HARVEY CUSHING IN EUROPE 1929
From a photograph by Arnold C. Klebs on the Axenstrasse

Harvey Cushing

A BIOGRAPHY

By

JOHN F. FULTON

Springfield · Illinois

CHARLES C THOMAS : *Publisher*

1946

CHARLES C THOMAS, PUBLISHER
BANNERSTONE HOUSE
301-327 East Lawrence Avenue, Springfield, Illinois

Published simultaneously in Canada by
THE RYERSON PRESS, TORONTO

FIRST EDITION

Printed in the United States of America

TO

KATHARINE CROWELL CUSHING

"Live as to die tomorrow
Learn as to live for ever"

Attributed to ISIDORE OF SEVILLE, *fl.* 630 A.D.

Preface

WHILE he lived Harvey Cushing had stimulated a generation of medical students, many of them profoundly, and it was evident that a record of his life, particularly of his early days at Yale, Harvard, and the Johns Hopkins, would prove a source of inspiration to students for many generations to come, as had his biography of Sir William Osler. And having been made aware that a biography might be called for and remembering what the preparation of the Life of Osler had entailed, Cushing made a thoughtful provision in his will that a sum of money be set aside to help defray the expenses of compiling an account of his life, should his wife and his literary executor "feel that the publication of my biography might be of interest or help to medical students." He further stipulated that ". . . any royalties from such biography and all royalties from any of my own writings and publications . . . shall be paid to Yale University for use by it in connection with the project hereinafter set forth for the Medical Historical Library."

Thus, in preparing an account of Dr. Cushing's life, selections from the voluminous source materials have been made with the medical student primarily in mind. But since Cushing's personality had so many facets, and since he drew as many of his friends from the lay public and from scholars in other fields as from the medical profession, it has seemed desirable to prepare a record that might also be of interest to non-medical readers. For this reason, and to bring the biography within the compass of a single volume, the detail of his clinical years has been deliberately curtailed, particularly with regard to the more technical phases of neurosurgery and brain tumor pathology.

Cushing's pride in his forebears, especially in the three generations of physicians immediately behind him, is evident in the story of his lineage and his own early days vividly set forth in the family papers collected and annotated over fifty years and systematically assembled for binding shortly before his death. His diaries and case histories were kept in the same meticulous way and were illustrated with many freehand drawings which gave evidence of his remarkable gift of draftsmanship. He always urged medical students to cultivate their artistic talents, for a fracture, he contended, is more easily drawn on the case record than described in words; and similarly, anatomical relationships, as Leonardo and Vesalius well knew, can be much more readily grasped through the medium of the eye.

In all he did, Cushing was a perfectionist—on the parallel bars and at tennis, in the experimental laboratory and the operating room where he constantly attempted to extend the horiozns of medical science. He was equally painstaking in the attention he gave to his writing and to the collection of his great library. He had the temperament and the sensitive perception of an artist, but he also had the enduring patience of the scientist; indeed, there seemed to burn in his soul something of Pater's hard, gem-like flame that sustained him in his vigorous yet simple way of life. Along with an unyielding devotion to principle there was warmth and gaiety and humor which lightened the way and proved a source of unending delight to his family and his host of friends, both young and old.

* * * * *

To those who have helped in the preparation of this volume, the compiler owes more than he can easily confess. Dr. W. W. Francis, who shared Cushing's "latch-keyer" days in Baltimore and who perused the Life of Osler three times in manuscript, has read the manuscript of this biography and has left it enriched in countless ways. Dr. Cushing's loyal secretaries, Miss Julia H. Shepley who kept his war diary in France and later assisted with the 'Osler,' and Miss Madeline E. Stanton who served him from 1920 until his death, have both helped in collecting and arranging the source material and they have contributed notably to the editing. I am similarly much indebted to Miss Elizabeth H. Thomson for her typing and her constructive scrutiny of the entire text, and to Mr. Frederic G. Ludwig of the Yale University Library for his technical skill in preparing the illustrations for press. I wish to thank the publisher, the printer, and Mr. Reinhold F. Gehner who has designed the book and arranged the illustrations; also Mrs. Henrietta T. Perkins who, with Miss Stanton, has compiled the index. Finally, all whose letters are quoted in the following pages have my warm thanks, and my gratitude likewise goes out to "a still larger number, whose names do not appear, yet who have lightened this labor of love by innumerable kindnesses."

Yale University,
June, 1946.

J. F. F.

Contents

Preface vii
List of Halftone Illustrations x
List of Abbreviations xii
I. The Cushing Lineage and the Western Reserve 3
II. Parents and Early Days in Cleveland . . . 11
III. Bright College Years: Yale 1887–1891 . . . 33
IV. Harvard Medical School 1891–1896 . . . 53
V. Halsted and The Johns Hopkins 1896–1900 . . 110
VI. A Year of Travel: Broadening Horizons 1900–1901 161
VII. Physician and General Surgeon 1901–1907 . . 202
VIII. Neurological Surgery: The Birth of a Specialty 256
IX. The Pituitary Body: Years of Rapid Development 271
X. Academic Calls. Planning a University Hospital 330
XI. Settling in Boston 1912–1914 353
XII. The Harvard Unit in Paris and After 1915–1917 387
XIII. Base Hospital Number 5 1915–1918 412
XIV. Postwar Problems: The Institute of Neurology 443
XV. Literary Pursuits: Osler Biography 1920–1924 . 456
XVI. Growth of a Clinic: The Life History of Brain Tumors and Electrosurgery 1925–1928 . . 514
XVII. Final Years at Harvard 1929–1933 569
XVIII. Return to Yale 1933–1937 634
XIX. The Closing Years 1937–1939 685
Appendix A: Harvey Cushing's Will 716
Appendix B: Degrees and Honors 719
Index 723

Halftone Illustrations

Harvey Cushing in Europe 1929 . . . . *frontispiece*
Matthew Cushing Homestead . . . . *following page* 4
House of David Cushing, Jr. 4
Cushing Tombstones at Stafford Hill 4
Erastus Cushing's House and Office 4
Erastus Cushing's Certificate, New York Hospital . . 4
Erastus Cushing 4
Henry Kirke Cushing 18
Betsey Maria Williams 18
Betsey Maria Cushing 18
Harvey Williams Cushing 18
Alleyne and Harvey Cushing 18
"The Crew of the [Illegible]" 36
A Sophomore at Yale 36
H.C. in a Backward Somersault 36
Touched for a Contribution 36
Yale Freshman Baseball Team 36
H.C. and Friend (J. Sanford Barnes) on Yale Fence 36
The Yale Fence 36
Microscopical Anatomy 100
Patients Sketched During Clinic 100
The South Side, M.G.H. 100
Chatsworth 1894 100
The Johns Hopkins Hospital Library 148
The Johns Hopkins Hospital 148
The Cushing Bookplate 148
The Great Lakes Trip to Duluth 148
"At the Turn of the Century" 148
Max Brödel 148
Surgical Resident Staff, J.H.H. 1899 148
Friends at the Hopkins 148
The Town of Berne 180
Theodor Kocher 180
Hugo Kronecker 180
Social Life in Berne 180
Professor Charles S. Sherrington 180
Nos. 1 and 3 West Franklin Street, Baltimore 244
Cushing's Baltimore Study 244
The "All-Star" Operation on 5 October 1904 244
H.C. at his Laboratory Desk 1907 244
An Early Johns Hopkins X-ray 244
Cushing's First Patient With Brain Tumor 276

Gasserian Ganglion Operation .... *following page* 276
Motor Area of Human Brain 276
Cushing's Suboccipital Exposure 276
The Tarbell Portrait 340
Dr. Cushing and Betsey in 1910 340
Mrs. Cushing and Children in 1910 340
The *Tabulae Sex* of Vesalius 340
Mrs. Cushing and Sir Henry Head 340
Development of Acromegaly 340
No. 305 Walnut Street, Brookline, Massachusetts... 372
Some Members of the Saturday Club 372
Unofficial Opening of P.B.B.H. 30 April 1913 372
Surgical Staff of P.B.B.H. 1914 372
Leaving with the Unit 436
Officers of the Unit, May 1917 436
John McCrae and "Bonneau" 436
Sir William Osler 468
Walter E. Dandy and H.C. 468
Family Group at Little Boar's Head 1921 468
H.C. Viewing an X-ray Film 564
Surgeon and Patient 564
Three Surgeons 564
Swedish Visitors 564
The Instrument Table 564
Student and Teacher 564
Two Physiologists 564
H.C. and Otfrid Foerster 596
A Dressing 596
Welch and H.C., February 1931 596
A Consultation 596
The 2000th Verified Brain Tumor 596
John Homans and the 2000th Tumor 596
Arnold C. Klebs 612
H.C. and Vittorio Putti 612
Leaders in Scientific Medicine 612
The Harvey Cushing Society 1932 612
Le Docteur, *honoris causa,* Paris 1933 612
Yale Members of the National Academy of Sciences 660
Listening to a Paper at the Beaumont Club 660
"Lulu" and H.C. 660
H.C. after his Oxford Degree 660
H.C. and Sir Charles Sherrington 660
Doctor of Science, Oxford 1938 660
Harvey Cushing Society on H.C.'s 70th Birthday 692
The 70th Birthday Dinner 692
Respite from Croquet 692
Watching the Croquet at Tea Time 692

List of Abbreviations

A.A.A.S.	American Association for the Advancement of Science
A.C.K.	Arnold C. Klebs
A.E.F.	American Expeditionary Force
A.M.A.	American Medical Association
B.C.H.	Boston City Hospital
B.E.F.	British Expeditionary Force
B.M.C.	Betsey Maria Cushing
C.A.M.C.	Canadian Army Medical Corps
C.C.M.C.	Committee on the Costs of Medical Care
C.C.S.	Casualty Clearing Station
C.E.S.	Committee on Economic Security
D.G.M.S.	Director-General of Medical Services
E.F.C.	Edward Fitch Cushing
H.C.	Harvey Cushing
H.K.C.	Henry Kirke Cushing
H.M.S.	Harvard Medical School
J.H.H.	Johns Hopkins Hospital
K.C.	Katharine (Crowell) Cushing
M.G.H.	Massachusetts General Hospital
N.R.C.	National Research Council
P.B.B.H.	Peter Bent Brigham Hospital
S.G.O.	Surgeon General's Office, U.S. Army
W.O.	William Osler

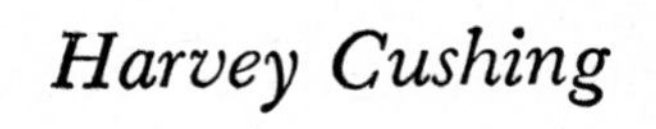

Harvey Cushing

"The writer of biography who can muster the strength of mind sometimes to leave his shop, and in the open to meditate upon his trade, must often be abashed at its facile presumptions. If he strive to recall the flow of his own life, he will find that it has been full of mystery to himself—and to others, to his friends even, or to his very housemates, much more mysterious. How hardly, then, shall he explain the life of one whom he has never seen, who lived perhaps in a far land, on other times, amid an alien people. Yet so assured are men of the resurrective power of literary scholarship that they have not hesitated to attempt the recall of such remote and misty persons as Abelard or Zoroaster. But, after he has once felt this sense of futility, the biographer will always wish to make some preliminary reservation. He will undertake to deal fairly with his reader, to be diligent in gathering knowledge of his subject, to order it carefully, to ponder it strictly and sympathetically; but he will not undertake to portray the elusive personality in all its fulness."

(Ferris Greenslet, *Walter Pater,* 1903)

CHAPTER I

The Cushing Lineage and the Western Reserve

HARVEY WILLIAMS CUSHING, the youngest of ten children of Betsey Maria Williams and Henry Kirke Cushing, M.D., was born on the Western Reserve of Connecticut in the town of Cleveland, Ohio, on 8 April 1869. His forebear, Matthew Cushing, who had settled at Hingham in the Massachusetts Bay Colony, came to this country on the ship *Diligent,* sailing from Gravesend on 26 April and arriving at Boston on 10 August 1638. Matthew's descendant, David Cushing, Jr., a country doctor, was the father of Erastus Cushing, M.D., who emigrated with a young family in 1835 to the Western Reserve. Erastus was the grandfather of Harvey Cushing [H.C.].

There is an element of true romance in the story of the Cushing family and the Western Reserve: how Erastus left the Berkshire hills of Massachusetts and travelled to the Western Reserve by the Erie Canal, and how a grandson of Erastus returned to New England, proud of the vigorous race of physicians from which he sprang, to occupy important chairs, first at Harvard University and then at Yale whither his Western Reserve loyalties had led him in his youth and again in his closing years. His forebears in medicine had all been general practitioners: David, Jr., Erastus, and his father, Henry Kirke. With this strong medical tradition they revered those who had taught them the art, and each deemed it a prime responsibility to pass on his knowledge to a new generation of students. Thus if Harvey Cushing followed the profession of medicine at all, it was inevitable that he would attempt in the first instance to become a good doctor and a good teacher. How it came about that he made himself one of the first physicians of his time, a teacher of great eminence and literary capacity, and, in addition, the creator of a new field of surgery, will be the theme of this volume.

Five generations of the Cushing family have been traced in England, beginning with Thomas of Hardingham, Norfolk, and his son, William Cushing, both of whom are mentioned in a deed of 1466; William's first testament is dated 20 September 1492. John, the eldest of William's seven children, whose will is dated 21 February 1522, begat eight children, the second of whom, Thomas, also of Hardingham, died there in April 1558. His fifth son, Peter, a centenarian of Hingham (Norfolk) was the father of Matthew who came to America in August 1638 and in the same year settled at Hingham in the Massachusetts Bay Colony.

Matthew Cushing (1589-1660), the founder of the Cushing family in the New World, was deacon of the Reverend Peter Hobart's church at Hingham. His wife, Nazareth Pitcher, who died on 1 January 1681 at the age of ninety-six, had borne him six children: Daniel, Jeremiah, Matthew, John, and two daughters. The fourth son, John (1627-1708), married Sarah, daughter of Matthew Hawke of Hingham, and had twelve children. John served as Deputy to the Colony Court in 1674, and for many years thereafter he was also prominent in the Colony Government; from 1689 to 1691 he was appointed Selectman, and in 1692 Representative of the General Court at Boston. Matthew (1665-1715), John's third son, had eight children by his wife Deborah Jacob (also a native of Hingham), the sixth of whom, Josiah Cushing, removed to Rehoboth, Massachusetts, and became the father of David Cushing, Sr. (1740-1821).

David Cushing, Jr., M.D., 1768-1814

For those who concern themselves with heredity, Harvey Cushing's most interesting progenitors were the physicians in the direct line of his descent. David, Sr., was the father of David, Jr., the first physician in the family. In 1876 William E. Cushing, H.C.'s eldest brother, set down an account of David, Jr., which had been based on talks he had had with his grandfather Erastus:

> My grandfather's personal knowledge of our line goes back only to his grandfather, David Cushing, who lived in Rehoboth, Massachusetts, near Providence, Rhode Island. He was a farmer comfortably well off for the time in which he lived. He had five children, one of whom, David, studied medicine, and left home about 1793 [actually 1796] to settle in the newer country. The tide of emigration at that time was moving from Connecticut and Rhode Island and Western Massachusetts up into Vermont, which had only quite recently been erected into a State and had the distracting question of its ownership finally settled. And while emigrants from Connecticut came up the Housatonic valley past Pittsfield and Lanesboro, those from the East came over the road on the other side of the mountain, running through Cheshire and Adams.
>
> At a place in Cheshire township called *Stafford Hill* was a large tavern, the usual place of resort for all travelers over that road, and my grandfather remembered seeing as many as fifty sleighs at once standing there of a winter night.
>
> Being thus on the line of emigration, Stafford Hill was a thriving place; and David Cushing, Jr., finding that a physician of the village had recently died—a Dr. Jenks, or Jinks, or Jenckes, as the name seems to have been indifferently spelled—decided to settle there, worked into a practice, and in course of time married the widow, Mrs. Jinks, who had been left with five children.
>
> He prospered; bought a farm, on which he lived, though he did not manage it himself; and was a share-holder in the first cotton factory established in South Adams. He lived at Stafford Hill until 1811. The hill towns of Berkshire County

MATTHEW CUSHING HOMESTEAD
Which stood on Main Street at Hingham, Massachusetts
from 1638 until burned in 1866

HOUSE OF DAVID CUSHING, JR.
The birthplace of Erastus Cushing and the last house to remain standing at
Stafford Hill, Cheshire, Berkshire County, Massachusetts

CUSHING TOMBSTONES AT STAFFORD HILL

Those of David Cushing, Jr. and Freelove Brown are in the foreground. H.K.C. had all the stones reset in 1907

ERASTUS CUSHING'S HOUSE AND OFFICE

On Euclid Avenue in Cleveland as they appeared in 1851. His horse-drawn gig stands before the office door

View of the New-York Hospital

WE the Physicians and Surgeons of the

NEW-YORK HOSPITAL.

Do certify that Erastus Cushing hath attended the practice of Physic and Surgery in this Hospital during the Session of 1822 & 1823—

In testimony whereof we have hereunto subscribed our names this 17th day of February in the Year of our Lord 1823—

Physicians	Surgeons
David Hosack M.D.	Wright Post M.D.
Peter C. Tappen	Valentine Mott M.D.
John Watts Jun. M.D.	Alex H. Stevens M.D.
	John C. Cheesman M.D.
	Kearny Rodgers M.D.

ERASTUS CUSHING'S CERTIFICATE FROM NEW YORK HOSPITAL

Dated 17 February 1823 and signed by David Hosack, Valentine Mott, and others

ERASTUS CUSHING
From a snapshot taken late in life with "Jack," who played the piano. E.C.'s nose closely resembles that of his grandson, Harvey

ERASTUS CUSHING
Posthumous portrait by W. H. Brough, now in the Cleveland Medical Library

were at first the most prosperous; people avoided the valleys for fear of malaria; but gradually the manufacturing towns in the valleys increased in wealth and relative importance, the owners of the hill farms moved down to the lower villages, and the hill towns diminished and little by little disappeared. Dr. David yielded to this state of things, and in 1811 moved to the village of South Adams. (Four years ago—1872—there was but one house remaining on Stafford Hill [that of David Cushing, Jr.]).

During the winter of 1813-14 that region was visited by an epidemic of malignant pneumonia, and the Doctor was used up by overwork. He was attacked the following summer by typhoid, and died Sept. 30, 1814, at the age of forty-seven.

He was a tall man—some 5 feet 10—and spare. He had a fine head of hair, though not profuse; it was black—not the dead Indian black—but somewhat wavy. His eye was very prominent and very blue, the cornea being clear and not at all congested. He was a forehanded man, and well off for those days. (The regular charge for a visit was 12 to 25 cents, according to circumstances.) His medical library would even now be thought a large one, and for those days was very exceptional. He was a thinking and sensible man, and you always knew where to find him.

His wife lived until 1843, when she was eighty years of age. My grandfather saw her last two years before her death. She was then "straight as Alice" [H.C.'s sister]; the skin of her face and hands was still fresh and clear; her hair was silver-grey and very abundant, and fell below her knees. She was of "slow and gentle speech." In her later years she was sometimes seized during sleep with attacks of complete numbness and immovability, from which she could be roused only by being touched by someone; and consequently she never slept alone. One night she spent with one of her daughters, who rose early to get breakfast, and left her lying in bed awake; but on going back to her found her dead. The attack must have come upon her when no one was at hand to rouse her. Her mother was an alert little lady of French Huguenot descent; and her father, Mr. Brown, was a well-to-do farmer in northern Berkshire County. She had three brothers in the Revolutionary Army, all of whom fought at Bennington; and she used to tell how her father, on the day of battle, kept going out of the house and putting his ear to the ground to listen for sounds from Bennington, thirty miles away.

In David, Jr., we thus find the prototype of Harvey: a "forehanded man" who brought together a medical library[1]—"a thinking and sensible man, and you always knew where to find him." In 1934 Harvey made an expedition to Stafford Hill with Mrs. Cushing where they found two grandchildren (Bowen) of Lydia, sister of Erastus, still living on property inherited, along with some furniture, from David, Jr. Mr. Eugene Bowen subsequently presented H.C.

[1] A number of David Cushing's books have come down through the libraries of Erastus and Henry Kirke to H.C.'s collection. "We were surprised," H.C. wrote in 1910, "at the number of David Cushing's books and by their rather unusual character, there being many of the important monographs of the time, some of which must have been imported at great expense from England." One finds, for example, Quincy's *Pharmacopoeia officinalis et extemporanea: or a complete English dispensatory*, London, 1782; Cullen's *Lectures on the materia medica*, Philadelphia, 1775; van Swieten's *The commentaries upon the aphorisms of Dr. Herman Boerhaave*, London, 1771.

with David Cushing's Windsor chair. Another heirloom in the possession of the Bowens was Freelove Cushing's [bed] warming pan.

The Western Reserve of Connecticut

When Harvey Cushing died in 1939, the Cushing family had been associated with Ohio and the Western Reserve for more than a century. The extraordinary series of events which led the Connecticut Colony to have a large western land grant "reserved from conveyance" for purposes of settlement is nowhere more vividly recounted than by Harvey Cushing himself:[2]

> Had they [the Pilgrim Fathers] not in their religious enthusiasm set up on the shore of Massachusetts Bay a theocratic form of government intolerable to those holding less rigid views of theology there might have been no subsequent separatist movements. . . . Had not a concession been made to Connecticut alone of all the states, whereby out of the newly formed Northwest Territory she was given title to a strip of land due west of Pennsylvania, 120 miles in extent between the parallels of her colonial charter, supposedly equivalent in size not only to her New England area but also to the Susquehanna Company's claim which she perforce had relinquished; had not Connecticut accepted this compromise, agreeing in return to set apart certain townships in the territory in quit-claim for those of her citizens who were entitled to land-bonuses from the Government; had not all these things taken place this piece of land would not have been thus '*reserved* from conveyance,' the term Western Reserve of Connecticut would not have come into being, there would have been no Western Reserve University, no Western Reserve Medical School, no necessity of reviewing these episodes from past history today.
>
> So Connecticut alone of all the thirteen colonies came to have bestowed upon her in those days of reconstruction a certain portion of the Western lands from which she had been virtually dispossessed. She however had not made so good a bargain as appeared, for when the new Reserve came to be surveyed it was found that a large part of it south of the 42nd parallel lay under the waters of Lake Erie. Even now there is a good deal of confusion 'down East' in regard to the amazing size and extent of these Great Lakes. Only a yesterday or so ago a New England lady on her first visit west of the Hudson stepped from a residence in Bratenahl on to the grassy terrace bordering the lake, with the exclamation, 'And pray what body of water can this be?' . . .
>
> Soon into this new country, like a surging tide, swept the Connecticut immigrants. In ox-drawn, canvas-covered wagons, the forerunners of the prairie schooners of later days, they came overland, for the most part, across central New York by way of the Mohawk and Genesee Turnpike through Cherry Valley and the country soon to be made famous by Fenimore Cooper's novels—or so at least they came until the opening (1825) of the Erie Canal, which practically paralleled the old cross-country trail. And here in the Western Reserve they finally established what was said to be 'the largest, strongest and most characteristic single, compact colony in the West, the last distinct footprint of Puritanism.'
>
> A scant six years after the first driblets of this wave of immigration reached here the 'Enabling Act' was passed whereby Ohio emerged from the Northwest

[2] *The Western Reserve and its medical traditions.* Cleveland: Privately printed [1924], 33 pp.

territory into full-fledged statehood (1803), by which time, though Cleveland was but a scattered hamlet, there must have been some 10,000 settlers in other parts of the Reserve and some 40,000 elsewhere in the state. Those who bought their individual holdings from the original Connecticut Land Company at something like fifty cents an acre were almost wholly people of Connecticut stock and of English lineage. . . .

Cushing continues his story with a reference to his own immediate family and their migration to the Western Reserve:

Tradition is largely a matter of sentiment and the possession of sentiment, in accordance with the code of unwritten laws which largely guide our actions, is something we are not expected to betray, unless perhaps in the family circle. But this I feel to be a family circle made up in large measure of those whose ancestors with mine were early among those vigorous souls who left New England a century and more ago to open up and to leave their stamp upon this new country—on its form of government, on its form of worship, on its schools. . . .

My own forebears on the distaff side were of Connecticut origin and seven of my grandparents in three generations, though not among the actual vanguard, were fairly early settlers and took up lands in Painesville, Boardman, Canfield and Warren. The two earliest, so far as I know, Haynes Fitch from Norwalk and Comfort Mygatt from Danbury, came with their families in 1804, and the last, Ebenezer Williams, came from Windsor as late as 1811. The son of this Ebenezer has left an account of their journey which describes the Cherry Valley Turnpike even at this comparatively late day as a 200-mile piece of corduroy of such a nature as fairly to jolt one's bones asunder. It was near the first of December when they finally made Buffalo, where representations of the impassable state of the Cattaraugus swamps and woods led them to sell their ox-drawn wagons and to take passage on a new and staunch schooner, the "Little Belt" which lay at anchor in the Niagara River. Three weeks elapsed ere a favorable wind permitted them to set sail; and before reaching their destination (the mouth of the Cuyahoga, I presume) a severe winter storm overtook them and drove them back to Presque Isle [Erie] where they were finally landed in safety. From there, after much labor and toil, they made their way overland in midwinter the seventy-two miles to Painesville 'through an unbroken and primeval wilderness awaiting the woodman's axe.'

Then followed a description of the migration of Grandfather Erastus and his family in 1835.

Erastus Cushing, M.D., 1802-1893

Erastus Cushing,[3] the second child of David, Jr. and Freelove Brown (Jinks), was twelve years of age when his father died. His boyhood was passed at Stafford Hill and South Adams (Massachusetts) where the family had removed two or three years prior to his father's death. He was later for two years in Lenox Academy, presumably in 1818 and 1819; in 1820 he began the study of medicine with William L. Tyler, M.D., of Lanesboro. In the winter of 1822-1823 he attended the course of instruction at the New York Hospital. His

[3] The details concerning Erastus Cushing are based on notes set down in 1892 by his son, Henry Kirke Cushing.

certificate, dated 17 February 1823, bears the signatures of David Hosack, Valentine Mott, and others.

On his way to New York for his medical training Erastus had travelled from Albany in a sloop packet, and was one week on the voyage, visiting West Point while becalmed in the neighborhood. Steamboats were in use, but they were slow and expensive, while the sloops were well equipped and provisioned, and very comfortable. He had anticipated returning to New York the ensuing year to graduate, but for economic reasons he took the course at the Berkshire Medical School at Pittsfield, the Medical Department of Williams College, which had been established in 1822. His Berkshire diploma bears the date 24 December 1824. In the Pittsfield Athenaeum Library are bound volumes containing the graduating theses of students of the Berkshire Medical School. The volume for 1824 contains twenty-two theses, including Erastus Cushing's on "Cossium Maculatum"—a plant yielding a narcotic poison.

His son states that it was a good school with a bright faculty. A fellow student was Mark Hopkins, afterwards widely known as President of Williams College; his roommate was a Dr. Sabin, later a well-known physician of Williamstown. After his graduation Erastus continued for two years actively employed with Dr. Tyler. On 23 July 1826 he married Mary Ann, daughter of Abial and Charlotte Platt of Lanesboro, Massachusetts. "Their wedding excursion," H.K.C. writes, "was to Niagara Falls by way of the Erie Canal, but shortly before completed."[4] He continued in practice in Lanesboro for several years, and in the winter of 1834-1835 attended the course of lectures in Philadelphia at the Medical Department of the University of Pennsylvania. But the arduous work in the severe climate of the Berkshire hills had already begun to tell upon his health, and shortly after leaving Philadelphia in 1835 he journeyed West seeking a community where the weather would be more temperate. H.C. writes of his grandfather's migration:

> In search of a place of abode Erastus came west visiting Buffalo, Detroit, Wooster and Columbus; but the place above all which took his fancy was the village of Cleveland through which he passed when on the way to see his brother who had already come west and was living in Ashtabula County. Accordingly, in the following year, in October of 1835 to be exact, he brought his wife and three children here over the water-ways via the Erie Canal to Buffalo and thence by sail to the mouth of the Cuyahoga. One recollection of their arrival I may mention, for on landing at the Gittings warehouse at the

[4] The children of Erastus and Mary Ann were born in Lanesboro; Henry Kirke, *b.* 29 July 1827, father of Harvey; William David, *b.* 12 June 1829, who married Caroline Shaw of Lanesboro and died in Cleveland 30 July 1874; Charlotte who died in infancy; Cornelia, *b.* 10 May 1835, who married George P. Briggs and died at the age of 23. Neither William nor Cornelia left children.

foot of Superior Street, the commercial center of the town in those days, and ascending the steep bluff to the level of the flat plateau on which lay the scattering village, the first object that attracted their attention was a white cat which they saw in the distance crossing the road from "Squire" Case's house, where the postoffice now stands; and somehow this was regarded as an auspicious omen. For it might have been a black cat.

In a series of papers on pioneer medicine in the Western Reserve, Dr. Howard Dittrick of Cleveland has given a vignette of Erastus:

One of his colleagues still living[5] remembers him as a gentlemanly old man with smooth-shaven face, finely chiselled features and rather pointed nose. A slight stoop of the shoulders developed with his advanced years. The kindliness which characterized his disposition and expression was revealed in sympathetic eyes and pleasant voice. It inevitably won friendship and professional success. He was ever the distinguished though unassuming gentleman, as he walked about clad in his long black cape, his hands clasping his arms. He was both small and slender, and he differed markedly from his son and grandchildren. Many of us recall the tall stature and erect and dignified carriage of Dr. H. Kirke Cushing and his sons, in whom quick and almost abruptly alert movement was characteristic. These traits were almost entirely absent in Dr. Erastus Cushing, whose calm and kindly serenity was a happy memory to all who knew him. He was a devout churchman, faithful in attendance at the Old Stone Church. His declining years were blessed by the same gracious charm which had ever made him beloved. He lived to witness much progress in the city he had chosen for his home, for it was not until the 14th of April 1893, in his 91st year, that he died of pneumonia.

Erastus was highly regarded as a physician, and some idea of his relations with his patients can be gleaned from the following letter:

Erastus Cushing to H. H. Coit — *Cleveland, Ohio, 21 Feby 1850.*

Kind Sir, From the description given in y^r^ note I am disposed to view the ill from which you & yours are now suffering as more allied to scarlet fever than Quinsey. Notwithstanding you may not have had the eruption or other evidences that would clearly mark it as such. With that view of the subject, I would say—Medicate but moderately—at most onely keep the bowels gently open with Rhubarb or Rhubarb & Magnesia combined. If that is not adequate to it—precede the same with Blue Pill at bed time, & the other in the morning.

Some local means to the throat—& if there is much internal [discharge] with offensive secretion—a gargle of Borax dissolved in strong sage tea & sweetened with honey will be as well as any thing. Make use of it freely & frequently during the day. This is perhaps about as definite as I can consistently be in directing means under present circumstances. If there are any farther enquirys that you may wish to make—write me as definitely as you can & I will answer you accordingly. Yours truly, ERASTUS CUSHING.

[5] Dr. William T. Corlett (*b.* 1854). Dr. Corlett writes (4 Aug. 1945) in reply to a question about Erastus' nose, "His nose was not in my recollection a prominent feature, possibly slightly roman, but in harmony with a somewhat meager frame of slightly below medium height. He lived at that time in 'The Forest City House' which was situated on the Public Square. His son Kirke Cushing I knew for many years, but not intimately. He was slightly taller but also inclined to be thin, without much beard on his face. He had a less kindly smile than his father, was short of speech and to the point."

Erastus Cushing retired from practice in 1873 at the age of seventy. For the next two decades he was to continue a familiar figure in Cleveland, and his grandson recalls, "I can see him now, hailing a horse-car and bowing with dignity to the driver." Although sound intellectually, he was somewhat crippled physically, and finally demurred at his granddaughter Alice's visits because he was unable personally to see her to the door when she departed—an attention he could not fail to show his guests.

In retrospect it seems clear that few of Erastus' personal characteristics were passed on to his eldest son, for Henry Kirke Cushing did not have the easygoing, sunny nature of his father. H.C., on the other hand, inherited much from Erastus—his physique, his nose, and his innate kindliness. He also derived traits from his mother, but anyone wishing to complete the pattern of his heredity will be obliged to look to his paternal grandmother, Mary Ann Platt, and her line. Study of their family papers indicates that they were shrewd in business and made hard bargains—though it would be boldness to suggest that such prevalent New England traits are heritable.

CHAPTER II

Parents and Early Days in Cleveland

SEVERAL traits, well developed in David Cushing, Jr., and in Erastus, emerge conspicuously in Harvey Cushing's father, eldest son of Erastus Cushing and his wife, Mary Ann Platt of the town of Lanesboro, Massachusetts.

Henry Kirke Cushing, M.D., 1827-1910

Henry Kirke Cushing [H.K.C.] was born on 29 July 1827 at the old Platt house in Lanesboro and received his earliest education in a neighboring rural school. When he was eight his father, Erastus, conducted his small family first by carriage and then by the Erie Canal to Buffalo whence they took passage by lake boat to Cleveland where they landed on 20 October 1835. He thus grew up as the son of a busy pioneer doctor and during his boyhood years was left largely to his own resources. Within ten years of their arrival at Cleveland his father had become affluent enough to send Henry Kirke East to Union College in Schenectady, New York. He entered in the autumn of 1845 and was graduated with high academic standing in 1848. He returned to Cleveland and began at once to study medicine as an apprentice to his father, at the same time attending lectures during three academic sessions (1848-1850) at the Cleveland Medical College, an institution which he was later to serve as Professor of Midwifery, Diseases of Women, and Medical Jurisprudence. On his father's insistence Henry Kirke then proceeded to Philadelphia for a year where he again acquitted himself most creditably, but owing to his father's illness in 1851, he returned to Cleveland without having had the usual year of interne experience in a Philadelphia hospital, a circumstance to which he frequently referred with regret in later years. "The lack of those hospital years of training," he said, "has ever been regretted and has been a hindrance in many things." A letter which Erastus addressed to Henry Kirke soon after his arrival in Philadelphia is much in the vein of the letters which Henry Kirke in turn wrote to his son Harvey at Yale:

Cleveland, Ohio,
6 May 1850.

E.C. to H.K.C.

My Son, Agreeable to promise when you left home, I write you at this time enclosing in the same envelope some letters for you and Dr. Hopkins—to Doctor Tickner & some other medical gentlemen in the places you will visit. I suppose you are by this time fairly engaged in the business of yr. journey (i.e.)

seeing and hearing whatever there may be of interest in the places where you are and the regions of country you may pass through.

Self reliance, intelligence and a manner of address & utterance free from affectation will secure you a reasonable degree of attention and respect in whatever correct circle of society you may chance to be placed in or amongst. If favoured with health, I have confidence you will have both a pleasant & profitable journey; and how is your health now? And how think you the change of habits for the time is probable to affect you? I hope favourably, still it's too soon to expect any decided influence from it yet.

Since you left home I am not aware that anything of interest has transpired worth relating in this vicinity. I think your mother desired you to call on Mrs. Prentiss Dow when you arrived at N. York. Mrs. Dow however is not there. She arrived here yesterday on a visit to her friends. As to myself the week since you left has been one of much industry by me or with me. I find that your aid in the office was more than I should have appreciated but for the experience I have had at a previous time. Should it occur to you that you have neglected any arrangement that you wish to have completed here, write me and I will do whatever I can to aid it. Say to Doctor Hopkins that I have given attention to the little matters he left with me and that I should be gratified to hear from him when he has leisure to write. Let me hear from you soon. ERASTUS CUSHING.

After his return to Cleveland Henry Kirke soon found himself in a busy practice, first in association with his father and later in an independent office, and by 1860 he was firmly established. In 1861, when President Lincoln called for 7,500 volunteers for three months' enlistment, he offered his services and entered the army on 26 April as a battalion surgeon. In the summer he re-enlisted for a second three months, but resigned on 6 September 1861 and returned to his Cleveland practice. He re-entered service, however, on at least three occasions between 1861 and 1864 as a member of the Ohio Volunteer Militia. The many letters to his wife and family written while serving with the Northern Army reveal an unusual knowledge of military history, and they often contained as much detail about military strategy and tactical difficulties of the terrain as they did of matters medical. In later life H.K.C. studied all phases of military and naval history and became one of the first authorities on the subject in his community. His children have said of him that while he read widely in history, botany, and astronomy, he hated poetry and could not abide a novel.

To his many friends in Cleveland Henry Kirke Cushing appeared a shy, somewhat austere and puritanical individual, slow to make friends and quite unbending in his conduct and interpretation of ethical principle. Those who knew him more intimately, however, saw another side of his nature which comes out to some extent in his letters to his son Harvey at Yale and later at the Harvard Medical School; but he was much better known to his older children. His first-born, William E. Cushing, has left a vivid memoir which may be quoted in part:

. . . He was absent from home, with his regiment, nearly four months in 1861. After Shiloh he responded to the call of the Governor of Ohio on behalf of the U.S. Sanitary Commission and from there returned in charge of a boat-load of wounded Ohio Volunteers. . . . After Gettysburg he responded to a like call, from the Christian Commission, and was there for some days at work among the wounded; and again similarly for some days in Virginia after Grant's campaign had opened in 1864 with the Battles of the Wilderness. Of course at times he was briefly away on professional business, going somewhere with or to a patient. But with these exceptions, I have no personal recollection of his being away at all, before his final retirement from the practice of his profession; nor of his taking a "day off" at home, for rest or relaxation (before that retirement) except when compelled by illness. That is to say, for the forty-odd years of his medical practice, his life (as far as I know) was absolutely vacationless, and of constant unremitting hard work.

He had naturally the gift of being skilful, "handy" with his hands, and liked to "tinker" with them. Mending locks, repairing leaky faucets, making an obstinate clock go, patching a worn book-binding or a torn leaf, were among the things of that kind he would do and find entertainment in. . . . He could draw a little; I believe he was given some drawing lessons when a lad by the man who drew the pencil sketch of him at that age, which was and I suppose still is, somewhere among the family archives [in H.C.'s volume on H.K.C.], and who also drew the collection of sketches of the well-known Cleveland men of that time, which Eckstein Case borrowed from Charles Gale last year to show to H.K.C. and get the missing names supplied by him. Mother used to say that the drawings H.K.C. made to illustrate his lectures at the Medical College during his first professorship were "beautifully done." Here and there in his notes on the Franklin portraits are bits of sketches—a cap, a part of a head, or something of the sort, to show some identifying feature of the picture he was referring to. I am sure that his manual skill and dexterity were of such a degree as to have been helpful to many a patient of his. His bodily movements were quick, alert and graceful.

The actions of his mind were also quick and direct. When he had, or believed he had, his premises, his mind moved rapidly to its conclusions; and the conclusions and the reasons for them remained with great definiteness, clearness and distinctness, and he could express them without any waste of words and without leaving the hearer in any doubt as to what he meant. And he rose to an emergency with instant courage and without being confused or unbalanced by it.

I think a psychologist would have said that his mental reaction-interval was unusually short. Alice has some stories of the quickness with which he got out of tight places while driving his electric runabout. I recall only two occasions of his being pressed into service as an expert witness; and I was told of the unusually effective impression he made by Sam Williamson with reference to one of those times, and by John Lowman with reference to the other. I think Sam Williamson said that H.K.C. was the best medical expert witness he ever heard testify. (I never saw him on the stand, myself.)

He was an attentive and good observer, and on general principles preferred to try to find out a thing by observation—when opportunity offered—rather than by asking; at least rather than by asking strangers. In going about in the touring car he chartered during the week of his Berkshire visit of 1907, he sat by preference in the front seat beside the chauffeur; and he told me at the end of the week that he had paid some attention to the man's doings and had at length become pretty well satisfied that if anything had happened to the man, he (H.K.C.) could have driven the car home. But he made it plain to me that he had not asked the man any questions about the "modus." . . . I have forgotten what image of an elephant set him off on the inquiry, a year or two ago, whether elephants were by nature pacers, as he perceived that one had been represented by the artist to have that gait. At any rate the inquiry amused him, and failing to find in his books anything to settle it, he improved the opportunity of the visit of a circus to town, and arranged to meet me at the proper time to go from my office to St. Clair Street to see the parade. It contained plenty of elephants, they all paced, and with a satisfied nod at me he turned homeward.

He had in his library from a long time back, some books on the stars, and he knew the constellations quite well and kept enough track of the planets to know which the bright ones in sight at any time were. He told me once that he took some pains to learn the constellations, because he thought they would thus become (as they did) better company for him on the long night walks which were so often necessary in going to and from patients' houses, especially in the times of no streetcars, or few streetcars.

He liked trees and plants. He liked to see plants grow; and of late, to make them grow, in so far as his small garden plot allowed. When Newhall's book on the *Trees of Northeastern America* [1890], planned to enable one to distinguish these trees by the leaves alone (or principally), came into the household in the early or middle '90's, he caught the fever, as some of the rest of us did, and took pleasure in noticing the individual trees he passed in his walks or drives, and in making sure of the names and kinds of any as to which he had any doubt. I think none of the rest of us were quite as bold as he in entering yards of other people and plucking sample leaves in case of need.

He liked to observe animals and birds, wild or domestic, and to get and read books about them and their ways. His discovery of the waltzing mice in the bird-store window, not many years ago, set him to inquiry and reading on that subject which he often recurred to with enjoyment. The annual return of the sapsuckers to the Norway birch in front of his house, and their performances over the sweet and intoxicating sap, he always watched for, and the date of their first appearance he would note down each Spring in his diary or notebook.

The deep vein of sentiment and feeling that was in him he was shy of expressing (and his natural reticence became intensified when this was involved) so that it was only on rare occasions, and then rather by sidelights, that one caught glimpses of it, by his permission. His abounding sense of humor found its expression in ways which were so quiet that one might almost call them gentle, and on the rather rare occasions when something was so funny that he was forced to laugh or chuckle unduly long, there was something almost apologetic in his manner, as though he were a little ashamed at finding himself a little out of his own control.

It was his interest in the family history, I believe, which set him to taking the *Boston Transcript* of late years, because the *Transcript* had a genealogy page once or twice a week. But having begun, he found he liked the paper, and so kept on with it. His other eastern daily, the *New York Tribune,* is a matter of longer standing; that is to say, he took the *Semi-Weekly Tribune* for many years, certainly as far back as the Greeley time, or even before the time of the War of the Rebellion; and finally changed to the daily. The *Semi-Weekly Tribune, The Independent* and the *New York Evangelist,* are the only papers, beside the *Cleveland Leader,* which as I remember came regularly to the house while I was a boy.

Few men could have been more highly regarded professionally in their community than was Henry Kirke Cushing. He gave freely of his time at the Cleveland Medical College in promoting better medical education; and he was ever conscientious in attending and encouraging meetings of the local medical societies. He frequently entered into general discussion and had an unusual faculty for quietly settling differences among the members. Unlike his tenth child, H.K.C. published little. Local journals carried an occasional transcript of a discussion at a medical meeting, but H.C. states in a volume of family papers that, as far as he could ascertain, his father published no formal case reports. His only detailed paper, issued after his retirement, is historical in nature, being based on a lecture presented at a meeting of the Johns Hopkins Historical Club on 23 May 1904 on the Franklin-Heberden inoculation pamphlet of 1759. The paper, which reviews in some detail the history of the inoculation controversy, is thoroughly documented and displays among other things a knowledge, unusual for those days, of technique in bibliographical description. H.C. records that his father was most reluctant to allow publication of the paper in the *Johns Hopkins Hospital Bulletin* (vol. 15, pp. 276-285). H.K.C. had brought together a large collection of iconographical material relating to Benjamin Franklin which the trustees of his estate presented after his death to the Western Reserve Historical Society. The collection, known as "The H. K. Cushing Franklin Collection," has been described in some detail in the *Annual Report* of the Society for 1919.

Although he started in a general practice he specialized fairly soon in gynecology and obstetrics, giving lectures on these subjects at the Medical College. His advice was frequently sought in difficult cases, and by dint of working for forty years without a vacation he managed to keep the wolf from the door and to educate the seven children who reached maturity. He had a penurious streak that amounted to more than frugality and thrift, but this trait is understandable in the light of the many responsibilities which he carried. When Harvey was in Harvard Medical School he sent him this advice: "My experience is that you spend more money in the end when you check than when you pay from your pocket. In the latter case you know perfectly just how you stand. My advice to you is never to have a bill anywhere, unless it is absolutely impossible, and then to pay it in person, and take a receipt, and keep it. That is my own way: for having many demands upon my income, but a small part has ever been left for my own personal wants. I have thus been obliged to keep the closest watch upon my outgoes, and that is easiest done by knowing how much or how little is in my pocket. I could of course have that from my check book, but that is in the drawer, and only occasionally regarded. . . ."

It was a family tradition never to speak, even in the privacy of the family circle, about personal affairs, and no one in the family ever dreamed of enquiring about H.K.C.'s patients. In all such things he was not only silent but unconsciously secretive. And there were times when, for no apparent reason, he would become silent and speak to no one in the family for days at a time. The reason was never asked but the assumption was that someone had offended. His wife accepted these episodes with philosophical calm, putting them down to overwork and fatigue—for an obstetrician can never determine the hours of his work.

Betsey Maria Williams Cushing, 1828-1903

Harvey Cushing's mother, Betsey Maria Williams [B.M.C.], was an even-tempered, forceful, and kindly woman with a deep-running sense of domestic responsibility and a strong love of family, and along with these homely virtues she had humor, grace, and an inner gaiety of spirit which Harvey inherited in full measure. She came of pioneer Western Reserve stock, her paternal grandfather having been one Ebenezer Williams (1769-1843) who had migrated in 1811 to the Western Reserve from East Windsor, Connecticut, to settle in Painesville, Ohio. Ebenezer's fifth child, William, married Lucy, daughter of Zalmon Fitch (1785-1860), another early settler in the Western Reserve originating in Norwalk, Connecticut. Lucy Fitch's eldest daughter was Betsey Maria Williams, born on 3 March 1828, the mother of Harvey Cushing. Both families were in themselves close-knit, with strong family traditions, and from both sides she inherited resourcefulness, spiritual independence, and a quality which, in the eastern part of the United States, is known as "middle-western enterprise."

There is no better way of giving insight into Cushing's nature, background, and inheritance than to record a brief, unpublished memoir which he wrote in 1934 concerning his mother to whom he had always referred affectionately as "B.M.C." He heads the tribute, "Something of B.M.C. by her youngest son."

. . . After the failure of the "Day & Williams Glass Manufacturing Co." in Kent, Ohio, because of the law against imported labor thereby preventing C. T. W[illiams] from bringing over his annual lot of Belgian glass blowers, he and Uncle Day (Edward L.) closed their works, sold their places on the hill in Kent, Ohio, and moved to Cleveland. There C.T.W. for a few years taught Greek in the Public High School and incidentally gave my cousin, Perry Harvey, and me enough extracurricular French to enable us to pass creditably in 1887 our entrance examination for Yale which we went to Chicago to take.

B.M.C. (C.T.W.'s elder sister and my mother) must have started him in French as well as in music, but from the latter angle she had good material to work upon as the Williamses were all musical and it even drifted down through B.M.C. to her own children, two of whom, Alice and Harry, were natively musical, and

Harry's son, Kirke W., so much so he would have taken up music as a profession had his father not been opposed. Two of C.T.W.'s children, William Carver and Day, made it their profession and Uncle Ed's children and grandchildren have all been musically gifted. It added much to the enjoyment of the frequent family gatherings and most of the games that were played on such occasions, as the family Christmas parties, were games set to music—"Here we go round the Barberry-Bush," "The Day's far spent and the Night's coming on," etc.

The memories of one's mother are in the nature of things among the most vivid of all memories. I think being read to aloud before being sent to bed is my earliest remembrance, and after my "Now I lay me, etc.," having poetry recited to me until I went to sleep. This was at 786 Prospect Street where we moved from the house on [10] Euclid Avenue near the Public Square when I was about four years old. There was a day school for the neighbors' small children just across the street conducted by a Miss Freeman which I attended before going to the junior public school on what was then Sterling Avenue not far away. About the time of this transfer in schools, I recall having a sharp attack of scarlet fever when I was perhaps six. I was quarantined in so far as to sleep on a cot alongside the double bed in which Father and Mother always slept, and it was characteristic of her that she not only did all the nursing and doctoring for me but saw to it that while convalescing I kept up with my lessons by games that were educational. It was made play that I should write out the menus for my meals, for example, and to my lasting chagrin the other children howled with delight at my spelling of "bananna"—to this day I've never been quite sure whether there are one or two n's, or none at all.

She had her own medicine cupboard which served as a medium for all the family doctoring—paregoric, eye drops, a nux vomica with gentian mixture, etc. H.K.C. was never bothered about it, as I suppose is true in all doctors' families. The only time he ever had to be "called in," so far as concerned me at least, was some years later when I got a Colles fracture doing a "fly away" from a horizontal bar at the old Y.M.C.A. gymnasium which I frequented between 1884 and 1886, being middle man of a three-high combination of tumblers in which capacity we once were exhibited at a charity show. I was scared stiff when told he had been sent for, but he was kindness and tenderness itself, reduced the fracture and whittled out a splint to fit the radial curve—no questions asked about what foolishness I had been up to.

We were strictly brought up—punctuality at meals—Sunday School and Church, etc.—and were duly spanked for our peccadillos, I think by both parents, Father's favorite weapon being the back of a hair brush on the open palm or the same on the buttocks while across his knees until we got too big for that. I'm sure it was good for us and probably hurt them the most. I think my last one administered by Mother was for being caught with a dime novel of the sort I'd been forbidden to read. It was a ten-penny thriller of the day giving episodes in the life of Dick Deadeye or some other Western bandit of noble sentiments who never robbed or offended the ladies. For some mysterious reason these stories were taboo and consequently irresistible when loaned by a friend.

All of us were expected in small ways to share in the work, for it was a house in which there was no loafing and sitting about. Cutting the grass, watering the garden, raking the house-road, sweeping the walks were tasks handed on from brother to brother and assumed—for a time at least—with certain pride. As I recall it, I, being the youngest, came in the end to inherit all these chores together, and being the smallest, was accustomed to wearing some elder brother's outgrown shoes or made-over clothes, which wasn't so pride-engendering.

We and our cousins, of whom there were many, were all collectors of something or other—postmarks, postage stamps, trademarks, coins, butterflies, birds' eggs, etc., and the family stamp collection which had been begun by Grandmother Cushing when with Uncle George P. Briggs and a Mr. and Mrs. Dow she went abroad (in the 'sixties, I believe) was a notable one. As one brother after another went off to college it was handed on to the next to care for as was the butterfly collection, which in a way atoned for the inherited chores. Then there were, first and last, a multitude of pets. The older boys had a pigeon loft in the barn where they bred fancy birds, tumblers, pouters, and such, and I think provided the family with squabs. There was also a small chicken yard, and they went in for bantams. Then there were various caged birds in the house; ring doves, paroquets, etc., and living in the barn were pet cats galore, all of which were taught to jump through our hands; and we used to race them from the horse block to the open barn door. Alongside the barn was a so-called playhouse, chiefly given over to a carpenter's bench where Father used to make and mend things like bookshelves, and so on. He was skilful at any form of handicraft.

It was a small back yard but room in it for such games as "Duck and Drake" or "Sheep-fold-down," and for Mother's garden; also a croquet set and some fruit trees: quince bushes, peaches and cherries I chiefly remember. The neighbors too had fruit trees from which we poached I fear—poached cherries always tasted better than our own. There was a big willow and a tall poplar, both of which Father had planted by simply poking a stick into the ground. And there was a cemetery for our many pets which had gone to another world, among them two dogs, I believe. After these had passed, Father let it be known that he did not want any more dogs around the house—the parting was too painful. And when N. M. Anderson finally gave me a white and tan spaniel for my very own called Jack, the dog was hid in the barn. There it was of course finally discovered, and when questions were asked and he was told it was my dog Jack, he remarked that from his observation the dog had better be called Jill—and let it go at that. Jack became a famous trick dog and besides the ordinary things could play the piano (there were always two for eight-hand duets) at command, carry messages about the house always to the right person, and would run half a block to meet the paper-boy and bring the paper home. Father always assumed an air of unawareness of the dog until one day he found her proudly sitting on the seat of his buggy which had been left at the front gate. He took for the first time a comprehending look at the dog and succumbed, got in and drove off with her on his visits. After that they were inseparable.

These reminiscences of the back-yard flora and fauna have led me momentarily away from Mother to whom I must return as we sooner or later always did with cuts or bruises or torn clothes or hurt feelings. She was quite used to it, having begun life taking care of a succession of younger brothers and sisters as her stepmother brought them one after another into the world. She then started in with her own ten, seven of whom grew to maturity. Each one of them got from her the rudiments of their education at odd times when she wasn't making or mending their clothes and cooking much of their food and putting up the preserves and all that. Yet she never seemed to be hurried and was never known to show impatience. Her day was planned to get the most out of it, and, often singing at her tasks, she went at them from early till late with an untiring enthusiasm.

I can see her now, on her knees in her bedroom and at the same time her workroom, cutting out shirts or night dresses or something of the kind with a *Delineator*—a familiar paper of the day—open before her from which to take her

HENRY KIRKE CUSHING
From a photograph used for the portrait which now hangs in the Cleveland Medical Library

BETSEY MARIA WILLIAMS
Before her marriage to H.K.C.

BETSY MARIA CUSHING
In 1900

HARVEY WILLIAMS CUSHING
At about two years

ALLEYNE AND HARVEY CUSHING
About 1880

measurements. Then she would gather everything up neatly and go busily to work on the sewing-machine with which she was expert. And there were always stockings and socks or mittens to darn, most of which she had of course knitted in the first place. While this was all duty which I think she enjoyed for the simple joy of creating useful things, she at the same time was an expert needle woman and her usual Christmas presents to her sisters would be things like doilies she had made or a piece of lace or some rugs she had woven. She used to make the most amazing rugs out of old Brussels carpets which we children would unravel and prepare for her by matching the colors into skeins. The color designs she would make up out of her head as she went along and they had a surprising Turkish-rug-like effect.

As Cleveland grew prosperous it became increasingly dirty and the annual spring house-cleaning which took about two weeks was something everyone but Mother would gladly have let go by the board. We regarded it as comparable to washing behind the ears—an unnecessary frill as long as you couldn't see it yourself. All carpets up, all pictures and curtains down, all walls washed or rubbed off with loaves of old bread or repapered if necessary, all books (and the house was full of them) taken down and cleaned. The chief 'out' about it was that after the carpets had been thoroughly spanked in the back yard and the floors washed, they had to be tacked down again if good enough, or ravelled for rug-making if not.

Then the Sundays of my childhood were days of spiritual house-cleaning and I can't say that I look back on them with pleasure though they may have been restful, which was their secondary purpose. A bank holiday in London always gives me a feeling of Sunday. No toys were allowed—no games—no books except those doled out at Sunday School. We all went by streetcar to the Old Stone Church of which Mother was a pillar, and afterwards those who were strong enough walked the mile and a half out Euclid Avenue to our house for a family dinner with Grandfather Cushing always present. There was of course always a blessing said at meals. After that the servants were let off and Mother got the supper, meanwhile listening to her volunteer helper's catechism and next week's Bible verses which had been committed to memory during the day.

All this in time began to relax. Morning prayers were given up, and blessings at the table. Father relinquished his Sunday School Class, I suppose about the time we moved up town, and stopped going to church altogether after his friend, Dr. Haydn, stopped preaching. Will and Carolyn and Alice were regular churchgoers, but I don't remember that Harry and Ed attended church after going to college. Mother was the last one to go with any regularity and the Hon. Richard Parsons who was also a churchgoer once remarked that he wouldn't feel at home in Heaven unless his pew was behind hers.

I think for some years after first setting up housekeeping they got along without any servant and there was one particularly bad time—just after the War, I believe—when Father fell on the icy steps of the old Medical School and wrenched his knee which was a little stiff the rest of his life. It went into a "white swelling"—presumably a tuberculous arthritis—and he was on his back for nearly a year, Mother doing all the nursing; and meanwhile, one after the other, the children all came down with whooping-cough. I think it must have been about the time of the carte-de-visite photo with Harry and Alice in which she looks (for her) somewhat hollow-cheeked.

Except for Father's buggy which was constantly in use and the horse-car line which passed the house, there was no means of transport; and of course the telephone was not yet. So among other things Mother went every day on foot to the local market across from the Sterling Street school and perhaps once or twice a week to the larger market in town. We of course by this time had servants but they were limited to a cook and a combination chambermaid and waitress. No choreman was needed, for Father would not have entrusted the furnace to one, and I can now hear the grate being shaken down, the fire bed being broken up by the long poker and the three shovelsful of anthracite unerringly shot into their place on the glowing coals before the furnace door was shut and his step could be heard as he felt his way up the cellar stairs—to emerge not infrequently with an abrasion on the top of his bald head from knocking into furnace pipes. All artificial lighting of course was by gas and I have no remembrance of any lamps in the house for reading or otherwise. Even sulphur matches were expensive and one of our tasks was the rolling of paper tapers, "quills," with one of which I have often lit my way as a child, half terrified, upstairs to bed. . . .

As the older boys began to drift off one by one to college and George to the army, there was less for Mother to do but I don't remember that she particularly changed her ways or became any less active. Time never hung on her hands. There was a period when I was still in Grammar School when she had her own horse and buggy, my chief recollection therewith being of a daily half hour's drive with her, after our noonday dinner and before returning to school, when she would hear my spelling lesson over and over till she thought I knew it. Later on when I was in High School she always helped me with my Latin and Greek.

If I remember aright, this horse of Mother's called Nannie (a joint venture between Mary Harvey and Betsey Cushing) was kept in our barn and was attended to by Father, his own horse and buggy being always kept in a public livery stable on Sibley Street. Father was always interested in and was supposedly a good judge of horses, but he sometimes got fooled. This mare Nannie had a predecessor named Betsey Trotwood whose chief interest in life was to get her tail clamped over the reins while she kicked out the dashboard. Then Father on another occasion, when he was well along in the seventies, went down to Kentucky and bought himself a saddle horse which had a stall in our barn and which he attended to himself. By this time Ned (E.F.C.) was back at home and beginning to take over a share in his practice so that he had a little more leisure. But one day while Father was trying to identify some birds on a side path at Gordon's Park, this horse stumbled and pitched him off on his head, fortunately with no ill effects—other than that it was the last time he ventured to get into the saddle.

Harry (with his wife and three children) had come back to Cleveland by this time (1892) to take the Chair of Geology at the Western Reserve, and Father built a house for him on Case Avenue, next door to the E. P. Williams' house and I suppose a relic of Zalmon Fitch's real estate ventures. So there were small grandchildren to engage Mother's interest and attention and they passed much of their time in our back yard. And a year or two later Ned returned home from abroad and lived in the house until the time of his marriage (*ca.* 1897) to Melanie Harvey. Being quite unattached and not yet very busy in his profession, he devoted himself to Mother and they read or played games together or went out somewhere almost every evening. I've always envied him in this for he was the only one of the boys to whom the opportunity fell thus to repay her in a measure for all she had done for us by real companionship in her later and more leisurely years.

Will had married in 1884, not many years after his graduation (at the top of his class, may I add) from the Harvard Law School, and he would drop in almost daily. Harry was away, except for his vacations, for about fourteen years; George was permanently away after his army enlistment; and I was never back except for summer vacations, after entering Yale in the autumn of 1887. To all of us during these years of absenteeism she sent off without fail a long weekly letter. And the winter of 1900-1901 when I was in France and Switzerland she always wrote me in French though I don't suppose she had had any practice in it since before she was married. There certainly were never any French books about the house to read—certainly no French novels, which were regarded as highly improper even for adults, and for the young, nothing short of demoralizing. . . .

Mother in her later years had some added income to expend—next to none of it on herself, I may add. She was an inveterate giver and was always taking little surprise presents to people, and her favorite Christmas gifts to the young were subscriptions to magazines, the last bit of writing found on her desk being an attempt to make out her list of renewals for the coming Christmas.

During the time of which I have spoken when Ned was again living at home, he introduced her to playing-cards which in earlier days would have been looked upon as instruments of Satan. Games of solitaire amused her and there used to be lively bouts of bezique and perhaps even whist at which all the older children at least were expert. These things with her reading and sewing and fancy work occupied her evenings while Father was busy over his Franklin collection and the genealogical studies, usually in his room upstairs. Whether reading aloud or to herself, she had her book or magazine propped on a sort of wire rack common in old days so that her hands were disengaged for some crocheting or knitting that required no close attention and could be done reflexly. . . .

I have no recollection of Mother's ever having had a day's illness until the few months before her death on October 21, 1903, in her seventy-sixth year. Even then she was not confined to bed until just before the end but with help got up and dressed every day. During these last months Father scarcely left her. His devotion was rare to see, more like a young lover than the austere, unbending, silent doctor-man we children knew. In the last picture we have of her (taken by H.P.C.) she was wrapped up and sitting in the sun at the back of 786 Prospect Street. She was holding a nasturtium Father had picked for her from her favorite border along the fence making the boundary of her garden which she loved to plant and cultivate. It is the only period I remember her when she was not working at something. To while away the time she would recite poetry by the hour, many of them things she said she had learned in childhood and not thought of for years. She had an extraordinary memory—far better than any of her children unless Will and Ned be excepted.

What may have been the cause of her death I don't quite know. Ned and I both thought it was a parietal lobe tumor as one of the first things she observed was a sensory disability of her left hand, and I think she acquired a left hemianopsia. Nothing was said to Father about it and he asked us no questions nor did she. What Father may have thought I don't know, but he wrote in the genealogy book "died of cerebral haemorrhage," which of course may have occurred at the end. She had headaches and was ready to lie down in the afternoons but she never complained. Father scarcely left her side and to the end they shared the same bed as they had done for fifty-one years. This had been so even during those long spells of silence when he might go for a week or two without speaking to her—to any of us, for that matter. Whether he was on edge about something at these times or absorbed and worried about his patients, I never knew, or asked. After her death all his pent-up appreciation of and affection for her showed itself in his collecting all the old photographs of her he could find and having them framed and put in his room as well as distributed to the children.

For the next seven years before he followed on, aged eighty-two, he and Alice lived together in the old house into which so many of us had once been crowded. He was erect, alert, active and interested in his affairs to the end, but it is fortunate he did not live for another year. Ned's untimely death at forty-eight would have been hard for him to bear.

Miss Julia Parsons, an old friend of the family, had this to say in 1940 of the Cushings as she recalled them in the early days:

> . . . Dr. Kirke Cushing . . . I remember . . . as a stern father, too much so as I remember, in his treatment of his sons. Their mother was the one to whom the boys turned for the few indulgences permitted. In the Old Stone Church the Cushing pew was just in front of ours, and every Sunday it was filled by the, I think, six boys, the eldest sitting next to the stiff upright form of his father, who never seemed to relax. *My* father, with only one son, was very envious of the larger family, of whom his special favorite was the youngest and beautiful little boy, Harvey, who sheltered his impatience at the confinement against his mother in the further corner from the unindulgent father.
>
> My father would take a small lozenge, I think a peppermint, from his pocket, pass it to me with a motion to slip it over to the small Harvey, who with a fearful look at the unbending authority at the end of the pew, got it, looking up at his mother whose smile assured him that he might accept it with a quiet conscience. My father's respect for Mrs. Cushing as a mother and sagacious woman was unfailing.
>
> The small Harvey was a delicate boy, and I have often wondered how he could go through so strenuous a training and keep his nervous system fit for the delicate and wonderful operations that made him famous. . . .

Harvey Cushing's Brothers and Sisters

Henry Kirke and B.M.C. had ten children:

William Erastus	*b.* 23 September 1853	*d.* 19 December 1917
Charlotte	*b.* 20 January 1855	*d.* 8 February 1855
Julia	*b.* 9 March 1856	*d.* 12 April 1856
Cornelia	*b.* 26 September 1857	*d.* 15 September 1858
Alice Kirke	*b.* 23 February 1859	*d.* 26 April 1918
Henry Platt	*b.* 10 October 1860	*d.* 14 April 1921
Edward Fitch	*b.* 24 June 1862	*d.* 24 March 1911
George Briggs	*b.* 26 April 1864	*d.* 7 April 1939
Alleyne Maynard	*b.* 5 August 1867	*d.* 26 April 1903
Harvey Williams[1]	*b.* 8 April 1869	*d.* 7 October 1939

Only seven reached maturity. Of these *William Erastus,* the eldest,

[1] After 1899 the middle name was dropped in H.C.'s formal correspondence and in his published writings; only his Yale classmates continued to use it consistently.

went to Western Reserve and then to the Harvard Law School. He was probably nearer to his father than were any of the other boys, but H.K.C. was ever the austere parent and until Harvey came along he almost never showed favoritism. William relates the following anecdote:

> My first year out of College was a pretty aimless drifting one, I had an idea of going into newspaper work, which came to nothing; and like other boys ignorant of the world I did not know where to start. I tried to get a teaching position but did not succeed. Finally Grandfather Cushing suggested to me that I study law. It was a new idea, but it soon came to appeal to me. Grandfather's suggestion also was that if I cared to go to a law school (Harvard or anywhere), he would pay the expense of it. When I reported this to father (feeling relieved that the way was open without it being a burden to him, for this was during the hard times that followed the panic of 1873) he said that he would send me to a law school if I wanted to study law, but (to my surprise) that he didn't wish anyone but himself to pay the cost of the education of a boy of his.

William married Miss Carolyn Kellogg of Pittsfield, Massachusetts and practised law in Cleveland until his death in December 1917.

Alice Kirke Cushing remained at home unmarried, and after B.M.C.'s death in 1903 she kept house for her father and ultimately inherited the property at 786 Prospect Street, many family papers (those that H.C. had not purloined), and most of the family effects. Shy and somewhat austere, Miss Cushing had an active mind and was widely read both in history and general literature, and she became an authority on English church architecture without ever having travelled abroad. She also had a retentive memory and was given to quoting poetry at length and with seemingly little effort. Like Harvey, she made a point of preserving family papers, but after her death in 1918 (when H.C. was in France) her brother Henry placed many of her books and letters in the rubbish heap, thus disposing of much that might have had historical interest.

Henry Platt Cushing ("Harry") was graduated from Cornell University in 1882 and became one of the foremost geologists of the country. He studied at Munich in 1891 and 1892 and was appointed to the chair of geology at Western Reserve the following year. He headed a geological survey to the Glacier Bay region of Alaska in the early '90's, and the official maps of that area now show a glacier and a plateau, north of Glacier Bay, named after him. He died in April 1921, after thirty years of service to Western Reserve. Henry Cushing's son, Kirke, went through Harvard Medical School with a distinguished record. To the deep grief of the entire family he capsized in a canoe and drowned shortly after his graduation. Alice, the elder daughter, died of typhoid at seventeen. Cornelia, who married the Rev. Vivan A. Peterson, still resides in Cleveland.

Edward Fitch Cushing ("Ned") was the only other child who became a physician. Following in the footsteps of Henry, Edward took his academic degree at Cornell in 1883 and then went on to Harvard, where he received his M.D. in 1888, thus incidentally paving the way for Harvey who followed him at the Harvard Medical School several years later. He was a pediatrician and was appointed in 1894 Associate Professor of Pediatrics at Western Reserve. A few years later he occupied the chair of pediatrics. "An enthusiastic and inspiring teacher, he was admired and loved by his students and house officers. His influence over the young men under him was remarkably stimulating." Edward, like his father, also took an active part in the affairs of the local medical societies in Cleveland and he did much to stimulate the development of the Cleveland Medical Library. He was gifted intellectually and, like others in his family, he had an unusually retentive memory. He died prematurely of an inoperable cancer of the rectum at the age of forty-eight. His death, while at the height of his career, plunged the family into grief, particularly Harvey, who had always been very close to him. A few hours before his brother's death, Harvey was impelled to set down this thought:

EDWARD FITCH CUSHING

A sketch of brother Ned while "reading Parkman" made by H.C. in August 1896 on a Great Lakes' steamer

> In a short while I shall be the last of the Cushing doctors. A little more than a year ago there were three of us. Neddie is dying in a near room in a most beautiful and ecstatic euthanasia. . . . He smilingly told me that Harvey [his son "Pat"] had the 'touch'—that the 'kitchen' preferred him much to the head of the house. Pray God, he has—for it must go somewhere. Too rare to be lost in any family who has it. Some Cushing doctor in the future may know what I mean—the thing that puts a patient almost immediately under your control and in your confidence with a trust that fails not. . . . Pat at thirteen quieted him in a moment, and the others, all falling over themselves in devotion, made him jumpy. This is something quite apart from the spirit of research which is in our modern type [of physician].

Edward's son, Edward Harvey ("Pat") to whom H.C. refers, lived up to his early promise and became a physician—the only living Cushing doctor of his generation in the family.

George Briggs Cushing was a somewhat eccentric bachelor who fled the family circle early in life to join the army. He became a Jack-of-all-trades without gaining particular distinction in any one. Toward the end of his life he became an active leader of the Boy Scout movement in California. He died in April 1939.

Alleyne Maynard Cushing was a boy of great promise and Harvey's immediate contemporary, there being only eighteen months between them. They grew up together and in physical appearance resembled one another closely. Temperamentally they also seemed to be much alike as children, both exhibiting the kind of impetuous zeal which characterized Harvey throughout his life. Alleyne, however, did not apply himself at school and did not go on to college. Frail in health, he eventually developed tuberculosis but recovered and made several unsuccessful attempts to establish himself in Cleveland. His father then urged him to go westward where he apparently fell into bad company and, much to the grief of the family, was found dead in Douglas, Arizona, in April 1903 with a bullet through his head and a revolver lying close by. Investigation made it doubtful that he had committed suicide, but the case was never fully solved. He had been away from home for ten years. H.K.C. announced the unhappy tidings in two brief notes to H.C. The first, on 26 April 1903, said merely: "We are just informed of the melancholy death of Alleyne, by his own hand, last night in Douglas, Arizona. No particulars thus far. Will write as soon as they are learned." The next day he wrote again:

> Since my note of yesterday which was broken in upon by the dispatch about Alleyne, further advices suggest the strong probability of murder: no circumstances of the matter are yet known to us. It occurred at Douglas, Arizona, where Alleyne had gone early in the month, as he wrote me at the time, when he thought he might find some employment. Telegraph and railroad connection is very roundabout, and we are hoping for answer to inquiries hourly. Will keep you informed of all we hear. Aff. FATHER.

No further information reached the family, however, and the case was dropped. Since Alleyne had been the companion of his boyhood, H.C. was deeply disturbed by the tragedy and for many months thereafter he slept badly and continued to refer to Alleyne's unhappy fate.

Harvey Cushing's Childhood and Early Education

Cushing's parents, who had been married on 17 June 1852, had lived in rooms on East First Street in Cleveland, where William was born in 1853. The next year they moved to Sheriff Street (now East Fourth), evidently an unhealthy place for the next three children all died on these premises in infancy. In 1860 they moved to a house at 10 Euclid Avenue which had been built on the Zalmon Fitch property, and it was there that Harvey Cushing was born on 8 April 1869. He did not remember his birthplace for in 1873 business interests had encroached on lower Euclid and the family betook themselves to a more spacious house at 786 Prospect Street (renumbered 3112 in 1908) to be near Grandfather Erastus, whose house and office were near by at 967 Euclid. Harvey's youth was thus spent in Cleveland, and he remained there, save for summer excursions up the Great Lakes, until he matriculated at Yale in September 1887.

On 15 June 1910 Mr. Newton M. Anderson, Harvey's Cleveland high school teacher, wrote to him from Asheville School in North Carolina in reference to his appointment as Professor of Surgery at Harvard: "I saw it all twenty-seven years ago and have had the greatest delight in watching the materializing of my vision. You surely have become all that I hoped and dreamed you might be, and I think I placed my standard for you at the very top notch." The pride of a teacher in a successful pupil is inevitably deep, and it was especially real in the case of Newton Anderson and Harvey Cushing. Before describing their relationship, however, Harvey's boyhood may be briefly outlined.[2]

Harvey was an unusually attractive baby, as a photograph taken at the age of two bears witness, but he was in no sense a precocious child. He evinced signs of unusual energy and spirit at an early age; also a rather conspicuous streak of determination amounting at times to stubbornness. When he was less than six years of age, the following jingle was perpetrated upon him at a family party:

"Pepper Pot, Pepper Pot, when you were young
They tell me you had a most fiery tongue."

Mr. A. F. Harvey, H.C.'s cousin, writes of their boyhood:

> As small boys we played all the boyhood games, such as pull-away, duck and drake, one old cat, tag, hare and hounds, shinny (on grass in summer and on ice in winter), base-ball, foot-ball (sort of a Rugby game) and later, tennis. We made and flew our own kites. We cut out of trees and made our own shinny sticks. We made our own outdoor skating rinks by flooding someone's yard. We went swimming almost every day during the season. This necessitated a walk of two or three miles across-lots, unless one of us was lucky enough to pry a horse and buggy off one of our families. In all these athletics Harvey was adept, and was one of the most graceful boys I ever knew. We had a gymnasium in the loft of a barn, and here again he excelled in tumbling as well as in all uses of rings, parallel bars and turning bar. As we came into young manhood he became an exceptionally graceful dancer.

Other details concerning his boyhood are well described in his memoir of his mother.

[2] For many of the details I am much in the debt of Dr. Cushing's Cleveland contemporaries, including his cousins the late Mrs. Edward F. Cushing, Mrs. A. D. Baldwin, and Mr. A. F. Harvey; Dr. William Corlett, Miss Mary C. Goodwillie, Mrs. Abram Garfield; also Mr. Charles A. Otis, the late Dr. George W. Crile and Mrs. Crile, Dr. J. J. Thomas, Mr. and Mrs. Samuel Halle, Mr. J. Milton Dyer, Mr. Alexander Taylor, Rev. Vivan A. Peterson, and many present-day Cleveland physicians including Drs. Clyde L. Cummer, Howard Dittrick, Harold Feil, and Louis Karnosh.

At the age of six, Harvey was entered in a private primary school directly across the street from his house at the corner of Prospect and Kennard Streets (now East 46th Street). He stayed there for two years and then entered the Sterling Street Grammar School which, as Mr. Harvey recalls, was midway between the Cushing house and that of the Harveys. There is little information concerning his six years there, but thanks to the generous efforts of Dr. Harold Feil, a full transcript of his record during the four years at Central High School has been made available.[3]

Harvey Cushing entered "Central" in February 1883 at the age of thirteen years and ten months, and was graduated on Friday evening, 24 June 1887. J. J. Thomas, his classmate, recalls that on entering the school Harvey was "a short, chubby little fellow, wearing short pants and a little bob-tailed coat, very fashionable at that time for young boys." He and Dr. Thomas had taken the classical course at Central, and Cushing stood eleventh in a class of eighty-three students, with a final average for the four years of 89.34. His cousin Perry Harvey was twelfth with a grade of 89.19. The top student of the class was one A. Lynch whose average was 93.4. In examining grades in individual courses, it is interesting that Cushing's best grades were in mathematics (arithmetic and trigonometry; average 95); he also stood very well in Latin which he had studied throughout his four years (average 92); rather less well in Greek which he had studied during his last three years, and he was poorest in English history in which he scored a grade of 75 during his first year.

He was president of the class during his senior year, and at the class entertainment on 16 December 1886 he is listed on the program with Taylor Boggis as giving a tumbling exhibition, as well as taking the part of "Mr. Highflown" in the class play on the same occasion. He did not participate in the Commencement program. Dr. Thomas recalls that the Central seniors paid a visit to the seniors of West High School. As president of the class Harvey was obliged to respond to a speech of welcome, but owing to embarrassment his speech "was a complete flop."

It was during his years at high school that Newton Anderson came into H.C.'s life. Mr. Anderson was born in Cincinnati and after graduating from the University of Ohio had been employed in 1879 by the Bell Telephone Company to install the first telephone exchange at Liége in Belgium. He returned to the United States in

[3] The high school building, which was abandoned in 1940, had been erected in 1878 on East 55th Street at a total cost of $74,000. This sum was inadequate for the completion of the tower which was made possible in 1892 with the installation of a three-faced clock through a gift of Mrs. John D. Rockefeller, Sr.

1881 and served as instructor in physics at the University of Ohio. In September 1883 he became teacher of physics at Central High School and began almost at once to agitate for a course in manual training. Cushing had studied physics under him in 1883-1884 (grade 89) and had assisted him in the apparatus room and received some instruction in the use of tools. The following summer (1884) Anderson took Harvey Cushing, Perry Harvey, "Al" Harvey, and "Ed" Williams—all cousins—up the lake on a fishing expedition, spending most of the summer at a small farm-house near Sault Sainte Marie. On alternate mornings Anderson took two of the boys down the river to fish and made them row back against the current. The following winter (February 1885) he bought an island of some twenty-five acres situated in Lake Huron near the Sault River. He first took the boys to the island during the summer of 1885, along with others from Cleveland, some fourteen in number. To this camp Cushing returned in the summers of both 1886 and 1887, and some of his earliest letters date from these camping expeditions. In his appreciation of his cousin Perry Harvey, H.C. gives a vivid description of the camp:

> To this island we gave the name Maskenoza—the Indian word, I believe, for a pike which it somewhat resembled in outline—and there we passed most of the following summer [1885], felling spruce with which to build our camp, cooking our own meals, supplying with gun and rod most of our provender, exploring the neighboring country so full of border history, and in leisure time surveying and mapping our small domain. That winter a staunch 42-foot schooner was built in which, on the eagerly awaited close of school, eight of us sailed from Cleveland to our beloved island, another eight having preceded us by steamer to get the camp rebuilt and in running order before the arrival of the schooner with its crew.

Herbert McBride, aged sixteen, kept a diary of their first summer at Maskenoza and his sister, Mrs. George W. Crile, has generously made this available. It starts:

> With a party of 14 we left Cleveland at half past 11 on the night of July 3rd, 1885. A pleasanter night could not have been wished for. The water was as smooth as glass. Before we started, we chose lots as to our stateroom. Three boys went in one room, one slept in the upper berth and two in the lower. Avery Adams, Harvey Cushing and myself drew room number 3. It was said in the morning that voices in our room were heard clear to the other end of the boat, but of course I do not know anything of that.

McBride in a letter of 10 July goes on:

> The island is just covered with trees and underbrush. It took us until afternoon of the first day to clear away a place about 40 ft. square. We cleaned away the trees and were constantly on the lookout for lumber as it was after dinner and our prospects for shelter were not very good. Our first meal was very slim—menu: hard tack, oatmeal, crackers and water.

On 16 July:

The boys eat the greatest lot of pancakes you ever saw. We have them regularly once a day and each fellow takes about 12 or 14. That's no fish story and they are corking big ones besides. We have got the flagpole up and it looks splendid. Mr. Anderson has just got the sail to the big boat done. Yesterday, one of my squad days, the boys had splendid fishing. Ten of them caught about 40 with an average of three to three-and-a-half pounds a piece. There are more pike biting now than anything else, but the halfbreeds say the bass will begin to be thick about the last of the month. We cannot eat all of the fish now that the boys are fishing every day, so Mr. Anderson has begun to salt them.

Several of Cushing's own letters, the first antedating this period, are filled with amusing turns of boyish enthusiasm. From them we incidentally learn that he had become an ardent entomologist. The first is to his brother William:

H.C. to W.E.C. [*c. 1877*]

Dear Will, I want you to come home. We have got a new hen, and I have been making some things for Christmas. Has it snowed there yet? We have got some new dining-room chairs. Grandpa Cushing gave them to us for a Christmas present and Harry and Ned went to Kent [Ohio] and we had two turkeys on Thanksgiving and one the day after. Papa made me a man and it was made of wishbone and it was made of a turkeys wishbone and it had a feather in its hat and it had wire arms and mama mad some clothes for it and I am going to hang it on the Christmas tree. Ed says: it is so cold that you had beter pull down your vest to keep warm. and Ed broke a great big piece of our bed. now I will tell you about Jinks' [Alleyne's] man who has got a stand-up collar and it has a different cind of clothes. And I forgot to tell you what I made for Christmas I made some disected pictures and that wish-bone man and I have been knitting a mat. and George took off that box that was on the old sled and it made it look offel pretty. and I am sorry that I made that blot. and up in your room the window blew wright in and papa came up stares and fixed it up as well as he could. and Alleyne says that he likes that story that you gave him and I like those two storyes that you gave me that are about Thanksgiving and Chester hog. I think that I will not write any more this time and I will tell you the rest when you come home. becous you are comeing home soon. your aff. brother HARVEY.

Cleveland,
H.C. to B.M.C. *17 July 1885, 7 a.m.*

Dear Mama, As you prophesied, Jinks got your letter Sunday morning, when he went for the mail, and as you said your's was the first letter you ever wrote to me. I suppose this one is the first I ever wrote you. I want to tell you about the big storm we had here Thursday night. The first I knew of it was being disturbed by Ed's getting up to see if it was raining in either of our windows, and such a racket was going on that—as Brer Remus says—"I dident know which minuet was gwine to be de nex." The thunder boomed and the lightening pealed, at least it *peeled* all the bark off Mr. Ed Harvey's big oak tree which was struck during the storm. The Higbee's went up the lakes yesterday and the Mitchels are going today so there won't be much interest in Sunday School and Church. When Aunt Mamie and the Boys were coming up to Earlville to take the train, Uncle Day drove Aunt Mamie, and Will the boys, but they must have gone to slow for the boys got left and had to come up on the Connotton at 6 o'clock. Clarkie is going to stay down until Friday when [name illegible] is coming up with him to stay over night. Al [Harvey] and Grouse are going down to have their pictures taken together, and I have to be down at 10.30 to have my teeth Buffetted. Aunt Mamie let Perry, Al and myself take Nannie and go down to the lake and she stood just as still all the time. I learned to swim a little yesterday, at least I can keep myself up in the water, but I don't know whether I make any progress or not. Those new black stockings fitted me exactly right. I wish they all did as well. It is getting almost time for breakfast so I guess I had better close with love to William E. H.W.C.

P.S. I was going to try and make a life preserver out of cork but Grandpa C. said it would not be safe and he would rather buy me one, but I don't want to ask him to do that so I am at a loss to know what to do about it. He said I could get one at the rubber store but that bit of knowledge don't do me any good, for I haven't the money to buy it with. HARVEY.

Camp Maskenoza,
H.C. to B.M.C. *Tuesday, 10 August 1886.*

Dear Mother, As I omitted in my last letter to send the money and insect pins which you requested I thought I had better send them on to you. I did not expect to have a chance to write today for I am on squad with Burt and Al but all the boys except 3, not on squad, have gone seven miles down the Michigan coast to a trout stream and those three—Ed, Will and Morris—have just gotten back from fishing with 27 lbs of pike &c after we had waited dinner for them two hours, so that now the dishes are all cleaned up and as they had dinner so late, we get out of getting a hot supper. Burt and I are writing and Al and Ed are pounding the table and urging us on so that we can go in swimming together.

I paralyzed myself yesterday over to Detour by finding that I weighed 127, a gain of 13 lbs since I left home which I will immediately have to work off at the "Gym" on my return. I have got a great many more insects this year than last, every 5 minutes somebody yells out "Oh Harve! Whats this?" and I have got so used to it that I just say "I dunno, stick it in the cyanide bottle" and when I come to look them over I have to pin for a good while before I can get them pinned not speaking of setting any of them. I don't see how I came to go away with only 2 p. of D. and about 12 of the other kind. I have to wash a p. of D. about every 3 days. Expect us Tuesday morning. Love to all, HARVEY W. CUSHING.

In another letter to his mother (12 Aug. 1887) he writes:

I wish I had brought up a butterfly net this year, for there are more on the island than I have seen before. There is a crysalis formed on the rafters right over my bed and yesterday Jack brought in a big hawk moth caterpillar, but we could not find out anything for him to eat. So today I let him go as he was getting very meagre. One of the boys brought in the funniest shaped skull I ever saw, which is not saying much, but we could not imagine what it was so I have preserved it to show to father.

And again the following spring (15 April 1888) a letter harks back amusingly to a problem that had come up while he was in camp the previous year—indeed was never to be wholly downed:

> You and Father both got into me last week for spelling wrong. I am mighty glad you did for thats the best way to learn and I don't blame you a bit for I used to be noted for being about the worst speller in the Grammar School class. Father says I ought to keep a dictionary beside me all the time but its the words I ought to know, and suppose I do know, that I misspell. I remember that last summer up to the lakes I got a letter in which you said I had been spelling "sure" shure all summer and hoped I would deign to change. Don't you recollect how we used to drive the Kicking Nanny up and down Sterling Avenue before dinner while you tried to drill the afternoon spelling lesson into me with such words as "ichthyophagous." That must have been about five years ago.

McBride attended St. Paul's School at Concord, New Hampshire, and on 20 December 1885 he wrote to his mother: "Yesterday morning the first persons that I saw [on] coming into the depot were Horace Hutchins, Rollo Watson, Perry Harvey, Harvey Cushing and Ed Williams, who had come down to welcome my return. The train was an hour and a half late. Papa said they were down there when the train was due at 6 o'clock." And two days later he wrote: "Yesterday afternoon five of us boys went down to get Mr. Anderson a Christmas present. We all put in fifty cents and got him a scarf pin at Mr. Hubbard's. It was very pretty, but of course nothing very elaborate at that price. . . . Mr. Anderson goes down to Columbus today to spend Christmas. Now, since the manual training school has got started it seems to be getting along first-rate. They have got some of the roof beams up and he hopes to get into it by the last of January sure."

The Manual Training School

This early reference to the Manual Training School requires some explanation. During 1884-1885, Mr. Anderson, on behalf of the parents of twelve boys including Harvey Cushing, C. Avery Adams, Herbert McBride, Perry Harvey, Horace Hutchins, George Collins, and Edward Childs, had rented an unused barn on the property of Mr. E. H. Harvey; and there they began their first manual training course. In the spring of 1885, after enlisting the interest and support of a number of Cleveland citizens, Anderson was able to purchase the ground on the north side of Carnegie Avenue, west of what are now the Pennsylvania Railroad tracks, and by February 1886 had built and equipped the three-story brick building referred to in Herbert McBride's letter of 22 December (1885). This came to be known as the Cleveland Manual Training

School. Instruction was provided in carpentry, wood-turning, forge, bent metal work, mechanical drawing, and machinery. The Manual Training School functioned as a private institution until the spring of 1890 when it was incorporated into the Cleveland Public School system, the forerunner of our technical high schools.

Anderson was convinced that manual dexterity played an important part in the intellectual training of boys, and all of Harvey Cushing's contemporaries in Cleveland have suggested that this early training contributed notably in the shaping of his subsequent career as a surgeon. In referring to Anderson, Mr. Allyn F. Harvey writes: "For myself I can say that he drilled us very thoroughly in the handling of small boats, propelled by oar or paddle, up to thorough ability to handle a 46-foot schooner yacht; he taught us a lot about being independent and made us so by the duties he inflicted upon us during these summer vacations. We were all undoubtedly better disciplined and better prepared for life from the teachings of this man, and from association such as we had with him." Many years afterwards Cushing recalled: "We embryo carpenters progressed to a course of wood-turning with lathes and a year later to metal work at a forge—like so many blacksmiths learning to strike when the iron was hot—the best possible cure for youthful indecision."[4]

[4] *Yale University Library Gazette,* January 1937, p. 49.

CHAPTER III

Bright College Years: Yale

1887–1891

THE municipal high schools of the western states early became distinguished for their excellent vocational training, but in Harvey Cushing's student days, even as now, they were likely to provide a relatively poor background in languages and literature, often insufficient to meet the requirements for entrance to an eastern college. Both H.C. and his cousin, Perry Harvey, had help in French from their uncle, Charles Tudor Williams, formerly of Kent, Ohio, and H.C. had additional tutoring from his mother who was accomplished in French. The entrance examinations for Yale were held in Chicago, and H.C. was doubtless relieved when the following handwritten letter arrived from the Secretary of the University:

F.B. Dexter to H.C. *6 July 1887.*

Dear Sir, Your examination at Chicago was satisfactory, and the formal certificate of admission will be sent you, as soon as the testimonial to character from the Cleveland High School, or the principal teacher you have been under, is received, as required by our catalogue. Yours truly, F. B. DEXTER.

This letter and the formal admission certificate were found carefully preserved in the first of two college scrapbooks which were kept systematically throughout the years at New Haven. In them H.C. placed memorabilia of every description: menus, programs, news cuttings (especially those relating to athletic events with which he was in any way connected), photographs, and even examination papers. One could reconstruct his college years with little difficulty from these meticulously kept volumes, but an even richer source of information was discovered in the letters exchanged weekly with his parents in Cleveland. The correspondence extended from 1887, when he entered Yale, to 1910, with a few breaks between 1896 and 1900. The letters are intimate documents of great human interest, portraying with clarity Cushing's rather slow emotional and intellectual development. They also throw valuable light on the state of collegiate and medical education at Yale and Harvard during these years. It is curious that in writing to his father and mother Cushing seemed to take it for granted, probably with reason, that neither parent would show his letters to the other.

He arrived in New Haven on 17 September 1887 and went directly to 166 York Street where he was to share rooms with his cousin, Perry Harvey, in a rooming house which is still standing. He wrote his father the next day:

[*166 York Street*]
H.C. to H.K.C. *18 September 1887.*

. . . We arrived here about 3 and came right up to the house finding Miss Prescott in the midst of fixing our rooms. She had just kalsomined and it smelled so bad that we could not sleep in the bed room last night and as Perry had a cold we could not let in much air. They are third story rooms or rather attic rooms and there are only two small windows, one in each room, which is a great drawback as there is not much light admitted and the front wall slants so that we can't hang anything on it. The landlady had procured two beds and had put matting on the floor beside the kalsomining, which alas comes off very easily on clothes. There is a small bureau, book-case, and washstand as well as two closets which constitute our furniture at present besides a round table so you see that we will have to get tables and lamps. We have been scratching around getting meals since we were here, last night we got into a tony place where we had to pay 65 cts. for a poor meal and this morning we got a ten o'clock breakfast at another place for 15 cents and are waiting to make out a dinner and supper at Mr. Ladd's where we are asked to tea. Miss Prescott says she will take an eating club of 6 or 7 boys if we can get it up, but we are waiting to see what kind of boys the Freshmen are who have got the floors below us. She says she expects them tomorrow. . . . We took a walk this morning under the wing of Will Williams out to the Athletic field which unfortunately is two miles from the campus with no St. car lines connecting. We also looked around at the buildings, some of which are very old and dingy looking and are a great contrast to the Williams buildings which I saw Friday on a drive from Pittsfield. . . .

To his mother he wrote on the same day: "You see I have not been here long enough to become enthusiastic about it and it is not a place to become so at first sight." Later (6 Nov.) he sent her a sketch of his room showing how he had eventually arranged it.

It was not long before he found himself in the full swing of college life at Yale. Mr. George T. Ladd, mentioned in the letter, was his second cousin, Ladd's mother having been Elizabeth Williams, a cousin of H.C.'s mother. Ladd was the Professor of Mental and Moral Philosophy, and he and his wife stood *in loco parentis* both to H.C. and to Perry Harvey during their college years. Writing to his sister Alice on 2 October, H.C. mentions other social contacts:

Prof. Seymour, or Digamma as he is called, kindly invited Harry Hurd, an Elyria boy named Ely, Perry and myself to tea Wednesday where we had a very pleasant time. Prof. wanted to be remembered to all the folks. He said I looked for all the world like Will, not to speak of Mother. I had the worst time in Pittsfield with the resemblance people saw in me to the family. Mrs. Kellogg thought I was the "spittin" image of you. Last Sunday night we cousins all went over to Henry Thompsons and sat around his log fireplace and sang "to the tune of Will's light guitar" which he has learned to play.

In an early letter to his father (16 Oct.) Cushing describes the freshman curriculum and mentions the names of his instructors:

We have now got well into the full swing of recitations. Chapel at 8.10, first recitation at 8.30, second at 12 and third at 5, varied by only one on Saturday, and it takes almost all the time between recitations to get the next lesson; besides this week we have had to do 29 original propositions for our geometry teacher, extra, which we have to do in ink. I have got already 25 of them but don't have to hand them in till Tuesday. Mr. Moore, our geometry man, is a stinker if I may use that expression and the only one of our tutors who is not liked. We have Mr. Taft for Livy, Prof. Seymour for Homer, Prof. Phillips for Algebra and Mr. Cushing[1] for Cicero, Mr. Bridgman (son of the Cleveland man) for Greek prose and Mr. Moore for Geometry. Our program is very queerly arranged. You see there are six tutors and six studies and the class is divided into six divisions so every tutor is engaged at the same time. I forgot to say that we have German at the 12 recitation Mon., Wed. and Fri. of Mr. [Alfred] Ripley, the great tennis player. He is mighty nice to some of the boys who can't get on to the pronunciation easily. To go back to the program. Tomorrow for instance I have Homer at 8, German at 12, Livy at 5; Tuesday, Geom. at 8, Gk. Prose at 12, Cicero at 5 and so on through the program going around like a wheel.

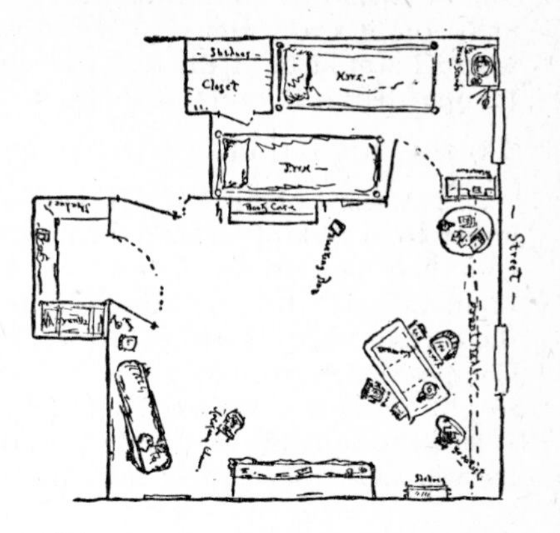

ROOMS AT 166 YORK STREET

Diagram of the quarters occupied by H.C. and Perry Harvey during their first semester at Yale. From letter of H.C. to B.M.C. of 6 November 1887

Later (18 Feb.) he writes:

. . . We finished the "De Amicitia" the other day; now we have to get Cicero's Select Orationes. They are giving us our fill of Cicero. We have read the Senectute and Amicitia and are reading his letters to Atticus which are about the hardest Latin prose, and now we have to start in on the orationes. I am getting tired of him and I wish they would give us a change.

And again (19 Feb.):

. . . There is one subject, especially, that we have just taken up, and one that I never had very good drilling on, which I have to grind over like everything and it is a kind that is hard to study on, that is Latin Composition. The first week or two that we had it I got terribly down in the mouth and thought my place in the first division was gone sure, but Mr. Cushing told me I was picking up in it so I don't feel as disgusted with it as I did. The worst part of it is that half of the lesson you can't study up for; what he gives

[1] The "Mr. Cushing" mentioned as a Latin instructor was William Lee Cushing, B.A. 1872, M.A. 1882, and Instructor at Yale, 1887-88; he appears not to have been an immediate family connection of H.C.'s.

us to get outside I can bone up but he always gives in the last part of the recitation a long sentence in English which we have to turn into Latin almost as fast as we can write, which some of them can do, but I get a low mark on it every time. If Mr. Cushing wasn't a high marker I don't know where I would be. I think I have got a pretty good mark in Mathematics and I hope that will counterbalance it somewhat.

To this his father replied sternly (23 Feb.):

. . . A word about Latin Composition and all other studies that come hard, either from lack of acquaintance or aptitude for them. The necessity of putting your best capacity into them, of working hard upon them, is what develops brain capacity, just as training is needed for good bone, muscle and pluck in the race or tug of gymnastic or outdoor sports. Every victory gained over Latin Composition is a preparation for success in the hard things of life wh. come to all. So work away at it and feel that after all it is a blessing in disguise. Difficulties squarely met and overcome by faithful work are the tests of character wh. show the reliable man from the fair weather crowd of sailors.

YALE COLLEGE, FRESHMAN CLASS, FALL TERM, 1887.

Text Books.	1st Lesson.	Recit. Room.	Instructor.
Livy, Bks. 21 and 22. Edited by W. W. Capes.	First Introduction; 1st and half of 2nd page of text.	185 Lyceum.	Mr. TAFT.
Homer's Iliad, Tyler's Ed.	18th Book, Lines 1—17.	184 Lyceum.	Div. Master. Prof. SEYMOUR.
Graphic Algebra.	1st Chapter.	E, Atheneum.	Prof. PHILLIPS.
Kelsey's Cicero De Senectute.	English Introduction.	D ~~F~~, Atheneum.	Mr. CUSHING.
Jackson's Prose Comp'n.	Page 31, all, and page 56, Ex. 19.	G, Atheneum.	Mr. BRIDGMAN.
Chauvenet's Geometry.	Bk. VI., 1st 4 pages.	T ~~D~~, Atheneum.	Mr. MOORE.
German 10 A.M. Mon. Wed. & Fri.			Prof. Ripley

College Prayers, 8.10 A. M. Recitations in Latin. Greek and Mathematics, immediately after Prayers every week-day; at 12 M. ~~from Monday to Friday~~ Tues. and Thurs. inclusive; and at ~~8 P. M.~~ ~~on Tuesdays and Thursdays~~. 5 from Monday to Friday inc.

(over)

Further insight into Yale's pedagogical habits of this period may be gained from a passage written to his mother (25 March 1888):

They have laid out our work for next term and I have three new subjects though only one new tutor, Mr. Abbott whom I like very much though I have only recited to him once; still you can tell pretty well by one recitation. He has Horace. We have Mr. Cushing in Demosthenes in which he gives about as long lessons as he did in the "Amicitia." Mr. Moore is trying to drive some Analytical Trigonometry into us. We still have Mr. Taft in Cicero's Letters, Prof. Ripley in German and Mr. Bridgman in Herodotus. Mr. Bridgman has taken a new wrinkle lately and he takes someone out of the division to look up something extra besides the regular work. Last time he called on three of whom I was one. He gave the other boys their subjects and told me he wanted me to get the account of the battle of Sardis by Nicolaus Damascenus Olympiodorus and read it and write out a comparison of his account and that of Xenophon and Herodotus. So I have got a Greek book here from the library as big as a dictionary, containing

"THE CREW OF THE [ILLEGIBLE]"
Summer of 1884
Back row: N. M. Anderson, P. W. Harvey
Front row: A. F. Harvey, E. M. Williams, H.C.

A SOPHOMORE AT YALE
From a photograph taken in January 1889

H.C. IN A BACKWARD SOMERSAULT
Off the steps of the old Yale gymnasium

TOUCHED FOR A CONTRIBUTION
But the pockets were empty. On the old Yale campus

YALE FRESHMAN BASEBALL TEAM
In Spring of 1888. H.C. in front row center

H.C. (right) AND FRIEND (J. Sanford Barnes)
ON YALE FENCE

THE YALE FENCE
From A. G. Howland's painting

the relics of his writings, which I have to peruse before Wednesday morning. It sounds interesting, don't you think so?

Saturday medical lectures were also mentioned: "We have to attend every Saturday noon a medical lecture which I hope will become more interesting as we get on, but it has been pretty slow as yet."

Yale College during Cushing's undergraduate years was in a state of transition from a small and rather self-satisfied teaching institution, which offered social advantages to the sons of its more wealthy alumni, to an institution of learning with graduate schools and a broader university outlook. Until that time the Academical Department had almost completely dominated the scene. The theological and classical faculties had been in the ascendant, but Yale had also developed in its Sheffield Scientific School a group of men of outstanding reputation in the field of science, including Benjamin Silliman in chemistry, James Dwight Dana in geology, Othniel Charles Marsh in paleontology, and Josiah Willard Gibbs, the world-renowned mathematical physicist; and when Charles Eliot as a young chemist was made president of Harvard in 1869, he sought to steal several of Yale's best scientific brains.

During Cushing's years in New Haven the Laboratory of Physiological Chemistry was being developed by Russell Chittenden, and Cushing came to be influenced by Chittenden and by the students who flocked to him: men such as Elliott Joslin, now one of our foremost diabetes specialists; Graham Lusk, who later took over the Department of Physiology at Yale; and Lafayette Mendel, who succeeded Chittenden in the chair of Physiological Chemistry at Yale—these and many others; but it is probable that he did not appreciate until many years later the extent of his debt to men like Chittenden, Joslin, and Mendel. It was to Yale College that Cushing became attached emotionally, but one cannot contend that Yale College made a serious student of him, for he was more interested in baseball, the social contacts of the Fence, and the "gym" than he was, for example, in the library, which, surprisingly enough, he confessed to having visited only once in his four years.[2]

Financial problems loomed large throughout H.C.'s college years and those at medical school. His father could not afford to be lavish with a tenth child, and he insisted on the strictest accounting. At the beginning of the freshman year H.C. was in constant penury; an appeal for funds went off on 16 October:

[2] His memory seems to have failed him here. In November 1888 he borrowed Packard's *Guide to the study of insects;* and in January 1891 his wife-to-be, Kate Crowell, visiting Yale with her mother, caused him to enter the library again, this time the Chittenden Library, opened in 1890, a photograph of which was preserved in his scrapbook.

I have to again send a supplication to you for money. It seems as though you sent me just a day or two ago that $40 which, in making out my accounts last night, I find to be too small to pay my board bill for $12, which comes in every other Friday, next Friday being the one. Perry and I have each subscribed to three college papers. Everybody is expected to take all of them but I did not take the Courant. I took the News—a daily which costs four dollars; it is almost a necessity as all the notices etc. are printed in it. I also take the Record, a bi-weekly for $1.50 and the Yale Literary Magazine for $3.00. Perry takes the Courant in place of the Record. If you would like I will send them home after I have read them so you can see what they are. The News and the "Lit" are very good papers but I can't say much for the Record. I paid Miss Hotchkiss $12.00 for two weeks board. I just paid Miss Prescott today $12.00 as my share of the rooms for four weeks. Last Wednesday I got stuck $10.00 for the support of the crew, and I consider now that I was pretty lucky as Perry got stuck $25.

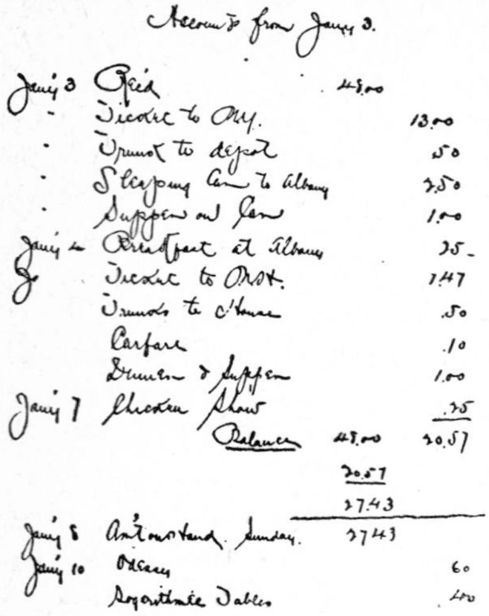

EXPENSE ACCOUNT
A page from one of H.C.'s accounts submitted each month to his father

There were similar appeals every month or so during the next eight years, since Henry Kirke could never bring himself to supply funds spontaneously. A similar streak of penuriousness often came out in his son in later years; but unlike his father, he could be as pound-foolish as he was penny-wise, and many instances could be cited of H.C.'s spontaneous and at times lavish generosity. In some of his more frantic appeals for funds, there are touches of humor, as on 13 April 1890:

Dear Father, I meant to write to you for some more money two weeks ago but somehow was interrupted & kept putting it off till we went on the trip, and then thought I would wait till I got back to New Haven, as the trip does not necessitate any expense on our part, but I got back here with ten cents in my pocket, five of which I spent for a paper this morning leaving me with quite a small capitol [*sic*].

I have felt very much, during the last few days, like the man who having been short of funds for some time, procured in some way a five dollar note and meeting a friend said "I have here a five dollar William" and, when asked why he called it a William, he said he didn't know it well enough to call it Bill.

H.C. at this time also began to develop his powers of description, nowhere better exemplified than in his letter on the blizzard of '88, an event to which he often referred in later life:

New Haven,
H.C. to B.M.C. *Sunday, 18 March 1888.*

Dear Mother I suppose you have had full particulars of the storm by this time from the papers, though for some days communication and travel were stopped, but as the weather usually has to take up a good part of my letters as of most peoples I will give you my account of the blizzard which I think comes up to Harry's storms. One of the boys in the class who comes from St. Paul says it beats any storm he ever saw at home. You know I wrote a week ago of what fine weather we had been having for three or four days. Well when we went to bed it had started to rain and came down pretty fast but we supposed it was just a passing shower but you may judge—by the way, Tot has stayed over at Will Rhodes—my surprise on getting up to see that there had been a snow fall but the wind was blowing hard and the air so full of snow I did not know how deep it was till I came to go out the front door. I had put on my boots and an old pair of trowsers but little good they were for when I looked out the snow was just on a level with the steps and went up to a big drift in the middle of where the sidewalk was, extending along this side of the street, that time, about five or six feet high. The blocks along here all have high basements so the stoops are rather high and I knew I could never flounder through that snow but I climbed down the broad rail at the side of the steps feeling for it in the snow with my feet till I could reach and climb up on the porch of the next house which is set a little in front of this and thus after I had got to the second stoop I could get out and walk alongside of the drift in only two or three feet of snow. In that way climbing along, I at last got down to breakfast, a walk of about three minutes taking me about twenty. The wind was terrible, sometimes you couldn't head up into it and the air was so full of fine snow which stung your face like needles, that you couldn't see across the street. I never appreciated before how any one could get lost so easily in a blizzard but several persons were frozen right in the streets during the night. The Freshmen were the only students who were not given some cuts. All Sheff. was excused for 48 hours and most of the upper classes in the Academic. It was something terrible going to and fro recitations. Lots of boys who had gone home the day before to spend Sunday did not get back till yesterday. Four trains were snowed up here. It kept on blowing as hard and snowing harder if anything all Tuesday and by that time food began to be rather scarce in town.

We didn't have any milk for three days and Miss Prescott moaned around as though she was starved. Men went around the streets where they were passable on horseback with big bags of bread hung across the horses distributing it. When I got home Tuesday afternoon the snow had drifted up my window, which is set back a little from the gutter, so bad that the room was most dark which I wrestled with till I got most of it away. The boys went around with some of the queerest costumes on you ever saw. I got my boots so wet the first day I couldn't wear them again so I laced those high shoes up around the bottoms of my trowsers and thus kept the snow out very effectually as they are quite water tight. Most every one wore these big white sweaters right over their clothes and a big toboggan hat pulled down to meet it, and high rubber boots.

Some of the houses were snowed up so bad that the people did not get out at all for about two days; but by Wednesday the wind went down though it snowed harder than ever, and big flakes, most all day. The streets were full of men digging paths, and I thought Miss Prescott was going to wait for a thaw but late in the afternoon she bartered with a man to clear a path which is only wide enough for one person to walk comfortably and big walls of snow over your head on both sides. Though we were mighty thankful for that since we had to make use of the porch next door, still, in order to get out. Most all the stores closed Monday and Tuesday and some of the boys who went down town through the snow to get rubbers couldn't get in anywhere. But "It's an ill wind" &c for the newsboys made a fortune selling their papers for ten and twenty cents and the first day the N.Y. papers got here they charged a quarter for them. All the soda water fountains and such charged fabulous prices and one of the boys from N.Y. told me that the hackmen up there charged ten and twenty dollars to take people down street. The street cars haven't started to run yet, they use big bobs instead. I never saw so much snow in my life. I am getting terribly short of clean clothes as neither the washerwoman nor laundryman came last week. We didn't get any mail from outside till yesterday. I could go on talking about the storm all the afternoon but I have come to the end of my paper so I will stop. Love to all, HARVEY.

Athletics

Some insight into Cushing's character can be gained by following his activity in sports and his abiding interest in games and athletics of every description. He was fascinated by the alertness, agility, and delicate coordination of an adept tennis or baseball player, and the fascination remained through the years no doubt for the reason that a similar delicacy of muscular control has much to do with success in surgery. The tight-rope walker and the troupe on the flying trapeze likewise intrigued him, and he never tired of the circus. In addition to watching feats of muscular skill, he invariably visited the "freaks" at the side show—and Cushing it was who first proved how giants and dwarfs came to be; but of this more later. H.C. had already shown prowess in athletics at high school in Cleveland and at Camp Maskenoza. In January of his first year at Yale, his mother enquired whether he was having any exercise. He replied (29 Jan.):

I started in training with the Freshman base ball team just for the exercise for I haven't the ghost of a show to get on, as there are 40 men trying and mostly fine players. But it has made me feel better ever since, as you are compelled to be at the gym an hour a day to exercise and to go to bed by ten o'clock. That's one of the good things about training for some athletic team—though I haven't been able to get to bed on time always. I have to be at the gym every day, and those men who smoke and drink have to swear off and the Captains of the teams look after them too. We are going up to the Ladds with Al Cre[hore] tonight and Perry is hurrying me up so I will have to stop. Bert McB[ride] was just up with his room mate.

This marked the beginning of Cushing's career in Yale athletics, and it almost caused a split with his puritanical father, who had made Harvey promise before leaving for college not to drink, smoke, or consort with those of easy virtue; and above all things he was not to indulge in organized intercollegiate athletics! H.C. was soon taken on the freshman baseball team, and he played shortstop in matches on 21 and 23 April, and 2, 14, 19, 23, and 26 May 1888. The game on the 19th was played against the Harvard freshmen at Cambridge, Massachusetts. Anticipating trouble with his father, he sent the following diplomatic enquiry, emphasizing incidentally the advantages of being entitled to sit on the Yale Fence:

. . . I want to ask you if you have any serious objections to my playing ball with the freshman nine as long as I don't let it interfere with my studies which I hope you can trust me not to do. I know you object to intercollegiate contests of any kind and I suppose the game they play with the Harvard freshmen nine comes under that head, but there is no fuss made about the freshman game as there is about the "varsity" and there is not the same end in view, that of college supremacy in athletics; but the freshmen are not allowed to sit on the College fence unless they beat the Harvard freshmen. And it's an honor to help win the fence for your class. I don't know as you know what the fence is in relation to the College unless you have heard of it from some Yale man. I suppose it does more social work in the College than anything possibly could. Will Cre[hore] told me he had become acquainted with more men at the fence in the hour after supper when all the upper classmen meet there for a short time together and talk & sing. It is the original fence that was put up around the first building.

His father promptly replied (1 May):

The chief item in your letter in your estimation, as it certainly is in mine, is that relating to your connection with your class base ball 9. The convictions I hold and wh. you are well acquainted with, concerning the methods wh. have grown up about College games, and contests, are no less strong than when you left home. Indeed, the more I hear of them the more settled do I become in my belief that they are an evil of the first magnitude. I will not object—in words—to your playing in games at New Haven but cannot assent to your accompanying the club to games or contests anywhere else, or in going anywhere else as a spectator simply of class collegiate or interstate athletic associations.

When his father discovered that he actually intended to play at Harvard, the floodgates of wrath were opened (7 May):

Dear Harvey, I will try to reply to your letter calmly, though I do feel sore and disturbed over the unhappy position you have brought us into. I carefully explained before you went to New Haven, that we were going into a partnership with mutual responsibilities and duties. I was to supply the means, and you to conduct yourself to my approval while the partnership survived. Among the conditions I insisted on, and wh. I understood you to assent to, were those that you would not smoke, drink or be guilty of any immoral conduct or join a College ball club or boat crew. . . .

I cannot believe that you have forgotten our arrangement. It looks to me as if in the glamour and excitement of College sentiments and surroundings, you have reasoned yourself into the feeling that if you only kept in the first division it was none of my business what else you did. . . . Now if you cannot withdraw without hardship to others for this Harvard Contest I shall say no more about it, but when that is through with, *that must be the end of that sort of thing absolutely and for good.*

Two comments more on your letter and I have done. You say if I will consent to your playing in this game, you "will try and keep out of them." I must have an explicit promise *that you will keep out of them.* You say that it has been an incentive to you to study and keep a good stand. Is it necessary to do your best as a scholar that you be a ball player? Are there not other and better and all sufficient inducements without that?

Harvey replied to each point raised in his father's letter, but indicated that he could not properly withdraw from the team just before it went to Harvard. In a postscript he mentioned that he was quite "broke" and needed funds. His mother wrote him that his father had not been well (a recurrent boil) and advised him to be patient. Unfortunately the Harvard team won; however, the Yale freshmen won the return game on the 26th in New Haven, which brightened Harvey's spirits not a little. His pleasure in having acquired the privilege of sitting on the Yale Fence was set down in naïve enthusiasm:

I have had more enjoyment out of our privilege to sit on the fence this last week than in anything since I have been here, and I guess every one else in the class has. Every evening after supper for an hour or two before you have to study there is always a crowd there talking and singing. I have become acquainted with more boys there than in ten times the amount of time elsewhere, and boys whom I had never seen before. It is the only place one ever sees any of the "Sheff" boys and connects them more to the College proper than anything else. Then if you have ten minutes or so before going to Chapel or recitation there is one place where any one else, who is in the same position, will go and you are always sure to find someone there you know and want to see.

The problem of baseball arose more acutely the next year when he was asked to play on the Yale Varsity nine. A persuasive letter was immediately (27 Mar. 1889) sent off:

Dear Father I want to come to you again with a matter which I know is very distasteful to you. I agreed last Spring not to play ball again in College.

Noyes the Captain of the University Nine a short time ago came and asked me to play and I remembered my promise and told him my father wouldn't like it. Well, I thought that settled it but he came around again and talked to me and said that everyone ought to do their best to help the College in athletics as long as it did no harm to their studies and he said that he was sure Professor Richards or the Dean, Prof. Wright, would write to you if I wanted. I went up and asked Prof. Ladd's advice, as you told me always to do, and even he thinks there not only is no harm in it, but it is quite an honor to be on the nine. He said, if you were willing, he would be very glad to write and tell you just what he thought about it. If I should play ball and get on the Nine there is one thing which would perhaps result which would be worth more to me, or any one, than you can imagine and that is, I would have a chance of an election into a Senior Society. I don't know whether you or any one, except a Yale graduate, knows what it is to get an election to Skull and Bones or Scroll and Key. It is the one, the greatest honor a man can receive in College and is the one thing more than any other sought after by everyone from the time of entering college to senior year and unless I can get an election through athletics I am afraid I will be left out. I hope you know, father, that I fully understand what you sent me here to college for and I have tried faithfully to do my best and do every thing which would please you. Perhaps you will say that you didn't send me here to play ball. Of course you didn't, that is to play ball to the neglect of my studies, but if I do just as hard work in my lessons at the same time and simply take my daily hour of recreation in that way, in preference to a worse one perhaps, I don't see what difference it makes. I know you don't like the going around the country but it only is on an occasional Saturday and then to some college where one meets men from different places. And the faculty have supervision over the schedule so that no recitations are cut.

. . . If I can't play I will probably be soured on by the whole college as everyone knows who has a chance for the Nine and I never heard of anyone refusing before, when they had a chance. I do hope you will give a favorable answer or at least will write Cousin George about it. I would willingly forego a Junior society which I see you have not got a very good impression of, if I can play. Affectionately, HARVEY.

H.K.C. apparently did not answer for no reply is preserved, but he evidently gave in gracefully because there is no further reference to baseball in any of his subsequent letters.

On one of his trips with the team, Harvey visited the White House and met President and Mrs. Harrison. Thus on 28 April 1889:

The Glee Club gave a concert in Washington, Monday night, and Mrs. Harrison gave a reception to them after the concert. When she found out that the Nine were there too she invited them to come and the man that brought the invitation said it made no difference about dress suits, which we didn't happen to have. Some went around there after the concert, and the President and his wife and Mrs. McKee were brought into the big reception room, and we all lined up, about fifty of us counting the Glee Club and Banjo Club, and one by one were introduced to and shook hands with the Presidential couple. The Glee Club stayed quite late but we didn't feel much at home without dress suits and so only stayed a few minutes. It was quite an experience. He is the first President I have seen, I think. No, I heard Ex-President Hayes one night at the Music Hall with you, but I don't know as they are any different from other people. The Pres. is very small, much to my surprise, and looks very tired and I guess it didn't rest him very much to shake hands with a crowd of young fellows, especially as his handshake is very weak.

Amos Alonzo Stagg, who pitched for Yale from 1886 through 1890, writes (16 Mar. 1940) of H.C.'s prowess in baseball:

The baseball seasons of 1889 and 1890 were the last two of the five championship years that I pitched for Yale. Those were Harvey's sophomore and junior years. His first year he played on the freshman team. In looking up the records, I find that, in 1889, he played some games at short stop but mainly at right and center field. In 1890, he played chiefly right field. I do not know what position he played in 1891. Taking the Harvard and Princeton series of 1889, Harvey stood in fifth place in batting average among the players of Harvard, Princeton and Yale. . . . My remembrance is that Harvey was good at batting and in fielding and in base running.

He was also adept in certain gymnastics such as tumbling and turning on the parallel bars:

Amatures [*sic*] from all the Athletic Clubs around here and from several of the colleges were here and a good many of them were Champions of their particular branch of athletics. Your humble son went in the first night on the horizontal bar and got the prize, not because he could do anything on it but the other men could do less than that, so it was a pretty poor exhibition you may imagine.

One of his classmates at Harvard Medical School later recalls:

His compact, beautifully-formed muscular body was well known. I remember him standing on the stone steps of the old Medical School (now part of Boston University) with a lighted cigarette in his mouth and turning a back somerset landing on the bare sidewalk with the cigarette still going. His cigarette was an important part of his life then. He scorned the smoker who did not inhale and said that when he drew the smoke deep into his lungs, he felt every nerve tingle to the ends of his fingers and toes. His skill at sleight-of-hand is of course well known and his trick of pulling little wads of cotton and other things out of impossible places mystified his fellow dissectors until they knew him better.

College Societies

Throughout Cushing's four years at Yale there was much correspondence with his father about college societies. As might be expected, Henry Kirke Cushing disapproved of them on principle, much as he had of athletics. But he gave in to Harvey's determined desire to join a sophomore, junior, and finally a Yale senior society. In his sophomore year H.C. had joined the ΔKE fraternity, a society from which he evidently derived pleasure and satisfaction. On 2 February 1890, he sounded his father out about a senior society:

Do you, father, as an outsider know anything about the two Senior societies here. You may not know anything about their present standing but if you do I wish you would write and tell me about it. I have about made up my mind to go to "Keys" if I am a good enough man to get an election simply for the reason that much the better men are going that way in our Class. I think that my chances of going to "Bones" are better and that if I should I would perhaps meet better men when I get out of college. I wish you would say nothing of my writing you on this subject for of course I have no reason to feel confident of getting an election to either Societv but a man has to make a stand either one way or the other.

If his father replied to this, the letter was not saved. On 18 May H.C. mentioned that "Tap" Day was near: "The Elections for

Senior Societies are given out next Thursday. If I am one of the lucky ones to be tapped I will let you know you may be sure. It is perhaps the greatest honor a man can receive in his College Course at Yale." And on 25 May he announced his election to "Scroll and Key:"

> The most important news of the week which I have to announce was my election to 'Scroll and Key'. Perry Harvey, Ned Hale, Will Rhodes, San Barnes, Hoppin, Cooley, & Atterbury, are men of whom you have heard me speak and who were in the lucky fifteen. I guess Bill Graves [Dr. William P., later of Boston] is the only one you know who went the other way. I won't attempt to tell you what fine things the Senior Societies are acknowledged to be, what a position they hold in the College World and what good they do a man, for if you don't already know something about it, it would make too long a story. The initiations are next Tuesday so that I am not free for very long to talk on the subject. Perry and I have received congratulations from numerous Yale people.

There were no further references to his senior society after his initiation, but he became as much in earnest about his societies as about sports. A classmate, Mr. John B. Townsend, recalls (in 1940):

> When Harvey Cushing was a junior at Yale, he had the idea that the standard of the junior societies ought to be raised. At that time, there were sophomore societies and they seemed to exert more of an influence than the junior societies, which seemed to him all wrong. He went into the matter seriously, as was his wont in all things, and he succeeded in doing excellent work along these lines. He was instrumental in limiting the numbers, which, at that time, were indefinite and he also introduced into the meetings of the societies something of a serious program, which tended to increase the respect with which they were held.

Another friend, C. R. L. Putnam, who met Cushing when he entered the Harvard Medical School fresh from Yale, writes:

> Harvey Cushing in his undergraduate days was a real Yale man—believing in the great importance and seriousness of athletic victories—and in the social honors associated with "Tap" day at New Haven, and told how the great Heffelfinger after a defeat by Harvard had cried all night in spite of the efforts of his roommate to comfort him. To young Cushing this seemed natural as he had lost his chances for college success. (Heffelfinger later won all the honors, but at this early game his error contributed to a spectacular Harvard victory.) Cushing belonged to Scroll and Key and explained that this society sought to reward merit in all fields—choosing eminent athletes, a few distinguished scholars, the editor of the Litt, etc. During his medical school days, the one thing that he did besides study—but his studies were always very broad, far outside the curriculum—was to write every two weeks to some fellow member of "Keys" in rotation.

Senior Year

The sophomore and junior years slipped away, and Cushing had acquitted himself creditably, but not brilliantly, in all but one or two of his subjects. The courses of study which he elected during his four years, with grades based on the old Yale system of 400 units, are shown in the table below.

Year 1887–88		Year 1888–89		Year 1889–90		Year 1890–91	
Courses	Standing	Courses	Standing	Courses	Standing	Courses	Standing
German	302	English	284	Chemistry 82	350	Physiol. Chem.	363
Greek	232	German	268	History 20	328	English 57	290
Greek	302	Greek	301	Men. & Mor. Sc.	300	Ancient Lang. 64	315
Latin	210	Greek	279	Men. & Mor. Sc.	278	History 20	322
Latin	325	Latin	212	Math. 98, 97	345	Law 19, 18	238
Latin	304	Latin	287	Polit. Econ. 7	297	Psychology 3	308
Math.	345	Latin	142	Physics	300	Soc. Sci. 15	307
Math.	343	Math.	330	Physics	315	Zoology 101	379
				Physics	294		
				Physiol. 86	337		
Average	315		292		315		312

N.B. Scale of marking at this time was 0–400, 200 passing — General Average 308

Professor George L. Hendrickson, Emeritus Professor of Latin and Greek Literature at Yale, has given an illuminating appraisal of Cushing's academic record (16 Dec. 1939):

> It was interesting to see Cushing's College record, & somewhat shocking too to see how much time was spent on Latin & Greek without making a real classicist of him. Unfortunately in those days the theory of instruction was discipline rather than acquisition & facility. We do better now. . . . The entries are of course for each of the 2 semesters, but the basis or scale is throughout 4 (or 400), the method still in vogue when I first came to Yale. The origin of it is I believe disputed, but as explained to me by Dean Wright it comes from the square (made by ruling of the class book) after each man's name for each day of the term or semester, thus □ and a dot in any corner, or along the line between the corners indicated quickly the grade of a man for each day. Two, or 50 per cent, was passing grade, while 3 just touched honors, 4 was almost never given. For convenience of fractional division 1, 2 & 3 are treated as 100, 200, 300. Thus although 300 is strictly speaking 75% yet in practice of that time it was considered a high mark, where now 75 is only a quality grade.
>
> Thus Cushing's Greek is relatively high & better than his Latin, & the latter not so bad by standards of that time except for the lamentable 149 & 143 in Spring Semesters, when apparently base ball proved a dangerous rival. The total average of 308, though only a little above 75%, would have been looked on as a tolerably high mark, perhaps the upper 1/3 of the class or above.

In high school days and in camp Harvey's interests had turned toward botany, zoology—indeed, to all the natural sciences, and one can trace during the college years the growth of his interest in medicine. A visit to his brother Ned, an interne at the Massachusetts General Hospital, is described in a letter to his mother (20 May 1888):

I had a mighty good time out of the trip as I had a long visit with Ned all yesterday morning in which time I "did" the hospital, so to speak, under his guidance. . . . He took me through his wards and introduced me to the men who are working there with him; all whom I met, I liked very much. I had no idea the place was so big. As he was on duty in the operating room the latter part of the morning I went up on the benches and sat with the medical students and watched him operate for a while and then went back to the hotel where we had dinner and drove out to Cambridge. They have got some fine buildings out there and lots of ground but I wouldn't like to go there, I don't like the bull pup and pink shirt feeling.

But his full interest in medicine did not culminate until his senior year. This can again be closely traced in his letters home. On 10 October 1890 he removed a dog's brain, evidently for an "anthropological" collection and at the request of the Professor of Moral Philosophy.

"I can imagine myself getting up in his class, composed one half of Theologues and Medical students, and discoursing on that dog's brain. May it not smell bad." A few days later, after mentioning his various collections, we find him searching for the cranial nerves of a frog (26 Oct.):

Dear Mother . . . I tenderly secreted the family stamp album in the penultimate drawer of the butterfly case, not as a monument for my fine collection of beetles, in whose destruction both Alice and the moths had a hand, but to preserve it from the dust with which it used to be covered whenever I returned home. I hope the moths haven't attacked the backs of the stamps for lack of beetles to chew on. I'm sure I don't remember whether I did anything with my coin box or not. I thought I left it in its accustomed place.

I will chronicle this week's events if you prefer that to "cronicling" them. I have discovered during the week those spinal nerves which I told you I was looking for in my frog and am at present vainly struggling with his cranial nerves which are very small and have a great faculty for eluding discovery.

But it was his course in physiological chemistry with Russell H. Chittenden (1856-1944) that really stirred him and centered his energies on the study of medicine.

H.C. to H.K.C. *2 November 1890.*

. . . I am getting along very well, I think, in my Physiological Chemistry course though it takes about all the time I can spare from my other work. The little drawing which I can do, rough though it is, helps me very much for we have to illustrate our note books, and some of the best men in the class can't do that sort of work at all. They have furnished us with microscopes which are very fine ones, I judge, to allow a class to use. They are a German make. Prof. Smith wants us to learn to use them and keep both eyes open, an accomplishment I have not acquired as yet. If I try it, all I can see is the side of the instrument. He can look into the instrument with one eye and use the other at the same time, to guide his pencil in copying what is on the slide. I find it pretty hard on the eyes. We have to furnish ourselves with all the accessories. I never understood before how they measured little things, like blood corpuscles, which we have been doing with the micrometers furnished.

11 January 1891.

. . . You will probably like to know how we are beginning this 1st term but there is not much to tell of any course except the Physiological Chemistry. The other work goes on in the same lines as last term being merely a continuation of it. The chemical work has its laboratory in one of the wings of the old Sheffield house. It is very light and finely equipped as far as I can tell. Each one of us (there are about 10 in the course) had a great abundance of room and a large amount of apparatus of different sorts, in cleaning and arranging which we were kept busy a whole afternoon. Thursday and Friday we started in, in earnest, taking up the subject of albumin, its reactions, coagulation, diffusibility or rather nondiffusibility, which is about all of the ground we have covered. I hope that my impromptu dialyser is dialysing nicely at this moment. Chittenden is a very interesting man and I think he will make the course so, although it has the reputation of being the hardest course in College. Our text book is a "Handbook for the Physiological Laboratory" edited by Sanderson and though called a handbook it is as big an armful as Geo. Ladd's book, and costs *too* much money.

1 February 1891.

. . . I have sort of off days occasionally and Friday was one of them. From the moment I went into the laboratory nothing went right for I started off by breaking a large water bottle which, though my own, bored Chittenden a good deal for he is a scrupulously neat person and anything of that sort annoys him. After that I couldn't break enough things, and fail in enough experiments, inwardly swearing at everything in the room, myself principally, during the rest of the afternoon. I could not get any decent crystals of the Leucine, with which we were working, and stayed three quarters of an hour after the others till I finally succeeded in getting some very nice ones, thereby scoring a few points with Prof. Chittenden, I hope, to offset the rest of the day.

22 March 1891.

. . . I had a talk with Prof. Chittenden about my work with him and he says he is very glad to let me work other hours if necessary and to help me as if in the class, which is an unhoped for privalege and seems almost like private instruction. It's the finest course I have had here and ever expect to have in that line of work and I would not be willing to lose any of it for the sake of college base ball which happily is not necessary.

Prof. Ladd wants me to come back next year and go on with the work. We have just been working on the Chemistry of the tissues and are now working on brain tissue which we will about finish by Easter. I was very much overwhelmed the other day when he laid a pamphlet on my desk on "On Neurokeratin" of which I had asked him something the day before, ignorant of the fact that he and Kühne of Heidelberg University who together published the pamphlet had first studied the body.

In April, Professor Chittenden asked H.C. to return the following semester to have a special year of study and research in physiological chemistry.

H.C. to H.K.C. *26 April 1891.*

. . . I had quite a talk with Prof. Chittenden one day about coming back next year and he urged me to do so if I can afford the time and expense. He has every year about three post graduate students and it really amounts to almost private instruction under a remarkable man instead of scrabbling along with a big class in a medical school. Besides men who have been under him are allowed to omit six months, in the medical school in New York at least, which would be rather pharsical after the work here. I will get from him some day an outline of what the work is exactly so that you may see. We have got down in our study of digestion as far as the intestines and have been examining glycogen thoroughly and the bile acids and pigments for the past week—very interesting.

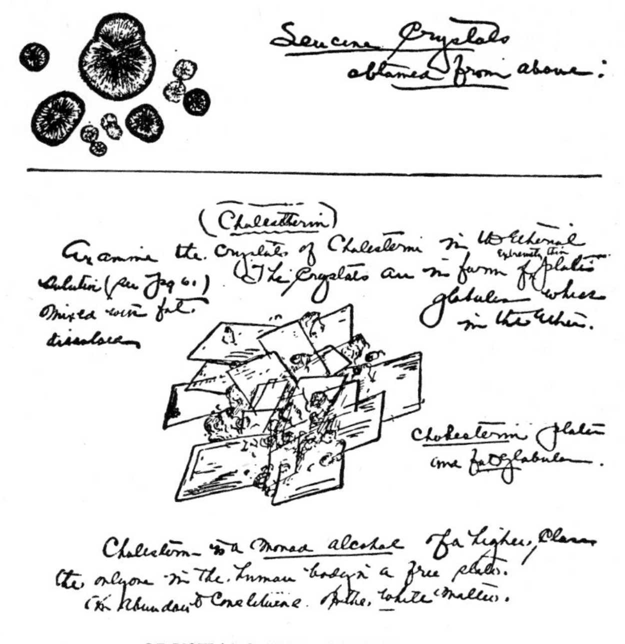

CRYSTALS FOR CHITTENDEN

Above: Leucine crystals from H.C.'s notebook for Professor Russell Chittenden's lectures on Physiological Chemistry. *Below:* Cholesterin crystals (from same notebook)

H.C. to H.K.C. *12 June 1891.*

. . . Prof. Chittenden has given me a special exam which I have next Monday and he probably will want to know what I expect to do. As I have heard nothing from you I suppose I shall say "No" to his offer.

H.C. to B.M.C. *14 June 1891.*

. . . My examinations have all been encountered but one and successfully I hope. That one however I care most about as it is with Prof. Chittenden for whom I would like to do well. I have it tomorrow. I took down my note book, which I had just finished writing up, to the city yesterday to study, but with fear and trembling for it represents a whole term's work, and having nearly lost it up at Amherst once before, I was pretty careful of it, and was greatly relieved to arrive in New Haven without having lost it as well as the ball game.

In recalling Cushing's work in physiological chemistry, Professor Chittenden wrote after Cushing's death (4 Dec. 1939):

When Dr. Cushing was an undergraduate at Yale he was in my course in physiology during his junior year, and during his senior year he took my course in physiological chemistry, so that I had him for two years. He was an earnest student, one who worked hard and faithfully, and while I did not consider him brilliant at that time, he made such an impression upon me that I encouraged him to come back for a graduate year, offering him a position as assistant in the laboratory. He was much interested in physiological chemistry and seemed interested in the proposal, but after talking it over with some members of his family it was decided that he had best go directly into the Medical School. In later years, on several occasions, he called my attention to that proposal and how near he came to becoming a biochemist.

There were also other medical contacts during his senior year. In November his classmate, Grosvenor Atterbury, introduced him to his medical friends in New York. Cushing's description of the episode is, as usual, vivid and amusing:

H.C. to H.K.C. *29 November 1890.*

. . . Have you ever heard of Dr. Stimson in New York? He is an old Yale man and a cousin of the Atterburys. Grove A. was quite sick with a headache Thursday night and Dr. Stimson came in to see him and we got talking about Medicine and he promised to take us down to the hospitals the next morning while he made his rounds. I was very glad of the chance and so Friday morning he turned up and took us, first down to the New York Hospital of which he is first officer and we went his rounds with him. Grove had enough very soon for I looked around at him, when the Dr. was examining a poor cus with a bad fracture above the elbow, and Grove was as white as a sheet and, saying he would wait for us outside, left the ward quite expeditiously. Dr. Stimson said the New York was probably the wealthiest in the country and if that is the case I was very much disappointed in it. Dr. S. thinks there is no place like New York for work though he was not educated there himself. He is a very skillful surgeon I guess from what the Atterburys said of him. There was one queer case of cleft palate there: a small boy whose two front teeth were right on the end of his nose and in the photograph taken before the operation was about the worst looking deformity I ever saw. Now he's a very presentable looking boy but for the red scar on his lip. Aren't dislocations of the hip quite uncommon accidents? There were about six of them there. The Mass. General has a handicap on the New York places in having lots of room. We were going down to Chambers Street hospital but I took compassion on Grove and we went up in the Century Magazine offices as an antidote where he felt more at ease among books and drawings. I am very much obliged for the clippings you have been sending. They will help me with my scrap book which I have had to neglect almost entirely this fall from lack of time to search the papers &c for clippings myself.

Later in the year he had contact with Dr. Bryson Delavan of New York:

H.C. to H.K.C. *1 March 1891.*

Do you know anything of Dr. Delavan in New York. He knows Dr. Lowman and Dr. Allen I believe and served with Lowman in a hospital somewhere. I mention him because he gave us a talk on medicine last night which was very interesting. He told us a lot about the history & growth of the art or rather science of Medicine, about the men who have done the most for it, of all of whom he had pictures and many of whom he seemed to know personally. Sir James Paget, Lord Lister, Pasteur, Virchow and a lot more I don't at present remember. He told us about the Berlin Congress at which he was present, about Koch, his paper and how everything got so exaggerated, and then he went on to tell us about the schools and the study of Medicine & surgery, their recent advancement &c. It was mighty interesting and he must have talked about an hour and a half. These Saturday night talks about what is going on in the outside world are I think one of the most pleasant and interesting features of our society life, the only drawback being that every man in College can't have the same advantages. Hart Lyman gave us a nice one a week ago on Newspapers and other people on law, politics, &c. Senator Dubois came way on from Washington to talk to us. A man can't help congratulating himself every day for the opportunity of meeting these men on the same level, which a Senior society here gives him.

In writing Dr. Delavan many years later (17 May 1939), Cushing referred to this address in the following terms: "I well remember the informal talk you gave one night to our crowd in C.S.P. on the medical career. At that time I was disposed to take up architecture, and indeed was making vague plans with Grosvenor Atterbury to open an office in New York with him, but that, like other undergraduate plans, soon went by the board." Dr. Delavan added (29 April 1940): "The address which seemed to have influenced Dr. Cushing in the choice of a profession was made in the presence of a quiet group of seniors of whom he was one. They were carefully selected men of a particularly fine class. The other leading professions were represented in the same way on other occasions about that time. I had no means of knowing what effect my own remarks had made upon my young friend."

And so Harvey Cushing came to the end of his senior year at Yale well pointed toward a medical career. He had considered other possible professions, but not too seriously. His gift of drawing and his close friendship with Atterbury had made architecture pleasant to contemplate; but he was to wait fifty years before undertaking active collaboration with his classmate when they planned the library that was to house H.C.'s collection of books. An academic career in chemistry or in physiological chemistry had also been considered. Either one would have allowed him further years at Yale, but both plans were ultimately abandoned.

His college years had been bright. Not only had he acquitted himself creditably in his course work, but he had achieved what was more important to him at the time—distinction in athletics. And most important of all were the warm friendships he had formed in his class. He continued his close association with the Cleveland contingent of course—Perry Harvey, Herbert McBride, and Al Crehore—and added many new friends with whom he kept in touch throughout his life, among them Grosvenor Atterbury, Starling Childs, and F. C. Walcott; and for any of his 186 Yale classmates he was ever ready to lay aside his work, no matter how preoccupied he might be.

In later years, Cushing often alluded to his student days at Yale, but never more vividly or with greater depth of feeling than in his appreciation of his devoted cousin, Perry Harvey:[3]

> . . . It may be said without disrespect to a thriving young scientific school, that in our undergraduate days Yale was still Yale College. And in those happy-go-lucky times, the then library on the western boundary of the old campus was to us merely a building and not a collection of animate books, the necessary tools of education.
>
> I remember once—and only once—taking a look within its gloomy portal and wondering how anyone could choose to waste the all too fleeting days of youth in that dismal place, where *Lux* was dim and *Veritas* had the musty smell of mouldering calf. All faces were set toward a lure, not far beyond, that needed no advertising, for there at least with patience and good luck, after the perspiring candidates for the teams had bathed, one might get a brief turn with a bar of soap under one of the two (or was it three?) public showers. . . .
>
> All this comes back to me with a deep-seated nostalgia for something that is forever gone—meaning of course one's physically vigorous youth for want of which nothing can ever again be quite the same. And since this period of life may be taken to close with graduation from college, it is on the cherished memories of our youthful intimacy that I somehow just now feel disposed to dwell, though it obliges me as of old to flutter after Perry into a light meant to be focused on him alone. . . .
>
> . . . We passed much of the next four years, as I have indicated, sweating in the old Gym to qualify for our chosen forms of sport—he as a brilliant half-back on the eleven; I as a mediocre outfielder on the baseball team. And lest anything in my opening paragraphs be construed as disparaging of the life and opportunities here in the Yale of our time, even at the risk of fomenting a debate with the gifted orator of the class which graduated last June, I venture openly to say that "*Those* were really the days."[4]

Yale thus gave Cushing something rich and vital that he carried with him through life, something that stirred him to the depths whenever he returned to New Haven, something that brought him again to Yale after a life crowded with almost every honor that could come to a man in medicine.

[3] "Perry Williams Harvey, 1869-1932. Books and the man." *Yale University Library Gazette,* January 1937, *11,* 43-52.

[4] Heckscher, A., II. *These are the days, 1935: 1936.* New Haven, 1936, 204 pp.

CHAPTER IV

Harvard Medical School

1891–1896

AFTER leaving Yale at the end of June 1891 Cushing spent the summer with his family at Cleveland. During his years at Yale and Harvard there is little to indicate how he passed these summer holidays at home. A few hints, however, are found in letters written after he had returned to New Haven or Boston. He had become, among other things, an amateur photographer; he had apparently spent considerable time during the summer of 1891 trying to persuade—or surprise—his father into being photographed, his father, like his grandfather, having a special aversion to the camera. Photography had thus been added to the diversions of fishing and camping trips up the Lakes that were always a part of his summer schedule. Frequent allusions to his "leaf books," one of which is still preserved among his memorabilia, indicate also that he and his father and brother Ned were active in observing and collecting botanical specimens.

In September Cushing entered the Harvard Medical School. The reason for his choosing Harvard is not entirely clear. During the spring of 1891 Chittenden had urged him on several occasions to return to Yale, but as late as the middle of June he was still undecided. His brother Ned had been graduated from the Harvard Medical School, and H.C.'s decision to follow in his footsteps was apparently made during the summer while he was in Cleveland.

The Harvard Medical School was founded in 1783 and had been situated after 1846 on North Grove Street. In 1883 it moved to a new, and for its time, spacious building on the corner of Boylston and Exeter Streets which was said to represent "the acme of convenience and suitability" and was believed to be adequate for at least three generations. Already, however, in 1891 as Cushing's letters home indicate, the students were cramped for laboratory space, due to altered concepts of laboratory teaching and to the great advances which had occurred in American medical science in the '80's and early '90's. The curriculum at the Harvard Medical School had passed through various vicissitudes. In the early 19th century it was excellent, as judged by contemporary standards, having been largely influenced first by the Scottish schools and, beginning about 1830, by the French. Between 1840 and 1869, however, teaching had become stereotyped, and despite a number of efforts on the part of the faculty itself,[1] little was done to vitalize it until Charles W. Eliot became President of Harvard in 1869. As David Cheever has recently pointed out:[2]

> [Prior to Eliot] it was essentially a proprietary school, with a curriculum of four months of lectures during each of two years. In addition to attendance at exactly the same lectures in succeeding years, the students were required to spend their additional eight months of each year and one succeeding year in an apprenticeship to some acceptable practitioner, or indeed in one of the very few available house-officer posts at the Massachusetts General Hospital or in the recently established Boston City Hospital. It was only necessary for the student to pass perfunctory examinations in five of the nine lecture courses in order to obtain his degree.

President Eliot changed all this, much to the consternation of the faculty, and especially of Henry Jacob Bigelow, the Professor of Surgery. When Eliot, who had taken to attending meetings of the medical faculty, was asked why all this change was necessary, he made his celebrated retort, "I can tell Dr. Bigelow the reason; we have a new President."

Cushing entered the Medical School after it had benefited by Eliot's farsighted reorganization. The School had been given full status as a postgraduate division of a great university, liberal endowment had begun to accrue, and by 1891 teaching was on a plane superior probably to that in any other existing American medical school. The faculty included Thomas Dwight, Parkman Professor of Anatomy, who had succeeded to the chair after the retirement of Oliver Wendell Holmes (1883); Charles Sedgwick Minot, who taught Cushing histology and took charge of the Department of Histology and Embryology in 1892; Henry Pickering Bowditch (a grandson of the mathematician, Nathaniel Bowditch), Professor of Physiology (who had, at Eliot's instigation, studied abroad with Claude Bernard and Carl Ludwig and established on his return the first laboratory in the United States devoted to experimental physiology); and Edward Stickney Wood, in charge of medical chemistry. In the clinical years instruction was given by John Collins Warren, Reginald Heber Fitz, David Williams Cheever, Frederick Cheever Shattuck, Maurice Howe Richardson (who also taught anatomy), John Homans, and others, all men of wide repute.

[1] *Practical views on medical education.* Submitted to the members of the American Medical Association by the Medical Faculty of Harvard University. Boston, D. Clapp, 1850, 7 pp. [Signed by Jacob Bigelow, Walter Channing, John Ware, John B. S. Jackson, O. W. Holmes, Henry J. Bigelow and E. N. Horsford.] See also the unsigned editorial in the *Boston Medical and Surgical Journal,* 1866, p. 63 [by J. C. White].

[2] Cheever, David. "The turn of the century—and after." *New England Journal of Medicine,* 1940, 222, 1-11.

1891-1892

The transition from New Haven to Boston was difficult for H.C.; in fact he early developed an uneasiness about Harvard which he never quite overcame, despite the passing of the years and the fact that he made many warm friends in the University. On arrival he wrote at once to his mother:

H.C. to B.M.C. *27 September 1891.*

As you see I have reached the scene of my future operations. I have secured a very nice room here at the Tremont House for the magnificent sum of $1.50, as good as if I had secured a whole suite, for a bathroom is situated right across the hall which I can frequent at will and where I have already spent time sufficient to erase from my person the dirt gathered in large quantities on my journey. As you may imagine the ride to New York was rather trying but all discomfort was forgotten on meeting Star Childs, Brewster, Barnes, Atterbury and Hoppin who went up to New Haven with me. I stopped over there for a few hours & saw all my friends, Profs Wright & Chittenden and many other people, and though I had not much more than enough time to say 'how do do' and 'good bye' it cheered me up very much. . . . I think there are going to be between 15 and 20 Yale men in the Harvard Law School this year, mostly my classmates and some of them pretty well equipped already so that they will make a good record there I am sure.

The next day he added: "The last four hours have gone slowly by, sacaraficed [*sic*] for the purpose of securing a lodging place, but I have not accomplished much more than to get a pretty good composite picture of a landlady whose name is legion and whom I do not admire. It seems to me I never saw so many people before who were all utter strangers & it's most depressing. . . ." His father offered timeless advice to a son starting on a new adventure. On the envelope H.C. had written in pencil, "a Chesterfield letter:"

I was very glad to receive your letter, and to know something of your experiences and feelings in making way in a new place. It had been my plan to go on with you, and be of such comfort as I could in seeing you settled for the winter's work. But your grandfather's illness of course negatived that.

The taking up new threads in a great new city is a trying and discouraging process. You can imagine what it is like to one who must do it without help from letters and friends. . . . You will undoubtedly find every day now making you more at home in your new work. As it is likely to be the front entrance into the work of life, deliberation, constancy, zeal and painstaking endeavor should mark each day. . . . Unusual opportunities have been and are being placed at your control. There is no reason why you should not do as well in Boston as Will and Ed[wd] have done. . . .

Be careful with whom you make acquaintance. It is not every bright and agreeable man that it is safe to tie to. Men go astray in great numbers (even at your age and older) under the temptations of one kind and another that insidiously beguile. Playing cards for money, tippling, and frequenting haunts of immoral women are the three chief ways in which young men have wrecked themselves in my observation. . . . I have come of late to the conclusion that there is a growing laxity of morals in these regards in the present day. . . .

Then H.C. ran into a Yale man, Class of '89 [Henry Sage], who was "invaluable" in the matter of lodging places, "washer ladies," etc., and immediately his outlook brightened. He eventually settled at 32 West Cedar Street, at the foot of Beacon Hill, which was within convenient walking distance of the Medical School. Some of his first impressions and experiences are recorded in his early letters:

H.C. to H.K.C. *3 October 1891.*

I am just about to go over to supper and tho't as I had a few minutes I would write you a line to say that I am at last about settled down in my new quarters which are as comfortable as could be expected. I have added one piece of furniture at my own expense, namely a desk which I needed badly as there was no table in the room & the good landlady refused to get one. My boarding place is but a moment's walk & the table at present is excellent. I have a bathroom quite handy, a good closet, folding bed &c. I also secured a lamp as there was none here and the gas not particularly good. I got off my chemistry all right and am going on with Prof. Wood in Medical Chem. which he advised me to do as I have already had some of it in New Haven.

Am rather at a loss to know what to do about a microscope, the one Dr. Minot recommends costs $81.00 here which is beyond my means at present. I have applied for one of the school microscopes which I may not get as the class is very large & many can't afford to buy them. I'm sure you'd advise against purchasing a cheap article. If I can get a school instrument temporarily I would like to order a Leitz microscope from abroad if I can get some one to bring it through for me. Ed Harvey might do it. Dr. Minot says if it is shipped thru the custom house the duty brings it up to the cost here, so that wouldn't pay. How medical books do cost! I have already squandered $20.00 for them & fear I must get more. They are beautiful books though—the Quain especially. Tell Ned I've subscribed for the medical journal, but get it free for the first three months and ask him when his subscription runs out & when he wants me to forward them to him. My matriculation and laboratory fees cost me $131.00 so that with traveling, hoteling, buying a desk, lamp, books, stilographic pen &c &c the handsome sum you presented me with has much dwindled. I have about $20.00 however which should last me some time now. Excuse this scrawl. I must get some new pens.

H.C. to B.M.C. *4 October 1891.*

. . . I am just beginning to feel a little at home & am learning to find my way around thanks to a small map which I purchased and which used to come out at almost every street corner. The weather has been ideal since the first two days which were rather warm—not a cloud in the sky and a cool breeze—such blue skies as are foreign to Cleveland. It is lucky for my personal appearance that Boston is a clean place as otherwise my wardrobe would all have been in the dirty clothes bag by this time. I hope today to get hold of a washer lady thanks to Sage who has been invaluable in all such things. Work begins in earnest tomorrow at the school where a very large class has entered and a much better appearing one than I had anticipated. Give my love to Grandpa and the people at 786.

H.C. to H.K.C. *6 October 1891.*

The *bona dea fortuna* shone on me yesterday and I was the last man to receive one of the school microscopes. Thirty men were drawing for 3 of them at the end, when my name was drawn, the last one. Pretty lucky wasn't it? They are just like the one I used in New Haven so I can manage them easily. Am already "in medias res" and very busy. Thank you very much for your kind letter. I hope it may help me to prove myself worthy of my father.

H.C. to H.K.C. *9 October 1891.*

I received your letter with enclosed P.O. order yesterday. You have probably got my letter saying that I have a school microscope, contrary to my expectations. The money should keep me going for some time. Am liking the work very much so far but wish the class was not quite so large which would make it more manageable. It's pretty hard for the last 30 or so of the 100 to get seats in the lecture rooms so that good standing room is in demand, which fortunately I haven't had to resort to as yet. The weather still continues clear but colder.

H.C. to B.M.C. *10 October 1891.*

I think I will take time by the forelock and write my letter to you tonight, as I have time now and may not have tomorrow. Two or three of the Cambridge boys are coming in in the morning and we are going to hear one Phillips Brooks preach, provided we can get into the church, and as they probably will stay in all day I may not have opportunity for letter writing. Last Sunday Sage and I wended our way out to their legal haunts and tomorrow some of them are coming in to return the visit. Dr. Phillips Brooks preached a sermon to the Harvard men last Sunday night at their chapel which we expected to hear but the church was so crowded fifteen minutes early, when we arrived, that the best I could do was to catch a glimpse of him from the door. Tomorrow will be his last Sunday at Trinity so that I imagine everyone will be there and we are going to try and arrive early enough this time to enter the portals at any rate. I have got pretty well settled in every way by this time and things are going pretty smoothly. My domestic affairs which I suppose you are interested in are in good shape. An estimable woman answering to the name of Duffy controls my washing—of linen &c I mean—and promises to rival Mrs. McVene. She also does darning which is something I had to do myself in New Haven though more often with a big D than with a needle. My boarding place is a great success and I think the good landlady is a wonderful economist or else losing money daily on her table.

At Yale H.C. had given a full account of his academic work in his letters home. At the Harvard Medical School he did not go into as much detail, even in the letters to his father, concerning the character of his studies. This is especially true of his first year, and is perhaps due to the fact that because his brother Edward had preceded him, H.K.C. was already acquainted with the work of the Medical School. Such details as there were are contained in letters already quoted and in the following:

H.C. to H.K.C. *23 October 1891.*

. . . Things are progressing all right so far at the School and I am, as every one is, apparently, very much interested in everything. We began yesterday our laboratory work in Medical Chemistry and though it is so crowded that two men must work at a desk built for one, I like it much and can put in hours intervening between lectures there in time it would take me to go way to my room and back. I have this afternoon been examining the urine of a J. Sullivan who I think is suffering from acute nephritis & I hardly think it can be the pugilist.

Tell Ned I have called on Dr. [Maurice] Richardson about six times and finally found him in today but so busy that he asked me to call again which I hardly think I'll do. Also that Dr. Scudder wants him to be here the first Tuesday in November if he is coming on about that time, so that he can attend one of their Warren Club meetings which comes off on that date. . . .

H.C. to H.K.C. *31 January 1892.*

I must write you today for more funds as I have run down so low that this morning I thought best to save five cents and read another man's paper as I might need the same for carfare on one of these unpleasant days. I have been meaning to write you for some time past but fear that I have not much to say so that my letters home don't seem to be much more than a handshake. I haven't had any dissecting to do for a long time so that without its distracting influence Anatomy has been more or less of a grind. We have begun one quiz in the same with Dr. Scudder and have a very good class; among them Joslin, Edes, White and Painter are *very* good men, something our class seems to abound in. The quiz has a stimulating though a very discouraging influence in one way—namely, that one finds out how much more other men can learn and remember, in the same length of time, than he. Joslin and a man named Mix I think will head the class in the examination line at least. Painter I like very much. He is slow, but hangs on to everything he gets. He hails from Great Barrington, Mass. and is a great big solid whole-souled creature such as one likes to meet.

Did you know there was a Cushing besides myself here at 32 W. Cedar? His father is Major Cushing of Co. B of the IVth Light Artillery, I think; now stationed at Newport.

H.C. to H.K.C. *Saturday, 27 February 1892.*

I just received your letter this afternoon with enclosed P.O. order which I will get rid of Monday. Not being satisfied with that I must write for more funds for other purposes. Dr. Scudder announced at our last quiz that he would like to have our fees by the next meeting, viz. $20.00, which I thought rather queer inasmuch as we have hardly begun the course. The next meeting being Monday he can not have mine as I have none to give him & must wait a few days. We have been holding the quiz on Saturday afternoons but changed this week to Monday as the preparation for the same prevented us from going to the Saturday operations at the Hospital. I therefore went today for the first time since the holidays and enjoyed them immensely with the aid of a borrowed opera glass. An amputation, excision of the knee, removal of an enlarged testicle, a perineal section, a breast & especially interesting was the removal of a plate of teeth from a woman's oesophagus without ether, the same having been swallowed six weeks ago. Made up a very interesting two hours, when hunger bade me leave. . . .

H.C. to H.K.C. *6 March 1892.*

. . . I have an idea that I will get my third part—a head—tomorrow when the last round of parts this winter is given out. I am rather glad as I think I did much better work last fall, when dissecting, than I have since, when perhaps I have had more time. When one's time is *entirely* filled up it seems to be easier to work. I'm sorry to say that the night dissecting is prohibited which will be rather unfortunate especially on a head, as two men can't work at the same time, and three weeks is none too long, but as we have been over much of the anatomy of it I will be able to work faster. . . .

To augment these letters there is a vivid description of H.C. as he appeared to one of his classmates, Charles Russell Lowell Putnam. The clarity of this picture indicates that even then Cushing gave hint of his destiny as a leader in medicine:

During his first three weeks at the Medical School, he hardly spoke to his fellow students, but had found out a great deal from Samuel Jason Mixter, Demonstrator of Anatomy, and Charles L. Scudder [a Yale graduate (1882)], one of the Assistant Demonstrators—both of whom had been friends and admirers of Ned Cushing.

From the day his class was turned into the dissecting room, Cushing became as *eminent* among his fellows as he continued to be among his colleagues throughout his life. His first "part" was a right upper extremity, and before a day was passed all the students as well as the teachers were watching the progress of Cushing's dissection. Dr. Mixter had placed him near a window, which in the old gas-lighted room was important, and groups of two's and three's often came for a few minutes at a time to watch. Cushing himself talked little. First he sharpened his scalpel carefully and frequently, then he raised his skin flaps so as to keep as many of the cutaneous endings of the nerves as possible intact. At the end of three weeks, he had not only his intercosto-humeral intact, but a multitude of anastomoses from the clavicle to the finger tips. He took the same care of the tissues to avoid drying as he afterwards took in his cranial operations. I should say that he showed his professional preëminence from the start. After the early weeks, he began to talk freely to his fellow workers—but first he stated his intentions. "I have decided to be a leper," he said, and with that phrase he refused practically all social invitations that would have wasted his evenings. . . . Cushing, "the leper," lived in a boarding-house on Charles Street where there were no other medical students, but young business men and others lived there.

H.C.'s accounts of social activities and items of general interest were usually found in letters to his mother. The following are typical of the lighter vein in which he was wont to write to B.M.C.:

5 December 1891.

. . . My Christmas vacation begins two weeks from Tuesday next and if all goes well I will leave that afternoon on the first train for the West. The vacation will be very welcome as a breathing spell in which to catch my 'secundum ventum' so to speak, for I never got so winded in any race before. It seems as though my head leaked somewhere so that things ran out faster than I could shove them in which is rather apalling [*sic*] to think on as it predicts complete emptiness. Perhaps I can stop the shoving and take time to find a plug for the leak during the vacation.

I found a note on my desk on getting home tonight from Star and Harry Mosle asking rather profanely what my office hours are and stating that they would be in tomorrow at one o'clock for which I am very glad as I haven't been able to get out there for a long time and have missed them most every time they have come in. Those embryo lawyers at Cambridge seem to have more time at their disposal than the prospective pill givers as the latter are kept busy from early morn till dewy eve has long passed. . . .

20 March 1892.

. . . Having been very busy this week I got behind in some lectures which has compelled me to grind today so that you see I am in an unpleasant state of mind all round. I went the other night to see Mary Goodwillie who has gone now to Miss Hersey's, and had a very pleasant call. I like Miss Hersey *very* much, & never saw such an energetic person. She left Mary & me to our own resources for about half an hour & returned with a package of eight letters which she had written meanwhile. I asked her about it & she said they were letters, not notes, & also said that she had been away from home since 1872 & had written home every day without fail which made my eyes pop out. I saw a picture over there, a large photograph of von Moltke & two officers at the siege of Paris, which I'm going to buy if it costs a leg. It must adorn the new office.[3] Tell Aunt Louise I eagerly accept her invitation. A former mistake will not be repeated.

A letter of 3 April announces an honor which had come early to H.C., election to the Boylston Medical Society. It also mentions Ernest Amory Codman, destined to become his close friend. They worked together throughout their four years in medical school and were responsible for an important contribution to surgical science (see page 93).

H.C. to H.K.C. *3 April 1892.*

. . . Our April vacation begins Wednesday, the 6th, and I hope to be able to get some dissecting to do to keep me busy part of the time. I have not done half of the work I should have liked on the head I have just had and hope to keep it over the vacation.

If I can manage it and if you agree I should like to go down to New Haven for Saturday and Sunday and renew my youth for I feel about a hundred years old, and am very glad of the approaching recess & will be glad of the opportunity of giving up the pill for the pillow. . . . Ned will appreciate how the Public Gardens appear at this time with their gorgeous array of crocuses &c. A little rain is all that is needed to turn everything green in a night. Codman and I were elected to the Boylston Society Friday night.

Later in the year examinations hung heavy over H.C.'s horizon; and well they might have for Professor Dwight's anatomy "final" in the spring of 1892 is one with which probably few American medical students of the present generation—coddled as they are on growth-substances and hormones—could easily cope. The questions were as follows (no choice):

1. With what bones does the malar articulate?
2. With what bones does the internal cuneiform articulate?
3. What are the crest, angle, and spine of the pubes?
4. What part of the capsule of the hip is the strongest, and what strengthens it?
5. What muscles are inserted into the greater tuberosity of the humerus?
6. What muscles are supplied by the ulnar nerve?
7. What group of muscles is supplied by the obturator nerve?
8. Where does the phrenic nerve arise? Along what muscle does it run? What does it supply?

[3] This was evidently later procured (though not at the extravagant cost here threatened) as it hung in the offices of the Surgeon-in-Chief at the Peter Bent Brigham Hospital for twenty years.

9. How is Hunter's canal formed, and what is in it?
10. What arteries supply the stomach?
11. What is the difference between a Malpighian body of the spleen and one of the kidney?
12. Where does the Eustachian tube begin? Where does it end? What is it made of?
13. What structures are in the interpeduncular space of the brain?
14. What vessels go to the right auricle?
15. How many kinds of muscular tissue are there, and what are their microscopical peculiarities?

The physiology examination is more modern:

1. Why is the combustion warmth of an article of food not an absolute measure of its nutritive value?
2. Describe the process of bread-making.
3. Are the chemical or the mechanical functions of the saliva more important? Why?
4. How is the gastric juice modified in fever?
5. How may the amount of blood in the body be determined?
6. How does the contraction of the heart-muscle differ from that of ordinary striped muscle?
7. How is the temperature of the body regulated?
8. Why is the motion of the blood in the capillaries uniform?
9. What are the most important functions of the cilia?
10. What is meant by "glandular activity"?
11. Explain the importance of afferent nerve impulses for the production of voluntary motions.
12. What is the effect of removing the cortex cerebri in the higher animals?

A few additional allusions to his work at the end of his first year occur in April and June letters:

H.C. to H.K.C. *30 April 1892.*

Money is a dangerous thing to have in one's possession, there is so much temptation to spend it, and feeling wealthy from your donation I have yielded to the temptation and done nothing but spend, all day. I have settled up with my landlady, board lady, and washer lady, ordered a suit of clothes a sample of which I secured to send you but have mislaid somewhere, bought a new anatomy which I have wanted for some time—a Macalister—and lastly purchased for two dollars a cast of a gentleman who looks something like this and whom perhaps you will recognize as being a Grecian boxer or something of the sort. This person is now nicely decorated with his cutaneous nerve supply showing, and copied from a similar one at the school. He quite adorns my desk, my only other bric-a-brac

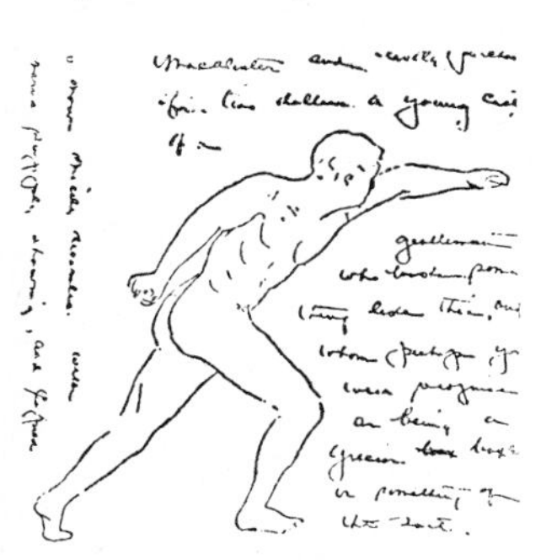

being a skull and an enlarged copy from the triumvirate doctor kodac. The work is beginning to pile up fast at the school as the lecturers are hurrying to finish their work laid out before June 1st which is pretty near at hand, so that there is more work than ever and whether it's the weather or the fact that I'm tired, I find it comes harder. I have been doing a little urinary work every day since the dissecting closed and would like to try and get it off next fall though the regular exam. comes in Feb'y. Do you think I can get some of it to do at home next summer?

Examinations are not far off and I feel fairly safe on the Anatomy but fear that I have neglected the Physiology more than I ought. I hope I may get a fair mark in them especially as there are so many good men in the class who will get high ones that the comparison would not be pleasant.

H.C. to B.M.C. *18 June 1892.*

. . . I have already struggled with one of my exams and also a part of next Thursday's and so feel somewhat relieved of their burden. I was feeling pretty mean the first part of the week and Codman took me down to Nahant where his brother has a house—there we studied some but as the thermometer was over 90 most of the time we spent most of our two days in the water. It was about my first experience with salt water and it certainly eclipses fresh, as far as swimming goes that is, not as a beverage. . . .

H.C. to H.K.C. *18 June 1892.*

Physiology next Thursday winds up the year's work. I want to stay here 24 hrs. or so to arrange about a place for next fall. [Charles F.] Painter wants me to stop with him in Gt. Barrington a day or two which I said I would do. This will probably bring me home Wednesday or probably Tuesday (28th). Will let you know definitely later. I got through the Anatomy all right I hope. Sixty dollars I think ought to settle me up with wash, lodge & board ladies & get my ticket home.

P.S. Just rec'd a postal from Dr. Pratt to the effect that I was appointed one of Dr. Scudder's assistants in the Out Patient Department next Fall. The appointment—so-called—is no credit to me but due to Dr. Scudder's kindness.

H.C. to H.K.C. *25 June 1892.*

I have got a chance to substitute in the M.G.H. for a couple of days next week while one of the men goes to Commencement Exercises. I think I had better accept it. Will not get home probably till Friday. Please tell Mother.

During his first years in Boston, Cushing was drawn to some extent into social activities although, as some of the previous letters indicated, he tried to avoid entanglements. He accordingly developed the habit of being somewhat casual, both about invitations and the social amenities, especially when he hoped not to be invited again, for he was jealous of any interruption of his work. However, when Yale friends were involved, it was different.

H.C. to B.M.C. *Sunday, 21 February 1892.*

. . . Tomorrow, being a holiday, most of the boys have scattered so that I fear it will be a lonely day for me. I got a letter from Melanie in New York begging me to come on to Mrs. Coles to spend the day. I almost made up my mind to do it & to stop over last night in New Haven but finally thought I had better not, partly as it's what I want to do during our Easter recess and partly because Charlie Howland had asked Star Childs & myself to go up in the country to his uncle's place with him to spend the day. I just heard from him saying that his plans had fallen through & now I must glorify G.W. alone. I went again to the Symphony concert last night & enjoyed it nicely though 'twas rather deep for me to understand. Friday afternoon I went to a tea at the Wards, given for Mrs. Dr. [Paul] Thorndike. Not knowing anyone I expected to be extremely bored & was. Dr. Holmes I believe describes such an occasion as "Giggle Gabble Gobble Git." The rest of the large company were wildly carrying out the first three fourths of his description when I did the last not staying long enough even for the gobble.

He did go to New Haven during the Easter recess and his enduring nostalgia for Yale appears in the letter he wrote his mother:

H.C. to B.M.C. *145 Farnam College, 10 April 1892.*

To think of sitting here in a college room writing my Sunday letter as of old. Al Harvey is just across the desk fooling with his scrapbook and I can almost imagine it is Tot [Perry Harvey]. This is the cheapest place to visit I ever saw. I am being fattened at the training table with the nine and have had beds galore put at my disposal. Everything is just about as it was last year except that many familiar faces are missed, which will be much more noticible in two or three years for I seem to know a good many men still though their names are very elusive.

I left Boston yesterday morning & after a short debate left all my books with it though I don't seem to have entirely escaped medical people for I heard Dr. Delavan last night give a talk on Medicine, its history &c to the men, which however was very pleasant. He told me that he was a classmate of Dr. Lowman's at the College of Physicians and Surgeons and asked many questions of Dr. and Mrs. L. which I was unable to answer, not knowing either of them. Charlie Cooley and George Eliot were in town, the latter having just come on from Cleveland so had much to talk about. It makes me live again to be here, and I look forward to my departure with much displeasure which will probably be this afternoon. Excuse this scrappy letter but I can't sit still long at a time. Many thanks for the birthday present. It was the cause of my being here.

Although Yale men had priority among the distractions he permitted himself, music was another he tolerated and possibly even enjoyed, though he himself could play no musical instrument. The generosity of Dr. Charles L. Scudder, who has already been identified as a friend of Ned's and one of H.C.'s anatomy teachers, enabled him to attend more concerts than might otherwise have been possible.

H.C. to B.M.C. *27 March 1892.*

. . . I went to the Symphony again last night with George Hitchcock who came in from Cambridge for that purpose. As a large part of the ticket holders were at the Italian opera which is now in Boston we appropriated boldly two desirable seats & fortunately were unmolested. Dr. Scudder is going South for a three weeks' vacation and he has kindly entrusted to my care his Symphony ticket and also his ticket to the Handel and Haydn Society for the Creation and Passion music so that my savage breast may be soothed whenever I desire. . . . I received an invitation the other day to a Maskenoza Club Reunion which brought up many pleasant recollections. Sorry not to have been there.

H.C. also willingly took time out for family friends from Cleveland, and in a letter to his mother in which we find him passing judgment on young Paderewski he also mentions his pleasure at seeing such friends as Mary Goodwillie, Mary Root, and also Katharine Crowell whose company he seemed particularly to enjoy:

H.C. to B.M.C. *27 February 1892.*

. . . I went this afternoon with [Henry] Sage to hear the good gentleman whose name resembles a sneeze give a piano recital. Has Paderewski been to Cleveland? If he has not, I hope he will & that you will go and hear him play. Simply listen, don't look for he resembles a personified crysanthemum [*sic*] to my mind. But for all his looks I never heard such playing. I enclose the program, on which I have underlined the pieces I liked best, probably as they were the only ones with which I was familiar. The others were rather over my head, much to my regret. I begin to feel quite musical having been to three concerts since I came to Boston, four in my life I believe, & I can say Chopin through my nose with the rest of them. Whenever I hear a familiar piece I seem to associate it with Tuesday mornings at 786 and Alice's eight hands, and realizing where we became acquainted I have much to thank Alice for.

I discovered Mary Goodwillie and Mary Root at the concert, it being the first time I had seen them though I knew they were in Boston & in fact staying on the same street, but my calling hours are limited. Kate Crowell is also here though she was not at the concert and it will give me great pleasure to escort them to the sanctuary tomorrow where I have been a stranger for some time I'm ashamed to say.

In his next letter home there is evidence that even in those days he found it difficult to change his clothes in the evening for calls or callers:

H.C. to B.M.C. *6 March 1892.*

. . . Elijah Boardman came in last night and I persuaded him to stay over night so that we have had a pleasant visit together. I have just come from church where I proudly escorted Kate and Mary G. leaving them there to communion. Elijah retreated to his legal surroundings, refusing to accompany us to the sanctuary. Dr. Babcock of Providence preached a very good sermon. I haven't had much time to see & be polite to the girls except, as they are staying right across the street, to drop in after dinner in the evening & spend about a half an hour in saying howde'. Not having energy to dress up on said occasions, I go looking more or less like a tramp and beat a hasty retreat before other callers may come. As my mind is occupied with nonconversational subjects these days, I fear that I am not a very entertaining caller & for this reason also retreat early.

It was wholly out of keeping with custom in his emotionally rather inarticulate family to mention affairs of the heart, but he did relate—in restrained fashion—one incident which seems to indicate that Kate Crowell, of all his friends, had the power to divert his mind from its usually level course.

H.C. to B.M.C. *13 March 1892.*

. . . I saw Kate Crowell off Friday afternoon and came very near being carried to Worcester. We took the train at the Columbus Avenue station where it only stops for a minute. Kate's section was the last one in the last car and by the time I had seen her settled and spoken to the porter the train had started. I naturally went to the rear door and found it locked and hurried forward then, managing in some way to get by the line of men who were in the narrow passage way beside the stateroom. By the time I reached the forward platform I found that locked also, the vestibule doors being closed, but I got hold of the conductor & he opened them and I swung off just about in time for had the train been going much faster or had I been much older I would have stayed on, which I was strongly tempted to do anyway, but time and money prevented.

1892-1893

During the summer of 1892 H.C. spent less time than usual in Cleveland. On 28 August we find him at Pittsfield en route to Boston, and on 5 September he writes that he is already settled in new lodgings, this year at 89 Charles Street, where a Dr. Sears[4] had his office. A letter to his mother is characteristic:

H.C. to B.M.C. *5 September 1892.*

. . . I went yesterday afternoon to the Arnold Arboretum which proved very interesting but will require more than one visit to be even superficially looked over. I think I shall stay here at 89 Charles permanently as I am getting accustomed to the noise and find that a constant racket is better than an interrupted one as I had last year. I found a little Wedgewood pitcher and sent it to Mary Briggs. Its only redeeming feature was its cheapness but I guess it will do. I should have liked to be in Pittsfield tomorrow but do not care to ask to be let off.

It is evident from two interesting letters from his father that during this summer vacation also he and his father had been interested in ornithology and in "botanizing." On 11 September, he had sent his father a duplicate "over cup white oak" leaf which he had just found, probably at the Arboretum:

Cleveland,
H.K.C. to H.C. *24 September 1892.*

Many thanks for your two letters to me since you bade us goodby last. I was interested in the slim waisted oak leaf, and the *anser*-footed maple (I have not forgotten all my Latin, you see). I think your summer's interest in leaves will do much to aid development in critical observation of things. It is a good thing to have acquired on general principles, and especially valuable to a physician. By the way, Dr. Scudder in his occasional lines to Ed takes opportunity to commend your efforts as an assistant in a way most pleasant and satisfactory to us all, and as I have no doubt it is to you to know it. It must of course require hard work, and close attention and application during the novitiate, but it will make everything easier and far more satisfactory when that shall have been completed. . . .

H.K.C. to H.C. (in red ink) *27 September 1892.*

. . . I foraged the other day under the Chisholm oaks for acorns. So far as I can make out, there are two sorts—those of the Scarlet, and Black oaks. Have saved some, and noted the trees from under which they were gathered. I was attracted to the spot by a very large gathering of black birds at work under the trees. They were gobbling the acorns in great style. They easily separated the cups from the nuts—i.e.—they dropped off when the blackies picked up the nuts, and then they swallowed the acorns whole, usually with one, or by one

[4] Dr. Henry F. Sears, then an Assistant in Pathology at the Harvard Medical School.

gulp; sometimes it required two efforts for the downing. The birds were only at work under the scarlet oaks. I presume the black oak acorns are bitter, though with the shell on this would not seem to be a serious objection.

I saw not long since a statement in regard to the diverse ways in wh. various birds manage acorns. I remember it said that wild pigeons and wild ring doves swallowed them whole, of course minus the cups—that some woodpeckers broke open the shell with their beaks, and then ate the fragments, but I don't remember that the article referred to blackbirds. At any rate I was surprised to see such small birds make such easy work of going the entire swine. This note looks like an advertisement of "Dr. John Tripp's Blood Purifier"—but it is the best I can do at this writing.

A letter of this period to his brother William seems to substantiate the fact that H.C.'s chief pilfering ground for botanical specimens was the Arnold Arboretum:

B-town,
H.C. to William E. Cushing [*September 1892*].

Dear Will Your offering at hand—much interested. He's no foreigner. I have a sample [dried seed of some shrub glued on] serupticiously [*sic*] plucked at the Arnold Arboretum, but have just found to my sorrow that I have lost his name. I will renew the acquaintance next time I go to the A.A. for I like the shrub nicely & will report to you. Have seen some fine trees &c since leaving home notably a hornbean—a hop—at G. Barrington about 3 ft. in diameter, but have had little time to look about lately. Will send you a Kentucky coff. tree (leaf only) some day so you can identify the Rockefeller trees.

Just before the term started he spent a week-end at Annisquam with his Yale friend, Henry Sage. The vivid letter describing his brief holiday presents early evidence of his remarkable powers of observation (encountered previously in his description of the blizzard of '88) and also shows something of his propensity for lighthearted humor:

H.C. to B.M.C. *18 September 1892.*

Thanks to Henry Sage I have been spending a glorious Sunday up on the north Coast of Cape Ann, at a small place called Annisquam or Squam for short, four miles from Gloucester & where his mother and many other charming people including artists galore spend the summer in the most informal way. They live in an old boarding house which looks as though it had been thrown together haphazard and in which a conversation can easily be held between the servant on the first floor and a third story lodger, provided the other guests remain quiet pro tem. This thin walledness naturally only adds to the informality and easily formed acquaintance between the boarders. The bathing, boating, good substantial table set, beautiful walks and superb views to which the presence of a porch covered with easels, palates [*sic*], brushes & half finished canvasses attests, seem to more than atone for any other inconveniences.

We left here on the three o'clock boat yesterday and after a beautiful sail through the harbor past Nahant, Beverly, Salem, Magnolia & Norman's Woe, into fishy Gloucester—her harbor crowded with sturdy craft and docks covered with fish and lined with old storehouses containing all the paraphernalia necessary for supplying the seamen and their schooners on their long cruises—all very interesting—thence a fine drive to Annisquam—arriving just in time to climb the Squam rock and see the sunset—a regular blood orange one—it's a luxury in this part of the world to get water between yourself and the setting Sol who usually drops onto the dry land. An evening spent in looking at pictures wishing for money to buy some of them, for many were beautiful & dirt cheap compared to city prices for such things. The next morning Henry took me on a long walk to the Dennison homestead built in 1727 & a dandy it is though on its last legs—then on to a rock known as the "Whale's Jaw" from which is a beautiful view for miles on every side.

We had a rough tramp through woods of all sorts, pines & ash aplenty, birches, alders, maples—the red ones just in their glory—butter-nut, oak, quantities of heavy laden barbery bushes & others without end—over country roads we went chasing over boulders, fences, fields for short cuts, more woods and always more boulders, over one brook and swamp in which I had of course to fall so that my white tennis jeans assumed from the waist down a greenish brown aspect which would have become the skirts of a white birch but not so with mine, and after a three-hour tramp as you may imagine I arrived a much bedraggled object at the starting point. It was part of the game however, and made all the more fun for ourselves as well as for the country people we met. A salt water swim, change of clo., lunch and return home at 3 this afternoon about completes in outline the tale.

Have enjoyed the papers sent on very much, especially the Psychology one. Would like to send it to G. Ladd as the scene is evidently New Haven. Lectures commence about the 29th, I think, which I dread as with the hospital it means much work.

Early Clinical Work

Maurice Richardson did much to influence Cushing's surgical thinking in the early days and he developed a great fondness for the eager young medical student which was warmly reciprocated. Little did either realize then that Fate had decreed that one would ultimately succeed the other as Moseley Professor of Surgery at Harvard. That the friendly relationship between the two men was fostered by H.C.'s brother Ned is apparent in his letter of 16 September 1892 from Cleveland:

Dear Harvey, Glad to hear that Maurice has asked you to assist him. The work is good fun and will help you in the way of the M.G.H. appointment, for Maurice's backing counts at the hospital—I owed my appointment largely to him, and got to know him as his 2nd year assistant.

Hope the O.P.D. work is proving satisfactory. Have you sounded Scudder as to the afternoon surgical out-patient work at the Children's Hospital? I should think possibly you might get something to do there in the afternoons. Write me something about the treatment of fresh and septic wounds now in vogue when you get time. Have you encountered old Jim Mains? Remember me to him if you do. You had better have the Med. Journal sent to your address if you care for it. I supposed you would have done so, but the paper has come regularly to me. . . . Affectionately, Ed.

Two weeks later H.C. writes further of his work with Scudder:

H.C. to H.K.C. *1 October 1892.*

Have just received your letter with enclosed check for which many thanks.

The week has gone by like a flash. School opened Thursday though practically not till tomorrow: still the creak of the grindstone is in my ears. We have arranged with Dr. Scudder to get off in time from the Hospital to attend lectures &c. When my turn comes to remain I can easily secure the notes of some other man. Tell Ed that I have been apportioned to Dr. [William W.] Gannett's Auscultation division as he has the first 40 men alphabetically and this just includes the C's.[5]

The first references to his second-year course work occur in a letter to his father of 9 October. Of particular interest is his reference to the purchase of Osler's Textbook:

Have been buying books right and left—& wish they were cheaper. Osler's Practice of Medicine,[6] a Therapeutics &c &c at about $5 per pound weight. I have bought a Ziegler—please tell Ned so that he won't send yours as his letter promised to. Hope I shall like Pathology—have a splendid teacher, at any rate, in Councilman from Johns Hopkins. Theory and Practice is fairly appalling. I left a little thin book about the size of a school catalogue at home, containing some Histology drawings. Will you ask Alice or someone to look for & forward it? Hope it won't be too much trouble.

The term progressed rapidly and Christmas holidays were upon him before he realized it. Early in December he wrote, "I have settled my fate as far as the Christmas vacation is concerned and accepted an opportunity to work in the medical out patient department [Massachusetts General Hospital] for this month." Since it involved mornings only, it gave him a chance to work over materia medica (which he keenly disliked) and auscultation. He added: "Dr. Richardson's demonstrations have begun and are good fun though they have not given us much dissecting to do as yet." Cushing and Amory Codman served during the course as Richardson's prosectors, which gave H.C. an excellent opportunity to perfect his skill in dissection. On New Year's he wrote to his father about his first month of real clinical experience, mixing it with a little family genealogy:

I have just come from a breast operation which Dr. Scudder kindly asked me to etherize—I met there a Dr. Benjamin Cushing of Dorchester who filled me full of genealogy as I washed instruments. I couldn't follow him perfectly but his grandfather was a 'Benjy' of Hingham where this Benjamin was born. He knew Frank "Juni," has rooted about Hingham, England, and probably knows some things which would interest you. He wanted to know all about the H.K.C. branch but as I could get no farther back than David and Goliath I have sent him the paper which you made out for Major C. last year.

With yesterday my out-patient engagement wound up. I don't know how much I have learned there except to ask people with more or less grace—"How are your bowels?" One good old creature told me his were in Ireland. I presume

[5] There were 122 students in the second-year class, the number having fallen from the original 171 who entered in 1891.

[6] This was the first edition of Osler's famous text, which had then just been published. It weighed 4 lbs. 7 oz.

he didn't quite catch the drift of my question. I hope it has made me a little more at home with a stethescope in my ears—though I still feel a good deal like a great big mosquito with a formidable proboscis buzzing about and prodding an innocent creature here and there. I also hope Materia Medica will seem less dry.

Clinical training was now in full swing, for in those days it came earlier in the medical student's course than now. To students who may feel insecure and discouraged during the early years in medical school, there is no more heartening tonic than the entries in a brief "line-a-day" diary which H.C. kept for one year from 1 January 1893 (during his second and third years at Harvard Medical School). He served occasionally as an anesthetist, sometimes as a surgical assistant; he had also to examine and present cases and to use his wits in an emergency dispensary. One of the first patients anesthetized died under the anesthetic before a class of students at the Massachusetts General Hospital on 10 January 1893—a circumstance which had a profound effect on the sensitive young medical student and caused him to devise, with Amory Codman, improvements which are still in use in all operating rooms. All this and much else is found in his brief entries. The diary for the entire year obviously cannot here be given in full, but some idea of his activities, his thoughts, and reactions can be gained from a few random entries.

January 1893

Sunday, 1 January. Etherized for Dr. Warren at St. Margaret's. Carcinoma of breast. Met Dr. Benj. Cushing. Gloucester at 6.15. Rain.

Monday, 9. Saw M. H. Richardson perform oesophagotomy and remove a teaspoon from the oesophagus of a crazy woman who had swallowed it. Twenty minutes. More snow.

Tuesday, 10. Have promised to substitute at M.G.H. for [Frank] Lynam for a week.[7] Strangulated hernia case—woman died on table before the Class. Had

[7] Two weeks, as it turned out. He wrote home on 15 January: "I have been substituting at the Massachusetts General during the week for one of the men who is laid up and have enjoyed it very much. Those house officers are about as hard worked men as I have ever seen. Every day is twenty-four hours long for them with a vengeance." And on 22 January there is further mention: "I wound up my hospital substituting last night at eleven o'clock and returned gladly to 89 Charles Street and bed." Dr. Lynam (now of Duluth, Minnesota) recalls that when he asked Cushing to substitute, "He was not as anxious for the position as I had expected; said that he had anaesthetized only a couple of times but consented to try it, I being at his elbow. Of course the first case had to be one of a strangulated hernia of some 48 hours or more duration. I explained to him that if things turned out to be as they looked on the surface that the woman would die during the operation. I told him that the first one that I had troubled my conscience for weeks, in fact until I saw it happen to someone else. I had been sure that I had killed the man with too much ether. The patient went true to expectations and lasted only a few minutes. Later I went down to the Laboratory where he was doing work for me. He seemed very reticent and at last said, 'Will you get someone to take my place?' I said 'Of course, but it isn't on account of this case, is it?' I got a half negative answer and then he said 'I think that I won't study medicine.' I was a little aggravated and said 'It *is* this case, and after all the trouble

had Strych. Gr. 1/60, Atropine 1/60. Brandy sub. cu. and Nitro Glyc. 1/100 gr. Am pretty low in mind.[8]

Thursday, 12. Another cervix and perineum. A pretty poor etherizer I. Lynam a good fellow. Paraphymosis reduced. Codman's friend w. carcinoma of lip. Did not operate. Chute and I helped care for a negro who fell from a wagon, on way home.

Friday, 13. First [Ward] E operation—double tubo-ovariotomy in Trendelenburg position. Encysted hydrocele at 38 [Commonwealth Avenue] w. Dr. Porter—A. K. Stone assisted. Promised latter to help in a bandaging course w. policemen.

Saturday, 14. Big operating day. Etherized well but don't seem to hit it off with the house officers. 2 strictures—leg amp. Sarcoma of back. Vaginal exam. &c. Got thru. at 6.30 G.C.H [itchcock]. here tonight.

Tuesday, 17. Alexander operation—E. A miserable catarrhal patient. Codman's N.H. friend—took out lip and glands in neck for examination. Behaved well, Dr. P[orter]. a beautiful operator. Still cold and bright.

Thursday, 19. Hard luck again etherizing. Ovariotomy in E and a cervix in Glass room who behaved bad—had to put string in tongue. Dr. P. must think I'm a clumsy dunce. Slightly warmer.

Saturday, 21. Has been a good day. Operated to 4. Excision of both testicles. Porter leaves a piece of one. Amputation. Copied Kraske's records for Cabot. Beer in the flat. Missed Star [Childs] and Hitch.

Thursday, 26. Bishop Brooks' funeral today. Many thousand must have seen him lie in state at Trinity. Etherized for Cabot at 37 [a nursing home] for ovariotomy. Urine exam tomorrow. Ground all evening with White. Headache most all day. Stopped nicotine. Moderate and clear.

Saturday, 28. Saw first Cheyne-Stokes respiration in an aortic insuff. Skated on the Garden at 10.30. Poor ice.

Monday, 30. Still working over the poisons. Contemplate taking some myself. A note from W.S.G. thinks he has "onaemia" and wants a blood doctor. Joslin gave me a ticket to art exhibit. Frozen up again and slippery ± clear.

Tuesday, 31. Sandwich Island [Hawaii] revolution—Annexation (?). Ground all day with White.

February 1893

Wednesday, 1 February. Rain & ice—examination this A.M. Did fairly well but as usual left out part of a question—studied up a lot of unnecessary things,

---

that I went to to explain it to you.' He said that he appreciated my trying to let him down easily. I turned on him and said 'You are one d——d fool.' He then consented to continue for the rest of the week.

"Either at this time or later he substituted for me again. Dr. Arthur T. Cabot had a case of cancer of the bladder. He was sent home, and being near by, we irrigated his bladder for him. Cushing took this over. When I came back, he said 'The man died.' Dr. Cabot was anxious for an autopsy, so I went over to talk with the man's wife. They were right in the middle of the wake. When I told her what I had come for, she screamed and called us all names. The assembled mourners jumped up and grabbing whatever was handiest started for me. I easily led the parade for quite a distance. I began to feel like a jinx."

[8] Dr. [John W.] Cummin writes 8 April 1942: "An examination of West Surgical records under date of 10 January 1893 shows that on that day Dr. C. B. Porter operated on a woman, J.A., for a strangulated hernia. He found a sac filled with gangrenous black intestines floating in pus. She had been given ether (but the name of the etherizer is *not* recorded). The patient failed rapidly and though stimulation was given died in a few minutes."

like Dragendorff's method &c. Heard Dr. Senn on Bloodless Hip Amputation at the surgical meetings.[9] Maurice had Codman & me to help a lad to the fore— much embarrassment.

Thursday, 2. They have passed the Athletic rule at N.H. [Yale], keeping out all but undergrads &c. I admire them for it. Have had scraps w. Scudder about it.

Friday, 3. Copying up Pathology Notes. Am much interested in immunity &c. Sternberg's article in the Journal, Tyndall's floating matter &c. Been raining and freezing for 2 days so that the electrics can't get along. They sit still & hum.

Saturday, 4. Helped Sears w. pleurisy baby in South End. Washington Heights & fine view. Glare of ice. City Point—ice boats &c. Theatre. Lion Tamer-Wilson w. Hitch in Eve. Very cold since last night & ice everywhere.

Sunday, 5. Star to dinner. Skate on the Basin w. White & Whitmans. Supper w. the Scudders & Theodore at Brookline. Cold & clear—beautiful day.

Monday, 6. Began Anatomy Quiz w. Conant. Rain.

Tuesday, 7. Monks' Clinic for 1st time. First autopsy. Beautiful sunset over the bridge [rough little pen & ink sketch]. Walked across w. Codman & Putnam. Cold wave coming.

Wednesday, 8. Skate on the Basin. Cold.

Thursday, 9. Another skate on the Basin after dinner. Cold.

Friday, 10. Moffitt read a fine paper on "Rest Cure" at the Boylston. He is an exceedingly bright man. Rain all day—colder tonight.

Saturday, 11. Etherized—Cabot—at 38 Commonwealth Ave.—abdom. hysterectomy—cancer. Studied all day. Hitch came in about 10 o'clock.

Sunday, 12. Lunched at the Wards. Met an entertaining and much traveled old gentleman. Mr. Silsby [Silsbee?].

Monday, 13. Great joke on T. D[wight]. at the School who mistook a bear's foot skinned for child's—Inspector brought it—found in drug store. Girl opened it & fainted away. Conant's quiz on Abdomen. Don't know much about sections. Snowballed on my way home. Snow, rain and *slush.*

In the next entry and those which follow later in the year he frequently adds at the end of the last line numerals, e.g., "11.30," indicating, Pepys-wise, his hour of retiring.

Friday, 17. Call from C. Warren & Gardner Perry. Been fine day but snowing tonight. Very cold last night 10° or thereabouts. 11.30.

Saturday, 18. Hardest snow this winter—24 hrs. A foot or over on a level. Putnam to lunch. Saw Hopkinson Smith's "Summer in Venice" picture—very fine. G.C.H. in eve.

Sunday, 19. Painter this A.M. Stone to dinner—Herbert Parsons in eve. Went out to Warrens w. Wint. Snowing again.

Monday, 20. Dr. Warren opened the abdom. cavity in operating on an empyaema of Shattuck's before the class—peritonitis, recovery.

Tuesday, 21. Etherized a circumcision at M.G.H. for Lund. Left for New Haven at 4. Saw George Case w. little avail. A fine Zs. Many '91'ers there.

[9] He gives a more detailed account of Senn's paper in a letter the same day to his father: "He is German looking—has an unmistakable German accent and bearing and his paper was characteristic of one of them in its detail and careful preparation. I was very glad to have seen him as well as the local celebrities who were present, many of whom I had never had pointed out to me before." Senn's book, *The pathology and surgical treatment of tumors,* published in 1895, became one of Cushing's principal reference guides during his last years in Boston and his early years at Hopkins. His well-grangerized copy is still preserved in his library.

Coats' tatoo, Hatch's imitations of Prof. Tyndall &c. Ned and John Porter's political repartee. Left hall about 7.30 for Troubadour but found instead of clear sky &c. about 6″ of snow so did not tramp w. the gang to campus. Wallace led the Fleece session. Home about 6 [a.m.]—bed about 7, slept till 12—dinner at the Commons with Al. Saw the new gym. wh. is certainly a marble palace. The gym equipment seems perfect. Team have own rooms, baths &c—about 60 men at table—The Zs' [of the senior society] paper on "Typical College Men" good. Left at 3.30 & got here [Wednesday] late for Gannett's Quiz on Pericardium. Still snowing and cold—also blowing much.

Thursday, 23. Patrick Henry's advice to young men is "Never argue because it's 10 to 1 you won't convince your opponent—& it's 10 to 1 if you do convince him he wasn't worth convincing."

Friday, 24. About 4 inches more snow last night. Good clear day today. Good sleighing.

Saturday, 25. Most everyone in house down with the 'Grippe,' wh. Calkins started. Shows it's contagious. Snow = to 4″ water & more coming down this P.M. Met Hallowell at M.G.H. Helped Scudder w. wen in back. Snowing. 10.30.

Sunday, 26. Dinner at the Joslins w. Edes, Painter, Dolliver, Miss Painter & ? Called on Major & Mrs. Cushing. She is a fine, hospitable type of Southern befo' the war woman. Had an interesting talk w. Major C. about model yacht racing. He described an ingenious rudder of lead they used & of which they had many weights for different winds. An inverted rudder so that the vessel was kept automatically before the wind. A puff made her tend to run up into it but the rudder by its weight swung round. [Pen & ink diagram]. 12.

Tuesday, 28. Etherized for A.T.C[abot]. Mrs. B. breast. Cancer recurrent. Also M.H.R[ichardson]. amputated a foot wh. he wants me to dissect. We are now trying to dissect a fat axilla for his demonstration. Snowing again tonight. Bed early as headache. 9.30.

March 1893

Friday, 3 March. Maurice on shoulder & arm. Monks gave interesting talk at Boylston on advantages of foreign study—the places to go & their different systems & courses. He thinks it's a good thing. Rec'd a box from Asheville from Laura G. Williams full of oak leaves & acorns. Grover inaugurated. 12.30

Monday, 6. Dissected all day and finished the foot for Maurice. 11.15

Thursday, 9. Dissected all day on an elbow for Conant. Have promised A. K. Stone to help in policemen's bandaging course wh. Brooks is giving. Painter is going in too. A wretched day. Rain & wind & water. 12.30

Friday, 10. Dissected in A.M. Conant demonstrated Elbow. Large fire near Albany depot—went down w. White. $4,000,000 loss. Boylston Soc. Warren read on shock. 11.15

Saturday, 11. Saw w. Edes some fine pictures at the St. Botolph Club—a Millet—a Meissonier of a Cavalier & horse getting a drink at a tavern wh. was wonderful. Some Corots with their willow greens. Also liked one of Cazin's of a field of grain, poppies &c after a storm, very much. Drizzling. 11.30.

Tuesday, 14. Dr. Strong died from septicaemia—infected at a laparotomy last Thursday. A gangrenous appendix. Beautiful day. 11.30

Saturday, 18. Etherized poorly for Cabot this A.M. An ovariotomy at 37. Went to Natural Hist. Museum this P.M. Good place. Bad tooth. Pretty cold. 11.30

Monday, 20. Warren told pathetic story of Dr. D.'s death from cancer of tongue at Clinic this A.M. Tried to cut it out himself w. cocaine in a fit of desperation. Didn't go to Conant's Quiz. School w. Edes & dissected. 12.15

Wednesday, 22. Shattuck told an old hypochondriac to remember the Eleventh Commandment—"Fret not thy Gizzard" & forget all the others if necessary. Gannett in eve and to Puritan Club w. Codman. Planned trip to Cape Cod with him for Easter. 12.30

Friday, 24. Bad grouch this P.M. Boylston in eve. Selva read a good paper & showed apparatus for Pott's disease. Monks talked about technical memory, memories &c. Went with him to look up a subject—suggested anthrax.

Sunday, 26. Asked to Warrens but didn't go. Dined at Codman's. His sister talked "family" all the time. Went to Museum w. him to see the Bronze by D. C. French for the monument for the sculptor, Martin Milmore. A relief representing death as an angel stopping him in his work [small thumbnail indication] chizeling on a sphinx. Called at Wards. Star & Hitch to tea.

Thursday, 30. Walked out to park w. Codman. Saw first robin. Gannett this p.m. Bandaging class w. policemen & given by Goldthwait. Painter told story of H. I. Bowditch & quack. B. told a man he had ph[thisis] & lung full of cavities. He went to a quack who said liver trouble. Man better for a while & then died. Ob't an autopsy and all there. Lung full of holes. Quack admitted it & said if B. had done as well by the lungs as he had by the liver man would have lived. Drizzling. Still stupid. Smoking.

Friday, 31. Conant finished up the demonstration. Page read & Cobb reported on hemorrhoids at Boylston—they use only clamp & cautery at the M.G.H. A most gorgeous night—full moon. **12.**

Two letters are inserted between diary entries because they amplify the details of H.C.'s activities:

H.C. to H.K.C. *3 April 1893.*

I just received your letter and enclosed all right. I am very much grieved to hear about Grandpa. I suppose the general infection in the case of a lax pneumonia such as you describe offers a very serious outlook. I hope you will telegraph me so that I can come home if it comes to the worst. [Erastus Cushing died 4 April 1893.]

Our Easter vacation begins tomorrow and I expect to stay here in Boston. I must write a Boylston paper for the 14th of the month and have been rather at a loss for a subject. I think however I shall write about Anthrax. It is not a very practical question from the standpoint of practice but its intimate relation to the germ theories of infection, immunity &c makes it interesting historically at least. I hope I can make something out of it. Dr. Conant who has been taking Dr. Richardson's place as demonstrator during the latter's absence on a vacation finished up the course last Friday so that there is one more thing off my hands. There is much good dissecting still on the subjects, which Codman and I hope to get time to finish up. I have just received notice to the effect that I have been elected into the Union Boat Club. I applied for the same last fall and had forgotten all about it till now. The gymnasium and boat house are very convenient, being only a hundred yards from here on the river basin. I should like to join and get some regular exercise but will leave it with you as to whether you think it is worth the $30.00 initiation fee required. Ned can tell you about the status of the organization and its members.

H.C. to H.K.C. *Sunday, 30 April 1893.*

I must write you again for some more money and the approach of this spring time makes me realize that I must have a house-cleaning soon. My under clo.

are Chinese puzzles—my socks all have windows a plenty and my respected washerwoman says my shirts are not "worth the washin' "—hence I must ask for an extra donation.

We have been having a great treat in the shape of some lectures by Dr. H. C. Wood of Philadelphia on Therapeutics. The Medical School Association has secured him—and it certainly is "Therapeutics dramatized" when he is compared with the sleepy lecturer we have had during the year. It is a pleasure to hear a man let himself out in this conservative town, and judging from the number of staid old professors & doctors who attend, they enjoy it as well as the younger part of the audience. He has been lecturing on Digitalis & other Cardiants & is going to give three or four more lectures on opium &c. Dr. Richardson finished up the demonstrations finally Friday but he has asked us to do some more dissecting for him so that the time when I expected to get at the real School work of the term in earnest is again put off. I have had a chance to come in on the tail end of the surgical course & finish up the material—tieing arteries—amputating &c which is great fun though we have had to work at all hours of the night at it. I read my Anthrax paper on the 21st—don't think it was very good. Codman read a good paper last Friday on some theories of rheumatism which wound up the Boylston for the year.

I have etherized quite a number of times lately for Drs. Porter and Warren, and had a case last Thursday which behaved very much like the Shepard one in New York—apparently an oedema of the lungs. They worked over him nearly all day and I think he pulled through—he was all right the last I heard. Bad cases seem to run my way.

April 1893

Monday, 3 April. Shattuck hypnotized a girl at Clinic. Warren gave his "wooden leg" lecture at M.G.H. Etherized for Dr. Porter who removed for 4th time some tuberculous glands of the neck. Councilman gave exhibition of slides at demonstration. 12.15.

Wednesday, 5. Vacation. Etherized Master R.S.L. for Dr. Warren. Cosmetic ear operation. To Riverside with Porter all afternoon. Beautiful day. Skunk weeds. 12.

Thursday, 6. Fast day. Etherized a Mrs. Cushing at No. 2 for a breast. Anthrax this P.M. Whitman back from Chicago. Says he went thru. Cleveland like a dose of salts—effects of Chicago water. No more word from home—expect to leave tomorrow. 3" of snow last night, did not stay long. 11.

Sunday, 9; Monday, 10. Letter from Mel [Melanie Harvey] staying in N.Y. Met Mr. Atterbury & for N.Y. at 4 w. him. Reading the "Rt. Honourable." On Monday saw Grove's shop. To N.Y. Hospital (180 ± beds) & shown about by Dr. Barstow. To Dr. Weir's Clinic w. Osler [Cushing's first meeting with Osler] & Howell. Shown about Anatomical Dept. Met Dr. Eliot, their quiz master. Saw Hart, Fisher, Dr. Delavan & others. Lunch w. Howell & short call on Armstrong just going up for exams at St. Luke's. To Imperial and call on Mel & Cousin Mattie. Atterburys to dinner w. Mr. & Mrs. Higgins. Grove & I stayed home & talked. Saw his sketch book &c. Rained & warm.

Tuesday, 11. To Imperial in morning—Bratenahl's office—Will Carey at Century said that Miss Phelps engaged—Ethel not home—Mary Chisholm & + Clevelanders at Winsor. Saw Josh Hartwell. Atterburys to lunch. W. Gustave to Vanderbilt Clinic—Roosevelt—Sims' beautiful theatre there. McLane does all operating—best now in N.Y. Call on Mr. LeBourgeois w. Mel. Farewell to Atterburys & dinner w. Harveys, Hollidays & Bratenahl. Saw Low's ceiling at

Waldorf Hotel—talked in eve, and left on 11 train—men in N.Y. working like dogs.

Wednesday, 12. Arrived at 6.30 ±. Found Vicar of Wakefield from Kate.

Friday, 14. Beautiful warm day. Willows & elms quite suggestive of green. Got Burrell's Anthrax case. Dined at Codman's. Councilman told us about the fattening of geese—tie them up in bags in wh. are two holes. Raining tonight.

Tuesday, 18. Etherized for Warren on breast case at No. 2. Dissected the dura of one side for Maurice and ruined it & consequently discouraged tonight. Can do nothing but Anthrax & little of that. Don't see when I shall get in any studying. 11.

Friday, 21. Read Anthrax paper at the Boylston—not very successful. Headache all day. Chas. Howland to dinner. Rain—clear. 11.

Sunday, 23. Tied arteries all day at School. Star to dinner. 10.30.

Monday, 24. Warren Clinic on Cranial Surgery—Codman & I cleaned up subject for Maurice's final demonstration. Conant's quiz & dissected vulva till 12. Puritan Club w. Lord & Codman. Mayflowers—primroses—arbutus &c. Beautiful day. 1.30.

Tuesday, 25. Birthday present from Marian Phelps [of Cleveland]. Dissected all A.M. Pathol. in eve. "Find out what sort of advice a man wants and then give it to him." 11.30.

Wednesday, 26. Materia Med. in A.M. Finished female perineum for M.H.R. & he complimented us. Gannett in eve & amputated at School w. Lord, Codman, & Moffitt till 12.30. Calkins is writing a paper on smells & says "Sufficient unto the day is the odour thereof." 1.

Sunday, 30. Dedham w. Kate and Mary Goodwillie. Stayed to tea. G. Fred Williams there. Beautiful day—dog tooth violets. 12.30.

May, 1893

Tuesday, 2 May. Spent evening w. Kate and M.G. Read "The Dove Lady." Am seriously worried about myself. I have been able to do no studying for some time. Sit and stare at my books—so stupid I can't read words or say anything. Suicide about only alternative—don't wonder that people turn to it. 10.30.

Saturday, 6. Amputation in A.M. Gradually making way w. Rameses II and the old woman. '95 won Race. Yale 5, U. of P. 4. Harvard 7, Princeton 0. 12.

Friday, 12. Materia Med. till 11.30. Etherized Mrs. H. for Porter. Excised super. maxilla—eye—frontal sinuses—down to brain—great operation. School & finished up Rameses II. C.S.P. [Scroll and Key] dinner at Union Club. Good time. Baldy Cooley there.

Monday, 15. Etherized Mrs. W. at 366 Commonwealth. Conant and Brooks. Abdom. hysterectomy. Patient did poorly. Long operation—Conant's quiz—an A in medical chemistry. Beautiful warm day. 12.

Tuesday, 23. Very hot day 90° ±. Row at Union Club in afternoon. Tried to grind in eve s̄ avail. Cannot keep my mind, if I have any which at times I doubt, on any work. Really serious—have not smoked for some time 10 days ±. Mary Chisholm married.

Wednesday, 24. Fine day. Couldn't stand it and smoked again—after about 10 days. Bet Williams $10 on Athletic results—crew and nine. Gannett tonight. Hate myself these days. *Stupid.* 12.

Friday, 26. Etherized Mr. Pierce 476 Beacon—"Litholapaxy" for Cabot—successful. Councilman lectured twice today. Wrote to Miss Stiles in eve & grind till 1.15. Raining tonight. 1.30.

Wednesday, 31. Went to Nahant w. Codmans [for several days]. Rather cold for first few days but got warm enough by the 5th. Got our meals for 2 days, then to Club. I could not study very well—was grouchy because Codman learned so much faster than I that I came back after 6 days—not a very pleasant guest. We studied, not for long hours, & meanwhile took walks, threw the ball about or indulged in single stick exercise. A lovely view from the cottage up the coast toward Beverly, Marblehead &c past Egg Rock.

June 1893

Thursday, 15 June. Materia Med. exam this A.M. Did poorly. No memory, but be good, as Miss Stiles says, and let those who will be clever. Rowed in afternoon. "Pop" concert w. Codman in evening. Sultry.

Friday, 16. Ground till 5. G.C.H. to dinner & went to Circus. Saw gorilla, mandrill—Laloo the double Hindoo boy—&c. 11.30.

Wednesday, 28. Saw sheepskins given at Centre Church [New Haven]. Joslin told me I got the first 100 ever given in Pathology. Ashamed of knowing so little & having such luck. Alumni dinner with the Class. Al Crehore in town. Practice at field—Winston there. Negotiated for New York practice w. Harry Brooks. Good Bye to Clevelanders. C.S.P. Women ostracised. Left at 2 w. Ripley & Phelps.

Friday, 30. Yale wins by six lengths. Gibson here at house. Went on Peary's last trip. *Got 100 in Pathology*—first time it has ever been given. A in Anatomy and C in Therapeutics and Materia Medica. Rowed in a shell for the first time this P.M.

This brief diary of Harvey Cushing's is a poignant human document. Countless students have experienced similar periods of depression, usually when doing work of high order as he was doing in medicine. Many men with careers of conspicuous distinction have passed successfully through similar experiences; and some have sought the escape of self-destruction. Francis Galton, the great English geneticist, was forced on several occasions to leave Cambridge because of his feeling of utter frustration and inadequacy; Weir Mitchell had a parallel struggle, as did William James, the eminent American psychologist. The fact that H.C. won a similar battle is deserving of comment.

The academic year ends with amusing letters to his father and mother which indicate that he is beginning to recover his normal spirits:

H.C. to H.K.C. *18 June 1893.*

. . . I expected to start in this week with one of Ned's colleagues Paul Thorndike at the Dyspensary but he has gone down to Cumberland Gap where the meeting of genito-urinary men is now being held, and he said I had better wait till his return next Tuesday. This gives me a week and I shall gladly spend most of it as I have today and may go down to good New Haven for two or three days later and renew my acquaintance with baseball as I have told Mother. This I fear will not please you much as I know you were never very partial to the above-mentioned acquaintance, but if I can help the team any, as the Captain thinks I can, I shall gladly go. Then it gives me two or three days there sans expense. I don't know why they should want me for they all know more about the game than I ever did. I have told them this and they remain deceived. . . .

It has not been a very satisfactory year. We are just on the border line of practical work and have reached in theory the stage where things are no longer definate and assured and as I am not much of a theorist it's been pretty hard. Then the year has been broken up a lot by the out-patient work I did, the hospital substituting and Dr. Richardson's work for which we had to cut all the Therapeutics lectures, and that made some difference. It's over with now, however, and I hope I have gotten as much out of it as I ought. It certainly has been long hours. I have succeeded in getting a place at the Children's in the afternoons during July but for only 2 days a week and hope later to get in the other two. It depends on how much I can get out of these appointments as to my homecoming. If I find it profitable I shall stay on into August—if not, I'll leave the last of July. Dr. Porter, Jr. got me the place at the Children's & said come when you can and stay as long as you please, which was a very broad invitation surely.

H.C. to B.M.C. *19 June 1893.*

I will draw you some views of H.W.C. *Before* and *After* taking his examination this morning. I think that yesterday was the first time in many moons that I have missed writing you on Sunday. I found that I had miscalculated somewhat on the amount of matter which I had to go over so that I had to work up to the last minute. This was partly due to the fact that I was cajoled into taking Friday night off and going to the circus with the law school delegation who came in town after one of their long five-hour examinations and insisted on my going with them, when they found that I had till Monday. We had a very fine time and saw everything which the Circus had to present from the new gorilla to the old bearded lady. While gleefully watching the monkey collection, Hitchcock took occasion to tell us of the good Irishman who asked his companion while they were in the park in New York & apropos of the names which are being given to the animals there now—if he could tell whether the O'Rangs and the O'Tangs came from Kilkenny or Cork—which amused me greatly. . . .

BEFORE AND AFTER

1893-1894

Before settling down for his summer at the Children's Hospital, he had an interesting week-end at Plymouth with Winslow Whitman, a friend at Charles Street. "Being a Plymouthian," H.C. wrote his father, "he goes right back to 'the Rock' being the eighth direct from Gov. Winslow." "I was interested," he continued, "in something Mrs. Whitman told me which brings the landing in 1620 ridiculously near. A relative of hers who died not long since at the ripe old age of 98 remembered an old man, 'Grandfather Thomas' by name, who lived to be over one hundred and who was present at Perygrine White's funeral & remembered it well. Does not that make the country seem pretty young?" Later in the month he writes his mother of an excursion to Cambridge:

25 July 1893.

. . . I amused myself this afternoon, having been left in lone possession of 89 Charles Street, by a trip to the University Museum at Cambridge, and consequently I have that glad-to-sit-down feeling which sightseeing brings and with which you must have become familiar during your Chicago stay unless you patronized 'Sophomore' chairs and gondolas largely. I went out particularly to see the Ware glass flowers or better the so-called "Blaschka collection of glass models" and the like I never saw before. Perhaps you have heard of them. They are the most perfect things imaginable from huge century plants down to minute clusters of flowers, ferns, leaves, blossoms and berries and many low forms of plant life. It seems hard to realize that they are not freshly picked, and the most exquisite colors you ever saw. They are made by some German glass workers, I believe. Then there are magnified parts of the dissected flower when it is small. They would certainly delight you and also the leaf collectors of the family. They also have a fine collection of birds, insects and animals all of which are especially attractive as they have none of that dusty, motheaten appearance so common in like collections. I was admiring an enormous walrus and thinking of Gibson's tales about them in Greenland when the guests were politely requested to depart.

A few other details of his hot summer can be gleaned from his line-a-day diary:

July 1893

Saturday, 9 July. Dispensary in A.M. Did a septic phymosis circumcision. Children's in aft. Helped Proctor w. plaster casts &c. Dinner at Dr. Porter's. Etherized (?) a Mr. H. at Jam. Plain for C. A. Porter. Allie a corker. Man damned him up & down.

Tuesday, 18. Dispensary in A.M. Children's—Lund told story of eminent Dr. in Phila. Son came home one night edged & insulted a policeman who chased him home. Pol. banged on door & aroused the Dr. who came to window & inquired cause. *Pol.:* "Your son told me to kiss his ——." *Dr.:* "Can't you wait till morning?"

Wednesday, 19. Etherized a stricture divulsion for Cabot at St. Margaret's. I do despise etherizing. Got my man's urine at hospital and found Tubercle Bacilli in the sediment. Much pleased. Hitch came in in eve and we went to see Sandow.

Friday, 28. Fooled w. surgical case at Library all day. Row in 'Kelpie' up to 2nd bridge. Just beginning to feel at home in a shell.

Saturday, 29. Dispensary and Children's—learned diff. betw. varus and valgus shoes, Thomas knee splint, Taylor back brace and hip splint &c. Rather poor day. Letters all evening.

Early in August his father had further word on the subject of funds. Although H.C. was never free from financial worries during his years in medical school, he had come to treat them as routine and his requests, dispatched at least once a month, were usually amusing:

H.C. to H.K.C. *August 1893.*

Being much reduced in pocket I have been looking for your regular monthly letter and P.O. order but Ned writes me that you are very busy over some trustee work and that you want me to account for myself. I'm afraid you will find me an expensive luxury though I don't know as I come in that latter category.

Having broken one of my molars over some boarding house tapioka [*sic*] I hied me to a worthy dentist and while there had him doctor me up for the time being as I think he is a good one. You may have heard from him as I asked him to send the bill to you. I also have got a new black coat to take the place of the old one, defunct. This with my board and room up to the tenth, washer lady for the month, railroad fare and an expedition which I have promised to make to Falmouth Sunday to see the Ed Harveys & which will cost three or four dollars will bring me up to about $120.00. If you are poor like everyone else in these strange times, the coat can wait a month as I have but just received it and the bill has not turned up. Unless something unforseen turns up I shall leave here Wednesday next.

Externe duties at the Children's and at the Massachusetts General Hospital kept him in Boston until after the second week in August. He then took a brief vacation, but it seems to have been rather a busman's holiday for his diary reveals that he assisted at an operation in a country farmhouse near Oberlin, Ohio, and he also worked in some of the Cleveland hospitals.

August 1893

Saturday, 5 August. Dyspensary. Children's. Poor day. Proctor made a cast of my hand. Blowing & w. thin plaster.

Thursday, 10. Etherized a Philadelphia Dr. for Cabot. Recurrent appendicitis between attacks.

Thursday, 24 [Cleveland]. To Oberlin c̄ [Dudley] Allen. Assisted in appendix case in a country farmhouse. Rural operation. Called in evening by Drs. Ashman & Spence to Lakeview for another case. Decided to delay.

Friday, 25. Etherized above case at Charity. Went to Lakeside & etherized a vaginal dilatation &c.—saw Children's ward. An unfortunate scrap wh. Ed keeps out of, going on betw. the Weber & Cushing factions. Papers have taken it up.

The diary habit became strongly entrenched in Cushing, and his student diaries, his travel diaries, and his war diaries show his unusual talent for catching the essence of a person, a situation, a panorama, or an experience in a few telling words; and augmenting the verbal description there are his facile, amusing sketches. The first of his many travel diaries records a week spent at the Columbian Exposition at Chicago in September 1893. The account is embellished with some of his early sketches and contains his expense account, set down in his usual meticulous fashion. It appears that on Wednesday, 13 September, he started with $91.84 and managed to reduce this sum to $3.58 by the following Wednesday. His expenses during the first three days were entered as follows:

Start c̄ $91.84

September 13—Wednesday and Thursday Expenses	
Fare	15.00
Sleeper	2.00
Porter	.20
Carfare	.10
Crackers and hotbox	.13
Admission	.50
Breakfast	.35
Central	.10
Launch	.25
Cliff Dwellers and	.25
Catalogue	.10
Beer	.10
M	.05
W	.01
Dinner at Winder[mere]	1.35
Admission	.50
Boat	.25
Cider Orange	.05
	21.29

	91.84
	21.29
On Hand	70.55

Friday	
Breakfast	.50
Paper	.02
C Hotel	3.50
Admission	.50
German Foreign Bldg.	.25
Orange Cider	.05
Carfare	.05
Java Cocoa	.10
" Entrance	.20
" Theatre	.25
Ferris Wheel	.50
Cairo Street	.10
Beer	.50
Intramural [railway]	.20
Baby Javanese	.02
	7.74

	70.55
	7.74
On Hand	62.81

The Exposition itself must have afforded welcome relaxation and it no doubt elevated his depressed spirits, for he seemed to be amused by everything and the most trivial and inconsequential details are set down. He visited buildings of all the nations and found himself fascinated by the extraordinary exhibits from Japan—for this was the first real glimpse that any Western nation had had of Japanese art and culture. "The Japs' dancing," he commented, "was entirely a graceful pantomime, using hands and fingers to signify the spokesman." The Bedouin dancing girls "all have their hands and nails stained with senna." But the sketches are the most diverting part of the diary. A letter to his father after his return to Boston indicates special interest in the art of the Orient:

1 October 1893.

I have had one of my 'Jap' photographs framed which I have just been hanging. This has reminded me that I departed without leaving the names of those Ned and I got for you, which I hope have been delivered ere this. The first one was a view of Tokio from a hill (the name I have forgotten)—Atago Yama—on the outskirts. On the left is a drinking fountain put there with the summer pavilion, for the chance wayfarer. The donor's name is on one of the posts.

The middle picture is a long road lined by the big pink-stemmed cryptomeria (fifteen miles of them) leading from Tokio to Nikko where as you know are the tombs of the great Shoguns, the gateway to one of them being shown in No. 3. The Jap who gave me the pictures said it was the tomb of Ieyasu, the founder of the Tokugawa line. I knew nothing when I bought the pictures of Ieyasu or other Shoguns but an article in the Nineteenth Century for September which Ned gave me says that he was the big Shogun of all Shoguns. For this reason I

THE CHICAGO EXPOSITION 1893

am inclined to think that Mr. Jap may have said that about the gateway because this man's name was first at his tongue's end though I may be doing him an injustice. I hope the pictures will interest you. . . .

A few random entries follow for the months before Christmas:

September 1893

Sunday, 24 September. Walk c̄ Kate in Gardens & home to dinner. Call on Boardmans and Chisholms.

Monday, 25. Theatre c̄ Boardmans. John Drew in *The Masked Ball.* Opened (too wide) an abscess of neck in little Etsansburger girl—darn clumsy fool—rattled. Melanie got home.

Saturday, 30. Fitz first clinic on anaemia. Edes case. Tried in vain to work on paper. Row at 5. Abe Garfield to dinner. Fixed up room c̄ casts &c.

October 1893

Wednesday, 4 October. [William] Richardson's first lecture in Obstetrics. Called on Mary Goodwillie at Miss Hersey's. Met Miss White, Mrs. Colt's niece. Ground up quiz for Amerman. Willie Dal[zell] married.

Monday, 16. Too long lecture today. Cold. Codman came in in the evening c̄ his dog which he shot in the back as it leapt a wall after a partridge.

November 1893

Wednesday, 1 November. Hand ball. Heard T.D. lecture on Thorax c̄ Sears. Ground bones for Amerman till 1 p.m. Refused a scholarship of $250 from Councilman.[10] Recommended Edes.

Wednesday, 15. Read surgical paper. Dr. Frank Watson present. Codman came up courageously and asked questions. Watson complimented me on paper. Not so Proctor who talked to a friend most of the time and then told how he had performed some operations on tuberculous patients.

Friday, 17. Joslin read great paper at Boylston on diabetes. Ogden reported a case.

December 1893

Saturday, 2 December. Fitz threw me down on a case of acute endocarditis wh. really was merely a myocitis. B.C.H. in aft. and hand ball.

Wednesday, 6. [David W.] Cheever gave his last lecture on Professional Ethics—great send off. Amerman gave me a pen.

Friday, 22. Left for home c̄ Irv. at 5 P.M. Prodromal symptoms of Ye Grippe put off by whiskey & phenacetine. Codman & Mr. Hall on the train.

Cushing's artistic talent, which was well illustrated in his diary of the Chicago Exposition in 1893, comes again to the fore in his student notebooks. It was one thing to draw an artistic figure of a microscopic section, but quite another to catch the likeness of a patient lying in bed in respiratory distress. When attending clinics during the winter of 1893-1894 he almost invariably made a sketch of the patient in order to fix symptoms and general appearance in his mind. On 26 January one finds the pained expression of a woman suffering with gallstone colic; a week later a distinguished-looking sailor, aged 62, is depicted in respiratory distress with Cheyne-Stokes periodic breathing. A group of these exquisite vi-

[10] There is no record of his father's reaction to his having cheerfully turned down a $250 scholarship on the grounds that someone else probably needed it more than he. Dr. Councilman's proposal must, however, have been a source of gratification.

gnettes selected at random from many hundreds scattered through his medical school notebooks indicate their artistic quality.

Although Cushing sketched off and on until the end of his life, the artistic perfection of his work seems to have been at its height in his early thirties. Thereafter it suffered from disuse, and following

ON THE STREETS OF HAVANA
From travel diary of March 1894

the war he frequently complained that he could no longer catch a likeness. When editing his war diary in 1935 he attempted to redraw some of his rough sketches and found, to his chagrin, that he had lost his 'touch.'

Cushing spent a few days in Cleveland with his family during his Christmas recess. On returning to Boston he had ten days' service at the North End Hospital, after which he fell ill of a severe attack of tonsilitis and evidently failed to take care of himself, for it recurred in more severe form several weeks later and he was obliged to take a week off. He records that his landlady attempted to cure him with 'Rock and Rye.' This was not the first of such illnesses for throughout Cushing's student years he had been addicted to severe upper respiratory infections, and while at Yale he had had recurrent attacks of a conjunctival affection ('pinkeye' in his letters) which was never adequately diagnosed.

Early in March brother Ned appeared in Boston somewhat unexpectedly, possibly having been prompted by his father, and took Harvey off on a fortnight's trip to Cuba. They sailed from New York on a small ship, the *Yucatan*. A full and particularly well-illustrated diary was kept of this trip from which a few representative entries and sketches have been selected at random.

FROM H.C.'S HAVANA TRAVEL DIARY OF MARCH 1894

Sunday, 4 March 1894. We threw some rolls to the gulls this morning and Ned spoke about their keenness in knowing what boats to follow—for instance great crowds follow the big Cunarders way across as there is abundant table waste all of which is thrown away whereas the meagre French boats on which everything left over is served up again in a new style are accompanied by only a few less knowing birds. The whole appearance of things changes hourly and it's getting very warm. The Purser says that the boundary line of the Stream is so sharply marked that one could sit in a rowboat and have one's hand in two kinds of water which are 30° different in temperature and that they mix no more than oil and water.

Tuesday, 6. Friend Forrest, whose name was pronounced with such a velvety sound in Cleveland, proves very amusing. We were conversing on the subject of 'been' when he told me the story of the Englishman who was dining in Boston & the waiter gave him some bean soup when he asked for his broth. After he had finished he asked the waiter what it was, "That's bean soup, sir," the waiter told him. "Yes, yes, I know, but what is it now?"

Wednesday, 7. . . . These gay Cubans summon one by a prolonged 'pist'—through the teeth instead of a Christian call. We tried to obtain stamps at the Post Office but were referred to a cigar store as they did not keep them at the P.O. The victoria man landed us at the Hotel & we like true plebians then boarded a Street Car wh. took us to the Botanical Gardens, a rather unkempt place but the double row of Royal palms would have been grand anywhere. There were a lot of negro convicts at work there in shackles.

From there we went up to a strange old castle where some Spanish toy soldiery are stationed and we were regarded as spies. We traipsed about the very old fortress with its moat, queer old vine-covered walls & port holes. Strange underground houses over whose roofs we tramped. We tried to gain an entrance but the guards refused admission to the curious. The view from the hill was beautiful and the guns could probably sweep Havanna at will as easily as could our eyes. Very ragged & feeble soldiery however controlled the place.

Friday, 9. Weather perfect. June-like day. After early coffee & fruits, Dr. Burgess & his boy took us over to the Hospital San Lazar where we saw many curious forms of leprosy. Tuberculous & others not ulcerating. Some very rapid. One negro with huge elephantiasis of the leg & leprous cond. & another c̄ elephantiasis of the lid of eye. Many had been in years, the non-ulcerative type; after an amputation the sore closes over leaving a good looking stump. Mostly China-

SCENES IN CUBA
From Havana travel diary of March 1894

men—all allowed to have opium wh. is right. Nothing is done for them & they seemed rather proud to show their lesions.

The foundling hospital with its 700 children was seen. The Sisters of Charity run it as in all Catholic countries. Children rec'd up to age of 5, big as can be got in the box, as Ned said. They have a box like this [rough indication] in the wall—the baby is put in sometimes s̄ any clothes & the cord just cut—the box turned from the street & the child passes into the inside & a bell rings. They are kept a long time, the girls until they are 23. Taught embroidery—singing—& that's about all. The place was ill kept but they said the children rarely died, though Ned spotted rachitis, syphilis, seborrhoeas, favus &c galore. The younger attending physician knew little about them. Nearly 100 are admitted during the year. The courts, with fruit trees &c inside the enclosure were very interesting & the long corridors &c had a very foreign look. . . .

That [the prison] was one of the most interesting places I have seen, 2500 prisoners, mostly murderers, of all nationalities put off together by races. Such a place for the study of faces and criminal physiognomy: I never saw such a lot of brutal faces gathered together before. Convict labor is in practice but the men are allowed to keep what they make. The prison is large and the best-conducted place I have seen in Havanna. Manuel Ribero showed us about & took us to the Hospital grounds which are beautifully kept. The hospital—morgue—&c are well ordered.

His general reactions to Cuba are interesting. Other diary entries indicated that he was utterly disgusted with the bullfight, as well as with some of his fellow travellers whom he had moments of thinking would be better in the ring than the unfortunate blind-folded horses. He seems to have returned somewhat refreshed from the Cuba trip, but he evidently had not recovered from his attacks of grippe and he continued physically weak and in a rather "low" state of mind until the end of the year. Ned, some weeks after returning from Cuba, developed a severe case of typhoid fever.

Early in January H.C. had begun to think of plans for the following year. The Class of 1894 at the Harvard Medical School was the last three-year class, and the majority of students took their degrees in that year. After months of indecision, he elected to remain for a fourth year. Early in February he wrote to his father:

. . . I have just succeeded in winding up my medical paper over which I was struggling while at home—friend Michael Murphy having had complications galore with his rheumatic fever so that I had to write more than I bargained for. Dr. Sears kindly reviewed it for me and as criticisms naturally were numerous I had to rewrite large portions. Sears has moved this week to a less humble abode on Marlborough Street and we are all sorry to lose him. . . . Is there any chance that you or Ned will come East this spring? If not, I want to use the poor medium of a pen to discuss a fourth year with you. The men who are taking it at present seem to be very much disappointed in it. I imagine that the change of curriculum next year has made a good deal of difference in the attention given it now. More of this later. I have not been vaccinated and hardly think it's necessary now. I forgot all about it in fact when I was at the North End.

On his 25th birthday (8 April 1894) he wrote his father of an opportunity to work under Osler at Johns Hopkins, but later, having failed to hear further from Thayer, decided against going.

Here is a letter from Dr. Thayer which Dr. Storer has sent to me. Evidently Thayer wrote him to ask if there were any men who wanted such a position and I was probably the only one in the school whose name he knew. He seems to think it's an unusual opportunity. I suppose if the applicant is wanted it means work under Osler. I submit the same to you and Ned.

I wrote home last night to Mother telling of spring weather here at last. Today there are about three inches of sleet on the ground and it has snowed incessantly all day. Such is the uncertainty of our spring months. I have been spending this, our 'Easter' vacation, in the endeavor to construct a clinical paper for the course in children's diseases but without any very marked success. It may be foolish for me to think so but it does seem as though, since that miserable Grippe, I am not capable of nearly as much or as good mental work and am sometimes so forgetful it scares me. Please thank Ned for me for those Kodacs.

It's too bad they panned out so poorly from bad films. Thank you for the P.O. order rec'd a few days ago. Most of it is now lying in Mrs. Mortimer's coffers. I shall need some more before long to replenish portions of my wearing apparel and will advise you of the cost of the same.

A few weeks later (13 May) he writes: "I am now writing you while Codman sits here grinding over my Surgery notes and swearing at my writing. I wish I had his fourteen hours a day energy and enthusiasm. I get 'woozy' after about three." Later in the month (20 May): "The last of my friends or acquaintances in the school went up for their hospital examinations last week. I know none of the men who are going to take a fourth year and consequently will feel very much deserted." He refers again to his health early in June:

I lead very much a hermit life these days which is not very cheerful to say the least, especially as I sit most of the day over lecture notes and books thinking of everything under the sun except the work before me, Ned principally these last few days, and finally go to bed just where I started in the morning only 'grouchier.' Dr. Phelps, the man who has taken Sears' place here, got laid up and has gone away on a vacation. Abe left some time ago and Thursday Erdman left for the Great City to go into the Central office there so that there is no more telephoning home. When was Ned first taken sick and how long did he keep at the grindstone before he gave up? I have had no data whatever except the bare fact that he is sick with a probable typhoid. Has he had any typhoid cases lately and do you suppose he got it from a patient? I'm mighty glad we took that trip. It ought to make him better able to withstand an illness.

There followed in June a long letter to his father which summarizes both his work for the year and his future plans. The letter is of considerable interest from the point of view of the history of the Massachusetts General Hospital:

H.C. to H.K.C. *11 June 1894.*

I am overjoyed to hear from Mother this morning that Ned has greatly improved. I have worried a plenty about him and anxiously awaited the evening mails which have usually brought word of him from you or Mother, but heard nothing from Friday till this A.M. [Monday]. I didn't write home yesterday as I was grinding most all day and all my spare moments were taken up in hating myself as I seem to be on the royal road to chronic dyspepticism which is not cheerful in contemplation nor predisposing in any decent mental work. Having experimented with the usual drugs in vain I am reduced to living on a starvation diet and *chewing gum,* think of it.

We had our first bout last Friday in Obstetrics and I am happy to say I got an A in it but it is about the easiest subject and the best taught so that there was no excuse for anything else and everyone got high marks. This morning we had Theory and Practice with Fitz and 'difficilimus' it was. Thursday Clinical Medicine and Saturday Surgery which has been so wretchedly presented to us that no one seems to care particularly about the outcome. We wind up Tuesday the 20th and I have expected to go down to New Haven for Triennial for four or five days and have engaged a room with Perry but if you think on Ned's account I had better come home, or if I can be of any service whatever to you there, I will gladly sacarafice [*sic*] the New Haven trip. What does Ned expect to do when he gets about? Not go to work I hope. . . .

Mother says Ned has asked about my plans &c and if he is well enough you may present him my love and compliments and relate the following. There have been great revolutions at the M.G.H. on the Surgical Side. They have a new Service, the South Side, so called. Elliot, Harrington and Mixter have been taken into the house. Allie Porter, Brooks, and Jim Mumford have received the Out Patient Services after much delay & controversy on the part of the trustees, Thorndike, Lund, Balch & others being long considered in the race.

The student house officers have been shifted all about and are much disgruntled as Services have been changed, shortened, and none of them are to work in the Out Patient department any more, this work being done by members of the School who expect to be candidates for hospital appointments. This is a great disappointment all round and greatly diminishes the value of the Service as it means so much longer time etherizing and washing instruments & the like. I am rejoiced that I did not go up for that last examination and shall go up for the *Out Patient appointment* August first. It is a four months' service, of course only morning work and the men in the upper classes and those passing the best examinations have the running of the department under the visiting surgeon just as the hospital externes used to.

In July I expect to be in the women's out patient Medical with A. K. Stone to get up the gynaecology I have slighted this year and in preparation for next year's work. I shall be up at the Children's two, perhaps four, afternoons a week and was very fortunate in getting the place as many applied; I, early. Joslin, Hewes, Denny and White have received the medical appointments and Codman, Putnam, Dolliver and Hill the surgical ones at the M.G.H. Joslin easily leads the class. "Eclipse first & the rest nowhere"—in my estimation. This is about all, I think, except that everyone is much exercised about Ned's illness & asks regularly about him.

If you favor my New Haven sojourn I must petition for $25.00. I think without doubt that I can get away for two or three weeks in September, but could not very well now as I want to start in on time at these various clinics July first.

First Trip Abroad—July 1894

By the end of June H.C.'s brother Ned had recovered sufficiently from his typhoid to travel, so a trip to England with H.C. was planned. They sailed 30 June on the *SS. Cephalonia* from Boston and Codman and other friends saw them off. On their trip they had been joined by their uncle, Edward Williams of Cleveland, and his wife. The crossing was uneventful save for a few minor family crises, for Ned, the invalid, and Harvey, the worn-out medical student, seemed unable to accept with equanimity Uncle Ed's occasional outbursts to waiters and others who served them. These incidents seem not to have spoiled the trip, however, and H.C. gives a spirited, but in most places a rather telegraphic account of their experiences, accompanied as usual by innumerable sketches and memorabilia. His first impressions of England as they arrived in Liverpool and travelled to London were promptly set down.

11 June. Awaked at 6. Liverpool harbor—bath in muddy water. The tender met us and after feeing Chon "the Boots" & others we with our baggage put off for English soil. The Customs house is passed by us easily—Uncle Ed gets stuck for his tobacco—Ned and I stand off and laugh at him, very mad. "My wife's trunk—haven't got the keys" &c. The Inspector finds some pounds of Johnson's Mixture, pipes &c on which E.P.W. pays much duty and barely escapes incarceration. To Lime Street Station. Take 9.45 train, foolishly buying 1st class tickets at 29*s*. Don't know whether they take us for fools or Americans. Beautiful country. Lunches at Crewe and Litchfield. The green hedges, poppies, buttercups, Manor houses, timbered and half timbered houses style of Elizabeth, old Cathedrals and minsters everywhere—very beautiful trip by the London and North Western—through Rugby &c. Arrived London 2.20 at Berkeley [Hotel] per bus. Aunt Louise naps while the Eds and I take bus to Bank for money. Walk down Gr. Victoria Street, Victoria Embankment, Trafalgar Square, to Berkeley, &c. Rain.

. . . Meet at Berkeley & go to Cheshire Cheese—a bully hour—meet 3 good spirits—a Mr. Murray (?) M.P., an Irishman, and two friends. Mr. M. says the Dr. Johnson tales n.g. He has been there regularly for 40 years. They gave us some Cheshire punch—"Old Leather bottel"—with clout removed from a shoe sale—Black Jack—&c. Gray Beard jug &c. —very old—fine sanded floor. Ride home in a cab very merry after half and half punch, stewed cheese &c. Uncle Ed says it's the finest hour he's spent in months. Bed. Snuff taking at the O.C.C. Luxurious sneezes on all sides.

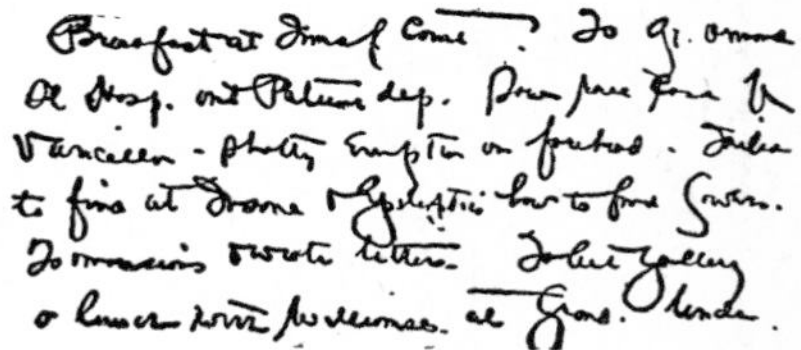

AFTER "RUBENS"
(?Rembrandt)
From travel notebook 1894

While still in London they made a two-day excursion to Oxford, driving up in a four-in-hand.

Wednesday [*18th*]. We took a trip to beautiful Oxford on the Ace, one of the coaches plying about London run & owned by a lot of London swells who keep them up at their own loss merely to get pleasure in driving four in hand when they want. [Time table of "The Ace" inserted]. We changed horses every ten miles on the way making 40 horses in all. A fine lunch at High Wycombe & passing through a lovely country & over wonderful roads. At Oxford I looked up Hal Tweedy & find him at the old Parsonage No. 1 Banbury Road. We walk about to St. John's—Magdalen—New College—the University Barges on the Isis &c—& after a talk we separate—& "So to Bed" as Pepys says. Ned goes to town.

Thursday [*19th*]. The next morning we spend a delightful two hours in going about. See the President's house at Magdalen. Christ's where we are shown the kitchens & Mr. Watson's rooms in the noisy quad. The Broad Walk—Addison's Walk, New & Merton &c. To town at 12.15. Lucy sleeping most of the way while E.P.W. and I consumed Gorgonzola cheese. In the afternoon I do some shopping, go to Museum &c. Ned & I shake hands.

In all, they passed some ten days in London sightseeing, and after dispatching Uncle Ed safely off to Paris, Edward and Harvey made a quiet trip to the peaceful hills of Derbyshire, stopping at the "Rutland Arms" in Bakewell. They wandered through hills, scaled the "Peaks," and visited Chatsworth, Haddon Hall, and other places of local interest. On returning to London they remembered their profession and began to seek out places and persons of medical interest. Most notable were their visits to Thomas Barlow and Jonathan Hutchinson.

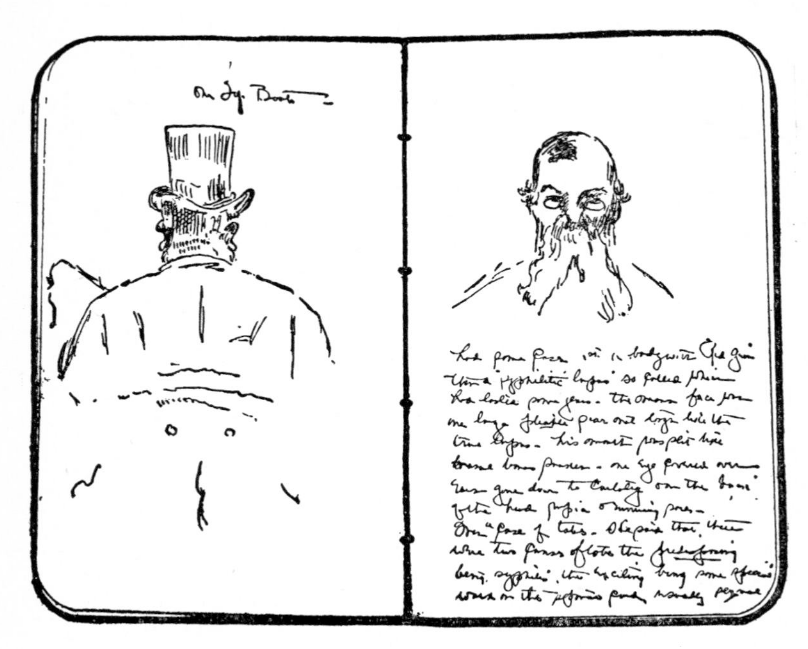

THE CABBY AND JONATHAN HUTCHINSON

Monday, 30 July. . . . Go to Gt Ormond St Hospital & make a visit with Dr. [Thomas] Barlow. Five cases of chronic rheumatoid arthritis in children. English indifference. To Army & Navy stores—pipes, umbrellas, book for Codman—to our Victoria tea place—to W^{mses} stopping all along to look in at windows—bought strop.

31 July. Breakfast at Inns of Court. To Gt Ormond St Hosp. out patient dep. Saw rare case of varicella—spotty eruption on forehead. Failed to find at Insane & Epileptics how to find Gowers. To Mansions & wrote letters. To Art Gallery & lunch with Williamses at Grand. Uncle Ed sends Lucy home—Ed goes to South Kensington, I to Westminster service & at 4 to Jonathan Hutchinson's, 211 Gt. Portland St. A most interesting 2 hours. The dear old man had some cases—1st a baby with "Red Gum" then a "syphilitic lupus," so-called, which had lasted some years—the man's face was one large pliable scar not tough like the true lupus—his mouth was slitlike—nasal bones sunken—one eye covered over—ears gone down to cartilege & on the back of the head rupia & running sores. Then a case of tabes. He said there were two causes of tabes, the predisposing being syphilis. He also showed a boy 17 yrs old—absolutely hairless and s̄ panniculus adiposus whatever—the skin showing all veins &c beneath like an anatomical plate—nails &c rudimentary. He had another case just like it. In one the mother had always been bald but her several daughters were robust and fat. Also a case of intestinal obstruction by gallstone diagnosed and operated on by Arbuthnot Lane & recovering. No pain of any sort before the obstruction. J.H. does not regard op. advisable however. He says the obstruction is from spasmodic contrac. of the musc. coat & the thing to do is to give full surgical anaesthesia. The diagnosis can be rarely made however.

1 August. The Red Letter Day. A rapid breakfast at the Vienna café. To the Children's Hospital and visit with Owen. He is a *dandy*—spoke to me & had me try to diagnose some cases. I was not very keen. A boy with spastic paralysis—beautiful increased reflexes. A tuberculous shoulder joint in a little child wh. I did not recognize. A case of Molluscum Contagiosum wh. I thought was Millia. Saw him open a big abscess—& he invited us to dinner at the Saville Club—I was too rattled to regret.

Got a haircut at [blank] & met the W[mses] & drove with them & a top boots to Kew Garden where we tramped about for a time, then to Richmond where we had a fine dinner of trout & the inevitable champagne wh. he—Uncle Ed—seems to think is always indispensable. We ride home through Richmond Park where the Gt. Grandson's christening recently was. Home by Hyde Park. Go to Mansions for a time & then back to Almands leaving a note for Owen.

2 August. We scrabbled through a breakfast at the Mansions. I go to tailors of which I am getting very tired—to Army & Navy Stores, that irresistible place. Attempt to go by underground to Paddington Station of Sherlock Holmes' fame but find I will be late so jump into a "What Ho" as Ned also has to do from another quarter of the town—train for Windsor. We reach there, get a carriage & are driven to the Castle—are hustled through the State appartments—which can't touch Chatsworth & come out into the rain with the crowd, tired & very cross. Climb the tower, go through the Chapel which are the most interesting parts of the whole place—Prince Albert's mausoleum, where also are buried Dukes of Clarence & Albany, is a beautiful place. St. George's Chapel also is fine & in the Chapel of the Knights of the Garter much like Henry VIIth Chapel—some beautiful tombs are in the Chapel—the prince imperial, Princess Charlotte &c. Too many Americans take the shine off from any place however.

3 August. A great day and the last in London town. We got a fine breakfast at the Grand of oatmeal, chops & the usual English things & then go to the British Museum of Natural History which is exceedingly interesting. . . . We lunch in the building, & then start for the living animals at the Zoo but wander into Madame Toussaud's Museum & spend the afternoon there. A very entertaining place. The Napoleon Collections are very valuable historically. The American ones were Lincoln, Garfield, Grant & were frights. The Chamber of Horrors. Hare & Burke & others—history of crime &c.

They returned from Southampton on 4 August and reached New York on the 10th—all still on speaking terms, although even Harvey and Ned had twice fallen out with one another during the rigors of the trip.

1894-1895

Shortly after returning from his trip abroad, H.C. entered upon his fourth year at the Harvard Medical School. Things seemed to go rather slowly at first, and on 7 October he writes: "I don't think much of the fourth year as yet and am very glad of the opportunity for hospital work. So far there have been only three exercises for 4th year men." Actually the year was devoted chiefly to work in the hospitals as an unappointed house officer. Early in November he writes: "I am still running the G.U. clinic at the M.G.H. as the man who was to take my place has been unable to come. I think I am learning enough to make it worth while." A month later: "I have to all intents and purposes just started in with the fourth year this week, and find that new textbooks and an ophthalmoscope and laryngoscope are demanded. . . . Thank you for urging me to take a fourth year. I think I am getting and am going to get much out of it. The clinics are mostly fine. . . ." As usual, he found relaxation at the Boat Club, but he writes on 9 December: "I have taken unto myself a new method of recreation, viz., hill climbing. Since going to the Boat Club takes too much time, for hand ball is such a seductive sport I never know when to leave off, I, instead of going there, gird up my loins about 5.30 and climb Beacon Hill for a half or three quarters of an hour."

From the following letter to his father (12 Dec. 1894) we learn of his experimental work with Edward Hickling Bradford, the Boston orthopedic surgeon, who later became Dean of the Medical School: ". . . I am doubtful about the home coming. I have a fine opportunity to do some work with Bradford in the line of bone fillings.[11] He wants to make some investigations for his operating on tuberculous bone cavities. It is a good chance to do some original work and in addition an opportunity to get acquainted with Bradford. . . . If we can get ready for work by week after next, I will stay here." However, he did go to Cleveland for a brief Christmas holiday, returning to Boston on 3 January. There was little to record during January. On 3 February he wrote a somewhat disgruntled letter to his father about his examination in medical jurisprudence:

> . . . Thank you for the P.O. order. I finished my exams Wednesday but have only heard from Legal Medicine in which I got a B. This shows the uncertainty of examinations. I think I went into that exam better equipped than for almost any other one since I have been in the School, having followed the course two years and gone over it all with Painter shortly ago as his hospital had prevented his attendance at lectures. It is somewhat consoling that no A's were given however. The questions were much too long for the time allotted. . . . I have

[11] The *Boston Medical and Surgical Journal* for 15 November 1894 (*131*, 489) carries a review on recent progress in surgery by H. L. Burrell and H[ayward]. W. Cushing in which Martin's experimental work (*Centralblatt für Chirurgie*, 1894, No. 9) on filling bony cavities in dogs with plaster of Paris and base-plate gutta-percha is described. Bradford had set H.C. the problem of repeating Martin's observations. The results were never published.

decided nothing about the hospital. The M.G.H. is all torn up at present and they don't seem to know "where they are at." The house officers are shifted about unceremoniously so that they don't know under whom they are serving and there seems to be an attending surgeon to about every three patients. All this is somewhat exaggerated but things do seem to be very much at sea there.

On the same day he wrote his mother: "I am through my examinations, I rejoice to say, and it requires but four more before I am 'full fledged' and will be no longer simple Mister." In the same letter he announced the opening of the new Boston Public Library: "The new public library is opened at last and the great American public to the number of 10,000 daily have been visiting and tracking mud into it. The necessity of signs beseeching people to wipe their feet seems to exist even in 'cultured' Boston."

Later in the month H.C. gave to his brother Ned some additional details about the M.G.H. appointments and again mentions his work with Bradford (18 Feb.):

I am much bored over the M.G.H. appointments, or rather lack of them, for they are at present determined to give none this Spring but to wait till next July when the next class will send up some men. I believe at the last exam, which was to fill Barney's place & for which, under the circumstances, I could not apply, only one man went up, which has rather disgusted them. They have put the externes back in the O.P.D. again. This is the fourth time they have changed the service in the last two years. Painter is now at the M.G.H. as perhaps you know. Allen is making advances to come to Cleveland & take the Orthopaedic Chair.

I operated on the dog again yesterday & filled two more holes with cement which Bradford & I have been tinkering over. Jim Skillen [the anatomy diener] is in a bad way, having had two or three mild apoplectic seizures in the past two months. Once he fell & cut a large gash in his forehead and is now in bed under Fitz's care. Phelps who as you know took Sears' place at 89 Charles St. is at the B.C.H. convalescing from an acute appendix which I had the pleasure of diagnosing at four o'clock one morning & getting Scudder to confirm my youthful opinion. Phelps' appendix, however, and he have been separated.

Ether Charts

When Cushing, as a second-year student, was called upon to give anesthesia for the first time, he was greatly disturbed by the inadequacy of the methods then in use for administering the volatile anesthetics. Untrained and inexperienced students were often enlisted to give the ether sponge, and the surgeon, generally impatient, insisted upon a depth of anesthesia so profound that there was frequently but a small margin of safety. As mentioned earlier Cushing had had the painful experience of having a patient, whom he was anesthetizing, die before the class, and others of his student acquaintance also had had similar experiences. His classmate, Amory Codman, was likewise dissatisfied with the procedure for giving anesthetics, so he and Cushing between them worked out a system of continuous recording which enabled both the anesthetist and the surgeon to tell at a glance the condition of the patient, as indicated by pulse and respiration. There was no convenient method available at that time for estimating blood pressure, so that when Cushing

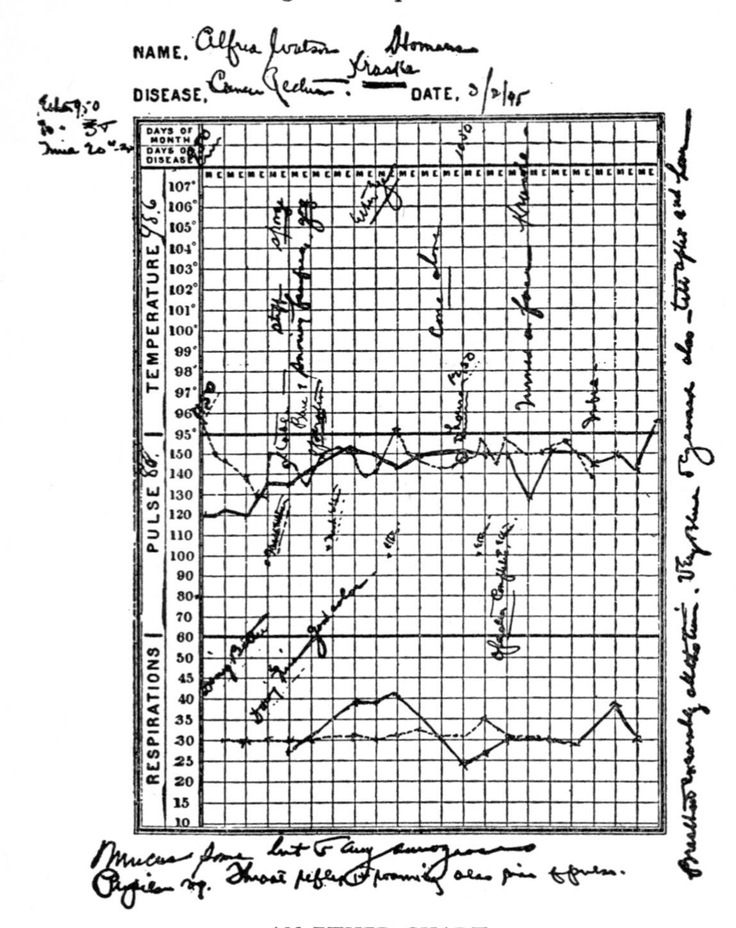

AN ETHER CHART
One of the charts introduced by Cushing and Codman in 1895 to increase safety in surgical procedures

several years later saw the Riva-Rocci pneumatic device for recording human blood pressure at Pavia in Italy (see page 190), he seized upon it and brought it back to the United States. Thereafter his ether charts, as the anesthetic records of Codman and Cushing had come to be called, included a continuous blood-pressure record in addition to pulse and respiration.

H. K. Beecher has recently described these anesthesia records,[12] and he reprints Cushing's long letter to Dr. Washburn in which their early experiences are described. It should be pointed out that whereas Codman had his house pupilship at the Massachusetts General before Cushing, H.C.'s diary of 1893 indicates that he (Cushing) had already been giving ether for M.G.H. surgeons as early as December of 1892, which considerably antedates Codman's appointment as house pupil. Of the ether charts preserved at the M.G.H., the earliest of Cushing's is dated 2 April 1895—a case of osteomyelitis operated upon by John Homans.[13] An example of one of these early charts is given in the accompanying figure. A letter from Dr. Codman about the charts and a few paragraphs from Cushing's letter to Washburn may be quoted:

227 Beacon Street, Boston,
E. A. Codman to H.C. *9 February 1920.*

Dear Harvey: Having nothing better to do lately I have been trying to put my effects into order again after the volcanic dislocation caused by the war and incidentally by the renting of our house. . . . One of the things I cannot bear to dump in the wastebasket is a collection of ether charts which we made 30 years ago! In connection therewith I find a long *unpublished* paper on 'Etherization,' in which I described *vividly I think* but somewhat tediously the process as we then knew it. I must say I have never read anything better on the subject. I recall that the reason for not publishing it was that I took it to 'Coll' Warren, who regarded it as too frank for the good of the hospital, for it described in detail the case which I lost in the O.R. because I was paying attention to some tomfoolery which *you* (who had come in from the theatre), were entertaining us with, while the poor devil was inhaling vomitus! I also spoke of the case which stopped breathing under ether and interested you in Brain Surgery. So I send you these charts to destroy with some solemnity, for you and I are the only persons that give a —— for them. Do they give less ether per hour now? Sincerely E. A. CODMAN.

Cushing's account written in 1920 to Dr. Washburn began by recalling the patient who died before the class. He continued:

To my perfect amazement I was told it was nothing at all, that I had nothing to do with the patient's death, that she had a strangulated hernia and had been vomiting all night anyway, and that sort of thing happened frequently and I had better forget about it and go on with the Medical School. I went on with the Medical School but I have never forgotten about it. Now, to come back to these ether charts. Codman and I resolved that we would improve our technique of giving ether, which in those days in the large majority of cases meant crowding the patient to the second stage of anaesthesia as quickly as possible, and for the most part we used old sea sponges.

In order to make a game of the task before us we made a wager of a dinner

[12] Beecher, H. K. "The first anesthesia records (Codman, Cushing)." *Surgery, Gynecology and Obstetrics,* 1940, *71,* 689-693.

[13] Viets, H. R. "Notes on the formative period of a neurological surgeon." *Harvey Cushing's seventieth birthday party.* Springfield, Illinois, Charles C Thomas, 1939, p. 118.

as to who could learn to give the best anaesthesia. We determined to let the test of satisfactory anaesthesia rest with the patient's behavior in the ward, and though I have forgotten just what was our scale of marking the cases, a perfect anaesthesia was supposed to be one in which the patient was sufficiently conscious to respond when left in the ward with the nurse and did not subsequently vomit. You will recall that in those days we had no ether recovery room in general use, except for the Saturday clinics.

I think we both became very much more skillful in our jobs than we otherwise would have become, owing to this competition, but it was particularly due, I think, to the detailed attention which we had to put upon the patient by the careful recording of the pulse rate throughout the operation.

Abdominal hysterectomy
for fibroid tumor in Ward E
Sat. morn - March 9.
at 10 a.m. - J Homans

NOTE FROM JOHN HOMANS, SR.
6 March 1895

Although both Cushing and Codman made light of these early anesthesia charts, they stand historically as one of the principal American contributions to the technique of surgery, and similar records are now kept by every careful anesthetist and surgeon. The charts were not only a milestone in surgery, but, as Viets has pointed out (*loc. cit.*), they were also a milestone in Cushing's own career:

Of more interest to us, however, is the record of a patient with a compound fracture of the skull, operated upon on April 24, 1895 by William M. Conant. Cushing made the following abbreviated notations on the back of this record: "Patient had fearful hemorrhage from brain sinuses. Pulse kept along very well and finally went out all at once and could not be felt at wrist. With pressure which checked the hem. the pulse finally came back a few beats at a time, as an engine starts up from a way-station, and finally became pretty regular. 120-110-100." On the front of the record is another jotting, "Bled enormously," and finally, a follow-up note, "Waverley and disch. O.K.," indicating that Cushing had followed the patient to the convalescent home in Waverley, near Boston, and had found out that the man was ultimately discharged as 'well.' In this one case is found much of the groundwork on which Cushing later built his career as a neurological surgeon. One notes the scientific attitude, the carefully kept record with its illuminating comments, the interest already evident in neurological surgery and the following of the patient to obtain the end-result. The problems of intracranial hemorrhage and anesthesia, moreover, already fixed in his mind, were to occupy him for many years after this incident of 1895, for neurological surgery could not be advanced before these fundamentals had

SKETCHES FROM BERMUDA
Notebook of March 1895

received adequate attention. It is safe to say, however, that the observations recorded here were the starting points for a series of innovations which were to revolutionize his chosen field of endeavor.

Toward the end of March (13-31) of 1895 H.C. had another two-week holiday with his brother Ned—this time in Bermuda. He kept a full diary with sketches, photographs, and voluminous memorabilia, and the account also includes detailed descriptions of nearly all of the exotic flowers and shrubs of the Island—hibiscus, bougainvillaea, oleanders, and night-blooming cereus—in addition to the birds, many of the fish, and the trees. Between moments spent in delineating local flora and fauna, they evidently had a hilarious time—for there seem to have been Yale and Harvard classmates in each hotel (as well as a number of friends of the opposite sex), all less interested than the brothers Cushing in the indigenous flowering plants. Before leaving H.C. remarked: "We have begun to have a curious feeling of proprietorship in the place & find ourselves making excuses for weather &c to the newcomers."

On reaching New York on 1 April he found a letter from "Abe" Garfield at the Murray Hill Hotel telling him of his appointment as house officer for the following year at the Massachusetts General Hospital:

89 Charles Street,
Abram Garfield to H.C. *27 March 1895.*

Dear Squishing, Excoriations arrived safely. Wish you would use more care so that such letters would arrive between meals. Great consternation. I suppose you received Dr. Scudder's and our note but in case you did not—you got the first hospital appointment and Goodwillie and I have decided that you are a hog of the worst sort. Hastily, Boo.

A formal letter from the Hospital in longhand contained the welcome confirmation.

Following his holiday, H.C. was assigned for a few days to the M.G.H. Convalescent Home in Waverley (a suburb of Boston), where students and house pupils spent part of their service. The psychiatric division, McLean Hospital, had just been moved to a new site, also in Waverley, the first patients having been transferred from the old quarters at Somerville in April 1894. Dr. John W. Cummin, a friend in the Medical School, writes (10 April 1942):

In our day the [Convalescent] Home was in charge of Miss Scott (or Scottie as she was called) and there was a nurse in constant attendance who did the simpler dressings. The three externes divided up their four-month service into equal parts and one externe was always at the Home for supper and breakfast. He took an early train to Boston, always going to the Hospital through the 'Hole in the Wall' on the way. At the hospital his duties consisted of etherizing and doing urines, etc. On his arrival he often found basins of dirty instruments used in emergencies at night which it was his first duty to clean, in addition to all instruments used during the day by his service (the cleaning of the night emergency instruments fell to the externe on Convalescent Home duty, whatever the service which had used them). The externe left the hospital in time to catch a late afternoon train, did dressings after supper, was on call during the night, and did any necessary dressings in the early morning before starting for the hospital.

Contact with the mental and neurological cases at Waverley did much to crystallize H.C.'s interest in neurology. After completing his month's service, he returned to Waverley to spend most of July in further work.

Massachusetts General Hospital
Boston Mar. 16 1895

Mr. H. W. Cushing
Dear Sir:
At the meeting of the Board of Trustees held yesterday, you were elected Surgical Externe of the Hospital. The Secretary asks me to inform you of your appointment.
Yours truly,
John W. Pratt.
Resident Physician

FIRST HOSPITAL APPOINTMENT

Boston,
H.C. to B.M.C. *Sunday, 16 June 1895.*

. . . Yesterday I finished my last examination in the Harvard Medical School and glad I am. If I had known what a struggle it was to be I don't believe I should ever have had the sand to begin. However, I don't suppose it will be long before I will wish that I was back again. I have stopped playing 'rus' lately and have returned to 89 Charles St. while another man takes my place there. I was loath to leave as Waverley and Rue Charles are two very different places. . . .

H.C. to H.K.C. *7 July 1895.*

I have been flying from pillar to post so during the last three months that I hardly know where I am 'at.' A few days after the examinations were over I gave up Waverley to my co-worker Hall and came back to 89 Charles St. After a few days more I had to go into the house to substitute for Cogswell who was away on his vacation. On his return last Friday I shuffled back to 89 Charles St. again and tomorrow Hall comes in from Waverley to go into the house, so out to Waverley I go till the first of August. The past few days I have been spending my nights in gathering into many boxes the spoils of my four years sojourn in B-town. Said boxes will probably straggle into Cleveland at intervals during the next few weeks. There should be five of them in all, and I hope there will still be room for B. Trotwood in the barn if you see fit to deposit them there. I also send you a tin box containing three papers which represent eight years of my existence and many dollars from your generous pocket.

The papers to which he referred were evidently his diplomas from Yale and Harvard—which are still carefully preserved in a large album in which he subsequently placed his honorary degrees. It was perhaps characteristic that he did not bother to go to the Harvard Commencement exercises to get his diploma in person—for he was "busy at the hospital."

However he was awarded the degrees of M.D. and A.M., *cum laude,* on 26 June 1895; and a record of his grades during his four years at the Harvard Medical School lends no weight to his frequent expressions of discouragement over his inability to work properly.

First Year 1891-1892	
Anatomy	A
Physiology	B
Medical Chemistry	A

Second Year 1892-1893	
Advanced Anatomy	A
Pathological Anatomy	A
Therapeutics	C

Third Year 1893-1894	
Theory and Practice	A
Surgery	A
Obstetrics	A
Dermatology	B

Fourth Year 1894-1895	
Clinical Medicine	A
Clinical Surgery	C-50 A
Legal Medicine	B
Operative Surgery	A
Children's	A B
Bacteriology	A
Operative Obstetrics	A
Clinical Obstetrics	C

The Massachusetts General Hospital 1895-1896

Cushing had in reality begun his formal appointment as House Pupil at the Massachusetts General Hospital in April 1895, spending his first four months in the so-called "externe" service. His "interneship" proper began on 1 August.

H.C. to H.K.C. *Waverley, 13 July 1895.*

Your two letters and enclosure rec'd all right. Thank you for your congratulations. I hope I have not entirely wasted the years spent in pursuit of these sheep-

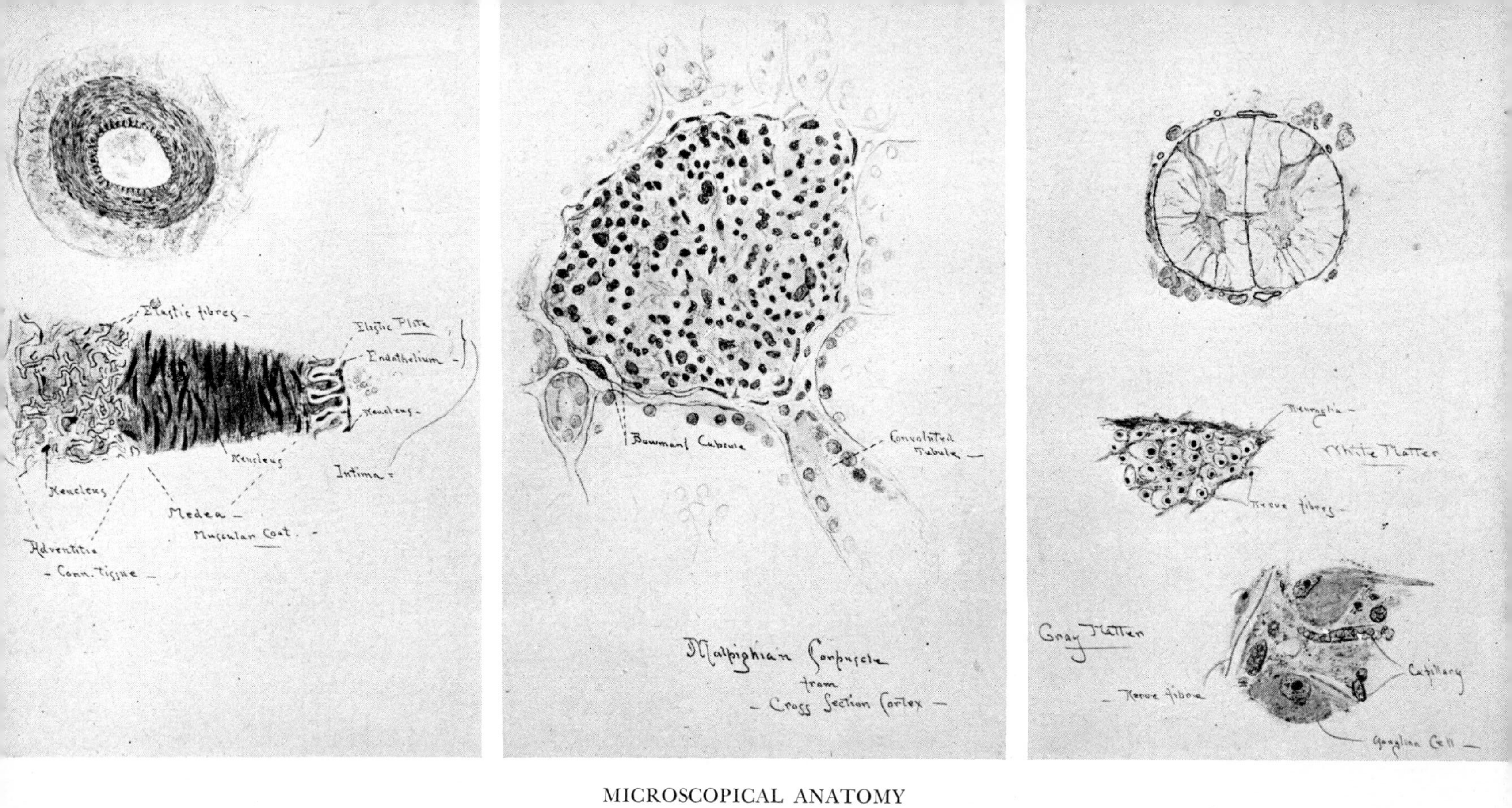

MICROSCOPICAL ANATOMY

A selection of drawings from H.C.'s histology notebook kept during his first year at the Harvard Medical School

PATIENTS SKETCHED DURING CLINIC

THE SOUTH SIDE

Massachusetts General Hospital in July 1896

Back row: H.C. (Senior), J. W. Cummin (Externe), J. C. Hubbard ("Pup"), F. S. Newell (Junior). *In front:* Dr. William M. Conant, Visiting Surgeon

CHATSWORTH 1894

Sketch taken from H.C.'s diary of his first trip to England

skins. I did not get a Commencement day program as I was housed at the M.G.H. at the time and my parchments were brought to me. I will try to get one for you. The hospital will be my next abiding place as the Externe service is only four months, and I began in April you know. Perhaps I will have to go in before to substitute again as just before the change in service i.e. every four months the house officers try to crowd in a vacation. Perhaps I can get home for a brief period about Thanksgiving time, four months away. I shall write you if I ever run short of funds. After August 1st living will be cheap. My two year old suit does very well for hospital and Waverley at present. I may need a new one in the fall.

In August he wrote: "... Work prospers. I am ensconced in the Out Patient mornings and do several interesting dressings and a multitude of odd jobs during the rest of the day. It's a great place here with a constant succession of curious and interesting cases." During his year as an interne Cushing's letters home were less frequent and less informative than those of his medical student days, but one can follow him through his excellent clinical histories which are preserved in the record room of the Massachusetts General Hospital. As Viets has pointed out *(loc. cit.)*, his histories were always detailed and were usually accompanied by a sketch, the latter being often more illuminating than a photograph of the same clinical entity.

In October plans had been made to go with his brother Ned to Baltimore, and they actually made the trip on 21-22 November. They met Drs. Thayer and Finney, and also Osler and Halsted. In recalling the trip later H.C. remarks (Halsted papers, p. 3): "I had been down on my first visit to the J.H.H. with my brother during my M.G.H. house-officer days and became enamoured of the place. For even a short visit was enough to show an outsider something of the spirit which permeated the early group of workers there. I subsequently applied through Thayer for a position on Osler's service, but Thayer made no response, being presumably much engrossed in his studies on malaria. Then Halsted was approached and though a position was offered, there was apparently some hitch which left me in doubt so that plans were made to go to Vienna for a year in company with C. A. Porter. Indeed, I believe our passage had been engaged for October, 1896."

Cushing's first letter from Halsted arrived soon after his trip to Baltimore, and on the basis of it he made his plans for a trip to Europe.

1201 Eutaw Place, Baltimore,
W. S. Halsted to H.C. *7 December 1895.*

Dear Dr. Cushing: I was much pleased with what you said in the letter which I received from you a few days ago, but I fear that I cannot answer your principal question. You will understand my embarrassment if you will pause a moment to think about it. There will undoubtedly be several men on my staff with ambitions the same as yours. I prefer not to know who these men are, and shall try to forget what you have confided to me, so please do not expect to become my house surgeon. I think it would be well for you to go to Europe as soon as you can, and to remain as long as possible before coming to us. I am sure that you will be more useful to us, and that the position here will be more useful to you if you can arrange to be abroad six months or more. If you should go abroad I would advise you to spend most of your time in studying German. It is very necessary nowadays for a medical man to have a thorough knowledge of German so that he can read medical German quite as well as English. You probably know that there is little if any scientific work done in this country in medicine, and that most of it is done in Germany. If you cannot go for so long a time as six months I do not think that it would be worth while to go at all just now. Possibly two or three years later when you have finished your work with us you might be able to go abroad for a longer time. The short trips abroad which enable one to run from one clinic to another are very pleasant, and are more or less useful to men who have had a good deal of practice. Such a trip would be more valuable to you two or three years hence than now. Six months or a year in Europe just now for the purpose of learning German thoroughly would be of great benefit to you. With kindest regards, I am Yours very sincerely Wm S. HALSTED.

His father commented:

967 Prospect Street,
16 December 1895.

Dear Harvey: "Ned" has shown me Dr. Halsted's letter which you sent him. On its face it is, as plainly meant to be, noncommittal. Between the lines I read (perhaps not correctly) that he thought approvingly of your attitude Johns Hopkinsward, but in view of many possible contingencies did not deem it wise to make promises or hold out anything definite. . . . It has been my conviction that you should have the opportunity of going abroad for a year or so before settling down to professional work. Unless something unexpected develops it will, in all probability, be as well for you to go on the expiration of your term at the M.G.H. as at any other time. The German seems to be put in strong relief in Halsted's letter, and you can perhaps do a little with it in preparation, as a diversion from the Hospital grind. . . .

Meanwhile, plans for Europe went on apace:

H.C. to B.M.C. *22 March 1896.*

Ten days more and I shall be on my last hospital lap—four months as Senior, a person of some relative importance in this little world of ours. Four months, which will seem but little more than another ten days, and I shall be one of absolute insignificance in your big world—it must be a terrible drop. I am already making some plans about Germany—courses, their times of beginning and desirability—men to see, and places to go for the first German grind.

Many of the men who are now abroad and beginning to turn their faces homeward will be anxiously looked for for advice—Denny, one of my classmates, sailed yesterday for Genoa, from which place he expects to work his way through Austria, Germany and England with the purpose of mapping out his work for the fall, bears many commissions from the half dozen of us who will probably follow. He can secure places in some of the select courses which we, coming later, might miss. The winter semester begins in October I believe. This will give me some time to trot about with Neddie and work at the language. I have four places under consideration to settle in: Bonn, Göttingen, Stuttgart and Freiburg. The latter seem very attractive to me and are highly spoken of. I expect to see my old New Haven German teacher, who lives here, and ask his advice about localities.

This is all very visionary however and four months to come seems longer than when it's just gone by—and I need not hurry—like the old Woman of Crewe—

There was an old woman of Crewe
Who wanted to catch the 2:2
The porter replied do not hurry
Nor scurry—nor flurry—
It's a minute or 2.2.2.2.

Perhaps you know this famous jingle.

Between times there were flashes of humor such as the following enclosed in a letter to his family:

7 April 1896.

—Dr. Cuison—

Family History. Excellent, though father and one brother are physicians.

Past History. Born fatigued nearly twenty-seven years ago lacking a few hours as far as anyone knows. Measles, Scarlet fever, etc.—cared for by his mother—General health good—habits questionable.

Present Illness. Limped into Mass. "Hospitle" c̄ the following history. Not being used to exercise and not of sound mind was persuaded twenty-four hours ago by a youth of questionable character to ride a horse. Patient was sadly contused and tossed about for two hours. Did not lose consciousness. Was somewhat nauseated.

Phys. Exam. Attitude peculiar—seems to prefer standing. Marked genu varum. Considerable tenderness of adductors. Ecchymosis over tuber ischii. Further examination s̄ note. Is a dark faced, poorly developed young man c̄ signs of premature age, having two gray hairs. Looks as though he might have seen better days.

Prognosis. Good.

Treatment. Massage. Advised to continue his former sedentary life.

In April came two more letters from Dr. Halsted which caused H.C. to abandon for the time being his plans for Europe, and he then made formal application for an appointment at Johns Hopkins:

1201 Eutaw Place, Baltimore,

W.S. Halsted to H.C. *15 April 1896.*

My dear Dr. Cushing: I am sorry to have to tell you that beginning with next Spring it is to be our policy to fill all the places on the staff of the Johns Hopkins Hospital with graduates of the Johns Hopkins Medical School. If you care for a place on my staff before next Fall, I can probably give it to you. You might in this way secure a place on the staff, and if satisfactory to both of us, remain for a year or more here and then go to Europe, possibly with the privilege of returning as house surgeon or first assistant. You will understand, of course, that I cannot promise you anything more than a trial. This is as much as I can promise any one who has not worked with me. I shall have a vacancy in June, for which there are already a number of applicants, two of whom have been internes in the hospitals in New York. I have not promised the position to any one as yet. Yours sincerely, W. S. Halsted.

I should very much like to have you come before May 10—for several reasons.

24 April 1896.

Dear Dr. Cushing: Last night Dr. Garrett, one of my assistants whose term expires next month, called to see me to ask if he might be allowed to remain on the Staff until the coming Fall. This fortunately straightens matters nicely for you, for I said Yes to him, & he is the interne whose place you were to fill.

You need not report for duty until Oct. 1st '96. This will give you a short vacation. Kindly send me a formal application for the position and also for form's sake, a letter or two from those who know you best. I shall probably leave town early in May for Europe & should like to submit your name to the Medical Board before I sail. I shall be very glad to have you on my staff. W. S. HALSTED.

Halsted's second letter was promptly passed on to his father:

H.C. to H.K.C. *M.G.H., Boston, 30 April 1896.*

Thanks for your letter and enclosure. Here is the finale in the Baltimore matter—which seems to have fallen on its feet so to speak. I have sent my formal application endorsed by Councilman, Shattuck, Porter, Warren, Richardson and Elliot. I hope I may not prove unworthy of their commendations. The carbuncle is better. I hope your cough is the same.

For some reason H.C. did not take Halsted's letter of 24 April as settling the matter and on 10 May writes, "The Baltimore matter is still in abeyance of course. I have only handed in my application for the place. The appointment is for October 1st. This will give me two months to get rested and bone German."

Early Use of X-rays

During his year as a House Pupil at the M.G.H. Cushing helped to inaugurate the clinical use of X-rays. He and Codman again collaborated and Cushing, later in the year, carried the new technique to the Johns Hopkins Hospital where he also set up an X-ray unit. Röntgen's discovery of a new kind of ray had been announced at Würzburg, Germany, on 28 December 1895. In January and February of the following year discussions of the "X-rays," as they were immediately called, began to occupy medical and scientific meetings throughout Europe. Edison, Elihu Thomson, and others commenced experimentation immediately, and by February 1896 American medical journals began to carry X-ray photographs. An exposure of part of the human hand appeared in the *Boston Medical and Surgical Journal* for 13 February 1896. On 15 February Cushing wrote to his mother: "Everyone is much excited over the new photographic discovery. Professor Röntgen may have discovered something with his cathode rays which may revolutionize medical diagnosis. Imagine taking photographs of gall stones in situ—stone in the bladder—foreign bodies anywhere—fractures &c &c. Mary Crehore sent me two photographs, one of a hand showing in a most mysterious manner the bones of the hand and a ring on the finger which were outlined in a misty way by the normal outlines of the hand. The other of a fracture of the forearm showing the bony displacements.

It's fearfully uncanny. We won't be able to have any secrets if people can take photographs through stone walls &c. Some letters have come from the men abroad telling of the wonderful things they are doing in Vienna with the X-rays."

There is no indication in this letter that a tube was as yet available at the M.G.H. Dr. Codman, writing many years later, states that John Collins Warren brought back a tube in the spring of 1896,[14] but the tube used by Cushing at the M.G.H. appears to be one that he himself had helped to purchase, as is indicated by the following passage in a letter of 10 May to his mother: "We have at last succeeded in having an X-ray machine put in for which I have subscribed largely and hope the conservative staff will ultimately remunerate us for it. It is great sport—very useful in the Out Patient to locate needles &c. We could look through the chest readily this morning—count the ribs—see the heart beat—the edge of the liver, etc. It is positively uncanny. I will send you some photographs." From this, one must infer that a tube or tubes had been in use at the Hospital for some weeks. Dr. Codman, writing in May 1940, mentions that Dr. Warren had probably obtained his tube not from Röntgen but in England where the focus tube was actually developed. Continuing, Codman writes: "Thomson (Elihu) invented the double focus tube[15] for alternating current at almost the same time in this country. My recollection is that Dr. Warren brought the tube home at my request, because I had read of it in the *Lancet* or *B.M.J.* . . . I don't think that I have ever written anything on the early X-ray days except what is in the Preface to my book, *The Shoulder,* pp. viii to xi incl."

By June, F. H. Williams of Boston had published a note on the

[14] Development of the permanent X-ray Service at the M.G.H. was due to the imagination and energy of the Assistant Apothecary (appointed in April, 1892), Walter James Dodd (1869-1916), a British cockney by birth who had entered upon a scientific career after the manner of Faraday, as janitor in a Harvard chemistry laboratory, to become one of the foremost roentgenologists of this country. But as a pioneer in X-ray he was also a martyr who after years of patient suffering died of his carcinomatous X-ray burns. In his capacity as apothecary he had developed a photographic unit for the Hospital, and on learning of Röntgen's discovery he set about at once with the cooperation of the Ziegler Electric Company of Boston to make a suitable tube. His first effort (still preserved at the M.G.H.) did not work, but in March 1896 he purchased from Swett and Lewis of Bromfield Street, Boston, a tube that did work and with this he obtained the first successful roentgenograms at the Hospital. (Macy, J. A. *Walter James Dodd; a biographical sketch.* Boston, 1918, p. 19.) The tube to which Cushing refers on 10 May as having been bought by him was probably a second tube of the same type, and it is possible that he retained it and carried it with him to Baltimore, since he started to take X-ray photographs within a few days of his arrival at the Johns Hopkins.

[15] The much improved double focus tube mentioned by Dr. Codman was first described by Elihu Thomson in October 1896. ("Description of Thomson X-ray and double focus tube," *Electrical Engineer,* 21 October 1896.)

use of X-ray fluoroscopy for detecting the presence of tuberculous lesions in the lungs.[16] Cannon's celebrated experimental work with the X-ray on the motility of the intestinal tract was commenced in December of 1896 when he was a first-year student in the Harvard Medical School. Codman assisted him in his early experiments.[17] Codman and Cushing activated their X-ray focus tube by a hand-driven static machine, and prolonged exposures, *e.g.*, as much as twenty minutes, were essential to get a clear plate. Codman appears to have spent more time working with the tube than did Cushing and eventually suffered from X-ray burns and serious impairment of his health. Cushing's first formal report on the use of X-rays was made to the Johns Hopkins Medical Society in May 1897[18] and had to do with two cases of gunshot wound of the spine in which the projectiles had been localized by use of the X-rays.

* * * * *

Cushing's final hectic days at the M.G.H. are briefly described in two letters to his father:

H.C. to H.K.C. *18 June 1896.*

Yours rec'd promptly, c̄ enclosed check. Had a great 24 hours—the past. Started the morning with usual dressings—had a bad cut wrist with tendon sutures in acc. room—followed by a subglenoid disloc. of humerus. Several operations by Dr. Conant—till 3 P.M.—an emergency extrauterine pregnancy. Lunch. Two histories in afternoon—one case a cancer of caecum probably—a gunshot wound of abdomen at 7.15 P.M. Operation 3 hours long—intestinal resection &c.

Raft of small things in acc. room the rest of night it being June 17th—lacerated common cracker hands—gunshot wound of thigh—fractured leg, et cetera. Stayed up with gunshot belly man till he died at 7.45 A.M. Picked up about 4 A.M. after an intravenous infusion remarkably but no use. Just about to take a bath before breakfast when in piled a crushed foot—from a trolley car—Chopart's amputation—H.W.C.

Breakfast. No time for ward visit—hysterectomy for fibroid—hydrocele of Canal of Nuck—extirpation of rectum for cancer—put a fracture up in plaster in P.M. and I am now very feeble. Several operations tomorrow. No place in the country does the work the M.G.H. does. I am only one of thirteen.

17 July 1896.

Please send me a check for 100.00 to wind up my affairs in good old Boston town. I hate to leave it. Nearly six years is it not? I have got to buy some things—shoes &c—pay some bills for books—send some boxes &c home. I don't see how I am going to do it all & wind up my work to get away August 1st.

I keep well & sturdy but fear that I will make a pretty poor traveling companion for Ned. I dread the let down from this place of high tension. Would that I had six months more service.

[16] Otto Glasser's excellent biography of Röntgen contains a bibliography of 1,044 papers on X-rays published during 1896.

[17] Cannon, W. B. "Early use of the Roentgen ray in the study of the alimentary canal." *Journal of the American Medical Association*, 3 January 1914, *62*, 1-3.

[18] *Johns Hopkins Hospital Bulletin*, August-September 1897, *8*, 195-196.

H.C.'s contemporary comments on M.G.H. surgery are few, but they are pungent. The work of John W. Elliot, C. B. Porter, Maurice Richardson, and William Conant he held in high esteem, but some of the others operated by the clock. For example, on 12 April 1896, he writes: "Not operating much. Considerable sepsis in the house. No wonder, these men operate about the way a commercial traveller grabs breakfast at a lunch counter."

A man of H.C.'s driving energy could not live long without arousing animosities among those with whom he was thrown. He was a severe taskmaster, demanding of others a standard of performance similar to that to which he himself aspired. Franklin S. Newell who served under him at the M.G.H. and who later came to occupy the chair of obstetrics at the Harvard Medical School writes on 6 April 1942: "He was recognized as perhaps the ablest man in his class at the Medical School and was an extremely hard worker. As house officer I was his junior and suffered severely in that position for a year. He was an extremely hard man to work with, whether one was over him or under him, as his tremendous ambition for success made it impossible for him to allow anyone else to get any credit for work done. As you know, when he wanted to be he was one of the most charming people in the world, but working with him I found that he couldn't tolerate anyone else in the limelight."

But there were others who felt differently. In the summer of 1896 William Graves, a classmate of Cushing's at Yale[19] and later a colleague at Harvard (Professor of Gynecology), wrote a letter which forcefully illustrates Cushing's favorite dictum that great teaching stems always from good example:

Moosehead Lake, Maine,
William P. Graves to H.C. *July 1896.*

Dear Cush, . . . I want to try to tell you how grateful I am for what you have done for me this year. You have made all the difference in the world in my work, and I don't know what I should have done without you. I have to thank you not only for what you have consciously done, but also because hearing of what you have done in the School, and watching you do things at the Hospital has been much the greatest inspiration and stimulus that I have had this year.

When I was teaching I found that the greatest satisfaction I could have was to discover that I had unconsciously or consciously inspired a boy to try to do something worth doing. If I can make you realize this feeling in my own case, it is the only way I can hope to repay you at all. I wish I knew how to express just what I really feel, but I can't.

I am perfectly satisfied with your advice about the Harvard Medical School, especially since I have seen the Hospital. This has been much the best year I have ever spent and I owe much of the satisfaction of it to you. . . . It is unnecessary

[19] After he left Yale Dr. Graves had been obliged to teach for several years before entering Harvard Medical School.

for me to tell you how much interested I am in your own success. That is well enough assured anyway. . . . I hope the summer will do wonders for your health, and that you may start in your work next fall with iron legs. Affectionately yours, WILLIAM P. GRAVES.

An exchange, many years later, between a patient, Cushing, and Dr. Charles A. Porter gives still another picture of H.C.'s days in surgery at the M.G.H. The patient was one on whom he had operated when a house officer.

Warren, Massachusetts,
Mr. Frank H. Linnehan to H.C. *4 January 1930.*

My Dear Doctor, Please excuse the liberty I am taking in writing to you: but I have been putting it off for years and years, and now something compels me to write to you. I wonder, Doctor, if you ever think of the days of long ago in the Mass. General Hospital, when you and young Doctor Porter used to sit on the bed of one of your patients and talk over things: and of the many operations that patient had gone through to save his right leg—and how the best Physicians in the Hospital could not save the leg, and wanted to take the leg off, and how you encouraged the patient to hold on to the leg until you became House Doctor and you would guarantee to save the leg—and how I was your first Patient to go under your knife when you became House Doctor: and you in one operation saved the leg that all the other Doctors wanted to take off.

That operation Doctor to me seems to be one of the greatest of your many many big things in your life. The leg today is as sound and strong as a twenty dollar gold piece—after giving it the hardest of abuse in hard labor.

I sometimes wonder Doctor if my leg would be of any use for clinic purposes or lectures, or could in any way help out the cause of good surgery. At this time Doctor I want to thank you a thousand times over and over again, for your great kindness to me in those dark days of long ago. Wishing you and yours all of nature's greatest gifts—Health Happiness and sunshine.

To this H.C. replied (6 Jan.): "I can't tell you how pleased I am to have had your letter. That was a long time ago when we agonized over your poor leg, and I am so glad to know that it has stood you in good stead this long time. Perhaps some day when you are in this part of the world you will drop in to see me." And to "young Dr. Porter" he wrote: "Those were days when we used to sit on the side of a bed together and make many plans, few of which have ever come to fruition. However, this letter seems to indicate that we once, at all events, did a good job together. Just how sound and strong a twenty-dollar gold piece may be I don't know. I don't often see 'em. If you would like to have F.H.L. send in his leg for any clinical purposes or lectures, the opportunity is yours. But it's a nice letter out of a remote past that I hand on for recollections' sake."

But perhaps the most objective picture of H.C.'s student and interne days will be found in his reminiscences in his Ether Day Address many years later:[20]

[20] "The personality of a hospital." Ether Day Address, M.G.H., 18 October 1921, *Boston Medical and Surgical Journal*, 1921, *185*, 529-538.

Even long after Bigelow had passed, when surgery had risen high on the wave of Listerism and was beginning to invade the body cavities, and even though our existing chiefs at the time: Porter, Warren, Homans and Beach, Richardson, Cabot, Elliot, Mixter and Harrington, were men of unusual character and attainments, the Bigelow traditions still dominated and those of us who had never seen him nevertheless felt the influence of his commanding personality. . . . To be acceptable, the physician requires a special combination of head and heart; the surgeon of head, heart and hand—a rarer combination which comes partly by gift and partly by training. I know of no better example of this combination at its best than my talented and lamented predecessor in the school, Maurice H. Richardson. . . .

Up to our lights back in the '90's, surgery in its transition stage was done here exceptionally well, and there was a healthy rivalry between the services, of which there were then three—East, West and South—each with its own distinctive personality. How looked down upon were we of the newly established "South" by those of the other services, each with its long and enviable genealogical list of internes scratched upon the lid of the senior's desk. My brother, I remember with amusement, was shocked to find that I was not on the East side which had been his. But each of us felt his own service to be the best, and endeavored to make this assured by establishing traditions better, if possible, than those of the others. So with my contemporaries of the short-lived "South" I look back with an enduring sense of obligation to our four chiefs—to that resolute and picturesque pioneer John Homans, who twenty years before had been privately advised not to do ovariotomies here, yet persisted in so doing: to C. B. Porter, master of operative technique; to Jack Elliot with his brilliant gifts and uncanny surgical instinct, and to the youngest of them, William Conant, most generous and considerate of his hard-working juniors.

To place the time for a younger generation, we were just beginning to count the leucocytes in the blood, to operate for appendicitis in the interval, and hesitatingly to expose the gallbladder through a small opening, for the upper abdomen was still largely a closed territory. . . . A good deal of it, to be sure, in retrospect appears somewhat old-fashioned and we were misled in many ways. We operated too much by the clock; the wealth of material was utilized in no way except for added experience; cases were insufficiently studied before operation; our fracture dressings were so neat and laboriously made we would hesitate to take them down to see if all was well beneath; we disdained the students, forgetting how recently we had been of them; there was rather too much display and operative rivalry at our Saturday morning public exhibition of skill; too much of the week's hard work was postponed for a prolonged Sunday morning visit which left us with no day of relaxation; there was no spur whatever to productiveness, no encouragement to follow up a bad result, whether to its home or to the deadhouse.

But in spite of the weaknesses in his medical training, so apparent from the perspective of twenty years later, Cushing had been intensely interested and stimulated throughout his student years in Boston and he was reluctant to leave when the time came for him to take up the next phase of his career.

CHAPTER V

Halsted and The Johns Hopkins Hospital

1896–1900

WHEN Cushing arrived in Baltimore in the autumn of 1896 to take up his duties as William S. Halsted's Assistant Resident in Surgery, the Medical School of Johns Hopkins University and its Hospital were new and vigorous institutions. Johns Hopkins—bachelor, Quaker, and wealthy merchant—had amassed a considerable fortune which upon his death in 1873 he had left for philanthropic purposes, as had Peter Bent Brigham of Boston in 1872. Hopkins placed his fortune in the hands of wisely chosen trustees with the stipulation that the seven million dollars be divided equally—one half to found a university, the other to establish a hospital. For the development of the University the trustees had made the fortunate choice of Daniel Coit Gilman, once Librarian of Yale University, and for the Hospital, John Shaw Billings of the Surgeon General's Library, one of the foremost scholars in the history of American medicine.

The trustees moved slowly, laying their plans with caution. Gilman and Billings followed their good example, exercising particular care in their search for staff, since both believed in spending their money on men rather than on bricks and mortar. The plans for the University, however, materialized more rapidly than those for the Hospital. Within three years it was possible to dedicate Johns Hopkins University and announce as the nucleus of a faculty six distinguished professors: Basil L. Gildersleeve in the classics; Henry Augustus Rowland in physics; Janus J. Sylvester in mathematics; Ira Remsen in chemistry; George S. Morris in philosophy; and Newell Martin, the talented pupil of Thomas Henry Huxley and Michael Foster, in biology (and physiology). Huxley came from England to give the inaugural address, and since the powers-that-be at the new University had been advised that Huxley was a nonconformist, the ceremony, much to the consternation of the orthodox board of trustees, was conducted without music or theological accessories.

The Hospital, on the other hand, was under construction for nearly twelve years (from 1877). The original faculty consisted of Billings, who held the title of Professor of Hygiene, Ira Remsen, and Newell Martin. William H. Welch, who was called from New York to the chair of pathology, joined them in 1884. Instead of fretting over the slow progress of the hospital building, Welch occupied the first year of his professorship by taking a trip abroad where he spent some time with the foremost pathologists of Europe: Weigert at Leipzig, Cohnheim at Breslau, and Frobenius at Munich. He also met Koch but did not work with him. Welch returned late in 1885 and during 1886 quickly developed a flourishing laboratory of experimental pathology around his new chair, the first full-time post in pathology to be established on a university basis. A group of enthusiastic young investigators immediately came to him—men such as Franklin P. Mall who later became Professor of Anatomy; William T. Councilman, H.C.'s warm friend, who was appointed to the chair of pathology at Harvard in 1892; Simon Flexner, who subsequently developed the Rockefeller Institute; William S. Halsted, who was to become Professor of Surgery at Johns Hopkins (1889); and Walter Reed of yellow fever fame. It was a remarkable group, and in turn it soon attracted the best brains in the field of medicine on the North American continent.

Both Welch and Gilman had had their eyes on William Osler who was doing so much to enliven the medical department at the University of Pennsylvania, whither he had gone from Montreal in 1884. In 1888 Mr. Gilman made a definite proposal which Osler accepted on 3 October. Osler rapidly organized his clinic during the early months of 1889, and, like Welch, he began at once to attract younger men of outstanding ability. By this time the chiefs-of-service had been appointed; they were all young—Osler 39, Welch 38, Halsted, 37, and Howard Kelly (whom Osler was responsible for bringing to the Hopkins) only 31. Henry M. Hurd, who had been selected to serve as Superintendent of the Hospital, was 46—no doubt a fortunate circumstance since he might otherwise have had difficulty in making his youthful chiefs-of-service toe the line.

The Johns Hopkins Hospital was dedicated on 6 May 1889,[1] and on this occasion there were prayer and proper melody. As Osler pointed out years later, "The opening of the Johns Hopkins Hospital in 1889 marked a new departure in medical education in the United States. It was not the hospital itself . . . it was not the men . . . it was the organization. For the first time in an English-speaking country a hospital was organized in units, each one in charge of a head or chief." The new Medical School with its Hospital organized on these unconventional lines received its first students in the autumn of 1893, when Cushing was just completing his second year at Harvard, and

[1] Chesney, A. M. *The Johns Hopkins Hospital and the Johns Hopkins University School of Medicine. A chronicle.* Vol. I: Early years, 1867-1893. Baltimore, 1943.

the first class was graduated in June of 1897. On the occasion of this, the first graduating ceremony to include the Medical School, William Welch had spoken in this vein:

. . . This occasion is of significance not to this University alone but to the history of medical education in this country. What is significant is not the addition of a new medical school to an already overburdened list, but it is the completed organization of a medical school surpassing in its standards of requirement all others now existing on this continent.

The opportunity was afforded me four years ago at these graduating exercises to present in some detail the organization and aims of the new Medical Department then about to begin its work. It is not necessary to repeat what was then said. The plans and purposes set forth upon that occasion have been in the main realized. . . . You will remember that professional education is not completed at the Medical School. You have learned only a relatively small part of the entire contents of the science and art of medicine. It is much if the student takes with him upon graduation a knowledge of fundamental principles, some practical familiarity with the nature and treatment of cases of disease and injury, the ability to use instruments of his profession and above all correct methods of work and a trained scientific spirit of investigation. . . .

Cushing had come into this stimulating atmosphere in October of 1896. Osler was then 47 years of age, Halsted 45, Cushing 27 (and still unmarried).

* * * * *

After leaving Boston on 31 July 1896, H.C. took a month's holiday with his brother Ned, his cousins Mr. and Mrs. Edward Harvey, and their daughter Melanie, visiting Nova Scotia, Prince Edward Island, the Gaspé, and Quebec, Montreal, and several intermediate points. The diary of the trip is crowded with lighthearted anecdote and innumerable sketches.[2] Remembering his experiences and Ned's on their trip to Europe it is amusing to find him recording, "Ed Harvey has brought for our careful perusal two books—'Is life worth living' and 'The art of living together'—much needed literature." He was alert to every aspect of the changing scene—new country, new faces offering continual stimulation—and the brief descriptions chosen at random through the diary are interesting not only in themselves but also as an earnest of what is to follow throughout all his future travels.

[From Halifax to Mulgrave] The road is lined with beautiful red wild roses,

[2] The journal, designated "The Diary of the Ready Shifters," is more extensively illustrated than some of his journals of later date and, although highly amusing throughout, is of less general interest than his other travel journals. Hospitals were visited at all the chief centers, but he does not record incidents of special moment save for passing reference to the fact that "Macewen of Glasgow" was at the Royal Victoria Hospital on 23 August 1896. It is not clear whether H.C. met him then—probably not, for there is no reference to such an encounter in Cushing's lecture given many years later in Macewen's honor.

goldenrod, pink tassels of orchids, huckleberry bushes, alder. Many fine maples and birch with their light green standing out well before the dark of the evergreens.

[And on Prince Edward Island] The three genties later cross the windblown sand dunes which look to me much like the Shinnecock dunes of sweet memory—fine dry sand drifted and packed hard like snow with long grass growing in tufts in it—a fitting background for the lovely wide beach and lowering sky we found beyond. . . . Great fields of waving wheat—white acres of potatoes—woods of spruce and hemlock, groves of large beech—balm of Gilead—silver-barked birch shining against the dark evergreens—fertile country, looking as though every farmhouse was full of milk, butter, eggs, and mutton chops 2″ thick.

[On the Gaspé] A bold red sandstone bluff with abrupt and precipitous shore led out from the town (Percé) in a sweep to the eastward making the little harbour, full of fishing vessels—humble craft but sturdy assuredly. At the end of this bluff was placed a cross as though Jules Cruvier [Jacques Cartier] himself had put it there. . . . The fog lifted just enough for us to see . . . the bold headland, Cape Gaspé, with its light sturdily facing the broad tumultuous Atlantic. The Gaspé basin astonishes and charms. The shore with . . . waterworn cliffs with great sworls made by the waves—caverns—and a fine gray beach above which on high palisades are built the little fishing houses . . . the banks then sloping off across fertile areas of cultivated land to the pine-clad vertebrae through the centre—a veritable Rameses II cut in stone guards the most seaward point of the high promontory and an absurd Irishman's face looks toward the town. . . . A smooth sea—warm sun—the passage close to the wild towering shore whose headlands project into the sea menacingly. . . . And then never to be forgotten—Quebec, the romantic, is before us, every window in its buildings reflecting the gold of the western sky, and hanging in the dark blue over the frowning citadel, the crescent moon softens, blesses—the most beautiful sight I have ever seen. We were very quiet and had little to say.

[Quebec] The Sisterhood is of the "flesh & blood" at the Hôtel Dieu, nursing remedial ills. Other branches have the incurables—foundlings &c. A very old order—one year of probation—a year with the white veil and, if final orders taken for life, with the black veil. We found there was an especial feast today—the "annunciation of the Virgin." The sister gives us a quiet corner where we see the procession which brings tears to my eyes. Down the long corridor, chanting, come about 70 nuns, the Mother Superior bearing the Cross; the probationers—all in black with bonnets—the white veiled nuns and those with the black veil last. They slowly advance, going into each ward in which the Chapel had been especially prepared & lit up with candles. They kneel, chant, and pass on in slow procession—like a bit out of a play—most of them young—many with very beautiful faces. It was a very sad spectacle to me for some reason, though I suppose their lives are very useful ones compared to many. The sister told us their duties were combined between 7 hours a day prayer and meditation and the rest nursing. The novices learn nursing by "observation" alone; there is no instruction. . . .

[Montreal] To the Grey nunnery where after a long wait I am hurried through the long corridors and see the usual pathetic sights of bastard children deserted—turned over to soulless creatures who in an English land teach them a foreign language. The poor peaked children—everything done in unison with their fellows—automatons in life. The youngest foundlings I could not see. The old men and women were smoking and knitting away their remaining days.

H.C. was equally vivid in describing the amusing incidents of the trip—Ned's preparing a mustard plaster for Cousin Mattie's stitch-in-the-side. "Neddie makes a delicious fat poultice of mustard & flour, spreads it on a plate and rushes out as though it were a golden brick." His description of trying to empty coffee beans out of Melanie's trunk after they had drunk some "medicine" procured by the landlord to counteract the fatigue of a strenuous day speaks for itself: "Nothing would do but Cousin Ed must empty the trunk out of the window. So he piled out with it and I too to save his life and the trunk. Both were hanging by our abidoes [abdomen] when E.H.H. howled out to be dragged in, leaving me holding the gaping trunk over the road below and any chance passerby. In some unaccountable fashion we both—trunk and I—got back into the room, which was strewn with people in attitudes of intense agony, shrieking at our plight. There was as much coffee as ever in the trunk."

SPILLING THE COFFEE BEANS

Cushing had become much attached to his work in Boston, and Melanie Harvey recalls that he was a very unhappy companion at the start of their trip since he hated leaving the Massachusetts General Hospital. On 5 August he wrote his father: "Having good time—the only thing that reconciles me about leaving the M.G.H. It was the hardest thing I have ever done. Was having a good service. Had several very good laparotomies myself." And again on the 16th from the Château Frontenac: "Got batch of letters from you. Glad to hear from Halsted. It was a curious note, but characteristic, I presume." Cushing had left Boston still uncertain about his post in Baltimore. The formal application for an Assistant Residency at the Johns Hopkins Hospital, which he had submitted the preceding April, had not been acknowledged, and Dr. Halsted himself had gone to Europe. The letter from Halsted received at Quebec therefore gave him welcome reassurance:

1201 Eutaw Place, Baltimore,
William S. Halsted to H.C. *10 August 1896.*

Dear Dr. Cushing, I have just received your letter, and am surprised to hear that I have not told you already positively that you might expect the appointment. You will be appointed without doubt, for I nominated you before leaving town in May. I shall see to it that a room in the Hospital is arranged for you on or before the first of October. Please pardon me for not signing this letter. Yours very sincerely, W. S. HALSTED, per S.

Although reassured by Halsted's letter Cushing deemed it an odd document, and on reaching Cleveland (where he spent September) he consulted various friends about the appointment. Hunter Robb, one of Osler's original house officers, recalls:

SKETCHES OF CANADA
From the "Diary of the Ready Shifters," August 1896

. . . I was perhaps partially instrumental in getting Dr. Cushing to go to the Johns Hopkins . . . ; he came to see me in Cleveland and asked me what I thought about his going as an interne on the Surgical Service at the Hopkins. I strongly advised his doing so, as I believed that it would give him the opportunity to develop fully his abilities. I was at the Hopkins some months after he began his service there, and had a few minutes to chat with him, and I gathered that he was not altogether pleased with the way his work was going, and he said that he did not think that he would stay very long. I advised him to stick it out a bit longer and he said that he would. I was at the Hopkins about six months later and saw Dr. Cushing again, and I asked him "Well, Harvey, how are things going now, and how long do you expect to remain," and he replied with a broad smile, "Indefinitely."[3]

Halsted's confirmation of his Hopkins appointment caused H.C. to give up his plans to go abroad with his friend, Allen Porter, who wrote him a generous letter wishing him Godspeed in Baltimore:

"New England Express Line,"
C. A. Porter to H.C. [*Summer 1896*].

Dear Harvey, I was sorry not to see you—and say Goodbye. I wish, now that I am on the way—even more than before—that you were going with me. We have had such a good time together, scrapping over diagnoses and all that, that I am looking forward very much to meeting Professor Cushing of Cleveland, or wherever else you go, as one of the pleasures to come. You will learn a great deal at Johns Hopkins on the scientific side and all that—but you must be sure not to unlearn a lot of things—I will grant 3½ [hours] to a breast if you wish—and that blood saving is valuable—but I only grant such a time when it is necessary, never to the surgeon who says that he has got 3 or 4 hours for what only requires 2 hours hard work. So please combine their methods & scientific spirit with some of our Boston *"Gimp."*

I wrote Billy Thayer three weeks ago for Dr. Baltzell's address. He is abroad and I wish you would find it out for me and send it to Baring Bros. *with* a letter from yourself. If that photograph is a good one—of myself—I wish you *would* send one to my father. Will write you. Sincerely always, ALLEN PORTER.

Transplantation always caused H.C. some initial unhappiness, and things in Baltimore when he arrived in late September were indeed very different from Boston. His first letters home, both written on 4 October, convey his state of mind:

J.H.H., Baltimore,
H.C. to B.M.C. *4 October 1896.*

Dear Mother You see I am located at last, surrounded by the four high bare white walls of a room recently occupied by one named Blumer [Dr. George Blumer of Yale]. My sole adornment consists of an old-time discolored photograph of Neddie on the mantel. My few books look very lonesome in the corner of a huge book case. I am occupying a similar position in this big room. There is a small iron bedstead in one corner covered with mosquito netting, an evidence of summer needs. . . . I am a very humble member of a large staff here. I have been given a part of a ward with a few patients as a starter and have not as much to do as is salutary. Everyone is very kind, however, and I expect soon to feel more at home. Had a very pleasant 24 hours with Dalzell. They sent many

[3] The year before, Ned had also conveyed to H.C. something of Robb's enthusiasm for Halsted, "I have seen much of Robb in the past three weeks and have been interested by what he has to say of Halsted & the Johns Hopkins. He says that to his mind there is no surgeon like him in the land, that his aseptic technique is perfect, and that the scientific manner of his work, keeping at it from the laboratory side simultaneously with his clinical & operative work is a revelation to a man. In talking over your offer with him he says strongly that if a place is available after you finish your M.G.H. service, take it by all means—that a year there would be worth five abroad &c &c. Think it over."

kind messages to you. There is a small daughter in the family aged 6 months who is very cunning.

H.C. to Alice K. Cushing *4 October 1896.*

Dear Alice I left behind my blue heavy winter sack coat and vest. . . . Am not having a very good time here as yet. Everything is very strange. Have seen Mr. Goodwillie a couple of times, which cheered me up much. Hope you are getting along all right.

The Goodwillies, old friends from Cleveland, did much to help H.C. adjust to his new surroundings. To his father he wrote with candor about his early impressions of the Hopkins Hospital and the surgical service:

H.C. to H.K.C. *15 October 1896.*

Will you please forward to me my Quain Vol. II on Histology. I miss my books very much. The library here is rather inaccessible. Am hard at work doing little things. Am much disappointed to find the Hospital a very sloppy place and the work of everyone most unsystematic, i.e. on the surgical side. Dr. Halsted has only operated once this month and rarely appears. Hope things will clear up or I can't stand it.

H.C. to B.M.C. *17 October 1896.*

. . . Baltimore is a curious place—slow hardly expresses it. I bought a couple of books last week at the one book store, Cushing & Co. by the way. They were delivered in six days. My surprise and disgust caused the man I spoke to great amusement. This is one illustration of several such experiences. The house staff are a new sort of men to me, all but one or two, southerners—the one I have seen most of—named Hoke from Georgia—son of a Confederate Major General and educated at the University of North Carolina. He has just left unfortunately. It's curious to be with so many men with whom one has absolutely no association or mutual acquaintances. It's a good experience—and that's what we look for, experiences. Medicine of course is an all sufficient bond. . . .

H.K.C. promptly told his somewhat impetuous son to be patient with Baltimore:

H.K.C. to H.C. *18 October 1896.*

Dear Harvey In accordance with your note I posted to you yesterday the section of Quain on Histology. Would it not be worth while to send on to you such of your books as it would be useful or comfortable to have? It could easily be done without very much expense, and I should be glad to see to it for you. You have not referred to the microscope which I hope reached its destination safely. How about the new lens and its cost? Plainly your experience at "Hopkins" is not all that you anticipated or wished. It may eventuate as at the M.G.H. You thought you were going on the least desirable side of the house, but in the end, found it the best end. Things are unlike; you are among strangers; and I hope opportunities for profit may seem more hopeful after a time. At any rate you will have to make the best of it, hopefully, until fair trial has been made. This I have no doubt is also your own judgment and intention.

If you think you could use a wheel [bicycle] profitably, you had better have one, and it can be obtained either there or here as may be deemed best. I of course do not know the various brands or their characteristics. But if you get one, get a good one. Would you care for a Cleveland paper? Much rainy and cold weather through the month. Affectionately FATHER. [P.S.] I enclose a ten for ballast, for I suspect the other contents are light weight.

To his mother, H.C. expands upon the curious eating habits of the Baltimorians, and he rails like the usual restless house officer about the hospital food; having this out of his system he turns naturally to a description of the town itself whose attractions he views with his usual alert eye:

H.C. to B.M.C. *1 November 1896.*

There are a lot of men working over in the laboratory and as much of my time is spent there I see a good deal of them, Carter especially. I believe I've introduced him to you *per epistolam*. He was good enough to take me over to his house to dinner today so that I escaped our house dinner which is one of three very bad meals we have a day. These Baltimorians have more ingenious ways of serving up viscera than I imagined possible. Good muscle is a rarity. Oysters we never see. It's most curious. The Marylander serves his chicken fried. Sunday mornings we have griddle cakes and sausage served together—a general custom and an insult to good digestion the equal of beans and fish balls. Water is looked at somewhat askance. Everyone drinks milk with all meals. As a consequence I am getting very stout and weigh more today than I have for two years.

The only thing to see in Baltimore I saw with Mr. Goodwillie last Sunday—Druid Hill Park—pronounced 'Drudill' Park. A large tract of rolling woodland of some 700 acres with most attractive little gullies where one can wander away from the hoi polloi, for crowds congregate there Sundays. The woodland is left entirely to nature, except for the good roads cut through it and contains some of the most magnificent primeval forest trees I have ever seen. Huge red, black and white oaks—tulips very high; monstrous buttonwood with startling white upper branches almost like a birch; many beautiful beeches; persimmons, with the most puckering fruit I ever tasted, heretofore unknown to me—sassafras, chestnut, an occasional ash and bass wood—and many more. I never saw such a collection of fine trees in one locality. I wish father could have been there with us. Mr. Goodwillie is at his best in the woods. It was a very enjoyable afternoon. . . .

Within a short space of time, Baltimore had begun to work its charm and a letter to his mother toward the end of the month shows that he had perhaps modified his earlier belief that there was "only one thing to see."

H.C. to B.M.C. *21 November 1896.*

Baltimore is a homely, homespun sort of a town. The few streets with which I am acquainted are architecturally most monotonous. Rows of unbroken brick fronts as alike as Streptococci, the only ornament being a landing and three white marble steps leading to the brick pavement. The streets—the residence streets—are deserted—at night an occasional glimmer of lights from a 3rd story window alone indicates any habitation. Mr. G. says the people all live in the backs of the houses. I should think they would get as far away from the front elevation as possible—and the gutters. . . .

On certain days in the week, here, everyone wears a huge market basket. If one follows a market basket he comes in due time to the second oasis—that is if he follows an empty one. Lexington Market is immense. Mr. G. and I had planned to go a-marketing last Saturday night. We missed connections so I went alone. Lexington Market makes a basket almost essential to one's wardrobe—I never saw so many things worth taking home in one. The butcher, the baker, and the broom stick maker sleek and ruddy stand in their stalls and slice off great bologna sausages or our Maryland fresh biscuits or anything you like into the gaping basket. Fruit—the apples especially attracted me and I bought some huge shiny Northern Spies and though somewhat ashamed carried them home in a paper bag. Candy; all sorts of bread stuff; flowers; vegetables; meat—miles of it. Can you imagine a hundred yards of skinny, skinned rabbits, hanging on a rope with a row of grinning darkies behind them? It's the sort of market one only expects to read about. I wandered about and munched and acted the Northern Spy for about an hour, till my 'abido' got sore from countless encounters with the corners of heavy laden baskets. When you go to the Lexington Market, don't ride home in a jerky electric car or you may step into a basket of eggs instead of one of meat and bread.

At long last, H.C. decided to accept Baltimore as Margaret Fuller had the universe. On 30 November he reluctantly admitted: "I am beginning to get used to things here and though not wildly enthusiastic hope I am making it pay." Things became even brighter toward Christmas when Mrs. Harry Fielding Reid invited him to dinner with her family.

H.C. to B.M.C. *23 December 1896.*

I have no share in the performance [Hospital Christmas party] but Gynn—Gwyn, or however he spells his name [Norman B. Gwyn], a Canadian who is in charge of the medical side of Ward G, has combined with me and we have planned to have some stockings for the children of the ward on the morning of the 25th. Preparatory for which we assailed a 10-cent toy store yesterday and purchased a multitude of squeaking animals, tin trumpets, "wonder puzzles," alphabet books, sawdust dolls, some ridiculous jumping jack rabbits and what not with a large consignment of candy (there is paregoric in the Ward). These purchases we lugged home in the snow. The proprietor told us 48 hrs. was too short a time to think of delivering them. Such is Baltimore. I reached the hospital with a tin trumpet and the head of a rabbit protruding from my great angular bundle. Mrs. Reid has most kindly asked me to share their Christmas dinner so I shall have a taste of something besides what an institution can offer. It was very good of her. There are to be one or two other people there so I am not intruding on a family function.

CHRISTMAS GREETINGS TO K.C.

Halsted

After Halsted's death in 1922 Cushing wrote a biographical sketch, the first paragraphs of which give an excellent objective description of the man under whom he had worked in his early Baltimore years and who had had a profound influence on the development of his career as a surgeon:

. . . A man of unique personality, shy, something of a recluse, fastidious in his tastes and in his friendships, an aristocrat in his breeding, scholarly in his habits, the victim for many years of indifferent health, he nevertheless was one of the few American surgeons who may be considered to have established a school of surgery comparable, in a sense, to the school of Billroth in Vienna.

He had few of the qualities supposed to accompany what the world regards as a successful surgeon. Overmodest about his work, indifferent to matters of priority, caring little for the gregarious gatherings of medical men, unassuming, having little interest in private practice, he spent his medical life avoiding patients—even students, when this was possible—and, when health permitted, working in clinic and laboratory at the solution of a succession of problems which aroused his interest. He had that rare form of imagination which sees problems, and the technical ability combined with persistence which enabled him to attack them with promise of a successful issue. Many of his contributions, not only to his craft but to the science of medicine in general, were fundamental in character and of enduring importance. . . .

Before going to Johns Hopkins Halsted had investigated the anesthetizing effect of the then little-known and newly introduced drug, cocaine, completely unaware that it was habit-forming. Although he had the strength of character to overcome what at first had been a serious habituation to the drug, he was the victim thereafter of indifferent health, and was in consequence frequently absent from his clinic. We have it, however, on unimpeachable authority that at the time of his death he had not touched cocaine in many years.

From all that can be gathered from the records, chiefly Cushing's letters home, there was nothing clear-cut or decisive about his relationship with Halsted. He states on one occasion that Halsted had ordered a set of books for him and again after he and Kate Crowell had called on the Halsteds he writes: "The Professor himself is doubtless the best man in his specialty in the country which of course makes being his slave a most valuable experience. I am very fond of and admire him immensely." Indeed, there seems to have been respect and admiration on both sides. Halsted wrote in a letter to Welch on 14 July 1922, just two months before he died, "I embrace this opportunity to express my indebtedness to Harvey Cushing, for thirteen years my brilliant assistant, for his zeal in elaborating these courses [laboratory operative courses] and placing them on such a substantial basis that they are now regarded as one of the dominant features of the surgical curriculum for the third-year medical students at the Johns Hopkins University and are being adopted by other medical schools of this country." Their relationship, however, had none of the warmth and affection which existed between Osler and Cushing, or Welch and Cushing.

In the introductory note to the volume of Halsted letters and memorabilia assembled after his death, Cushing set down some of his early impressions of 'the Professor':

The surroundings at the J.H.H. were strange enough after what I had been through at the Massachusetts General. The talk was of pathology and bacteriology of which I knew so little that much of my time the first few months was passed alone at night in the room devoted to surgical pathology in the old pathological building looking at specimens with a German textbook at hand. . . . Meanwhile I had plenty to do, in addition to my duties as a house officer in Ward G and in the newly opened children's ward off the Broadway corridor. With the aid of a small X-ray tube, I began taking Röntgenograms, the first at the J.H.H., and the old discarded static machine relegated to a room in the private ward had never been put to better use. Later on, I also started a class in orthopaedics, of which I had learned something at the Children's Hospital in Boston; gave a course of lectures to the nurses; and subsequently encouraged Baer to take up orthopaedics as a specialty and sent him with letters to Boston which gave him a start. . . .

It was most disconcerting to me, after the hurly-burly of the M.G.H., to have my new Chief come, as it were apologetically, some day into Ward G; ask if he might be allowed to examine a particular patient; to have him spend an hour fiddling over a patient with cancer of the breast who had recently been admitted; and then to have him depart saying he was tired and would be able to do nothing more that day. If he were sufficiently interested he might ask that he be permitted to do the operation; and if he came and did operate, so soon as the breast was removed, leaving the huge closure and skin graft to Bloodgood, he would depart with the tissues. These he would study and ruminate over for an interminable time, meanwhile tagging innumerable areas which he wished to have sectioned—a duty which devolved upon the house officer. It was incumbent upon each of us to make all the clinical, bacteriological and pathological studies for every patient in our charge—a good system for reliable house officers, which unfortunately all are not. Due to it, a great deal of most valuable material at the Hopkins in those days was either imperfectly worked up or not worked up at all. I personally owe to this system what little I know of histological pathology and my early bacteriological studies, some of which got into print, would otherwise have never been made.

Elliott Cutler, one of Cushing's younger contemporaries, throws additional light on the relationship between Cushing and Halsted in the first days of their association.[4] This incident illustrates the striking contrast between the point of view of the surgical school at Hopkins and that at Harvard:

Cushing went to Baltimore to work under William Stewart Halsted. Being a newcomer he was not allowed in the operating room his first day there, though a patient from his ward went to be operated upon. It was with great misgiving that the young Cushing watched two and even three hours go by, while the great master took such exquisite care with each cell that there would be no injury to the patient. Finally when the patient returned to the ward after some four and one-half hours in the operating room, young Cushing was ready with restoratives and the customary medication that he had been ordered to give

[4] "The art of surgery." *The Aesculapian*, 1940, *31*, 3-18.

to surgical patients when a pupil at the Massachusetts General Hospital. When he was about to administer these medicaments, for he recalled from his days as a pupil at the Massachusetts General Hospital how ill those who returned from the operating room were even after a hurried procedure of minutes, not hours, Dr. Halsted entered the ward.

Dr. Cushing spoke up and said, "I am carrying out the usual procedure."

Noting the Trendelenburg position, Dr. Halsted said, "Is my patient ill? This is unusual. Let us examine her." Examination revealed a normal pulse rate and normal respiration. He then noted the hypodermic and said, "What is in the syringe?"

"Strychnin," said Cushing. "It will do the patient good."

Dr. Halsted asked a third question. "What do you think strychnin will do for the patient?" Having been educated in a school where memory and orders were the rule, Cushing did not know. He was then informed by Dr. Halsted that he should read up on strychnin. "If your reading convinces you that strychnin is good for the patient, by all means use it," said Halsted. Young Cushing never gave the strychnin, and he learned a great lesson—never do anything to a patient without understanding the why and wherefore.

While things were going slowly during the first months, H.C. carried on with his X-ray studies and he has given us this account of them:[5]

No X-ray photos had been taken at the J.H.H. when I came down in the fall of 1896. Codman and I had been fooling with some exposures at the Mass. Genl. using an old static machine, and he continued for about ten years more until it had obviously affected his physical condition. We had of course no idea of burns or ductless gland disturbances &c. [H.C. brought a fluoroscope with him from Boston]. There was a large static machine in Ward C in Balto. at the time and I got a small 4″ tube and began making exposures, spending many an hour in a temporary dark room off the old amphitheatre with Rodinal as a developer. The [X-ray] prints in this paper were among the first taken with an exposure of anywhere from 20 to 30 minutes and I think fully a dozen trials must have been made. It is extraordinary that there were no burns and no personal injury. A Willyoung brand of coil was secured about a year later and I did all the X-ray work until I became resident succeeding Bloodgood.

On 6 November 1896 one Lizzie W. entered the emergency ward on Cushing's service, having been shot in the neck by her bartender husband during a family brawl. The bullet had entered the cervical region and was lodged somewhere in the neck. The woman showed signs of paralysis on one side of her body and sensory impairment on the opposite side. H.C. inferred that the bullet must have reached the spinal cord. The old static machine was activated and a number of first-rate plates of the cervical spine were obtained, disclosing the bullet as lodged in the body of the 6th cervical vertebra. Voluminous studies were made of this, H.C.'s first case of spinal cord lesion; there were detailed sensory charts illustrating the familiar Brown-Séquard syndrome and innumerable notes and sketches. The case was

[5] Written on the inside cover of the reprint on "Haematomyelia from gunshot wounds of the spine" and dated 19 February 1911.

reported at the Johns Hopkins Medical Society meeting on 3 May 1897.[6] This excellent paper stands as H.C.'s first formal piece of writing. He mentions his 'maiden effort' in a letter to his father:

H.C. to H.K.C. [*Undated—? 9 May 1897*].

I have not communicated with home or with anyone much of late. I am trying to shoulder almost more work than I can carry at present, and only the thought of home on June 1st keeps me agoing. Walker, one of the staff, has left and I have taken up his ward in addition to my own which is a pretty heavy job. Last Monday I read or rather talked before the Medical Society on a case of haematomyelia from gunshot wound, which represented a good deal of study especially as it was my maiden effort and I wanted to make a good report. I had to talk as my paper was not finished as I hope it will be before I leave.

Tomorrow I've got to start in on a large drawing which Dr. Halsted wants for a Surgical Society meeting and I seem to be the only one accessible at present to make it. To crown all, my patients are all grunting and groaning, temperatures elevated and what not so I am nigh distracted and am going to bed. With apologies for this doleful note.

1897

The year began auspiciously for H.C. with an unexpected visit from his brother Ned and Melanie Harvey who surprised him by announcing their engagement—news which caused great family rejoicing:

H.C. to B.M.C. *21 January 1897.*

I have been having a very nice visit from the happy pair. It's a good thing and I am delighted. I never saw Neddie so jolly nor Melanie as sweet, which is much to say. Mr. Goodwillie just gave us a Baltimore dinner of oysters and lobster. Roasted oysters opened right before your eyes and swallowed instanter. Neddie will tell you about it.

They are going over to Washington tomorrow to see the Congressional Library, Congress in session and other interesting things. I wish I could go along. They are having a beautiful time. Tomorrow night they return here for dinner and leave at 8.30 for home so that this missive will appear but little ahead of them. Howard and Mrs. Ellis turned up here this afternoon to see Miss Fitch. I met them by accident and showed them about the hospital. The Robbs are also here frequently being in town pro tem. Quite an influx of Clevelanders. Neddie and Melanie are a great team. It couldn't have been better.

After the engaged couple left, H.C. plunged into work. "I have done little but hospital work since Neddie left," he writes (31 Jan.), "and have been busy all day today [Sunday], quite like old times at the M.G.H. when days in the week were all alike." A few days later: "I am getting more used to Baltimore—don't mind their carelessness and slowness and unreliability now that I expect it. I wouldn't choose to dwell here however." On 7 March he took time off to attend McKinley's inaugural:

[6] "Haematomyelia from gunshot wounds of the spine. A report of two cases, with recovery following symptoms of hemilesion of the cord." *American Journal of the Medical Sciences*, 1898, *115*, 654-683.

The Johns Hopkins Hospital,
H.C. to B.M.C. *7 March 1897.*

Thursday dawned a glorious clear springlike day and after a hurried ward visit I hied me to a B. and O. train about 10 o'clock. Mr. G[oodwillie]. and Prof. Reid went earlier. It took us three mortal hours to make the trip because trains were pouring into Washington from all sides and there were not enough tracks to use in getting the empty cars out again. I had no time to spare in looking about the Capitol grounds though I was landed quite near them and I did not attempt to see the inauguration ceremonies but made my way, after casting a longing glance at the new library, down crowded Pennsylvania Avenue to the Standard Oil Office. The crowd was enormous. A solid wall of people 20 deep lined the avenue on each side but fortunately we were allowed to use the avenue between, till just before the parade. The crowd of sightseers in itself was a 'sight to see' and I immortalized portions of it with my trusty Kodak as well as the Capitol and later the parts of the parade which interested me most. After a great struggle I penetrated the crowd at the Standard Oil Corner, found Mr. G., was given some lunch, and settled myself in a window corner to await the procession.

It soon appeared and I was as pleased as a child. The regulars made their usual business-like showing. It's always interesting and gratifying to see them. The militia also. The City troops were magnificent and were greeted by rounds of applause. Then a handsome carriage with John Sherman, another man, McKinley bowing and smiling on all sides—Grover sitting very solemn and dignified under his hat. I should like to know what his thoughts were. He was really the centre of interest to me. They were the first Presidents I have ever seen. No, I forgot Benjy Harrison. One Easter in Washington the Nine was asked to a reception at the White House. We all went—were lined up—shook hands with the little man and, feeling very ill at ease, departed immediately. I had almost forgotten it. Well: the parade went on for some hours—I saw several notables I was glad to recognize—Genl. Miles, Horace Porter—many foreign dignitaries—Genl. Howard who was greeted by such shouts from the crowd at our corner that he finally took his reins in his teeth and waved his broad brimmed hat with his only hand to them.

Then there were miles of troops from various states often with the Governor riding ahead—bicycle companies—light artillery—Marines, Naval reserves—old soldiers ad lib. till we got tired and hied us homeward. It was probably my first and last association with an inauguration ceremony. I wish father had been there. I had many questions to ask about the troops and notables I could not get answers to.

Then came the welcome rumor, later confirmed, that Halsted had decided to invite H.C. to become his surgical resident in succession to Joseph C. Bloodgood:

H.C. to H.K.C. *30 March 1897.*

I must write for some more money. My wardrobe needs replenishing chiefly in the matter of shoes, socks and shirts and I suppose if I am coming home to see Neddie cross the Rubicon I must procure me a frock coat at some period not far distant.

I have been receiving congratulations from various sources as being the next Surgical Resident to succeed Bloodgood. I don't know what particular qualities I have to fit me for the position and I have heard nothing from Dr. Halsted though he has been very nice to me on all occasions. I therefore know nothing of it and only tell you as it's the prospect which keeps me here, hoping that it will not go beyond you. Bloodgood goes either in June or October. I have made no inquiries. If Neddie gets married in June as seems to be fated, I hope to go on to New Haven to my Sexennial after the event, and to make a small trip to Boston to keep in touch with things and people there and get some records I want. I will know by that time whether another or myself is to be Resident. I hardly think it would be profitable to me to stay in any other capacity much longer.

5 April 1897.

Your nice letter received. Enclosure O.K. Dr. Halsted approached me today and offered me the much envied position. I am naturally much elated. I hope I will prove worthy of his confidence. I don't know when Bloodgood will leave —probably not till October.

His father promptly replied to the good news:

967 Prospect Street,
6 April 1897.

I am glad to hear from you, that Dr. Halsted's tongue has been loosed to your relief and satisfaction after so long a time of suspense. I congratulate you heartily upon this outcome of your somewhat uncertain relations in "Hopkins," and have no doubt you will "fill the bill" to the reasonable satisfaction of all. Why does Dr. Bloodgood hold on so much beyond his heretofore anticipated time of departure from his place in the Hospital?

Years later reference is made to the appointment in his unpublished notes on Halsted:

After a year in the wards I was offered the Residency, though Bloodgood stayed on in the Resident's rooms for another twelve months while writing his monograph on hernia.[7] There were other candidates for the post, men who had been there longer than I, men better grounded in the fundamentals of surgery, and whom I perhaps excelled in only one thing, in operative technique. Finney and I had both been schooled in this under C. B. Porter, a brilliant technician, though from the Hopkins point of view not what would be called a great surgeon. Both Finney and I must have profited much from the Boston school of operating surgeons who, be it said, were most scornful of the Hopkins and its inartistic rubber-gloved methods of operating. However, to one who was familiar with the postoperative care of cases under each system, there could be no question which was superior, at least from the standpoint of end results.

Too little mention has been made of the long and warmhearted letters that B.M.C. sent at frequent intervals to her son. They contain endless family news and much sly humor and reveal a broad mind and lovable spirit. A letter setting forth her cosmic worries about the administration in Washington has a curiously modern ring:

Cleveland,
B.M.C. to H.C. *13 April 1897.*

Thanks for the pictures [of the inaugural parade]. They are like all your Kodaks very nice and clear. But the great distance from the objects taken does

[7] Bloodgood, J. C. "Operations on 459 cases of hernia in the Johns Hopkins Hospital from June 1889 to January 1899." *Johns Hopkins Hospital Reports,* 1899, 7, 223-567.

not lend enchantment in this case, for they are so small that it is difficult to distinguish one man from another. Except in the case of one individual, who evidently wanted to cross the street, and the way he has one leg lifted for that purpose is very funny. Between Mr. McKinley and the spectator is an obtrusive tree, so that his dignified head cannot be seen. What a mess the whole world seems to be making in the administration of affairs! Speaking of Mr. McKinley reminds me of this present Congress, and the way in which it seems to be managing the vital business of this land. When I read the papers I groan over the miseries and the mistakes. The Greeks, the wars and rumors of wars, Cuba, the floods and distresses on the Mississippi, the famine in India, and the stupidity of mine own countrymen, till I think I will read the news no more. "When ignorance is bliss, 'tis folly to be wise." And who knows, anyway, what is right, and what is wrong? "The Lord reigneth,—let the earth rejoice." That is all that gives one any feeling of security.

Melanie and Neddie were in here yesterday when your letter came. She was pleased with the pictures. Your message to Neddie last week gave special pleasure—that is, the prospect of a good visit from you in June. . . . I have to hunt up three wedding gifts this week—one for Anna Gardner, one for Alice Paddock, and one for Bessie Metlin. Of course I shall give Melanie a piano. That is my stereotyped wedding gift for my sons' wives. . . . Your loving Mother BESSIE M. CUSHING.

A month's leave of absence[8] from his hospital duties allowed H.C to be in Cleveland for his brother's wedding on 9 June, to return to New Haven for his sexennial reunion (as he had counted on doing since March), and then go on to Boston to renew friendships and take a look at M.G.H. medicine after a year's absence:

M.G.H., Boston,
H.C. to H.K.C. *25 June 1897.*

I have been having a most pleasant and profitable time here and will stay till Monday, 28th, noon. It has been good to get back here and the men have put me up in the house. I could live here in Boston with great joy. It's the most attractive place, other than medically, that I know of and professionally without a peer. I have been devoting myself to X-ray work and to orthopaedics, going to clinics, seeing most interesting things all round. I could profitably spend a month here. The M.G.H. is the biggest operative place I ever saw. Yesterday there were seven cases of acute appendicitis admitted to the house. Think of it. Hope you are all well.

In July some uncertainty still surrounded his status as Resident, but the letters received from Halsted reassured H.C. of his position and his future.

The Johns Hopkins Hospital,
H.C. to H.K.C. *13 July 1897.*

The aspect of things has changed somewhat. Bloodgood has not succeeded in completing the work he had laid out for himself and is coming back for another year. Both he and Dr. Halsted are away and I have only heard from the latter by letter. He talks of dividing the work and honours &c which hardly seems feasible to me. I think he is somewhat embarrassed by the new plan as I most

[8] By taking the month of June off H.C. missed the impressive ceremonies of the first class to be graduated in medicine from Johns Hopkins University.

certainly am. I am not sure but that it will be a good opportunity for me to go abroad for the winter to return here or not as you think best. At present I am Acting Resident under Dr. Finney who has apparently declined the Maryland Hospital appointment. We are having a good service and I have as much as I care to do this weather. More later.

17 July 1897.

I am acting resident by Dr. Hurd's especial request. I rather wished to have one of the other men take it but he said Dr. Halsted expected me to.

Cushing's appointment as Resident indicates that he and Halsted had come to understand one another, and from the tone of Halsted's letters during the summer of 1897 it is clear that "the Professor," as he was generally called, held Cushing in high esteem and had come to depend upon him for teaching. Unfortunately only one side of the correspondence has been preserved, but the letters can be given here without particular comment since they fully explain themselves:

High Hampton, Cashiers, N.C.,

W. S. Halsted to H.C. *5 July 1897.*

My dear Cushing: Your letter, received a day or two before I left Baltimore, interested me very much indeed, & I am heartily obliged to you for the interest you take in Roentgen photography. The marvelous results which you saw foreshow, as you say, a limitless future. I had intended to remain in Balto. until Saturday, July 3, in order to have a talk with you, for Bloodgood is eager to remain at least a year longer; but a telegram from my wife caused me to leave town quite suddenly. She was 38 miles from the Railroad in the mountains of N.C., a moonshiners' country, & seemed to have her hands very full. I presume that Bloodgood has, by this time, had a talk with you about your respective futures. I agreed with him that it would be greatly to his advantage to remain a little longer or until he could work up certain things, which I committed to him long ago, for publication. He appreciates clearly the fact that he stands in your way & is perfectly willing to divide the work & honours with you, leaving the details to me—

I have a plan, the details of which are not worked out, which I shall submit to you in the Fall if you care to remain. I hope that you will think it advisable to stay with us for a few years more, at least; we had counted very much on your assistance in the teaching staff next year. Please write to me when you have time; for I await your decision with some anxiety. I should be glad to hear about Mrs. Miller when you write. Sincerely Yrs W. S. HALSTED.

P.S. Please say to Dr. Hurd that to reach me by telegram he must address the message to Hendersonville, N.C. From Hendersonville, by telephone, to Brevard, from Brevard by telephone to Sapphire, N.C. From Sapphire the message will be sent to me in Cashiers on horseback. W.S.H.

. . . Will you do me a very great favour? I am unable to attend to the request of Dr. Körte, to send him the journals for which he asks in the enclosed memorandum. Will you be so very kind as to hire some one for me either to abstract the articles referred to or to procure the journals & send them to Dr. W. Körte, Potsdamerstrasse 99, Berlin? Körte is perhaps the best surgeon in Berlin today. He is surgeon-in-chief to the Spital Am Urban. I saw a great deal of him & some of his work when I was in Berlin last year. I beg of you to *hire* some one to do this work for me. I should not venture to ask you to attend to this for me if I did not feel sure that you would do precisely what I request, viz. *hire* some one for the task. W.S.H.

High Hampton, N.C.,
W. S. Halsted to H.C. *18 July 1897.*

You really must not, for a moment, contemplate leaving us. If necessary, we shall have to create for Bloodgood a fellowship in Surgery or something of the sort, anything to make your position desirable & entirely satisfactory to you. If you would like to have the details worked out before you decide I shall be happy to do so at once, with the cooperation of yourself & Bloodgood. I have plenty of time for correspondence & deliberation in this country. I would ask you to take another vacation & pay me a visit so that we might discuss the matter fully, if the journey to this valley was not such a long and difficult one. We had hoped that you would lend us a very considerable hand in the teaching next winter & shall be much embarrassed if you conclude that you cannot stay. But your own interests are the only ones to be considered & I will not urge you to remain if you cannot believe that Bloodgood's presence in the Hospital will not interfere in the least with your progress. . . . Yrs sincerely W. S. HALSTED.

High Hampton,
W. S. Halsted to H.C. *21 July 1897.*

It is very kind of you who must be worked up to your limit to keep me so thoroughly informed as to the progress of things on our side of the House. I consider your suggestion for the ether convalescents an admirable one & hope that you may be able to institute the plan at once. Inasmuch as you are operating in the Amphitheatre you can easily do as you propose & in the Fall we can probably persuade Dr. Hurd to give us another room. I am grateful to you for such suggestions & hope that you will never hesitate to criticise freely what you consider existing evils. . . .

I heartily appreciate your kindness in attending to Körte's affair. I shall try to convince him that some of us are worse than others. I see that Credé has made the hit of his life, perhaps immortalized himself, by the promulgation of his views on silver in Surgery. He has quite forgotten that there is a Johns Hopkins Hosp. & dates his use of silver back to his in-utero term when his father employed nitrate of silver in Surgery. I am glad that you are interesting yourself in our "John" [the hospital orderly]. I shall write to Dr. Hurd at once about the food which is served to the orderlies. John told me about it just before I left town & I had hoped to speak to Dr. Hurd about it then. I think that John's salary should be increased & have several times spoken to Dr. Hurd about it: I shall make another effort on my return, but in the meantime should like to pay John $5. a month on my own account. Will you be kind enough to attend to this for me, & kindly find enclosed my cheque for $16.50–$1.50 to reimburse you for your outlay on Körte's behalf & the remainder for John, in 3 doses, p.r.n. If you can arrange for a long vacation for John I should be more than glad & would cheerfully compensate him for what he might lose in salary during his absence. I enjoy your letters very much & hope that you may find time to continue them. . . . Sincerely yrs W. S. HALSTED.

High Hampton,
W. S. Halsted to H.C. *29 July 1897.*

Dear Cushing The expression "old maids of both sexes" which amused you so much last spring I found the other day in Huxley's lecture on the *Origin of Species* (1860)—Can't you in return for this information send me something good to read? Perhaps you could order me a lot of stuff from the bookstores—Stevenson's *Ballads & Essays* (I have read his stories); anything very new in philosophy, & some trash & farcical stuff. I have loaded my trunks with nothing but heavy reading & I am tired of it for the moment—I have read all of Kipling's things, I believe, except some scattered poems etc. I don't care for blood & chivalry very much—My man is waiting for the mail so wishing you a happy & successful summer, I am yrs most sincerely, W. S. HALSTED.

W. S. Halsted to H.C. *4 August 1897.*

Dear Cushing It was truly a disgusting pity to lose your beautiful case of circular suture. You have the satisfaction of knowing that your peritoneal cavity was all right, but those who do not know you might look wise. I have had but one circular intestinal suture in Baltimore, I believe, & that was in a hopeless case, so considered. I need hardly tell you that I am in hearty sympathy with your efforts to correct some of our many bad habits. We have never had a man on the staff who understood the management of his assistants or, indeed, who had served in a well conducted hospital. It is a discouraging fact that good precedents are so often forgotten & bad ones seem to take such deep root. During the first 2 years of the Hospital I spent many hours in the wards trying to stimulate or develop in the internes a taste for neat dressings. Unfortunately one must have the proper anlage as well as be trained for these matters. I shall return to Baltimore towards the end of this month for I am uneasy about Mrs. Miller & should not like to make the mistake of postponing operation too long. Your letters give me a very clear idea of her condition & I am truly obliged to you for them. With kindest regards to the Millers & others, I am Yrs very sincerely, W. S. HALSTED.

Cushing's relations with Halsted continued cordial, as they did also with Bloodgood with whom H.C. shared the responsibilities of the surgical residency for nearly a full year. H.C. especially enjoyed, however, the intervals during which he was in sole charge. He writes on 7 August: "Everything prosperous here. I am having a good service and shall hate to give it up in the fall or whenever Bloodgood comes back. I am taking advantage of and living in the present. Something, perhaps the change of hands, has made the Surgical Service boom for this time of year." And on 15 August: "Dr. Halsted came up from the North Carolina mountains yesterday to operate on a case and fled the town again today. Too hot for him."

Cushing had been much interested in the syndrome of appendicitis from his contact with R. H. Fitz in Boston and his assistance at some of the first operations for the condition.[9] The new operation had been performed several times at the Hopkins prior to his advent in Baltimore, but the results had not been particularly encouraging and Halsted was still reluctant to recommend it. On 9 September 1897, H.C. had operated on a patient with a ruptured appendix

[9] Appendicitis as a pathological entity was first fully described by Reginald Heber Fitz of Boston in 1886 ("Perforating inflammation of the vermiform appendix; with special reference to its early diagnosis and treatment." Reprinted from the *Transactions of the Association of American Physicians,* 18 June 1886). The M.G.H. surgeons had at first been reluctant to operate, for this was still the transition period from antiseptic to aseptic technique. One of the first patients to have an inflamed appendix successfully removed was Dr. Alfred Worcester of Boston. The operation was performed by J. W. Elliot.

(J.H.H. No. 6913) who died ten days later of peritonitis. Consequently when he himself developed an acute colic in his lower abdomen and diagnosed appendicitis, he had misgivings, but he nevertheless implored Halsted to operate quickly. Just before going to the operating room (28 Sept. 1897), he left a note in the room of his friend C. N. B. Camac: "As I have often told patients, there is a certain amount of danger in all operations, similarly some danger in getting on to a street car—about even they are. *Quae cum ita sint* I write you a small missive giving you the privilege of distributing my things, books &c. among the Staff. 'Auf wiedersehen,' I hope." Although H.C. could not quite perform the operation himself, he wrote his own case history which is a model of directness and brevity:

Complaint. Appendicitis.

Past History uneventful as far as present illness is concerned. No previous attack at all resembling appendicular colic remembered. Patient has always been strong and well. For past year has had some periodic attack of indigestion due to poor food, and has been, during this time, apt to suffer from constipation.

Present Attack (Sunday 26 Sept., 22 hours before operation). Had been feeling perfectly well but tired from loss of sleep for a few nights. At 4 in the afternoon, after a wretched dinner, began to have paroxysmal attack of abdominal cramp. At first not severe and without definate localization. Took an 1/8 gr Calomel. "Cramps" became more severe and left some soreness during interval. By 9 P.M. pain was pretty constant with exacerbations and had become located below the umbilicus but localization was never very definate and never markedly in the right iliac fossa. Some tenderness was apparent at that time quite below and to the inside of McBurney's point. Bowels moved naturally about this time s̄ giving relief.

Pain continued quite severe during the night requiring morphia gr 1/10 at 5 A.M. *Tenderness* had become quite distinct at this time but not marked. It was appreciated rather as soreness when pressure used for its detection was removed. (As though pressure had driven out some congestion and relief of pressure allowed return of it. HWC) This same sensation was appreciated on evacuation of the bladder which caused no discomfort when distended.

8 A.M. (16 hours) Leucocytes counted by Dr. Strong. 13,000. Temp. 101. Cond. much as during night. Pain and slight tenderness alone. Absolutely no muscle spasm though patient found it impossible to straighten up when on his feet.

9 A.M. Consultation with Drs. Halsted and Osler. Operation not advised.

12 Noon. Leucocytosis. Dr. MacCallum. 23,000. T 101.6. Condition otherwise the same. Given 1/6 morphia by Dr. Halsted. *Vomiting.*

2 P.M. To operating room. Temp. had reached 104.2. This steady *elevation of temperature* (pulse not affected) without remission and the increasing number of *leucocytes* were practically the only definate guides to the local condition found, c̄ *vomiting. Pain* though severe was never either in site or severity characteristic. *Tenderness* never was marked or at the usual site. *Muscle spasm* was practically absent till a very short time before the operation. Bladder symptoms present (cf. site of appendix found at op.). Last *evacuation* before anaesthesia was quite painful. Abdomen was scaphoid during whole period. [Operative note was left to the surgeon!]

Subsequent History. Abdominal wound broke down on 5th day. Cultures. Infection probably superficial. Silver suture removed s̄ causing particular pain. Lower ½ of wound broken down subcutaneously and irrigated with HgCl through a small opening. Began to take solid food; no further abdominal symptoms (6th day). Out of bed; wearing abdominal support (10th day).

THE JOHNS HOPKINS HOSPITAL.

NAME Cushing

Complaint – Appendicitis

Past History uneventful as far as present illness is concerned. No previous attack at all resembling appendicular colic remembered. Patient has been always strong and well. For past year has had some gradual attack of indigestion due to poor food, and has been, during this time, apt to suffer from constipation.

Present Attack (Sunday Sept. 26. 22 hours before operation)
Has been feeling perfectly well but tired from loss of sleep for a few nights. At 4 in the afternoon, after a wretched dinner, began to have paroxysmal attacks of abdominal cramp. At first not severe and without definite localization. Took an ⅛ gr. Calomel. "Cramps" became more severe and left some soreness during interval.
By 9 P.M. pain was pretty constant with exacerbations and had become localized below the umbilicus but localization was never very definite and never markedly in the right iliac fossa. Some tenderness was apparent at this time quite below and to the inside of McBurney's point.
Bowels moved naturally about this time s̄ giving relief.
Pain continued quite severe during the night requiring morphia gr 1/10 at 5 a.m. Tenderness had become quite distinct at this time but not markedly. It was appreciated

point

A CASE OF APPENDICITIS

H.C.'s clinical history of his own case of 27 September 1897

Discharged (17 Oct. 1897). A sinus persists in the centre of cicatrix. Paralysis of that part of right rectus between incision and median line. Considerable soreness on pressure on both sides of incision. All reflex acts aided by abdominal muscles as sneezing, coughing, blowing nose, defecation &c cause pain in wound. Standing without abdominal support not s̄ great discomfort.

This somewhat trying episode was eased by many evidences of friendship and affection. Brother Ned came on from Cleveland shortly after the operation, and Halsted, Bloodgood, and Osler kept the family fully informed. The ever-gracious and thoughtful Richard P. Strong, then a surgical house officer, had written to H.C.'s mother:

Johns Hopkins Hospital,
R. P. Strong to B.M.C. *29 September 1897.*

My dear Mrs. Cushing: Although quite unknown to you I am taking the liberty of writing you a line about your son. I have just come from him and he has given me your address. Dr. Bloodgood with whom I have just been talking and under whose care, together with that of Dr. Halsted, your son is, tells me I may write that everything is favorable and that he regards him as entirely out of danger. I thought it might comfort you to know this from us. Please accept my sympathy at being separated from your son during his sickness and for the anxiety which his illness must have caused you—but rest assured that he has every comfort and attention we can give. Very sincerely, RICHARD PEARSON STRONG.

By way of introducing myself may I say that I am one of your son's assistants on the surgical staff here.

And soon there were pencilled notes from the patient himself:

2 October 1897.

Dear Father Everything very prosperous hereabouts. No symptoms whatever at present and hope not to have to stay in bed the usual full time. Everyone most good to me. My room full of flowers and good wishes. Halsted wants me to take a couple of months off duty when I get up. I think it would be a good chance to get in a solid crack at German and get a vacation at the same time. I should like very much to get on one of these North German Lloyd steamers and go right over were it not so lonesome. What say you.

7 October 1897.

Dear Mother Beautiful weather—an easy convalescence—kind friends—plenty to eat, read, &c. The time passes very quickly. I am so well that they have taken off my special nurse which means little more than that I have no one now to hand me the many little things I want. . . . School has opened with 70 new students, incl. 12 women "bad luck to 'em" and their patron saint Mrs. Garrett. I believe in it but little. It's a bad time of year to be laid up when things are just starting out but it's the fortune of war and we must make the best of it.

Already Cushing had become a great favorite with his patients on the wards at Hopkins. "What I really wanted to say," wrote one, "was that as I went from bed to bed I used to hear such things as this —'The doctor was certainly kind tonight and I really minded the pain much less,' or 'It would be so different if the doctor were not patient with me,' or as another old body said, 'If the doctor comes down to say goodnight, I am sure to sleep better.'" The children on his ward sent H.C. some flowers during his convalescence from the appendectomy, and he responded in poetry—the only verse, as far as is known, that H.C. committed to paper. It ran:

DEAR CHILDREN—

To pay up for his many sins
In cutting deep holes through your skins—
And tieing you to Bradford frames
And other things which have no names—
Dr. "Cushong" took some "Efur."

II

He screamed and made a dreadful fuss,
And wrung his hands and made a muss
Of everything in reach. " 'Cause why?"
Just 'Cause. It was quite wrong to cry
For nothing more than "Efur."

III

They took him down upon a truck
Like any one of you, whose luck
That day might have been ill. "Dear me,"
He cried, "Quite scared am I." You see—
Like you he feared the "Efur."

IV

He had to breathe it just as you
Have done and slept and never knew
A thing until at last, awake, he found
Miss "Sherring" there, and safe and sound
He'd come out from his "Efur."

V

And now he thanks you one and all
From Mary short to Claud so tall
For those pink roses, a delight
They were, so sweet and fresh they quite
Make up for taking "Efur."

Although popular with his patients, H.C. was a stern taskmaster and he did not always court the favor of his nurses. At a Christmas party at the hospital Mrs. Max Brödel recalls that one who had chafed under his criticism in the operating room perpetrated the following:

"C" is for Cushing
So cussedly clever
He can be polite,
But he hardly is ever.

"C" is for Cushing
So cleverly cusséd
If he ever gets sick,
He will never be nusséd.

His convalescence was also brightened by the following notes from Welch:

5 October 1897.

Dear Sir, Upon recommendation of the Medical Faculty you have been appointed by the Trustees for one year Instructor in Surgery with a compensation of $100. Yours very truly, WILLIAM H. WELCH, Dean.

5 October 1897.

My dear Dr. Cushing In sending you this official notice I wish to congratulate you upon the appointment. Above all I congratulate you upon the successful result of the operation, about which I have been kept informed. I hope that your convalescence will be speedy and that after a good vacation you will be as vigorous as ever. It is well that you have said good riddance to that appendix of yours. Yours sincerely, WILLIAM H. WELCH.

On 11 October he wrote his father:

Up in a wheel chair today. Feeling well enough to go to work tomorrow. Have taken a few steps and will get my feet in a few days. I feel the need of getting to work as soon as possible. They have given me the Resident's place with the usual salary and an Instructorship in Surgery in the School with $100[00] per annum much to my gratification. I will not take the two months and shall consequently give up the Germany trip for the present. I ought to be able to fix things so as to get away by the first of next week and will look for you sometime the latter part of this [week?] if you feel able to come on. I shall be very glad to see you and have you see what the J.H.H. is like.

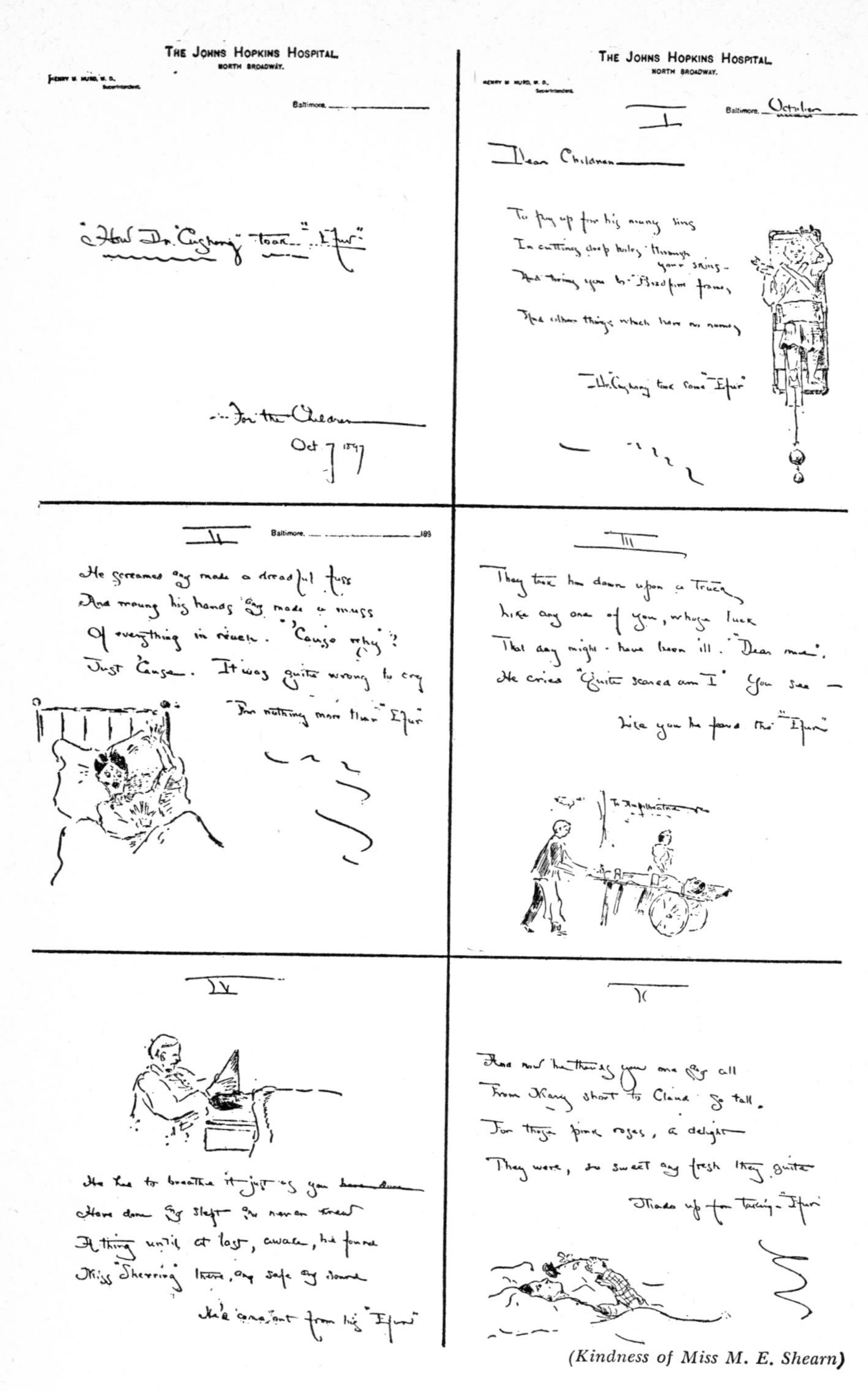

THE JOHNS HOPKINS HOSPITAL
NORTH BROADWAY.
HENRY M. HURD, M.D., Superintendent.
Baltimore, ________

"How Dr. "Cushong" took "Efur""

—For the Children
Oct 7 1897

THE JOHNS HOPKINS HOSPITAL
NORTH BROADWAY.
HENRY M. HURD, M.D., Superintendent.
Baltimore, October

I

Dear Children—

To pay up for his many sins
In cutting deep holes through your skins—
And tiring you by "Bread from frames"
And other things which have no names
Dr. Cushong took some "Efur"

II

Baltimore, ________189

He screamed and made a dreadful fuss
And moving his hands and made a muss
Of everything in reach. "Cause why"?
Just 'Cause. It was quite wrong to cry
For nothing more than "Efur"

III

They took him down upon a truck,
Like any one of you, whose luck
That day might have been ill. "Dear me",
He cried "Quite scared am I" You see—
Like you he feared the "Efur"

IV

He had to breathe it just as you ~~have done~~
Have done and slept and never knew
A thing until at last, awake, he found
Miss "Sherring" there, and safe and sound
He'd come out from his "Efur"

V

And now he thanks you one and all
From Mary short to Clara so tall,
For those pink roses, a delight—
They were, so sweet and fresh they quite
Made up for taking "Efur"

(Kindness of Miss M. E. Shearn)

HOW DR. "CUSHONG" TOOK "EFUR"

By 17 November H.C. was well enough to go to Camac's wedding in New York and on the 21st he writes his mother from Baltimore that he is "gradually drifting back to work." Shortly, he is again in the midst of things.

Johns Hopkins Hospital,
H.C. to H.K.C. *1 December 1897.*

We are very busy here. I have just been operating on a gunshot wound of the abdomen—four perforations—good case but 24 hours old and I fear too late. Am standing the work very well. Busy with a clinic of students every morning for two hours. . . .

12 December 1897.

I am quite busy. The proof of my Haematomyelia article has been here on my desk untouched for several days. I don't think much of it now that I have it ready for publication. I hope it is worth it. My days are crowded with clinical things much like old M.G.H. days plus a greater responsibility and more operating. I don't think it's the best sort of rut for me partly because it's the easiest one. A little more study and laboratory work such as I had last year is what I need most.

My gunshot man made an uninterrupted recovery. I have looked up the house cases and find only three recoveries. All were in high perforations. Interesting in that possibly the microorganisms from high in the tract are less virulent. A good chance for some experimental work on dogs. . . .

1898

Although there is little mention of Osler during Cushing's first two years at the Hopkins, his influence and that of others in the School had clearly begun to show itself in H.C.'s newly developed interest in books, bookplates, and the acquisition of a library. His bibliophilic taste, fortunately for him, was encouraged by his father, and throughout this and the succeeding years books are constantly mentioned in his letters. During his convalescence from his appendicitis the opportunity to read appears to have whetted his appetite, and one of his first interests on recovery was in obtaining a suitable bookplate. He had begun systematically by first collecting representative bookplates; he then proceeded to design one of his own carrying the family crest and the Cushing motto, *Virtute et numine.*

New York,
Dodd Mead & Company to H.C. *21 December 1897.*

Dear Sir: In reply to your favor of the 20th, we would say that we duly received your letter, containing suggestions and sketch for your Book Plate, and forwarded these promptly to our artist, who promised to let us have a sketch to submit to you before Christmas. We expect to receive it some time this week and will mail it to you just as soon as it is received. Yours very truly, DODD, MEAD & COMPANY.

H.C. to H.K.C. *26 December 1897.*

Here is the artist's sketch of the book plate after a rough design I made. Do you approve of it? There are a few minor changes I would like to make, e.g. a less jaunty position for the crest, some spots on the hands, etc. I think he has done quite well. The medical insignia I think he has made very unobtrusive. This is a Merry Christmas gift. Return it with criticisms please.

H.K.C. to H.C. *28 December 1897.*

The book plate sketch meets with great approval from all who have seen it, as almost all have. The general effect can hardly be improved. Regarding your suggestion of the uppish location of the crest, I would ask if it does not relieve what otherwise might be the too formal look of the general parallelogram. The crest, with the coat of arms, however, could be carried a little to the left, and dropped a little, as well, where it would not encroach on the blank left for inscription more than at present. Personally, I do not quite like the skull, unobtrusively as it has been managed. Ned however likes it, and you and he are the ones I should like suited.

How would the Caduceus of Mercury strike you in place of the skull (the ex libris fold crossing over the large loop of the entwined serpents), or being worked into the opposite lower corner from the coat of arms? The ovoid letters about the caduceus enclosed are not a part of it, and could be used, or not, or modified as preferred. Ned's diploma is dated 1888—not 1887 the year he went into the hospital.

H.K.C. to H.C. *9[45] o'clock p.m.*

I posted you a hurried line at tea time anent the book plate. Some further reflection leads to this further communication. Would it not be well to omit skull and snake, leaving the sketch otherwise just as it is, unless the initials can be easily introduced. Of course I would not introduce the Caduceus either. . . .

The Cushing motto is "virtute et numine," by valor and divine aid. This, or any other, better liked, might be selected. I would like you to order such a plate that might serve us all, perhaps, acceptably, at my expense. Of the bookplate I presume 1500 prints would be needed for immediate and future use. If you *present* the plate, I will pay for the printing of that no. of the impressions. . . .

H.C. to H.K.C. *27 February 1898.*

Book plate submitted to you for further suggestions or approval with Dodd Mead's note. Let me know soon what are your wishes about it. You see I have only ordered a medical one. . . .

There is no indication in this correspondence that either father or son knew who the Dodd Mead engraver was. It turned out that the book plate had been entrusted to Edwin Davis French, one of the most celebrated of all bookplate designers and engravers; and the Cushing plate, signed "E.D.F." is listed as No. 115 in the official history of French's work. Incidentally, it is one of the few designed by an owner.[10] "D.C. 1789" and "E.C. 1824" on the left perpendicular limb of the plate refer respectively to David and Erastus Cushing. On a later impression done in Boston from the original plate, "K.W.C. 1919" was added for Kirke Cushing, son of Henry Platt Cushing; later still "E.H.C." was also added for Edward Harvey

[10] *Edwin Davis French. A memorial: his life his art.* New York, privately printed, 1908, p. 50.

Cushing who graduated in 1923 from Harvard. The bookplate, usually signed, gradually found its way into the majority of H.C.'s books. In later years the process of pasting them in proved too time-consuming and for a long period the plates were put into only the more prized of his possessions, for it was not a task he delegated. Eventually in New Haven a small "etiquette" was made and since it was a gummed label and did not require a paste pot to put it in place, it came to be used almost to the exclusion of the larger plate.

Whether or not the bookplate was responsible for a quickening interest in collecting, incidental references to books begin to appear more frequently in letters home.

H.C. to B.M.C. *26 December 1897.*

Old Virginia is delightful. I hope I can find spare moments to read it. Some mental telegraphy told you that I was in need of socks and handkerchiefs. I was sent some very nice books indeed. Mrs. Carter sent me Dr. Holmes' life and letters—and Will and Carolyn's "Ambroise Paré" has been longed for for some time. . . .

H.C. to H.K.C. *5 February 1898.*

Many thanks for the Trousseau. I have read none of him and doubt my ability to do so but I am glad to number it among my possessions. There is a certain satisfaction in owning some books even though unread. The twenty dollars was very welcome. It will take me on a trip to Savannah by boat some time this month. I think I need to get away for a while. We have had a couple of deaths from Streptococcus infection (not my cases however) which have knocked me out so that I lie awake and see chains of streptococcus devils on all sides. It's hard to get away. When people are sick I have to live with them and when they get well I don't feel like pulling out, consequently I stay along. . . . I have heard nothing from the book plate since I sent it on for improvements but hope to soon.

20 February 1898.

. . . I understand that there is to be a medical library in Cleveland to be located on Prospect Street. Splendid thing and very much needed. I hope they will get a good collection and good librarian. . . .

Curious accident in Havanna was it not? The Maine might have selected a more suitable place for such a catastrophe if she is responsible for it. A fearful loss of life certainly, but less horrible than the losses from fire like the Paris Bazaar and such where people have time to become frightened and fight for life.

27 May 1898.

Have you a set of Darwin's Works? I have cast my eye on one of Appleton's sets which are most attractive complete, half russia 15 volumes for 36.00. Shall I get them for my shelves and read them for my brain or are yours complete and enough for the family? Fine day today.

In the midst of correspondence about books, the bookplate, and the "Maine," news came from Ned of the arrival of another male Cushing—Edward Harvey, better known from the day he was born as "Pat."

H.C. to H.K.C. *Baltimore, 21 March 1898.*

. . . What good news it is for 967 Prospect Street! I am delighted of course and am anxious to get home and see the youngster; "Pat" I believe he is dubbed. I will enclose a card and beg you send some flowers for me to Melanie, unless she is surrounded by a bower already. We are very hard at work and I have three half written papers on hand and am driven nearly distracted with the littles of life. The house is very full and I must operate constantly to keep the work down. Many very interesting cases; Dr. Halsted appears seldom, as he is preparing a paper for the American Surgical Association. I sent the book-plate on to Dodd, Mead & Co. despite its snakiness; we hope to hear from them soon. Dr. Halsted told me that he had sent to Germany for a set of the Transactions of the German Surgical Congress with all the discussions in full, which he had seen advertised for sale. I was aghast at the announcement and told him I would like them very much and would have to let you give them to me for a birthday present, which somewhat amused him. They really constitute a surgical library in themselves. . . .

Then came the bill for the bookplates (4 April): "Here is the huge bill. I hope it has been worth it. Everyone hereabouts admires it immensely. Dr. H[alsted] I think is going to have a plate made."

During his years in Baltimore H.C. records that he entered the Halsted house only four or five times. But a Halsted dinner was an occasion.

H.C. to Katharine S. Crowell *7 January 1898.*

Glad to hear from you. I went to dine at the Chief's last night—a most interesting dinner, truly Chesapeake. I'll try and remember the courses—

I. Caviar and thin slices of dry toast as an hors d'oeuvre

II. Bouillon

III. Roast oysters—huge ones—brought in on a great dish of silver, an old hunting prize won by Mrs. H's grandfather in the palmy days of the South. We were supposed to help ourselves and had to open the oysters instead of having the Mädchen do it. They *were* good. (The big dish was planted right in the center of the table.)

IV. A terrapin stew made in a chafing dish from the real $50.00 bird picked out of a lot by the Professor himself and boiled and skinned and picked by him before the dinner.

V(a). An asparagus course I forgot.

V. A wonderful quail arrangement with a whole bird in the middle of a block of a salty quail jelly. Also a slice of paté de foie gras.

VI. Omelette soufflé, I believe. Very delicious at all events.

VII. An ice served in most curious and quaint dishes.

VIII. Crackers and Camembert cheese.

IX. Fruit, candy et cetera.

Many rare wines at intervals appeared. Some old Madeira 60 years old, think of it. Also from Grandfather Hampton's cellar. Lastly coffee made in the library. The berries were picked out and roasted that afternoon. Ground in a quaint old brass arrangement before us and brought to boil over the fire [sketch of the pot]. I never tasted coffee before. I wish you could have been there.

Then there was a litter of five 6-weeks-old dachshunds [on display!] with their father and mother who came from some famous kennel in the Black Forest where some one of the Chief's German admirers lives. They have pedigrees a mile long. I wanted to steal one to send to you. They were jet black glossy little fellows with brown faces and paws and not a white hair. The mother is a prize winner named Madie. I started this hurried scrawl to you early in the evening. I got called to the ward and it's now past midnight. Life is not a bed of roses. . . . Goodnight, from your affectionate but very tired HARVEY W. C.

In February 1898 he gave another vivid description of a visit to the Halsted household:

H.C. to B.M.C. *20 February 1898.*

Kate appeared at the Goodwillies' Wednesday. I took her over to the Halsteds to call and see the dogs yesterday. The Chief and his wife are certainly queer people. A great magnificent cold stone house full of rare old furniture, clocks, pictures and what not in topsy turvy condition, cold as a stone and most unlivable. The dog room upstairs and the Chief's library alone have fires in them. Such independent people. Mrs. H. met us or received us in the 'dog room' in a large dirty butchers apron. Such a blunt outspoken plain creature you never saw. They are so peculiar, eccentric, so unlike other people yet so interesting doubtless because of their oddities that one is inclined to shelve his thoughts about them alongside of those of people from fiction—Dickens perhaps. She was a daughter of Gen'l Wade Hampton, perhaps you know. Used to be in charge of the operating room here at the J.H.H. The Professor himself is doubtless the best man in his specialty in the country which of course makes being his slave a most valuable experience. I am very fond of and admire him immensely.

I went to the Yale dinner last Tuesday but found that I was down for a speech and wisely beat a retreat before coffee time. I don't care to speechify unprepared.

But despite books and other interludes, clinical work was always uppermost in his mind. One of his early contributions (which incidently indicates an association with Osler) had to do with a splenectomy. Cushing is credited with having been the first in this country to remove the spleen for Banti's disease. A farmer from Fincastle, Virginia, had come to the Hopkins Hospital 9 March 1898 complaining of recurrent gastro-intestinal hemorrhage for some nine years and Osler made the diagnosis of Banti's disease and recommended splenectomy. The operation which was carried out a few days later[11] has been listed as the twelfth case of Banti's disease cured by splenectomy, the first dating back to Spencer Wells in 1851. The patient's progress was followed in the course of the next forty years through the exchange of letters, and in 1928 Cushing congratulated his former patient on his fourth marriage.

In April Cushing took a short and solitary holiday at Old Point

[11] See "Two cases of splenectomy for splenic anemia. A clinical lecture 21 January 1920, to third-year students, telling an old story." By Harvey Cushing. And: "A report on the pathologic changes in splenic anemia (written in 1900, but not published)." By W. G. MacCallum. *Archives of Surgery,* July 1920, *1,* 1-22. See also: "Unusual spleen cases." By A. P. Jones. *Annals of Surgery,* June 1939, *109,* 960-961. I am indebted to Hugh H. Trout for giving further information concerning the case. Dr. Trout had followed the patient for many years at Dr. Cushing's request.

Comfort, but he was back within a week and reported on 14 April: "We have been operating today for a batch of Naval surgeons, doing intestinal sutures on dogs." Apparently his tendency to disappear into the laboratory caused him some trouble as is suggested by a crisp letter at this time from the Superintendent of the Hopkins Hospital:

Johns Hopkins Hospital,
Henry M. Hurd to H.C. *11 August 1898.*

Dear Dr. Cushing: I write to suggest that some more orderly and definite arrangement be made for the efficient administration of the surgical department. I have tried to see you this morning but have not succeeded in finding you. There seems to be at present a lack of responsibility *somewhere* for the routine care of patients. For example, yesterday a surgical patient in Ward C needed immediate attention about 3 o'clock and although every effort was made to find a surgeon, no one could be found until finally Dr. Mitchell, who was not in the service, was secured, and no surgeon was found until after 6 o'clock. There should be someone constantly on call in view of accident cases and emergencies. I write to ask that you will kindly arrange for such service. It is hardly sufficient excuse for a resident officer to claim that he was engaged in laboratory work, and hence could not be found. Very truly yours, HENRY M. HURD, Supt.

On the back of this letter is noted: " Poor Hurd after a very bad breakfast. The occasion of some warm words between H.M.H. and H.C. and subsequent apologies."

The Spanish-American hostilities were naturally very much on everyone's mind, and even before declaration of war inroads were being made on the Hopkins staff.

H.C. to B.M.C. *20 April 1898.*

This war is getting to be a serious business. Finney is Surgeon General in the state militia and gets called off in a day or two supposedly with the Maryland troops to Cuba. This curtails our house staff very much. I wish Cuba could be towed out to sea and sunk. The Professor is away in New Orleans at a surgical meeting so that I have the house on my hands and am rather busy.

. . . My correspondence is large and often of necessity neglected till evenings when with the help of a stenographer I turn off a large batch of it. Stenographers, however good they may be, on occasion are the ruination of personal correspondence. One forgets how to think through the point of a pen and feels more at home tramping up and down the room. Old patients, friends, doctors, all have to be corresponded with *ad nauseam.*

In the midst of the Spanish War agitation and while Halsted was attending the meeting in New Orleans, Mrs. Halsted was seriously injured, suffering a fractured pelvis and severe concussion when her horse ran away. H.C. went to the house and seems to have taken charge (we find him writing about the accident on 23 April to Kate Crowell with Halsted's quill pen) and to have remained in residence until Halsted returned. Mrs. Halsted recovered, and although an inarticulate woman she was particularly grateful to those who attended her.

1201 Eutaw Place, Baltimore,
June 1898.

Mrs. W. S. Halsted to H.C.

My dear Dr. Cushing, Ever since my smash up I have said at intervals to "the Prof." I wish I could have an opportunity to thank Dr. Cushing as well as the other M.D.'s for patching me together so successfully & starting me on the road to recovery. Yet this afternoon I never alluded to the subject.

I hope you will not think that I do not appreciate your kindness & the mere fact that we were interested in discussing other matters is no excuse. I feel of course that a great deal of my prompt & happy recovery is due to the very prompt & skillful attention that I received & though the war & Cuba were of interest I should have realized that gratitude is always a thing that it is well to express. Hoping that I may see you before I leave for the summer when I may have a chance to thank you better, I am very sincerely, CAROLINE HALSTED.

Local Anesthesia

While Halsted was away from the clinic during the autumn of 1897, there were several operative deaths in the clinic from improper etherization. Students of the Medical School, as in Boston, were often called upon to hold the ether sponge with little knowledge of the hazards involved. While an assistant resident, H.C. could not reorganize their practices with regard to anesthesia, so he began to experiment with block anesthesia produced by cocaine infiltration of suitable nerve trunks, a procedure which Halsted himself had been largely responsible for introducing but which for many reasons he had abandoned in his own clinic. H.C.'s first major procedure appears to have been an amputation at the shoulder in a boy with a sarcoma of the humerus, and for the purpose the whole brachial plexus was successfully blocked. Later, he did an amputation at the hip, and finally developed a successful local infiltration technique for hernia. The latter procedure formed the basis of an important early paper on cocaine anesthesia first communicated at the Johns Hopkins Medical Society on 8 May 1898.[12]

Since Halsted's early work on local anesthesia from which Cushing received his initial stimulus is not widely known,[13] it seems proper to include here a letter which Halsted wrote late in life to Osler describing the circumstances surrounding his introduction of local anesthesia:

[12] "Cocaine anaesthesia in the treatment of certain cases of hernia and in operations for thyroid tumors." *Johns Hopkins Hospital Bulletin,* August 1898, *9,* 192-193. See also: "The employment of local anaesthesia in the radical cure of certain cases of hernia, with a note upon the nervous anatomy of the inguinal region." *Annals of Surgery,* 1900, *31,* 1-34; and: "Observations upon the neural anatomy of the inguinal region relative to the performance of herniotomy under local anaesthesia." *Johns Hopkins Hospital Bulletin,* 1900, *11,* 58-64.

[13] The best account with many of the relevant citations (but omitting Cushing's pioneer paper) is to be found in *Surgical papers by William Stewart Halsted,* Baltimore, Johns Hopkins Press, 1924, vol. 1, pp. 167-178.

High Hampton, Cashiers, N.C.,
W. S. Halsted to Sir William Osler *23 August 1918.*

Dear Osler, Thank you for your kind permission to reproduce your cut of the famous case of arterio-venous fistula. I wish that I had known more about the subject when your patient was in Baltimore. You will, I believe, be interested in my little paper on the subject which should soon appear in *Surg., Gyn. & Obstetrics.*

Yes, I published 3 or 4 little papers in 1884-5 in the *N.Y. Med. Jour.* on the subject of cocaine anaesthesia. They are not creditable papers for I was not in good form at the time. But I anticipated all of Schleich's work by about 6 years (or five). We discovered that very mild solutions & even water would produce anaesthesia if properly injected—injected so as to produce distension & anemia of the tissues. We also injected all the accessible nerves in the body—sciatic, internal pudic, brachial plexus, inferior dental, etc. I did not know until 1914 that Richard Hall of N.Y. (son of Rev. John D. Hall) my 1st assistant at Roosevelt Hosp. had described an operation which we performed together in my house in N.Y. A rich & influential woman permitted me in 1885 to excise her inferior dental nerve (Paravicini's method) for the trigeminal neuralgia, under cocaine. I injected the nerve opposite or rather above its entrance into the canal before incising the mucous membrane. On exposing the nerve I clamped it with a specially designed broad (1.5 cm.) forceps to insure the excision of a long piece. The final snip of the scissors through the nerve divided a large artery, probably the internal maxillary. The patient's mouth filled with blood as if poured in by cupfuls. Tom McBride, whose patient she was, rushed out of the room, not wishing, as he told me afterwards, to be present at the death. Gauze plugging finally arrested the hemorrhage. The patient was put in my bed & 2 trained nurses summoned. For 2 nights I slept in the same room & then transferred her to my service at the Presbyterian Hosp. She made a good recovery. It is odd that I happened in 1914 to be attending a meeting in Berlin of the Deutsche Ges. f. Chirurgie when this case was referred to by Rehn. I asked him how he knew of it. He said that Richard Hall had published it. I have since then seen this case mentioned in German articles. Apropos of this, it interests me to recall a visit I made to Vienna in the autumn of 1885, when I showed Wölfler (Billroth's 1st assistant) how to use cocaine. He had declared that it was useless in surgery. But before I left Vienna he published an enthusiastic article in one of the daily papers on the subject. It did not, however, occur to him to mention my name. Having occasion to have a tooth attended to by Thomas, the famous American dentist of Vienna, I showed him how to inject the inf. dental nerve from within the mouth. He became so enthusiastic on the subject that he requested me to inject the inferior nerves of 2 assistants whose teeth he filled while they were insensitive. Corning's book[14] on cocaine anaesthesia was based almost entirely on my work. He was a student of mine & followed my work with cocaine closely. One of my papers was entitled "A report of about 2000 operations with cocaine" (approximate title).[15] The list included some major operations such as amputations, exsections of joints, excision of axillary contents.

[14] Corning, J. L. *Local anaesthesia in general medicine and surgery, being the practical application of the author's recent discoveries.* New York, D. Appleton & Co., 1886, 103 pp.

[15] Halsted, W. S. "Practical comments on the use and abuse of cocaine; suggested by its invariably successful employment in more than a thousand minor surgical operations." *New York Medical Journal,* 1885, *43,* 294-295. ["To be concluded"—but it never was, owing to Halsted's illness.]

You will perhaps recall that when the J.H.H. opened we were employing local anaesthesia much as we do today. This was some years in advance of Schleich. Poor Hall & 2 other assistants of mine acquired the cocaine habit in the course of our experiments on ourselves—injecting nerves. They all died without recovering from the habit.

I might mention that we discovered the effect of anemia in prolonging almost indefinitely the anaesthetic action of cocaine. Consequently we usually employed the Esmarch bandage when operating on the extremities. You will, I fear, regret having asked the question which has brought forth this rambling reply. Woolsey, Hotchkiss, Walter James & Christian Herter were students of mine at the time we were making these experiments & took part in them. Will you give our love to Lady Osler. Ever yours, W. S. HALSTED.

Cushing was not aware of all this when in Baltimore, and when Welch told him after Halsted's death, H.C. reproached himself for having been so impatient with Halsted in the early days. As MacCallum has said: "Those early victims were quite innocent of any knowledge of its [cocaine's] habit-forming character, and secondly, he [Halsted], almost alone of the many who fell under its influence, conquered it through superhuman strength and determination and came back to a splendid life of achievement."

* * * * *

H.C. managed to squeeze in several holidays during the summer of 1898. In June he and McCrae spent ten days at Fredericksburg, Virginia, where "War with Cuba seems most remote and evidently these long-whiskered Virginians have as little ken of wearisome current events as we." More evident was the spirit of the Civil War and while at Fredericksburg he asked his father to send him the Civil War volume describing the campaign there. During mid-July he was in Boston, after which he gave his mother a racy account of his recent travels:

Pittsfield, Massachusetts,
H.C. to B.M.C. *18 July 1898.*

Dear Ma, I have been gadding about so promiscuously and been so occupied that I have hardly known what minute is gwine be de nex! I spent a very profitable and most enjoyable week in Boston after a very brief stay in Providence. I stayed with Codman and spent my time hospitaling and renewing acquaintances. Everyone was most cordial and it was a delight to be in "The Hub" again. Sunday and Saturday on the North Shore with the Goodwillies and some friends of Codman at Manchester next door to the Boardmans. I am at present enroute for New York and have promised to stop over 24 hours with the Chapins in Lenox. My train is late or I would have been able to go up town and see Mrs. Kellogg. I am very hot and covered with cinders and have but 15 minutes before the Lenox train goes out. Possibly it's time I spent 15 minutes with my Ma. You are far enough away not to mind the grime which covers me. I will be in New York the rest of the week doing much the sort of things which occupied me in Boston. Hope to stay with Grove Atterbury. This should bring me home Tuesday or Wednesday of next week for a brief stay.

Katharine Stone Crowell

Katharine Stone Crowell, the daughter of William and Mary Benedict Crowell, was also of Western Reserve pioneering stock. She had grown up in Cleveland on Prospect Street (No. 937), a few blocks away from the Cushing household at 786. Harvey and "Kate" had known one another since early childhood. Kate was an attractive and high-spirited girl with a ready wit and deep-running loyalties. Her outward gaiety was tempered by steadiness, love of family, wide reading, and an eastern schooling—and she seemed to understand Harvey better than he did himself. Mr. A. F. Harvey, H.C.'s cousin, recalls that during the summers when the boys at Cleveland were home from eastern colleges there was a gay round of dances, picnics, and boating parties, and that Harvey and Kate were always among the gayest and most lively members of this younger set. Miss Mary Goodwillie has given a vivid description of these summer festivities:

> . . . Cleveland, being a lake city, has a pleasant summer climate and in the '80's and '90's trips to New England or the Adirondacks were not as customary as they have since become. Many of the town houses had wide lawns and deep "back-yards" and piazzas where young people would gather in the evenings for "porch parties." One of these favorite meeting places was the home of Mr. W. J. Boardman on Euclid Avenue in what is now the business section of the city. Here baseball and tennis parties made many an afternoon's entertainment. Then there were the country places on the Lake shore within an easy street car ride from town. "Breezy Bluff," where the Crowell family spent every summer, and Brightwood, the hospitable home of Mrs. Edward Williams, were the spots where a group of young people most often gathered. It was a group that had grown up together—Perry and Al Harvey, Bert McBride, Ben Crowell, Will Rhodes, Irvin and Abram Garfield, Al Chisholm and Lew Smith, and their Yale visitors, were some of the boys; while the girls included Kate Crowell, Ray and Reba Williams, Melanie Harvey, Mary Goodwillie and her sister, "Harry"; also Josephine and Nina Boardman, and with them often a visiting belle from Farmington School.
>
> Social life was much simpler then than now but none the less gay and happy. Harvey's brothers and sister Alice were shy and retiring, but he entered easily into all the youthful pleasures around him, and was always a central figure in any gathering and extremely popular with everyone. His quick wit and amusing ways brought many a laugh then as they did all through his life. He was a graceful dancer and greatly enjoyed the summer dances at the Country Club. Tennis also figured prominently in his life at this time and he kept an expertness that enabled him to defeat some of his most adept young assistants even in his later years, when moving freely had become more difficult for him.
>
> Other vacation pleasures were trips up the Great Lakes as far as Duluth. These were made on the large iron ore barges which had officers' quarters accommodating most comfortably the small parties that were made up each summer. Another vacation feature was "Uncle Ed Williams'" house parties at the Castalia Fishing Club near Sandusky. Harvey was nearly always a member of both these expeditions. Young people then naturally sang when they were together and music was a great part of the summer evenings, led by the musical members of the Williams family. Long years afterwards, when Harvey and

Perry Harvey got together they would spontaneously break into the old songs, and vie with each other in their memory of tunes and words.

It would be a mistake to look upon Cushing, as many did in later life, as a man whose time was wholly restricted to work. It is true that he found it difficult to unbend in later years with those who had not been close to him in his youth and this is particularly well illustrated by the friendly attitude which he retained to all his Yale contemporaries as opposed to those of the same vintage at Harvard.

By the summer of 1890 H.C. was more often with Kate Crowell than the others, and in November 1891 she sent him her picture at his request. After the summer of 1892 they had reached an understanding, but no formal announcement of an engagement was made until ten years later. In February 1898 Kate came to Baltimore to stay with the Goodwillies. During this visit Harvey introduced her to the Halsteds and also to the Oslers, and in March, after she had returned to Cleveland, he brought things to a head by writing Mrs. Crowell, "Aunt Ca'line" as he called her, requesting her daughter's hand. He waited anxiously for four days for a reply, meanwhile writing six somewhat frenzied letters to Kate fearing (after four years working up to it) that he had acted too precipitately. On 12 March he was greatly relieved when he received a most gracious and warm-hearted reply: "Of all the attractive men I have known," Mrs. Crowell wrote, "there is no one to whom I could trust her as I can to you, and from this you must form my estimate of you for you've known how fond I have always been of you and your ways. . . . In taking her you may have to take me. Have you thought of that, though I do hope to spare you?" Formal announcement of their engagement was not made until February 1902. Meanwhile, during July 1898 we find them off with the Ned Cushings and Harvey's mother on a trip up the Great Lakes to Duluth. The amusing diary of the trip is designated "The initial journeying of Pat"—since Master Edward Harvey Cushing, aged four months, also accompanied them.

Pat makes the Captain's acquaintance

At noon Mother and Pat were persuaded to go. Pat was prepared for the worst. Mother fortified herself with a dozen black parasols and six small opera bonnets, a combination to delude the sun. We hied ourselves to the good steamer *Castalia* in the evening escorted by H.K.C. We found the boat in the black clutches of one Cuddy Mullen, who threatened to pour coal into her from midnight to morn: most distressing news to all but Pat, who had insinuated himself into the good graces and whiskers of a deep voiced pirate who guided us along a dark, shinbarking, precipitous ledge, between the Cuyahoga and Cuddy Mullen, and tumbled us into the side of his boat, for he was Captain Allen, our host for the voyage.

There follows a spirited description of Duluth:

Duluth was built originally on the bias and has since been boomed which resulted in its distribution up along the amphitheatre-like hillside where it remains scattered. There is a large church, a $400,000 High School & clock tower with Westminster chimes. Here is a bird's eye view of Duluth. It was on its way farther west but was wrecked and thrown up on the shore at the apex of the lake where it has remained. . . . We found a busy lot of people aboard & around the *Castalia* in the morning grimly shoveling out coal into whirring brown hoist buckets. Breakfast over we boarded a tug which took us, Pat and baggage, to town where we quartered ourselves at a barbarian caravansery, the Spaulding House, big, pretentious, uncomfortable.

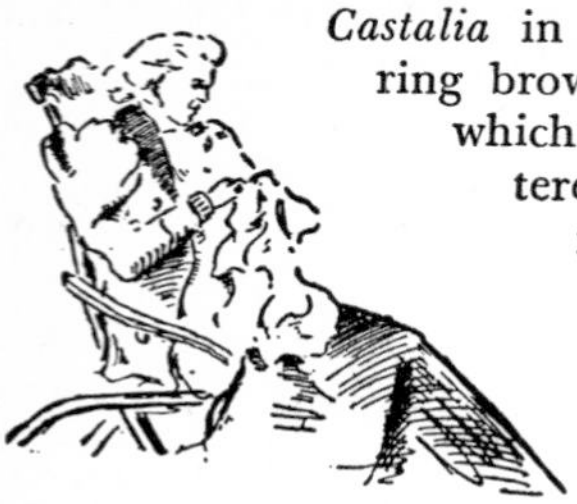

K.C.

Neddie and Melanie retire early: while Mother, Kate and I seek out the incline road and scoot up the hill to the pavillion where we get a fine moonlight view of the lake and St. Louis bay and see a few acts of a vaudeville performance which is not quite up to Mother's ideals though Kate and I are much amused. La danseuse Mother thought would have danced better if she did not kick. A Mr. Zicker did some parlor tricks and we departed & so to bed.

The trip to Duluth with Harvey's family brought Kate very much into the fold, and the prolonged courtship which followed unconsciously stimulated Harvey in his work—unconsciously but most powerfully—for he was now determined to rise to the top, not for himself alone, but to please the girl he loved so tenderly and with such fierce Victorian reserve. His letters (which reached her almost daily for many months) are those of a man with prodigious energies, all of which were now, by his own romantic spirit, concentrated on achieving the highest goal, for he constantly reiterated that he was working only for her.

* * * * *

The Spanish-American War gave Cushing his first contact with military medicine and surgery, and cases of typhoid perforation of the gut which he operated upon (several from the troops) formed the basis of two of his early papers.[16] The Maine had been sunk on 15 February—the night of his Yale Alumni dinner, but war was not declared until 25 April and Santiago de Cuba did not fall until 17 July (Manila fell 13 August). Late in August H.C. was called to meet a trainload of typhoid patients from the Fifth (Baltimore) Regiment who had been sent up from Alabama:

H.C. to Katharine S. Crowell — *The Johns Hopkins Hospital, 28 August, Sunday 4* P.M.

I got up at daybreak after four hours of sleep, struggled into some very old

[16] "Laparotomy for intestinal perforation in typhoid fever. A report of four cases, with a discussion of the diagnostic signs of perforation." *Johns Hopkins Hospital Bulletin,* November 1898, *9,* 257-269. Also: "Laparotomy for intestinal perforation in typhoid fever. A report of four cases occurring in 1898." *Johns Hopkins Hospital Reports,* 1900, *8,* 209-240.

clothes unbathed and unshaved, fortified myself with a cup of 'chicory' coffee in Ward C, lit a pipe and rumbled off in the shackely old borrowed ambulance which called here for me. We had not long to wait for the transportation train which backed down the long siding by the forlorn Calvert Street Station. All the police patrols, eight in number, the cross town hospital ambulances, the Maryland N.G. (National Guard *not* No good, very good in fact) Ambulance and some carriages with a large crowd of anxious and teary people were all kept away from the train which fortunately was accessable to me under Finney's wing. I never have, nor expect to see 150 such emaciated, wan, forlorn, ragged, dirty creatures as were carted in on that train of six old disreputable sleepers. It was enough to make a strong man weep. As one of them told me, "We are and have been rotting." Perhaps a hundred of them, so called convalescents, were furloughed and one by one tottered off from the train with their packs, gaunt, haggard, feeble. It would have wrung your heart. They did not even have carfare, many of them. And then the sick ones, big heavy fellows, their skins hot as a live coal, not sick long enough to have lost flesh and made carrying easy. . . . It took us two hours, but it was one of the greatest privaleges I have ever been granted. We could have done it all day and General Griggs thanked us with tears in his eyes. The train was foul beyond description. Imagine an old Pullman sleeper, with shabbiest of fittings, crowded with sick, many lower berths with two people, dirty clothes & equipment scattered about everywhere, no thought whatever of keeping the patients clean, and pans & cups & old hats & shoes and dirt and haggard bearded young faces.

The next day he went down to Alabama for another trainload.

H.C. to H.K.C. *29 August 1898.*

I am going to Huntsville, Ala. on a hospital train today to bring up some sick soldiers. I went down yesterday to meet a train load of sick Maryland troops with Finney. It was *awful.* I never saw such terrible specimens of humanity. Pictures of Reconcentrados hardly equal to it. Filth, disease, rags. Hope not to be gone more than a week. Will write you occasionally meanwhile. In haste, HARVEY.

The *Baltimore Sun* for 30 August carried the following:

The hospital train which Sunday brought 111 hollow-eyed members of the Fifth Regiment home will start south again early this morning, and in a few more days another lot of invalid soldiers will be in the hospitals of Baltimore. . . . Dr. I. R. Trimble will be in charge of the second expedition, as he was of the first, but has selected another staff of physicians to go with him, those who went on the first trip being exhausted. Those selected are Dr. Eugene L. Opie and Dr. Harvey W. Cushing, both of the Johns Hopkins Hospital, and four orderlies from the same hospital.

A few days later H.C. described to his father his second experience in bringing back the wounded, making some interesting comments on the dangers of freedom of speech in wartime:

Baltimore,
H.C. to H.K.C. *3 September 1898.*

Got here this morning & to bed after a one-hour soak in the tub at 4 A.M. Very hard trip but most interesting. Picked up about 40 typhoids at Huntsville, many right out of the camp which sounds worse than it really is. The men are much to blame and there are many extenuating circumstances. I was very agreeably surprised. The men of the V Maryland all very thin of course, but seemed in good spirits and reports are much exaggerated. The great trouble is that everyone grumbles and kicks at everything and in this great North American republic even in times of military discipline a growler in the ranks has his say to the papers and his people take it up and the whole pot of discontent is thus kept stirred up. I was very agreeably disappointed in the hospitals & camp. In Atlanta they have everything in the hospitals that we have except enough and perhaps able enough men to do the work. The patients are as well off there as they would be here and I think we brought away men much better left there.

I have innumerable questions to ask you and observations to recount but 'vita brevis.' I must wait till I can see you. There is much work to be done here now. A new staff came on duty while I was away. The weather here is frightful. Heat! We suffered little from it however during our trip. Huntsville is a garden spot. Cool—beautiful. Ideal place for an encampment.

Autumn found the Hospital and School settling down to busy routine and there is little of moment to record. Letters home give the best idea of the demands made upon a conscientious assistant resident:

H.C. to H.K.C. *25 September 1898.*

Busy days. Up all night with a little girl—question of typhoid operation—operated at 5.30 this A.M. Have been hustling ever since. My desk is piled high with manuscript, unanswered letters, pamphlets, etc. Hopeless utterly. Am working up this difficult typhoid perforation question to report at the Southern Tri-state Med. Society next month. Hope I can make a good paper out of it. Have you ever seen any cases? We have had 3 this fall. Cooler weather here. Dr. Osler is sick and McCrae spends night there so that I am high cockalorum in the house with Thayer away and I don't love it at all. School opens soon, which means more things to do. I am thriving under it and never felt better.

H.C. to B.M.C. *22 October 1898.*

I leave for the Sunny South tomorrow night for a few days. To read a paper at a Southern Medical Society being my supposed—to get some rest and recreation being my actual—object. I have just been over taking supper with the Goodwillies, i.e. Mary and her father. McCrae or I or both are there most every Sunday night and eat up everything in the house. This is no exaggeration. Mary used to look startled at a third help but has long since grown accustomed to the length of our appetites. I'm afraid we will have to stop taking our preceding walk. This is about my only exercise during the week and appetite follows in its wake to the depletion of the G'willies' cupboard. They have a new darkie named Sparrow: most appropriate. He gathers up the crumbs after us. Even this requires industry. We are having fine weather—clear, cool. I am called to see an appendix case. Darn. Hoped to get some sleep.

H.C. to H.K.C. *29 October 1898.*

Arrived home safely. Had a very interesting and profitable trip. Did more talking than I thought I was capable of. An empty wagon makes the most noise perhaps. Hope I gave them some things to think about. Dr. Halsted has presented me with 25 volumes of the Transactions of the German Surgical Society. Very valuable and I'm happy enough over it.

My present ambition is to get a *Century Dictionary* which I need at my right hand. Here is a prospectus of a good edition for $69 instead of $100. Would you

THE JOHNS HOPKINS HOSPITAL LIBRARY
From a photograph by H.C. in 1899-1900

THE JOHNS HOPKINS HOSPITAL
The main entrance viewed from the South. From a photograph by H.C. in 1899-1900

THE CUSHING BOOKPLATE

Designed by H.C. and executed by Edwin Davis French. The most recent form of the bookplate has the initials of Kirke W. (son of Henry P.) and Edward H. (son of Edward F.) added, *i.e.*, "K.W.C. 1919" and "E.H.C. 1923"

THE GREAT LAKES TRIP TO DULUTH

The first day (*from left to right*): B.M.C. with Pat, H.C., K.C., Mrs. Ned Cushing and Dr. Ned

The second day (*from left to right*): H.C., B.M.C., Pat, Dr. Ned, K.C. and Mrs. Ned

"AT THE TURN OF THE CENTURY"
From an undated photograph of H.C. sent by the late W. G. MacCallum, believed to have been taken in 1900 or 1901

MAX BRÖDEL
From a sketch by H.C. dated 27 January 1900

SURGICAL RESIDENT STAFF, J.H.H. 1899
James F. Mitchell, H.C., M. B. Clopton

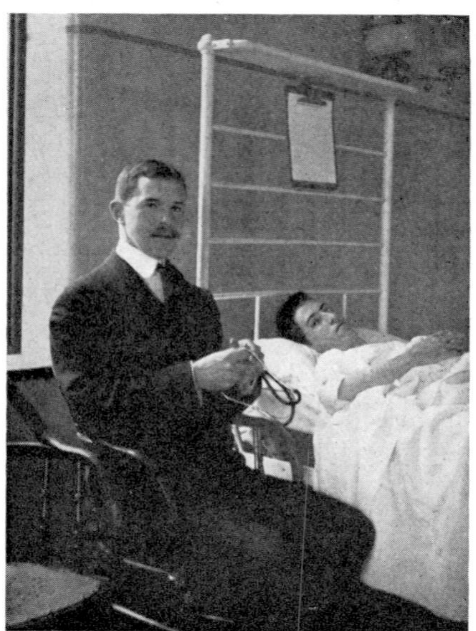

FRIENDS AT THE HOPKINS

J. C. Bloodgood — Henry M. Hurd

Thomas McCrae — Thomas B. Futcher

From photographs by H.C. *circa* 1901

get it if you were I? In a lump or on the installment plan? Please send back the slip.

15 November 1898.

Have given up the *Century Dictionary* idea on your advice and will get the small book which you recommend. I have been very busy as usual. My last monograph is completed and went to the printers today. It will probably appear in the next Bulletin.

General Barnett is staying with the Goodwillies. I saw him there last Sunday. He had some very flattering things to say about you and your Loyal Legion papers which apparently are the striking features of the meetings. I hope you write more easily and correctly than your youngest hopeful. I have had some interesting things lately. Operated on a spinal meningitis case and drained the subdural space. Also had an extirpation of the spleen for primary splenic anaemia: the first splenectomy [for anemia] at the J.H.H.

1899

In 1898 Cushing's interest in bacteriology had grown, and 1899 and early 1900 may properly be termed his bacteriological years, for during this time he was seriously tempted to follow the subject as a specialty. His experiences with typhoid and his pioneer work on the surgical handling of typhoid perforations had done much to crystallize this interest, as had his contacts with Welch, Livingood, Simon Flexner, and also Norman Gwyn.

The early part of the year brought two notes from Osler (among the earliest from W.O. that H.C. had preserved):

1 West Franklin Street, Baltimore,
William Osler to H.C. *9 January 1899.*

Dear Cushing: Your paper on Typhoid Perforation is tip-top. Send one, please, to Dr. Ker at the Fever Hospital, Edinburgh; also to Dr. T. K. Dalziel, 196 Bath Street, Glasgow, Scotland. Sincerely yours, Wm Osler.

William Osler to H.C. *6 February 1899.*

Dear Cushing: Your paper on perforative peritonitis in typhoid fever should come into our Studies in Typhoid Fever, Series III, for the Reports. Won't you look it over and make any corrections you see fit and let me have it on Wednesday? Very truly yours, Wm Osler.

He also had a somewhat brisk missive from W. W. Keen who was preparing a book on typhoid and surgery:

1729 Chestnut Street, Philadelphia,
W. W. Keen to H.C. *26 January 1899.*

My dear Dr. Cushing: Thank you very much for sending me your paper on intestinal perforation. On page 25 I notice your dissent from my opinion, but I hardly think that you state it quite exactly. I certainly do advise delay till the immediate symptoms of shock have passed away, but my only statement (on pages 225-6) as to the second twelve hours is "that all things considered, it has been the most favorable up to this time." In the fourth paragraph on page 25, you have misquoted the name of my assistant as Westfall. It should be Westcott. Yours truly, W. W. Keen.

Cushing's work on typhoid quickly received recognition abroad, and he subsequently rewrote his first report for translation into French.[17] In his personal reprint of this he has written (Dec. 1929):

When I was in Paris in the autumn of 1900 I called on Dieulafoy who was anxious to learn something about our results in operating for typhoid perforation, no recoveries at the time having been reported in France. I told him what I could about it and he asked if I would write a paper on the subject to be published in the Archives.

This was the result. A nice young fellow named Lecène translated the paper for me and before it was published Dieulafoy wrote something, I've forgotten where, in which he stated that he had made the acquaintance of Dr. Johns Hopkins *(sic)* of Baltimore who had given him reason to believe that perforations in typhoid were everyday affairs, or something of the sort, in America. I never met Lecène again though he occasionally sent me his papers, and the notice of his death came as a great shock to me when I saw it in the *Lancet* [23 November 1929] yesterday.[18]

H.C.'s later work in the bacteriological field, carried out largely during 1899, brought him into touch with Theobald Smith, Walter Reed, and others whose early papers on types of paratyphoid bacilli he subsequently bound up with the following note (dated 14 Sept. 1935):

In the old days of the Hopkins everyone was engaged in some sort of bacteriological work and had a pet organism which he was ardently cultivating. Young, I recall, had a strange bug that one day was a bacillus, another day a coccus, either in chains or pairs, and we called it the original Adam bacillus. The general impression was that Young had slipped up on his technique, but I suppose he had gotten hold of a pleomorphic organism such as E. C. Rosenow has in later years been concentrating upon.

Halsted expected his house officers to make their own bacteriological studies and with the help of Flexner in Welch's department we somehow managed to get the work done, though there was a vast amount of neglect of these chores on the part of those who were not interested, and they were many.

Typhoid fever was prevalent and Keen had just written a book about the surgical complications of typhoid fever; and during my last year as resident I happened to operate, on March 6, 1899, upon a young negro for a costochondral abscess of the rib which had followed a prolonged fever, possibly typhoid, with relapse. Cultures were taken at the time of the operation and it proved to be what Flexner called a blue typhoid, for instead of acidulating litmus milk it failed to do so. Somehow or other I got stirred up about this and began pursuing the matter at odd times between operations and at night, and enjoyed immensely studying and taking photographs of the variable gas production and color changes in different media.

Naturally I began sending around for cultures of similar organisms that had been described, and had some correspondence with Walter Reed, James Carroll, Theobald Smith, General Sternberg, and others. General Sternberg had a bacillus "X" which was much discussed at the time—"X" being an unknown quantity—

[17] "Sur la laparotomie exploratrice précoce dans la perforation intestinale au cours de la fièvre typhoïde." *Archives Générales de Médecine,* January 1901, *197 (n.s.5),* 14-26.

[18] Lecène died at the age of 51, as fate would have it, of typhoid contracted while operating on a case of cholecystitis.

and someone suggested my calling this one bacillus "O," so it was called bacillus "O" in a paper I wrote on the subject, with a very long title, published in the Johns Hopkins Bulletin for July-August 1900.[19] I have no copy of this paper to add to this present collection, but a copy is in my collection of reprints, Vol. I, No. 14, in which I find that several letters from Walter Reed and others have been bound.

The present collection of reprints has been knocking about among my possessions and was finally brought here to New Haven when my things were cleared out *en bloc* from the Brigham Hospital three years ago. Among them are a few other letters which serve to indicate how much interest at the time was being taken in the question. Undoubtedly it was a very valuable experience for a young surgeon and I don't know that I have ever engaged in any side issue that interested me more. I even thought of going on in bacteriology and began making a study with Louis E. Livingood in Welch's department—a study of the bacteriology of the upper portion of the alimentary canal.[20] Livingood's untimely death in the *Bourgogne* disaster obliged me to finish the study alone; and as I soon went abroad, that ended my bacteriological activities.

Cushing's bacteriological interests almost carried him to the Philippines where Flexner was sent with Lewellys Barker on a government medical mission arising out of the American occupation of Manila. In his letter to his father he sounds much disappointed that he had not been one of those selected to go:

H.C. to H.K.C. *15 March 1899.*

Thanks for the $20.00. Very acceptable indeed. Great excitement here about Barker's and Flexner's departure. They go tomorrow to the Philippines to study tropical diseases under J.H. University auspices and with government patronage. Such an opportunity comes to few and but once. They come home in October round the world. There was a remote possibility once that I might go along. They have 3 assistants—Barker to do the clinical, Flexner the pathological work. Everything is to be placed at their disposal. I never saw such stimulated men. They are capable of great things and I look for much from them.

Before Flexner departed, H.C. submitted another bacteriological paper to him for criticism.[21] An interesting exchange of letters followed:

[19] "A comparative study of some members of a pathogenic group of bacilli of the hog cholera or bac. enteritidis (Gärtner) type, intermediate between the typhoid and colon groups. With the report of a case resembling typhoid fever, in which there occurred a post-febrile osteomyelitis due to such an intermediate bacillus." *Johns Hopkins Hospital Bulletin,* 1900, *11,* 156-170.

[20] "Experimental and surgical notes upon the bacteriology of the upper portion of the alimentary canal, with observations on the establishment there of an amicrobic state as a preliminary to operative procedures on the stomach and small intestine." *Johns Hopkins Hospital Reports,* 1900, *9,* 543-591. ("Contributions to the science of medicine dedicated by his pupils to William Henry Welch on the 25th anniversary of his doctorate.") Louis Eugene Livingood (1868-1898) left for a holiday in Havana on the French Paquebot *La Bourgogne* July 2; as he was leaving he addressed an affectionate note to "My dear old bacteriologist né Cushing" which he signed "Yours for ever." The disaster occurred on the 4th. Memorial services were held at his home in Reading, Pennsylvania on July 20.

[21] "Acute diffuse gonococcus peritonitis." *Johns Hopkins Hospital Bulletin,* May 1899, *10,* 75-81.

Chicago,
22 March 1899.

Simon Flexner to H.C.

Dear Cushing, Your paper will be returned today by my brother. I went over it on the train to Louisville and made a few minor alterations. The paper is very convincing and, of course, important and I hope you will bring it out without much more delay. I regret that I kept it so long, but you will understand why I did so. I failed to see you just before I left the Hospital. I did not mean to say good-bye for I shall return for a period in September and then from time to time, I trust, afterwards. . . . Sincerely, SIMON FLEXNER.

Johns Hopkins Hospital,
11 April 1899.

H.C. to Simon Flexner

My dear Flexner You and Barker are sorely missed. The empty table at the end of the dining room is a constant reminder of your absence. John has decorated it elaborately with folded napkins, colored glass &c—a sort of in memoriam token of esteem. It is even more gorgeous than our Thanksgiving feast of Priapismus decorations. Poor Max Brödel has not been able to finish the famous sketch as he has been laid up with a bad streptococcus arm for two weeks in Ward C. He was very ill for a time. I feared a general infection. The Professor operated on him and opened up his arm widely and alas! picked up his ulnar nerve with a clamp. It's a sorry thing for Max—left arm fortunately, but it precludes any piano playing of course for a long time from inability to separate his fingers. I hope it will entirely regenerate but it's a slow process, I fear.

The gonococcus paper was returned. You were good indeed to go over it as you did. I still regard it as an imposition. Your conclusions I have adopted. I did not dare be quite so positive myself. I am much interested now in a paracolon post-typhoid general infection with osteomyelitis of the rib. I am working on the fermentation and indol reactions with great delight. The organism is much like Gwyn's. It is agglutinated by the patient's blood in dilution 1-600. . . . Very sincerely, HARVEY W. C.

1, Calle Malacañan, Manila, P.I.
23 May 1899.

Simon Flexner to H.C.

Dear Cushing, Many thanks for your good letter. I am glad to know about your doings in Baltimore; nothing interests me more. I am mourning Brödel's hard lines, but I am hoping too that in time the trouble will right itself. . . . You will be interested in our progress here. It has, of course, taken time to get things under way—more time than we expected at the start. But it is clear now that we should have been better prepared for certain unavoidable delays. At this time we are started, have a laboratory in the 1st Reserve Military Hospital, where there are 1000 ± sick & wounded. Strong who is on duty there has been delightful and self-sacrificing to a degree. This hospital together with the 2nd Reserve Hospital has been opened to us freely. Through the local health officer we have also had the general civil hospitals opened to us.

Our work thus far we have limited to certain kinds of cases; we thought best not to spread too much. We are studying the dysenteries, malaria and incidentally typhoid fever, the latter by means of the Widal test. Amoebae are common in the dysenteries and amoebic abscess of the liver is an occasional complication. We are studying the blood sera of dysenteric patients with reference to its power over Shiga's bac. dysenteriae, and thus far have gotten a number of positive reactions —in amoebic cases. We are searching the stools also for that organism. Thus far in our experience malaria is not common. Yesterday however we had an autopsy on a case of sudden death from acute malarial infection.

Beri-beri is common among the natives and thus far we have had three autopsies. We are planning some experimental work on this disease in connection with monkeys which are plentiful around here—but not easy to catch. There is a leper hospital here and today [I] did two autopsies on leprous individuals—one man and one woman. Both had extensive external lesions; neither had visceral lesions. We are very busy—as busy as one dares be in this climate.

The rainy season has just set in. One wonders where all the water comes from. A typhoon was threatened yesterday, but we got only a whiff of its end. The bamboo in our garden rocked and shook and beat against our walls until we feared for safety of the house.

The war continues although there is no severe fighting just now. We spent a couple of days at the front—at San Fernando—and saw the active operations. Everyone is expecting peace; but each day there are casualties at the outposts. The troops are being worried and harassed in this petty way; and now that the rains are upon us, the next moves seem uncertain.

Our garden is a dream of tropical beauty and luxuriance. We have our own banana trees and the most gorgeous and varied foliage and flowers. All kinds of curious animals abound in the tall grass and in the trees and the night air is filled with a medley of strange and weird sounds.

The Filipinos are now docile; they were not always so to the Americanos. They are however a problem, I fear. Freedom for them is at present impossible. Their best men insist on this and the wisdom of their demand is evident. They are however not without possibilities. My regards to Futcher and the boys generally. Sincerely, SIMON FLEXNER.

Between times, the informative letters home continued. In February he had gone up to New Haven (22 Feb.) "to help celebrate a Society function," and afterwards he stopped off in New York with the Atterburys, where he met Mr. Albert Herter, the artist, and heard Tannhäuser with the Crowells. On 4 April he gave Tom McCrae a dinner at Baltimore, all in the best Hopkins tradition. On the 25th began the centennial of the Maryland Medical and Chirurgical Faculty for which Welch arranged an exhibit of books and portraits "of extraordinary interest." In early June he slipped off to East Radford, Virginia, on a fishing trip with Mr. Goodwillie. During the winter he had entertained hopes of going abroad, but this plan had again to be abandoned.

H.C. to H.K.C. *4 June 1899.*

Many thanks for your kind note and enclosure. Your gifts certainly encourage my small attempts at medical writings. Glad you liked the last paper. I wrote it while I was at home with my sore finger, mostly at your desk. Dr. Halsted sails Tuesday for England where Dr. O has preceded him. Bloodgood I believe is likely to accept a call to Philadelphia. [Dr. Hunter] Robb also I have heard may go there. Mrs. R. has been on here for a nurses' graduation. My hopes for foreign tour may have to be postponed as it seems not unlikely that we will be short-handed in the fall.

Brödel is giving me regular German lessons—in return for my care of him when he was laid up with his septic arm. . . .

On 1 July he writes: "I am not feeling my oats exactly at present having the whole surgical house on my hands most of the time and the responsibility and general disinclination to work are rather wearing." A further reference to bacteriology occurs on 2 September: "Work goes on apace. Have just had two successful intestinal resection cases and my first Gasserian ganglion resection."

In connection with his bacteriological preoccupations Cushing had an interesting exchange of letters during August and September with Theobald Smith, Walter Reed, and others to whom reference has already been made. Thus from Boston came the following:

Harvard Medical School,
Theobald Smith to H.C. *27 August 1899.*

Dear Dr. Cushing: I have a few copies of the bulletin you refer to and I am willing to part with one of them if you will eventually deposit it in the Hospital library. I also send you a reprint of a non-motile member of the same group. For 18 months past I have been testing the serum reaction of the members of the group I now have, with blood from an immunized guinea-pig and rabbit but the results are not yet in shape for publication. The agglutinative reaction I at present look upon as a good means of classification for parasitic or pathogenic characters but I question whether it should decide phylogenetic relationship. This brings up your query concerning the grouping of these forms. I am unable to make any definite statements on this point and I believe that the nomenclature must remain a tentative one until a broader name than any now in use can be given. Pathologists are apt to emphasize too strongly pathogenic characters whereas these are probably the last to be assumed in the process of parasitic adaption and the first to be lost. The other questions you raise are in part discussed in the articles mailed to you. I shall be pleased to aid you in your important work in any way possible. Yours very truly, THEOBALD SMITH.

At the same time H.C., who evidently believed in going to the top when he wanted information, approached the country's leading authority on yellow fever and had a prompt reply:

Surgeon General's Office, Washington,
Walter Reed to H.C. *29 August 1899.*

My dear Doctor: Your kind favor of yesterday comes at an opportune moment. Of course, you have read Sanarelli's criticisms of his American critics, which appeared in the Med. News of August 12th, & in which he says that Carroll & I have made the stupid blunder of "mixing" our cultures! I will be glad to send you a reprint of our reply, which will, also, appear in the same Journal. Now concerning the culture that I gave Flexner, let me say that this was from the blood of Dog 443, injected with a culture of the original *B. icteroides* which Sternberg got in Roux's laboratory. At that time we had no culture of the hog cholera bacillus in our laboratory, nor had we ever worked with it—so that your culture is one remove from Sanarelli's own original *B. icteroides.* I will take pleasure in sending you within a few days two other cultures of *B. icteroides* isolated from yellow fever cadavers in Cuba, *one* of which will be the original culture as taken from the blood. With kindest regards, Sincerely yours, WALTER REED.

On 30 August, Reed sent him the various bacterial cultures for which he had asked, and subsequently there were letters from Reed and his collaborator, James Carroll:

Walter Reed to H.C. *Washington, 9 September 1899.*

My dear Doctor: I would appreciate it very much if you will be so kind as to send us a culture of *B. enteritidis* (Gärtner), *B. typhi murium* & your culture of the hog cholera bacillus. Concerning your inquiry, I may say that we have made no investigation with the bacilli mentioned in your letter. Please pardon the unavoidable delay which has occurred in replying to your kind note of Aug. 31. Very truly yours, WALTER REED.

James Carroll to H.C. *Surgeon General's Office, Washington, 15 September 1899.*

Dear Dr. Cushing: Dr. Reed is out of the city for a short time, and in his absence I beg to thank you for the cultures you so kindly sent us, and which were handed me by Dr. Wellington this morning. I am especially anxious to try the effect upon them of Sanarelli's serum and of dried blood from y. f. cases. We feel particularly encouraged by the results already obtained.

It is delightful to know that the results you have obtained are so strongly confirmatory of our own, as regards *B. ict.* and *B. chol. Suis.* I will hand your note to Dr. Reed immediately upon his return. Again thanking you for the cultures, Very sincerely yours, JAMES CARROLL.

After Halsted had returned from his prolonged summer holiday, Cushing, who had been at work all summer as Resident, repaired to Washington for several weeks in November to work in the Surgeon General's Library. He later visited Flexner at Philadelphia shortly after the latter's return from Manila. On 16 November he was in Boston attending Amory Codman's wedding and renewing his old associations:

H.C. to B.M.C. *16 November 1899.*

Codman was married today and I do not know when I have seen a more simple and beautiful wedding or enjoyed one so much. His bride was a Miss Bowditch who lives up on a high wooded hill (Bowditch Hill yclept) in the centre of Jamaica Plain. There were no frills at the wedding. No scarf pins, no white gloves, no elaborate floral decorations and house upsetting. They simply got married. I was very much of an outsider but they were all very nice to me and I helped nail up the laurel and hemlock branches about the house yesterday with the family. Mrs. Bowditch it turns out used to know 'Carrie Kellogg' very well. I wonder if Carolyn will remember anything about her.

I have been having a beautiful time here in Boston staying at Allie Porter's, seeing a great deal of a great many doctors, looking over the School and as you see, not entirely being occupied with Codman's bridal performance. We are having beautiful weather and as I have not been here since '96 when people were in town, I have made the most of my opportunities. Strange how much pleasanter a place this is than New York. Do you not think so, Ma dear, in spite of the occasional hill to climb. I do not see many changes. Boston was built well and comfortably in the beginning and the only alterations and additions seem to be on the edges. I hope you are all well. Aff'y HARVEY.

He returned to Baltimore on 20 November and was soon again hard at work with his two assistants, James F. Mitchell and M. B. Clopton. On 4 December he writes: "Prof. Remsen's Chemical Lab. burned out last night." And on the 23d: "Most of the hospital people have gone off for the holidays. My staff of seven is curtailed to two and all of the Chiefs, Halsted, Welch and Osler, have gone to their respective homes." On the 26th: "I went across town to the Goodwillies to dinner with McCrae and sent a telegram to the home party on my way back which I presume appeared. . . . I am gradually accumulating quite a respectable library which is a great delight."

1900

In academic life there is nothing more gratifying than a call to another university. A proposal had been made in December 1899 that Cushing return to Cleveland to join the Department of Surgery at the Western Reserve under Professor Dudley P. Allen. In these circumstances, only one thing can be more satisfying than a call, and that is a serious effort on the part of one's own institution to retain one's services. Welch wrote to him promptly on 1 January:

Journal of Experimental Medicine,
William H. Welch to H.C. *1 January 1900.*

Dear Cushing, The position offered you in Cleveland is certainly a tempting one. I do not know enough about the conditions there to judge whether there may be any serious drawbacks connected with it. If you are really to have a separate surgical service, entirely independent of Allen's, and the arrangements are made without creating serious antagonisms, it may be the best thing for you to accept. I wish that we could offer you some position here attractive enough to keep you with us for some years. I am sure that the Faculty would coincide in any recommendation which Dr. Halsted might make, but I am not clear what could be done in the way of promotion. I feel confident that you are equal to any position in surgery which can be offered here or elsewhere, but the right opportunities unfortunately do not present themselves very often, as our medical schools and hospitals in this country are organized.

I hope that you will talk the situation over with Drs. Halsted and Osler. Much as it is for our interest to keep you with us, it would not be right to stand in the way of your best interests for the future. If you see your way clear to remaining here, I shall rejoice. Happy New Year. Very sincerely yours, WILLIAM H. WELCH.

The Johns Hopkins Hospital was never lavish in the salaries paid to its junior staff, but there are intangible factors that cause younger men to stay at such institutions, and Cushing after a good deal of hesitation elected to remain, even though in the end the University gave him very little in the way of rank or remuneration. No doubt the wise and kindly advice offered by his mother helped him reach a decision:

I have thought very much about our conversation in the Library Café at Washington, and canvassed the pros and cons in my own mind, as to your future course. And it has seemed to me in some of the times of thought, that life is such a brief span at the longest, one should try to put self and self interest on one side, in making so momentous a decision, and let higher aims and purposes influence one's judgment. In the first place one should put duty to the

Master. How best can I work for the good of others? should be a supreme question. And then the father who has done so much to help you fit yourself for your life work, should have due weight given to his wishes and opinions. What those may be I have no means of knowing, except from his little remark to Dr. Osler about having spared you for so long. I am trying to bring *myself* to acquiesce in whatever decision you may make, if you will only make it in accordance with this question, "Where can I do the most good?"

His father withheld advice for a time, but later wrote:

My conviction is that you are much better off where you are than you could be with anything offered here. Every year you stay in Baltimore will add increasingly to the advantages of your opportunities. In this time, largely, you have been establishing a foundation, the superstructure is now in the making, and will be recognized as the earlier work would not have been.

It does not matter so much what your title is, or what your relative rank is: the great thing is the opportunity to do good work and to have it recognized. It may be difficult for the powers that be to arrange at present any advancement for you in name or place. My suggestion is that you henceforth say nothing further about going away or make any plans in that direction.

A letter home just at this time tells of his many activities, including the preparation of a paper for publication on forty-eight hours' notice:

H.C. to H.K.C. *28 February 1900.*

I have been very much occupied of late—Mitchell [the Assistant Resident] laid up with measles (cutting his teeth, Dr. Hurd claims); another man off on the ill list, with a house brim full of hard work. In addition I tried to write on 48 hours' notice a paper for Dr. Gould for the Phila. Med. Journal.[22] This was done in two nights' work: all night practically. I had the matter well in mind and was interested to see what I could do on a push. It was out of favor to Gould who had been disappointed in some manuscripts at the last minute. I think it's better than some of the things I have let ripen too long so that the sentences have become too involved from rewriting. Dr. Hurd says the preface to a book is always the most difficult to translate into a foreign language because it's always written last and worked over. Hence translators always leave it to the last. I suppose a paper brewed over too long acquires the same faults. . . .

Expect to read a Gasserian Ganglion paper at Keen's request in Phila. on the 20th of April so will have to fly away from Carter's wedding. Perhaps I can come on a few days earlier. My Festschrift paper for Welch's volume is about completed. Brödel is drawing a portrait of him for it. Most of the papers are extraordinarily good—rather ultra-scientific perhaps.

Welch thanked him warmly for his contribution:

935 St. Paul Street, Baltimore,
W. H. Welch to H.C. *14 May 1900.*

My dear Cushing, I wish to thank you more emphatically than I have yet done for your contribution to my Festschrift. I was greatly pleased to find Livingood's name there in association with yours.

Your paper is of very great value and I confess that I had not realized how

[22] "Exploratory laparotomy under local anesthesia for acute abdominal symptoms occurring in the course of typhoid fever." *Philadelphia Medical Journal* [Special typhoid fever number], March 1900, 5, 501-508.

thorough a study you had made of the bacterial flora of the intestine under varying conditions. Your observations are certainly of great practical importance, as well as of scientific interest. This testimonial volume has been a source of the greatest pleasure to me and I trust that all of the contributors know how deeply I appreciate this manifestation of their affection and loyalty. Believe me, with the kindest regards and all good wishes, Very sincerely yours, WILLIAM H. WELCH.

The development of medical illustrating at Johns Hopkins was due to the backing which Kelly, Mall, and Cushing gave to the most celebrated of medical illustrators, Max Brödel, whom Kelly had brought to the Hopkins in 1894.[23] Brödel and Cushing, arriving at much the same time and having an instinctive insight into one another's personalities and interests, fell almost literally into one another's arms. A close and deeply cherished intimacy developed between them, and Brödel looked upon Cushing as his most gifted pupil—a "pupil" in the sense of one who as a surgeon received only casual guidance rather than the more formal courses in medical illustrating for which Brödel later became celebrated. The illustrations in his paper on trigeminal neuralgia,[24] being done in half-tone, reflect Brödel's influence; but Brödel stated emphatically on more than one occasion that Cushing executed them himself with only occasional suggestion. The plate of the base of the skull showing the Gasserian ganglion is one of the best, but it was sadly reproduced when it was published.

H.C.'s flair for catching a likeness was most evident when, on 27 January 1900, he did a skillful crayon sketch of Max Brödel, sitting in an easy chair. The correspondence between the two men extended over the next four decades and their letters cast many interesting sidelights on the history of medical illustrating in this country.

During this period Cushing was made a member of the Hopkins Committee on Graduate Instruction (2 Feb.), and in that capacity devoted much thought to clinical teaching. The load which he carried in this connection was unusually heavy because of Dr. Halsted's irregular attendance at the clinic. In his Halsted memorabilia, Cushing put together a series of communications received from Halsted during his absence from the clinic for a week "with the exception of Thursday when he came over in answer to a note to operate on a boy whose stomach was full of nails." Typical is the note received on 12 March with Cushing's annotation appended:

[23] Cullen T. S. "Max Brödel, 1870-1941. Director of the first development of art as applied to medicine in the world." *Bulletin of the Medical Library Association,* 1945, *33,* 5-29.

[24] "A method of total extirpation of the Gasserian ganglion for trigeminal neuralgia. By a route through the temporal fossa and beneath the middle meningeal artery." *Journal of the American Medical Association,* 28 April 1900, *34,* 1035-1041.

1201 Eutaw Place, Baltimore,
W. S. Halsted to H.C. *Monday, 12 March 1900.*

Dear Cushing I should like to hold a clinic on goitre on Friday of this week. Do you know of any cases that we could send for? Sincerely, W. S. HALSTED. [The first time this year I have had a lead as to the proposed subject for the clinic on Friday. All local goitre cases sent for. 'The Professor' operated Mar. 15, Thursday, on Arthur Schritt 'the ostrich'—H.W.C.]

Cushing's plans for a trip abroad, which had been brewing since the summer of 1896, were at last coming to realization. He had spoken tentatively of the plan off and on during the year, and finally on 10 May news came of his being granted a year's leave of absence. The arrangements made for his trip are as usual related in his letters home:

H.C. to H.K.C. *10 May 1900.*

I have had no chance to answer your note of May first. I am quite occupied and have not very much ambition for work—a bad combination. It will be a relief to get away on June 23. The Faculty have granted me a year's leave of absence. I have been unable to corner Dr. Halsted and get any satisfaction from him about future work here. He sails for Europe himself June 7, 1900. I think Flexner will go with McCrae and myself.

H.C. to B.M.C. *24 May 1900.*

. . . I do not know when I will sail. McCrae has passage engaged on the *Teutonic* 20th—Flexner on the *Traube* 16th and the Oslers & Jacobs on the *Campania* 16th. I hope I can get a berth on one of these boats. At present I am limited to the *Servia* sailing the 23rd. These dates are June of course. Will let you know definately as soon as I know.

H.C. to H.K.C. *6 June 1900.*

Your note of the first with enclosure remains unanswered; also the June 5th letter which has just arrived. Forgive me for my seeming neglect. I will have too many things to do before sailing to think of coming home, sorry as I am to say so. Dr. Halsted sails tomorrow. Finney is away on his vacation and Mitchell also so that I am pretty much alone and the house is very heavy, with postgraduate responsibilities also. I shall be glad when it is all over. Have had a good deal of night operating (typhoid perforation last night) and the private patients I must now take care of. I hate to touch them, there is so much to lose and nothing to gain, but occasional thanks.

H.C. to H.K.C. *20 June 1900.*

The letter of credit has been received all right. It's an impressive document and looks like a Marriage Certificate. My arrangements are about completed—books packed and pictures put away after much labor. Very cool weather here. I leave for N.Y. Friday a.m. [22d].

He finally sailed on 23 June on the *SS. Servia.*

* * * * *

H.C. had thus completed four years, first as Assistant Resident and then as Resident Surgeon at Hopkins under Halsted. He had been given a much freer rein than would have fallen to the lot of most men in the same circumstances. This was due in part to the fact that he proved himself able to carry the responsibility of a large surgical clinic, but more particularly to the fact that the "Professor" was in poor health and was seldom at the clinic. Cushing summed up his experience with Halsted thus:

> I saw relatively little of him during my three years as Resident, less and less as he perhaps began to feel that I might be entrusted with the bulk of the routine work. A great deal of this was of course major surgery and the assistance was very poor. There was at the time a rotation service for house officers who were only on surgery for four months; and as Young soon was side-tracked into urology, there was no one of any experience to give anaesthesia for prolonged cases like breast cases or for serious conditions such as intestinal strangulations and the like. It was owing to this that I took up local anaesthesia without getting much moral support from the 'Professor.' I little realized at the time the reasons for this.
>
> He had few private patients, indeed was too difficult of access and too much away to build up a consulting practice. . . . We sometimes went out of town with him to operate, less often in private houses in Baltimore. An operating trunk was prepared for these occasions and a large part of the staff would go along—most elaborate performances they were, for which he charged prodigious fees.
>
> He stood the summer heat badly and usually went away sometimes for six months at a stretch. . . . Under this régime I became perhaps a little too independent and his letters hint that I may have been too prone to put myself on paper. I can understand better now how this must have annoyed him and I think it was true in the case of all of his assistants that when they began to write he was ready to let them go.
>
> I sensed this in time and felt that I had better get away. I had spoken to him the year before of an ambition to go and work with Kocher in whose *Verletzungen der Wirbelsäule* I had become interested through my studies of a case of haematomyelia. He did not know Kocher but went on to Berne that summer [1899], passed some time there, and became greatly attached to him, regarding him, I believe, as the leading surgeon on the Continent. They were very much alike in their surgical methods and had a common bond of interest in the goitre question.
>
> Kocher, however, was a man of prodigious and incessant industry, whereas Halsted took things very easily, not to say lazily, in the eyes of his juniors. This, I am now quite sure, was due to ill health during the period of my residency and I lament that at the time I did not fully appreciate it. There is a series of notes apparently written in the spring of 1900 from 1201 Eutaw Place—quill-pen notes which show something of his irregularities under which I must have fretted considerably.

CHAPTER VI

A Year of Travel: Broadening Horizons[1]

1900–1901

ENCOURAGED by his father and his brother, as well as by Osler and Welch, Cushing spent fourteen months abroad in 1900 and 1901—an experience that was to prove one of the most valuable of his career. He had worked unremittingly for ten years, and his friends, aware of his talents, but recognizing that his intellectual outlook was still somewhat restricted, had for some time been urging him to travel. At first he was reluctant to consider it for he was eager to marry and become established and he was not certain that European clinics had much to offer. He thus approached them with skepticism and, as his journal attests, he actually found much to confirm this view. Subsequently, however, the critical impatience of his first youthful reactions became less imperious as his familiarity with the personnel of the clinics and laboratories broadened into friendship and understanding of their various problems and backgrounds. He had gone to Europe a self-assured and somewhat provincial young American with many a deep-rooted prejudice; he returned a cosmopolitan with a greatly broadened point of view on medical matters, and a deep respect for European culture and tradition.

The political situation in Europe at the opening of the century was not exactly calm, but it is not apparent that H.C. gave much thought to Continental politics or affairs of state at that time. It is clear, however, that this year of travel opened his eyes and his mind; for when 1914 came, knowledge of Europe quickened his perception of the issues involved in the First World War and incidentally gave emphasis to the futility of isolationism and the need for preparedness. Throughout his life Cushing's politics were tinged by frugal Ohio republicanism—a tendency which his Yale senior society no doubt strengthened—but he was too intelligent to have been an isolationist. His outspoken internationalism dates from 1900, and despite his Cleveland background he found himself in complete sympathy with the foreign policies pursued by Franklin Roosevelt prior to the Second World War.

[1] Donald H. Barron, Associate Professor of Physiology at Yale, who knows Berne and its university traditions, has assisted materially in the final revision of this chapter.

In planning his trip Cushing gave first place to study with men whose interests were neurological, *i.e.* Kocher, Horsley, and Sherrington, although twenty years later he remarked that he had no idea then that he would eventually specialize in neurological surgery. Kocher, the Professor of Surgery at the University of Berne, whose treatise on lesions of the spinal cord resulting from damage to the vertebral column had been Cushing's handbook in his study of similar cases, was commonly acknowledged at that time to be the foremost surgeon of Europe. A conscientious, painstaking individual who kept detailed clinical histories and studied his cases with utmost care, Kocher had attracted to the University clinic patients and graduate students from all over the world, and through his writings had influenced surgical thought as have few other men in modern surgery. Horsley, surgeon at University College Hospital, London, was at the height of his career and was carrying out investigations on the functions of the brain and spinal cord to clarify his work in neurosurgery. Charles S. Sherrington, then at Liverpool in the chair of physiology, had attracted wide notice through his work on decerebrate rigidity and the functions of the sensory nerves to muscles; he was also beginning a detailed study of the motor area of the monkey and anthropoid brain.

Cushing's plan had been to go first to England and later to the Continent, but he found Horsley preoccupied and everyone else in England on their holidays, so he altered his plans and, after a brief trip in France, settled himself in Berne.

* * * * *

Cushing crossed on the *Servia,* arriving in Liverpool on 2 July. The voyage was a quiet one, but he found some amusement in his shipmates:

H.C. to B.M.C. *RMS. Servia, 29 June 1900.*

... There is a large crowd aboard—not many attractive people: mostly pilgrims to Rome and Cook's tourists; many English people who have been spending two weeks in "the States" and who think we are queer, I doubt not. I heard a woman from Illinois ask a young English woman who had been absent from the table for a meal or two, "Have you been under the weather?" "Oh no," she replied, "I've been up under the awning." I thought it worthy of *Life.* My roommate has proved to be a very amusing fellow—an Irishman, a few years removed, who has a very keen sense of humor. . . .

He stopped in Leeds to visit Sir Arthur Mayo Robson (1853-1933), at that time surgeon to the Leeds General Infirmary and an authority on the surgery of the abdomen—a reputation which led to his selection as president of the surgical section of the International Medical Congress at Paris the following August. H.C. records that Robson was an attractive person with great talent and tremendous energy, "a two-steps-at-a-time-upstairs kind of man." After they had seen many of his private patients in various nursing homes, Cushing went to Robson's home, "Moor Grange," at Far Headingly to spend the night before proceeding to London. This was the beginning of a warm friendship and mutual respect, and we find Robson writing to H.C. later: "Very many thanks for your monographs. What splendid work you are doing in the Johns Hopkins Laboratories. I envy you your possibilities. I feel that I should very much like to come to be a student with you. I hope you had a good time in Paris after we met. . . ." H.C. arrived in London on 3 July and was invited to join the Horsley family at breakfast at 35 Cavendish Square the following morning. His impressions of Horsley as recalled many years later have been set down by one of his students:

A BOAT ACQUAINTANCE

He found Horsley living in seemingly great confusion: dictating letters during breakfast to a male secretary; patting dogs between letters; and operating like a wild man. H.C. gave him a reprint of his paper on the Gasserian ganglion, whereupon Horsley said he would show him how to do a case. They drove off the next morning in Horsley's cab, after sterilizing the instruments in H.'s house and, packing them in a towel, went to a well-appointed West End mansion. Horsley dashed upstairs, had his patient under ether in five minutes, and was operating fifteen minutes after he entered the house; made a great hole in the woman's skull, pushed up the temporal lobe—blood everywhere, gauze packed into the middle fossa, the ganglion cut, the wound closed, and he was out of the house less than an hour after he had entered it. This experience settled H.C.'s decision to leave London; for he felt that the refinements of neurological surgery could not be learned from Horsley.

Having abandoned his plan to study with Horsley, Cushing devoted his time to exploring places of interest in London. Osler was spending the summer in England "brain dusting," and this summer of 1900 brought H.C. into intimate contact with him for the first time. With characteristic generosity W.O. introduced him to many of his friends in medical circles; indeed, he must have gone out of his way in this direction for we find H.C. attending a number of senior gatherings in which he would not have been spontaneously included. In his letters home and in his diary are many references to W.O.'s sponsorship:

[*69 Torrington Square, London*].

H.C. to B.M.C. [7] *July 1900.*

. . . I have been having an interesting time, chiefly medical. Have met some prominent people thanks to Dr. Osler. . . . I would have liked to see the regatta or the Cricket (Oxford-Cambridge) match which is "on" this week but one thing or another has intervened. The weather is unusually cool, "the season upside down" in common parlance, and very little rain at the present time. I religiously carry a "brella" and have had a sponge squeezed over me only once. It is hard to become used to a frock coat and tall hat in the morning hours and I feel as though I were going to somebody's wedding each day when I saunter forth. . . .

He wrote his father on the same day:

. . . Mr. Horsley has been very kind; also Dr. Osler. His name is a passport anywhere. He gave a stirring address at the "Polyclinic," Jonathan Hutchinson's postgraduate hospital, the other night. I met Sir William Broadbent, Malcolm Morris, Ewart the heart man, and some other nabobs there. Dr. Jacobs and I went down to Guy's Hospital this afternoon and had a profitable visit. It's a fine place, less old foggyism than in our comparatively young institutions as the M.G.H. for instance. The old Guy's Museum is remarkable, second only to the Hunterian which surpasseth my highest anticipations. Dr. O. told me he had sent you a reprint of his Elisha Bartlett essay. I hope you received it. We went into the old Church at the South End of London Bridge, St. Saviour's, where Beaumont, Fletcher, Gower "the father of English poetry," Shakespeare's brother and other poets and dramatists are buried. It's a treat to go about with Dr. Osler. He gets at the meat of things in an extraordinary way. At Guy's we looked over some of Addison's, Bright's, Hodgson's old pathological and clinical reports—very interesting they were.

Drs. Halsted, Weir, "Col" Warren and Keen have been elected honorary members or fellows of the R.C.S. Very nice is it not? The Professor will be most pleased and Dr. Warren must be walking on air.

He also mentions Osler's lecture in a diary note:

5 July. Heard Dr. Osler's lecture at the Polyclinic [on "The importance of postgraduate study"]. Very well received and a splendid address. Met a lot of prominent people. Amused at a brief conversation between Mr. Hutchinson and Sir William Broadbent. A distinguished looking man passed and bowed as we were talking. *Sir W.*: 'Who is that, do you know his name, Jonathan?' *J.H.*: 'I don't remember exactly but it's the name of a bird.' *Sir W.*: 'No, I think it's the name of a fish.' The man's name turned out to be Turtle.

Dr. O. is a big man here—even bigger than in his own country and just as nice.

With Jacobs he later called on Sir William Broadbent, popular private consultant, well known for his studies on aphasia and on the pulse:

Sir William Broadbent gave us each a copy of his third edition with inscription. A dear old gentleman who refers to himself as being 'on the shelf' which possibly is the effect of Dr. Osler's lecture the other evening.

As is usual in English houses apparently, an M.D.'s waiting room is his dining room where we attended our call. Sir William's pictures interested us—many of them; proof and signed engraving of his 'dear old friend' Sir James Paget. A photo of 'our Princess.' Sir William is physician extraordinary to the Queen. It was amusing to hear him speak of Jonathan Hutchinson—'Poor man,' he said, 'John Hunter also died plain John.' Plain John—two of them will long be remembered. Hughlings Jackson's portrait was also there: lifelong friends. H.J.'s motto was 'Error is preferable to Confusion,' Sir William's 'Chaos is preferable to Error,' and hence they had many discussions. . . .

Other diary entries indicate that he made the rounds of some of the larger London hospitals: The National at Queen Square, Guy's,

St. Thomas', St. George's, University College, frequently in the company of Jacobs. Everywhere there was a cordial reception; H.C. liked the people, but could find little to praise on the wards or in the operating rooms. His mind, fresh from an active residency, must have been filled with comparisons, and the youthful impatience which marked his contacts with Horsley is expressed in "miserable laboratories," "dreadful careless techniques," and other similar comments in his diary.

If contemporary endeavor failed to impress him, the records of the past constantly engaged his attention. To the Hunterian Museum of the Royal College of Surgeons he returned again and again, "a wonderful place." This was a wholly new experience which could not be prejudiced by comparison. The horizons were broadening; and Osler evidently continued to keep an eye on his pupil:

15 July. Left Paddington at 10:45 for Twyford, thence to Wargrave on the river where found the Oslers at the 'George and Dragon.' After a delicious lunch at which I first made acquaintance with cold veal and ham pie we, McCrae, Dr. and Mrs. O. and Revere, rowed down the river to the next lock and then back along the narrow 'back water.' It was a perfect day and a delightful experience. We had our basket lunch and camped out on the bank of the stream till we were put off as trespassers, much to Revere's anger. He made an attempt to attack the 'rude man' with a boat hook. We all nearly expired with mirth though it was not a very proper performance. Revere is an extraordinary but not the best behaved child. . . .

The following Sunday was likewise spent with the Oslers who had in the meantime left the Thames for their cottage in the south of England.

Swanage, Dorset,
H.C. to B.M.C. *22 July 1900.*

Dear Mother, I have escaped from sweltering London town to this place due to the cordial and repeated invitations of Dr. Osler. It is an ideal seaside resort not overrun (as yet) by many. This old comfortable house situated right on the water with a table groaning with English goodies, big soft feather beds, and in a countryside of great interest, is perfect. Would that I could transport all of the family who are gathering about your table over here for the afternoon. I came down yesterday morning and we drove in the afternoon over to Corfe Castle or its ruins which date back to Saxon days, and in their ruined state back to Cromwell. Would that Mr. Oliver had seen fit to preserve the Castle. It must have been a wonderful pile. And with all of their gunpowder they only succeeded in demolishing it in part. . . . The Oslers have come down here for several years and have a cottage into which they will escape about August first. We are just opposite the Isle of Wight and the coast line is beautiful. Rocky shores, great chalk-white cliffs, rolling downs, heather in abundance, and flowers of all imaginable varieties, everywhere—a beautiful clear sea. . . . McCrae and the Chief show the effect of their week's outing and are brown and fat. They work on some literary things in the morning—play golf—bicycle, swim, sail and otherwise disport themselves during the day. . . . Have promised to be best man at a wedding—one Crockett, an M.D. from Boston, and Elizabeth LeBourgeois, Mrs. [Robert]

Chapin's sister, are to be married at Chelsea at noon. Crockett I do not know very well but the poor man has come over here all alone and needs some moral support. . . .

After this short respite the social pace quickened. Jonathan Hutchinson gave a dinner for Osler to which Cushing was invited. His lack of worldliness at this time is well illustrated by a diary entry which describes the dinner; although he had been well schooled at Halsted's table, the serving of wine in quantity seemed to astonish him.

24 July. Marylebone Carnival today. Chiefly interesting in that it almost made me late to Mr. Hutchinson's dinner for Dr. Osler, as the roads were all blocked. The dinner an extraordinary affair—I felt rather out of it—Sir William Gowers—Sir William Broadbent—Sir James somebody [Crichton-Brown inserted above] of Edinburgh F.R.S. &c. &c., a royal neurologist in whose laboratory all of Ferrier's original work was done. I sat next to him and on the other side was Dr. Church, the government appointee to go to South Africa to investigate the Army medical affairs. Dr. Manson of mosquito-malaria fame, Mr. Butlin of St. Bartholomew's, Dr. d'Antona (the neurosurgeon) of Naples, another Sir somebody Hara who wore his decorations, and two other men I did not know. Elaborate and delicious, long-course dinner with much wine of which they all drank heavily. I was astonished. The amount of alcohol consumed here is extraordinary anyway. Working men never pass a 'pub' without a peg and their betters (?) are really *no* better. The question is 'What wine?' not 'Shall there be wine?' . . .

H.C.'s activities reached a climax with the Centennial celebration of the Royal College of Surgeons, 25-27 July. At the end of the first day he wrote to his father:

69 Torrington Square, London,
25 July 1900.

It is hotter than the hinges and I have come home to sit . . . for a few hours preparatory to the 'Conversazione' this evening to be held at the College of Surgeons. Such receptions are very poor things but I go, firstly because I have rec'd an invitation and they are scarce, and secondly because I want to see the big men who have gathered for these Centenary exercises. This morning at a demonstration of the Museum by Prof. Stewart there were a lot of distinguished foreigners—v. Bergmann, Kocher, Koenig, etc. etc. You can imagine my joy when Maurice Richardson, Drs. Warren and Keen, Dr. Weir of New York and Dr. Halsted came in. It was pleasant to see some home people. The Professor looks well. He has been making a visit at Breslau with Mikulicz seeing some intestinal surgery, resections &c.—a daily performance there. Tonight's occasion will be a very formal one, I presume, with people in uniform, academic costumes, wearing orders and the like. Tomorrow comes the formal giving of the honorary degrees at London University. I wonder what the Professor will do for a 'robe and hood.'

It's a bad time to do medical things here of course and I have profited little by my stay other than to become acquainted with the hospitals and to meet some people—this and studying French which is my daily work. I am going to Paris the first of the week and I think I will be about ready to come home in a month more.

The diary entries of the next few days record the events that apparently interested him most:

26 July. Examination Hall in A.M. Saw the laboratories with the Chief and he took me afterward up to the College of Physicians. Many interesting portraits—Reynolds, Lawrence &c. Saw those of Radcliffe, Mead, Askew, and Baillie, also Gold Headed Cane and subsequently found a book about it in an old shop.

Afternoon exercises at London University were remarkable. Such a brilliant gathering I have never seen. The Fellows of the College, Lord Lister and all the rest sat on the platform—Sir William MacCormac in the centre with the two censors on each side—Marquis of Salisbury with his Oxford Chancellor's gown, the Earl of Rosebery on the other side with a D.Sc. gown. Then in a double row in front and facing them were the people to receive the honorary degrees—a wonderful collection of famous men in uniform, academic gowns, wearing elaborate orders & decorations &c. The two Spaniards looked like old monks with their yellow & black robes & bald heads. Lannelongue was gorgeous in a gold & black uniform trimmed with green, and the Italians & Russians also were fine; v. Bergmann was covered with decorations and perhaps next to the Prime Minister received the most applause. MacCormac was rather awkward in his presentations and his address could hardly be heard. Keen responded for the American recipients with some graceful remarks about the Queen who if not Queen of our persons was Queen of our hearts &c.; v. Bergmann spoke in German, Lannelongue in French and one of the Russians read an English reply. It was a great sight. . . .

27 July. Morning at College of Surgeons seeing old Hunterian relics with "Col" Warren, Richardson, J. W. White, Osler, McCrae &c. Afternoon at Guy's Hospital with Bryant. Met a lot of people. Saw Howse, the Senior Surgeon and 1st Vice President of the College, operate under an old Listerian spray. Most extraordinary sight. They (the youngsters) made all sorts of apologies for him. . . .

Bryant took me while at Guy's out to the old George Inn just around the corner. It's unchanged from the days of Pickwick when Sam Weller blacked the boots there. A nice old lady was delighted to show us about—old four poster beds, a lovely glass 'doored' china closet.

28 July. . . . Stopped in at Rolleston's to call in the late evening to pick up McCrae. R.'s a daisy—interesting talk and saw many fine old books. Sir Humphry Davy was his grandfather [actually his great-uncle] and most of his things have come down to Rolleston.

Cushing thus stayed the month out in England enjoying the unusual social and scientific contacts made possible by the Oslers. His initial reaction to Horsley as a surgeon softened as he came to know him better as a man. Their relations were always cordial, and Cushing came to admire Horsley's determined and aggressive sponsorship of animal experimentation and his scathing excoriations of the antivivisectionists. He later picked up, apparently from a second-hand bookseller, an interesting early letter of Horsley's on this subject:

25, Cavendish Square, London,
Sir Victor Horsley to R. Fielding Ould *25 October 1892.*

Dear Sir I have asked my friend Mr. Stephen Paget to send you what little literature the Association for Research possesses.

I hope that you will not permit Miss Cobbe's name to be referred to as that of a 'lady.' A woman who is proved by her own writings and by exposure in the Law Courts to have systematically falsified the published statements of scientific men for 16 years and to have termed them murderers etc. has no claim it seems to me to the title 'lady.' Much harm has been done to science work by non-recognition of her dishonesty a final instance of which I give in *The Times* today. Yours with best wishes, VICTOR HORSLEY.

Significant in the light of Cushing's later development is the interest aroused by the Hunterian Museum at the Royal College of Surgeons. His interest in John Hunter probably dates from this time, and the brothers, John and William, came to mean almost as much in Cushing's life as did Vesalius. When writing a year later about Haller he compared him with John Hunter, pointing out that when Haller died he left no one to carry on his traditions—he had had many pupils but none of them was trained to take his place. John Hunter, on the other hand, founded a school.

... The one note missing in what was to be Haller's greatness is that he did not become a great teacher, did not become responsible for renowned personal disciples, founded no great school, as he was capable of doing, and lived as an example of the concentration of learning in the individual. How different from Boerhaave, who, though possibly possessed of less extraordinary mental capacity, yet could diffuse knowledge, and whose influence was the guiding star of many great followers: even John Hunter, who drugged himself before undertaking his lectures, to such an extent did he dread and dislike them, and yet who could count Jenner, Abernethy, Cline, Astley Cooper, and others among his pupils. How different with some of the great moderns like Carl Ludwig, whose disciples before his death filled countless professional chairs in universities the world over.

French Medicine and Surgery

Cushing left Britain at the end of July and spent the next three months visiting hospitals in France and French Switzerland. His diary notes during this period were cryptic, bilingual, and more ungrammatical than usual, since his sentences often started in English and ended in French (and it would be difficult to say which was more casual—his French or his English); but much can be gleaned between the lines of his telegraphic entries. The first three weeks of August were spent in Paris, during which he made systematic use of a pocket *Guide Médical Parisien* which had just been published. He visited many of the larger hospitals and before each visit he evidently looked up the principal personnel of the hospital in order to be well posted in advance of his visit.

The days immediately following his arrival in Paris (2 to 9 August) were spent at the meetings of the XIIIth International Medical Congress, the first gathering of this character he had attended. The Congress was opened by the President, Dr. Lannelongue, in the Salle des Fêtes de l'Exposition with ceremonies which reflected the international repercussions of the assassination of King Humbert of Italy but five days earlier. Indeed, the very existence of the Congress had been threatened by reports of a wholesale massacre of ambassadors and other Europeans at Peiping, and the official mourning in the European capitols which followed the death of the King of Italy added a final note to the confusion which marked the entire proceedings. In his letters home H.C. dwells on the social side of the Congress rather than on the scientific papers, which one gathers were rather dull:

H.C. to H.K.C. *Paris,*
3 August 1900.

. . . The large meeting took place yesterday in the Salle des Fêtes in the Exposition Grounds. Such a hall I have never dreamed of. There were about 7000 of us in a small patch on the floor below the huge platform which held the delegates from all countries in uniform and full dress of all kinds. We all were in evening clothes from 9 a.m. till six when I escaped and donned my sack suit, never having had such an aversion to a white tie and 'swallow tail' before. Virchow, von Bergmann—I could not begin to give the names of people. There are more receptions to follow—one at the Elysée by the president. Paris is beautiful beyond words—stimulating. London, dull, dusty, with its continuous roar used to fatigue me: a nap in the afternoon, tea at 5 o'clock are necessary. Nor sleep, nor tea is essential here. The Exposition in spots is lovely. Am living with Jacobs at Rue de Castiglione, a very moderate room. Dr. Osler unfortunately has been called home—his lawyer brother is ill. . . .

On the 6th he sent additional details to his mother:

. . . This evening we go to the Luxembourg. It will be a treat to see the palace and gardens on a festal occasion of this kind. . . . Paris is a wonderful place. I think I will like it better than London in the end—*i.e.,* when I have a little more ability to understand and be understood. I like the Parisian medical people immensely. They are much more like Americans than are the English, curious as it may seem, in appearance and manner. Such a hospitable lot I have never encountered. . . .

Many years later H.C. recalled an episode of these days which proved that sometimes even boredom can bring results of positive value:

. . . Late one afternoon three of the congressionists, A. J. Ochsner, W. J. Mayo and myself, thoroughly wearied and fed up with listening to a succession of papers presented in polyglot tongues we could ill understand, sat gloomily on a stone balustrade of the Pont d'Alexandre overlooking the Seine. If I am not mistaken, the idea of this club [Society of Clinical Surgery] was conceived during the course of our conversation that midsummer afternoon.

This proved the incentive for the formation of one of the most stimulating and prolific surgical organizations that we have had in the United States.

He wrote his father on 12 August:

. . . The medical ceremonies associated with the Congress are finished and I have come over on the other side of the Seine to escape from people and my native tongue. My room would amuse—perhaps shock you—but it is clean, cheap and comfortable enough, though I can rap my knuckles against the ceiling with ease and have difficulty in protecting my papers and clothes from destruction when I take my morning bath—in the washbowl on the floor. I must invest in a rubber folding tub and would have obtained one in London but expected to secure one which MacCallum has and which has descended by inheritance through several hands during the past year. . . .

The medical meetings have been interesting, chiefly from a social standpoint, sizing up people and also for the privaledge [*sic*] it has offered of ingress into places like the Luxembourg—the Hôtel de Ville, the Palais d'Elysée, etc. Loubet gave a most elaborate reception there Friday afternoon—an outdoor theatrical performance, gorgeous in its effects, in the beautiful garden and the several thousand people hardly could be found. . . .

To "Ned" he wrote in lighter vein about his surroundings:

6 September 1900.

Dear Neddie Are you familiar with the smells of an old house in the "Quartier Latin de Paris?" If not, you have new sensations still to encounter. Not even the Old Corner itself is more picturesque and variegated. The street, rue des Sts. Pères, from which I have just ascended "les vieux escaliers tortueux" is lined with boulangeries, patisseries, épiceries, brasseries and other things essentially Parisian which I shall not mention. To the "Schneiderian" membrane the picture is of the impressionist school—with vivid colors. The stairs, above mentioned, leading up to my box on the 4me étage remind me of an old buffalo robe with snarled brown hair. The lower floor of M. Koch's apartments were [the rooms] of Victor Hugo whose old clothes still hang on the corner of the four poster which he occupied between novels. By the way some enthusiast has written a description of the V.H. collection of things here—published by the Century Magazine not long ago—possibly Will will remember it. I wonder if he laid any stress on the smell—he should have. To continue—another pair of stairs to ascend which without a mis-step required a week's training and I know what we are going to have for dinner, there being a predominating flavor of choux fleurs à la Marie de Maison with a dash of potage du pain—and a little bit of everything else. All of which is educational and helps one with the language.

THE LATIN QUARTER

Here H.C. moved easily into a continental way of life. The mornings were given over to "hospitaling," the afternoons to sightseeing and French lessons "à la Berlitz." The evenings were devoted to French novels and history or the theatre.

Paris,

H.C. to Katharine S. Crowell *4 September 1900.*

I have settled down to a life of virtuous domesticity. . . . It is a new sensation to pass by the Louvre without wondering which was Henry the IVth's, which

Catherine de'Medici's—to walk by the various shops without waiting to scan the attractive things in the windows—to cease to wonder who are the various people and where from—to no longer carry a map in one's hand and a Baedeker in one's pocket. A frugal existence it is—le petit déjeuner while half dressed in my room—a French lesson at nine—an exploration of some kind until noon—another frugal repast at noon, usually in a cremerie to which I bring my own loaf and where I fill up on dairy products: a bottle of cold milk, bread and butter and some *crème fraiche* to which Grove Atterbury introduced me and under the influence of which I am growing rapidly s-t-o-u-t. I presume it's the same thing as Devonshire cream of fame. Then I come home feeling like a young calf and work till seven when I dine here with M. Koch and his son Gene—all of which is time profitably spent, I trust, and a method of living "à bon marché."

Every visit to a Paris hospital was a revelation to Cushing; the conditions in the wards, the casual attitude of the medical men toward their patients, and the carelessness of their clinical records shocked him repeatedly. After visiting a hospital near his lodgings he records in his diary:

. . . Found as usual that the "Chef de Clinique était en vacance" but was directed to the surgical wards by the Concierge, where in the Salle de Malgaigne I was directed to the pavilion d'opération. There I found a M. le Dr. F., a stumpy little man who paid no attention whatever to me and whom I hated, not for this reason but because he slapped a patient and did not seem to know his business. He explored a deeply icteric woman who did not seem to have had her history taken and closed her up (after finding malignant disease—I think he called the nodules "marrons"—in the liver) most carelessly. Their technique is good though they have too many whiskers, espec. the assistants, one of whom would have made a good Pan. The visit "au lit des malades" was distressing as usual—poor, old, dirty, over-crowded wards, perhaps the best they can do under the circumstances; women examined publicly, men bared promiscuously—no histories to be seen—careless examinations—ragged looking temperature charts and so on ad infinitum. F. wore gloves (rubber) during his visit and the usual linen butcher's costume and apron. An acute appendix case was discussed and allowed to wait and there were rows of "Salpingite," the patients' names and diagnoses being written on old pieces of slate hanging over the heads of the cots called beds which were straggling about everywhere. The nurses I thought were good and I liked their plain linen gowns and caps. F. started in to do his gallstone case with one assistant (the red whiskered Pan above) cleaned up and a woman to give chloroform—the patient being stripped and cleaned up during the performance.

In all this confusion Cushing discovered a notable exception in Dr. Henri Hartmann, a member of the Paris Faculty of Medicine on the staff of the small Hospice d'Ivry, whom he met by chance at lunch in the Café Voltaire. The acquaintance broadened rapidly into friendship, and H.C. made several visits to Hartmann's laboratory and clinic during late September; there, while watching Hartmann operate, he made notes on methods for determining whether the inside of dressings was sterile, and drawings of the intestinal forceps used and of a special operating table. After an evening at Hartmann's home, he "came away laden with reprints and impressed with the amount of work he [Hartmann] did." Some of the reprints were sent on to Halsted with a letter (the only early letter to Halsted so far uncovered):

Paris,

H.C. to W. S. Halsted *28 September 1900.*

Dear Dr. Halsted I send to you today some reprints with Dr. Hartmann's compliments. He is far and away the best man I have encountered—I must even include Mayo Robson. His intestinal work is beautiful and the pylorectomy which he describes in one of the papers he does very quickly and simply. The preliminary work on the subject by Cunéo, I believe Young reviewed in the Maryland Journal recently. Hartmann's treatment of his wounds and operative technique in general would gratify the most critical individual. He has a splendid lot of young men at work with him—among them Mignot who was the first to succeed in producing experimental typhoid gall stones. Hartmann is at work at Hôpital de la Pitié at present, being Ferrier's remplaçant. Was pleased to hear him call his pylorectomy in the Clinic the other day, in reference to the totality of the extirpation, "une petite Halsted." Yesterday he gave a two-hour "dry" clinic on two cases—a gland in the groin and a small fistula in ano. It was a most interesting performance.

Toward the end of August H.C. made a ten-day trip with Grosvenor Atterbury, his Yale classmate, to Auvergne, that picturesque country in the south of France in and about the town of Le Puy-en-Velay. On this trip he kept a separate diary in which he made a number of exquisite sketches, some in water color, which again exhibited not only his powers of observation but the growth of his artistic talent.[2]

Le Puy, Haute Loire, France,

H.C. to H.K.C. *27 August 1900.*

You will doubtless be surprised to see the postmark on this letter—no more so, however, than I am to be here. In July 1893 the Pennells described (*Century Magazine*) a place, unnamed, which they called "The most picturesque place in the world" ending up their account, which was beautifully illustrated, with the aggravating question "Do you not wish that you knew where is the most picturesque place &c. &c."

The Atterburys did know and Grove and I have come down here for four or five days—would gladly stay a month. The Pennells' description is none too enthusiastic. I doubt not that we have found their hotel. The country from Clermont down—we stopped over night in Issoire—is one series of geographical surprises and, as Mrs. Van Rensselaer has said, "of verdurous delights." These *puys* or peaks are most extraordinary things—each one with a castle—a ruined château or an old 11th century church perched up on the summit in most inaccessible fashion. Happily the Pennells' indefinateness has succeeded in preserving Le Puy—a foreigner is rarely seen and the good people are unspoiled. Grove's sketch book is in constant use and I spend my time exclaiming at every vista, keeping the diary and reading French. I sent Alice a book on the cathedrals which has some pictures of the place and I will send along my notebook in time. . . .

[2] The full text of this notebook with some of the illustrations was reproduced in December 1944 (*A visit to Le Puy-en-Velay: an illustrated diary.* By Harvey Cushing. Cleveland, The Rowfant Club, 1944, 40 pp.)

Following the trip to Le Puy he spent two more weeks in Paris working at his French, writing, and doing general sightseeing. On 11 October he wrote his mother of his impending departure for Lyons. "Paris I leave with many longings. I have enjoyed my sojourn here so much. I have only one thing against it—'it's hell for horses.' I never felt so sorry for any animals before."

In Lyons, at that time the foremost medical center in provincial France, H.C. experienced a real awakening through contacts with a number of men of unusual background and intellectual capacity—Nové-Josserand, Ollier, Jaboulay, as well as Poncet who had attained international prominence by his attendance on President Carnot when he was assassinated in Lyons in 1894. Cushing spent the week of 12-18 October in their several clinics which offered a wide variety of opportunities for surgical experience. By this time he had come to recognize that there were good surgeons in France as well as poor ones, and he realized that he could learn much more than he had anticipated, but praise he gave sparingly: "I wonder if I am trying to find a perfect surgeon."

Through Louis Dor, the Lyons ophthalmologist, and his learned father Henri (1834-1912), H.C. heard something of the difficulties of French medicine—the traditional aspects of promotions and appointments—and obtained a glimpse into the life of a Continental scholar.

Lyons—12 October 1900. . . . Called on Dor (Louis) son of a Dr. H. Dor who married a Scottish woman and, thanks to her, L.D. talks English like a native. Very delightful enthusiastic fellow—knew Councilman in the Engadine (I believe when C. was there with his wife). Dor is an ophthalmologist but such a one as the following description will relate. He took me to see a patient who had lost his cornea and ant. chamber from a hot iron. The man came to Dor after 8 days just as the slough had separated. The lens fell out and iris was prolapsed. Dor replaced them, covered the wound with a graft of a rabbit's whole cornea which he sewed in place and covered with one of the thin glass arrangements for astigmatic eyes. I saw the man 8 days after this—graft taken—slightly opaque. Probably will have vision. I suggested covering eyes of Gasserian ganglion patients in same manner—Dor laughed and said "that is not necessary if you cut the cervical sympathetic. Jaboulay always does in ganglion cases." . . .

Further details went to his father in a letter of the 15th:

H.C. to H.K.C. *Lyons, 15 October 1900.*

I have just passed a most delightful evening with a Dr. Dor and his father here in Lyons. Ophthalmologists both of them, M. Dor fils being as well Prof. Poncet's Chef du laboratoire pathologique, hence my acquaintance. He is a most interesting fellow—has done some excellent bacteriological work of permanent value—some work in comparative pathology—has a command of languages which makes me green with envy, his four or five only stop short at Russian—is an Alpine climber of note—a bibliophile—and an expert ophthalmologist if

I judge aright. His father caps all this, however; but I must tell you of my curious visit. Having asked Dor to dine with me in return for some past favors he said no, you must come and take dinner with my father—and gave me the address of a place on the outskirts of Lyons where the Rhone winds around the high hill to the west of the river. It was dark of course when I arrived and I found a narrow, dark, cut-throat alley leading precipitously up the side of the hill. By the aid of many matches I found No. 55 and rang the bell. There were no windows, mind you, only abrupt walls miles high with an occasional heavy portal. The large door swung open and I entered a little stone chamber containing a lamp in a niche in the wall which dimly lighted a bare flight of stone steps. I climbed these to the first landing, hoping to find a concierge. None. The same sort of little chamber as below. I went up another cold flight—another little room. Another and the same thing without sign of life. After five of these landings I began to get worried and would have retreated to consult the street number again which

OLLIER OF LYONS REVERDIN OF GENEVA ROUX OF LAUSANNE

was not very distinct, when I was encouraged by a voice somewhere above to venture further and I finally arrived at the living part of this strange dwelling. I had merely gone up the front steps cut in the rock, heaven knows when. I have no idea what the house looks like by day but the rooms were large and irregular and full of old books and furniture and a very delightful old gentleman. He took me out on a terrace which overlooked the city and the river with its many bridges and lights, and on the other side, behind us, was a large garden with three large terraces and a tea house and fruit trees and ivy. Imagine my sensations, stumbling onto this strange abode

We sat down to a very delicious dinner and afterwards I was as well served intellectually, for the old gentleman pulled down books on books, 15th Cent. and thereabouts—Fabricius, full of original water colors; original, perfect Vesalius Anatomy; Ambroise Paré; Haller; etc., etc. And I have walked home by the river wondering whether I will wake up in the morning and find it untrue.

On the 20th H.C. went from Lyons to Geneva where he spent the day with Auguste Reverdin, the Professor of Surgery at the University of Geneva, going on to Lausanne for ten days in the clinic of César Roux (1857-1934). Roux he found "a rough diamond, son of a peasant who had worked his way into one of the best clinics in Switzerland. He is a worker—I spent six to seven hours a day in his clinics usually beginning at 7 a.m. He is perhaps best known for his goitre operations and gastro-enterostomy procedure, both of which are good. It's marvelous to see him enucleate a goitre (no anesthesia whatever, not even any morphia) in from eight to twelve minutes for the entire operation." The Lausanne experience is well described in a letter written to his mother a day or two before his departure for Berne on the 31st:

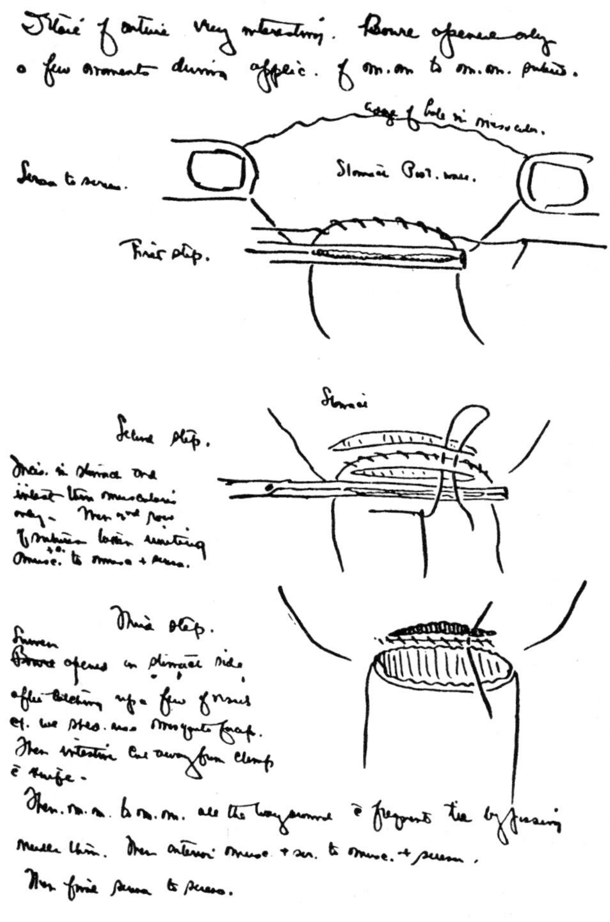

GASTRO-INTESTINAL ANASTOMOSIS
Diagram made at Roux's clinic

H.C. to B.M.C. *Lausanne,*
26 October 1900.

Lausanne itself is not so interesting as Geneva but the University here is excellent, drawing many, many foreigners from the world over. About half the medical school are Russians, and half of these women. Curious creatures they are. Roux, the Chief Chirurgien, is an interesting man—looks like Kipling—does excellent work and comes nearer to being the kind of man I am looking for than anyone I have seen. Stilling, the pathologist, also I like very much. Have just come from a delightful lunch with him, his wife and two assistants in Stilling's laboratory; one of them a nice Englishman named Bellamy. Mrs. Stilling—most attractive—is a sister of the Louis Dor of whom I wrote you from Lyons, and whose father I dined with one night in that curious place on the hill. Have also been pleased to encounter here Wm Walter Phelps' daughter Frau von Rottenburg, who is very much the same person she used to be when I knew her through the Boardmans. She is staying at Ouchy, the port of Lausanne, with her children, one of whom has been threatened with some bronchial trouble—nice children, much more American than German but with the good points of both kinds. Have been gathered into the family most hospitably, which is easier here than it would be at their home in Bonn doubtless, since they are rather prominent people, 'His Excellency' being Curator of the University—rather more than President I judge. He was Bismarck's devoted ally, as perhaps you know, and went out of political life with B. Bismarck, von Moltke and others were frequent visitors at their home, and Frau von R. has told me many interesting tales of them. She is the most enthusiastic American, in spite of her 10 years or more as a German matron.

Berne

At Berne Cushing divided his time between experimental work in Kronecker's laboratory at the old Hallerianum, and Theodor Kocher's clinic. The University, at that time one of the foremost in Europe, had had an interesting history since Berne, as the capital of Switzerland and a continental crossroad, served as the meeting place for scholars and intellectuals from every corner of Europe.[3] Its faculty was composed of men of unusual attainment. Hugo Kronecker, a student of Helmholtz and one-time professor extraordinary in the laboratory of the great German physiologist, Carl Ludwig, had been attracted to Berne at the height of his career as an experimental physiologist. Hermann Sahli (1865-1933), the Professor of Medicine and Director of the University Clinics, was as widely known as any internist in Europe. Men of similar stature held chairs in the fields of history, philosophy, and the physical sciences. H.C.'s first reactions to Berne were set down in a letter to his father:

Pension Kunchel, Berne,
H.C. to H.K.C. [*Postmarked 5 November 1900*].

I have found a boarding house a stone's throw from the hospital and it is a relief to get away from hotel life again. . . . You would laugh could you see me in this place. I have not got the people at the pension straightened out yet and only know that there are two Russian medical students, one timid young shrinking Polish thing named Imbricheck (spelled phonetically) another a buxom creature, Madam Lalamson, who has an amusing small boy named Boris—the landlady and her sister who seem to be very nice people named Lanz; a huge creature named Tagonala presumbly Italian, occupation unknown, and three or four others, diagnosis in abeyance, but all women (I think)—that is excepting Boris and one youth, also medical, who comes in for supper.

[3] Feller, R. *Die Universität Bern 1834-1934*. Berne, P. Haupt, 1935.

. . . Curious how much Kocher is like 'the Professor' [Halsted]—careful, painstaking work, elaborate technique, and all the rest which we have in Baltimore. A marked contrast to Roux who is brilliant, showy, rapid in his work. A great teacher from his startling ways of expressing things and his ability to draw—he is always at the board. It's striking how much better people seem to talk in French than in any other language. I went today to Olten with Prof. Kocher to a medical Versammlung where about 300 of the Swiss-German section were gathered. Olten is a small town—the hub of the Berne-Basle-Lucerne spokes. It was very interesting to see them—great big men of the type one sees at our American Medical Association congresses. None of them, however, were good talkers—even Kocher has awkward address. Kocher's son Albert is Chef de Clinique and has been very kind. There are many rather unfamiliar things—goitres predominating. They are well on toward their 2000th case of partial extirpation and I think there must be at present ten or twelve cases awaiting operation—most of them for symptoms of dyspnoea—an occasional cretinoid child. Kocher fils was bemoaning the fact this morning that they rarely could obtain at autopsy a normal thyroid for comparative observation, about 99 per cent of all thyroids being in some measure pathological. Dr. Kocher has offered me a place in the laboratory and possibly will give me something to work on. If not, I will go on with some things I started in Baltimore.

THEODOR AND ALBERT KOCHER

Berne itself is the most picturesque town I have seen—has an interesting history—was one of the old walled towns of this part of Switzerland and the old gates, the peculiar 17th century architecture, the arcaded streets etc. are curious and interesting. I am starting with German again with some difficulty since I find my trolley wheel from short custom runs easiest on the French wire. . . .

Further details concerning Cushing's reactions in the first few days can be gleaned from his diary:

Berne. 1 November [*1900*]. . . . Kocher's clinic in A.M. Elementary lecture at 8 A.M. by Dr. Arnat on wounds—Albert Kocher operating from 9 to 2. A.K. looks and acts much like Bob Huntington—tall, fair, gentlemanly fellow—but the operating!!—the J.H.H. outdone. It's easily seen why 'the Professor' thought so highly of their work. Detailed technique, tedious operating, absolute hemostasis—intervals between operations to encourage pesplanus &c. &c.

Strange contrast to yesterday A.M. Roux did six operations in two hours—Kocher fils did two in six hours. A goitre extirpation and repair of a small hole in a cleft palate twice operated. Except that he is more composed—"tranquil"—he works like Bloodgood. Emphasized importance of not dividing muscles in neck operations since asymmetry always results even after suture. . . .

2 November. Kocher's clinic—very tame after Roux—managed much like ones at the J.H.H. Case hydrocele—ranula—foreign body in elbow—fibroma of breast. Kocher operated—slow, clean, careful. . . . Amused at request to sign my name in Guest book which begins with W. S. Halsted—Johns Hopkins University. . . . Many cases of goitre awaiting operation. They are approaching their 2000th case. Kocher told me of his first attempts when it was almost impossible to get cases as all before the antiseptic days had died from infections. . . .

Kocher is a slight, rather cadaverous little man—neat in his appearance with a sparse, gray, closely cropped beard, very large and prominent upper teeth which make his actual smile rather ghastly and make him appear to smile often when he does not inwardly do so. I have seen almost no surgeon who did not suffer from some form of inhibitory relaxation at the operating table. K's takes the form of the Professor's—he is kindly sarcastic in his impatience—his *"Schwester, Schwester"* long-drawn-out, with the usual *stupid* at the end, must be hard to bear and is usually followed by an embarrassed flush.

H.C. found, however, that Kocher had good days and bad days and sometimes he appeared to dally most unnecessarily during an operation; he was also at times irascible. On the 6th, for example, "his inhibition relaxed this morning and he was needlessly sarcastic to the poor head nurse who does most of the assisting—the kind of Halsted sarcasm which hurts more than a good cursing out." In his notebook H.C. listed many points of Kocher's technique which he hoped to introduce at the Hopkins when he returned, one in particular being the method of draping the head for operations on the head or neck.

H.C.'s diary gives an interesting sidelight on the state of medical education in Switzerland at this time: "The poor students here have a surfeit of lectures, little practical work apparently, and no ward opportunities, not even visits. All patients are brought to the clinic." He also felt there was too little opportunity for postgraduate study.

Soon after his arrival at Kocher's clinic he had asked the "Professor" for a problem on which to work. Kocher promised one but he took his time about it and after two weeks' waiting H.C. decided to go on to Heidelberg. He was on the point of leaving when, on 19 November, he called on the elderly physiologist, Hugo Kronecker, "a lovely old gentleman enthusiastic about Welch, Bowditch, Chittenden, etc." Kronecker was much impressed by the restless young American and intimated to Kocher that he would be glad to have him do his arbeit at the physiological institute. But Swiss academic formalities had to be observed and before Cushing could start work the Professor (Kocher) must pose the problem. On the 24th: "Another week gone by in waiting for Kocher's 'proposition' promised on the 3d of the month. Called on him in despair last night." The next day Cushing received a formal invitation from Kronecker, evidently at Kocher's instigation. A day or two later Kocher's proposition arrived written in English:

1. Will you try, with the aid of Bertels in Kronecker's laboratory, to decide the question, if in compression of the brain the small veins and capillary vessels are dilated by stasis or compressed? by making an injection during a compression experiment in an animal and without that? Dog or calf would be necessary. That would be an excellent step towards better knowledge.

2. Make 1 or 2 experiments on a calf's head freshly killed with a solution which would circulate as easily as blood (ask Kronecker what the best liquid would be) and take the pressure in carotids, in sinus long. and transversus, in Vena Jugularis and cerebral pressure according to [Leonard] Hill's method, to measure the pressure as well as the quantity of liquid floating through a brain in normal state and with artificial compression with a bag of Lysbang. Notice the height of pulsations in the carotid, vena jug. and in cerebral liquor.

Professor Guillebeau at the veterinary school would certainly be willing to help you at my recommendation. . . .

3. Commotio cerebri. Is there with a commotio cerebri a pouring of blood out of the cranium veins and arteries or not?

4. Compressibility of sinus durae matris.

This was all Cushing needed. The problem was one in which he became at once intensely interested and in the course of an incredibly brief space of time he had obtained a body of highly significant data.

Outside of the laboratory H.C. was also busy, for the Kroneckers were very hospitable and he was soon involved in social functions, along with H. C. Jackson and J. B. Solley, Americans who were likewise studying in Berne.

Berne,

H.C. to H.K.C. *30 November [1900].*

. . . Today I made my debut into Berne—my social debut that is—having been asked by Professor Kronecker to dinner *i.e.* at 12.30. (Prof. Kronecker I may not have explained is the physiologist in whose laboratory I am at work. He is a kindly little man—a great friend of Dr. Bowditch—a leader in his particular branch and quite a favorite with American physiologists, many of whom come over here to work.) . . . Jackson was there, Dr. Asher (Kronecker's assistant professor), and a German gynaecologist named Shicking who is working here also. . . . Well I learned many queer things—such as the necessity of wearing your gloves until you sit down at table and other curious formalities. . . . Jackson, who apparently knew little more than I, was finally made to understand that he was expected to escort Miss K. to the table which, mind you, was not ten feet away in the room adjoining the one in which we sat. Prof. K. gave me his arm and Dr. Asher in a funereal frock coat brought up the rear. Well, it was too funny all through—an elaborate repast (Jackson and I regarded it as our Thanksgiving dinner) with several courses and wines and a bottle of champagne was opened and *Die allgemeine Physiologie* toasted, everyone was formally clinking glasses with everyone else and by the time dessert was finished I was as full inside of my belt as the salt solution frog which I just left at the laboratory appeared to be. It was a relief when we got up and everyone shook hands all round and said *Mahlzeit* and we formed procession again to the next room where coffee was served. After coffee Prof. K. played on the piano and we danced—yes danced—a curious kind of German waltz and there was much discussion as to whether the Anglo-Saxon or rather the American method of dancing was more aesthetic than the German. This all took place in a small room no bigger than our sitting room at 786 and was too amusing and curious for words. Then we all shook hands again and Prof. K. gave two lectures during the afternoon and Jackson and I went back to our respective arbeits.

The Kroneckers live in a strange little house or in the second story of a little building whose ground floor is occupied by two stores. Apparently no one is expected to work here without taking part in social functions with the university "set." Jackson is already regrettably deep in matters social. However, calling apparently is easy—the prescribed time being Sunday morning between 11 and 12.30, church being at 9.30. More of this anon. I am puttering over an arbeit for Kocher on the question of condition of blood vessels (intracranial) during cerebral compression. Have accomplished nothing as yet.

H.C. filled much of the rest of his Berne diary with reference to Kocher's clinics, but he mentions enough of his own research to enable one to complete the story.

12 December [*Berne*]. Two weeks past spent in Kronecker's laboratory for the most part. Attempting injections (intracerebral) without much success and irrigating frogs' legs without much more. Prof. K. has been most kind—yes, *rather* old [61 years], though he 'hangs on' with determination, whether in the laboratory or climbing the Niederhorn with Jackson and myself through 10 metres of snow. I gather too that his glutei are less lame than ours and his pulse less rapid than ours at the summit though he reached it half an hour later than we. (Jackson 165; guide 129; Cushing 123-116; Prof. K. 130). . . . A most interesting evening was spent last night at Prof. Zimmermann's at a professorial 'Referierabend.' Prof. Kocher reviewed Crile's work on shock which has just appeared in the University College reports. It was fine to see him dissect the work and pick out the essential and interesting things—and it interested him much.

HERMANN SAHLI
The Professor of Medicine at Berne

Prof. Sahli as usual took the other side of the question, criticising Crile's charts, especially the composite ones. Kronecker thought very little of the work. After a long discussion in which Müller, Gérard, Strasser and the rest took part we consumed a large part of the various beverages and eatables which decorated the dinner table about which we had been sitting and which had been geometrically set out like a Renaissance garden and as though a reward of merit for our two hours of abstemiousness. Asher informed me the next day that these meetings were sacred and guests never invited. If so, they were all very cordial to me. Sahli I like more and more. He is the slow, sure worker reaching his fixed conclusions only after deliberation—Kocher is quick, grasps essentials immediately, is perhaps more often wrong. . . .

17 December [*Berne*]. . . . Memories of Haller, the great Swiss physiologist and poet, cling about Berne in many ways. His old house in the town—Pavilion Haller at the Insel with a tablet erected in 1877 I presume when the building was erected 100 years after Haller's death. The Physiologisches Institut is called the Hallerianum. His best and most enduring monuments are to be found on the shelves of Kronecker's laboratory library—12 or so ponderous tomes in Latin of his collected scientific works published in 1755+ and much quoted today. I keep running across his name whether in association with cerebral surgery or muscle fatigue problems. Haller died making physiological observations on his own exitus—with his hand on his pulse—"Nun schlägt es—es schlägt noch—es schlägt nicht mehr" and he died. Haller's descendant—sein einziger Nachkomme—is a cretin dwarf about four feet high known as little Haller who was saved from a myxoedematous death by thyroid extract and whose skin now misfits him as

THE TOWN OF BERNE

THEODOR KOCHER

HUGO KRONECKER

SOCIAL LIFE IN BERNE

Top: Dinner at the Kroneckers. Frau Kronecker, H. C. Jackson, Lotte K., H.C., The Professor, J. B. Solley

Center: H.C. and Jackson lunch with the Haags

Bottom: Skating in the Berner Oberland. In the foreground are Kronecker, H.C. and J. B. Solley

PROFESSOR SHERRINGTON

does that of a rhinoceros. I saw him today in the Haller pavilion of the Insel and wondered what his forebear would have thought—probably more of the miraculous treatment, of which he, physiologist though he was, never dreamed, than of his own flesh and blood degenerate from the national Krankheit.

One of the people who influenced Cushing's thinking at Berne was Leon Asher. In those days Asher was a slender young blade who conversed and gossiped in almost any European language on every conceivable theme, including science, history, metaphysics, and dancing. He had been a medical student in Leipzig and from the lectures of Carl Ludwig he had inherited a deep interest in the historical background of physiology. Although at first alarmed by Asher's explosive ebullience, H.C. became deeply interested in his philosophy as a physiologist. "Possibly Asher's 'Geist,' (*i.e.* laboratory geist) may excuse many things. He certainly has it, as his excellent papers on the lymphatic system bear out." Cushing continued:

I have had an interesting dinner with Asher this evening at a truly Swiss—what shall I call it, "Tummy Shop"? The Hôtel de l'Étoile—on a side street, some curious stairs and into a plain room with two long tables where he said the better class of peasants were wont to go for meals or wine when in town. We dined on a three-course dinner with good Swiss wine, a sweet omelette to end with, not forgetting black coffee and 'Kirsch,' the local liqueur; all for 2 francs 50 apiece. The best part of our dinner, however, was our talk or rather his talk which went all the way from Haller to Kronecker and took in everybody on the way. Johannes Müller (Berlin), the greatest of all according to L.A.: pathologist, physiologist, anatomist, physicist, and zoologist, and I know not what else, and great, as I can see, in that he had disciples and founded great principles. Virchow, DuBois-Reymond, Schwann, Kölliker the anatomists, Haeckel the great zoologist were all pupils of his and influenced by him, and always referred to him with greatest reverence. He must have been great—greater than Haller who had no disciples, no school. Ludwig too was great in this way, 200 of his pupils at one time having professorial chairs in one place or another. Interesting that Ludwig was something of a scapegoat as a youth—founder of one of the fighting corps in Heidelberg wearing a scar himself; he was pulled out of obscurity and saved from physical dissolution by Bunsen, the great chemist, whose assistant he became and who possibly was responsible for the kymograph himself. A fine pair of amateur photos of Ludwig are in Kronecker's Arbeitszimmer at the Hallerianum. Ludwig, most amiable in private life, was stern to a degree in classroom. Story about his severity to students who laughed at a decapitated rabbit. Very rarely vivisected before students. Wrote little, four or five papers. All his papers under the names of his arbeits-genossen—many written entirely by him. Asher says Stirling's five papers were all done by Ludwig or Kronecker.

Kronecker began his work under Helmholtz as a physiologist in Heidelberg and wrote his doctor's dissertation under him. Helmholtz of course with Ludwig and Bunsen are three great lights in middle of century and later. Kronecker then went to Leipzig as one of Ludwig's assistants from 1871-1876 or thereabouts at the time of great activity there. Then to Berlin at DuBois-Reymond's call to establish the methods of Ludwig's laboratory there; from there to Berne in 1887 or thereabouts. Helmholtz himself gave up the chair of physiology in Heidelberg as he said at his *Abreisend* dinner, because he was too old to take up necessary chemical and histological branches. Kühne was called at his instigation, a man of course preëminently great in these lines. Kühne was Asher's preceptor—Chittenden his favorite pupil I believe. Helmholtz himself going to Berlin as a pure physicist to fulfil the great things expected of him. More talk of His who originally came from Basle, and Kölliker, another Swiss anatomist. Curious how many there have been, and the great surgeons Billroth, his teacher von Langenbeck, Volkmann; of Virchow and Koch's controversy in Berne, and Virchow's delight in throwing down the tuberculin work and demonstration of tuberculous disseminations; of Robert Koch himself and his governmental backing and his backing of Ehrlich in turn, and I know not what more or how accurate it all was—and we walked back to the laboratory through the muddy Berne streets in a Bernese drizzle.

H.C. had indeed been stimulated by his evening with Asher—and what he remembered of it was essentially correct. Forty years later Asher was to recall with almost equal vividness his remembrances of H.C. in those student days:

I begin with Dr. Cushing's first day in the Hallerianum. Cushing came to Berne at the suggestion of Dr. Halsted who was a great friend of Professor Theodor Kocher, director of the surgical clinic. Halsted had advised him to see Kocher operate, visit his clinic and observe his way of taking care of patients, and especially to do some research work under Kocher—"eine Arbeit." Dr. Cushing at that time was a general surgeon and I believe it was then his intention to remain one.

Well, the subject which Kocher suggested was the study of the influence of brain pressure on circulation and respiration. Kocher told him he would have to do this research work at the Physiological Institute, the Hallerianum of Professor Kronecker, he being the right man for this kind of experimental work and having a well-equipped laboratory. Everyone in our laboratory was deeply impressed when Dr. Cushing appeared for the first time. From the very first he had all the eminent qualities and the great personality together with the wonderful charm which distinguished him all his life.

Besides the subject on intracranial pressure Professor Kronecker assigned Cushing a problem in nerve-muscle physiology involving perfusion of frogs. This gave Cushing the opportunity to learn a great deal about the experimental physiology of nerves and muscles. I well remember with what cleverness, using simple but effective methods, he managed to apply pressures of varied intensity to the dog's brain. He got up on a high ladder to fix a pulley on the ceiling of the room in the Hallerianum. It served to draw up by a rope the pressure bottle, which he used to raise brain pressure. He was a most assiduous worker and untiring in his efforts to master the physiological technique new to him at that time.

He divided his time between the Kocher clinic and Kronecker's laboratory. Kocher thought highly of Cushing; what I believe never happened to any other pupil of Kocher happened to Cushing: he asked him to operate and demonstrate Halsted's method of hernia operation. How much he was a favorite of Kocher was most strikingly revealed by the way Mrs. K. treated H.C. Very dignified but very shy, especially with foreigners, she often sent her maid shortly before lunch to the Physiological Institute with a small note inviting H.C. to interrupt his work in the laboratory and lunch with the Kochers.

H.C. was a universal favorite with everyone in Berne, but most with the ladies on account of his personality and his beautiful dancing. He continued up to the last several friendships of that time, so with Lotte Kronecker, with Jeanne

Michaud, and with Elsa Haag. The chief recreation of H.C. during the hard winter of 1900 was sledding—"schlitten"—with Kroneckers and young people. Parties were arranged by the former in the neighboring hills of Berne. H.C. bought a Grindelwald sled, which he named "Gee Whizz." How rapidly he raced down the snowy slopes! When H.C. left Berne he made me a present of "Gee Whizz" and it is still in the possession of my daughter Doris.

Personally Kocher was somewhat unbending and austere and little given to entertaining, but things were quite different in the physiological laboratory. As Asher indicated in his recollection of Cushing, H.C. became involved in a gay round of social activities soon after he joined the Hallerianum and was evidently looked upon by a number of hospitable families as a highly eligible young bachelor, and, not being too familiar with continental customs in these matters, he unwittingly gave several hopeful parents more encouragement than he had intended. His conversation was always quick and he seemed to have acquired considerable fluency in German. While in Paris he had written a letter home to his mother in impeccable French; being something of a chameleon, his diary notes and protocols of Berne days were half in English and half in German. Along with the German he also acquired a long black Oslerian moustache. In June 1939 he mentions this moustache in a letter to Dr. J. B. Solley of New York City who was with him in Berne: "At that time I was sporting a moustache by day and wearing a Schnurrbartbinde at night to keep its ends erect for a few hours at least in the morning. Proud as I was of it, it had a tendency to droop shortly after breakfast." In writing of their days in Berne, Dr. Solley describes one of their early experiences:

. . . Soon after I arrived Harvey took me one afternoon out on the Morat highway one mile to a skating pond in a field. Beyond the snowclad fields, dark grey-green woods and lower mountains to the southeast were the white peaks of the Bernese Oberland, gradually changing to orange-pink, salmon pink, deep rose to faint violet as the sun disappeared behind the western hills. We skated till dusk. On the way back we stopped at a roadside inn of the Swiss chalet type, set back among the lindens. At the long hitching rail at the roadside stood Swiss ponies and farmers' wagons, some with empty reed crates, others containing unsold pigs, ducks, chickens, and so on. Inside, the men sat around clean, uncovered round oak tables, the surfaces dark and smooth from long oiling. The walls were dark panelling, richly carved. Everything was clean. The men were quietly eating and drinking beer or ale or wine. Harvey ordered Swiss cheese—not the Hoboken kind, rye bread, sweet butter and two mugs of ale. A generous meal. We emptied plates and mugs. . . . Harvey did not go again, but I went as often as possible. Not until later did it occur to me that he had taken me there knowing that I could skate but could not coast comfortably "belly-whopper," or safely sitting up on account of my right game leg from anterior poliomyelitis at four. That was Harvey—ever thoughtful. . . .

H.C.'s research with Kronecker proceeded most satisfactorily. Among other things, he had established through his perfusion experiments that frog muscle is poisoned when exposed to sodium chloride alone, and that both calcium chloride and potassium must be added in small amounts to keep the muscle in a state of normal responsiveness. By the end of March he was ready to describe the results. Kronecker called him into the laboratory one evening to write up the paper; in his shirt sleeves with a large pot of hot coffee beside him, Kronecker began to dictate the full text of the paper to H.C. in German. Shades of Carl Ludwig! H.C. interrupted him politely but firmly by saying, "If you write the paper, it will not be mine and I would not feel free to sign it." Kronecker was apparently most surprised by this, but H.C. stood his ground and the ensuing argument lasted two hours. Ultimately H.C. wrote up the paper himself and it was published in the *American Journal of Physiology*.[4]

Cushing had also solved brilliantly the problem which Kocher had posed. Through the ingenious manoeuvre of placing a small window in the skull of an animal (under deep surgical anesthesia) he was able to observe by direct vision the effect of increasing the pressure within the skull. In the course of these experiments, he made continuous records of the animal's respiration and blood pressure, and found that as the pressure within the head is increased, the arterial blood pressure rises correspondingly, being maintained at a level somewhat greater than that of the intracranial pressure. If intracranial pressure at any time exceeds the arterial pressure, circulation to the brain fails and the animal dies.

Italy

Late in February H.C., having lost weight, began to worry about his health. He had developed a persistent cough at Christmas time, and several of his friends urged him to have a rest on the Riviera in an attempt to throw off his bronchitis. That he probably narrowly missed an attack of active tuberculosis at this time was indicated by the fact that old scars were found at the apex of his lungs after his death.

He left Berne for Mentone on 20 March on the night train. "I could get no berth," he wrote his father, "as traffic is heavy this way. . . . I finally bribed the porter to let me sit in his corner and smoke and read Dickens' *Italian letters.*" After a few days' stay at Mentone, he proceeded to Italy to make the 'grand tour,' visiting Turin, Genoa, Pisa, Florence, Bologna, Padua, Venice, Pavia, and Milan. At Turin he spent four weeks (24 March-20 April), principally in the laboratory of Angelo Mosso, the picturesque Italian physiologist, who was like-

[4] "Concerning the poisonous effect of pure sodium chloride solutions upon the nerve-muscle preparation." *American Journal of Physiology*, 1 October 1901, *6*, 77-90.

wise interested in problems of intracranial pressure and the circulation of the blood to the brain.

Cushing despite his experiences in Berne could not accustom himself to the continental attitude concerning the relation of professor to assistant, and his initial reaction to Mosso was unflattering. He refers to him as "an impressionist who writes monographs—yes, books—on a few chance observations and throws on his colors vivid and thick. . . . The parts of my experiments which correspond with his ideas he greets with enthusiasm and emphasizes them by giving me a poking shove with his fingertips under the pectoral margin which I dislike. When [evidence is] contrary or negative he leaves the room."

H.C.'s initial reactions to Turin are amusingly related in a letter to Katharine Crowell:

31 March 1901.

. . . I am wrapped up in a dressing gown and an overcoat and wish that I had stayed on the other side of the Alps where it was warm and the birds sang and there were signs of spring. . . . I am working and shivering in Mosso's laboratory during the days, learning something, I hope, taking one franc meals in a restaurant with a youth who is the other pensioner here because I can sap some Italian from him and give him some German in return over our cheese and macaroni.

I know nothing of Turin as yet—only its streets and the people on them. It's a Parisien-like place and I don't care much for it. I shall write in a few days that spring has come and Torino is a great place and I'm glad I came. . . .

He also wrote his father of his domestic arrangements:

H.C. to H.K.C. *Turin, 14 April 1901.*

I have put three weeks behind me here in Torino in some mysterious fashion. In the interim the time of year has changed and one sees the bare poles of winter through a shimmer of green, and great black patches have appeared in irregular fashion on the long line of mountains to the North—recently an unbroken stretch of glistening snow. Spring still seems reluctant, however, to step in—the elms show no signs of budding as yet and that most European of all trees, the sycamore maple planus, is equally backward.

I have been very hard at work—very well and not unhappy. Other conditions would have made this life intolerable. My routine is to answer a rap on the door by "Si, Si," at seven, an acrobatic bath in a washbowl à la 67 rue des Saints Pères de Paris, and the usual continental breakfast of a roll and café-au-lait in my room to follow. The laboratory before nine where I work till one, usually then two eggs and a plate of macaroni (wonderful food—sometimes in ribbons, sometimes strings, sometimes pencils with or without holes bored through them, sometimes mushy blobs, but always the same structure apparently) taken at a restaurant pension—then the laboratory again till seven, dinner at the same place as lunch, an Italian lesson from a bald Deutscher who lives here; back to my room to read the great lot of collected literature relative to my work, and bed by 12. Not a very thrilling existence as judged by this recital. . . . Great surprise by Mosso that I choose to begin my experiments at 9 in the morning. The Italian consumes a large meal at 12 and another at 7:30, thus spoiling both his morning and evening. No one works at night. I presume it would not take the foreigner long, however, to learn the same tricks of life.

My work has been pretty successful. At all events Mosso has evinced great excitement over it and says it is "ganz neu" if you know what that means. . . .

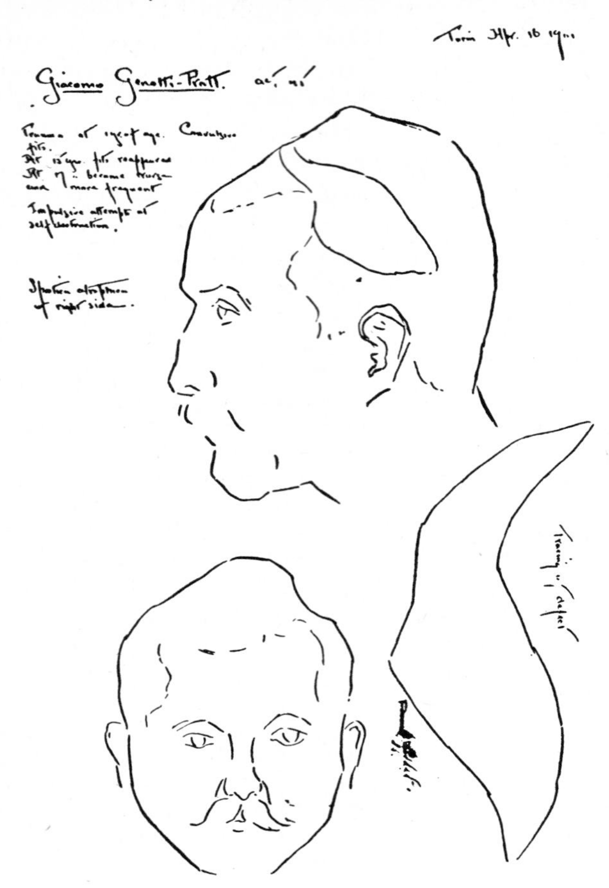

PATIENT OF ANGELO MOSSO
Showing cranial defect

On 6 April H.C. visited Mosso's asylum where he "made the acquaintance of a few hundred crazy people, among whom was a man with a hole in his skull." Mosso, long interested in the cerebral circulation as well as in the temperature of the brain, had studied a group of individuals with bony defects of the skull.[5] In one of his Turin notebooks H.C. describes a series of observations made on one of Mosso's patients which led him to conclude that there must be a reciprocal relation between the vasomotor nerves of the body

[5] Mosso, A. *Die Temperatur des Gehirns.* Leipzig, 1894.

as a whole and those of the head whereby, when the oxygen requirements of the brain increase, the blood vessels of the rest of the body, especially those of the skin, are caused to constrict, resulting in diversion of the blood from the skin to the brain. This diversion, he believed, was the basic mechanism by which blood pressure was increased when the pressure in the cranial cavity is elevated.

In the letter to his father of 14 April, H.C. had noted with some vanity, "Mosso has evinced great excitement over my work." He continued, "He wants me to stay a year and continue on the same lines, . . ." *i.e.* the repetition on dogs (dogs having been scarce in Berne) of his experiments on the effect of increased intracranial pressure. With Mosso's help, he had developed some ingenious new recording methods, the results of which Mosso urged him to write up and publish immediately. When the report was finished, Mosso wrote from Turin on 27 June 1901:

> Dear Dr. Cushing, I presented your work at once at the Academy of Sciences of Turin, but, I regret to say, that it was the last meeting but one and during the meeting the announcement was made by the president, that this year's volume was finished and that, therefore, the work would only appear in the next volume (November). . . . I therefore propose that your work be presented at the V Int. Congress [the Congress was to take place in Turin 17-21 September 1901] on account of priority. If you will allow me I shall present it myself, it will be published in November with two big charts. Please send me some original curves for the Congress.[6] Believe me, dear Dr. Cushing, Yours sincerely, A. Mosso.

The paper itself was clearly important and its summary may be cited:

> As a result of these experiments a simple and definite law may be established, namely, that *an increase of intracranial tension occasions a rise of blood pressure which tends to find a level slightly above that of the pressure exerted against the medulla.* It is thus seen that there exists a regulatory mechanism on the part of the vaso-motor centre which, with great accuracy, enables the blood pressure to remain at a point just sufficient to prevent the persistence of an anaemic condition of the bulb, demonstrating that the rise is a conservative act and not one such as is consequent upon a mere reflex sensory irritation.

Kocher, upon reading the manuscript, said of it: "Your paper from Mosso is clear, short, and convincing—has all the characteristics of a truly valuable and lasting contribution to our knowledge."

On 18 April a further report on Turin was sent to Kate Crowell:

[6] For some reason H.C. felt uncertain about Mosso's intentions, and wishing to make his results known at home, he sent a copy of his paper to Baltimore where it was published in September 1901 in the *Johns Hopkins Hospital Bulletin* ("Concerning a definite regulatory mechanism of the vasomotor centre which controls blood pressure during cerebral compression," *12*, 290-292). He moreover had the temerity to state in a footnote "reprinted from the *Archives Italiennes de Biologie* for 1901." The paper never appeared abroad, and there is no record of there having been further exchanges with Mosso after that date.

. . . It's a good thing my work is done here as I should be "ganz ein Verrückter." It's really been dreadful but I've had a great chance to work undisturbed in Mosso's laboratory during his absence in Paris and I've made a lucky find in some experimental work which won't make me famous but which will help me and some other people understand a little better some things about brain surgery. I shall put this in my bag tomorrow and flaunt my hand in the face of Turin and take the fastest train for Genoa of which I expect much—and hope to crowd many things into three or four days there—also my skin which doesn't fit any longer. . . . This chase after scientific facts is exciting but hard work and demoralizing.

Before he left Turin he saw the Giacomini Museum with its unusual collection of brains, skulls, and various anatomical anomalies, including the skeleton of a giant seven feet tall. There and in other Italian towns he made a point of visiting the hospitals and was impressed by the extraordinary service rendered by the Church to the ailing poor of various communities. It surprised him, on the other hand, that there was so little therapy in the hospitals—when an indigent patient entered an Italian hospital it was only to make the road to heaven more comfortable. Little effort was made to utilize the rich clinical material for scientific study.

Proceeding to Genoa on 20 April he spent several days visiting the hospitals, particularly the clinic of Professor G. F. Novaro, an able general surgeon. He spent the 24th in Pisa and on the 26th arrived in Florence where he was much interested in the Hospital of the Innocents:

It is with unbounded surprise that one finds an institution like the Hospital of the Innocents (1419) in the Piazza dell' Annunziata of Florence anything but old. It seems an anachronism to pass under the arches above which are the row of delicious medallions of the nephew of Luca della Robbia (1437-1528) and to find modern fin de siècle babes, not a few in most approved process of incubating. There are some two or three hundred children, most of whom I think I saw under the guidance of a hospitable and enthusiastic Sister. Rooms after rooms—for normal infants, for ill infants, for contagious disease entirely shut off from the rest of the hospital. Rooms for luetics, for cutaneous affections, a great incubator room, bathrooms, sterilizing room for mothers and infants—no, not for mothers, though 'twould be well if there were such things for most of these mothers. The greatest cleanliness, the most delightful cribs and an air of newness about everything from sterilized milk to lycopodium. The gold-medal-at-the-Paris-Exposition kind of place—a shock when one expected to find the incrustations of carelessness of five centuries.

By the 28th he had reached Bologna where he spent three days largely in antiquarian pursuits and for the first time he encountered the gorgeous écorchés of Ercole Lelli—"two figures representing complete perfection of the superficial muscles. It is hard to tell whether the artistic beauty of the pose or the perfection of the anatomical details to the very insertion of the tendon is the more occasion of delight."

From Bologna he went on to Padua, arriving on May Day. Here his antiquarian instincts were even more sharply stirred, for this was the place where Vesalius had done his work, where Fabricius had discovered the valves in the veins and demonstrated them to his young English student, William Harvey, thus sowing the seed for the

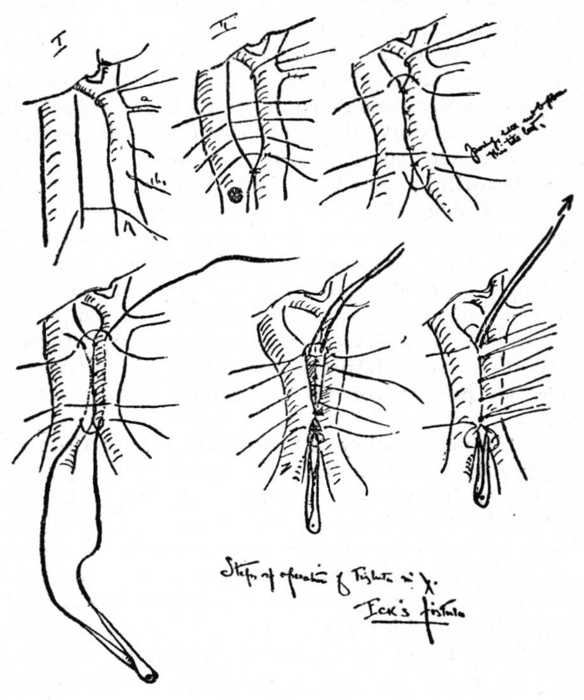

ECK'S FISTULA
Diagram made by H.C. while observing Kocher

great discovery of the circulation of the blood. Galileo had been there too. By the time H.C. reached Venice, his historical interests were almost at fever heat. He met the gracious Chief of the Venice Municipal Hospital, Davide Giordano, who "looks as though he had stepped down from a canvas of Titian, the same swarthy face, broad, low forehead, black eyes, curly, jet-black beard—a very characteristic type." From Milan on 5 May he sent his father a résumé of his tour:

. . . As you see I am about winding up my small tour in northern Italy. I arrived here this afternoon and have walked my legs off, firstly in the search for a certain Dottor Binda, secondly in my usual orientating tour of a new town. Tomorrow I hope to spend the day in Pavia, which is only a half an hour by the "little quickness," so called, hoping to see there a man who has a new blood pressure apparatus which I trust we can use in the operating room; also hoping to see something of the university. . . . I hardly know where the two weeks have gone to since my departure from Turin—on the other hand it seems ten weeks, since Florence, Pisa, Bologna, Padova and Venice have been included. It's not been so much of a whirlwind tour, however, as it sounds, since I have seen the things I wanted to see pretty thoroughly, and a glimpse at many other things which I shall remember less well, but still well enough to have made it worth while. Venice was enchanting. Perfect weather—a full moon—a dreamland city. It defies description. It's an extraordinary place exceeding one's fondest expectations. I just floated and sat about for three days and let it soak in. Would like to spend the rest of my days reading about it.

Next to this three days' dream, I think my pleasantest recollections center about the old university buildings in Bologna and Padua. The old courtyards are beautiful architecturally—kaleidescopic in their coloring & the walls and ceilings, staircases and corridors are simply crowded with inscriptions, heraldic emblems, tablets, reliefs, etc. galore. . . . The old anatomical theatre at Bologna is one of the most beautiful rooms I have ever seen—all in deeply carved wood, with great figures of Galen, Hippocrates, &c. and two figures, caryatides, supporting the canopy over the lecturer's desk which are exquisite, though meant to be simply anatomical muscle preparations. They were made by an old 'Professore' who was also a wood carver, artist, sculptor & what not. Fabricius' theatre in Padova of course is also interesting, though a simple pine well, with "standing room only" for six oval tiers of students. It's a great sensation to stand up there where Wm. Harvey, Malpighi, and others without end, have crowded elbows to watch the progress of the anatomical reawakening of the XVI hundreds.

I found Harvey's 'Stemma' as they call them, his student 'Coat of arms,' after a long search, being able to get no help from the authorities, even from the Secretary of the University, who was gracious and shrugged his shoulders and gesticulated much and referred me to the 'portinajo,' which I knew was useless, as a lira in the morning had failed to extract the information from him I wanted. Finally his face lighted up, and he and the 'portinajo' dashed off, I after them, and after a few corridors and many turnings, we wound up in a musty old room which had something to do with Galileo—guess he died there—and they both said "Ecco," and smiled; and I said "Damn," and smiled too. After we had parted I looked myself for an hour, and finally and unexpectedly found it, and said "Ecco" and smiled all alone. "Gulielmus Harveus Anglus." I have an idea that the students were divided into 'Nazioni' or nations, the ultra-montano—England, Poland, Germany Gallia, etc. and citramontano incl. the republics south of the Alps, and that there was a representative chosen from each of these groups of nations, and his arms were frescoed on, or cut in relief, in the old walls. . . .

At Pavia Cushing visited the Ospidale di S. Matteo where he found that a simple, 'home-made' adaptation of Riva-Rocci's blood-pressure device was in routine daily use throughout the hospital. H.C. promptly sketched it and was given a model of the inflatable armlet which he took back to Baltimore with him in August.

On returning to Berne in June he started to write up his results in detail and on 3 June was invited to demonstrate his brain pressure experiments at a "Referierabend" attended by the Professors of the Medical Faculty including Kocher, Kronecker, Sahli, Strasser, Zimmermann, Pflüger [the younger], Müller, Heffter, and several others. Fortunately the demonstration went off particularly well and Kocher, who had not hitherto followed the experiments in detail, was much pleased.

No word of Kronecker's experience with the independent American student having come to Kocher's attention, H.C. once again came

Dear Professor Kocher—

I would like very much to have your pass judgement on the paper before I go any farther with it. There are many questions I would like to ask.

Have I made it too long?

Have I put in too much detail and so left the principal points in obscurity? (I have left out purposely the detail of experiments)

Are there too many side points like Cerebrae pulse, Traube-Hering waves &c?

Are there too many illustrations? If not are they good enough to reproduce? Can the long Charts be reproduced as they are (i.e. the same size) and would you give one or two or three of them?

What shall I do about the translation? Asher has offered to do it for me but I dislike to ask such a great favor. Would prefer to pay to have it done.

Possibly these three last color sketches are better than the ones I gave you. The drawings are pretty accurate, also the colors though it hardly seems possible when one looks at them now. Would you be willing to let them go with my paper as well as appear in the Nothnagel?

I have made observations on exactly fifty animals so that I feel comparatively sure of most of the points though the earlier experiments naturally were very crude. On only eight (8) occasions however have I made any observations concerning

H.C. TO PROFESSOR KOCHER

Asking for criticism of his paper on intracranial pressure (13 June 1901)

up against the entrenched continental custom of the professor writing the pupil's paper. On the 5th he wrote: "Most extraordinary experience with K[ocher], who wished to go over my Arbeit before his departure for Glasgow. Planned for an all-night session, to my astonishment, and then proceeded to write the article as I went over my findings. This I told him was not my way and we had some pretty serious words, fortunately avoiding rocks. Apparently *Selbstständigkeit* [self-assurance] is an unusual quality. I was pretty plain with the Professor and told him he could write the article as his, or if he chose to have me publish it, I shall do all the work which he could correct and alter as much as he chose."

H.C. had his way and on the 13th he sent Kocher the finished manuscript which Asher had translated for him into German. Kocher evidently thought well of the manuscript and submitted it promptly to Bernard Naunyn, the well-known continental clinician, for publication in his journal.[7] Naunyn had himself worked on the cerebral circulation and since H.C. had failed to make reference to his work, Naunyn appended a peppery paragraph implying that there was nothing particularly new in Cushing's paper and that he was publishing it out of courtesy to his friend Kocher. Referring to this episode later in a letter to Arnold C. Klebs, H.C. wrote:

". . . You speak of Naunyn's uncomplimentary allusion to me in his *Errinnerungen*[8] and remember that he also spoke about Joslin though I don't recall whether Joslin was treated more or less kindly than I was. As a matter of fact, when I wrote that paper in Kronecker's laboratory I had very little chance to study the literature; if I had, I'd probably never have done the work. Asher, however, who knew the literature well, translated the paper for me and it was sent off to the Naunyn-Mikulicz Mitteilungen. At the end of the paper when published, Naunyn subjoined a "Bemerkung zu obigen Aufsatz." In this he goes on to say that he and Schreiber in 1881 made the same observations. My paper was nothing more than thunder for Kocher's monograph on Hirnerschütterung for Nothnagel's *Specielle Pathologie* and as Kocher at the time had the literature at his fingertips, I should have supposed that he would naturally have checked me up. I find in my reprint which I subsequently went over and

[7] "Physiologische und anatomische Beobachtungen über den Einfluss von Hirnkompression auf den intracraniellen Kreislauf und über einige hiermit verwandte Erscheinungen." *Mittheilungen aus den Grenzgebieten der Medizin und Chirurgie*, 1902, *9*, 773-808.

[8] "Zwischenein ging in Königsberg die grosse experimentelle Hirndruckarbeit vom Stapel, die ich 1881 mit Schreiber publizierte. Ich habe immer viel von ihr gehalten, doch wuchs mein Selbstgefühl gewaltig, als 1902 Cushings Arbeit über den gleichen Gegenstand erschien. Cushing ist tatsächlich an keiner Stelle über uns hinausgekommen. Dass er es dabei fertig gebracht hat, unsere Arbeit mit keinem Worte zu erwähnen, hat mich erstaunt, obgleich sie bei Kocher gemacht war. . . ."

abstracted that he had less reason for his protest than I feared he might have. But then, this is all past history and we needn't go into it. I was of course sorry to have given him any offence; nor did I know that I really had done so, for when I visited him afterward in Strasbourg on my way home he was very courteous. I have a sketch of him, I remember, in my notebook, and thought he looked a good deal like Robert Browning, and both of them looked more like a business man than a doctor or a poet.

Shortly after the Germans had invaded the Low Countries, Klebs made this penetrating comment about the Naunyn episode:

Nyon, Switzerland,
5 June 1940.

. . . I have good reason to think that behind Naunyn's bland and rather kindly appreciation of the 'characteristically American' there is something less kindly, a reproach of superficiality, such as Wenckebach in his obituary of Osler made about the *Practice:* "diese uns etwas oberflächlich erscheinende Werk." My reason is a remembrance of an after dinner conversation at Naunyn's house in Strassburg on the occasion of my farewell visit to him en route to America in 1894. N. had been an old friend and coworker of my father's and so I called on him and was invited with his house officers to dine. After dinner N. mentioned to the others my intention to go to America. Thereupon the oldest of them, the first assistant whose name I have forgotten—a big, husky, heel-clicking fellow with *Schmisse* in his unsympathetic features—quite contemptuously held forth: 'That one who has to leave here will go to America I can understand, but why one who can make his way here should prefer to go the way of defaulters, thieves and worse is incomprehensible to me." Naunyn and the others did not say anything or little to this, but it was clear enough to me that they shared the view. . . .

Now that the two modes of life have come to a great clash once more, now that the German might seems to triumph over their antagonists, I remember the sarcastic remark of a friend at the outbreak of the last war: 'We fight for the right to be inefficient.' . . . From these slight and apparently unimportant differences in behavior result the graver clashes that seem to bring our civilization to the brink of an abyss.

Harvey Cushing had indeed made an impression on many laboratories of Europe and his "Selbstständigkeit" was variously interpreted. His cavalier behavior in submitting his Mosso report for simultaneous publication in two journals no doubt injured his reputation, and it may have had something to do with Naunyn's treatment of him, for gossip concerning those of independent mind travels fast. The stand which he took, however, both with Kronecker and Kocher must be regarded as praiseworthy, even though he achieved his end with a bluntness and lack of diplomacy that must have considerably disconcerted men of their seniority.

Cushing left Berne on 27 June, going first for a brief visit to Strasbourg where he met von Recklinghausen, attended a lecture on toxicology given by Schmiedeberg, and visited the clinics of Hofmeister and Fürstner. Two days later he was in Heidelberg where he was received by Erb, the prominent neurologist. There he met Cohnheim, the pathologist, and performed an operation for Rudolf Magnus in his Institute of Pharmacology. Magnus had apparently asked him for pointers about exposure of the brain in animals; on the same evening he took H.C. up the Neckar on a picnic and gave him too much Swedish punch.[9] With scant mention of this episode he wrote his father about his reactions to Germany and the Germans:

Mainz, [Germany],
[30 June 1901].

H.C. to H.K.C.

. . . I saw all the big medical people—had a delightful visit in the old Bürgerspital with Naunyn the great Kliniker, who is one of the handsomest men I've seen over here—very unlike the usual German professor type, Hofmeister,

SCHMIEDEBERG FÜRSTNER ERB

Schmiedeberg, Madelung the surgeon (least interesting of all) etc. Was very lucky in catching them at their various clinics and so saw more in a day than I could have otherwise in a week. If you desire to find out more of them, you may consult later the diary of H.W.C. which is assuming uncomfortable dimensions from many pictorial inserts. There were many Americans there at work—one of the J.H.H. men with Hofmeister and Schmiedeberg's assistant in pharmacology, Faust, was once with us in Baltimore but likes it so much and is so much liked also over here that I presume he will stay.

It was all very different from plain old Berne of course. I was awakened early in the mornings by tramping feet goosestepping past my window, "Ich hätte die Ehre" and drum and fife corps which must make the people swear unless they find such matin performances useful as alarm clocks. Of course there are soldiers galore and the music and gaiety and the evening concerts must be very fine. . . . I went on to Heidelberg Thursday night where I found Solley and had another round of activity. Erb, Czerny, Arnold, all the big men I saw: also had the good luck to run across Kussmaul on the street. He is still a very sturdy-looking man, 80? perhaps, handsome as Lenbach's picture makes him out to be.

. . . Yesterday I went to a student *Mensur* [duel] which didn't please me greatly. What sport there can be in slashing up another man's face in cold blood is more than I can see. One man, a left-hander who seemed to be at some disadvantage I think got twelve gashes—lips, ears, cheek and forehead, and must have lost a

[9] When H.C. tasted Swedish punch again in 1929 (during a visit to Stockholm), he said it still nauseated him.

half litre of blood before the youth who seemed to umpire the function decided that somebody's Ehre was satisfied and the combatant might be sewed up. There may be skill in it but it's hard to understand—they stand perfectly rigid and slash with only a little wrist play, and no graceful body work or exercise as in French fencing. And their formalities and salutes and false politeness are dreadful. Absolutely *no* sign of what we would call fellowship. If that's sport here, give me baseball and a sunny outdoors and a few deformed knuckles [H.C. broke his left little finger at baseball].

Friday night with Cohnheim's son, Otto, a Swedish physiologist, and two or three other M.D.'s we went up the river, the Neckar, to a Gasthaus where a Swedish punch was brewed and after which we floated down in the moonlight past the old castle and the hills covered with blooming chestnuts. It was lovely, though I think I should have preferred it without the punch. Do you realize that we can read over here at this time of year at 9:30 without difficulty out of doors? The long twilights are beautiful. . . . I got into a 'Raucher' as usual hoping to smoke an after-breakfast cigarette when an old lady and a shower of baskets followed me so I missed my smoke which made me mad—madder because when we had almost reached Mainz she fumbled around in her packs and finally found a cigar which she proceeded to light and consume. . . .

PFLÜGER

Later there was a "delightful visit with the physiologist, Pflüger, who is said to be a boor and a hermit. A curious lecturer . . . never still a moment. An hour's talk with him afterward in the English he had learned to speak playing croquet." At Bonn he renewed an old acquaintance with Marian Phelps, formerly of Cleveland and now the wife of His Excellency Franz von Rottenburg. As H.C. had explained earlier to his mother (p. 176), von Rottenburg as *Kurator* of the University of Bonn was a powerful local figure who for many years had served as private secretary to Bismarck. Cushing stayed with them for two days and from the neurasthenic von Rottenburg gained some idea of the mentality of the Prussian ruling class.

A Month with Sherrington

Following his peregrinations on the Continent, Cushing crossed on 3 July to London, and after three days spent in seeing old friends and acquaintances (including Osler and Jonathan Hutchinson) he proceeded in accordance with previous arrangements to Liverpool on Sunday, 7 July. His first impressions of this city appear in an amusing note to his father written the evening of his arrival:

Liverpool,
H.C. to H.K.C. *7 July 1901.*

Do you know anything about Liverpool? Does anybody—except that it is where most of the transatlantic liners dump their hoards of passengers who step from the gangway to the train that whisks them to London? . . .

The afternoon was passed in orientating myself. I found Sherrington's house after some difficulty. He was away for the day. I wandered back through miles of treeless streets lined by unending rows of plain houses with no variations to break their monotony. The university and laboratories were locked and showed no signs of life. I hope Liverpool will wake up tomorrow. There are plenty of people about—all standing on the street corners or strolling aimlessly about. There is much to be said in favor of the English Sunday, but for a stranger it's deadly, especially after the music and gaieties of the day on the continent.

I saw the Oslers for a short time Thursday. McCrae does not arrive until this week some time. Sorry to have missed him. Friday I went up to Cambridge hoping to see the physiologists there—Langley, Foster and others but they were all away. Glad to have seen the Colleges however.

UNIVERSITY COLLEGE,
LIVERPOOL.

Physiology Laboratory
June 11. 1907.
[1901]

My dear Sir,

I shall be very pleased to welcome you in the Laboratory here, if you care to come to us. I do not expect to be here during the first half of August, but perhaps you would arrive early in July. Nor need my absence make any difference to your use of our Laboratory.

Believe me, with kind regards,
most truly yours
C. S. Sherrington

Dr Harvey Cushing

Unfortunately the diary of his stay at Liverpool is brief, and even by quoting the full text, only an incomplete picture can be drawn. H.C. was ever forthright in his first appraisals of people, and his initial uncertainties concerning Sherrington become the more diverting in the light of their warm friendship and mutual respect of later years.

12 July. No. 9 Princes Avenue in the care of one Mrs. Blossom. My first week has been consumed in the attempt to determine a line of work—Sherrington having no special suggestions—in finding out that an English laboratory may be in worse shape than an Italian one, and in watching two or three very interesting experiments.

The people. Sherrington is a great surprise. He is young, almost boyish if 36(?) [actually 43], nearsighted, wearing when he has not lost them a pair of gold spectacles. He operates well for a 'physiolog' but it seems to me much too much. I do not see how he can carry with any accuracy the great amount of experimental material he has under way. He has as many strings to his bow as Spiller, &

writes & publishes as much. As far as I can see, the reason why he is so much quoted is not that he has done especially big things, but that his predecessors have done them all so poorly before. It's a great surprise all through physiological work to find that practically all observations are open to dispute or various interpretations.

The simple point, for instance, concerning cortical stimulation which came up yesterday. It has been stated that only the crests of the convolutions can be stimulated. Letting out the fluid from the subarachnoid space & so emptying the sulci allows motor response to be obtained for entire precentral gyrus. Sherrington's observations during last two days show that the ascending parietal convolution is not irritable until one gets high up. This leaves a very small strip one convolution away *i.e.,* the ascending frontal for arm, face &c. I asked S. if the convolutions were not irritable as they dipped down. He did not know but found they were way to bottom. This makes a surface 2/3 or more greater than the exposed surface. Furthermore the slicing off of surface as done by many & subsequent stimulations prob. stimulated cells as well as tracts of corona radiata.

HUTCHINSON

Th[illegible]hole thing referable to experimental neurology much to my surprise is st[illegible] most crude condition. The problems offered are immense. S. goes at [illegible] fast. Few notes are taken during the observations, which is bad. S. says [illegible] he has a bad memory—putters around his laboratory till after 7 in the [illegible] trying to catch up on things & then is used up and doesn't begin till [illegible] eleven the next day.

[illegible]ünbaum the 1st Assistant—chemical side, is rather sarcastic—just misses being [illegible]ery nice fellow—is selfish.

Macdonald No. 2 is a jovial Scotsman wedded to his pipe—says his "pipe wants [illegible]o smoke." Very amusing man with a keen sense of humor.

Fröhlich who has come out of Wien with his young wife is working on sphincter subjects. I saw one of his experiments which S. did. Cat with hemisphere removed, post decerebrate muscular rigidity. Stimulation of various sensory nerves, muscular [nerves], &c. relaxes or increases this rigidity from stim. or inhibition. Same thing from stim. of spinal cord. One definate [*sic*] point where relaxation on same side was called out. Walking movements &c.—ear reflex—movements of tongue &c.

Cortical localization experiments

Chimpanzee—mapping out of areas—not in agreement with books.

Orang-utang from Borneo. Small-eared, red-haired fellow. Only done once before—Beevor and Horsley. I did the craniotomy for Sherrington who was afraid the skull was too thick.

Electrodes—single blunt-pointed platinum wire or else double as desired. If former used, a large electrode or big shovel. Two-cell battery, zinc &c. Use current strong enough to make exposed muscle contract. Prompt reactions on motor area, very weak ones over eye centres forward—& over occiput ditto. Evidently a different physiolog. arrangement. Motor areas do not run over a centimeter on inner side. Extraordinary how well the animals behaved—how long they lived. Today's exper. 9 hours—10 mins. for lunch—room temp. 87°.

Saturday. It does not come within the realm of everyday experience to be called upon to trephine a gorilla. This happened to me yesterday—the day before an orang-utang and the day before that I saw Sherrington do a chimpanzee. Experimentation on a large scale certainly—and expensive, Mr. Gorilla, though ill and unacclimatized, having been in Liverpool only 24 hours, cost 250 pounds.

Almost too human to be sacrificed for exps. of questionable importance. Sherrington has shown from them that the old interpretation of cortex is wrong —probably the precentral convolution is nowhere 'reizbar' [excitable] and over on the mesial surface only for a slight distance does irritability extend. Furthermore there are no inter-areas, as Horsley says.

The gorilla's motor area was enormous. Eight-hour observations in a room at 82-87°F. with Macdonald, Grünbaum, Fröhlich & the dieners. Hard work. The gorilla was anaesthetized in his cage with blankets about it. We also were almost anaesthetized at the same time. Grünbaum had a revolver so that if [it] came to the worst, there would be no scandal.

A few additional details concerning the week are given in the next letter to his father.

University College, Liverpool,
H.C. to H.K.C. [*14 July 1901*].

I have been having the most curious experiences during the past three days. I never expected to be called upon to trephine a gorilla but yesterday had that extraordinary experience. Sherrington has been going over the old cortical localization observations with some new methods and on the higher apes and seems to be finding some new things of considerable importance. I happen to have come just in time to see the work and to be of some assistance. In fact it takes many hands. Yesterday seven of us worked from two in the afternoon until ten in the evening in a hot-house room over the hardest kind of application—concentrated observation. I'm glad however that I do not have to take the responsibility of sacrificing these poor hairy *ape-like-men,* for such they seem.

Thursday a chimpanzee—Friday an orang-utang—yesterday a gorilla. Pretty expensive research is it not? The gorilla cost over $1000 and was a fine big specimen from the West Coast. He was ill however and apparently had pneumonia and I doubt if he would have lived more than a day or two. It's very difficult to keep them long alive here and this poor little man had only been in the country twenty-four hours. The bacterial flora of city air can hardly be endured by one who has spent his days in a mangrove swamp. . . . There are lots of monkeys in the 'ménagerie': several Macacus whose acquaintance I made first in Berne. They are very wild little fellows—one never catches them asleep (unlike the 'chimps'). A dog-faced monkey ("Fannie") very tame and friendly—a Bonnett, whose salaams and salutes at command are most comical. One of the chimpanzees with a large part of his motor cortex removed is a most delightful acquaintance. How he does like to have his chin scratched! The most jealous creature, however, you can imagine. If he sees you pat and play with dog-faced "Fanny" he gets mad and sulks.

Oh, they are a fine race—more human really than we are. I wish you were here to make their acquaintance with me.

A memorable week indeed, with the motor areas of three of the great anthropoid forms all subjected to study within a three-day interval. Cushing had turned up at a psychological moment in Sherrington's epic research, for there was probably no one anywhere in the world better qualified to make a surgical exposure of an anthropoid brain than he. Not only had he just been through five years of surgical training under Halsted, but he was also fresh from his experiences with Kronecker, Kocher, and Mosso during which he had studied the brain and cerebrospinal fluid pressure of the macaque. Sherrington was grateful not only for the surgical assistance which Cushing gave, but also for the remarkably clear drawings of the anthropoid brain which Sherrington later used when he and Grünbaum (whose name was changed to Leyton) came to report their results.[10]

16, Grove Park, Liverpool,
C. S. Sherrington to H.C. *8 September 1901.*

My dear Cushing, . . . After a pleasant time in France, and later in Sussex with my wife, I have got back here: I find a good deal to do in the way of photographing and studying those brains you helped us so much with. It will be some little time before I can get the things put together into a connected story. Among other helps most useful are your drawings—an excellent set of which, of the chimpanzee 'Miss,' I find you left here for me.

Your lesion was just as it should be—so also proved to be the one (post central) we made on the previous Saturday morning. I think you may like to have photographs of these, and when I get them finished I will send you prints.

My wife is not with me here now—still riding and driving about her old county in lovely weather—or she would I know join me in sending best regards to you. We shall always remember your visit to Liverpool—much too short a visit—with lively pleasure. Believe me Sincerely yours CH. S. SHERRINGTON.

Grünbaum, Macdonald, and all are away just now, including "George" [Cox, Sherrington's laboratory attendant].

During his brief stay in Liverpool Cushing took a great fancy to Alfred Fröhlich,[11] and he gives an entertaining account of the formation of their "Manx Club" and an excursion to the Isle of Man made with a view to studying problems of inheritance in tailless cats.

21 July. The Manx Club goes to the I.O.M. on a combined "Wissenschaft und Vergnügens" Excursion: the Fröhlichs, Pinels, and the foreign corresponding member. Object—scientific—is relative to the question are "Rumpies" real or artificial—like poets born or can they be made? The discovery of a three-day-old (eyes not open) family with two "rumpies" and one "stubbin" showing no signs of amputation settled the question. Further statistics given in a letter to H.K.C. The Viennese tripod get much enjoyment from the characteristics of the American member who sends for tea when he does not like his coffee instead of drinking it, and who objects to being over-charged for cats.

Isle of Man,
H.C. to H.K.C. *21 July 1901.*

The scientific desires of the 'Manx Club' have been gratified. We have discovered 10 cats during the past hour: 50% without tails ("rumpies"), 10% "stumpies" and 40% with the normal appendages. One family of 3, 2 blacks "rumpies," 1 yellow a "stumpy," all 3 days old. Mother a "rumpy," father un-

[10] H.C. reproduced one of the colored maps of the gorilla cortex in the meningioma monograph published in 1938 (p. 598). Several of his line drawings are included in Leyton, A. S. F., and Sherrington, C. S. "Observations on the excitable cortex of the chimpanzee, orang-utang and gorilla." *Quarterly Journal of Experimental Physiology,* 1917, *11,* 135-222.

[11] This was just prior to the time that Fröhlich was to publish his memorable paper describing the syndrome which still bears his name.

known. Also a large number of "stumpy" fowls. No three-legged men as yet encountered. Hall Cain seems to have a monopoly of the 'tails' of the island.

But the work on the anthropoid motor area went forward, and there follows another illuminating passage in his diary:

25 July [*Liverpool.*] Prof. S.'s explanation of the disparity of his and the old observations is that Ferrier, who did the earliest work on the monkey expecting wide areas [of representation], used strong currents and succeeded in calling out responses which he says, however, were not so distinctive as the ascending frontal convol. responses.

The cortical area for cutaneous sensation which must be present somewhere if we may draw an analogy from the usual aural &c. areas is 'unbestimmt.' Monk, Watt &c. would place it in motor area but this doubtless is wrong and only muscle sense is present there. Horsley and Schäfer place it in the gyrus funiculus but acknowledge that in its removal, which they found followed by sensory paralysis, they may have injured the mesial superior convolutions. Here lie Schäfer's shoulder over foot &c. areas.

Sherrington suggested that here may be the sensory area—the chimpanzee yesterday responded like a sensory response when this area was stimulated.[12] The motor responses are slow and different from the motor cortex ones, but each time when the animal was stimulated there it opened its eyes & was evidently the recipient of some great stimulus.

The month came all too quickly to an end, and several days before his departure he wrote a breezy letter to his mother, telling her of his plan to join McCrae in Scotland.

University Club, Liverpool,
H.C. to B.M.C. *29 July* [*1901*].

I missed writing you yesterday owing to the appearance of McCrae who came up from London en route to his ancestral country in the 'Hieland.' Being a year since I have seen him there naturally was much to be gone over and we talked almost without intermission from midnight Saturday when I routed him out of his bed in a hotel, until Monday, this morning, when work began again. It was very nice to see his cheery face again. I am almost the last of the laboratory-ites at present. The Fröhlichs departed for Vienna this morning thus dismembering effectually the Manx Club; Prof. Sherrington left for London and the Continent later in the morning, leaving me to finish an operation on a poor little chimpanzee who seems to be as chipper this evening and to eat bananas and to like to have his chin scratched with the same enjoyment he evidenced before a large piece of his brain was removed. What a useless and annoying organ it is after all! I shall probably finish up the small things I am doing by Thursday and hope to follow up and meet McCrae in Glasgow, spend a few days there and also in Edinburgh and possibly visit the Oslers in North Berwick. The 15th of August is drawing near indeed; I seem to have lived a lifetime since last I crossed the sea—curious too as it's been only a few weeks.

Saturday I took a bicycle ride with the Sherringtons to Chester—picturesque little town it is too! An ideal place for a University with all its history—its Cathedral and old towers & walls & quaint streets. Instead they are trying to have one established here. The 'University College' is only a piece of one whose

[12] A few years later Cushing found this surmise to be correct since on stimulating the parietal lobes of conscious human beings, sensations were experienced. "A note upon the faradic stimulation of the post-central gyrus in conscious patients." *Brain,* May 1909, *32,* 44-53.

other foot is in Leeds and head in Manchester. The people here are dissatisfied and want the whole shooting match.

The next few days were spent with Thomas McCrae near Glasgow. Very brief note was made of the current exhibition ("Some Whistlers in the fine new permanent art gallery &c. were pleasing. The Exposition itself very tame. McCrae refuses to shoot the chute with me.") and except for his drawing of "Ye sturdy Scot" and various photographs of the Exposition his attention seems to have been wholly focussed on things medical:

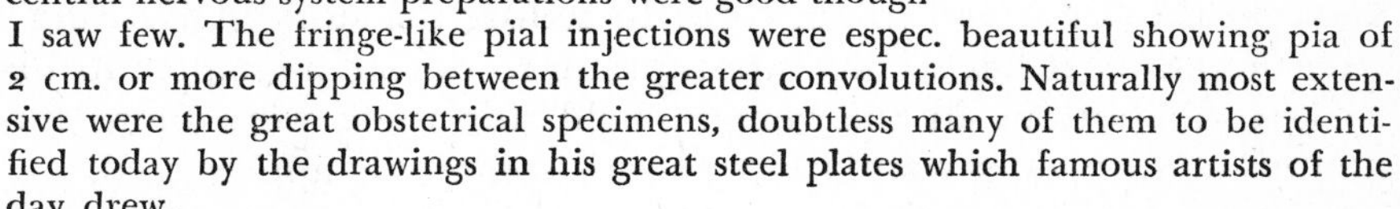

McCrae and I went out in the morning to the new Infirmary and after making inquiries about Macewen departed for the University buildings where under the guidance of Teacher and Prof. Young we had a most interesting two hours in the Hunterian Museum. William is for Glasgow what John has been to London. The former seems to have been the better brother of the two if less famous. The collection which Teacher has just been getting into shape is really wonderful—mostly Hunter's old things, the "wee ones" being preserved today as when he "put them up." The lymphatic injections on which he and John and Baillie and Cruikshank worked are fine—comparative illustrations from all sources—mercurial. Did he not get his idea from [Mascagni] of Padua, the discoverer? Many central nervous system preparations were good though I saw few. The fringe-like pial injections were espec. beautiful showing pia of 2 cm. or more dipping between the greater convolutions. Naturally most extensive were the great obstetrical specimens, doubtless many of them to be identified today by the drawings in his great steel plates which famous artists of the day drew.

Hunter was a fastidious worker and publisher. His lectures in the old School must have been famous indeed, illustrated by the preparations as well as by dissections. One thing to make W. deserving of fame was that he discovered John. A coin collector—a naturalist—a bibliophile par excellence. The old books are indeed a rare collection—manuscripts—several hundred or so volumes &c. &c. A librarian who reads is lost. Prof. Young says 'one who doesn't is' or words to that effect. Many old photographs—old paintings—the Reynolds Hunter—as an old man and with his famous retroversion of a gravid uterus in a jar—Sir Isaac Newton's death mask—Titian's painting of Vesalius, &c.

This visit to the Hunterian, as it turned out, may have been a significant event in Cushing's life and the idea of forming a library possibly crystallized in his mind as a result of seeing William Hunter's great collection. At all events, he often referred to it in later years; and a British review written in May 1944 of the catalogue of Cushing's library states that it is the finest collection of books left by a medical man since William Hunter willed his great collection to Glasgow.

CHAPTER VII

Physician and General Surgeon

1901–1907

TO HIS junior assistants, whether medical students or house officers, Cushing always offered the advice that they should make themselves first of all good physicians; and if they had a leaning toward neurological surgery, he also insisted that they should become proficient general surgeons before they specialized in neurosurgery—they must be as much "at home" in the abdomen as in the head. During his years at the Peter Bent Brigham Hospital in Boston, when his large neurosurgical clinic was flourishing at its height, he never permitted his neurosurgical patients to be segregated from other surgical cases; they all remained together on the wards. By this procedure he hoped to keep his men constantly in touch with the problems confronting the general surgeon.

And so in his own career he started as a general surgeon, and continued to operate in the wider field long after he had begun to concentrate on the brain and spinal cord. In telling the story of Cushing's life, therefore, it has seemed appropriate to devote a chapter to his early contributions in the general field, for these were more numerous and of wider significance than is commonly appreciated.

He had returned from his year abroad on the *SS. Commonwealth* which docked in Boston on 23 August 1901. On the 24th and 25th he visited friends at Little Boar's Head, New Hampshire; he spent the 26th in Boston seeing friends and catching up with news at the Massachusetts General Hospital. He then proceeded to Cleveland, via the Buffalo Exposition, and spent three weeks visiting his family and making plans with Kate Crowell for their wedding the following June. While in Boston he had missed William T. Porter, Editor of the *American Journal of Physiology,* but Dr. Porter wrote the next day: "I am very sorry not to have met you during your visit in Boston. May I ask whether you intend to practise medicine or whether you have chosen physiology as a career? You may be interested in knowing that there are two vacancies in this department." H.C.'s reply to this letter is not preserved; and while he always prided himself on his contributions to physiology, there is nothing to indicate that he took Porter's proposal seriously. When he reached Baltimore, however, he was still uncertain as to whether there would be a place for him in Halsted's clinic. During the summer Dr. Hurd, the Superintendent of the Johns Hopkins Hospital, had written him a cordial letter—most cordial for Hurd, since he was ever cautious and non-committal as H.C. had already learned during his four years as a surgical resident:

Baltimore,
Henry M. Hurd to H.C. *8 July 1901.*

Dear Dr. Cushing: I have delayed replying to your letter of June 14th until I could have a conference with Dr. Welch. We both feel alike in reference to your returning here, and hope that your future lot will be cast in with the Medical School. I am sorry to say that there are no available rooms in our building; in fact Dr. Halsted wishes to put on two additional members of the staff, for whom we have no room. No action has been taken in reference to any additional assistants in surgery. We all feel, however, that the teaching of the third-year students, as at present arranged, is extremely unsatisfactory. Last winter Dr. Halsted was called away frequently, and I suppose hardly met them a dozen times. Dr. Finney is becoming increasingly busy, and the inroads upon his time to do the teaching work are very great.

I am not in a position, of course, to make any definite statement, but I hope before you decide on any location you will come to Baltimore and have a conference with Dr. Welch, Dr. Osler and Dr. Halsted. Welch, Osler and myself are very anxious to retain you here, and we feel that in many respects this is the best place for you. I am sorry that I cannot offer you a room in the Hospital.

Everything is assuming its usual summer air at the Hospital. All the heads of departments are away, and everyone who can get a vacation is seriously considering where to go. Dr. Halsted is in North Carolina, but talks of going abroad. Dr. Welch is in Baltimore, but constantly talks of going to Atlantic City. Dr. Osler, of course, is abroad, as also McCrae. . . . I hear most favorable reports of your work abroad. With kind regards, I am, Sincerely yours, HENRY M. HURD.

"None of the faculty here," H.C. wrote to his father on 20 September, "so I will have no definite information before the first." Halsted had returned on the 29th but not until the middle of October had he made up his mind; there then followed a most revealing letter from H.C. to his father which is quoted in full because it discloses one of the most characteristic traits of Harvey Cushing's nature: namely, a burning personal pride which, throughout life, made it almost impossible for him to request anything from anybody. "What I disliked was the asking. I wanted offers." For years at Harvard H.C. could never bring himself to ask that his budget be increased, despite the huge growth of his clinic. He expected that Harvard, in recognition of his work, would increase it spontaneously; but Harvard failed to do so, and he never quite forgave those in administrative authority. Countless instances of this trait might be cited, and it forms the background of many of his reactions.

H.C. to H.K.C. *13 October 1901.*

The die is cast and I am to remain. I would dislike to dwell on the uncertainties of the first two weeks here which were rather forlorn. I do not quite understand why, when I regard the time from present perspectives, because everyone was apparently glad to see me and I knew I could have everything I asked for. What I disliked was the asking. I wanted offers. Everything, however, has come about satisfactorily, I think, and gives me a good line of work and all that is left is for me to come up to the scratch. I hope I will be able to.

I will have the 3rd year class once or twice a week, afternoons, in a 'Surgical Anatomy' course which means practical, regional, applied &c Anatomy and which will be followed in the Spring by an *Operative* Course for which I would like to use both cadavers and animals. Both courses are optional and with no examination which means presumably that the students will drop off toward the end of the course (especially if it's not good). Still it will be easier to conduct for the few, especially in the practical part, since the quarters are rather cramped. There is lots of work to be done in preparation as you may imagine. The people at the anatomical building, Prof. Mall especially, are interested and most ready to help in every way.

Besides this I will have, after all the backing and filling, the neurological side of the Clinic. Inasmuch as this was what really brought me back here according to a proposition from Dr. Halsted six months ago I rather hung on to it. I must work in the neurological dispensary mornings with Dr. Thomas and try to learn something in general about nerve cases—then I will have entry into the wards to see the house cases and one clinic a week with the 4th year surgical group on this material and a chance to operate on them once a week. Should I ever have any patients (I have one now with a boil and am worried to death about him. Curious isn't it? Have had a series of *16* on that leg of mine and regard them with indifference), I can take them to one of the private hospitals here, the Church Home or the Union Protestant Infirmary where most of the younger men do their work.

I hope to move in to 3 W. Franklin in a couple of weeks. There is much tearing up of carpets, getting of linen, building of bookshelves etc. at present in all of which the Goodwillies have taken an enthusiastic hand. Mr. G. likes to go down and smooth the old mahogany furniture; Mrs. G. would have the whole house rearranged for me and doubtless put Futcher on the 3rd floor; Mary just naturally likes to manage and plan; I am playing rather a passive part but am greatly delighted that they are amused. Later on I will pretend to keep afternoon office hours 2-3, and will have a 'yaller' shingle on the door. McCrae thinks I ought to hang out a transparency. . . .

It appears that after another two weeks H.C. had had a conference with Halsted. Writing of this episode later H.C. indicates that Halsted actually gave him very little encouragement:

My return to Baltimore was largely due to pressure brought to bear by Welch and Osler. After long delay, I was finally given an appointment one afternoon at Eutaw Place, the 'Professor' receiving me in his dressing-gown and slippers. He suggested that I take up and teach orthopaedics, which I could not very well do without displacing Baer to whom I felt somewhat responsible. So in a small way I started in with some work at the Church Home and Infirmary; and finally in the distribution of the teaching which we juniors usually arranged among ourselves Finney suggested that I take over the course in operative surgery which previously he had been giving on the cadaver.

In this way the dog course began with a selected group of 3d-year students in what was subsequently Florence Sabin's room in Mall's laboratory. It became a popular course and soon forced the building of the Hunterian Laboratory which MacCallum and I shared.

The Oslers

While waiting for Halsted to make up his mind H.C. once again began to see something of Osler.

H.C. to H.K.C. *29 September 1901.*

. . . Dr. Osler came Wednesday and I dined there the next night with Harris the bacteriologist also recently back from abroad. I gave him your greetings which pleased him and spoke to him about the Beaumont book. I never saw such a man: he asked me if I would care to see Beaumont's letters, several hundred of which he had gathered somewhere: correspondence with Alexis [Beaumont's celebrated patient with a fistulous stomach] for the most part, from the time of the first observations up to 1854 or thereabouts. Alexis must have been a rascal or his wife, and they must have led B. and Lydell a miserable life. Squandering and demanding money before allowing (and finally not allowing) a continuance of the work. Dr. O. has brought back a great pile of old books: very rare most of them and elaborately bound in Levant etc. old Linacres, Harvey's works, more Lockes etc. . . .

Although Cushing had had many contacts with Osler during his four years as resident at Hopkins, he apparently had not come to be on intimate terms with him until the summer of 1900 in Europe. By that time W.O. was at the height of his career and was well known in the United States and Canada not only as a brilliant diagnostician, but a gay, sunny personality whose wit, literary talents, and epicurean tastes were so widely appreciated and his popularity so great that he had ultimately to escape to Oxford in self-protection. Cushing's nature was basically different from Osler's but there can be no doubt that he attempted in many ways to emulate Osler's cheerful, outgoing ways and was profoundly influenced by the man, even to accepting stern criticism, for Osler did not hesitate to chastise.

1 West Franklin Street,
W.O. to H.C. (by hand) *3 March 1902.*

Dear Cushing I arranged with Dr. Hurd—he did not understand that they were your private patients. He must have you put on the Hospital Staff in some way officially.

You will not mind a reference to one point. The statement is current that you do not get on well with your surgical subordinates & colleagues. I heard of it last year & it was referred to by a strong admirer of yours in N.Y. The statement also is made that you have criticized before the students—the modes of dressings, operations &c of members of the staff. This, I need scarcely say would be absolutely fatal to your success here. The arrangement of the Hospital staff is so peculiar that loyalty to each other, even in the minutest particulars, is an essential. I know you will not mind this from me as I have your interests at heart. Sincerely yours, Wm OSLER.

1 West Franklin Street,
W.O. to H.C. (by hand) [*undated*].

Dear C. Do nothing of the kind! Who is free from faults—& failings! It is a simple matter—"Keep your mouth (as the Psalmist says) as it were with a bridle." Your prospects here are A.1. & we need you. Yours ever, W.O.

This reproof was no doubt timely for Cushing's stormy temperament was well known by this time, and there were some, less able than he, who would gladly have had him go elsewhere. Men of basic integrity generally accept honest criticism and it is to Cushing's credit that his respect for Osler grew with the years as the preface to his volume of Osler memorabilia clearly testifies:[1]

22 January 1920.

Beginning with the kindly admonition [not to neglect mention of juniors connected with reported cases] when I was a young Surgical house officer at the J.H.H. first trying my feeble literary wings, through letters to a few days before his death—these I find among my papers. There must be many more scattered among books and pamphlets and most of the letters received during the war period and about Revere are in my journals, at least all those I managed to preserve. It was Revere's death unquestionably that so undermined his health he was an easy prey to his terminal pneumonia. The note from Jersey on the 2nd anniversary of the boy's death addressed to 'Dr. Harvey' shows how great was his concealed emotion even then.

There are other letters among the Spielmann correspondence over the Vesal portrait but the extent to which the man influenced my own life, as he did that of all others with whom he came in contact, is shown by the notes and clippings and pictures which occur in all my books and papers. I had entirely forgotten the Baltimore scrapbook until I began to look over these accumulations. In it are found data concerning the Ship of Fools book club—the John Locke dinner—our presentation to him of the Dictionary of National Biography—the slip recalling Revere's annual celebration of Guy Fawkes' day—the notes from his text book describing the writing thereof—J. Wm. White's examination paper on the Textbook—the 'Fixed Period' address and something of the extraordinary reaction to it in the press which gave us so much anxiety and distress and which sent him to Oxford with a sorry heart I am sure. It undoubtedly had a great influence in checking contributions to the fund we were raising for the Faculty Library and Osler Hall and put the project in which I was greatly interested quite out of the question—namely the purchase of 1 West Franklin St as the future home of the Med-Chi Faculty.

Meanwhile K.C. has unearthed many old Kodak pictures among her things which were pasted in her "Willie book" and my journalettes—the "Oxford," "Budapest," "European Notes," "Harvard Unit in Paris," the Scrap Book of the London Med. Congress 1913, all contain much about him and 13 Norham Gardens and Lady Osler. When they left Baltimore many of the household possessions were scattered among the "latch-keyers," as we were called, for a lot of us were given keys and came and went at 1 West Franklin Street as though it were our home—and it was. To our lot fell the early volumes of the *Atlantic Monthly* which had been in the library of the senior Dr. Gross and W.O. wrote on the fly leaf:—

> This set came from Phila with the widow Gross when she undertook the care and education of one Egerton Yorrick Davis to whom the volumes were a daily comfort at breakfast at 1 West Franklin St. Baltimore
>
> Wm OSLER

[1] Written somewhat hurriedly before he had been asked to prepare the Osler biography.

This was true for he used to breakfast alone at 7.30 before others were astir and usually had an open page of the 'Autocrat' spread before him. He wasted little time on the morning "Sun." Then we were given some dining room chairs which we still have—and I the book shelves of Dr. Gross Jr. as well as the tall set of drawers his father used as an instrument repository. The last thing taken from the house was the door plate which Lady Osler told me to unscrew and keep the morning she departed and which I have had mounted on a block of the Virginia sand-stone from which the house was built. It was characteristic of her that the house was scrubbed from top to toe before she left even though it was known that its demolition was to take place. It began indeed the very next day as those of us occupying the old Carroll house next door can testify.

I know of no really satisfactory pictures of Dr. Osler. In his portraits and set photographs he always appeared somewhat dour and he was anything but that. The most characteristic features of all these pictures are the attitudes, particularly of his hands. In the innumerable Kodak pictures, on the other hand, he was almost always undignified and making fun—blithe and gay as was his wont. Possibly the best of these pictures is the one with Revere in a group taken in Oxford the year of 'Grandma' Revere's visit there.

There are innumerable things on Dr. Osler's trail that will continue to crop up for many years to come. One thing that I have seen no reference to in the many recent notices is the secret early history of the J.H.H. which is under lock and key to be opened in 100 years. It is probably an amusing skit on the early days. I once saw the book and he read a note from it about Halsted's courting of Miss Hampton.

After his plans for settling at 3 West Franklin Street had crystallized, he turned his mind to the Yale Bicentennial:

Baltimore,
H.C. to H.K.C. [*Thursday*] *17 October 1901.*

. . . I have some visions of going on to attend the ceremonies at New Haven Monday to Wednesday. This may not materialize for several reasons—financial, a dentist appointment Tuesday, and because I hope to come home for Harry Mosle's wedding Nov. 16th and can't make too many breaks. Don't be surprised however, if I write you from there in a few days. Would like to see the Hunter-Jenner-Cooper letters very much. Mumford came down from Boston and read us a paper on Jacob Bigelow (the father) last Monday [14th]. One of the best historical papers I have heard in a long time. Look for it in the *Bulletin* ere long.

Of course he could not resist the Yale Bicentennial, and in a note written from New Haven, 22 October, he describes it as "a great occasion." The Osler biography gives a vivid description of the great academic ceremony:

From October 21st to 23rd there was a gathering at New Haven to celebrate the bicentenary of Yale—an occasion which brought together delegates from countless universities at home and abroad, as is the way with such festivals. The exercises culminated in a ceremony remarkable in many respects, but particularly in that it gave opportunity to bring out the extraordinary qualities of two very unusual personages—Hadley, then President of Yale; and the man whom fate a short time before had made President of the Nation. Some threescore men of letters, of science, and statesmanship from various parts of the world were presented for degrees—John Hay, Marquis Ito and so on; from the Johns Hopkins were Remsen, Gildersleeve, and Osler; and, youngest of all, the Professor of Jurisprudence and Politics at Princeton University, by the name of Woodrow Wilson, to mention but a few of them. To each of these sixty as they were presented in turn, without reference to any notes, Mr. Hadley addressed himself appropriately and briefly in conferring the honorary degrees—the last of them on a man to whom, as a private citizen a few short months before, the invitation had been sent. Turning to Theodore Roosevelt, he said: 'But one name now remains,' whereupon an extraordinarily moving scene was enacted.

The "Latch-keyers"

Returning to Baltimore he now began to settle down to the year's work. As already indicated, he had decided to join forces with two close friends, both bachelors, Thomas B. Futcher and Henry Barton Jacobs; toward the end of the month Futcher and Cushing moved into 3 West Franklin Street, next door to the Oslers. From this address on the first of November he writes: "I have been a week here in the new quarters and am quite settled. No patients but plenty to do preparing for my classes. Futcher's week at housekeeping began today." Presently he started to use his first letterhead, designed after the style of those of Thayer and Osler.

The residents at 3 West Franklin were promptly given latch keys to the Osler household[2] and with this intimacy for nearly four years it is scarcely surprising that H.C.'s biography of Osler two decades later contained so much personal detail. These latch-keyer days were evidently gay and happy ones. The bachelors took turns in doing the housekeeping: when Jacobs brought in the provender (or telephoned for it!), they seemed to do very well; when H.C.'s turn came around, one gathered that they all but starved for H.C. was ever more intent upon working than he was on food. Writing to Jacobs in August 1938 H.C. reminisced about "the days when you and Tom Futch and I shared 3 West Franklin Street together. I never quite knew where you lived though I suppose it was on the second floor, sandwiched between your juniors. And then I think that Kate and I moved into your quarters, which led me to get so enamoured of those ecclesiastical bookcases in the middle room that Madame Carroll sold them to me when I went to Boston, along with the Shakespeare inkstand with its concealed bell that rings on twisting one of the books on the pedestal." In January 1932 when the Henry Barton Jacobs Room at the Welch Library was dedicated in Baltimore, H.C. recalled the latch-keyer days once again in a diverting bit of allegory after the manner of du Maurier. "The man-next-door" was, of course, W.O.:

[2] The original latch-keyers were Jacobs and William S. Thayer, but Thayer left No. 3 West Franklin Street after his marriage in September 1901. Dr. W. W. Francis, Osler's nephew, who was then a medical student at the Hopkins, moved into No. 3 whenever the guest rooms at No. 1 became overtaxed (which was often).

Once upon a time, long, long ago—almost a third of a century—there were three men who lived as happily together with what little they had as did Taffy, the Laird, and little Billee. There was primarily *the bearded one* [Henry Barton Jacobs], then *the bushy-browed one* [Thomas B. Futcher], and finally *the nondescript one* [H.C.] who had nothing beautiful and distinguishing about him and so belonged to the common herd of men. They dwelt on a side street of a most pleasant town, in a rented, four-decker house, on whose door appeared three shingles so well-polished as to intimate to the unwary that they were doctors of long experience. But as the bushy-browed one alone had that look of wisdom, which lured patients to him even against their better judgment, to him was apportioned the ground floor—properly speaking, C deck. To the nondescript one, who was least likely ever to be consulted, A deck was given over; and the bearded one, who was in a state of expectant hopefulness, occupied B deck, with an office up only one flight. . . .

One peculiarity of the abode was that the possessions of the owner, including innumerable mural cabinets and book cases which were carefully locked against prying fingers, left no wall space for the three tenants who, therefore, in their early days found it convenient to possess only one book apiece—a textbook of medicine presented to each of them by the man-next-door.

You are, perhaps, beginning to suspect the locus of this four-decker house, but you can have as yet no possible suspicion of who were its occupants. They differed considerably, not only in outward appearance and corresponding desirability as doctors, but in the way in which they did their marketing—a responsibility which was assumed in weekly rotation. The bearded one did his by telephone at a place with the jumpy name of Hopper Mac Something, which was costly. During the succeeding week, the eyebrowed one endeavoured to economize by sending a person named William to market, which left him no time to clean the steps and polish the shingles, which was bad for business. Hence, to even up on the third week, the nondescript one, like the little pig, went himself to market, purchased his gudgeons and chipped beef and cried "wee, wee, wee" all the way home.

Now this was all very pleasant and delightful and might have gone on forever had it not been for two things: *one* was that the expensive bearded one and the penurious nondescript one began each of them to cast an eye about for some one who might be persuaded to do their marketing for life. The *other thing* was the man-next-door. For he surreptitiously at about this time began leaving catalogues of second-hand books on decks A, B, and C—one at a time at first and then in such numbers they could not be overlooked. The eyebrowed one only had time to read them in bed, but the unemployed twain were at it—when not marketing—pretty much all day. Each two would warn the third to beware—to yield meant the beginning of the end—read the damn things but never send orders.

It was in vain. Each got the infection for which, like the common cold, there is no known preventive. So when mysterious brown paper parcels with foreign stamps began to arrive, there was, of course, some mistake—probably ordered by the man-next-door. But finally, when something all three had secretly ordered, each having previously warned the others "not to think of such a thing—the very idea of one pound ten for such a trifle and last month's market bills unpaid!"—when, I began to say, some item under these circumstances came by post to one of the three, there would, respectively, be gnashing of teeth and pulling of beards and eyebrows.

This, alas, however mournful to relate, was the beginning of the end. The bearded one said he could endure it no longer—he would take to himself a wife who would not double-cross him in his catalogomania. It was very sad, but the nondescript one soon followed suit, and then the man-next-door, who was the real cause of the mischief, fled the country, and it is easily understood what, in turn, the eyebrowed one was obliged to come to.

But the point of the legend is, that the bearded one, because of his peculiar method of marketing by telephone, got a grasshopper's start over the other two, and that is the chief reason, my dears, why we happen to be here today, listening to this old Aesculapian fable whose moral is clear.

Henry Barton Jacobs, a Harvard graduate of the Class of 1883 (M.D. in 1887), had left 3 West Franklin Street in the spring of 1901 to accompany his patient, Mr. Robert Garrett, one-time presi-

DR. HARVEY CUSHING.
3 WEST FRANKLIN STREET.

CONSULTATION HOURS:
2-3 P. M.

BALTIMORE. Nov 19 [1901]

Dear Father

Arrived safely this a.m. some three hours late however. Saw Alice for lunch, once more. [illegible] a life saving [illegible]. It was so generous that I dined on it but anyhow — [illegible] on it this morning and had [illegible] over, to resuscitate two Lexingtonians who apparently were famishing ~~apparently~~ as there was nothing to eat on the train and we were stalled 17 miles out of Baltimore by a break down until about 10 o'clock.

Lovely weather here. What a contrast to the slushy days at home. At least someone told me they were slushy. I did not have time to notice and am not much influenced by weather?

THE FIRST LETTERHEAD

dent of the Baltimore and Ohio Railroad, and his wife around the world. Mr. Garrett died in China, and sometime after Mrs. Garrett (*née* Alice Frick) had returned to Baltimore she married Dr. Jacobs (2 April 1902). Following his marriage, Dr. Jacobs retired from active practice, and over the years he and Mrs. Jacobs were important benefactors of Johns Hopkins University and Hospital and of many other institutions of art and learning. Their Baltimore home at 11 Mt. Vernon Place contained one of the finest collections of French art in private possession in the country.

Thomas B. Futcher, a brilliant Canadian educated at Toronto (M.D. 1893), followed Osler to Baltimore and served as resident on the medical service at Johns Hopkins Hospital from 1894 through 1901, while H.C. held the corresponding position on the surgical service. Being warm friends, they did much to bring the two services together. Futcher remained with the Cushings at No. 3 West Franklin Street until 1908. In 1909 he married Marjorie Howard of Montreal, daughter of Palmer Howard, the Professor of Medicine at McGill. The Futchers were much beloved in Baltimore and he practised there until his death in 1938.

The Mütter Lecture

During November H.C. had devoted most of his spare time to the preparation of the Mütter Lecture which he had been invited to give in December in Philadelphia. In the lecture he summarized the experimental work which he had carried out at Berne on the relation between intracranial pressure and the blood pressure. The lecture was one of his best and in a sense it marked another milestone in his career since it attracted wide attention both when given and after it was published. In it his prose begins to have a somewhat lighter touch than in his earlier, rather laborious papers. As with all of his writing, H.C. evidently wrote and rewrote the text many times, and the manuscript gives evidence of his having struggled with it even more energetically than usual. The paper is particularly well illustrated and includes colored sketches showing the appearance of the blood vessels of the brain at normal intracranial pressures and when pressure is elevated, as viewed through the ingenious window device that he had developed for making direct observations on the intracranial circulation. He had expected that his father was coming on for the lecture, and the next day he wrote to him expressing his disappointment:

Baltimore,
H.C. to H.K.C. *4 December 1901.*

I cast my eye about last night rather sheepishly looking for my pater during some embarrassing introductory remarks by Dr. Brinton. I am sorry you did not come on as I was rather looking forward to poking about Phila. with you today and to bringing you back here with me. The lecture went off much better than I could have hoped with a good audience despite a drenching night and a huge crowd afterward at Dr. Packard's to meet the guest of the evening. Everyone was very cordial and said complimentary things as a matter of course and formality. I was pretty tired and would have courted a railroad accident, a fire, or typhoid fever to have escaped the ordeal—rallied fortunately after I got up and saw it through well. Largest crowd they ever had at a Mütter lecture.

Have been spending the day largely with Flexner and saw much of the Philadelphia work. Flexner is responsible for the infusion of much of the new life and spirit. Was especially interested in the new Library—wish you could have seen the collection of Franklin engravings there, almost equal to yours—also in the Students' Club, Huston (?) Hall, membership two dollars a year which has closed every saloon in a radius of two miles of the University; the Museum of Anatomy etc. etc. Went over this afternoon to the old Penn. Hospital. First time I had ever seen it. Interesting, is it not? Flavor of the M.G.H. only more so perhaps. Founded in 1755—George the II—with fine old books, portraits, buildings, traditions. Wm. Penn himself, in lead, in the Yard has an interesting history. His two sons John and 'Fountain'? were moulders or something of the sort in London and cast this large figure of the father 'in plumbo'. It was discovered 10 years ago by a Philadelphian in an old junk shop in London and sent over. Wm. is too heavy for his lead ankles and about once a year breaks off completely or bends over 45° or so somewhere in the legs which look most rachitic now. The last double Pott's fracture has been badly repaired.

In the years that followed in Baltimore, H.C., in addition to starting to specialize in neurosurgery, made three highly significant contributions to medicine and general surgery: (i) clinical studies on

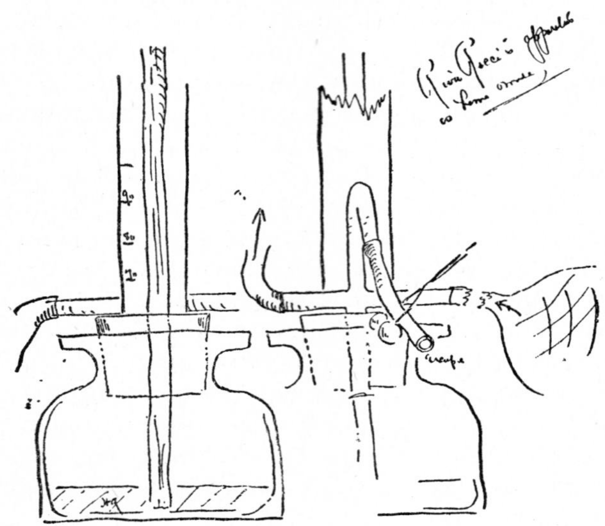

CUSHING'S DIAGRAM OF RIVA-ROCCI'S APPARATUS FOR DETERMINING BLOOD PRESSURE
From *Diary*, 6 May 1901

blood pressure; (ii) the establishment of the Hunterian Laboratory for Experimental Surgery; and (iii) the extension to the surgical clinic of Ringer's and Locke's studies on physiological saline.

Studies on Blood Pressure

Cushing's experimental work in Berne had been largely concerned with the regulation of blood pressure, particularly in relation to pressure within the skull. In the course of these studies it had become evident that the level of the blood pressure in an animal gives indication of the animal's physiological condition; if, during a surgical procedure, the blood pressure should fall unduly, the operator is forewarned that the animal's condition is poor. It will be recalled that during the years at the Harvard Medical School and the M.G.H., Cushing and Codman introduced ether charts so that the anesthetist could record the patient's pulse and respiration at stated intervals throughout an operation. At that time, however, the methods for determining the blood pressure had not yet been fully developed for clinical use. There was consequently no reference to blood-pressure determination in the early ether charts.

When Cushing saw the Riva-Rocci instrument at Pavia, he realized that it was exactly what was needed for use by his anesthetists during surgical procedures. Almost immediately on his return to Baltimore he developed a new anesthesia chart and insisted that blood-pressure readings be taken during all major operations. His first report, which appeared in the *Annals of Surgery* for September 1902, bore the title "On the avoidance of shock in major amputations by cocainization of large nerve-trunks preliminary to their division. With observations on blood-pressure changes in surgical cases."

Cushing had returned to Baltimore in September 1901; the following Christmas he went to a meeting in Cleveland where he told George Crile of the advantages of the Riva-Rocci apparatus over the Gaertner instrument which Crile was then using.[3] W. T. Councilman, who also attended the meeting, overheard their rather animated conversation, became greatly interested, and interrupted them in his usual halting, stuttering voice by saying, "What has this to do with the practice of surgery?" He apparently became at once equally interested in the matter and less than a year later (24 Oct. 1902), he invited Cushing to come to Boston, if possible with Crile, to "give a practical demonstration on the subject of your apparatus for measuring blood-pressure, and speak of the advantages of knowing just what the heart is doing in surgical operations generally." Both Crile and Cushing accepted, and a special meeting was held at the Boston Medical Library on Monday evening, 19 January 1903. The title of the program was "Consideration of blood-pressure." Crile spoke first on "Some observations on the methods of control in the blood pressure"; Cushing followed with a paper bearing the title, "Clinical value of blood-pressure observation." The papers were discussed by William T. Porter, James M. Jackson, and Richard C. Cabot.[4]

As a result of Cushing's paper, a printed circular was sent out in

[3] Dr. Crile refers to this in his monograph *Blood-pressure in surgery* (Lippincott, 1903) as follows (p. 358): "In the first part of the series of observations upon the human blood-pressure the Gaertner tonometer was used, when Dr. Harvey Cushing, to whom most of the interest in blood-pressure work in this country is due, brought the Riva-Rocci instrument to my attention. The latter instrument, especially with Cushing's modification, proved itself decidedly more practical."

[4] H.C.'s paper was published in detail in the *Boston Medical and Surgical Journal* for 5 March 1903, *148*, 250, under the title, "On routine determinations of arterial tension in operating-room and clinic."

February 1903 to all members of the Department of Surgery at the Harvard Medical School, requesting that a committee be formed to consider the "importance of blood-pressure observations in surgical diagnosis and treatment." The letter occupied three printed pages

DEPARTMENT OF SURGERY,

HARVARD MEDICAL SCHOOL.

FEBRUARY 1, 1903.

DEAR SIR:

The recent work by Dr. Crile on Surgical Shock and the representation by Dr Cushing of the importance of blood pressure observations in surgical diagnosis and treatment have produced a wide-spread interest in these methods of investigation of surgical problems and one which the Surgical Department of the Harvard Medical School desires to encourage in every way within its power.

To this end the Committee on Surgical Research has organized an investigation, in order to determine, so far as the opportunities in this community will allow, the extent to which blood pressure observations in surgical cases may be of value from a clinical point of view.

The Committee will be glad to receive the suggestions of all surgeons who may be interested in the subject, and they cordially invite your criticism of the following plan.

It is proposed that a representative of the Committee be appointed for each of the hospitals here concerned, the Massachusetts General, Boston City, and Children's. This representative of the Committee will provide the apparatus necessary for the estimation of blood pressure in clinical cases, and will give such

HARVARD BLOOD-PRESSURE CIRCULAR

and was signed by Herbert L. Burrell, Edward H. Nichols, and Robert B. Greenough. The committee was formed: it met and remet and deliberated at length on each occasion; eventually it was decided that the skilled finger was of much greater value clinically for determination of the state of the circulation than any pneumatic instrument. Consequently the work was put aside as of no significance.

Once, in telling the story, Cushing, much amused at recalling the details, repeated the following verses from Oliver Wendell Holmes' "Stethescope Song:"

> Now, such as hate new-fangled toys
> Began to look extremely glum;
> They said that rattles were made for boys,
> And vowed that his buzzing was all a hum.

Despite the deliberations of the Harvard committee, medical men throughout the country began to take an active interest in blood-pressure determination. Crile's book had appeared in the autumn of 1903 and the world at large fortunately turned a deaf ear to the recommendations of the New England committee.[5] Most interesting is an early letter from W. W. Keen:

W. W. Keen to H.C. *Philadelphia, Pa., 16 March 1903.*

My dear Dr. Cushing: I have received from Eimer and Amend the Riva-Rocci instrument. In acknowledging it, I suggested to them that a set of directions for its use should be sent with it, as I think few persons would know how to use it unless this were done. Secondly, I would like to know how you manage to prevent its being knocked over and broken, especially if the patient struggles any under ether. Any other hints as to its use also will be of service to me.

I have read with the greatest interest your paper ["On routine determination of arterial tension in operating-room and clinic."] and Crile's in the Boston Journal. I should like very much to have, say 200 to 250 words at the outside as to how to use it, *i.e.* the Riva-Rocci instrument, and the interpretation of the blood pressure for the new Edition of the American Text-book of Surgery. Of course it can only be a suggestion; not anything long. You can do it so much better than I that I am going to ask you to do me this favor. Moreover, please do not allow your modesty to prevent the mentioning of your own name, for if you do not put it in, I shall and very possibly may put it in wrong. I want to say, therefore, that "Cushing has pointed out," etc. Of course give credit to earlier investigators. . . .

In a letter to Ralph Major of Kansas City, written in April 1930, H.C. had this to say in reminiscence:

[5] Cushing's second report on the routine use of blood-pressure determination appeared in September 1902 in the *American Journal of Medical Sciences* (*124*, 396), in a paper entitled, "Some experimental and clinical observations concerning states of increased intracranial tension." Preliminary reports were also made at the Johns Hopkins Medical Society, 1 December 1902, by Henry Cook, a fourth-year student, and reported in the *Maryland Medical Journal* for February 1903 (p. 83), and again in the *Johns Hopkins Hospital Bulletin* by Briggs and Cook (1903, *14*, 92). This report was also made before the Johns Hopkins Medical Society, 17 November 1903. For early references to continental literature on blood-pressure determinations, see: a series of articles by N. Vaschide and J. M. Lahy on "La technique de la pression sanguine particulièrement chez l'homme," in the *Archives Générales de Médecine* for September, October, November, and December of 1902. The title of the Harvard Report is as follows: "The Division of Surgery of the Medical School of Harvard University—Report of Research Work, 1903-1904," *Bulletin No. 11* (March, 1904, pp. 1-41). The last sentence in the report summarizes the attitude of the committee: "The adoption of blood-pressure observations in surgical patients does not at present appear to be necessary as a routine measure."

. . . I brought the first Riva-Rocci apparatus to this country from Pavia in 1901 when I came back from my year abroad and introduced it into the Johns Hopkins clinic where Briggs and Cook subsequently modified it and got it put in a box. The original apparatus was of course simply home-made, and was perhaps as good as any of the more recent ones. . . . But I am not so sure that the general use of a blood-pressure apparatus in clinical work has done more than harm. Just as Floyer's pulse watch led to two previously unknown diseases,

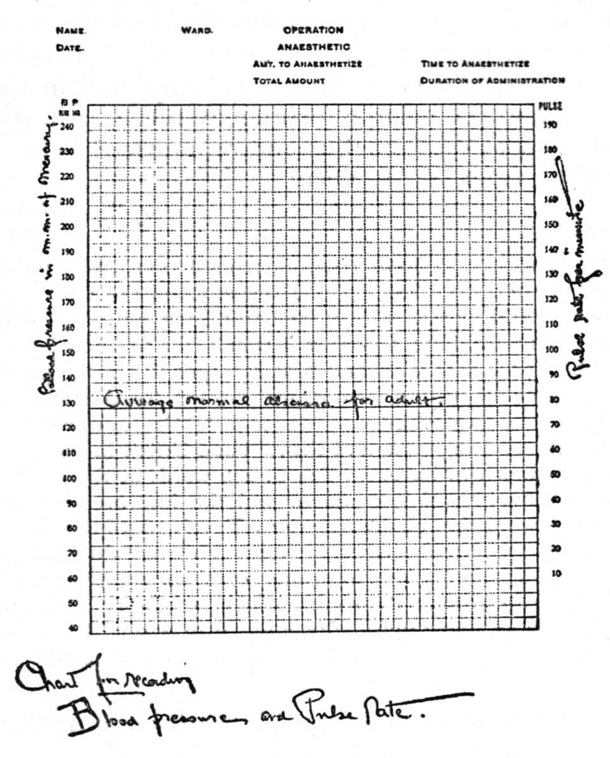

CUSHING'S ORIGINAL BLOOD-PRESSURE CHART
Introduced at the Johns Hopkins Hospital early in 1902

tachycardia and bradycardia, so the sphygmomanometer has led to the uncovering of the diseases (God save the mark!) of hypertension and hypotension, which have vastly added to the number of neurasthenics in the world.

An amusing anecdote concerning blood-pressure measurements is related by a Johns Hopkins nurse (and also by Jerome Webster). An inexperienced student nurse, who had heard vaguely about the blood-pressure cuff, was substituting as an anesthetist; at a tense moment in the operation she was suddenly told to take a pressure reading. A few minutes later Cushing felt something tugging at his pants' leg, only to discover that the student nurse was putting the pneumatic cuff on him!

The Hunterian Laboratory

In April 1903 a group of students addressed to Cushing an unusual letter of thanks:

Baltimore,
28 April 1903.

Dear Dr. Cushing: On account of the extraordinary interest taken in your course in Operative Surgery, it was voted at a recent meeting of the entire Third-Year Class of the Medical School, that we act as a Committee for the Class, to convey to you their high appreciation of the value of their course. The Class feels especially indebted to you, personally, for the originality in methods of teaching, the close personal attention and the clearness of presentation by which some of the underlying principles of Operative Surgery were impressed upon them. Very respectfully, G. LANE TANEYHILL, JR., W. R. KELLOGG, JOHN B. CARR.

It has been said that one of Cushing's most significant contributions to American surgery lay in the establishment of "The Old Hunterian," an experimental surgical laboratory in which junior students, as part of their curriculum, carried out on animals some of the more important procedures used in general surgery; with this as a background many of the students were led into various phases of physiological and surgical research. The Hunterian Laboratory became a model used by many schools elsewhere in the country, and was first described in 1906 in a paper entitled, "Instruction in operative medicine, with the description of a course in the Hunterian Laboratory of Experimental Medicine."[6] In 1920 Jay McLean, then in charge of the Hunterian, asked H.C. to set down his reminiscences of the early days:

Boston, Massachusetts,
H.C. to Jay McLean *24 January 1920.*

Dear Dr. McLean: As I promised, I shall send you some account of the origin of the Hunterian Laboratory, and also a set of the surgical papers published from the Laboratory during my regime though it is incomplete I fear. . . . Not long after my return in 1901 I was given a position on the Surgical Staff as an Assistant. The delightful feature of the J.H.H. organization in those days was the absence of any obvious departmental machinery and I hope it may always stay so. The Professor's junior associates practically agreed among themselves as to what they would teach, and they were allowed to go about it in their own way. Dr. Finney had for many years given a course in operative surgery on the cadaver and this he relinquished in order to give me something to do. Though untrained in laboratory methods except for my short period abroad in the physiological laboratories of Kronecker and Sherrington, I had been introduced to some experimental work on animals by Dr. Halsted, through an investigation we started together on parathyroid extirpations, though somehow we did not get very far with it. The third-year students occasionally attended these experiments as onlookers, but I always felt that they did not profit much thereby. The experience, however, so far as I was concerned, sufficed to make me think that something might be done with a course on animals at which the students should do their own operations, and such a course in operative surgery was started in

[6] *Johns Hopkins Hospital Bulletin,* 1906, *17,* 124-134.

the year 1901-2. There was of course nothing particularly new in this; the only novel features lay in the attempt to liken the exercise so far as possible to the actual performance of surgery as conducted on a patient in the hospital—the writing of a history, the keeping of an ether chart, the operative and postoperative notes, and complete formal postmortem examination in case of a fatality.

Through the kindness of Dr. Mall [Professor of Anatomy] we were permitted to use the northeast room on the ground floor in the anatomical building, the room in which Miss Sabin subsequently did her work. The course was offered as an optional exercise for third-year students, and I believe during the first year I took only two groups, with two tables of five men each—only twenty men in all. R. T. Miller, Jr. and H. T. Hutchins of the class of 1903 were the first volunteer prosectors. Despite its long hours, for we began at 11 a.m. and went on until late afternoon, the course proved popular beyond expectation and the next year, 1902-1903, there were many applicants, far more than could be taken. I believe that John Carr and DeWitt Casler were the two prosectors that year.

Dr. Mall badly needed the room in which we held these Friday exercises, and finally I made a formal request of the University authorities for a small inexpensive building to be erected in connection with the old dog-house which I believe is now the storage place for anatomical material. I think that the request would have received favorable action but in February of 1904 came the Baltimore fire with its financial losses to the University, and there was little prospect of securing support of any project needing money. A number of interested friends, however, Mr. H. M. Hanna of Cleveland, Mr. Robert Brewster of New York, and some others, came to my aid and subscribed a sum of $5,000, and with this I went again to the University with my appeal. The matter was taken into consideration but the decision was handed down that the sum was inadequate to put up a building in conformity with the other buildings on the Medical School lot. It was urged that all we wanted was a temporary barrack with a single room, which I imagined could be erected for the sum of $1,000 and could be fireproofed by using corrugated iron which would not look badly if properly painted. This would have left us with at least $4,000 as a fund to set the place going. The appeal was not accepted, and I can readily understand now why it was not. At all events we continued on during the semesters of 1903-1904 and 1904-1905 in the old quarters. It was enormously gratifying to find that the entire class would sign up for the optional course, and I have always felt that it was just as valuable if not more so, for those going into clinical medicine, as for the prospective surgeons.

During the year, I believe, of 1904, W. G. MacCallum, who had found that the facilities in the pathological building were inadequate for the type of experimental work he was interested in, entered into the conspiracy with me and we together made another appeal, which this time was backed up by the students, for a simple building which we could utilize for experimental work and which could serve as the centre of distribution for all the animals utilized by the school. To our great gratification our plans were accepted and during the year 1905 the "Old Hunterian" was erected, I believe at a cost of $15,000. The building, as you know, was divided into two equal parts, one for surgery and the other for pathology. We were left in rather a bad fix for the building was not at all equipped and we had the scant budget of $500 a year for our running expenses, and needless to say this sum was given over entirely to putting up partitions, animal cages, and the necessary furnishings of a laboratory, simple as they were. There is no doubt, however, but that its very simplicity was one of the charms of the old place. I think the animal yard was added later on.

We had a good deal of discussion as to what the laboratory ought to be called. I was in favor of naming it the Magendie Laboratory, but the anti-vivisection group in Baltimore were very active at the time and Magendie's name was anathema to them, so that at the suggestion of Dr. Welch we thought we would use John Hunter's name instead—hence the Hunterian Laboratory

JOHNS HOPKINS UNIVERSITY,
BALTIMORE.

May-June 1905

GRADUATE INSTRUCTION.

Operative Surgery.

Schedule of exercises showing operations to be performed.

1. Resume of abdominal operative technique in general. Incisions; use of gauze; methods of closure etc. Gastrotomy. Appendectomy.
2. Strictures of the oesophagus. Gastrostomy.
3. Physiology of the gastric secretion.
 Pyloric stenosis; malignant. Gastro-enterostomy.
4. Pyloric stenosis; non-malignant. Pyloroplasty. Gastric ulcer.
5. Surgery of the pancreas and biliary passages. Cholecystectomy etc. Powlow's pancreatic fistula.
6. Malignant disease of the stomach. Pylorectomy.
7. Intestinal resection and the various methods of anastomosis. Lateral entero-enterostomy.
8. Intestinal resections, continued. 'End-to-end' entero-enterostomy.
9. Gastroenterostomy. Roux's procedure.
10. Operations upon the large bowel. Resection of caecum.
11. The technique of amputations. Interscapulothoracic amputation.
12. Powlow's operation for isolated stomach pouch.
13. The surgery of the blood-vessels. Eck's fistula.
14. The technique of laminectomies.
15. The technique of craniotomies. Cortical stimulation.
16. Gunshot wounds of the abdomen.

SCHEDULE FOR CUSHING'S COURSE IN OPERATIVE SURGERY
Spring 1905

of Experimental Medicine. It was not a bad solution, for it mystified a good many people, who thought that the term had something to do with a pointer or a setter, and, after all, it did have something to do with them for we began to have a good deal of veterinary work.

This was brought about by the fact that in the course in operative surgery as originally planned, a good many animals with pathological lesions which were fit subjects for surgical procedures were utilized in the operative course, and the first paper, which appeared in the *J.H.H. Bulletin* of May, 1905, while the laboratory was in course of erection, was a collection of papers by third year students: Faris, Thacher, Ortschild and Beall of the class of 1906, describing a number of pathological conditions in animals which we had encountered during the session. . . .

The laboratory was finally ready for occupancy in the summer of 1905, and Philip K. Gilman, a graduate of that year, became the first surgical assistant there. He was succeeded a year later by J. F. Ortschild 1906, and there followed in the same position Lewis Reford of Montreal 1907, S. J. Crowe 1908, Emil Goetsch 1909, W. E. Dandy 1910, and Conrad Jacobson 1911.

I cannot adequately express the attachment we all felt for this homely and odoriferous old place—I use 'old' merely in an affectionate sense despite the vivid olfactory reminiscences. We had many amusing and not a few trying experiences with a succession of dieners, with unsympathetic antivivisectionists, the most militant of which we finally won over by an operation on her pet poodle who grew a large tumor on a portion of his anatomy which the prevailing styles for poodles ordained should be clipped.

We finally came to depend greatly on the offices of a cadaverous little man called Jimmie, to whom a monument should be erected, for how he managed to survive the buffets from the many departments of the School that wanted animals of the right size, sex and disposition at the right moment, how he managed with hose, mop and carbolic to keep the place tolerable under the rays of a Baltimore sun, how he managed to keep up the supply of animals in competition with the local society that collected and electrocuted them—all this is beyond me. I can see him now, tripping down Monument Street with his buckets of garbage from the hospital kitchen, and had it not been for his extraordinary moral control over the occupants of our kennels in his charge, their vociferousness would have driven the neighbors distracted.

The operative course was, I think, a great success though it was very hard work, and after the long consultation with the "family physicians" beginning at 11 a.m. followed by the appropriate operation, we used to find ourselves rather done up when the last animal was got to bed late Friday afternoon. I made the course, its methods and objects, the subject of an address at New Haven in February 1906, and though I find in rereading the preamble the expressions are somewhat callow, nevertheless I think the ideas, evidently borrowed in spots from Clifford Allbutt, are sound, and I still fail to see any inherent difference between medicine and surgery. The only apparent difference is due to the fact that different types of men are apt to select the two branches, but in the long run more eminent surgeons would have made good physicians than physicians good surgeons, though I could name many of the latter. You will forgive all this which may be beside the mark but I have been led into it for I feel that this third-year Friday exercise carried on in the Old Hunterian from 1905 to 1912 was by far the most satisfactory and profitable source of contact between student and teacher that I have experienced.

The second "Comparative Surgery" series was published from the Hunterian Laboratory by members of the class of 1907: F. W. Bancroft, E. S. Cross, G. W. Henry, W. D. Gatch, J. G. Hopkins, A. R. Dochez, W. von Gerber, and G. J. Heuer. This appeared in the Bulletin for December 1906, and a year later a third series, in which J. T. Geraghty, J. W. Churchman, S. J. Crowe, F. F. Gundrum, C. W. Mills, R. D. McClure, H. F. Derge, C. H. Bryant, H. M. Evans and A. G. Brenizer, Jr., of the class of 1908 participated, and it is a great gratification to me that so many of these men who since have done so well in their profession made their first small publications as undergraduates as an outcome of the operative course in the Hunterian Laboratory. In the preamble to this report which Ortschild[7] and I signed together there is a full comment on our stand as regards antivivisectionists; the set of laboratory rules which hung by the door for all to read is given; also a subject outline of the exercises of that year's course. There is comment too on the cordial relations we had established with the local veterinarians, a number of whom took the summer course offered to graduates.[8]

This was the last of the collected Comparative Surgery reports, for we had begun to get more interested in experimental work as our equipment was perfected. In 1908 a paper by J. R. B. Branch, later of the Hunan-Yale Hospital, and in 1909 papers by James Bordley Jr., by S. J. Crowe, by Lewis L. Reford, B. M. Bernheim, R. D. McClure, P. W. Harrison and S. Griffith Davis were published together in the April Bulletin. Reford's paper was the first of the studies on the pituitary body which came to engross us during the next few years when Crowe, Goetsch, Dandy and Jacobson were successively the assistants in the laboratory; and some of Jacobson's papers which have been long delayed in their completion are only now in press. Some of our conclusions were wrong, but all told it has been a useful line of investigation and has served at least to put the pituitary body on the map where it has since attracted more attention than it possibly deserves.

I have included among the papers one which was finished with Weed and Jacobson in Boston, though the work was begun in Baltimore and more credit should have been given to the Hunterian than the reprint records. I had hoped to keep up the traditions of the old place in the Surgical Laboratory here at Harvard, which has been successively under the direction of Dr. John Homans and Dr. William C. Quinby both of whom had worked at Baltimore in the Old Hunterian. The Arthur Tracy Cabot Fellowship here has been assigned to the assistant in charge of the laboratory, and the post has been held successively by Lewis H. Weed, 1912-13, Gilbert Horrax 1914, Samuel C. Harvey 1915, William S. McCann 1916, and George B. Wislocki 1917-19; and though to my everlasting regret I am unable to be in the laboratory as much as I used to be in Baltimore I feel that these men are first cousins to those of you who have succeeded Gilman, Ortschild, Reford, Crowe, Goetsch and Jacobson in the Hunterian. May the line continue to be as creditable a one to both Schools in the future as it has been in the past is my prayer.

I have said little in all this of MacCallum's and Whipple's department, undoubtedly much more productive than our half of the house. They will have to tell their own part of the story. It was really one laboratory, however, and we worked happily together and had not a few conjoint problems, on the surgical aspect of which we were privileged to take part. There were many workers from time to time, Bernheim, Stone and Staige Davis having worked more or less continuously during my last few years, as I presume they have continued to do; and Dr. Halsted always had a problem on foot and came to the laboratory frequently during its early days. His custom, to which I have already referred, of giving his juniors free swing with their own projects was what really made the laboratory a possibility.

[7] "J. F. Ortschild who succeeded Gilman as the assistant in the laboratory was a student of great promise. In the following year as a member of Dr. Halsted's staff he got a severe staphylococcus infection which settled in his hip and has left him an invalid these ten years but still hopeful of a recovery which will permit him to resume his career."

[8] "I find among my papers a prospectus of one of these early summer courses which we used to hold and which you may wish to keep with your records."

The most gratifying tribute the laboratory received was in 1912 when Abraham Flexner at the time the Rockefeller funds were about to be turned over to the University, recommended that $100,000 be utilized for the enlargement of the Hunterian Laboratory. Whether this is what led to the new building I am not sure, but at all events what you have come to call so soon the "Old Hunterian," like an exaggerated case of progeria became old before reaching its teens. Very sincerely yours, HARVEY CUSHING.

P.S. [handwriting] I'll have the papers bound and sent on to you.

Bertram M. Bernheim, one of the early Hunterian enthusiasts, recalls in a letter to H.C. many years later:

Those were wonderful days, those early days of the Hunterian, weren't they? How I wish they were back—with you in your old place. I shall never forget the stimulus you gave us all. My class (1905) did have the course in operative surgery, but I cannot recall whether it was given in the Anatomical Building or in the Hunterian, tho' I believe it was in the latter. My haziness in this regard is to be excused because if you will recall your facilities were so limited at that time that only part of the class (there were only 55 of us) could be accommodated. We therefore drew lots for the privilege and I lost. . . .

If my memory serves me right, Gilman ran the course. . . . I did not start to work under you till 1908, after I had been away from Baltimore for two or three years. After your departure things were sadly out of kilter at the Hunterian —until finally the full-time regime stopped all volunteers, like Stone and myself, from working. Nor am I at all convinced that the quality of the work turned out in recent years overshadows (or even equals) that done when you were here. But I may be prejudiced!"

Physiological Saline Solution

Through the physiological studies of Sidney Ringer and the later analyses of the British physiologist, F. S. Locke, it had become clear that physiological salt solution, so-called, would not preserve excised or exposed tissues in a normal state if the saline solutions were made up merely by adding sodium chloride to tap water. Ringer's work had been described in a series of papers published in the *Journal of Physiology* beginning in 1880. To the physicians and surgeons these disclosures might have seemed immediately applicable since medication is frequently administered by vein, and salt solutions are often given subcutaneously when patients for one reason or another are unable to take fluid by mouth. But the full significance of Ringer's work had not been appreciated in clinical circles until Jacques Loeb's papers appeared in 1900. H.C. as an active clinician did much to focus attention on the problem through a paper entitled, "Concerning the poisonous effect of pure sodium chloride solutions on the nerve-muscle preparations," issued in October 1901 immediately after his return from Berne.[9] Through direct infusion of the hind-leg vessels of a frog with solutions of differing ionic content he was able to prove that pure sodium chloride in a solution

[9] *American Journal of Physiology*, 1901, *6*, 77-90.

of 0.7 per cent abolished the capacity of the muscle to respond to stimulation of its nerves, but if potassium chloride and calcium chloride, .03 to .06 per cent, were added, the irritability of the muscle was restored and it would respond once again to nerve stimulation. From this, Cushing argued that solutions of saline administered to human subjects should have a carefully balanced ionic con-

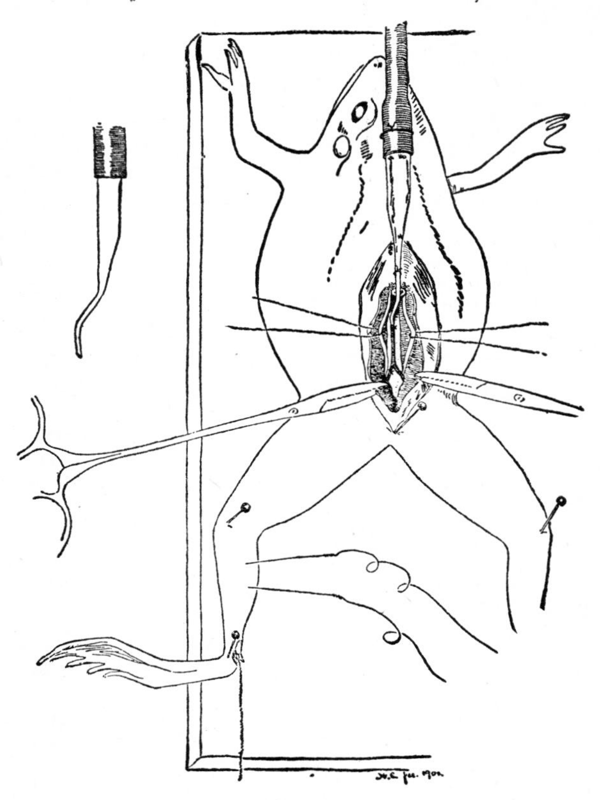

DIAGRAM OF PERFUSION EXPERIMENTS

tent. As recently as 1935 Elliott C. Cutler, Cushing's successor in the chair of surgery at Harvard, wrote to Cushing concerning this early work, remarking: "The curious part of this whole story is that no one has really worked upon this matter seriously since your publication, a matter which I am going to bring some day to Walter Cannon's attention at our lunch in the Brigham." To this H.C. replied:

11 February 1935.

Dear Elliott: . . . As a matter of fact, in the early years of the hospital, being uneasy about the sterility of the fluids, I ceased using them for intravenous therapy. I am glad you have put someone to work on the subject, for it is high time it was reviewed. It was Kronecker who put me to work on these matters.

I published a brief report based merely on muscle fatiguability to electrical stimulus in the *American Journal of Physiology* for October 1, 1901, page 77. Kronecker was so interested that he wrote some brief papers about it, one in the *Zentralblatt für Physiologie* for January 30, 1904, which had to do with Locke's priority. He also made a brief report in my name in the *Rendiconti della R. Accademia dei Lincei,* 1901, *10,* 145. Later on, for Cohen's System of Physiological Therapeutics (1902) I wrote a pot-boiler (Chapter V) on saline irrigations and infusions. I gave a formula for NaCl 0.9%, CaCl 0.026%, KCl. 0.01%, H_2O 99.064%. You must remember this was ten years before the opening of the Brigham Hospital, and what formulae may have been introduced there I do not know.

However, as I have said, it is just as well to forget about all these papers and for someone to begin again from the bottom. Just how the high potassium content got in the present Brigham formula I can't imagine.

The "pot-boiler" to which H.C. refers quite casually in his letter to Cutler bears the title "Saline irrigations and infusions" and is much the clearest statement of the problem in any textbook up to that time. A note on his own copy states that it was written while waiting for patients. In May 1902 a series of evening lectures was announced, and on the 20th H.C. spoke on "Saline infusions and their therapeutic indications. The lectures were never published.

1902

The calendar of events for 1902 and the years immediately following may be briefly summarized. In February Johns Hopkins University celebrated its twenty-fifth anniversary. "We have had a *remarkably* successful 25th anniversary celebration. Wish you could have been here. Great interest shown in it on all hands and much enthusiasm which the worst weather I have ever seen failed to dampen." In the Baltimore scrapbook various memorabilia of the occasion are duly preserved without detailed comment, but as with the Yale Bicentennial, an excellent description is given in the Osler biography:

. . . The birthdays of the Johns Hopkins fall at a time of year when weather conditions are unpropitious for the parading of streets in academic costume, and though worse than usual on this particular occasion, the weather could not dampen the interest of the group of representatives who had come from all the principal institutions of learning in the United States and Canada. Mr. Gilman's valedictory; the congratulatory address to the retiring President delivered by Woodrow Wilson, representing the alumni; the address by Principal Peterson of McGill, who could not refrain from complaining that the university was keeping Dr. William Osler from his Alma Mater, which wanted and needed him; the inaugural of Ira Remsen, the new President—these and the many other addresses need not detain us. Nor need the list of distinguished men whom Mr. Gilman then presented to his successor as recommended for various honorary degrees, among them Professor Wilson of Princeton University, 'whose vision is so broad that it includes both North and South; a master of the principles which underlie a free government.'

The ceremonies ended on Saturday night with a large alumni dinner at which there were so many to be called upon that when it came to the turn of President Alderman of Tulane University to speak, he glanced at the clock and said: 'Last week when this banquet began,' &c. It was two minutes past 12, and though there were other speakers to follow, it is time to end this account of an important episode in the history of the Hopkins, when its leadership first changed hands.

During the Hopkins celebrations in February he and Katharine Crowell announced their engagement; in May he begins to speak of his wedding plans.

The spring had been a busy one, with many meetings and papers, one on avoidance of surgical shock at the Medical and Chirurgical Faculty meeting on 24 April; on 4 and 5 June he attended a meeting in Wisconsin where he gave the annual address before the 56th annual meeting of the State Medical Society of Wisconsin in which he summarized his experience with cocaine mentioned earlier (p. 213).

Plans for the wedding had been shifted and changed every week or so for two or three months prior to the formal announcement of the engagement, but the date was finally settled upon for 10 June when friends of both families gathered in Cleveland in large numbers to celebrate the important event.[10] K.C. had been patience itself, for they had been strongly attached to one another for over ten years. H.C. had followed, perhaps too closely, the advice of his mentor, Vesalius, who had insisted that he who would marry a wife must not study medicine for there was not time enough for both.

When they returned to Baltimore H.C. took his bride to 3 West Franklin Street where for the next six years the one remaining bachelor latch-keyer, T. B. Futcher, stayed on as a member of their household. Mrs. Osler immediately took K.C. in hand, introducing her to the intricacies of marketing in Baltimore, and in countless other ways helping her to feel at home in her new surroundings.

H.C. meanwhile threw himself eagerly into the work of the new experimental course in surgery. Apparently he had not budgeted his expenses very carefully during the previous summer, which called forth a letter from the Dean:

W. H. Howell to H.C. *6 October 1902.*

Dear Dr. Cushing, The matter of payment for your services in connection with the graduate course last spring was brought before the Advisory Board at its meeting, Saturday, October 4. The members of the Board regretted very much that the proper recommendation had not been made last spring and were especially sorry to hear that you had been obliged to meet some of the expenses of the course. Inasmuch as the account for last year has been closed and could not well be opened without difficulty and explanations to the Board of Trustees, the following action was suggested and I hope will prove satisfactory to you.

1. It was desired that you should send in a bill for the amount that you

[10] They had intended to be married on the golden wedding anniversary of H.K.C. and B.M.C. but a cousin had preëmpted that date, much to their annoyance.

personally expended upon the course, as nearly as you can remember. This bill will be promptly met by the Medical School.

2. In payment of instruction in the graduate course during the coming spring it is the desire of the Board to make such payment to you as will meet also the services that you rendered last year. Very truly yours, W. H. Howell, Dean.

On 5 November he met Weir Mitchell for the first time. There were many exchanges between the two in the years that followed, and after Mitchell's death H.C. gathered together letters and other memorabilia into a volume for which he prepared an interesting introductory note, telling, among other things, of his first "Madeira Party:"

I well remember my first meeting with Weir Mitchell. This old program I have just come across gives the date as Nov. 5, 1902 and the scribbled notes on the back show how impressed I must have been as a youngster in his early thirties. On this occasion I had been asked by Mills to come over and discuss his paper on Brain Tumors. Little could I have known about the subject. I had perhaps had a case or two at the Church Home and Infirmary but could scarcely have had any successful cases at the time in question. But that's another story.

After the meeting Weir Mitchell waylaid me and asked if I cared to go home with him for a smoke and chat—that his son Jack and W. W. Keen were going. I accepted gladly and it was a memorable midnight session. I have always liked old men and S.W.M. seemed to me 'powerful old'—in years at least. But he said he was getting younger every day and would soon get back to his bottle. But it was not milk he produced. . . .

Mitchell's study or office at his home on Walnut Street was a delight. It was a capacious room dominated by two portraits—copies of the Reynolds' Hunter and Janssen's Harvey which hang resp^y in the Coll. of Surgeons & Coll. of Phys. in London. I remember his pointing out how clearly J. had portrayed Harvey's arthritic knuckles. Then there was a beautiful coloured bust of Dante, Keats' death mask, and in a glass case the head, recumbent, of a Roman, as I learned, who had been killed in battle some eons ago outside the walls of Ravenna. M. said it was of Guidarello Guidarelli and when he first saw the original in the museum of Ravenna he made a request of the Curator that he be permitted to have a copy made of the face. He was told that it was hardly possible and would cost a prohibitive sum—125 lire! He promptly made out a check and the Prof. of Sculpture at the local Beaux Arts did the work—an exact copy, even to the blemishes and stains on the old marble. "Jack," said he "I once wrote some verses on Guidarelli." Whereupon Jack got out a volume of his father's poems from the shelves which lined the wall and read the verses aloud. I have always liked this the best of M's verses perhaps due to this association. He subsequently gave me a copy of the book—pub^d by the Century Company in New York two years before, adding that the publishers had never been able to dispose of them.[11] There was one thing I failed to mention about the Guidarelli face, viz. that Dr. M. called attention to the fact that the lip was slightly drawn up on one side and M. said he had no doubt the original in Ravenna had been carved from a wax death mask.

There was much more about books after this and I recall Rob't Burns' copy of

[11] *The Wager and other poems.* New York, Century Co. H.C.'s copy bears the undated inscription "My dear Cushing, I send you this verse with thanks for the hospitality of head and heart. S. Weir Mitchell."

Pope, a presentation copy of Robinson Crusoe; and something brought up Mrs. Piozzi, whereupon Jack got down a copy of her Johnson which had in it a MS. letter about a New Year's sermon. The copy I think had belonged to Horace Walpole & later to Thackeray and M. chided Jack on his removing from its place an old foxed paper marker saying Horace had probably put it where it was and there it should remain. There were many other interesting association books —one of them a Harvey with a presentation note in H.'s script.

We must have lingered on from about eleven to three A.M., Dr. M. meanwhile smoking a succession of heavy cigars and he finally got out some old Madeira with a history of three times around the Horn. I saw him many times in later years. Once he stayed with us in Baltimore. It must have been in 1909 at the dedication of Osler Hall which accounts for my having come to possess his manuscript. The night before in looking over my few books he came upon the copy of his 'Lycian Tomb' which I had had put in covers from the *Century Magazine*[12] and he solemnly remarked, "Charles Eliot Norton told me this poem was the high tide of American verse." Mitchell was vain but he had much to be vain about. He eagerly lapt [*sic*] up adulation. . . . He was probably the most picturesque and many-sided physician of his time—and knew it. . . .

1903

H.C. started the year with a trip to Boston, made at Councilman's behest, during which he met Charles Eliot, President of Harvard. There is reason to believe that Eliot, with his unfailing insight, marked Cushing as his man, for the unrecorded negotiations which ultimately took H.C. to Harvard began at this time. Several years later, in mentioning this encounter in his account of the early days at the Hunterian, H.C. wrote: "It must have been at about this juncture, probably through the interest of W. T. Councilman, that I was first approached regarding the possibility of a transfer to Boston. I recall this because it was at a meeting with Dr. Councilman at President Eliot's house that he was told of this course [for teaching operative surgery], and he said: 'Why certainly, that is comparative surgery.' It was due to this chance remark that our first and some of the subsequent collections of papers published in the *Bulletin* and elsewhere came to be called Comparative Surgery." When the first report from the Hunterian appeared in 1905, H.C. sent Eliot a copy and had the following reply:[13]

Charles W. Eliot to H.C. *2 December 1905.*

Dear Dr. Cushing: I have read with pleasure the pamphlet on Comparative Surgery which you were good enough to send me. The name and the thing both seem to me very good. Very truly yours, CHARLES W. ELIOT.

On 24 January H.C. attended a dinner at the College of Physicians in Philadelphia which was evidently a rather sodden affair, if one can

[12] "Ode on a Lycian tomb." *The Century Magazine,* November 1907, 75, 85-88. H.C.'s copy (excerpted from the Century) is separately bound and inscribed by S.W.M.

[13] Inserted in H.C.'s bound reprints just in front of "Comparative surgery, with illustrative cases" (*Johns Hopkins Hospital Bulletin,* May, 1905) is the letter from President Eliot.

judge by the amusing note which he had the next day from his friend, A. C. Abbott, and from H.C.'s account to his father. From Abbott: "I am keeping my promise promptly in order to substitute something entertaining for the awful rubbish that you were forced to sit through last night. It was rough enough on me, who have a certain degree of *acquired* immunity, but for you, poor boy, whose haptophores are as yet receptive and unoccupied, it must have been close to deadly. However, it's all in the day's work. Don't let it keep you from coming again. You are always welcome."

H.C. to H.K.C. *25 January 1903.*

Dear Pater Attended a large dinner in Philadelphia last night given by the Entertainment Committee of the College of Phys. &c. Curious performance. Does it not strike you so? To have a large banquet once in two-three years. I think Dr. Mitchell gave the original sum whose interest was to be so expended. Object: promotion of good feeling between the members of the College—in the two schools I presume. Very nice to be invited however. Thayer and I went over together. There was much speechifying—Dr. H. C. Wood—good as usual. Made a strong plea for funds to make up $50,000 for a new building (fire-proof) to provide for the growing needs of the library. Some one has anon. given $50,000 provided an equal amount is raised. Dr. S. Weir M. also spoke—less well. The others—younger—still less well. Much tobacco, wine and eats. We dragged ourselves homeward on the 'owl train' reaching here at 2 a.m. Glad I went over however as I saw many interesting people. . . .

[P.S.] Hope to show the Hunter letter at the historical society ere long. May write you for that precious Franklin note introducing Shippen some day. Dr. O. *much* excited about it.

H.C.'s intimacy with Osler had grown during the preceding two years and in May he had arranged a dinner for W.O. at the Maryland Club at which those in attendance (house officers and staff)[14] presented W.O. with a 63-volume set of *The Dictionary of National Biography*, the last volume of which had just been published. The idea originated with Cushing and those who had attended the dinner had each contributed $15.00 toward the gift—a gift, be it said, which W.O. warmly appreciated, for the set of the "D.N.B." remained a fixture in the Osler dining room from 1903 until Lady Osler's death at Oxford in 1928. H.C., like W.O., had the dictionary habit and whenever a point arose that required verification, even during a meal, the appropriate volume of the D.N.B., or other reference source, was in the lap of whoever pulled it down first. Cushing arranged an amusing printed menu, embellished with some of W.O.'s brighter epigrams, including "Promptness is the one quality in a physician necessary for success." "One thing do I demand of my house physicians; they

[14] Those attending the dinner were: A. C. Abbott, Lewellys F. Barker, Joseph C. Bloodgood, George Blumer, C. N. B. Camac, John G. Clark, Harvey Cushing, Egerton Yorrick Davis, Jr. [Osler], J. M. T. Finney, Thomas B. Futcher, Norman B. Gwyn, August Hoch, Henry Barton Jacobs, H. A. Lafleur, Thomas McCrae, Stewart Paton, W. W. Russell, J. A. Scott, Frank R. Smith, W. S. Thayer, H. M. Thomas, H. Toulmin.

must put their affections on ice; there must be no 'Amaryllis in the shade,' and they must beware the tangles of 'Neaera's hair,' " etc.

Welch's dinners also were something of an institution, there being three categories depending upon the degree of distinction of the guest. Anyone who had experienced one of the No. 1 feasts might say, as was said of those of Peter the Great, that they were "parties to be remembered"—even if one's recollections of the end of the evening might have been somewhat dim. There were two such feasts in close succession, one on 26 April for Gamgee, the British physiological chemist, and another, a farewell dinner, on 31 May in honor of Dr. N. MacLeod Harris, who was leaving Hopkins to take the chair of bacteriology at the University of Chicago.

On 4 August, William Harvey, the first child of the Cushings, was born amid great rejoicing. With his usual promptness H.C. announced the good news by personal notes such as the following:

H.C. to Mrs. Harry F. Reid *5 August 1903.*

Dear Mrs. Reid Yesterday—high noon—an eight pound boy and, thank God, Kate doing exceptionally well. Very comfortable today with a normal temperature and writing a note. Doubtless she expects to go marketing tomorrow. Nice cool weather here. Thought 'you all' might like to know. Aff'y HARVEY C.

Letters poured in, as they always seemed to whenever anything happened in the Cushing family. Two pleased him in particular, one from Jacobs and the other from his old teacher, Newton Anderson.

Trouville-sur-mer,
Henry Barton Jacobs to H.C. *17 August 1903.*

Dear Cushing, Word has just reached this far-off land of the very good things which have been quietly going on in dear old No. 3 and immediately both I and my other half wish to send our warmest greetings to the new arrival and our heartiest congratulations to you and Mrs. Cushing. I have long known you could patch up and repair men, now I am overjoyed to know you can make them. So let the better work go on.

Asheville School [North Carolina],
Newton M. Anderson to H.C. *20 August 1903.*

Dear Harve, I see by the *Town Topics* that I should be congratulating you and I do so most heartily. I hope both mother and boy are well and will continue to be so. If I had an eye to business I suppose I should be sending you a blank application form but I will forgo that part for the present.

It would be hard to tell you how much I enjoyed my visit with you and how pleased I was to see you so happy. Now, then, you will be happier than ever. I expect you are beaming all over and that a poor wayfarer would get but little attention. I shall try to make another pilgrimage and have a look at the lad to see if he will be a worthy successor to his daddy. All is going well here and our outlook is good and bright. With best wishes to the wife and much love to yourself, I am, Sincerely yours, NEWTON M. ANDERSON.

Dr. McCrae wrote from London that W.O. hummed all day,

"O'er the garden wall the Cushing baby fell."

After the excitement of Bill's entry into the world, H.C. was saddened by the news that his mother was rapidly failing; she died on 21 October. Among his papers is a note on a copy of Henley's poem "Sundown." "Nothing," it reads, "could describe better the scene at Mother's funeral. It was a beautiful afternoon when we laid her at rest on the hilltop at Lakeview."

SUNDOWN

A late lark twitters from the quiet skies,
And from the west,
Where the sun, his day's work ended,
Lingers as in content,
There falls on the old, gray city
An influence, luminous and serene—
A shining peace.

The smoke ascends
In a rosy and golden haze. The spires
Shine, and are changed. In the valley
Shadows rise. The lark sings on. The sun,
Closing his benediction,
Sinks, and the darkening air
Thrills with a sense of the triumphing night—
Night with her train of stars
And her great gift of sleep.

So be my passing!
My task accomplished and the long day done;
My wages taken, and in my heart
Some late lark singing,
Let me be gathered to the quiet west,
The sundown splendid and serene
Death.

With H.C.'s increased activity and responsibility he still found time for literary pursuits. He had been working on both Garth and Vesalius; on 31 May he wrote: "Dr. Osler has started me on a Vesalius essay. He has turned over to me *pro tempore* a stunning copy of the '*De humani corporis fabrica*' with the famous plates etc. I want very much to collect photographs of the various portraits and as many engravings of V. himself as possible so if you run across any of them in your perusal of catalogues or see a notice of the sale of any of his books I wish you would let me know." At a meeting of Osler's Book and Journal Club on the 16th of December, H.C. made his first presentation on Vesalius ("The books of Vesalius") on a program at which Osler had spoken about the bookshops of Paris and London, and John Ruhräh on Fournier. Notes which he used for this address were found with his papers when the *Bio-bibliography of Vesalius* was being made ready for publication in 1943.

During 1903 private practice had increased and H.C.'s income had improved accordingly. His appointment as Associate in Surgery for the year brought him $500 instead of $350 which had been his stipend the previous year. Consultations were increasing and he was frequently asked to travel considerable distances, such as to Palm Beach on 15 March. On 2 November he wrote: "Also have operated nearly every day, a baby with an occipital meningocele, a removal of a thyroid for exophthalmic goitre, a brain tumor etc." One of his patients, Mr. Gerald W. Birks, who had been referred to him during the year for recurring attacks of facial pain ("tic douloureux") has set down the following moving tribute:

> . . . Dr. Ferrier discussed the possibility of the Gasserian ganglion operation, but evidently, then, looked upon it as a last desperate resort—a sort of polite way of committing suicide. So when Dr. Martin took me down to consult Dr. Osler and Dr. Cushing in 1903, it was like leading a forlorn hope. That consultation (if my memory holds good) resulted in Dr. Osler and Dr. Martin advising the major operation at once, with Cushing holding out for a peripheral attack on the fifth nerve. I was the youngest man he had ever seen with such a severe case of trigeminal neuralgia, and apparently I showed the results of having led a pretty decent life. So while guaranteeing six months' relief, he hoped for a permanent cure, and in plain English, I think he was still nervous over performing the major operation.
>
> The trouble returning in six months, almost to a day, the Gasserian ganglion operation followed. I came very near spoiling his record and Bell's paralysis put the eye out of business for some months afterwards. But *then* my troubles ended. If I remember aright that was his 19th case, and you may be interested to know that the sum of his fees for the previous eighteen amounted to less than $200.00. The financial side seemed to be his greatest worry—not for his, but for his patient's interest. When I at last got him to name a figure, which seemed to me a small price to pay for what he had done for me, I had to assure him over and over again that it would not inconvenience me before he would accept my cheque. I remember saying to him that as a business man I was going to return the compliment by prescribing for him. I pointed out that he would be just as good a surgeon if he were a better business man (I'm afraid my prescription had no lasting benefit in his case).
>
> And now as to my impression of the man behind it all. I think it was Schofield who said long years ago that "The cure commences when the eye of the patient meets the eye of the physician." At my very first meeting with Harvey Cushing I was impressed with that "something behind" which was so wonderfully exemplified in his great mentor, Dr. Osler. Something, quite intangible, in the personality—behind the skill and science—which made us patients trust his skill and science. And then, as with David Ferrier, his sympathy for us as individuals was profound—like Francis Thompson's "Hound of Heaven," he followed for years, with kindly sympathy, the lives of those his skill had helped.
>
> Harvey Williams Cushing—as was said of a greater than he—in very truth had fellowship with our sufferings, and so we, his patients, felt not only lasting gratitude for his skill, but lasting affection for the man.

Another activity arising out of his clinical work was the formation of the Society of Clinical Surgery, plans for which had been conceived during the Paris congress in 1900. The Society held its first meeting in Baltimore and Philadelphia on 13 and 14 November. H.C. was made chairman of the Committee on Admissions and he did much during the early years of the Society to foster its activities. Shortly before his death he brought together all of the early papers of the Society, with anecdotes and reminiscences, for ultimate disposition in the Society's archives. This interesting history of his favorite group of surgical colleagues remains unpublished.

Christmas was always an event in the Osler household and No. 3 West Franklin Street benefited as usual by the Oslers' generous impulses. A letter on the 26th indicates that Mrs. Cushing had received an illustrated catalogue of Johnsoniana to add to her Johnson collection, and H.C. a 1669 edition of Digby's *Souls and bodies* with the *Powder of sympathy* bound in; and from Jacobs in Paris came the Vernon plaque of Osler. Meanwhile, Bill, whom Osler had nicknamed "Pius" because he was born the day Pope Pius X was enthroned, had come to weigh eighteen pounds. In the same letter H.C. also speaks of his experimental work on the motor cortex of the dog's brain—a report which he had written for the Warren Triennial Prize in Boston, but which, if submitted, seems not to have won the Prize, and there is no record of his having published on the dog's motor cortex.

1904

There was much talk in the January letters of books and literary things. Osler's influence was everywhere clearly seen. Books had begun to arrive from Blackwell's in Oxford and "Mrs. Grossler," as W.O. enjoyed designating his wife (her first husband having been Dr. S. W. Gross), presented them with Dr. Gross' essay on John Hunter and his pupils. A copy of DeQuincey had come from H.K.C., and H.C. had reciprocated with one of Osler's favorite works, Gomperz' *Greek thinkers.*

In February he went to Montreal on a consultation referred to him by W.O. and apparently made a deep impression upon his medical colleagues in Canada. One of them, Dr. A. Schmidt, wrote W.O. [11 February]: "If Baltimore is the home of many men like Dr. Cushing, I don't wonder at your being so anxious to leave Montreal to go 'home.' Dr. Cushing is a charming personality, a most intellectual surgeon [and] an extremely skilled operator. He condescended to operate on the case I wanted you to see with so much of that grand simplicity so rarely seen." The *Montreal Gazette* for 6 February carried the following note: "A case of great interest to the medical profession at large will come before Dr. Cushing's attention today, and it is probable that he will operate upon it. It is a case of lesion involving all the branches of the Gasserian ganglion. The case is the first of its kind in Montreal."

On his way back he had an uncomfortable turn for in changing trains in Boston he received news of the Baltimore fire. Several days later Mrs. Cushing described their close call in a letter to H.K.C.:

3 West Franklin Street,
K.C. to H.K.C. *11 February 1904.*

Dear Dr. Kirke ... His [Harvey's] trip was cut short by a sight of the Monday morning paper in Boston—He had an anxious journey home, but found his family and friends safe. It was a strange thing, but all Sunday afternoon and evening [7 Feb.] there wasn't a man in this house. Dr. Futcher had gone to Washington at seven to see Mr. Hanna, and even the colored man was taking his Sunday off. About half past seven, when the fire was at its worst, coming right up Charles St. towards us, Dr. Osler came in to get us, and made us eat something and pack a few things, and send the baby away. Then Mr. Goodwillie appeared in a hansom and stayed here with Melanie, while I took the nurse and baby to his house. Came back and packed the precious Vesalius books belonging to Dr. Kelly, and sent them back with Mr. G., and then the worst anxiety was over. We could see the progress of the fire from the back windows, and the wind changed when it was within two blocks of us; and the fire burned everything right down to the water's edge. Nothing could stop it. It is a sad looking place.

In the Osler biography the fire was also described at length and H.C. adds: "From this devastating fire Baltimore reacted courageously, and a newer and better-built city soon emerged, but for a time many individuals and institutions were hard hit. Among them was Johns Hopkins Hospital, whose major properties from which rentals were returned now lay in ruins in the wake of the fire. Of all this there is little reference in his [Osler's] letters—except a word, after some days, to let Trudeau know that 'we are doing the Phoenix trick here.'"

Toward the end of the month H.C. was called, at W. W. Keen's instigation, to the chair of surgery at Jefferson Medical College in Philadelphia but, after careful consultation with Osler, and others, he declined (Ch. X). During March there was much correspondence to and fro with Henry Kirke in Cleveland about his Franklin-Heberden pamphlet, and on the 10th Osler sent the following cordial note:

1 West Franklin Street,
William Osler to H.K.C. *10 March 1904.*

Dear Dr. Cushing, Harvey has just been talking with me about your Franklin &c papers. I suggested to him that you should come down and read the paper before our Historical Club. It would be a great pleasure to have you here. Please come. You have not seen your grandson for months. His back is worth the visit....

They eventually induced him to come to Baltimore, and on 23 May he read his paper on "Notes suggested by the Franklin-Heberden Pamphlet of 1759," mentioned earlier (Ch. II).

A second meeting of the Society of Clinical Surgery had been held in New York in March; and on 13 April an impressive dinner was given by Welch for Professor Ehrlich, the discoverer of salvarsan; but H.C. appears to have left no record of the occasion, even though Ehrlich gave the Herter Lectures.[15]

In July Mrs. Cushing returned to Cleveland for a month and H.C. accompanied W.O., Futcher, and McCrae on a brief trip to England. Before leaving, he presented a paper on Pott's disease to the Laennec Society, another organization which had recently been founded by W.O. They sailed on the *SS. Campania* on 16 July, disembarking at Queenstown, following which they visited hospitals in Dublin on the 23d. H.C. stayed a day in Liverpool for a brief session with Sherrington—"much talk with Grünbaum about apes and the motor cortex." During this trip he acquired many books and also the beautiful statuette of Paré which has occupied his desk since that time. The account of this trip in the Osler biography is one of H.C.'s best pieces of descriptive writing. Speaking of Osler's activities on the trip over and at Oxford he says:

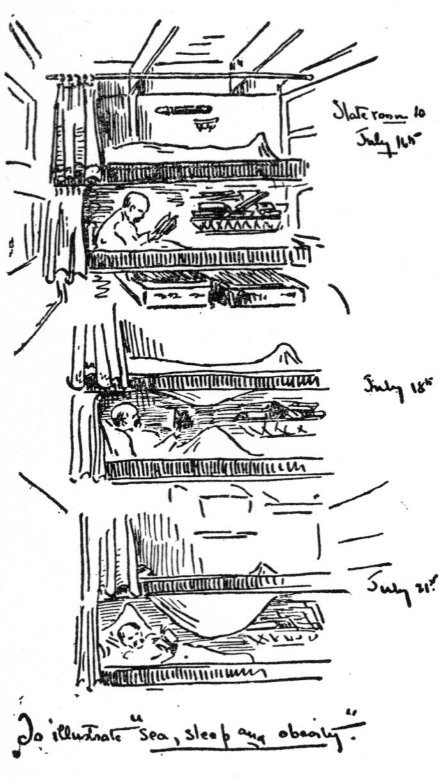

OSLER WORKING IN HIS STATEROOM
As depicted by H.C.

His habits aboard ship were interesting. His first act was to fill to overflowing the rack in his berth with books and papers he intended to use. Always the first awake, he stayed in his bunk all morning reading and writing for some four or five hours, and there was plenty for him to do, as his paper for the British Medical Association had to be put together. By noon he would appear on deck, free from care, the liveliest person aboard; and soon the half-dozen doctors on the passenger list, together with Francis Verdon, the ship's surgeon, were organized into the 'North Atlantic Medical Society' which met every afternoon at tea-time, and held its final meeting on July 22nd, when a fictitious programme of papers was presented, with amusing jibes on the various members.

Any one who would keep on Osler's trail during a first day in London must

[15] H.C. had appended this note to the abstracts of the Herter Lectures in his Baltimore Scrapbook: "These abstracts . . . were written by Dr. Welch from Prof. Ehrlich's lecture sheets—the lectures were in German of course—and they were so good that Prof. E. said it was useless to have the lectures englished and printed."

needs have good staying qualities. It is recalled that on this occasion, having been roused at 4 a.m. in the Mersey for an early landing, and having reached London by the boat train at noon, nothing would do but that the remnants of the N.A. Medical Society should go out to Haslemere and visit Jonathan Hutchinson. This was done, a delightful afternoon and evening being spent there, but when at midnight they got back to town the eldest member of the 'Society,' Dr. James Tyson, handed in his resignation. The pace was too much for him. The next day, a day of shopping and sightseeing, was even more strenuous. It began with the White Star Office; to Brown, Shipley's; to the tailor's in Savile Row, where it took about ten minutes to order and be measured for four suits of clothes; to the Ulster House ditto for overcoats; to the College of Physicians; to Sotheby's auction rooms in Wellington Street; to Maggs Brothers, &c.—to account for the morning alone. It was, of course, done in one of the picturesque old hansom cabs, long since vanished from the London streets. That evening, on dining with H. D. Rolleston, he casually remarked: "Do you think I'm sufficiently senile to become Regius Professor at Oxford?"—a remark which so misled Rolleston that when told later that Osler would accept, he emphatically denied it.

HONORARY DEGREE AT THE SHELDONIAN
Sketch by H.C.

During the Oxford meeting of the British Medical Association, Osler, at least in the eyes of his two young companions [H.C. and Futcher], occupied the centre of the stage, and it was not long before they heard to their dismay some rumours of the pressure that was being brought to bear upon him to accept the Regius Professorship. On the evening of the 26th, in the Sheldonian Theatre, came Dr. Collier's presidential address on the 'Growth and Development of the Oxford Medical School'—a timely subject. The customary vote of thanks was moved by Clifford Allbutt, and Osler in seconding it spoke most effectively in regard not only to traditions and ideals, but to the necessity of combining them with common sense. Though an impromptu speech, his familiarity with Oxford traditions and Oxford medical worthies was shown by his pointing out that John Locke should have been included among the long list from Roger Bacon to Henry Acland whom Dr. Collier had mentioned.

On the following afternoon, before a brilliant assemblage again in the Sheldonian, the Doctor of Science degree was conferred in Convocation upon Allbutt, Sir William Macewen, Jonathan Hutchinson, Sir Patrick Manson, and one or two more, with Osler the last; he receiving an unexpected and prolonged ovation which brought an unusual colour even to his dark skin. It was a busy and exciting week, with the usual festivities: a soirée at the Museum, a concert in the garden of St. John's, a garden-party at Blenheim and another at Warwick Castle, excursions on the river and elsewhere, in addition to the scientific sessions, at one of which he gave his paper, written on the steamer, on the Treatment of Pleurisy; and at the annual dinner in Christ Church Hall he must reply to a toast—'the Guests.'

In spite of the fact that he had often said his ideal of life would be to live within an hour of the British Museum and to have *The Times* on his breakfast-table, he had difficulty in coming to a decision, and so wrote to his wife. She got his letter at Murray Bay one Sunday morning, routed out Madame Rousseau at the telegraph office and cabled: 'DO NOT PROCRASTINATE ACCEPT AT ONCE.' This message he showed to his anxious young friends, though it was folded over with only the 'do not procrastinate' portion visible, so that they were left uncertain until the return home whether 'accept' or 'refuse' was the next word.

A few other impressions of Oxford may be quoted from H.C.'s diary:

Thursday, 28 July—dawned fresh and clear. . . . In the Anatomical Section [Gustav] Mann and Horsley on the thalamic region—very interesting talks—anatom. and physiolog. Horsley is a daisy. After lunch Tammas [McCrae] and I took a long walk 'doing' Magdalen—Merton—the Botanical Gardens—tea with Dr. Shadwell. Before, however, Mr. Phelps took us into the Quadrangle orig. of Merton College and in the hall there is a portrait of Wm Harvey, once Warden, of Erasmus who abided there &c. . . .

After the week in Oxford H.C. betook himself to Stratford, Warwick, and Leamington on 31 July and thereafter had a day in Cambridge and three days in London, during which he visited the British Museum and the London bookshops. A few paragraphs from his diary give details of his activities.

. . . Finding no trace of the Dryden funeral card at the B.M. I started on a morning's quest—first to the Dryden House in Gerrard St. where I procured one of their little monographs on the locality and its literary associations—to St. Anne's, Soho wh. turned out to be St. Mary's, to Southeby [*sic*] [Sotheby's list inserted], where I found an accountant who looked up the matter and found that a *Mr. Sidney Cockrell* of Walker and Cockrell, Cliffords Inn, Fleet St., had purchased the item for £3—'presumably for an American purchaser.' Quaritch had secured all the other things for fabulous sums.

To the Athenaeum publishing house in Chancery Lane where I got the copy and my cabby wanting to break away he took me to King's, publishers of Moseley's reprint which I ordered—then to Westminster Abbey, for a half hour until time to lunch with Tammas on white bait, roast and mash, and a tart. There we saw the Japs, Noguchi and two others. Wednesday afternoon passed in the National Hospital with Buzzard and T. McC. Not particularly edifying tho' they have a wonderful treasure of material. I was most interested in Buzzard's attitude toward operations—and in the cases of "*Lateral Recess Tumors*" which Horsley has been attacking—better *cerebello-pontine* growths.

They had sailed from Liverpool on the *SS. Cedric* early in August. On arriving in New York H.C. went immediately to Breezy Bluff, Glenville, Ohio, where Mrs. Cushing had been spending her holidays with her mother. He was back at 3 West Franklin Street on 1 September gloating over his latest acquisitions from London, among them some fine Vesalian items. Baltimore had been much shocked on learning of W.O.'s decision, and it was generally referred to as a public calamity. After Mrs. Osler had been reproached for her part in the decision, she nicknamed her husband "Public Calamity Number One."

During the autumn there was the usual round of Hopkins activities. Osler had given a dinner for Major Ronald Ross of malaria fame on 25 September. On the 5th of October the new surgical amphitheatre at the Johns Hopkins Hospital was formally opened. This was something of an event in the history of the Hospital. The occasion was marked by an elaborate ceremony for which engraved invitations had been prepared, and the proceedings were duly recorded in the *Bulletin*.[16] The Honorable H. D. Harlan, President of the Board of Trustees, spoke at length, stating that "our fiscal year had hardly opened when the great conflagration which devastated the business center of the city destroyed 64 warehouses, stores, and office buildings belonging to the Hospital and we were suddenly brought face to face with a loss of income of sixty thousand dollars a year . . . and a loss of endowment of about three hundred and eight thousand dollars." He went on to say that "Mr. John D. Rockefeller, after studying the situation, placed five hundred thousand dollars at the disposal of the trustees and thus rescued the Hopkins Medical School which otherwise might have had to close its doors."

In recognition of the occasion, Halsted's staff persuaded him to dedicate the new surgical theater by operating in it himself with his full staff. H.C. had scrubbed up as second assistant, but he managed to have innumerable photographs taken which he salted away in his Baltimore scrapbook. In 1937 Edwards A. Park and George Milton Smith became interested in one of these photographs and asked H. H. Young, J. M. T. Finney, and H.C., all of whom had taken part in the operation to set down their reminiscences of the event. The replies of Finney and H.C. are of interest not only for the immediate occasion, but for the light thrown upon an important milestone in the history of surgery: namely, the introduction of rubber gloves.

John M. T. Finney to George Milton Smith *1 December 1937.*

Dear Dr. Smith: . . . The photograph records the first operation performed in the new operating room of the Johns Hopkins Hospital and marks the dedication. The staff which surrounds Dr. Halsted is composed of his senior assistants—it is not his regular resident staff. The Professor is operating on a patient with osteomyelitis of the upper end of the femur. I remember the case

[16] "Opening of the Surgical Building and new clinical amphitheatre of the Johns Hopkins Hospital." *Johns Hopkins Hospital Bulletin,* December 1904, *15,* 379-389.

well. He was performing a resection. He is holding a wooden hammer bound with metal. Jim Mitchell was giving the anesthetic, I was the first assistant, Cushing the second, Joe Bloodgood the third. Hugh Young was the instrument man. Follis is disappearing in the background and F. H. Baetjer sits lost in contemplation on the steps. Baetjer was Resident Pathologist at that time and afterwards moved into X-ray work because of his interest in malignant disease and disease of the bone. The nurse is Miss Crawford. . . .

Observe that gloves are in use. This was certainly very early in the history of the use of rubber gloves in the operating room. The origin of their employment in surgical operations is interesting. Miss Caroline Hampton was Operating Room nurse. Dr. Halsted afterwards married her. It was interesting for us to see the interest of the Professor in Miss Hampton, which was at first entirely professional, grow into affection. Miss Hampton had a delicate skin and developed an eczema of the hands from plunging them into carbolic acid and bichloride of mercury solutions. For some time she was obliged to remain out of the operating room technique altogether. Dr. Halsted tried to help her. At first he painted her hands with collodion but of course this failed because with the contraction of the fingers the collodion covering would split. Dr. Welch used in his autopsy work a heavy pair of rubber gloves which he had obtained from Germany. They were a typical German production of the time. Halsted got his idea of using rubber gloves for Miss Hampton from Dr. Welch's autopsy gloves. He interested the Goodrich Rubber Company in making the gloves and they were successful. The gloves had long sleeves which came up to the elbow. Miss Hampton wore them with such success that Dr. Bloodgood said, one day, "What is sauce for the goose is sauce for the gander. Why should not the surgeon use the gloves as well as the nurse?" At first only the operating surgeon used them. For a time some members of Dr. Halsted's staff used gloves, some did not. But finally the use spread to the entire staff. The original gloves were stiff and unwieldy. The thickness was reduced gradually.

Really, Joe Bloodgood deserves the credit of having thought of extending the use of the gloves to the surgeons, but the Professor of course conceived the original idea for the protection of Miss Hampton's hands. So you see rubber gloves were introduced into surgery from the stimulus of the heart as well as the scintillation of the intellect, a case where Venus rendered great aid to Aesculapius.

Later, von Mikulicz of Germany visited Dr. Halsted's clinic, saw the gloves in use, was most enthusiastic and on his return to Germany published on the subject of the use of rubber gloves in the surgical operating room. Mikulicz is commonly given the credit for having introduced rubber gloves into surgery, but how they were actually introduced it has given me great pleasure to describe to you.

New Haven,
H.C. to George Milton Smith *13 December 1937.*

Dear Dr. Smith: Memories too many to retail are associated with this picture —my copy of which is labelled "The All-Star Performance." The most noticeable feature of the scene is that there is no sign of an audience in the seats. There rarely was for the reason I shall give.

You will see that "the Professor" as he was commonly known, though no one would have ventured to address him as Professor—has his broad back toward the seats as he hammers patiently with his favorite wooden hammer at an osteomyelitic cavity in the femur. You may not know that he was, back in the '70's, captain of the first official Yale football team, but that's another story. Jim Mitchell, you will observe, is giving the anaesthetic with the conical ether cone which was one of the Professor's many inventions. You will note, too, the absence of masks for we had not yet reached that stage though gloves were being used—it was *ca.* 1904.

The Hospital had never had anything but a makeshift operating room, and of all places, it was in the basement under Ward G, with no overhead light. There had been talk of the need for a better place for several years and finally in the summer of 1899, plans were being drawn to renovate Osler's amphitheatre, and just before the Professor went abroad that year for his usual long sojourn he turned some blueprints over to me and requested that I draw some plans for the upper story.

The main feature of these plans was an enormous window directly facing the audience whose pupils, reduced to pinpoints, could see little more than black shadows and the Professor's back. For good reasons I have always been sensitive about this and never confessed my part in it before. There is much more I might tell you about those early and happy days at the Johns Hopkins Hospital, but I shall spare you. Sincerely yours, HARVEY CUSHING.

On 27 October H.C. was off to Cleveland for a meeting of the Society of Clinical Surgery, but he was back again on the 29th for a dinner at 1 West Franklin Street to meet the distinguished German neurologist, Waldeyer. On 1 November came the celebration of the two hundredth anniversary of the death of John Locke at which Osler read his well-known essay on "Locke as a physician." Two days previously there had been a Locke dinner, with a menu drawn up in W.O.'s inimitable style. And from the sublime to the ridiculous, the Pithotomy Club—a ribald undergraduate organization—had a large feast on the 5th—to celebrate 'the gun powder treason and plot.' William W. Francis, Osler's scholarly nephew, who was living with the Oslers at that time, recalls, "There was also an exciting search of the cellar of 1 W. Franklin whence mysterious noises had been reported. To the delight of Revere and his pals, Guy Fawkes, looking remarkably like H.C. under his disguise, was finally discovered squatting on top of the furnace. This became an annual riot. I was in on the 1904 search."

During the year 1904 Cushing's neurosurgical interests had developed rapidly and in the next chapter an account will be given of his first general paper on the subject presented on 18 November at the Academy of Medicine at Cleveland under the title, "The special field of neurological surgery." The family were much amused by a local Cleveland paper which reported that "Dr. Harvey W. Cushing of Baltimore addressed the Academy of Music on Nemological surgery"!

During the previous two years under the stimulation of W.O., H.C. had been hot in the pursuit of the physician-poet, Samuel Garth, and his relations with Dryden. His paper, "Dr. Garth: the Kit-Kat poet," presented before the Johns Hopkins Historical Club on 12 December, is one of Cushing's earliest excursions into general literature; and it has stood the test of time. In the *17th Century*

News Letter for June 1945 the following allusion to the essay occurs:

A valuable but little known article on "Dr. Garth: the Kit-Kat Poet," was recently called to our attention by Louis I. Bredvold (Michigan) who suggested that readers of this News-Letter should know about it. After reading it, we thoroughly agree, and cannot understand how it has been overlooked by so many bibliographers, including the editors of the *CBEL*. Perhaps the explanation is that it was published in the *Bulletin of the Johns Hopkins Hospital* (vol. 17, No. 178, 1906, pp. 1-17) and so is off the beaten path of most literary investigators. The author was Dr. Harvey Cushing. . . . Though most of the available facts and anecdotes about Sir Samuel Garth, M.D., are included in Dr. Cushing's article, special interest attaches to his pages on Garth's famous medical poem, *The Dispensary*. Indeed Dr. Cushing's long account of "The Dispensarian Quarrel," which culminated in 1699, might profitably be reprinted in the preface to a modern edition of the poem.

Garth's name is also closely connected with Dryden's, largely because of the prominent part Garth played at Dryden's funeral. In the confusion surrounding that event Garth obtained permission from the Board of Censors to allow the funeral exercises to be held at the College of Physicians, some twelve days after the old poet's death. Dr. Cushing related how Garth presided at the funeral, issuing a printed invitation of which only two copies are known. In keeping with the non-ecclesiastical surroundings Garth delivered a funeral oration in Latin, concluding with an Horatian Ode, to the great dismay of Thomas Hearne and other pious contemporaries.

Dr. Cushing's later pages contain an account of Garth's life during the reigns of Anne and George I, with generous treatment of the Kit Kat Club. Though this article has been neglected by literary scholars, Dr. Cushing has performed a signal service to the memory of his distinguished predecessor. Both men combined medicine with humanism to the great benefit of their own and succeeding generations.

1905

Early in the year 1905 Cushing had cared for a youngster named John Carpenter, whose skull had been fractured by a baseball. Some twenty-five years later, a newspaper account of another accident on a college playing field called forth a letter from his one-time patient:

Gastonia, North Carolina,
John G. Carpenter to H.C. *27 October 1931.*

Dear Doctor You will probably not remember me as the chap you operated on at Johns Hopkins Hospital in 1905, which operation was the result of a blow on the head by a baseball at the University of North Carolina, but I have not forgotten your splendid surgery, and above all I have not forgotten your extreme kindness to me and your fine personality, and the interest you took in me. I noticed with regret the death of young Sheridan today, but I know everything was done for him that human skill could do, as I saw in the press that you treated him. I have been in the practice of law here for the past 24 yrs. Am prosecuting attorney of the largest district—which comprises with others the City of Charlotte, the largest town in the State. Have in my family 4 boys and 3 girls; pardon this letter but I have always been so grateful to you that I am writing this to express the hope that sometime I can see you when I am in Boston. With kindest wishes, and tenderest affection and gratitude to a great surgeon, but still, I think, the greatest thing one can be—a splendid, delightful courteous gentleman. I beg to remain, Sincerely, JOHN G. CARPENTER.

H.C. to John G. Carpenter *29 October 1931.*

My dear Carpenter How perfectly delightful of you to have written me such a nice note! I remember so well your coming to Baltimore for your operation, and I haven't heard a word from you these past twenty years. Should you ever find your way to Boston, it will give me the greatest pleasure to see you. I am glad to know that you never had any further symptoms from your old accident. Sincerely yours, HARVEY CUSHING.

This exchange is mentioned to illustrate H.C.'s unusual faculty for remembering his patients and keeping in touch with them. During 1905 he began to request all his neurosurgical patients to write him on the anniversary of their operations. This practice enabled him over the years to collect data concerning the end-results of his operations, and ultimately to learn of the probable life expectancy of patients having any particular type of tumor. At the time of his death in 1939 he was following nearly 1,000 of his living cases of verified brain tumor. If by any chance a patient did not write on the anniversary of the operation, a reminder was promptly sent out.[17]

But to return to the early months of 1905—they were particularly crowded because of fresh responsibilities at the hospital and plans for the departure of the Osler household for England. On 11 January H.C. read a paper to the Medical and Chirurgical Faculty of Maryland on "Surgical therapy in epilepsy." On the 16th he arranged a dinner for Dr. G.H.A. Clowes and on the 21st we find him in Cleveland reading his paper on Garth to the Rowfant Club. At the Clowes dinner something was said about Isaac Bickerstaff. In the next morning's mail came a letter from Welch, written sometime after midnight from the Maryland Club—a document which throws an interesting sidelight both on Welch and on Cushing:

Maryland Club,
William Welch to H.C. *17 January 1905.*

Dear Cushing, I have been looking up 'Isaac Bickerstaff.' It appears that Swift was the first to immortalize this name (it having caught his eye over a locksmith's shop in Longacre) in his famous controversy with Partridge, beginning in 1708. Steele was so pleased with it that he adopted it as editor of the Tatler (1709). The same pseudonym was later in the same century used by Benjamin West, the mathematician and professor at Brown University, in his Boston Almanacs.

Then there was a real Isaac Bickerstaff (also spelled Bickerstaffe) an Irish

[17] This work continues under the supervision of his former assistant, Dr. Louise Eisenhardt, who now directs the Cushing Brain Tumor Registry. She informs me at this writing (summer 1945) that there are 800 patients still living from whom Cushing had removed tumors of the brain or spinal cord. In due course Dr. Eisenhardt expects to publish a final report on all Cushing's cases.

dramatic writer with a checkered career, mentioned with details about him in a footnote in Boswell's Johnson (Hill's edition, vol. ii, pp. 94 and 97, New York. 1891). He lived from about 1735 to 1812 (?). See also articles 'Bickerstaffe, Isaac,' 'John Partridge' and 'Swift' in *Dictionary of National Biography,* article 'Astrology' in *Encycl. Britannica,* 9th Ed., and 'Bickerstaffe, Isaac' in *The Century Cyclopedia of Names. The 'Partridge-Bickerstaff'* pamphlets war is really most amusing and is credited with having given the death-blow to Astrology.

I enjoyed very much the dinner last night. What a clean-cut, nice fellow Clowes is! Very sincerely yours, WILLIAM H. WELCH.

References to Osler's impending departure occur in almost every letter during the early months of 1905. Mrs. Cushing gives a vivid picture of their activities:

K.C. to H.K.C. *20 February 1905.*

Dear Dr. Kirke . . . We see a great deal of the Oslers, making the most of our short time. I can't see how Dr. O. is going to get through the spring with all he has to do. I went in not long ago, and he called me into his study to see the portrait which is being done for the University. He was so busy skipping about that the painter was doing the figure from an obliging paralyzed man, whom he brought along for the purpose. Dr. O. just sits for the head. Many dinners are given for them, but Mrs. Osler has had to give up almost everything on account of a touch of the grip, which has set her coughing again. Tomorrow is the opening of the Phipps Dispensary (tuberculosis) and is expected to be a great occasion. Mr. Phipps is here with his piper, who acts as his valet and secretary; and Dr. Osler, Dr. Jacobs and Dr. Biggs of New York will speak.

Wednesday is the 29th Commemoration Day of the University, and Dr. Osler gives the address. It is rumored that the subject will be "New Brooms," and his successor will be named, but that may be only a rumor.

The Phipps Dispensary was opened on 21 February. Mr. Phipps was present and Hermann Biggs gave the principal address along with others by Osler, Welch, and Jacobs.

The next day, the 22nd, was throughout an Osler day. Such an unrestrained outpouring of appreciation for what he had done, of regret at his departure; such a demonstration of love and affection on the part of students, alumni, faculty, and community few teachers have ever received. Most men would have to live after death to know how others really regard them, but it fell to Osler's lot several times in his life to have paid to him in public the embarrassing tributes usually reserved for obituary notices. The university had never seen such a gathering of alumni. McCoy Hall was packed to the window-sills. Osler was the centre of the stage, at fifty-five with not a grey hair in his head, surrounded by his devoted friends of the past and present faculty, several of them, like Basil Gildersleeve, already beyond the allotted three-score years and ten. Suppressing his emotion, but with unwonted colour in his cheeks, he read his valedictory.

Osler's valedictory attracted wide attention, quite apart from the comment about chloroforming sexagenarians which was taken up by newspapers throughout the world, including those in England; it should perhaps be added that the public press in Britain accepted it more in the spirit intended than had the more serious-minded American journalists. Several days later H.C. mentions the "hot water" which Osler's farewell address brought upon him.

H.C. to H.K.C. *25 February 1905.*

. . . I sent you the other day Dr. Osler's Farewell Address. Poor man! It was written in about two days under great stress and he little thought what a bomb he was going to spring with his 40-60-80-year periods. There has been a perfect furor about it. He has been showered with abusive and threatening anonymous letters—the house besieged with reporters—telegrams galore from newspapers everywhere asking for amplifications of his views. The local papers have been full of it—many amusing and many serious things. The London *Times* comments on it all from a British standpoint saying how Dr. Osler's jocularities will enliven Oxford and wondering at the attitude which a supposedly humorous nation has taken toward his remarks. We have been in at No. 1 W. Franklin this evening, reading some of the extraordinary letters which have been showered on him for the past few days. The misunderstandingness of people passes comprehension.

Plans for a farewell dinner for Osler began to take shape and in February came a gratifying letter from Mr. Phipps, inclosing a check for $1,000 for the testimonial.[18]

St. Charles Hotel, New Orleans,
Henry Phipps to H.C. *25 February 1905.*

Dear Dr. Cushing: I am glad that you, Messrs. Welch, Brush, and Jacobs have a movement on foot to raise a fund toward the establishment of a suitable testimonial to Dr. Osler. This movement has my hearty concurrence, and I have pleasure in handing you my check for one thousand dollars in aid of the object. Dr. Osler well deserves the honour we are trying to show him: aside from this the library will be of great service to the University.

Let me suggest that a picture of Dr. Osler be painted and given to Mrs. Osler. This I am sure would be gratifying to his friends, and towards it I shall be pleased to contribute one hundred dollars. Yours very truly, HENRY PHIPPS.

P.S. Let Dr. Osler select the artist, and perhaps he would have more time in England to give the sittings.

Further details of Osler's last weeks in Baltimore are taken from two of H.C.'s letters to his father:

H.C. to H.K.C. *16 April 1905.*

. . . Meanwhile his portrait is being painted every few days for some university or society; he has several addresses to write and deliver; everybody wants to give him a dinner; and as usual his house is constantly full of visiting friends and patients that will not be turned away. . . .

29 April 1905.

. . . Everyone plays battledore and shuttlecock with Dr. Osler and yet he seems to submit with his usual equanimity and to have time for it all. He has given six addresses this month—the last one here Tuesday before the state faculty on 'Unity, Peace, and Concord'—the best thing I ever heard him give. He broke down in the middle of it and was awfully ashamed afterward—I don't suppose

[18] The testimonial was to have been a new library building at the Medical and Chirurgical Faculty of Maryland. Some $30,000 was pledged, but unhappily many of the pledges were withdrawn after Osler's much misunderstood 'Fixed Period' address in which he had alluded jokingly to the suggestion that those over sixty should be chloroformed (Osler biography, vol. 1, p. 677).

there was a dry eye in the house. Then he is hustling through a new edition of his text-book—seeing patients, mostly doctors' families, as usual—submitting pleasantly to the innumerable farewell dinners by all kinds of groups of people—keeping up his hospital clinics punctiliously—well! He remains a marvel.

Isn't it curious that his scandalously garbled remarks on retirement and old age should seemingly have led Mr. Carnegie to make his $10,000,000 gift toward the pensioning of retired professors. . . .

Toward the end of March he went with Mrs. Cushing for a vacation at Thomasville, Georgia, visiting their friends the Irelands and the Hannas of Cleveland. Since returning from his year at Berne, there had not been much time for physical exercise, and he writes amusingly of the disastrous consequences of a horseback ride: "I have not ridden on an animal's back since the summer that Alleyne and I had a pony [he had forgotten the episode in Boston in 1896]. . . . The late results have been ruefully incapacitating. My hind quarters have been completely unmanageable. It remained to have my right shoulder put out of commission shooting clay pigeons yesterday. I am unsymmetrically helpless and wonder what they will do to us today."

April and the early days of May were taken up with last-minute celebrations for the Oslers, and on 2 May a large subscription dinner was held at the Waldorf Astoria in New York to bid Osler farewell. W.O. spoke with great depth of feeling and showed little of his usual humor. The address ended: "I have made mistakes, but they have been mistakes of the head not of the heart. I can truly say, and I take upon myself to witness, that in my sojourn with you—

> I have loved no darkness,
> Sophisticated no truth,
> Nursed no delusion,
> Allowed no fear."

When the address was published, he later added the line from Tennyson's 'Ulysses,' "I am a part of all that I have met."

On 14 May H.C. wrote: "The Oslers go Tuesday, so there will be a shaking up. We have decided to remain here if the Carrolls will have us for another year, realizing that we run great risk of annoyance from the building operations. The chief reason for remaining on is the very small rent which they ask." No. 1 West Franklin Street was turned over to the wreckers immediately the Oslers had departed to sail on the *Cedric* on 19 May, and the bereft household next door felt little cheer at the rapidity with which all signs of their erstwhile neighbors were removed from view.

In going over the family letters one obtains many valuable sidelights from the exchanges between Mrs. Cushing and her father-in-law, for whom she had a warm attachment. "Harvey," she writes on

NOS. 1 AND 3 WEST FRANKLIN STREET, BALTIMORE

The Oslers lived at No. 1, the corner house on the left; the Latch-keyers in No. 3 at the right

CUSHING'S BALTIMORE STUDY

The church warden bookcases followed him to Boston and later to New Haven

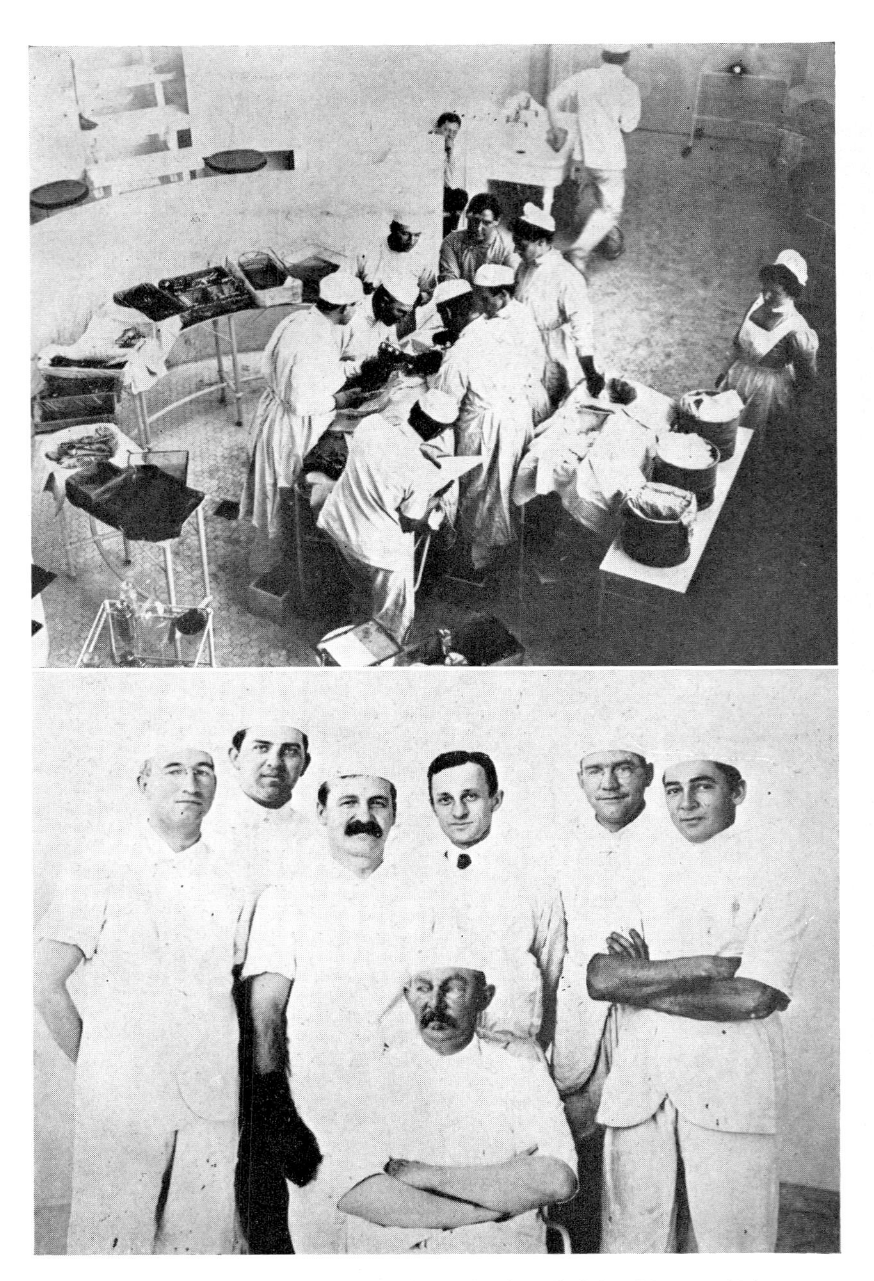

THE "ALL-STAR" OPERATION ON 5 OCTOBER 1904

Top: W. S. Halsted, operating; J. M. T. Finney, 1st assistant; Harvey Cushing, 2nd assistant; J. C. Bloodgood, 3rd assistant; Hugh H. Young, instruments; J. F. Mitchell, anesthetist; R. H. Follis, leaving; F. H. Baetjer, seated; Miss Crawford, operating nurse.

Bottom: Halsted's "All-Star" Team. Standing: Young, Follis, Finney, Cushing, Bloodgood, Mitchell. Seated: Halsted.

H.C. AT HIS LABORATORY DESK 1907

Before him are the photographs of Sherrington, Welch and Kocher

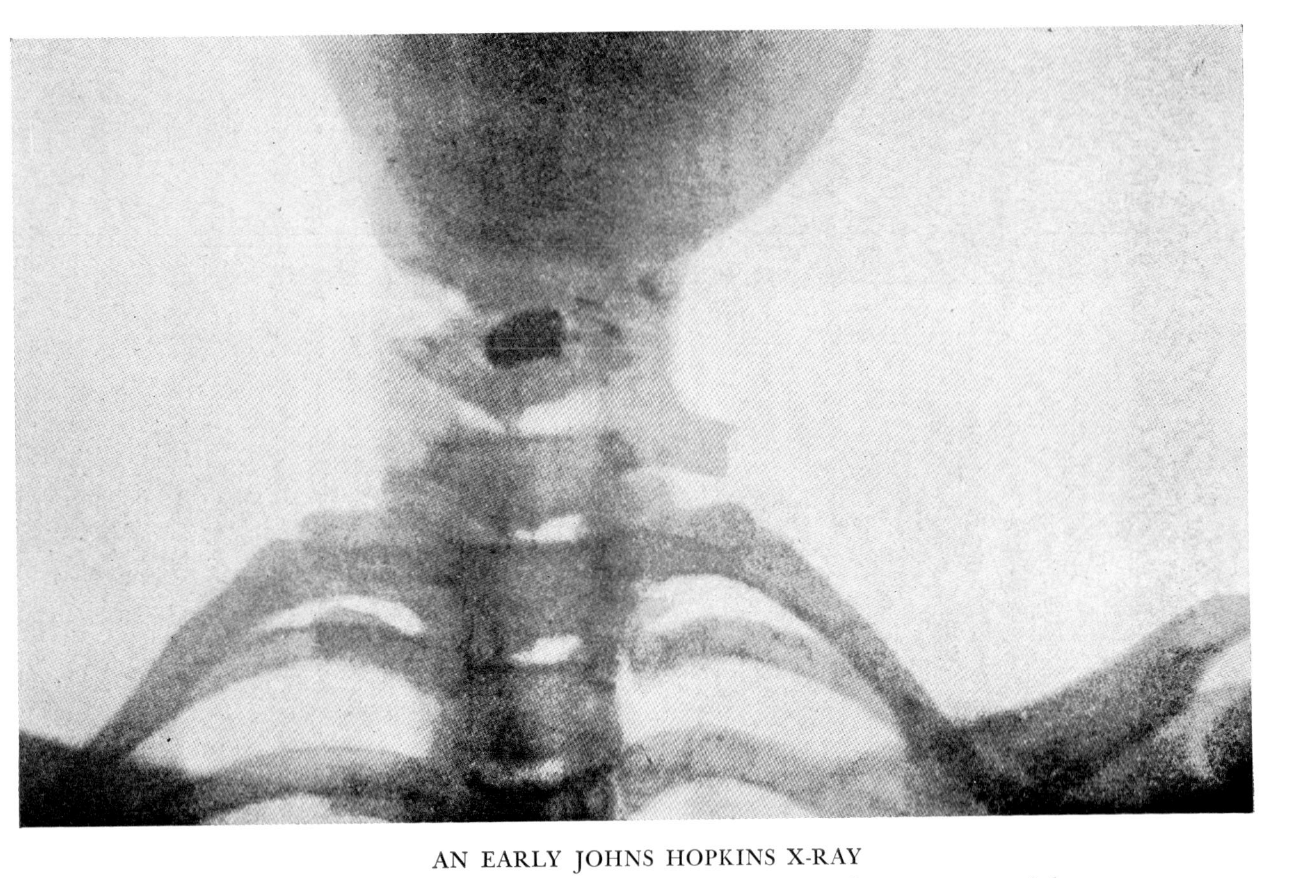

AN EARLY JOHNS HOPKINS X-RAY

Bullet in the cervical spine of patient Lizzie W. From H.C.'s first paper; one of the earliest X-rays to be taken at the Johns Hopkins Hospital

18 August, "goes in town at 8:18 so we breakfast at 7.30 and he comes out at 5.45 but always takes a whole day off on Sunday which he couldn't do in town." She is here speaking of the country cottage which they had taken for the summer near Elkridge, in Howard County, Maryland. In the same letter she adds, "Harvey seems to be quite busy, operating every day. He had a ganglion operation on Tuesday (impecunious—I wonder why all ganglions are impecunious?). I know that Harvey is well because he is in good spirits and eats two ears of corn and two large sliced tomatoes, and other things in proportion when he comes home at night." On Sunday, 20 August, H.C. speaks of getting his Garth paper ready for the printer and adds, "then for the next twelve months about all I can do will be to meet my word to Dr. Keen for a 200-page section on the surgery of the head for his proposed System of Surgery." This important monograph did not appear until early in 1908.

In October H.C. made a trip to Chicago and also to Rochester, Minnesota to attend a meeting of the Society of Clinical Surgery. His keen appreciation of the Mayos is indicated in a letter of 15 October written on his return: "Rochester, on the other hand, had no defects—at least none apparent on our short visit and of course their best foot was forward. They have built up a wonderful operative clinic and are well protected by an *able* staff of internists, specialists, &c, and are little likely to make mistakes. Both of the Mayos are charming fellows and lead a simple life in a simple community. They do as good and as much surgery in their own particular lines as any other two men in world. It has become worthily quite a Mecca for medical men."

By November they had moved back from Elkridge to 3 West Franklin Street where H.C. threw himself energetically into the work of the Hunterian Laboratory which had been built for him during the summer. He writes that he had turned back his $500 stipend from the University to enable him to employ Philip K. Gilman, a young medical student assistant, who took over much of the routine of the course in dog surgery. In the Dedication to his Cameron Prize Lectures given at Edinburgh in 1925 H.C. lists his Hunterian appointees and his assistant residents.

My Successive Appointees in the "Old Hunterian"		*My Assistant Residents in Baltimore*	
Philip K. Gilman	1905-1906	George J. Heuer	1908-1909
J. F. Ortschild	1906-1907	Samuel J. Crowe	1909-1910
Lewis L. Reford	1907-1908	Emil Goetsch	1910-1911
Samuel J. Crowe	1908-1909	William Sharpe	1910-1911
Emil Goetsch	1909-1910	Walter E. Dandy	1911-1912
Walter E. Dandy	1910-1911	H. C. Naffziger	1911-1912
Conrad Jacobson	1911-1912		

1906

There was much enthusiasm over the prospect of a visit from the Oslers who had returned to spend Christmas with Mrs. Osler's family, the Reveres of Canton, Massachusetts.

K.C. to H.K.C. *5 January 1906.*

Dear Dr. Kirke . . . Today we are quite excited over the prospect of seeing Dr. Osler, who arrived early this morning, it is rumored. He has been so pestered and worn out with reporters that he has to keep his movements very dark. Once in the hospital he will be hard to find. Mrs. Osler writes that they will lunch with us on Sunday. She and Revere come on from Toronto tomorrow night. There are so many entertainments being planned for them, they are going to be perfectly worn out before they leave Baltimore. We have not invited them at all, they are to ask themselves whenever they get a chance. Dr. O. wrote me from the steamer that he should expect "tea and extras" at No. 3 W. Franklin. Wish I could show you the beautiful copy of 'Counsels and Ideals' he sent me for Christmas done in green morocco with a grand gold monogram on the cover, something like this [large KCC]. . . .

Mrs. Cushing at this time was expecting her second child who was born on 27 January and was christened Mary Benedict for her maternal grandmother. In a long letter written somewhat tardily on 2 February, H.C. announced Mary's arrival and told of the goings on with the Oslers. Particularly amusing is the account of Osler's encounter with Mr. Sargent when sitting for Sargent's celebrated portrait of the "Big Four"—Osler, Halsted, Welch, and Kelly—which now hangs in the Welch Library at Johns Hopkins.

H.C. to H.K.C. *2 February 1906.*

. . . We have enjoyed the Oslers' visit hugely, and Kate has gloated on Mrs. Osler's stay in particular. She was in every day once or twice, and really made the last rather difficult weeks pleasant instead of trying. It was sad to see her go. Dr. Osler, too, has been in fine form, but has suffered the penalty of popularity to such an extent that he looked as ragged and worn out when he left on Tuesday as he did in May of last year after his strenuous few months of lecturing and submitting to the dinners which were forced down his throat. Mrs. Osler was full of tales about their Oxford life, which must be delightfully interesting. She is the mother of the Rhodes Scholars, who fill the Max Müller house where they have been staying, much of the time. Many of them they find to be delightful fellows.

Sargent had great difficulty in getting Dr. Osler satisfactorily on his famous canvas. Dr. Welch and the other men were put down almost at the first sitting to his satisfaction, but Dr. Osler proved too much for him. He has already painted him in and painted him out three times and seems to despair of getting the man he wants. He said Dr. Osler was like a chameleon, his color changing every day. The first day that the doctors four went into his studio he threw up his hands with delight and pointing to Dr. Osler said that no artist had ever had a chance of painting a man with an olive-green forehead. Dr. Osler said it wasn't olive-green, but Sargent said that was the way it looked to him and he was going to paint it so. Forty-eight hours later when Dr. Osler went in for a second sitting, Sargent looked at him askance and rubbed out what he had done and put in another man. Again a week later he went through the same process, all of which I suppose means that with the greater quiet and rest he began to get a good color and to fatten up as soon as he got away from this tumultuous life he was forced to lead over here.

In the same letter there occurs the first mention of a man who came to be one of Harvey Cushing's enduring friends—a man who, because of his personal affection for Cushing, decided just before his death to leave his magnificent library to Yale University where it would join that of H.C.

There is a nice man named Klebs, almost too nice to live in Chicago—who has been down here on an occasional visit, and who turned up again a day or two ago to say how-do-you-do to us and good-bye to Dr. Osler. He is the son of Professor Klebs, of the Klebs-Loeffler bacillus fame. A few years ago he was down here as a sort of cicerone for Dr. Babcock, the blind heart specialist in Chicago, who proved to be a classmate of Will's and a most charming man. I am now getting down to the reason for this preamble. Klebs, after returning home, sat down and dictated a long letter about his visit and its details, the people he saw and the things he had done, copies of which were struck off on a mimeograph and sent to his many relatives in Germany and elsewhere. This is his usual custom. One of the copies found its way down here, so that we learned what Klebs thought of us in a pleasant and indirect way. I do not expect Miss Humpton to mimeograph this letter, but I have got so much to say and so little time to say it in that I am going to 'Klebs-ize' this long-delayed letter to you.

It is curious that men of such strikingly different personalities should have developed such a profound bond of friendship and understanding, for Arnold Carl Klebs, with his Teutonic background and upbringing, his imperious nature that knew little restraint, differed utterly from Cushing. H.C. was a Puritan at heart, and while he too had a somewhat impetuous nature, he ruled himself with unyielding determination. He cared little for food and drink, while Klebs loved both—like Halsted Klebs was at heart a hedonist and an epicure. Klebs greatly admired the freshness and vigor of life in the United States, and Cushing to him seemed to exemplify everything that he liked best in America and Americans—he was industrious, he had a gay wit and a keen sense of literary values. After "A.C.K." retired to Switzerland in 1912, he corresponded, like Albrecht von Haller, with nearly every one of medical importance in Christendom, and a rich and unusual exchange of letters developed between the two men, extending from 1912 to the time of Cushing's death in 1939.

During Osler's stay in Baltimore a meeting of the Johns Hopkins Historical Club was arranged, devoted to the holders of the "Gold-headed Cane."

H.C. to H.K.C. *2 February 1906.*

. . . We had a Gold-headed Cane meeting at the Hospital on Monday night. I am sorry that Ned could not have been here. McCrae talked about the Gold-headed Cane and the men in general; Dr. Osler talked about John Radcliffe and his Oxford bequests and what they have grown into at the present day;

Futcher took up Matthew Baillie and gave a most delightful account of him; I said something about Mead and Askew and their extraordinary libraries. I have copies of the auction sale of both of them, with the prices marked in and many of the more prominent buyers, such as the King, the Museum, Dr. William Hunter, Cracherode and others. Dibdin also, in his Bibliomania, especially in the later editions which are so full of footnotes, has a great deal to say about Mead and Askew's wonderful collections of books. . . .

On 23 February 1906 Cushing, after repeated invitations from his friends in New Haven, finally agreed to read a paper at the Medical School. On his way he attended the Centenary of the Rensselaer Medical Society at Troy, New York. His paper at New Haven, read to the Medical Alumni Association of Yale, dealt with "Instruction in operative medicine" and was subsequently published in the *Yale Medical Journal*. During this trip he was sounded out about the possibility of taking the chair of surgery at Yale.

In the first months of 1906 Cushing had a lively correspondence with a Frenchman, who had recently come to this country—Alexis Carrel. There was something in the enthusiasm of the young foreigner that aroused Cushing's interest, but he did not seem an appropriate person for Johns Hopkins, so H.C. and Dr. Welch between them recommended him to Simon Flexner, who was then seeking personnel for the newly founded Rockefeller Institute. Shortly thereafter Carrel was taken on as a permanent member of the Institute staff. Carrel's letters of this period are uncomfortable documents, and in retrospect it is difficult to understand how men of H.C.'s and Welch's apperception should have sponsored a man whose standards and basic philosophy were so utterly different from theirs.

During the years 1905 and 1906 H.C. seems to have become more independent, both financially and professionally. His letters had become those of a man who had "arrived." He had acquired a competent office nurse and secretary, Miss Brinkley, who helped with his correspondence, but despite this, his letters home (and his father seemed to preserve everything) had become much less frequent and the details which were characteristic of the earlier letters are for the most part lacking. Only once in two or three months would he write a letter such as that of 2 February 1906. It has become, therefore, more difficult to reconstruct his day-to-day activities.[19]

The principal event in September was the dedication of the new buildings at the Harvard Medical School. He attended the two-day celebration on the 25th and 26th and described it with great en-

[19] On 24 April he attended the John Paul Jones Commemoration Services at Annapolis, but how he happened to go is nowhere indicated. Early in May the laboratories of the newly established Rockefeller Institute were formally opened. H.C. preserved in his scrapbook the invitation, which had been addressed to him and Mrs. Cushing, but it is not clear whether he attended. The family spent the summer at Westerly, Rhode Island, and H.C. paid them brief visits, but he managed to spend most of the hot summer in Baltimore.

thusiasm two weeks later in a letter home. In his Baltimore scrapbook all the programs and cuttings were carefully preserved; in several letters at this time he reiterates his great admiration for President Eliot:

H.C. to H.K.C. *13 October 1906.*

. . . Kate and I had a great time in Boston. The most interesting academic ceremony I have ever attended. I do so wish Ned and Melanie could have been there. It's worth going across the continent if only to hear Mr. Eliot speak. I think he's the *greatest* American. Doubtless you have seen the account in your papers but I will send on some clippings from the Transcript which perhaps Alice will read to you or you to yourself if eyes and letterpress permit.

It will be recalled that Osler in 1902 had chid H.C. for not getting on with some of his junior associates, and there are a good many anecdotes dating from about this time which indicate that Osler's letter had some basis; but there are also many anecdotes in another vein. From Miss Helen A. Adams, a head nurse in the operating room at the Johns Hopkins Hospital, came the following:

. . . As soon as I went to the Big Operating-Room as a pupil-nurse I realized he was a master of brain-surgery, and I 'cleaned up' as often as I could on his cases; when Head Nurse I did so on every occasion possible; they were the most interesting cases, each varied, and Dr. Cushing handled each so skilfully. Finally, I prided myself on knowing what kind of an instrument or dressing he would need and handing it without his asking—make the operation quiet. He greatly appreciated it. . . . One day when I was Head Nurse of the big general operating-room I had several rooms running at once, so was obliged to give Dr. Cushing the best senior I had. The nurse came out in about an hour, crying, and said she 'couldn't return to that room,' so I quieted her as well as I could. Soon after, the operation was at the stage where one of the assistants could close up the incision and Dr. Cushing ran out saying, 'Miss Adams, where is Miss. . . . .? I must see her to apologize for the sharp remark; I fear it hurt her feelings.' When one knows those very exacting, sometimes four-hour operations, and the great strain he was under, that showed his kind heart and sympathy for a pupil nurse!

I could tell you many anecdotes of him—I still correspond with the wife of a patient on whom he operated for a brain tumor. In a letter lately she referred to a day when the patient tried to talk but no one could understand. Dr. Cushing came in and spent a long time trying to see if he could get the idea. At such a time he was very gentle, and showed wonderful sympathy and unlimited patience in his efforts.

Jerome Webster tells of another characteristic incident:

. . . I recall during my first year hearing one about him which roughly was this (but could probably be corroborated by some of the men on the staff at the time). In the year 1906 or 1907, I believe, a patient with a brain abscess had come in and Doctor Cushing had examined the patient. On coming back to the ward later he saw the patient's bed surrounded by screens and asked the reason. When informed that the patient had died, he tore back around the screens, jumped on the bed and proceeded to give artificial respiration. He ordered the operating room prepared and, still kneeling over the patient, was wheeled up to the operating room and then turned the care of the respirations over to another and without scrubbing up went into the brain and found the abscess. I do not know absolutely whether the patient lived or not, but it was my impression that he did.

Closely similar is an incident related by Miss Margaret B. Hoyt, a student nurse:

> ... It was about 1901—I think—when Dr. Cushing was Resident Surgeon at the Hopkins. I was a student nurse on night-duty on the old Ward C. We had a patient (I think carcinoma of the tongue) who had a tracheotomy tube and he was very nervous about the cleaning of it. I don't know how it happened, but at this particular time the interne took out the outer tube as well as the inner one, and the man was choking badly. He ran out in the hall in the excitement and Dr. Cushing coming along the big corridor heard him, dashed down that slide to the lower floor, got hold of the man, and with his own mouth suctioned off the mucus, and put the tube back in. When he had finished, all he asked for was a glass of water and a basin to wash his own mouth.

Before anyone could realize it the Oslers had arrived again for Christmas, this time to celebrate the hundredth birthday of W.O.'s mother, in connection with which messages were received from the Archbishop of Canterbury, the Governor-General of Canada, Earl Grey, and the Johns Hopkins Hospital Historical Club. The story of the Oslers' annual visit to 3 West Franklin Street is once again told by Mrs. Cushing, who had arranged a large reception in their honor:

11 December 1906.
K.C. to H.K.C. [*finished on the 14th*].

> ... Our tea went off splendidly—we opened up the two big rooms downstairs and in spite of rain a perfect crowd of people came, almost every doctor in town and his wife! Mr. Simon Newcomb and a few others came over from Washington. Also the Secretary of the Navy and his wife, and after the tea was over about forty people stayed on to supper. It was great fun, and gave everyone a chance to shake hands with the Oslers. They are very well and seem to enjoy seeing their old friends. They are both staying with us, Revere going to Mrs. Harry Reid's—as Doris Reid is his dearest friend. Mrs. Osler's sister Mrs. Chapin came with them, but she could not stay for our "party." The house is full of flowers sent to her, and the doorbell ringing so constantly that we had to send for an old neuralgia patient of Harvey's, Henry Jones, colored, aged 89, to sit by the front door!
>
> They are delighted with little sister, and Willy and his "gottvater" [W.O.] have great romps together. They have written many letters to Santa Claus, and sent them up the chimney.

Although Mrs. Cushing makes light of the affair, *The Baltimore Sun* (11 December 1906) had this to say: "Doctor and Mrs. Cushing proved themselves splendid hosts. The house was transformed into a conservatory. Banks of American Beauty roses, evergreens and palms added to the beauty of the scene, and the odor of fragrant flowers filled the house. Mrs. Osler was the center of attraction among the fair sex." More than three hundred persons were listed as having been present, including, as far as one can gather, the entire faculty of the Medical School and Hospital.

The year ended with a slightly awkward situation which H.C. left to his wife to settle. Young Bill had persuaded Frank Ortschild, one of H.C.'s Hunterian assistants, to give him some guinea pigs for Christmas. K.C. dealt with the situation with her usual tact.

K.C. to J. Frank Ortschild *28 December 1906.*

Dear Dr. Ortschild Very reluctantly I am allowing Joe to take back those lovely guinea pigs, and don't dare mention it to Willy, but as you observed, pigs is pigs, and Dr. Cushing thought it best! They sat upon their cabbage, and seemed to enjoy apple peelings the best. With many thanks and regrets, and wishing you a very Happy New Year, I am Faithfully yours, KATHARINE CUSHING.

H.C. wound up the year with an attack of "flu"—the Osler visit having completely worn him out.

H.C. to H.K.C. *28 December 1906.*

We have had a 'grippy' Christmas—leastaways I have had and this morning I feel for the first time as though I were going to catch on again. Of all the depressing, rotten maladies this takes the cake and I wonder that anyone has been able to stand being under the same roof with me for a week. One's many bad qualities surge to the surface and among the cardinal symptoms of the disease may be mentioned paralysis of the hind legs, quarrelsomeness, irritability, loss of memory, despondency, dislocation of the attachments of the diaphragm, wasting of the gastrocnemii, and a hopelessness of spirit. Don't get it.

1907

Respiratory infections had disturbed H.C. during the autumn and after the Christmas attack he was finally persuaded to take a week off in North Carolina with Mrs. Cushing. He returned on 6 January much improved by the holiday. He had been coughing off and on for three months, and since his brother Alleyne had had a bout with tuberculosis and his father a tuberculous knee, H.C. was fearful that he, too, might be falling ill; but the response to a week's rest was so favorable that he ceased to be concerned about himself. On 19 January the Sargent portrait was formally unveiled.

H.C. to H.K.C. *20 January 1907.*

. . . We had a gala occasion last night at the unveiling of the Sargent group portrait. It is *wonderful*—a masterpiece of the highest rank. I wish you could have been there. The clipping which I will send gives but little idea of the interest of the occasion. Dr. Welch was at his best. Kate and I had dined with him beforehand to meet his nephew—a classmate of mine at Yale, Fred Walcott—and his niece. There and elsewhere we heard lots of the inside gossip in regard to the painting of the picture—the way S. happened to bring in the globe, the chance grouping, Sargent's delight in the men and interest in the work. The blacks of the silk gowns Cortissoz commented on as the marvel of critics and admiration of artists. I wish they had given Cortissoz' address in full—it was exceptionally pleasing. The people stayed till almost midnight admiring and talking about the picture.

Although he was devoting himself to his monograph on "Surgery of the head" for the Keen *Surgery,* H.C. spent the greater part of his spare time during 1907 arranging meetings of the Johns Hopkins Historical Club which, as one might have anticipated with H.C. as president and Futcher as secretary, had a lively year. On 2 January, while Osler was still in town, Mr. William A. Marburg had presented to the University at a formal ceremony, which H.C. had sponsored, the library of the Warrington Dispensary. Osler had long been interested in the vigorous group of Manchester dissenters who, in 1757, had founded the Warrington Academy which had attracted to its fold such men as Joseph Priestley, John Aikin, the physician-poet, Letitia Aikin (Mrs. Barbauld), and many others who had contributed so notably to the intellectual life of the time.[20] The Academy passed out of existence toward the end of the 18th century and it had come to W.O.'s attention that the library of the Dispensary, whither many of the Academy's books had gone, was coming on the market; with characteristic energy, no doubt aided and abetted by H.C., Osler prevailed upon Mr. Marburg to make this significant gift—one of the most important that the Hopkins Medical Library had had.

Other meetings were held on 14 January, 11 February, 11 March, 8 April (Cushing's birthday), 13 May, 11 November, and 9 December —the printed notices, with the programs, all being carefully preserved in H.C.'s Baltimore scrapbook. They must have been stimulating sessions—Lewis S. Pilcher spoke on "The Mundinus myth" on 14 January; on 11 February J. G. Mumford described Boston medicine a hundred years earlier; and on 11 March, Howard Kelly spoke on Walter Reed and H.C. read a paper entitled, "Notes concerning John Locke as a physician" (something that W.O. had evidently put him up to) but it seems never to have been published. H.C., however, retained his interest in Locke and eventually acquired a number of items from his library. At the meeting on 8 April, H.C.'s 38th birthday and Welch's 57th, Welch himself spoke on "The relations of physics to medicine" and Arthur W. Meyer, the guest speaker of the evening, discussed "The physicians and surgeons in Shakespeare." At the May meeting Dr. Welch gave a second communication on the relation of physics to medicine and Dr. A. Robin of Wilmington, Delaware, discussed the elements of John Syng Dorsey's success.[21] Things then lapsed as usual until November when Howard Kelly read a paper, "The barred road to anatomy," and J. H. Chatard, the guest speaker, discussed "Avicenna and Arabian medicine." The final meeting of the year must have been interesting since John

[20] "The Warrington Academy (1757-1786) and its influence on medicine and science." *Bulletin of the Institute of the History of Medicine,* Baltimore, 1933, *1,* 50-80; H. McLachlan, *Warrington Academy its history and influence.* Manchester, The Chetham Society, 1943.

[21] *Johns Hopkins Hospital Bulletin,* 1908, *19,* 127-131.

G. Curtis of New York described "Harvey's views on the use of the circulation of the blood," which formed the basis of his well-known monograph. At this meeting Dr. Hurd also gave an account of medicine in Mexico.

These communications given before the Club during the year have been listed in some detail to give an idea of the wide interests which men as busy as H.C., Futcher, and Welch found time to develop. Everyone who has set down reminiscences of the Johns Hopkins Hospital in those days has referred to the enormously stimulating atmosphere of the place, where men were able to work with almost incredible application and yet find time to relax with pleasure into the cultural backgrounds of the profession.[22]

Another event of the year was a visitation on 11 February from a young physician named Wilfred Grenfell. He came as "Master Mariner, Member of the Royal College of Surgeons, and Companion of the Order of St. Michael and St. George," to lecture at the Peabody Institute on his work in Labrador. On the program announcing the lecture is a sentence from Henry Van Dyke:

> I remember a night last winter when I sat beside my study fire in the small hours listening to the man who has given his life in the service of these people—a brave, steady, quiet voice telling of difficulties overcome and dangers faced and victories won against the black odds of ignorance and disease, making rather light of peril and hardship so far as his own part was concerned, brightening the darkest scenes with touches of irrepressible humor, giving pictures of human character and conduct so real and so vivid that they warmed the heart with sympathy, and bearing testimony not to be doubted of the power of plain religion to comfort and save plain folk in time of trouble.

Following this meeting Mrs. William H. Buckler started a Grenfell Association and invited H.C. to join.

West North Avenue, Baltimore,
Mrs. W. H. Buckler to H.C. *21 February 1907.*

Dear Dr. Cushing Miss Nutting tells me that you are interested in Dr. Grenfell's work. I hope she is right, for it is so remote that nothing but personal interest in the man, who is to my mind a hero, will help on the cause. I feel ashamed at helping to start a new Association, but it seemed the best way, & I hope you will forgive me for writing about it. Yours v. sincerely, G[EORGINA]. G[RENFELL]. BUCKLER.

Although we have no contemporary record of this meeting, it was evidently H.C.'s first encounter with Grenfell. They apparently understood one another and became fast friends, for among the most treasured possessions in the Cushing library are a number of Grenfell's notebooks and also some volumes from the first World War which Grenfell had annotated.

[22] Welch wrote H.C. "I do hope that you will be willing to continue in the presidency another year. We never had a more successful year of the club than the last one, but a few men must keep it going."

Little has been said concerning Cushing's relations with Halsted during the years following his return from Berne. Halsted at this time was still in poor health; he seldom appeared at the hospital, and in Cushing's files are a dozen or more letters each year from Halsted, most of them apologizing for failing to keep an engagement. There were many acceptances of dinner invitations which were usually followed on the day of the party by a note stating that his nerves were jangled and that he would be unable to be present. Occasionally he would appear for an operation and when he did, his technique was ever impeccable. In 1904-1905, shortly after the dedication of the new surgical pavilion, he was active and operated with considerable regularity for several months. Thereafter he tended to leave the clinic pretty much in the hands of his residents, and when H.C. made a bid for George Heuer, his Surgical Resident, Halsted was loath to have him go because he had placed most of the responsibility of the clinic during 1906 and 1907 in Heuer's able hands. Several of Halsted's letters to Cushing follow:

1201 Eutaw Place, Baltimore,
14 January 1907.

Dear Cushing It mortifies me very much indeed to be compelled to withdraw my acceptance of your kind invitation to dinner tonight to meet Dr. Pilcher, but my gastric upset & vertigo have not at any time quite disappeared & today having attempted a little too much I am paying for it.

Please express my regrets to Dr. Pilcher. And I had anticipated, with so much pleasure, his paper on Mondino. I shall expect Dr. Pilcher & yourself tomorrow evening at 7:30 at my house. It will be a small dinner of 6 or 8 doctors. Sincerely Yrs. W. S. HALSTED.

11 February 1907.

Dear Cushing I am very sorry indeed to feel compelled to ask you and Futcher to excuse me for Tuesday evening's dinner to which you so kindly invite me. It would, as I hope you know, give me great pleasure to come, and to meet Dr. Mulford [*sic*] again; but I have accepted Finney's invitation to luncheon on Tuesday and I know my nervous system too well to trust it to respond to a second round of dissipation in one afternoon. Please express my regrets to Mulford & believe me yours ever, W. S. HALSTED.

21 March 1907.

Dear Cushing I shall, of course, endorse with pleasure whatever you may recommend with reference to the salary of your boy Joseph in the laboratory. I regret very much that absence from town has prevented me from replying to your letter of the 4th instant until this morning.

By the way, I have just received a letter from Dr. Fölkens of Cleveland with reference to the dachshunds. He has apparently a fine litter at present and I shall bespeak two of the puppies. There are six in all, five males and one female in the litter. He does not state his price for the puppies nor send photographs, hence I am tempted to ask Dr. Howard to make the purchase for me. I realize that I have no right to impose on Howard to this extent but he is something of a sport and judge of dachshunds and might not object. I am exceedingly indebted to you for the interest you have taken in securing the dachshunds for Mrs. Halsted and me. I have corresponded with several dealers in the West and also with some New York men who took prizes at the last show with their dachshunds, but Dr. Fölkens, so far as I can judge, has the best dogs. Certainly none of the photographs which I have received from others indicate as fine points as your dogs had. Very sincerely yours, W. S. HALSTED.

P.S. As to the food for the animals, I too have felt that it was not of the right quality and had been contemplating speaking to you about it. It seems to me that we may be compelled to purchase food, as you suggest, unless the Hospital can treat us a little better. It is perhaps expecting too much of the Hospital to supply so many dogs with proper food but it does seem as if the waste from such a large hospital would be more than sufficient for our kennels. The waste from our own table in the country is enough, so far as meat is concerned, for quite a pack of dogs.

We find that it is not a good plan to feed much *meat* to dogs. The diet of our pack consists chiefly of corn bread, which is comparatively inexpensive. The trouble with this is, of course, the baking. Perhaps we might institute an oven in the laboratory or have corn bread baked for us in the Hospital ovens. Dogs are very fond of corn bread and thrive on it much better than on meat.

On 16 April, H.C. went to Washington to attend Simon Newcomb's dinner for Lord Bryce. Four days later the Spring meeting of the Society of Clinical Surgery was held in Cleveland. Then came the semi-centennial celebration of the founding of the Pathological Society of Philadelphia (10-11 May), and in June the meeting of the American Medical Association in Atlantic City. Thereafter the family repaired to Little Boar's Head, New Hampshire, for the summer and in August H.C. arranged a family expedition to the ancestral haunts of the Cushing family at Stafford Hill and South Adams in the Berkshire Hills of Massachusetts.

In December Osler, recalling the strenuous trips of the previous two Christmases, let Mrs. Osler come over alone to be once again with her aging mother, he having meanwhile lost his mother at the ripe age of one hundred years and three months.

By the end of 1907 H.C. was considerably more affluent than in previous years, but he was still to some extent dependent upon gifts from his father and on 29 October he was obliged to write a letter reminiscent of those of Yale and Harvard days confessing that he had overdrawn his Baltimore bank account and requesting some money quickly. "People," he says, "are slow in paying their bills these days," and he added that he had paid all his fall bills without realizing that he lacked sufficient funds. His father dutifully sent what was needed. Then a few weeks later he was offered a book likely to turn up only once in a lifetime—the pride of any medical book collector's heart, a first edition of William Harvey's *De motu cordis* (1628) announcing the discovery of the circulation—and he might have had it for $200; but was obliged to turn it down. After eventually acquiring another copy in 1927, it took him several years to confess that he had paid more than ten times this amount for it.

CHAPTER VIII

Neurological Surgery: The Birth of a Specialty

1895–1907

HARVEY CUSHING became widely known to the general public for his attainments as a "brain" surgeon. His reputation, even as early as 1908, had travelled far, and patients ultimately began to come to him from nearly every country in the world. The surgery of the brain and spinal cord presents difficulties of a highly specialized character which a lay reader cannot easily appreciate, and if there had not been opportunity to devote time and thought to the technical problems involved, little progress would have been possible. In England, Victor Horsley, at the request of his colleagues in clinical neurology, had begun to do brain operations in 1886[1] and, as far as England is concerned, it may be said that Horsley founded its school of neurosurgery. In France a considerable literature developed in the field during the 1890's which was summarized by Chipault in two large volumes entitled *Chirurgie opératoire du système nerveux* (1894).[2] There was also a growing literature in Italy, Germany, and Sweden. The first report of successful removal of a brain tumor was that of Francesco Durante of Rome who took out an olfactory groove tumor in May 1884.[3]

Interest in the surgery of the brain sprang from two sources: (i) the problem of how best to treat head injuries, especially blood clots and fractures, and (ii) the problem of removing tumors. All branches of surgery have tended to advance during periods of war, and the French neurosurgeons first appeared during and just after the War of 1870 when they had occasion to see large numbers of gunshot wounds of the head; and it was also in 1870 that the motor area was

[1] Horsley's first operation at the National Hospital, Queen Square, took place on 25 May 1886 with the eminent neurologists, David Ferrier and Hughlings Jackson, in attendance (Stephen Paget, *Sir Victor Horsley*, London, 1919).

[2] Chipault was a general surgeon of Paris who, late in life, had devoted much of his literary energies and some of his surgical activity to the subject of neurological surgery. Shortly after publishing this treatise he issued in 1896 an extensive work entitled *Travaux de neurologie chirurgicale,* an international compilation in which the contributions of neurological surgeons of all countries were assembled. In 1900 he also published a much more extensive three-volume work summarizing the advances that had been made since 1896.

[3] Cushing, H. and Eisenhardt, Louise, "Notes on the first reasonably successful removal of an intracranial tumor." *Bulletin of the Los Angeles Neurological Society,* September 1938, *3,* 95-98.

discovered—that part of the brain which, when stimulated, causes specific movements of the voluntary muscles. Hughlings Jackson had found that tumors, when situated in the motor area, periodically irritate the nerve cells there and in that way cause focal epileptic attacks, the so-called "Jacksonian seizures." Thus, if a tumor lies in the part of the motor area from which movements of the thumb and fingers normally originate, the epileptic attack caused by such a tumor will begin with an involuntary spasm of the thumb, and the spasm usually spreads quickly to the adjacent finger areas; later the wrist and the elbow may become involved. Since the nerve cells that control the face also lie close to those of the thumb, such a focal attack beginning in the thumb generally extends to the face.

The neurologists early realized that the only way by which a patient suffering from such a tumor could be relieved would be to remove the tumor. The first attempts in this direction, however, were discouraging. Ways and means for controlling hemorrhage of brain tissue had not yet been developed, and nine out of ten patients on whom operation was attempted died. Many general surgeons had made casual attempts to operate on the brain, but persistent failure discouraged them. In England, Horsley alone persevered in the early days despite disheartening losses. Like Cushing he was a man of driving energy, but he lacked patience and even though he had started more than fifteen years earlier, his surgical technique did not reach anything approaching the fastidious ritual of the Cushing school. A letter written many years later to Ernest Sachs, who had gone to Horsley on Cushing's recommendation, gives a reminiscent picture of what Horsley's technique had been:

H.C. to Ernest Sachs *Boston, 28 July 1933.*

Dear Ernest Do tell me whether you ever saw Sir Victor Horsley turn down a bone flap? I have an idea that he was too impetuous for this sort of fiddling, painstaking work which to-day we are accustomed to do. What's more, I think his large bone defects which he used to break up with his heavy forceps probably accounted for his good results, for other people that I remember seeing work thirty years ago used to chisel out little bits of flaps and then try to replace them without any understanding of the need of a postoperative wide area of decompression.

But you at least can tell me whether I am right about my conjecture about Sir Victor, peace to his ashes. Always affectionately yours, H.C.

Cushing's early interest in brain surgery cannot be attributed to any given circumstance or to a particular personality, but it is possible to trace the growth of this interest during his years of training. One recalls his having removed a dog's brain for Professor Ladd at Yale in 1890 and also in the same year his dissection of the cranial nerves of a frog. At the Harvard Medical School his lecture notes on the physiology of the nervous system are particularly full, and one finds him redrawing diagrams of the brain in which indication is given of the motor area as it was understood in those days. A page showing the nerve pathways from the eye and the so-called decussation of the

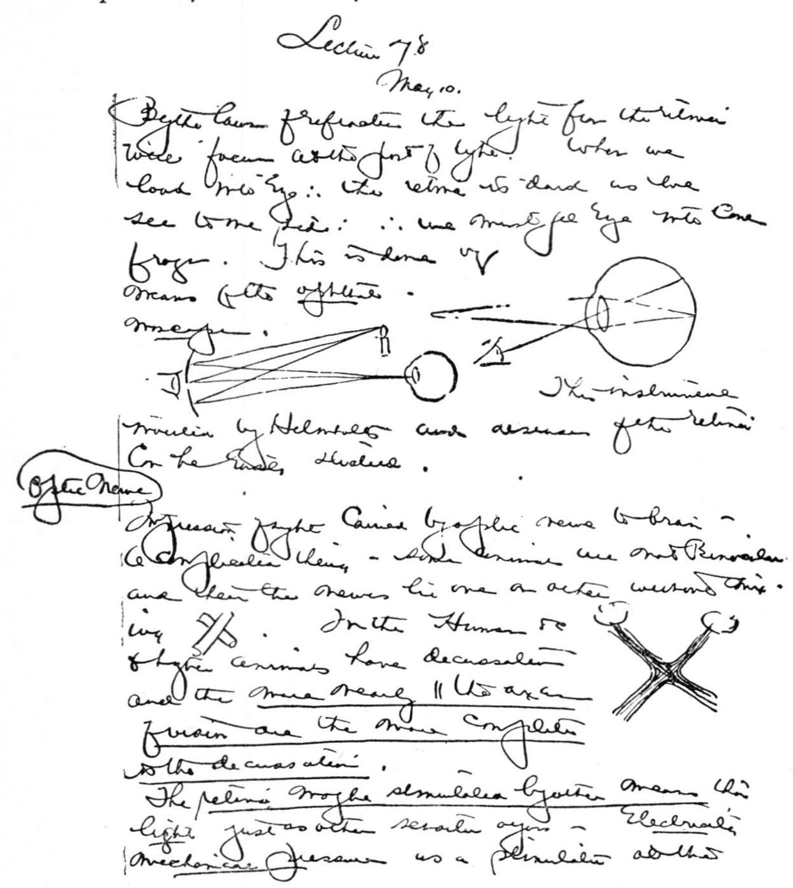

HARVARD LECTURE NOTES

A page from a physiology lecture at the Harvard Medical School 10 May 1892 showing H.C.'s diagram of the decussation of fibres in the optic nerve

fibres of the optic chiasm, which lies just above the pituitary gland, gives visual proof of his preoccupation with the nervous system.

During the second year at the Harvard Medical School a large part of his time was spent administering ether for various surgeons of the Massachusetts General Hospital. His line-a-day diary of 1893 indicates that he etherized at least 75 patients in the course of the year, and there is reason to believe that the number was considerably greater than this, for many such sessions undoubtedly passed unrecorded. During 1893 he did not do as much for John Wheelock Elliot as for Maurice Richardson and John Homans, but it seems clear that "Jack" Elliot, as he was known to his contemporaries, first turned Cushing's attention toward the surgery of the brain. Elliot had met Horsley in England in 1889 and he returned to Boston in 1890 deeply interested in cerebral localization; he urged his colleagues to permit him to deal with any cases of brain tumor that might come to their attention. Horsley, by this time, had reported on twenty such cases and W. W. Keen in Philadelphia had reported on three. It was not until 1895, however, that Elliot first operated successfully for an intracranial tumor.[4] During the summer of 1895 Cushing, who had now completed his fourth year at the Harvard Medical School, spent two months with Elliot during which time he assisted at two operations for brain tumors. Both cases had been studied by Cushing in some detail, and his carefully written notes can still be seen in the M.G.H. history room. On the back of the first case H.C. has written, "Elliot never had less bleeding in opening [a] skull." All of which suggests that Cushing had already witnessed other craniotomies which Elliot had performed. The patient in question was a 32-year-old male, Jordan Hunter by name, who had entered the hospital 9 July 1895 complaining of numbness of his right thumb and forefinger and severe headache. The symptoms suggested a tumor affecting the sensory area of the left cerebral hemisphere. The skull was therefore trephined over this region and an opening made "three-fourths of the size of a silver dollar, with centre about over the fissure of Rolando." The dural covering of the brain was lifted and the underlying brain substance thus disclosed "looked yellowish and somewhat unnatural." Elliot did not attempt to remove the tumor and the patient died eleven days thereafter. Cushing himself did the autopsy and left a detailed record indicating that the tumor of the brain was one that had spread by metastasis from a malignant tumor of the testicle. It lay "about a half-inch under the surface of the motor area." Although the case ended in a fatality, due no doubt to the highly malignant character of the growth, Cushing's enthusiasm was evidently high, for an accurate localized diagnosis had been made prior to operation.

Of even greater interest is a second patient, John Maloney, aged

[4] Codman states that Elliot's first successful brain tumor removal was carried out in 1893. A search of the M.G.H. records of that year fails to confirm this. The first successful case to be found in the M.G.H. files is that of Helena V. Hunter aged 22 who on 1 June 1895 had her left cerebellar hemisphere exposed. A tumor was found but not removed; eleven days later the right cerebellum was similarly exposed. The patient recovered and was much improved by the "decompression." She was closely followed by Cushing before and after her operation.

thirty-one, who had entered the hospital on 27 June 1895 complaining of a tender tumor of the vertex of his skull "somewhat spongy in consistence and having an enormous blood supply." Maloney had been struck on the head three years previously and a small lump began to develop two years later at the site of his injury. Operation was attempted on 2 July, again by Elliot, and a highly vascular growth was disclosed, deeply purple in color, but removal was not attempted owing to the bleeding. On 22 July Elliot made a second attempt. This time the vascular bone was removed and the tumor was "shelled out with the fingers, leaving pieces here and there adherent." The patient died a few hours later. Cushing wrote across the anesthesia chart, "Cerebral tumor No. 2. Have spec. of skull cap. Sarcoma of brain." The tumor was of the type now known as a meningioma which grows from the meningeal coverings of the brain, often as a sequela to an injury. It was this type of tumor that H.C. successfully removed in 1910 from Major General Leonard Wood. The meningiomas as a group were the subject of Cushing's last technical monograph issued in 1938 after he had settled in New Haven.

Both cases were ultimately reported by E. Wyllys Taylor,[5] who had studied the pathological characteristics of the tumors, and H.C. is given due credit for his autopsy report of the first case. Interestingly enough, Taylor invited Cushing to publish the report with joint authorship. H.C. declined because he felt that neither case had been sufficiently well studied prior to operation. He was probably not too enthusiastic about having his first published report based on two operative fatalities.

The experience in the case of John Maloney must be regarded as particularly significant, and H.C. did not forget him, for a photograph of the patient and his clinical history were incorporated in the monograph on *Meningiomas* (pp. 467-468), where in the text he remarks that the photograph had been salted away in a copy of Senn's monograph on tumors published in 1895.

Cushing did not often mention Elliot in his letters, but in 1921 when he gave the Ether Day Address at the Massachusetts General Hospital, "The personality of a hospital," he refers "to that resolute and picturesque pioneer, John Homans, who twenty years before had been privately advised not to do ovariotomies here, yet persisted in so doing; to C. B. Porter, master of operative technique; to Jack

[5] Taylor, E. W. "Two cases of tumor of the brain with autopsy." *Boston Medical and Surgical Journal,* 16 January 1896, *134,* 57-60. Dr. Henry Viets of Boston has also described these two cases in a brief comment entitled "Notes on the formative period of a neurological surgeon," given on the occasion of H.C.'s 70th Birthday Dinner, 8 April 1939 (see *Harvey Cushing's seventieth birthday party*).

Elliot with his brilliant gifts and uncanny surgical instinct." In the *Meningiomas* he speaks of him as "J. W. Elliot, one of the most brilliant and daring surgeons of his day, he ventured twice to trephine the skull for tumors involving the brain." Codman, in his obituary of Elliot, says, "It was not many years before Cushing's genius for detail made Horsley's prophetic ideas of practical importance to the patient with a brain tumor. For Elliot wrote nothing on this subject except one excellent paper on traumatic cranial surgery, but he did act as a successful local pioneer and in my opinion interested Cushing in his life work."

Codman reviewed to 1905 the twenty-eight cases of brain tumor which had come to operation at the Massachusetts General Hospital between 1895 and 1904 and, on the basis of the clinical records, he reached the following pessimistic conclusions:[6]

> . . . I may sum up the observations on brain tumor by saying that the reading of these records has made me personally feel that the chance of any success by radical operation was so small, that in any given case diagnosed as brain tumor, even if the symptoms gave evidence of a more or less exact localization, it would be wiser to do an operation simply for the relief of intracranial pressure, rather than to explore with the idea of removing the tumor. That surgical endeavor in brain cases should, for the present, aim rather at devising an operation which might give relief to intracranial tension without exposing the important motor area to trauma and strangulation through the opening in the skull. It would be particularly satisfactory if an exploratory operation could be devised which might serve at the same time to expose a large area for the inspection of the surface of the brain and when the flap was resutured could be so arranged as to prevent bulging of the motor area. Possibly this could be done by removing all of the bone in a large osteo-plastic flap, except the portion covering the motor area, and wiring this portion *in situ.*

During Cushing's year as a house pupil at the M.G.H. (1895-1896), there are occasional references to neurological cases, but none of them of such outstanding interest as those of Jordan Hunter and John Maloney. A search through the histories at the Johns Hopkins Hospital for the years 1896-1900 has disclosed a few neurological cases, the most notable being the two described in Cushing's first paper entitled, "Haematomyelia from gunshot wounds of the spine," which has already been mentioned in Chapter V in connection with his early use of the X-ray. When working up these cases he acquired an intimate familiarity with the literature of the spinal cord, both physiological and clinical, which established an interest in its functions that he retained throughout life.

[6] Codman, E. A. "Report of results in nontraumatic surgery of the brain and spinal cord. Observations upon the actual results of cerebral surgery at the Massachusetts General Hospital." *Boston Medical and Surgical Journal,* 1905, *153,* 74-76; other reports on the results of neurosurgical procedures by J. J. Putnam, W. N. Bullard, F. B. Lund, G. L. Walton and F. L. Jack follow on pp. 76-84.

Trigeminal Neuralgia

The end of 1899 and the first months of 1900 saw Cushing drawn more and more into the neurological field. There had been occasional neurological cases operated upon between 1897 and 1899, but in 1900 he began concentrating more and more upon disorders of the central nervous system and he himself wrote careful histories of all such cases instead of leaving them to junior house officers. One of his particular interests lay in the surgical relief of trigeminal neuralgia (severe facial pain), an operative procedure suggested originally by the Philadelphia neurologist, W. G. Spiller, and developed contemporaneously by a number of well-known surgeons. In February he was invited by W. W. Keen to present a paper on the subject before a joint meeting of the Philadelphia Neurological Society and the College of Physicians to be held on 20 April. For this he prepared an elaborate manuscript which was published promptly on 28 April in the *Journal of the American Medical Association.*[7] Although other surgeons had carried out the procedure before Cushing, this paper stands historically as an important landmark in the history of neurosurgery because of its unusual detail, and particularly because of the admirable character of its illustrations which Cushing had himself prepared. He seems to have felt, however, that this paper at Philadelphia had been something of a failure:

University Club, 1510 Walnut Street,
H.C. to H.K.C. *Philadelphia,* [*21 April 1900*].

I have been gadding about to a considerable extent. Had a nice visit with Flexner yesterday here. The meeting last night was "no great shakes." Barker was the only one listened to and worth listening to. Was much disappointed in Dana from N.Y. Abbe also. We dined at Dr. Keen's on Apollonaris and mushrooms. Am on my way back now though would like to remain here a day or two. The College of Physicians is a great place—fine old library and Museum.

By now, H.C.'s gifts as a draftsman had come to be of great service. His papers tended to become more and more copiously illustrated and they set a standard which has left its mark on American surgery. Commenting on Cushing's early work on the Gasserian ganglion, Horrax[8] notes that the operation was:

. . . in essence . . . a refinement of the so-called Hartley-Krause procedure, but because of this refinement a complete removal of the ganglion could be accomplished for the first time with certainty, whereas by the older methods, removal almost always had been either incomplete or uncertain. The operation described in this article is, to all intents and purposes, the same subtemporal

[7] "A method of total extirpation of the Gasserian ganglion for trigeminal neuralgia. By a route through the temporal fossa and beneath the middle meningeal artery." *Journal of the American Medical Association,* 28 April 1900, *34,* 1035-1041.

[8] Horrax, G. "Some of Harvey Cushing's contributions to neurological surgery." *Journal of Neurosurgery,* January 1944, *1,* 1-22.

approach which is used today for division of the sensory root behind the ganglion. Cushing's illustrations show that not only the ganglion but also the sensory root of the trigeminal nerve was extirpated, but it was not realized until the work of Spiller and Frazier[9] a year later that it was necessary only to divide the root, thus making removal of the ganglion superfluous.

In 1900 an important neurological case came under Cushing's care in the person of the great astro-physicist, Simon Newcomb, his colleague at the Hopkins. Physicians have varied in their practice but since the wide publicity which enveloped the case, and which was so embarrassing to the attending surgeons, arose from the naïveté of the patient himself, it cannot be regarded as a breach of professional confidence to give now H.C.'s brief statement of the facts, particularly since they incidentally indicated his convictions about dealing with patients whose outlook is without hope:

Simon Newcomb's operation happened the spring before my year's sojourn abroad. Barker and I were going to report the case, but I sailed some time in June, leaving much undone. I had known little enough of Simon Newcomb and nothing of *meralgia paraesthetica*—only that the old man was one of the peculiar geniuses of the early days of the University, large in brains but peculiar in habits—like Sylvester who used to pull a piece of chalk out of his coat pocket and do equations on the back of a cab if one were handy and the mood struck him while he was taking his absent-minded strolls—and Brooks, who would stand for hours in the old court facing Howard Street, hat in hand, head on one side, thinking of his friend the oyster and oblivious to the bipeds who passed by, nudging each other.

Simon Newcomb had worn crutches for years, or at least had possessed them, for they were not always worn; for when he had to catch a crosstown horsecar he did so in lively fashion with the crutches under one arm. His story he tells in his own words in his MS. of May 10, 1900, evidently written for Barker and me to use, but we must have been thoroughly scared by the newspaper notoriety to which we had been subjected. I believe Barker saw him first about March 20th, and immediately recognized the condition as Bernhardt's 'meralgia' of the external cutaneous nerve. As I recall it now, Bernhardt had reported the condition as having occurred to himself. I judge that the letter of March 26th was written before our conjoint examination when the operation was proposed. I was much interested at the time in local anaesthesia and he highly approved of trying it, but it is evident that he procrastinated considerably. . . .

What really happened was this. His operation went well enough and there was no difficulty in finding the nerve though the old gentleman was somewhat abdominous. He insisted on propping himself up on his elbows every now and then to see what we were doing, but unfortunately his centre of gravity intervened; despite this disappointment, however, he was much elated and kept up a running conversation during the procedure.

He did well enough subsequently . . . was bursting with gratitude and wanted to give us a fee which of course we refused though both needed it badly enough, Lord knows. I am sure it was out of the goodness of his heart that he retaliated as he did, for when he reached home he summoned the Washington representa-

[9] Spiller, W. G., and Frazier, C. H. "The division of the sensory root of the trigeminus for the relief of tic douloureux." *University of Pennsylvania Medical Bulletin,* 1901, *14,* 341-352.

tive of the N.Y. 'American', most vile of all news-sheets, and gave him the whole story. I once had a copy—indeed many of them were forwarded to us to add to our shame—and remember there was a full-page description with a large picture of the leonine S.N. directing an operation on his leg which two whiskered

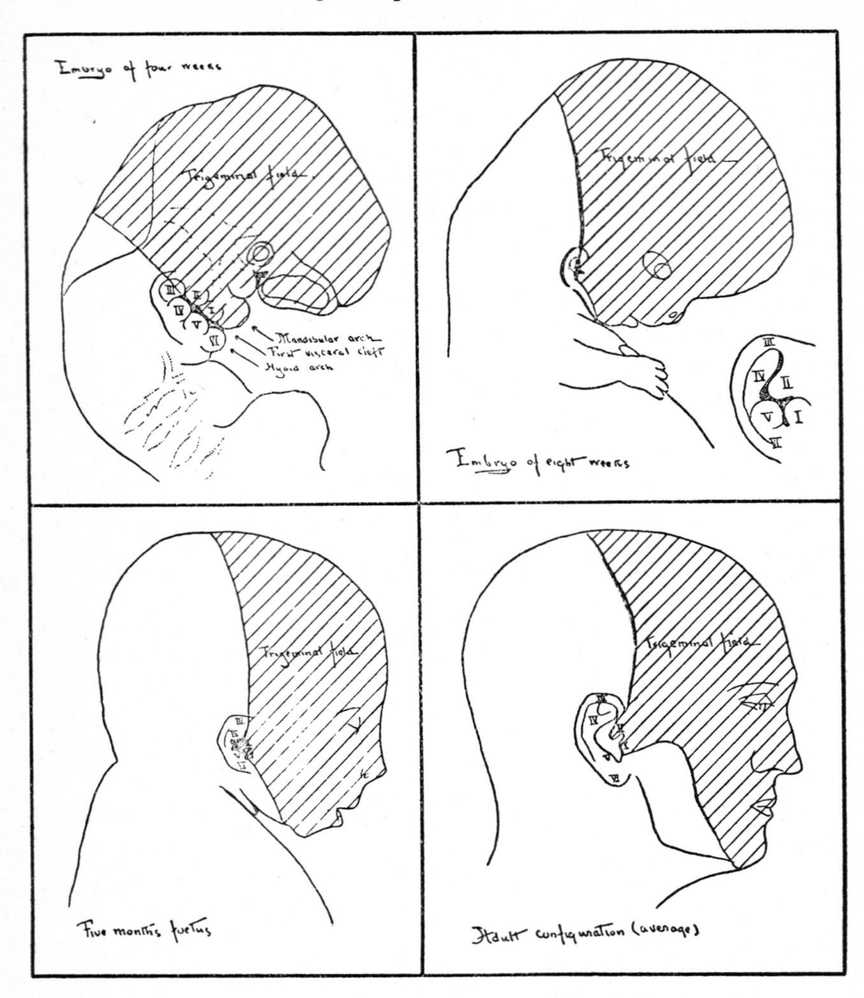

SENSORY DISTRIBUTION OF TRIGEMINAL NERVE

Cushing's diagram illustrating the embryological development of the trigeminal field. Note that the tragus of the ear belongs to the original mandibular arch of the four-week embryo (From *The Johns Hopkins Hospital Bulletin,* 1904, *15,* 230-231)

'Professors' of the J.H.H. were performing accordingly. It was long before we lived it down, and some of the letters I find I have preserved.

In spite of his great expectations—and possibly ours—he did not remain permanently well, though possibly as well as the neurasthenia of an intensive worker would permit; during my absence Finney operated again. On my return from abroad I saw a good deal of him, first and last, and became very fond of him and he was always making plans for us to go off on jaunts together. . . .

Then the sad part of the story. It's told in the brief notes I must have dictated from the J.H.H. histories on my leaving there in 1912. He saw Young in January, 1909. No one was told—least of all the patient—that he had a carcinoma. We all supposed, or at least I did, that a simple bar operation for prostatic trouble had been done. He subsequently had lumbar pains and spent three months in going about the country to get relief, and a diagnosis of osteoarthritis was made by Baer and he wore a brace to his great discomfiture. He finally came back in May, much worn down and, as always, expecting to find someone who could relieve him. Though not my patient, he finally appealed to me and I unearthed the fact that the nature of his bladder trouble had been concealed from him, and felt that he undoubtedly had a spinal metastasis. I had to tell him the truth. He was overwhelmingly grateful, berated those who had concealed the fact, said he had six months' more work on his book still to do, hoped he might live that long, had needlessly wasted the past four months, left the hospital that very day and fled to Washington and to work.

I saw him two or three times later at his home, always in a good deal of pain but always cheerful and speaking only of his work. People differ greatly. I had to tell M. the same thing a few years later in Boston. His family have never forgiven me and he refused to believe that the trouble was malignant.

When the newspaper publicity on the Newcomb operation reached Cleveland, H.C.'s mother again offered wise counsel (25 April 1900):

Dear Harvey boy, I wish to offer you my congratulations on your successful operation:—not so much because you have your name lauded in the newspapers—which is but an ephemeral fame—as because you have been able to do so much good to a great sufferer. Anybody can get his name in the papers, you know. That isn't much—sometimes. I am rather glad your *picture* did not appear, in company with those of other celebrities of the present day. Your Uncle Ed's was conspicuous one day lately, and was hideous. We are all gratified at your success. But to have the brilliant young surgeon of about 30 years thrown at us in such fashion this morning, gave us something of a start. Please forgive my comments. *And don't imagine that I talk!*

Cushing's preoccupation with the Gasserian ganglion operation and with Simon Newcomb's meralgia led to detailed study of sensory distribution, not only of the nerves of the face and lower extremities but of those supplying the skin in other parts of the body. His analysis of the skin areas of the face supplied by the various branches of the Gasserian ganglion's trigeminal nerve has become classic.[10] Following his Gasserian operations he spent many hours plotting the areas of sensory impairment on the face, noting that the posterior limit of skin anesthesia involved the anterior margin of the ear, including the "auricular vagus" and the anterior wall of the ex-

[10] "The sensory distribution of the fifth cranial nerve." *Johns Hopkins Hospital Bulletin*, July-August 1904, *15*, 213-232; also "The surgical aspects of major neuralgia of the trigeminal nerve. A report of twenty cases of operation on the Gasserian ganglion, with anatomic and physiologic notes on the consequences of its removal." *Journal of the American Medical Association*, March 11, 18, 25, April 1, 8, 1905, *44*, 773-778; 860-865; 920-929; 1002-1008; 1088-1093.

ternal ear canal. This, he pointed out, could have been anticipated from what is known of the embryological development of the ear in relation to the other cranial nerves. But he was not content with limiting his observations to the external surface of the face since several of his patients had complained of disturbances of taste following his Gasserian operations. Accordingly, another paper soon appeared describing the relation of the Gasserian ganglion to the taste buds of the tongue.[11]

All phases of the sensory problem began to engage Cushing's attention and in another series of observations he described the areas of skin affected when a sensory nerve from a given level of the spinal axis developed a virus infection ("herpes zoster"). The skin segment innervated by a given spinal nerve is known as a "dermatome," and Cushing set out to map the dermatomes of the entire body through study of the skin eruptions in individual cases of "herpes" and through analysis of sensory "levels" in cases of injury to the spinal cord. One of his pioneer papers in this series was on perineal "herpes" in which he elucidated the confusing distribution of the sacral nerve segments.[12]

Cushing also concerned himself at this time with the problem of peripheral nerve regeneration, and published several papers on ways and means of treating cases of facial paralysis by nerve anastomosis. In 1903 he was able to report his first successful case of regeneration of the motor nerve to the face.[13] On the basis of these studies he also contributed several chapters and diagrams to the 1905 edition of Osler's *Principles and practice of medicine.*

In November 1904 he made his first report upon the special field of neurological surgery in an address before the Academy of Medicine at Cleveland.[14] "I shall attempt," he writes, "to formulate some personal views concerning a branch of surgery which, in this country at least, largely owing to the allurement of other and more promising fields of operative endeavor, has hardly received the attention it deserves." He continues:

Through the generosity of Dr. Halsted, his junior associates have been given in

[11] "The taste fibres and their independence of the N. trigeminus. Deductions from thirteen cases of Gasserian ganglion extirpation." *Johns Hopkins Hospital Bulletin,* March-April, 1903, *14,* 71-78.

[12] "Perineal zoster, with notes upon cutaneous segmentation post-axial to the lower limb." *American Journal of Medical Science,* March 1904, n.s. *127,* 375-391.

[13] "The surgical treatment of facial paralysis by nerve anastomosis. With the report of a successful case." *Annals of Surgery,* May 1903, *37,* 641-659; also "Remarks on the surgical treatment of facial paralysis and of trigeminal neuralgia, with exhibition of patients." *Transactions of the American Surgical Association,* 1907, *25,* 275-280; discussion: 281-283.

[14] "The special field of neurological surgery." *Cleveland Medical Journal,* January 1905, *4,* 1-25.

a measure the privilege of directing the work in some of the subdivisions of his large surgical clinic, in order that they may concentrate their efforts toward advancement along particular lines. It has thus fallen to my lot, temporarily and under his guidance, to control the group of cases which present features chiefly of neurological interest; and it is upon the present possibilities and limitations, as well as upon the future outlook for this department of surgery, that I shall briefly dwell tonight. . . .

He then proceeded to describe how the work of Sherrington and his co-workers on the motor cortex of apes had assisted in the localization of tumors in the motor area, and he mentioned that reports of extirpation of such tumors were becoming more and more frequent, Horsley having recently removed successfully a series of tumors from the cerebello-pontine angle (tumors of the acoustic nerve). In a footnote Cushing adds prophetically, "It is not impossible that a diseased pituitary body may some day be successfully attacked." Although he had attempted brain tumor removals at this time, he had as yet no successful case to report, and he accordingly dwelt largely on the indication and technique for "palliative trepanation," which surgeons nowadays would designate a cerebral "decompression." The presence of an expanding tumor within the cranial cavity may cause extreme pain from rising intracranial pressure, and if a substantial bony opening is made, the intracranial tension is reduced.[15] The management of cases of traumatic injury of the head is also discussed and the wisdom of operating in cases of intracranial hemorrhage, particularly when occurring in the newborn.[16]

The second part of Cushing's report is devoted to the surgery of the spinal cord and the physiological problems involved in the management of cases of spinal injury; and he describes instances of dramatic improvement in cases of spinal compression caused by a tumor.[17] He ends his report with a discussion of the surgery of the peripheral nerve and the problem of peripheral regeneration.

In the space of a single lecture there was little opportunity for a discussion of technical procedures. This, however, came in his next major publication on neurological surgery, the preparation of which occupied the greater part of his leisure time during the years 1906 and 1907. When W. W. Keen invited Cushing to contribute a section on the surgery of the head for his five-volume *Surgery,* he had limited him to eighty printed pages, and he was not

[15] "The establishment of cerebral hernia as a decompressive measure for inaccessible brain tumors; with the description of intramuscular methods of making the bone defect in temporal and occipital regions." *Surgery, Gynecology, and Obstetrics,* October 1905, *1,* 297-314.

[16] "Concerning surgical intervention for the intracranial hemorrhages of the newborn." *American Journal of Medical Science,* October 1905, n.s. *130,* 563-581.

[17] "Intradural tumor of the cervical meninges. With early restoration of function in the cord after removal of the tumor." *Annals of Surgery,* June 1904, *39,* 934-955.

a little disturbed when H.C. coolly submitted a highly illustrated manuscript running to some 800 typed pages which was eventually compressed into a monograph of 276 pages and 154 illustrations. Since this monograph, which eventually appeared early in 1908, marks the end of an important period in Harvey Cushing's career, the present chapter may be appropriately terminated with a brief description of the book and an account of the sensation it created, both here and abroad—for as a result of this detailed monograph, neurological surgery became almost at once recognized as a clear-cut field of surgical endeavor. During the six-year period between his return from Berne and the completion of the manuscript on the "Surgery of the head," Cushing had not only succeeded in making brain surgery a recognized specialty, but he had begun to attract students who sought to learn his techniques and procedures. His first verified (by autopsy) case was operated upon on 21 February 1902, although on several occasions prior to that he had performed decompressive procedures for the relief of increased intracranial tension. He had also carried out many operations on the Gasserian ganglion (supplying sensory nerves to the face). During 1902 and 1903 he had a total of seven operations for intracranial tumor in which the tumor was actually verified at operation or subsequently at autopsy. In 1904 he had four more such cases and in 1905 eight, in 1906 ten, and the same number in 1907. On many of these patients he had operated more than once, and many others came to operation but died without verification of tumor.

During the first few years his mortality rates from operation were high, so high, indeed, that he was many times discouraged, and on more than one occasion the question was raised whether he was justified in proceeding. The "Summary of the surgical experience at the M.G.H.," published in 1905 by Codman did not help matters. Little by little, however, his results became more encouraging. The success of his ganglion operation had attracted wide notice (and it incidentally kept the wolf away from the door), and he also had some success in dealing with congenital malformations of the spinal canal known as meningoceles.

The chief advances during the six-year period were of a technical nature. The introduction of blood-pressure recording during operations had added to the safety of neurosurgical procedures in general, and he had also developed a number of ingenious devices for diminishing hemorrhage, including a cranial tourniquet[18]—now no longer used—that was of great value at the time, for ways and means

[18] "Pneumatic tourniquets: with especial reference to their use in craniotomies." *Medical News, N.Y.,* 26 March 1904, *84,* 577-580.

had not yet been developed for dealing with hemorrhage from the scalp. He also made many improvements in burrs and saws for opening the skull; and he developed electrodes for applying electrical stimuli to the exposed surface of the brain. On the scientific side he had laid the foundation for a broadly conceived program of study of the natural history of brain tumors, for he had soon recognized that some tumors were much more favorable surgically than others, and that some, if removed, had a more favorable prognosis; that is, some were slow-growing and tended not to recur, others returned with alarming rapidity.

The contribution to Keen's *Surgery* had a prompt and very favorable reception, as is indicated by the following letters:

Hotel Boston, Rome,
W. W. Keen to H.C. *24 November 1907.*

My dear "Cush" Yrs of Nov. 7 has just reached me. No, I didn't say hard things about you if I remember rightly tho I think I expressed serious regret that I had not had the pleasure & the opportunity of reading yr Chapter in MS. I hope very shortly to see it in print as soon as Vol III. reaches this side. You have no idea of the troubles of an Editor when e.g. a chapter of 20 pp. (assigned) reaches him expanded to 70 & one of 80 pp. to 196! At that rate the Surgery wd have to consist of 6 or 8 vols. instead of 5. If it exceeded 5 for which subscribers agreed to pay $35 who would pay for the extra vol. or vols.?

But you may be sure that any regrets are of the past & that I have no hard feelings for any one but only delight at the splendid Surgery you & the others have produced.

I am only sorry not to be home & able to send you at once the pamphlets you wish. You will find in my "Addresses & other papers" one on "Our Recent Debts to Vivisection" wh. may be of some help to you. (By the way when the reprints were sent to me labelled "250 Dr. Keen's recent Debts" how startled I was—seeing bankruptcy impending!) . . . I am having a splendid time in Rome, my 2d visit after 42 years' interval! If Mrs. Cushing has forgiven me, you may give her my kindest regards. Yours as ever, "BILL."

H.C. to H.K.C. *15 March 1908.*

I'm glad you liked the Keen Chapter. I bargained for a few of the reprints of which I sent you one. Some day I may improve on the thing somewhat and get Saunders to make a small volume of it—to be followed by one on the spinal cord and then on the peripheral nerves. Just now however this seems too remote for contemplation even—a symptom of spring fever possibly. For Spring seems to have come here today. Thunder showers, budding trees, forsythia in bloom and the like. It's a bit too early for me but I have learned not to accept these early Baltimore 'bluffs' and shall cling to my heavy clothes for a time.

My laboratory operative course has ended for the season and I shall have a month's breathing spell before the graduates come. There will be a goodly number of them I trust.

We are all flourishing. Willie and Schwester are very well and happy in their present big nursery. Much love from us all. HARVEY. I surmise that Perry is coming on here to have his appendix removed. We had a week of telegraphing but it did not seem necessary for me to go down, though on one occasion I was packed to do so.

1201 Eutaw Place, Baltimore,
W. S. Halsted to H.C. *25 April 1908.*

Dear Cushing You little know how much I have hoped for a copy of your "Surgery of the Head" in the form so kindly sent by you. I subscribe for Keen's surgery and had read much of your article with a great deal of interest & even eagerness, in that publication.

With this first edition as a nucleus we shall hope for a rapid growth of cortex, & in a few years to see an awe-inspiring tome on the subject of the Surgery of the nervous system. Very sincerely Yrs, W. S. HALSTED.

25 Cavendish Square, London,
Sir Victor Horsley to H.C. *1 May 1908.*

My dear Cushing I have now had the opportunity to go through your very valuable work on Head Surgery & congratulate you on succeeding in presenting a succinct & yet thorough account of such a complex subject. I hope & feel sure it will do a large amount of good for it is extraordinary what lack of knowledge of common methods still persists. I have been more struck with this since I have heard what customs still prevail in Europe. It seems that 20 yrs is not enough for principles to be realized & understood.

I hope you are very well. We are indebted to you for our friend Sachs who is now for 2 mos. in Vienna. Kindest regards & again many thanks. Yours as ever, VICTOR HORSLEY.

The next major development in neurosurgery was to come in 1908 when the surgery of the pituitary, which H.C. was already pondering in 1904, began actively to engage his attention.

CHAPTER IX

The Pituitary Body: Years of Rapid Development

1908–1912

FROM 1908 to 1912 one finds Harvey Cushing at the peak of his activity. The years were crowded with clinical and experimental work, and his primary attention during the period came to be centered on the normal functions and clinical disorders of the pituitary gland and the surgical treatment of its tumors. Shortly after returning in 1901 from Sherrington's laboratory (where he had met Alfred Fröhlich), Cushing had operated three times upon an unusual patient—a girl who had presented herself at his clinic in December 1901 complaining of headaches and failure of vision. He noticed incidentally that the patient was fat and that, although fourteen years of age, she had failed to mature sexually. He missed the diagnosis of his case and decompressed the brain, first on one side and then on the other; and while these operations relieved the patient's headache, vision still deteriorated. Thinking that she might be suffering from a tumor in the back of the head, *i.e.*, in the cerebellum, he made a cerebellar exposure at a third operation, and the patient died several days later. At the autopsy he was chagrined, but at the same time profoundly interested, to discover the presence of a large pituitary cyst which Welch called a "teratoma," but which we now know to have been a tumor that results from a developmental defect involving a structure to which the embryologist has given the name of Rathke's pouch.

A short time after Cushing had operated on this girl, a reprint arrived from Fröhlich[1] in which he described the case of a similar patient whom he had seen in Vienna in October of 1901—a boy, as it happened, who had also had headache and failure of vision and who, at the age of fifteen, was likewise fat and sexually immature. Fröhlich had described his case immediately and by so doing introduced into clinical medicine the syndrome that still bears his name. He had suspected the presence of a pituitary tumor and had persuaded the well-known Viennese surgeon, von Eiselsberg, to operate. The operation was successful in that the cystic tumor of the

[1] "Ein Fall von Tumor der Hypophysis cerebri ohne Akromegalie." *Wiener klinische Rundschau*, 1901, *15*, 883 and 906.

pituitary gland was drained and the elevated pressure in the patient's head thus relieved, but the operation was carried out too late to save vision.[2]

The fact that a correct diagnosis had been made in a case similar to his, whereas he had missed his own, was disturbing to anyone with Cushing's pride, and from that time on the pituitary became one of his prime interests; but since tumors of the gland were relatively infrequent and since at that time in the United States they were almost never recognized prior to death, few cases came to his attention until, largely as a result of his own personal efforts, he had taught successive groups of students and assistants to recognize an intracranial tumor, whether in the pituitary or elsewhere in the cranial cavity. Once physicians were on the alert for these and other brain lesions, patients began to flock to him—more, in fact, than he could possibly deal with—and by 1908 he was obliged to ask Halsted for permission to have his own assistant resident for neurosurgical cases.

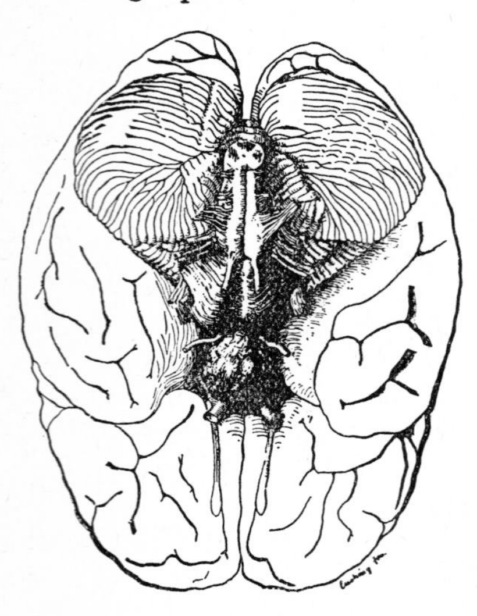

CYST OF PITUITARY GLAND
From Cushing's first case of verified tumor of the pituitary—a cyst of Rathke's pouch. The patient, first seen on December 1901, died after a third unsuccessful operation. Note that the cyst compresses the optic nerves. Drawn by H.C. for Keen's *Surgery* published in 1908

Cushing did not describe his case until November 1906. It was then reported along with a similar case under the title of "Sexual infantilism with optic atrophy in cases of tumor affecting the hypophysis cerebri."[3] On his own copy of the reprint he has written: "This certainly was feeling in the dark. H.C.

[2] The patient was still alive in 1939 when Dr. Fröhlich was obliged to leave Vienna to come to this country.

[3] *Journal of Nervous and Mental Diseases,* November 1906, *33,* 704-716. The patient is again described as Case III in his pituitary monograph of 1912. It is difficult to give undivided credit to a single clinical observer for the earliest description of adiposogenital dystrophy which the Fröhlich syndrome came to be designated in 1906 by Bartels, for Babinski had described a case in 1900 in which sexual dystrophy was mentioned without emphasis on adiposity. A year earlier, namely in 1899, Pechkranz in an article dealing with tumors of the hypophysis described an under-development of the genital apparatus as well as the femininity in distribution of the body fat and oedema of face and extremities sometimes associated with these lesions. It is clear, however, that Fröhlich's case history, recently reprinted in full in vol. 20 of the *Research Publications. Association for Research in Nervous and Mental Diseases,* first focussed attention on the problem. All early authors including Pechkranz, Babinski, Fröhlich, Cushing, Bartels, and others attributed the symptoms primarily to destruction

1912." The importance of the case was not fully appreciated at the time of the autopsy and several years later when Cushing asked the Department of Pathology for the tissue, it had disappeared. From then on he made insistent requests, which finally were granted, that he become responsible for the pathological study of all intracranial lesions encountered in his surgical procedures. This involved him in some difficulty with his colleagues, but fortunately for the future of neuropathology he was dealing with understanding friends such as William Welch and W. G. MacCallum. Later, when he went to Harvard, similar difficulties were encountered, but he was unyielding, and the result of his insistence has been the foundation of the Cushing Tumor Registry in which are preserved microscopic sections and the majority of the original specimens of all the 2000-odd verified brain tumors that came, during the next thirty years, in the range of his clinical experience.

1908

While his interest in the pituitary was developing, a succession of domestic events claimed his attention. A rapidly growing family had begun to make things difficult at 3 West Franklin Street and another member was expected shortly. During the second week in January they accordingly moved to a larger and more modern house at 107 East Chase Street—which had "electricity and all." They had been obliged to desert the other latch-keyer, Thomas Futcher, and he, being unable to stand the loneliness of it all, a year later married Gwendolen Marjorie Howard, daughter of Osler's close friend and teacher, Palmer Howard, Professor of Medicine at McGill.

For once H.C. reacted favorably to a move:

H.C. to H.K.C. *15 January 1908.*

We are in—slept here last night in fact. It's too good to be true—just what we wanted in the way of a house—so convenient. Baths!! without having to walk a mile. The desertion of Futcher is the only thing that clouds our present delight. Electric lights in the cellar even—they lure me to the furnace before I go to bed. I think of you barking your cranial skin on the pipes in the dark subterranean region at 786 where you have shoveled many a ton in years gone by.

Thanks for the check and the letter. I think I shall ask you to send me on $5000 of my account at the Savings and Trust. I shall need it and hope to replace it again soon. I enclose an order for the same though it may not be necessary. . . . Excuse this last sheet of 3 W. Franklin paper. . . .

---

of the pituitary gland. Not until Bailey and Bremer (*Endocrinology*, 1921, *5*, 761-762) proved conclusively that adiposity and genital dystrophy could be induced by lesions strictly limited to the hypothalamus without injury to the pituitary was it possible to separate the syndrome into its nervous and glandular components. Erdheim, however, had suggested in 1904 that the adiposity might be due to involvement of the brain rather than the gland.

And in a letter written the next day: ". . . Another request. Do you suppose you could send on those 3 Scroll and Key things—the emblem and the photographs—without too much trouble? . . . The new house is a joy, electric lights—a big water filter—gas and also big coal range—nice nursery—good laundry—'alles gut'." H.K.C. received other details about the new house from Mrs. Crowell, K.C.'s mother:

Baltimore,
Mrs. Crowell to H.K.C. *19 January 1908.*

Dear Dr. Cushing . . . "Sister" [Mary] continues her chatter in spite of disturbed household, with hammering carpenters, and finishing touches by all sorts of men. The new nursery with all the sun there is will cheer both children and nurse, the latter still suffering from a severe attack of grip. Harvey's rooms are beautiful ones, and his books almost placed. He and Kate appreciate and enjoy the many new conveniences, and a kitchen above ground—large and sunny—is indeed a luxury. I am to dine with Master Will today [Sunday] as his giddy parents go to the country for a few hours' change. We've had good weather, which always helps, and this week will, I hope, see them pretty well settled. There were many little odds and ends to do and the German carpenter who is established there for the time being is a host, turning his hand to anything that presents itself.

Dr. Futcher, I know, is lonely enough. William the waiterman was left with him, besides many household utensils of all sorts. These, however, scarcely make up for the family who have deserted him—the children, to whom he was devoted. On the other hand the Cushings will miss him. A nice man to live with if ever there was one. Combinations are not always so happy!

At this time H.C. records the arrival in Baltimore of Ernest Starling, one of the foremost among British physiologists: "Very interesting man. Expressed high appreciation of the Hunterian Laboratory. It and its work seem to have been the subject of discussion in the Anti-vivisection Commission testimony in parliament during the past year." During Starling's visit there was agitation, not only about antivivisection, but also about securing legislative support for a public health institution at the Maryland Medical and Chirurgical Faculty. Welch was of course heavily involved in the latter venture:

H.C. to H.K.C. *1 February 1908.*

. . .We have a large doctor party arranged to go to Annapolis Wednesday night—doctors and wives on a special train to hear Dr. Welch present arguments before the Legislature favoring State aid for a Medical-and-Chirurgical Faculty building where will be incorporated a central bureau for all organizations associated with matters relating to public health. We represent the 'Roman mob' in the play—merely to impress the law (and money in this instance) givers with our interest.

And five days later:

. . . I am filled up with speechifying for this month. Having presided at the Yale Alumni Banquet it seems incumbent on the holder of this office to go to other repasts so I am booked for the Johns Hopkins University affair on the 22nd and the University of Virginia dinner on the 29th. I despise them—not the institutions, but the speech making.

We all went last night to Annapolis—150 strong—to be present at a hearing before the Legislature in regard to a bill for state support for the Medical & Chirurgical Faculty. We are going to try to establish a great public health institution to take in nurses, druggists, boards of health, charity organizations &c. &c. The Osler fund will go for the main library room. Dr. Welch made a great appeal—it was splendid and ought to bring results. Have you seen his late historical addresses, by the way? "Medicine and the University" in the Journal of the A.M.A. Jan. 4. "The Interdependence of Med. & Other Sciences." Science, Jany 10. "Some of the Conds which have Influenced the Devel. of Am. Med. in Past Century." J.H.H. Bull., Feby. The last you would greatly like. I will send them if you have not seen them.

Starling was not the only visitor, for a few weeks later a young surgeon from Vienna, who had assisted von Eiselsberg in the operation on Fröhlich's case, arrived to see H.C.'s clinic. Cushing remarked that "the 'Centre of Gravity' seems to be shifting this way though it will be long before it gets on this side of the Atlantic. I rather think surgery attracts more over here than other things. . . ."

But there were also exciting events at home as is indicated by the following telegram of 18 May to his father: "A SEVEN AND THREE QUARTERS POUND SUFFRAGETTE LANDED AT FIVE SMOOTH VOYAGE TELEPHONE NED AND OTHERS." The Suffragette was christened Betsey, after B.M.C., and both she and her mother flourished. The family moved to Little Boar's Head a few weeks later, H.C. remaining in Baltimore until August. He continued to send his father new books as they appeared, usually with some interesting comment. The following is characteristic:

H.C. to H.K.C. *2 July 1908.*

I am sending you this book of Dr. Edes[4]—I presume he is the alienist whose son Richard was in my class at Harvard and who died from tuberculosis—a brilliant young fellow. I have not seen it but the *Hingham* matters attracted me.

It is hot here and lonesome. I am struggling over some medical papers long due and find little inspiration—for this or for letter writing. Kate sends good news from L.B.H. of a thriving family—Betsey gaining weight at the maternal dairy with incredible speed. The Goodwillies left for there yesterday and I shall swelter away till August 1st about which time I hope that you (and perhaps you and Alice) can be persuaded to make us a visit. Please cogitate seriously upon it.

H.C. had been re-elected president of the Johns Hopkins Historical Club and despite his increasing clinical burdens he and Futcher were always regular in their attendance at the meetings—the programs this year being as lively and as varied as the preceding year. There was usually a guest speaker and a dinner beforehand, most often at the Maryland Club. One of H.C.'s special dinners was held on 13

[4] *Parson Gay's Three Sermons, or St. Sacrement* by Robert T. Edes, M.D. "The lover of Colonial history will revel in this tale . . . a wonderfully readable story, full of Bateses, Lincolns, Cushings and recognizable local topography."

April for his old friend, George Adami, then Professor of Pathology at McGill.

The event which interested H.C. most profoundly during the year was Schafer's Herter Lectures. Professor Schafer had been working for many years on the physiology of the pituitary gland and it was he who in 1898 discovered the active principle of the posterior pituitary. His four lectures, 27-30 April, dealt with the following topics: "The ductless secreting glands and the doctrine of internal secretion;" "The structure and development of the pituitary body;" "The physiology of the pituitary body;" and "The pituitary body in disease: its relations to diabetes and acromegaly." Schafer was also an intimate of Osler's, so he and H.C. had much in common, and it is probably no accident that Cushing's experimental studies on the pituitary at the old Hunterian began in earnest shortly after Schafer's departure. From the experimental standpoint Cushing and his group at the Hunterian had an advantage over Schafer since he, although a brilliant experimenter, did not have at his command the surgical techniques essential for approaching the pituitary gland of higher animals.

During Cushing's stay at Little Boar's Head in August he sat still long enough to have his portrait painted by Edmund C. Tarbell, or at least to have it started. A photograph which has recently been unearthed suggests that the artist recognized the restless nature of his subject and did not demand his actual presence for more than the important details of head and hands. The portrait was executed at his father's expense for a sum which seemed a little surprising for those days—$2500. The correspondence in connection with it is tangled and amusing, and H.K.C. came to the conclusion that artists as a race of men were impossible when confronted with business details. After the portrait had been delivered, Tarbell, completely forgetting the initial deposit of $1000, submitted a bill for the full amount plus $75 for the frame, and H.K.C. seemed unable to fathom how any human being could be so careless. From Little Boar's Head H.C. wrote in the midst of the sittings:

H.C. to H.K.C. *7 August 1908.*

. . . I had expected you to be in this part of the world by this. Couldn't you and Will and Carolyn all come? I want you to see the portrait which Mr. Tarbell has begun—two days of sitting—head outlined, that is all. He has decided on an academic robe—sitting picture—arm on back of seat—perhaps pensive chin in other hand. I've left him entirely alone and just *sit,* where put. He is a very good fellow and talks amusingly. . . .

Months later a three-cornered correspondence was still going on, with H.C. trying to explain to his father the vagaries of an artistic temperament:

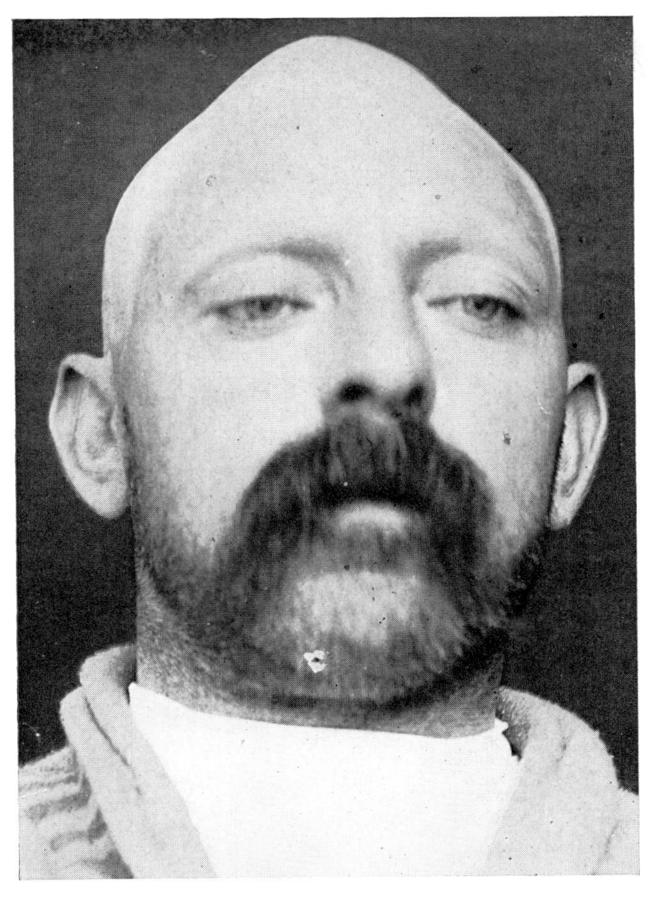

CUSHING'S FIRST BRAIN TUMOR PATIENT

The case of John Maloney whose meningeal tumor with bony overgrowth was operated upon by J. W. Elliot in July 1895 with Cushing assisting. The patient died and H.C. performed the autopsy (see p. 260)

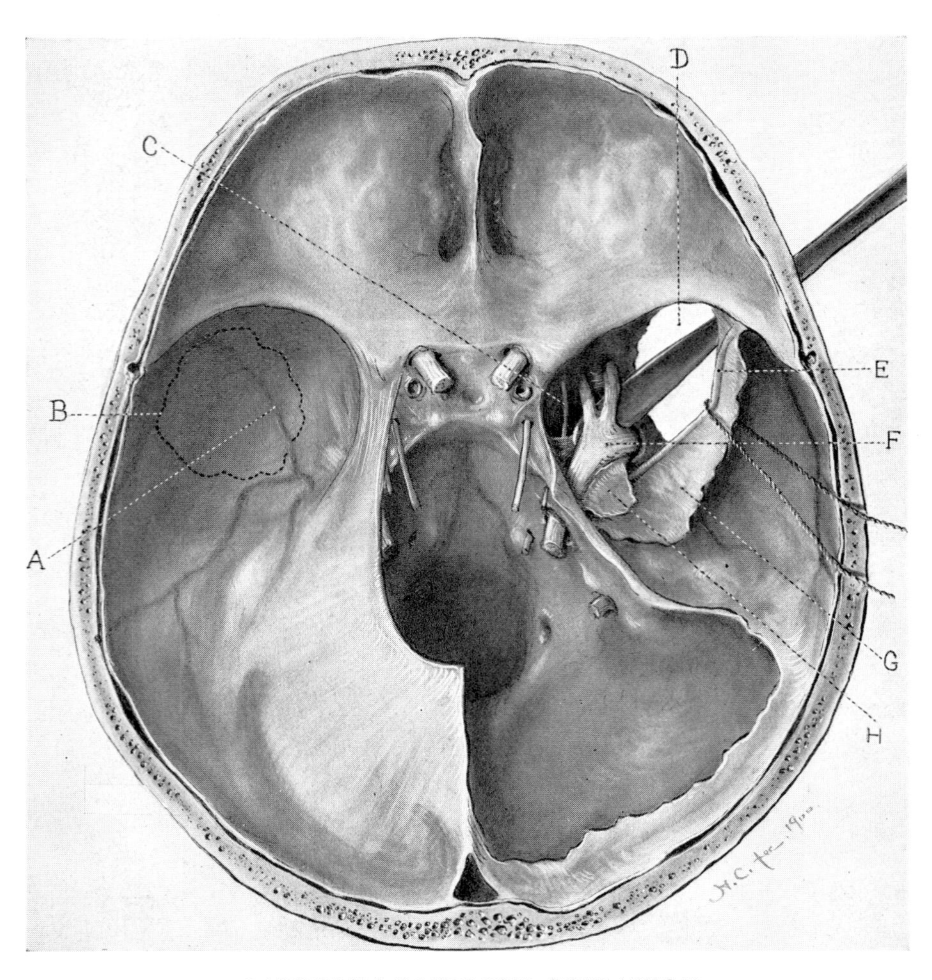

GASSERIAN GANGLION OPERATION

Cushing's beautifully executed drawing showing the position of the Gasserian ganglion at the base of the skull and its relation to the cranial opening, the meningeal artery, and the three branches of the trigeminal nerve to which it gives rise. *A,* Groove of middle meningeal artery; *B,* Site of bony opening; *C,* Abducens nerve (to eye muscle); *D,* Operative opening; *E,* Middle meningeal artery; *F,* Gasserian ganglion; *G,* Reflected dura mater; *H,* Dural covering of ganglion

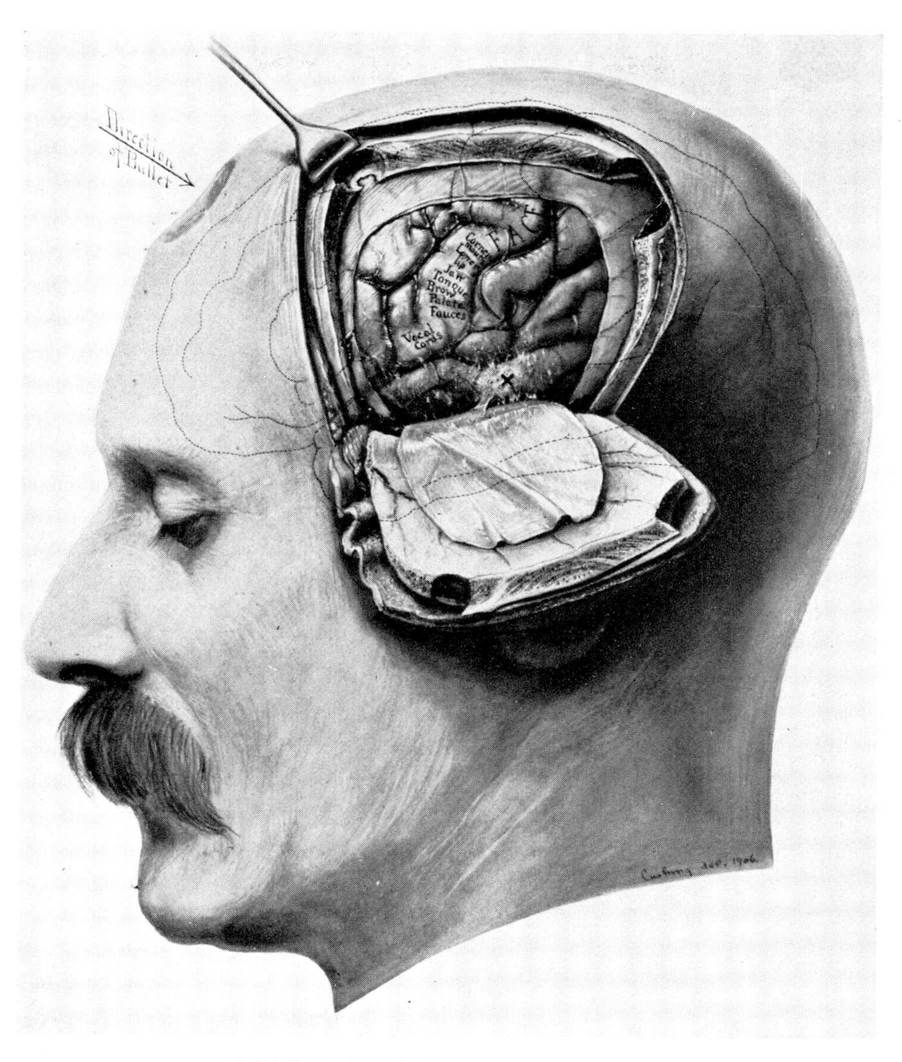

MOTOR AREA OF HUMAN BRAIN

One of Cushing's drawings of the exposed motor area of the brain; from the case of man having focal epilepsy secondary to a bullet wound in the speech area. Other motor points determined by electrical stimulation of the brain are indicated. Drawn by H.C. in 1906 and first issued in Keen's *Surgery,* 1908

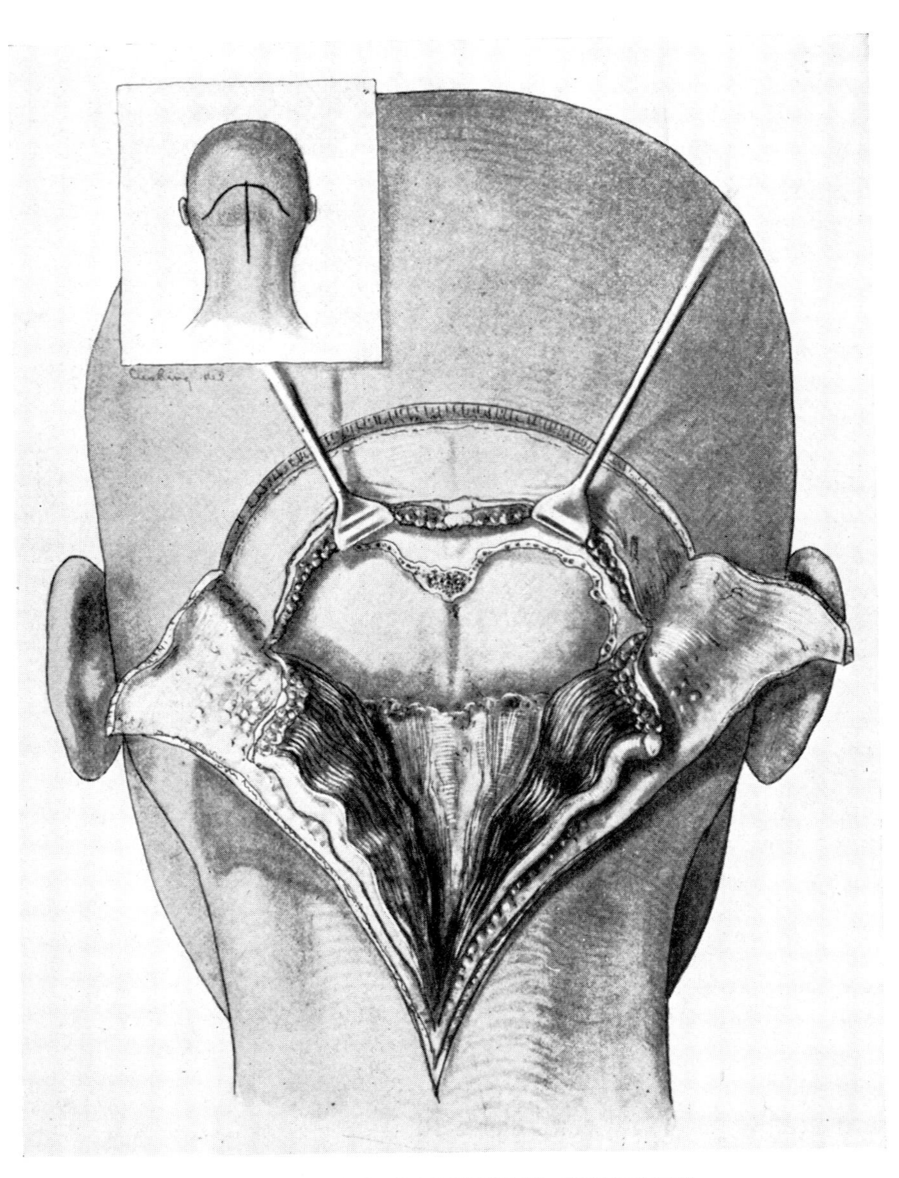

CUSHING'S SUBOCCIPITAL EXPOSURE

Drawn to illustrate his section on brain surgery in Keen's *Surgery,* 1908

H.C. to H.K.C. *7 January 1909.*

. . . Tarbell's failure to reply is, I think, only an indication of the typical irregularities of "people of talent." I have sent him a number of missives lately, not only granting him (for you) permission to use the portrait as he desires, but also in regard to a portrait of Ex-President Dwight which a committee of my classmates has decided to give to Tarbell if he is willing to undertake the commission. . . . [and have received no reply].

Edmund C. Tarbell to H.C. [*Postmarked 14 January 1909*].

Dear Cushing: . . . Do not let your father pay a cent until he or you get the portrait. Kindest regards from Mrs. T. and myself to you all. Sincerely yours, TARBELL. [When this note was written H.K.C. had paid the $1000].

H.C. to H.K.C. *29 April 1909.*

Your note in regard to Foster Brothers' bill [well-known picture framers in Boston] has just come. I think this is merely another evidence of Tarbell's artistic irregularities, for I suppose he is about as unbusinesslike as most people who engage in similar work, at least this is the reputation of most artists.

Everything was straightened out eventually by the following from Tarbell which placated H.K.C.:

Edmund C. Tarbell to H.K.C. [*Postmarked 30 July 1909*].

My dear Doctor Cushing: Thank you very much for the check for which I enclose a receipt. I am delighted that the portrait meets with your approval now that you have seen it in your home.[5] Dr. Harvey Cushing was a splendid sitter, I think the best I ever had, and also wonderfully interesting to paint. I am not surprised that he is the great surgeon that he is.

Again expressing my pleasure that you like the portrait, I am, Very sincerely yours, EDMUND C. TARBELL.

In October H.C. went to Boston with Dr. Welch who was to give the first Ether Day Address at the Massachusetts General Hospital to commemorate the introduction of surgical anesthesia, and his inimitable account (in his unpublished Welch memorabilia, vol. 1, p. 135) of how Welch drafted his address the night before on the Federal Express (and handed it the next day to the printer without changing a word) is one of the better of the many amusing stories about Welch:

On the evening of the 15th we took the Federal Express from Baltimore and dined leisurely together. As we were nearing Philadelphia he casually remarked that he had not yet written his address and perhaps had better go about it. I went back to his berth and got his bag from which he extracted a block of his familiar lined yellow paper which he always used and a handful of cigars. The dining room steward said he might smoke in the diner—a thing then unheard of —until we reached Phila[a] when the car would be taken off.

When we arrived there we returned to our car and found the smoking compartment full of drummers all smoking furiously. They moved up and gave Popsy a seat in the corner where like a Buddha he sat on his feet and began writing where he had left off with no apparent hesitation. He nevertheless was

[5] The original portrait now hangs in the library of the Cleveland Medical Library Association.

aware of what was going on and every now and then joined in the conversation which was general. The drummers one by one went off to bed and I finally got a seat and read until about eleven when I said I thought I would turn in and asked how far he had got. He counted the pages and said "Twenty-three minutes —you don't suppose they will expect me to talk an hour?" I assured him they would and reminded him that between Jacksonists and Mortonists who would be in the audience he would have to walk a tight-rope. This was an unnecessary caution—quite.

In the morning he said he had almost finished and we parted—he going to the Councilmans and I to stay with some friends. The lecture in the afternoon was admirable and took exactly 60 minutes. He had told me the night before that it took him a minute and a half to read one of the closely written pages on that particular paper—the reason he always used it. After the lecture Washburn asked him for the MS. which he surrendered. Washburn showed it to me and so far as I could see there were no corrections nor were there any paragraphs—each sheet simply full of close writing—40 in all. The address was set up, if I remember correctly, and the proofs sent to him for correction. They never heard from him and it was finally published as it stood.

Welch's address, despite the seemingly casual way in which the lecture was prepared, was outstanding—indeed it was a statesmanly appraisal of a controversy that had rent Boston medical circles for more than half a century. His criterion for the recognition of credit in the ether controversy was pragmatic. Since the beginning of time men had used vapors, alcoholic beverages, and other concoctions to diminish pain, but who was it who first convinced the world of the safety and feasibility of surgical anesthesia? This was W. T. G. Morton. Welch's judgment has had wide acceptance since it was based on a broad historical perspective which took into consideration the fact that scientific discovery is never the result of the work of one man alone but inevitably stems from a host of contributions of those who have preceded him. H.C. was profoundly influenced by Welch's point of view and frequently cited this Ether Day Address when priority seekers crossed his path.

Neurosurgical Assistants

As already noted, Cushing's neurosurgical clinic had grown so rapidly in 1906-1907 that he was obliged in the spring of 1908 to appeal to Halsted and the authorities at the Hopkins Hospital for a full-time assistant in neurosurgery. He asked for a house officer but he eventually received an Assistant Resident. He had had his eye on George Heuer, who had been Assistant Resident on Halsted's general service but being reluctant to ask for a man already committed to Halsted, he first surveyed other talent unattached to the Hopkins. Some months earlier (Jan. 1908) he had introduced Ernest Sachs to Sir Victor Horsley and on 16 May he enquired of Bernard Sachs, Ernest's uncle, whether he thought Ernest might be interested in the new post. The Assistant Residency would provide room and board and a stipend equivalent to that which Cushing himself was receiving from the University; namely, $500 a year. He later wrote to Ernest Sachs:

18 June 1908.

... I do not know whether it is worth while to go into your various questions in any detail, except to say that the position is an official one, that my material has grown so large that it is impossible for me to keep as careful track of the patients as I would like to do, and that I in consequence have been given the privilege of having a personal resident in neurology, who has no other connection with the surgical staff. It is necessary that the incumbent of this position should start in in October, and as you say you have planned to stay in Europe until the first of the year, this of itself would prevent me from giving you the position.

Possibly when you return you may wish to run down here and look over the ground and see what there is to offer for the following year. You may perhaps have heard that Mr. Phipps has given us a large sum of money for a psychiatric institute where our neurological clinical work is to be in all probability centered. . . .

Since Sachs would not be available in the autumn, Cushing finally summoned his courage and asked the "Professor" to release Heuer.

H.C. to W. S. Halsted *15 June 1908.*

Dear Dr. Halsted, I apologize for telephoning yesterday but I wished to speak with you in regard to the appointment of a personal house officer for next fall, permission for which you and the Trustees have so kindly given. Heuer has applied to me for the position and I have held him off hoping that I might get someone equally satisfactory from outside and particularly someone who had had a certain amount of laboratory training in neurological technique. I have been unsuccessful as yet. He tells me that you have held out to him the promise of some position on your staff and I wish to know whether it will interfere with your plans for the fall if Heuer should undertake the work for the next year.

I wished furthermore to speak about Ortschild. I gather that he will in all probability be able to return to work by fall. He has written me rather a touching letter to the effect that he learns that all of the positions on your staff have been filled for next year. Shall I tell him that this is the case or do you still regard him as a member of your house staff? I am sorry to trouble you with these things on the eve of your departure. If you think you can spare Heuer to me for a year the training in neurological matters may make him a more efficient assistant resident should you wish him to continue in your service afterward. Then we are all very anxious to see Ortschild have another chance.

Halsted's reply was more favorable than H.C. could have anticipated:

W. S. Halsted to H.C. *17 June 1908.*

Dear Cushing: It is quite agreeable to me to release Heuer for next year. I conferred with Dr. Hurd, however, with reference to his spending two months this summer with Mallory in Boston. We are, as you know, very shorthanded and I fear that it will be impossible to spare Heuer for so long a time. I had arranged with Reford that he should come back as late as the first of September, because he said he feared the hot weather in Baltimore during July and August would disagree with him. At his last visit to me he stated that it would be impossible, he feared, to return to Baltimore before the first of October, inasmuch as he had promised you to work during July and August in the Anatomical Laboratory. So you see it is pretty hard for us to keep up with the changes of plan.

As to Ortschild, I too have great sympathy for him and am sure that some place on the staff can be provided for him when he is well enough to return to duty. Wishing you and Mrs. Cushing a very pleasant summer, believe me, Sincerely yours, W. S. HALSTED.

Accordingly, in the autumn of 1908, Heuer entered upon his duties as Cushing's first Assistant in Neurosurgery (later designated Assistant Resident). In recalling his early experiences in this position Heuer writes (4 April 1940):

. . . You ask me if I recall when Dr. Cushing first became interested in acromegaly and gigantism. I was his Assistant in Neurosurgery from September 1908 to September 1909 and it was at that time or shortly before that he became deeply interested in the subject. Indeed, his interest was so great that he could think of little else. I recall the case he himself has commented upon, a man with acromegalic features but who had definite symptoms and signs of a cerebellar tumor. We had something of an argument. He told me I wasn't up on the newer things in neurology. He proceeded to explore the hypophysis. The patient died and showed at autopsy a large cerebellar cyst.

In 1907 a Roumanian surgeon, N. C. Paulesco, devised a new surgical approach to the canine pituitary which permitted a clean and complete removal of the gland. He reported that his animals invariably succumbed in a state of cachexia. Later in 1907 Cushing and his associate, L. L. Reford, undertook to repeat[6] Paulesco's experiments and reached the same conclusions. Now and again, however, following pituitary removal animals merely became fat and did not die. Further studies were therefore indicated.

Starting in September 1908 as a voluntary assistant in the old Hunterian, John Homans (son of H.C.'s preceptor of the same name at the M.G.H.) had joined in the pituitary study. Maurice Richardson had been instrumental in recommending him, and the letter which Richardson wrote no doubt pleased H.C. as much as any communication he had ever received:

224 Beacon Street, Boston,

M. H. Richardson to H.C. *31 July 1908.*

My dear Dr. Cushing, I suppose you are not in town now, but I am writing you in the hope that you may eventually receive this letter. I do not know why I should imagine you are not at work, except that it seems as if the younger men were more sensible than the older ones and saw the vast importance of taking a long rest in the summer, if for no reason other than the sharpening of their intellectual faculties and the stimulating of their ambition for original work in the fall. Men who do as I do keep themselves more or less in a state of fag

[6] "Is the pituitary gland essential to the maintenance of life?" (With L. L. Reford). *Johns Hopkins Hospital Bulletin,* April 1909, *20,* 105-107. Read at the American Physiological Society, December 1908.

all the time. Though I tire out my assistants, one after the other, I feel in the fall that I have blunted sensibilities and uninterested ambition.

I write in behalf of my assistant, John Homans. I suggested to him that the very best thing he could do would be to go to Baltimore and do some work under your direction. I realize that this may be perfectly impracticable; but I venture to write to ask you if you cannot take him as a post-graduate student, or in some capacity in which he can devote the coming year to work connected with surgery. I look upon him as one of the brightest assistants that I have ever had.

I feel that my men, although they make splendid practitioners of surgery, fail to get from me any inspiration toward so-called research work. Of course we are seeking all the time—and hoping that we shall find—knowledge in the fields of practical surgery; but it seems that the coming generation needs a broader field in which to work; that the men should be more than purely clinical observers. It is a good thing for a man to have a very broad foundation upon which to base special knowledge and experience. I feel, too, that we get to be very narrow in Boston. I advised Dr. Homans to go to Baltimore, and I found that my advice was in accord with his own wishes; and I have hoped that—of all the men there—you would be the one to direct his work. I hope later to have my son Edward get the inspiration of your example.

I feel, of course, a personal interest and gratification in your splendid career, and I know better than any one else in Boston what the splendid qualities are upon which that career is based. If you are not at home, perhaps you are in Europe, and perhaps I may be able to see you there at the Brussels meeting. Yours sincerely, M. H. RICHARDSON.

John Homans, who later became Cushing's associate at the Peter Bent Brigham Hospital and one of his most loyal friends in Boston, writes of his year in Baltimore and gives further details of Cushing's early experimental work on the pituitary:

. . . I went to Baltimore in the winter of 1908-09, because Dr. Maurice Richardson thought that Cushing was the coming surgeon of America and was very likely to be invited to come to Harvard. At that time he had established himself solidly as a neurological surgeon and was very active in the Hunterian Laboratory, carrying on research and giving a very popular course to students once a week in what might have been called the Art of Diagnosis, dividing the students into groups, including the family physician, the surgeon and several assistants. The family physician told the story, based on a hospital history, the surgical group made the diagnosis and the appropriate operation was carried out on the laboratory animal. The students "ate it up."

When I arrived in Baltimore in the autumn, Cushing had decided to interest himself particularly in the hypophysis. . . . He set Crowe and the rest of us to making hypophysectomized animals. It soon appeared that, though many of those died within a few days in a state of what was called *cachexia hypophysiopriva,* of which many photographs were taken showing dogs in extraordinary attitudes, some animals survived for many months. These animals were carefully looked after, but, on the whole, were passed by for the time being as freaks in which something had marred the completeness of the hypophysectomy. Finally, I remember that one of these animals died; an extraordinarily fat, loggy, sexless creature. I made the autopsy, merely noting the fact of the asexual adiposity which made no impression upon me whatever. One day Cushing caught sight of another of these animals while it was still alive, I am quite certain, and said at once: "Here is Fröhlich's asexual adiposity." From the fact that the animal was nearly or perhaps entirely without hypophysis, he judged that this represented a state due to hypophysial deficiency, as opposed to acromegaly which must represent an over-function of the gland. This latter condition was beginning to be recognized as such, but the asexual adiposity had been very confusing because this also seemed to be due to an enlargement of the hypophysis. Thus, it was Cushing's quickness and insight in connecting the hypophysial adiposity of the dog with the Fröhlich syndrome which straightened out the confusion and made Cushing the leader in this field. I remember well how quickly his imagination leaped from the hitherto overlooked fat, asexual dog to the whole picture of the hypophysial disease.

Cushing was devoting himself more and more at this time to his brain tumors, so that, as my winter in the Hunterian Laboratory went on, he spent less and less time there. It seemed impossible for him to get home at the end of a day's work. He would urge me to come in to tea but I soon learned not to expect him, but to turn up at the house on East Chase Street and join with others who took pleasure in Mrs. Cushing's sympathetic friendliness, kindly welcome and perfect tea. I had never seen anyone work like Cushing before and found it difficult to believe that he could enjoy life on this basis, but, as far as I have been able to discover since, his pace never varied, unless it became accelerated. One of the lessons of that winter was the enterprise with which everyone dug into the literature, much of which was Italian, and since we were expected to be able to master any foreign monograph, we soon learned to do so, deciding that scientific writing in a foreign language was perfectly understandable if one used one's common sense and accustomed one's self to the little quirks of the language.

Early in October Cushing had news that he had been commissioned a First Lieutenant in the Medical Reserve Corps with rank as from 5 July 1908, which, when the war came in 1914, gave him something of a head start as far as rank was concerned. At the end of October 1908 he attended the annual meeting of the Society of Clinical Surgery in Chicago, this being the surgical organization from which he always received the most stimulation. During the remainder of the year he was deep in clinical work, taking time out occasionally to attend local meetings in Baltimore. On 2 November he presented to the Hopkins Historical Club an account of early operations for brain tumor. From one of Mrs. Cushing's letters one gains a clear picture of his activities at this time—as well as a few domestic details:

28 October 1908.

Dear Dr. Kirke . . . Little Betsey is what you might call a "fine child," fat, with red cheeks and bright eyes—she looks very like Willy, only with not such a large head. Her hair has turned out to be reddish! She is the best baby, and has not kept her mother awake one night so far, which is a good record, as she's going on six months—altogether a perfect darling, and the whole household her slaves. Harvey takes more notice of her than he did of either of the others.

Harvey is expecting to leave tomorrow (Thursday) for Chicago—for his Clinical Society meeting, and will be with you on Sunday—he seems to be in good spirits and has had some very interesting cases this fall. His assistant in the Hunterian—by name of Crowe—is splendid—helping him a lot; and then he has the pick of the men in the hospital for his assistant in his operations, which makes all the difference in the world, instead of having a different assistant each time and it also means that there's someone on the spot all the time to watch the case after operation. It saves extra trips to the Hospital. . . . The Oslers have shut their house in Oxford, boarded out Revere, and will spend six months on the Continent—a thing Dr. O. has always wanted to do. They will spend some time in Italy. One of the Rhodes Scholars who has come back to enter the 3rd year here told us about it. I expect we shall have an interesting book on medical historical subjects as one result. . . .

One of the many visitors whom Cushing had attracted to Baltimore was a young Harvard psychologist named Robert M. Yerkes.

H.C. to Robert M. Yerkes *9 October 1908.*

Dear Mr. Yerkes: I am very much gratified to have received your letter saying that you are contemplating coming here for some surgical work. I have always been very much interested in your writings and nothing would give me greater pleasure than to be associated with you in any investigation that you may desire to make which concerns the surgery of the nervous system. I would be only too glad to place the privileges of the laboratory at your disposal at any time you might feel inclined to come here. Whether the routine prescribed course for the graduates would be profitable to you I do not know, but at least it might perhaps give you some inkling as to the present aspects of general surgical methods. . . .

Again, on 17 October: "I am afraid, in answer to your question, that *none* of our clinical material is 'thoroughly studied psychologically.' I trust, however, that should you be able to come down here for some work we may have some equally good opportunity as this case might have offered." And yet again on 5 February 1909: "I hope that at least we can help you with your surgical technique. I would not bother to read anything. It is merely a matter of surgical cleanliness, and learning how properly to handle tissues—not a thing you can get out of books." There was a further exchange, and Dr. Yerkes ultimately spent several months at the Hunterian in the spring of 1909. In thanking Cushing later, he wrote:

11 August 1909.

My dear Cushing: . . . I want to say again that the busy hours and days which I spent in Baltimore were as profitable as they were enjoyable. . . . You'll never know how you made my arms ache during the hypophysis operation on the one monkey which we sacrificed on the altar of science! I took it as discipline.

And now, thanks to your generosity, I feel competent to undertake any and all operations which my researches demand. Or rather I feel in a position to go ahead and work out my methods for I have a live working knowledge of aseptic technique. My own investigations are progressing finely. My family being away for the summer I am free to work day and night—and in consequence am accomplishing twice as much as usual. How the Hopkins Medical spirit impresses a visitor! I admire it hugely and wish we might imitate it here in Harvard Medical. . . .

H.C. replied on 29 August: ". . . The gratitude (and some apologies *re* the abandoned course) is mostly on our side. It's outrageous for a gentle soul like you to come to Baltimore for a few short weeks and make everyone, from the President down the line, regret that you are not a permanent member of our community. Hoping for many a reunion. . . ." Throughout the next months there was a barrage of Oslerian postcards from the various places the Oslers visited during their spree on the continent:

Paris,
W.O. to H.C. *19 October 1908.*

Dear H.C. Shadwell, Provost of Oriel, sails 22nd on the Cedric & will go directly to Bryce at the British Embassy. I am sure he would like to see Baltimore. Do write to him—he is a good soul in spite of his facial & cervical grimaces. We are very comfortably settled here—in Marguerite Chapin's Apt. Everything very grand so far. I have been prowling about the Bib. Nationale—spelling out some of Gui Patin's letters & getting oriented. So nice to hear such good accounts of the chicks. What darlings they must be. I hope your portrait is a success. Love to Kate & to Mrs. Futcher.[7] Yours, W.O.

Paris
W.O. to H.C. *8 December 1908.*

I was sending you the Harvey Diploma—but Rolleston says he has sent it. I have tried to head off your copy but if I fail—& it has gone—do what you like with it—some library preferably. I have sent to Med-Chir. & to the Hopkins. I am sending you instead a Servetus photograph which will interest you. I am looking up his life—intensely interesting. Love to the angels, *all four,* and best wishes for the new year. I wish you were here. Yours. Wm OSLER. My greetings to your father & Ned and Mrs. Ned.

On 20 November H.C. had the satisfaction of witnessing the dedication of the H. K. Cushing Laboratory of Experimental Medicine at Cleveland. He attended as an official delegate of Johns Hopkins University and was accompanied by William Welch who gave the principal address. The fact that a laboratory of experimental medicine should be named in honor of his father was particularly gratifying. It had been financed through a gift of $200,000 from Mr. Howard M. Hanna and Colonel Oliver H. Payne. They also had given an additional $17,000 for the purchase of apparatus. Professor George N. Stewart was the first director and has now been succeeded by Carl Wiggers, the Professor of Physiology at Western Reserve. The Cleveland *Plain Dealer* for 21 November quotes Dr. Welch as having said: "In the movement in this country for higher education upon a university standard, the medical department of Western Reserve University has maintained an advanced position in its requirements for preliminary training and in its educational standard. Although the main emphasis in the work of this laboratory is to be upon original investigation, I deem it fortunate that it is connected with an important university and in close affiliation with an excellent hospital. The real home of science is the university and there science should find the most favorable atmosphere for its cultivation."

In good Oslerian style H.C. wound up the year with a paper on his old friend Haller, which evoked a pleasant note from Welch: "I

[7] A characteristic Oslerian touch; there was no Mrs. Futcher at this time.

thought the meeting last night a great success. Your introductory remarks were just right and covered the ground admirably. I do not know how the Society, and indeed a good many other things here, would get on without you." On 30 December came word that he had been made a member of the Charaka Club in New York, a select body of medical historiophiles.

1909

A heavy schedule of clinical activity, lectures, and consultations continued in the new year. H.C. had been induced against his better judgment to go out to Cleveland to operate on a patient with brain tumor at the Lakeside Hospital—the family of the patient having been reluctant to bring him on to Baltimore. The operation was performed and after all seemed well Cushing returned to Baltimore, but the patient took a turn for the worse and died. On hearing the news, he wrote his father "I am grieved to learn that my Lakeside Hospital case died. It's poor business trying to do such things away from your own haunts." From that time on he made it a rule never to operate away from his own hospital. And on the basis of this decision, from which he subsequently seldom deviated,[8] he refused many urgent appeals from important personages and their families.

In the middle of January he was asked to see Major General Leonard Wood who was showing symptoms of a slowly growing brain tumor. The case had been referred to him by his old friend, Arthur Tracy Cabot of Boston, and it became something of a chapter in his clinical career. He decided to proceed conservatively and recommended that operation be deferred for a time.

In 1908 there had been an epidemic of cerebrospinal meningitis and a number of cases had come under H.C.'s care. Dr. Simon Flexner had recently introduced his well-known meningitis serum, and on 1 February H.C. gave an account of his experience with the disease, presenting the material in the discussion of Samuel Crowe's paper on "Prophylactic use of hexamethylenamin in cerebrospinal meningitis."[9] In this connection a letter from Flexner is interesting:

[8] Dr. Hans Lisser recalls (17 June 1940) an instance when, again against his better judgment, he did deviate: "I remember a less pleasant experience when I was one of a surgical team taken to Washington, D.C. (in 1911-12) where Dr. Cushing was invited by the President of the United States to operate on an army officer in the Walter Reed Hospital—an exceptional honor to a civilian M.D. For five hours Doctor Cushing explored the spinal column without discovering the suspected tumor. Much depressed we took the train home to Baltimore and the street car back to Johns Hopkins Hospital; Doctor Cushing got off the car at a point near his residence without having uttered a word to any of us all the way from Washington—not even a Thank-you, or Goodbye—he had failed and was dejected, not meaning to be unpleasant."

[9] *Johns Hopkins Hospital Bulletin,* May 1909, *20,* 154. In the previous year he had also published a paper on meningitis entitled "Obstructive hydrocephalus following cerebrospinal meningitis with intraventricular injection. Injection of antimeningitis serum." *Journal of Experimental Medicine,* July 1908, *10,* 548-556.

I am extremely sorry to hear that the young woman on whom you first used the antimeningitis serum has begun to develop paraplegia. I know of no similar complication, though of course it is always possible that the literature contains cases of the kind. I am greatly interested in what you say regarding urotropin and I see no reason why the drug should not be tried in all forms of meningitis. Whether or not it should be used to the exclusion of the serum is a question I should not like to assume the responsibility of answering. As far as I can judge, the serum when used promptly and freely will bring about the cure of most cases of meningitis. Whether, therefore, a new method of treatment should be tried, independently of the serum, is a moral question that someone else will have to pass upon. I see, however, no objection to using the urotropin internally at the same time that the serum is injected into the spinal canal. It is quite possible that together they may act better than either one alone, and, I should think, not interfere with each other.

At the end of the month H.C. went to Boston, partly to discuss plans for the Brigham Hospital, but principally to give an address before the Cancer Commission at Harvard which Councilman had prevailed upon him to deliver—the general theme being the pathological characteristics of different types of brain tumor. He stayed over until the 26th for a dinner given in his honor by Reginald Heber Fitz at the Medical Dinner Club, and attended by such old friends as Maurice Richardson, F. C. Shattuck, W. L. Richardson, and others who no doubt pressed him once again to consider transferring his activities from Baltimore to Boston.

In March 1909 H.C. received several interesting letters from Weir Mitchell with whom he had continued to correspond in desultory fashion over the years. The lure of historical conundrums was almost as great as that of clinical mysteries, and his eagerness evidently spurred many of his elders to exchange ideas with him and to enlist his sympathetic interest in their own pursuits. Thus Mitchell writes:

1524 Walnut Street, Philadelphia,
S. Weir Mitchell to H.C. [*March 1909*].

My dear Doctor, Garth always interested me & I have read him, which few can say. Thank you for a pleasant half hour in company doubly good. I send you a copy of "Pearl," [by Mitchell] which will explain itself. It is better poetry than Garth ever dreamed. I am at unfilled times busy with Harvey's autographs. To be sure that the three pp. I have of his m.s. are really his I had his earlier will photographed. The comparison of the m.s. of 1616 & that of the will seems to show a change from the almost unreadable English hand to a steady, beautifully clear Italian hand. Thayer, the expert, is now bewildered over this strange fact. I hope before long to write a little essay on Harvey, about whom I have some other matter of interest. The English M.D.'s are queerly neglectful—all of Harvey's lecture notes on the muscles remain in m.s., also various other medical m.s. not H's in the College of Phys[s]. I am bothering them about all these & about the Harvey portraits. You fell into a leisure hour, as I am about to go south for a breath of idleness, as we have been a bit too busy. Yrs. with thanks, WEIR MITCHELL. P.S. Is Garth's Harveian oration in print? Where? Address till 16th, Jekyl Club, Jekyl Island, Brunswick, Ga.

And then later from Jekyl Island: "Do try for those 'Mems' of Harvey. Try hard. Fothergill is another figure worth attention. I own his sleeve buttons." And still later: "I *must* have copies of the Harvey things, at all cost to whosoever can be competently bothered. Tell them I have for reference the full Harvey genealogy. Could I not get into direct relations with the people in question?" Mitchell's persistence is amusing and no doubt struck a sympathetic chord in H.C. who cultivated throughout life this same virtue in his historical as well as his clinical problems.

In April came news that the Oslers were arriving and forthwith H.C.'s veins seemed to run with ink. On 6 April he attended a meeting of the New York Neurological Society at the Academy of Medicine and presented a paper on "Some aspects of the pathological physiology of intracranial tumors"[10] which was an elaboration of the paper given in February before the Harvard Cancer Commission. H.C. was not often given to reading the same paper in two places but he was evidently enamoured of this one since he presented it first at Harvard on 25 February, then at New York; on 27 October he read it before the Chicago Medical Society, and on 29 January 1910 it came out of his pocket once more when he appeared before the Associated Physicians of Long Island. With further elaboration it was presented for the fifth time in June 1911 at a meeting of the American Neurological Association in Washington. He evidently felt that knowledge of the pathology of intracranial lesions needed dissemination, although he does hint in a letter to his father that there may also have been another reason. He moreover calls attention to his first operative encounter with the pituitary body of an acromegalic:

H.C. to H.K.C. *Sunday, 11 April 1909.*

I've had a very busy month and have done no letter writing. The Boston lecture went off fairly well and I gave the same thing in New York last week at a Neurological meeting and think I shall do it again for this Liverpool affair—the Wm. Mitchell Banks Lecture—booked for Aug. 4th. This tripling up saves much work though it is perhaps not the fairest thing, for the Boston people want me to publish it for them. 'Vita brevis.' I've promised to participate in the dedicatory exercises for our new State Medical Building May 13th for which Dr. Osler is coming and many others. Weir Mitchell is going to stay with us during the two days. Then there is a paper for the Am. Surgical Assn., the Neurolog. Socy., the Oration in Surgery for the A.M.A. at Atlantic City, the Chapter for Dr. Osler's System still to write and also the Budapest paper. It's the dickens! Kate has about decided to go with me and we probably sail on the Adriatic July 22nd for Liverpool, then to Oxford for a visit before going to the Continent and we should get back about Oct. 1st. I hope to get a good rest and some new ideas. All this means much work and as I have had many patients of late I shall probably give up the May and June graduate operative course which always has taken much out of me during these two months in past years.

[10] *Boston Medical and Surgical Journal,* 15 July 1909, *161,* 71-80.

We have been working hard over the pituitary body question in the Hunterian Lab'y and have made some progress. It seems to be an important gland and one which is surgically accessible. I have had one clinical case—an acromegaly patient. It is quite extraordinary how he has improved—quite a brilliant affair all round. Chas. Mayo sent him down to me from Rochester and the chap walked in to the clinic on his sixth day after operation when our Surgical Club was here—as much to my astonishment as to theirs. I think it is the first case in this country though there have been a few in London by Horsley and some Vienna cases, one of them an acromegalic.

Patients have been coming—most of them with brain tumors. I think the list would interest you, Boston, Vancouver, B.C., West Chester, N.Y., Washington, D.C., Batesburg, S.C., Morristown, N.J., Bangor, Me., Louisville, Ky., Ottawa, Ont., La Crosse, Wis., a South Dakota patient &c. . . . This letter is disjointed largely owing to Willie C. who is busily questioning me in regard to stamps. He sends his love to Grossvater in which the rest of us join. Betsey is weaned—a devil of a job. Kate fled to N.Y. and B. showed her native stubbornness by refusing food for five days before she gave in which she finally did abruptly and with a Well-I-give-it-up expression.

H.C. to H.K.C. *29 April 1909.*

. . . We expect Dr. Osler early next week, and I gather that he is going to stay here for a month, so there will be many activities of an unusual sort I doubt not. We are going to open the new Faculty Building the middle of May with three days of exercises, and I am booked for a short statement in regard to the collection of funds for the Osler Memorial and also have promised to give a paper at one of the meetings. . . . Weir Mitchell is coming down and will stay with us for a day or two; Flexner will also be here and the usual library representatives: Jacobi, John Billings, Fletcher and others.

I have just secured a tribe of monkeys, who are at present chattering in the laboratory. Yerkes has come to spend a month or two and I think he will be particularly glad to have the opportunity of observing them. They ought at least to be as interesting as dancing mice. Fortunately he has had a good deal of experience with the care of macaques and has laid down a definite dietary régime for the little rascals. They are really very comical, though they do smell bad.

The first account of experiences with tumors of the cerebellum was presented to the Johns Hopkins Medical Society on 3 May and in the subsequent paper[11] he gave statistical details on his first thirty cases. Tumors of the cerebellum became a source of particular fascination to Cushing and it is to be regretted that he did not live to finish a large monograph on the subject which had been projected in 1927 and in large measure drafted by 1929 in collaboration with one of his voluntary assistants at the Brigham. But he turned to other things, particularly the meningioma monograph and did not get back to the cerebellar treatise.

Osler arrived in Baltimore early in May and this time stayed with McCrae with whom he was slaving over the sixth volume of their *System of medicine*. There followed a round of activities that in retrospect seems breathtaking. On Monday, 11 May, Osler gave before

[11] *Interstate Medical Journal*, September 1909, *16*, 607-613.

the Hopkins Historical Club his celebrated lecture on Michael Servetus which, though much admired, has been criticized by experts for repeating some of the old inaccuracies. On Thursday, the 13th, Osler Hall was formally dedicated at the Maryland Medical and Chirurgical Faculty with the Governor of Maryland, the Mayor, Major General Leonard Wood, and other dignitaries in attendance. Henry Barton Jacobs was abroad and H.C. dutifully sent him the following full account of the ceremony:

. . . It was a great success. Weir Mitchell was at the top notch of his best form. He stayed with us at one hundred and seven, and told me *sub rosa* that he thought it was the best address he had ever given. I presume that you have received a programme, so that you know what were the other events of the day. The representatives of the various libraries were a bit tedious, at least that was true of Jacobi and of poor old Jimmie Tyson, but Farlow, representing the Boston Library made up for their longwindedness by a brief, delightful statement of the relation of the Boston and Baltimore medical people.

The special exercises for Osler Hall consisted of a report which I gave in your name, telling briefly something about the original movement to collect the funds and smoothing over the reason for our final determination to have a general building fund to supplement the Osler Testimonial Fund. I presume that you have already heard that the Marburg five thousand dollars has been easily duplicated, so that I was able to say that the fund in which we were particularly interested amounted to about twenty-five thousand dollars—really thirty thousand, though they have appropriated a large part of the extra five thousand. Dr. Welch followed my report, and as we expected he would said just the right thing in just the right way. There was a lot of amusing discussion, started by Dr. Brush and then followed by Weir Mitchell and Dr. Welch himself, in regard to on whom Dr. Osler's mantle had fallen. This was taken up by the Chief on the following evening very amusingly, when he laid aside his manuscript to say forcibly that there was no question of his mantle having fallen on Dr. Welch, but rather that everyone in the whole country had been from the first encompassed by Dr. Welch's mantle.

The Chief was in good form in the evening, and as usual left no name unmentioned that deserved to be mentioned. He even dragged in poor old Simmons for a tribute that ought to make Simmons reconciled to the bitter attacks that have recently been made upon him. I suppose you may have seen the scandalous reprint that has been sent to every member of the American Medical Association by one Frank Lydstron—at least I think that is his name. Lydstron has been employed by the patent medicine people to hire detectives to trace out Simmons' past, and it is perfectly appalling what they have uncovered—a homeopathist, advertising in the newspapers, and I do not know what all. I can't help believing, from the spontaneous burst of applause that followed this tribute of Dr. Osler's, that the attack has done Simmons more good than anything that could possibly have happened, for if in the face of this old record he has done what he has for the profession he deserves the best that we can give him.

The hall is really first-rate. The Frick room looks well, and Young and Ridge Warfield have hung the pictures in the very best taste. I begged to have nothing go in the Osler room except Dr. Osler's portrait, and this, with a few greens, was the only decoration there. I am sure that you would approve of this, and when you get back in the fall we can then see what we can do with the money that is left to finally and suitably fix up this big room. I think among other things it would be very nice to have a long decorative bookcase containing a complete set of the Chief's writings. We ought to have all the editions of the Text-book, etc. Edition seven, as you know, is out, with a note in the introduction telling of the Spanish and Chinese translations which are in progress. I think we will perhaps have a couple of thousand dollars to spend and I doubt not that we will be able to secure more. I found on looking over my correspondence with Robert Brewster that he said he would be glad to duplicate his original gift if we needed more money. I persuaded the committee to leave the Marburg gift until we could have a full meeting in the fall to decide what disposition had best be made of it. They were anxious to have it specifically set aside for the purchase of books, but there is no hurry about this and it would be best to have opinions from everyone before the matter is settled. I doubt not that with all the enthusiasm that was shown during the past few days here we could have raised a lot more money if we had seen the necessity for it and if anyone had had the ginger to start the ball rolling. Governor Warfield indeed told me that he wished to subscribe something himself some day and had only held off until he felt that we really needed the funds.

Dr. Osler has been in great form and looks very much better than he did when he was last here. He gave us a splendid paper at the Historical Club on Servetus. The room was simply jammed, and indeed at the new Library Building the place was packed beyond belief. I am so sorry that you missed it all. Your names [Jacobs and Mrs. Jacobs] were mentioned many times, and the cables from yourself and from Mrs. Osler came just in the nick of time. Mrs. Osler had given John Cook carte blanche for flowers and the place was a bower every day. . . . We must now do something handsome for Dr. Welch—something before it is too late for him thoroughly to enjoy it. Would it not be fine to have an annual subscription for a great pathological institute—the Welch Institute of Pathology. I doubt not that Mr. Rockefeller, Mr. Carnegie and Mr. Phipps would plank down anything we asked them to for such a cause. Please mull it over when you have time and let me see when you get back what can be done. Dr. Ellis dragged me into the Belvedere the other day and talked to me for an hour about it.

Mrs. Cushing and I expect to sail on the *Adriatic* on the 22nd of July, and after a lecture which I have promised to give in Liverpool we will drift on to Budapest for the Congress, and plan to get back here about the first of October. There are many places we hope to visit and many people we expect to see. I don't know whether Kate will stick it out for two months without seeing the Kinder, but at least these are our plans. . . .

Osler's address, "The old and the new," was in some ways almost as remarkable as his essay on Servetus given earlier in the week. Within less than two weeks, he gave other major addresses at the Harvard Medical School and, on 3 June, his well-known discourse entitled "The treatment of disease" was presented at Toronto. But H.C. ran him a close second, having presented a paper on "Alterations in the color fields in cases of brain tumor" at the American Neurological Association on 27 May and the Oration on Surgery, "The hypophysis cerebri" early in June at the annual meeting of the American Medical Association held in Atlantic City. On 16 June he writes to H.K.C.: "My oration went off very well, I think. Will send you a reprint when it is published—some weeks hence in the Journal. I think of little else than the pituitary body nowadays—a poor solace, however, for an empty house."

The next four weeks were crowded with a variety of duties, both onerous and pleasant. First there was a minor operation (hemorrhoidectomy), then a trip to the Western Reserve to see his Cleveland family, followed by the trek to Little Boar's Head with the children who were to be left there for the summer. And it is safe to assume that by 28 July when they sailed for Liverpool on the *Lusitania,* H.C. and K.C. both welcomed the brief respite on shipboard.

During this trip abroad, the first such jaunt that he had taken with Mrs. Cushing, he kept an informal notebook in which he pasted numerous postcards and photographs, but the usual sketches and diary notes are for the most part lacking. Such day-to-day entries as were made were usually telegraphic and often scarcely grammatical, but they give a clear idea of his interests and also indicate the ardor with which he had now come to pursue Andreas Vesalius. He had departed more or less unprepared for his lectures, which no doubt accounts for the fact that there are no entries in his diary on the voyage over. The trip was made at the invitation of the International Medical Congress which was being held at Budapest, and one gathers that his mind was more on the paper which he had promised to deliver than it was on sightseeing. His first responsibility, however, was the William Mitchell Banks Memorial Lecture which he gave at the University of Liverpool the first week in August.[12] This was based in part on his lecture on the pathology of intracranial tumors which he had originally given at Boston, but he had added a section on surgical treatment. His final paragraphs stressed for his British audience the same details he had tried to inculcate in his own countrymen:

> . . . In closing I may be permitted a word of admonition. Intracranial surgery from a technical standpoint is unlike all other forms of surgery in that the delicate structures involved cannot be handled with sponge and clamp and ligature as can the tissues of the body with which the surgeon is more familiar. It is far easier to do harm than good by the rough and rapid operative measures so commonly employed. Familiarity with special methods of manipulating a brain under tension, of controlling haemorrhage from the cerebral substance without insult to the tissues, of avoiding operative injury to the pia-arachnoid until actual extirpation is attempted, and countless other details which should be mastered first by operations upon the brain of animals are essential to success in this work.
>
> Difficult though it may often be, the craniotomy itself is the least important element in the operation; and though our surgical text-books for the most part dwell solely upon the methods to be employed in entering the cranial chamber, the vital elements are what may happen to the contents of the chamber while we are making the entry and how they are to be handled when the opening has been made. Earlier diagnoses and more prompt interference, a wider experience in overcoming the technical difficulties of these cases, coupled with the courage to work slowly and painstakingly, these things will lead to increasingly better

[12] "Recent observations on tumours of the brain and their surgical treatment." *Lancet,* 8 January 1910, *1,* 90-94.

results in this responsible work, the success of which depends so greatly upon detail, patience, and the expenditure of time.

The cryptic entries from his diary describe the remainder of their trip. Those who know Oxford will be able to read between the lines of the entries for the 9th through the 11th of August:

Aug. 9th, Monday. Oxford. Gorgeous clear day. Dr. Osler's lecture before the mob of 3000 Univ. Extension people—funny lot. An old Deutscher nearly fell down when handed Vesal's *Fabrica* 1543. To *Merton* and its 13th cent. library with the 2 chained books and fine old medical tomes. A Vesal with very broad margins (height of page 17½ in.—Dr. O's is 16½). An enormous Rhazes and many other incunabula.

To Christ Church by the way. The Burton books collected by Dr. O. had become much scattered. Copy of the portrait in the centre. The old priory: Dr. O's rooms: the common rooms &c. Ch.Ch. a curious foundation—all by their last names—so that the Regius Prof. is Osler to the youngest scholar. The Cathedral and College one. The Dean of Ch.Ch. appointed by the prime minister. All the holdings—and Ch.Ch. is very wealthy—came from the 32 priories demolished by Henry VIII. A portrait of Vesal at Ch.Ch. like the one in the Louvre but without the pillar and coat of arms. Attrib'd to Tintoretto.

Aug. 9th. p.m. A call on the Librarian (Mr. Sanderson?) of St. John's. Many fine old medical works, a 2nd ed. of the *Fabrica* and the only other Vesal item a *Radicis Chynae* 1547 Leyden Sub Scuto Coloniensi. These and most of the other books were from Sir Wm. Paddy's library 1554-1634—a great benefactor of St. John's and a remarkable character generally—Phys. to James 1st and friend of Bishop Laud. . . . Professor Macalister lectured in the evening on Vesalius. Very good and Macalister a very erudite man—anthropologist—bibliophile—archeologist —and much traveled.

Aug. 10th, Oxford. Saw Prof. Macalister off at the station and then to Dr. Osler's Servetus lecture—excellent! Gotten in shape from his Baltimore first delivery. To Clarendon Press with the party and Mr. Horace Hart the Comptroller.

Aug. 10th p.m. Barker turns up to dinner and afterwards a load—two motors full of the Frank Billings party from London. Dr. O. and I soon slipped off to the Bodleian to see the Stirling-Maxwell *Tabulae Sex.* He had written to several Stirling-Maxwells to try and get trace of them, for Sir William's possession of them and the 30 reproductions was known but no one has seemed to know of the whereabouts of any of the originals. With greatest promptitude Sir John had sent the original to the Bodleian for inspection and an accompanying one of the copies—the reproductions of which are rather disappointing.

The originals are bound in a sumptuous red morocco elephantine folio, the plates set in to much larger pages: with a book-plate specially for the work about a foot square. The plates are most interesting—the two circulations according to Galen separately shown—vena ad renem &c—We were much excited and I took about two rolls of snapshots of the Prof. of Med. for Barker happened in with another roll of films in the nick of time. May they turn out well!! At the Sherringtons for dinner with Ramsden the senior proctor: a Mr. Northcote and Miss Florence Buchanan. . . .

Aug. 12, Thursday. [*London*]. . . . Much of the morning at the Hunterian Museum with Keith (Arthur) the Conservator: also Wardy Atkinson. Keith has the spark and is rejuvenating the place. The Hunter things are endless and there is much new that I never saw before. Hunter's furniture—the table, library steps, chairs &c. The famous peahen with cock's tail feathers mentioned by John and forgotten till Keith identified it. Keith has a room of curios—'old trash' which all is of great interest when worked out. Wonderful lot of skulls—atrophics &c osteomas. National Hospital and a pleasant hour with our old JHH hanger-on Ward, and Gordon Holmes, A.K.W. [S.A.K.] Wilson, the surgeon Sampson? &c. Some tumor cases; a case of hypopituitarism &c. improving on thyroid. . . . Dinner with the Rollestons: Jex-Blake and Drysdale at 11 Upper Brooke St. Late home and to bed.

Aug. 13th, Friday. . . . Book shops. Henry Head at London Hospital an hour late. Henry Head's for dinner with Gordon Holmes. Much 18th Cent. talk. Fashion plates. Henley's desk. Head's method of working up papers, &c. K.C. much amused at Head's lively answering of the telephone: he being totally uninterested in the guinea.

Aug. 14th, Saturday. To St. Bartholomew's with Drysdale. Rather dull hour in the new buildings mostly. From the roof of them a view of the excavation disclosing a bit of the Roman wall—completely buried under the old Christchurch Hospital which has been torn down to make room for the Bart's extension &c. Once in the past an old "plague pit" was opened when they were excavating for a part of Bart's itself.

Sir James Paget's old quarters where the Bishop of Oxford and Stephen were born—most cramped, smelly, and forlorn. The windows look out on Little Britain into which the cattle overflowed from Smithfield in even later times and smelled and lowed all night probably. No wonder James could work late. St. Bartholomew's church and the Rahere tomb 12th Cent. The church has been repaired even since E.F.C. [Ned] and I saw it—the old forge removed &c. Other interesting things at Bart's: the old wooden figure of the licensed beggar (of the time of Chas. I) with sling & crutch which used to stand in front of the old entrance gate. There are many fine portraits: two Holbeins of Henry VIII: the famous Reynolds of Abernethy and a beautiful one of Pott: both in the great hall where the 200 directors meet.

Sunday, Aug. 15th. The Hague. A long day. We were turned out at the Hook about five o'clock or thereabouts: scrabbled into our clothes, grabbed a cup of coffee and whisked through misty, cow-covered Holland to this place—the hotel "Widow Dolan" where Kate says she stayed before. . . . An hour with the pictures —espec. the School of Anatomy, of course. Tulp's hands I think are the best part of it: but a wonderful picture. A Van der Meer of Delft, a splendid landscape &c. Paul Potter's Bull much stained is evidently a bull. In the afternoon after naps we took a long drive through the town—the House in the Woods &c. Lovely woods! In fact 'S Gravenhage pleased us much and we were sorry to go.

Tuesday, Aug. 17th. Leyden-Amsterdam. Two hours in a bookshop and another with Tendeloo. Luncheon: and a visit to the old university and to Boerhaave's lovely old house in the country. Beautiful drive. House now vacated by recent occupants. Nothing of old furnishings left but the great trees, box hedges, formal gardens show what a splendid residence it must have been. . . .

Aug. 18th, Wednesday. Amsterdam. Morning with Dr. Daniëls while Kate visits the Rijks Museum. We went first to a large private gynaecological sanitarium and waited and left. Then—what I wanted—to his medico-pharmaceutical museum. The Vesal portrait seems, according to him, genuine enough and possibly contemporary.

Aug. 19th, Thursday. Cologne. "Colonia Agrippina" of old. Antiquariats for me while K.C. in Cathedral, where I joined her later. . . .

Friday morning, Aug. 20. Basle. The Vesalianum—skeleton with bifid xiphoid. Platter's *weibliches Kind und Affe* above. Roth resurrected old covers of the skeleton case by Platter in which for 300 years the skeletons had been held, and has had them mounted and hung in the office room of the laboratory. The lettering of Latin verse is in gold on a dark green background.

On the tablet—*Skeletorum A. Vesalii nec non F. Plateri opera Basileae annis p. Ch. n. 1543 et 1573 paratorum, quae supersunt.* Antiquariat's on Baumling Gasse. Museum. Missed the portrait in the Aula. To Berne at 2 P.M.

Aug. 22nd, Friday p.m. Berne—Bellevue Hotel. Poor quarters. Met by Albert Kocher. Call on Kronecker: to Laboratory. Dinner at Kochers—sleepy.

On to Budapest

Monday, Aug. 23rd. . . . The Bastianellis were here [St. Moritz] and B. gave me a leather waistcoat and K. bought a large green Tyrolese mantle so that after a lunch we cheered and warmed up.

Aug. 26th. Munich to Vienna. Morning, after breakfast with Bastianelli and seeing Mrs. Paton, spent in old shops. Bought the 1st German Ed. of Vesal and the *Epitome*—to be bound. Wish I had had more time. . . .

Aug. 27th, Friday. Vienna. A telephone to Fröhlich brings him and his long locks—Hair Fröhlich—to the hotel. To the Kunsthistorisches Museum where we left K.C. and hied to the Allgemeines Krankenhaus—equal to all expectations of its size. Haberer was in charge of v. Eiselsberg's clinic—a clean-cut, pleasant chap who looked like Will Crehore. Lunch in the K. K. Volksgarten with Fröhlich. K.C. returns to the Imperial to await Mrs. F. and we visited Hans Meyer's department at the University. Interesting as showing the character of the man at the head, so deeply regarded that a great student petition kept him from going to Berlin. Everything is open in Meyer's building—Fröhlich, *e.g.,* has only a curtain over his door. Fröhlich and I visited the University before going to the Pharmakolog Dept. The balustrade was just being repaired after the last students' battle. We saw the great Aula—the books all out for house cleaning—and the inner court with the surrounding corridors where is the only monument to van Swieten in Vienna—*i.e.,* the only material one—a fat little bust.

The Aula itself magnificent—2 stories—very poor acoustic properties. Two blank squares on the ceiling where the pictures of the mad artist should have gone. Too indecent to put up. The Belvedere in which is retained the Vesal portrait is accessible only by special permission—a private—regal?—residence.

Sunday, Aug. 29th. Budapest. . . . Opening of the Congress in the Redoute. Very gorgeous but piping hot affair. Too 'much' people, too 'many' noise to hear or see. The Grand Duke in his swell uniform—Count Apponyi, Müller and the delegates. The Russians in their heavy fur uniforms must have melted. The Redoute a fine place for such a reception—the great staircase lined by gaily apparelled guards—one Major-domo in particular most gorgeous. Henry Head in his Cambridge scarlet and pink gown much admired. . . .

Monday, Aug. 30th. To the Congress to register—very well-arranged affair—with much literature gathered at separate stands. The Neurological Section and discussion of Frankl-Hochwart's paper. All very cordial. Showed the slides prepared for the surgical section. Oppenheim, Jendrássik, Levi et al. Dinner with Henry Head, the de Sarbós and "Sir Museum Radishes" [Eugène de Radisics] at the Hungaria. To the Lord Mayor's reception with them in the Redoute. Crowded and hot. Later to the garden for "citron." Most amusing evening with Sir Malcolm Morris and Mr. Jessop—who did not pay for their citrons. H.H. rather bored at Sarbó's threat to charge Edw. VII.

Tuesday, Aug. 31st. Luncheon at the Herczels at 1.30. Rovsing, Ceccherelli and others and wait until nearly 3 when Macewen, son and daughter stroll in. I tried to get away as the paper was booked for 3 but no—"Macewen first and the meeting postponed until 4 &c" so we dallied with the elaborate lunch and coffee & cakes on the porch overlooking the garden until 4 and were late. Saw Fröhlich on entering and he said I had been called on twice and would not be again. Krause was reading and after he had finished they called [on] unprepared me. It was late and most of the people had gone. Eiselsberg however there and spoke kindly of the work.

Wednesday, Sept. 1st. Dined at the Hungaria with the Thayers and was dropped by W.S.T. as Musser gave the signal to leave for the Court. Absurd arrangement with large red ribbons, smaller red ribbons and white ones. The first to be spoken to, the 2nd shaken hands with and the 3rd bowed to—this the most exclusive court in Europe. Rovsing and another big Dane finally picked me up and we drove over to be presented—a line of carriages a mile long. Stunning entrance to the receiving rooms—great staircase with red uniformed creatures having great eagle plumes in their hats and carrying halberds lined the steps on either side. An impossibly hot room considering the character of the people and we entered and waited in the 3rd class room while his Grand Dukeship talked hours with Musser *et al.* of the large red ribbons. De Sarbó finally rescued me and after one look at the Duke we left for the outer world. A beautiful view by moonlight of the 'Escalier' and of the monument to the 'saint' of Budapest. Thence to a café with the Langes and other bearded orthopaedists and their wives where we were missed by K.C. and Mrs. Thayer, they having gone to the theatre after the dinner.

Thursday evening, Sept. 2. The Dollingers' dinner at the Hungaria. A beautifully served and enjoyable feast for 200 guests, followed by speeches by representatives of the various countries. Prof. 'Chusching' got out of replying for America and Dr. Robert Lovett did finally respond. The dinner broke up after Prof. Ceccherelli of Parma threatened with all Italian violence an inoffensive old man from Fiume who had dared to address the assemblage in his mother tongue—Italian, Ceccherelli himself having responded for Italy in French, the official language.

Monday, Sept. 6th. Venice. A heavenly day—cloudless—a warm sun—a cool breeze. In and out of gondolas. St. Mark's—the Doge's Palace and finally at the end of the day to the Lido for a swim with numerous Adams and Eves on the sand. The return to Venice by sunset was lovely. A large meal and quiet evening 'at home' in the Danieli where there is much noise o'nights.

Tuesday, Sept. 7th. Venice. K.C. to the Accademia where she identified the Bellini type while I spent the morning in the Biblioteca Nazionale [di San Marco] looking at the Vesalius items. Careful notes of the *Epitome* of which they have 3 copies—two of them bound with others—one with *Tab. sex* and the 2nd with their *Fabrica* 1543. Discovered a living book worm—a silvery creature with a flat back and legs. He crawled out of his tunnel in the book as I opened it. Some of the volumes were sadly eaten. Photos of the *Tabulae sex.* One table without the signatures.

Beautiful old manuscripts in the library: Marco Polo's will and such like. The building itself: Libreria Vecchia begun in 1536 by Jac. Sansovinus. The librarian Frati and I found it difficult but I finally got the books. The Thayers join us at St. Mark's whence we go for lunch at the Café Cappello Nero after viewing much coral, pearls and amber in the windows. We lunched on fungi, snails and squids with cheese—S.T. consuming much mattoni Giesshübler or Nocera Umbra. After the purchase of amber hat pins—gondolas in quest of the old house of Aldus to which we had been vaguely directed from the library—near the church of I Frari. After a long search, many inquiries by Thayer in French of Italians, entry into a Schola, crossing of bridges & back, round and round the Archivio Centrale, we sent Mrs. T. and Kate into the S. Maria Gloriosa dei Frari and we asked further. . . . An old fellow across the Rio finally guided us to a place beyond the Campo San Stin to the Rio Terrà where he triumphantly pointed to a tablet at the end of the alley—to another person. Thayer undaunted 'feeling warm' walked on a few houses in the Rio Terrà and there it was—a cat perched on the balcony, a large fruit stand shaded by a great screen from the sun, hundreds of small imps of boys and a man dealing out boiled squids! for 10 c. There were two tablets—an old one undecipherable—the other: *In questa casa Che fu d'Aldo Pio Manuzio L'Accademia Aldina s'accolse E di qui tornó a splendere A'popoli civili La luce delle lettere greche.* "La scuola di lettere greche dello studio di Padova dell' anno 1876-1877 volle designato a' futuri il luogo famoso." The Frari was undergoing repairs and most of the pictures were removed to the S. Pantaleone where we saw Bellini's beautiful altar piece—with the enthroned Madonna and the musical cherubs and Titian's great madonna of the Pesaro family. The Titian and Danova tombs in the Frari are not much. Gondolas again to the Ponte di Rialto and thence back to the Procuratie Vecchie for chocolate.

Friday, Sept. 10th. Florence. A book hunt at Genelli's, Ricasoli 6 and elsewhere until 11.30 when I joined Kate in the Uffizi finding her in the Tribune. We then wandered through the other rooms and by the mile long passage between countless portraits of the Medici family to the Pitti Palazzo where a deal was made with one artist whom we saw painting the Sala dell'Illèade to make me a 60/70^{cm} copy of the Titian Vesalius for 200 lira.

After lunch to the Pretorial Palace Bargello. The court with the arms of the Podestàs is ever interesting—a gent was making a fine water color which we wanted. Upstairs in the chapel is the important portrait of Dante in one of the frescoes (Paradiso). We liked Donatello's bronze David—the youth with the rustic hat—much better than Michelangelo's marble one in the Piazza of his name where we were later.

Then to the National Library in the Uffizi shopping on the way at Bruscoli's shop, Condotta 4, for books. Though too late we did see the Savonarola Bible. A small, thick cut, 8vo volume much interleaved and with the most extraordinary marginal notes requiring a magnifying glass to decipher them. The librarian said they had all been transcribed—making a large thick volume of themselves. I think a Basle ed. of 1492 or thereabouts—or this may have been when America was discovered. Vesalius volumes also—a good *Epitome* and the usual things—the Venice Ed., a 2nd ed. *Fabrica* &c. Libreria Maglia Vecchiana. Then a drive to the San Miniato hill and the Piazzale Michelangelo with its wonderful view over Florence to Fiesole. Chocolate, and beer for the cocher. Home via the Viale Machiavelli and Porta Romana.

Saturday, Sept. 11. Florence. Morning at Olschki's. Bought an old Avicenna. To Genelli's, Ricasoli 6, again and hesitated over the Giunta ed. of Galen for £40 as the 1st volume was later than the other three. Vesal's chapters were amended &c.

Missed K.C. at the Duomo—she meanwhile having visited the Baptistery, Bigallo, Giotto's Tower, S. Croce, Or San Michele and Santa Maria Novella. . . . We saw the Palazzo Vecchio together. Fine lower court with Verrocchio's fountain and the carved pillars. Upper room where the 500 of Savonarola met. P.M. to the Laurentian Library but spent too much time in the S. Lorenzo Church with the tombs of the Medici and the Michelangelo things in the chapel so the Library was closed.

Sunday, Sept. 12th. Florence. A good day to see things in Florence is a Sunday. We start in with another view of the Battistero and see a crowd of waiting women with their 8-day babes as they have waited for the drones and kisses and crossings of the priests since this, the most ancient of the Florentine edifices was established—apparently always a Christian temple of the IIIrd and IVth century. Notable are the mosaic ceiling, the bronze doors of Andrea Pisano, and those on the north, the Gate of Paradise of Ghiberti, the baptismal font antedating 1371, the tomb of Pope John partly by Donatello, Donatello's Mary Magdalen etc.

Again a look into the Duomo—Santa Maria del Fiore—cold and dark and apparently empty though there was a large service going on in the north transept. Curious that our attention riveted on a small lizard carved on one of the blocks beside the great doors. Such was the detail everywhere. Such things were finished but not the great things like Michelangelo's Descent from the Cross—his chef d'oeuvre they say. Then to the Duomo Museum for the sake of the Cantorie with the reliefs of Luca della Robbia's singing children and Donatello's. Also the silver altar of the Baptistry. The Accadémia di Belle Arti—Michelangelo's David, the Botticelli "Spring" and the remarkable Fra Angelico's "World" picture. Perugino's portraits of two monks. A ride across the Ponte Vecchio to Via Romana and Casa Guidi where the Brownings sojourned. The Grand Hotel and lunch. In the Piazza S. Lorenzo is an awful statue of the father of Cosimo I. At a book stall in this square Browning picked up the "old yellow book"—the substance of *The Ring and the Book.*

Monday, Sept. 13th. Como and Villa d'Este. The Italian Lakes. Scarcely a glimpse at Como after the hour's trip out of Milan. Expectations of a return—the Brunate &c. We are fearful, from the start, of the Villa d'Este—too many autobusses &c. However a lovely spot and we try our best (both have colds in the head). A terrible place—much dress—much noise—crying Paolos—shrieking automobiles—all detracting from its lovely situation. While waiting for our rooms to be prepared we climbed along the old fountain up bypaths &c to a pretty lookout where we sat in the sun and added to our colds. Bellagio is what we want and the Grand Hôtel Bretagne suffices with a window looking over the lake. A good dinner and a prestidigitator in the evening amused the guests.

Tuesday, Sept. 16th. Bellagio. A walk through the town at the expense of a blue parasol, and £2 to enter Cardinal Serbelloni's gardens. We should have gone there for our rest and recuperation but decide that the effort to move is too great. A quiet afternoon in our room, tea and a walk away from the Bellagio neck seeing more villas and flowers and vistas. A good dinner again at the Bretagne with a band this time and a game of pocket billiards with a young English curate.

Paris. Sept. 20th. Monday and everything closed. Shopping for Kate and a hunt for old books after long sessions with Cook's about trunks &c. Luncheon at the café near the Luxembourg. Tea with the Woods at the Normandie.

Landing Sept. 28th, Tuesday at 11.30. Clear cold day: much wind: more Hudson-Fulton celebration. No difficulty at the customs owing to $100 of old books which disgust the inspectors. Across town to the 3 P.M. train with no second to spare among the procession and blocked streets and we part, on the run, as we had started for the train—two months gone by.

And so they reached New York on 28 September on the *SS. Kronprinz Wilhelm,* he returning immediately to Baltimore and K.C. to Little Boar's Head. H.C. was apparently much refreshed by his trip and gratified by the warm reception he had had in medical circles both in England and on the Continent. Many interesting patients were awaiting his return. He appears to have concentrated largely on his pituitary cases, and by Christmas time had developed plans for his pituitary monograph which he eventually completed two years later. He made several public appearances before the first of the year. On 27 October he read his paper on intracranial tumors for the Chicago Medical Society and on the 29th and 30th attended the meeting of the Society of Clinical Surgery at Rochester, Minnesota.

Clinical work occupied the larger part of his time during November and December but Christmas brought some relaxation which he described in a letter to his father:

H.C. to H.K.C. *25 December [1909].*

Dear Pater A fine snowy Christmas after a month of clear skies. People seem to regard snow as appropriate unto the day. We are up to our necks in "Goody-goodies" and "Just what I wanteds" and Willie is storming an enormous paper fort with an army of lead soldiers, life size, flags flying, bands playing and artillery in field action—from Marian. We are all equally overwhelmed with correspondingly welcome gifts. Such nice things, particularly from the home relations. The Goodwillies came in last night and helped us with the tree and stockings and tonight we are to have an oyster roast in the kitchen as we did last year.

Thanks much for your family contribution which has most opportunely helped us all out. Much love to you all. The day could only have been bettered by our being at home with you in Cleveland.

During the years 1908 and 1909 Cushing had become almost wholly absorbed in the study of the pituitary body and many regard this work as his most original and important contribution to medical science. He had been much stimulated by Schafer's Herter Lectures in April of 1908 and there were many exchanges between the two men in the next few years. Schafer's interest in Cushing's work is indicated in the following letter:

Marly Knowe, North Berwick,
Sir E. A. Schafer to H.C. *23 December 1908.*

My dear Cushing, Your results are very interesting. In view of them it is a little difficult to accept Paulesco's statement that mere cutting off the pituitary from the infundibulum is as fatal as entire removal of the gland. We are attempting to make out the metabolic changes which accompany partial or complete destruction—but metabolism experiments are always long & tedious.

We enjoyed having Baldwin with us in the summer & we had some fine golf together. We are looking forward to a visit from you (& Mrs. Cushing?) next summer—by which time I will try & furbish up a decent game. The course is delightful even now. It is generally mild here in the early winter and this morning we counted 35 different kinds of plants in flower in the garden & gathered a handful of roses from it. I shall be golfing every day for the next few days as we have a short holiday just now. But the days up here are too short for more than one comfortable round—although younger and more enthusiastic people sometimes take two.

I am not very surprised at hearing that it is the anterior part of the pituitary which is essential to life. Its extraordinary vascularity seems to indicate its importance: it resembles in that respect the suprarenal medulla. I suppose you are quite sure that in removing the anterior part the pars intermedia doesn't get injured & necrosed. With best wishes for the New Year from my wife & myself, Believe me Yours sincerely E. A. SCHAFER.

During the spring of 1909 H.C. had been working intensively with Drs. Samuel J. Crowe and John Homans and they ultimately issued together an important monograph entitled "Experimental hypophysectomy"[13] in which they established that the pituitary of animals, although probably not essential to life, normally exerts an important influence on metabolic processes of the body, and the disturbances which follow partial and complete removal of the gland are described in detail and correlated with the corresponding symptoms of pituitary disturbances in man. The most important early publication on the pituitary by Cushing himself is the discourse which he had presented before the Section on Surgery of the American Medical Association in June 1909.[14] In this paper he introduced the terms "hypo-" and "hyper-pituitarism," and by so doing paved the way for the clinical distinction now fully recognized between states caused by excess secretion of the anterior lobe (acromegaly) and states of diminished secretion such as occur when the pituitary is completely or partly destroyed.[15] The paper is so important from the point of view of Cushing's subsequent work and his ultimate publication of the pituitary monograph in 1912 that the summary is given in full:

Two conditions, one due to a pathologically increased activity of the pars anterior of the hypophysis (hyperpituitarism), the other to a diminished activity of the same epithelial structure (hypopituitarism), seem capable of clinical differentiation. The former expresses itself chiefly as a process of overgrowth—gigantism when originating in youth, acromegaly when originating in adult life. The latter expresses itself chiefly as an excessive, often a rapid, deposition of

[13] *Johns Hopkins Hospital Bulletin,* May 1910, *21,* 127-169.

[14] "The hypophysis cerebri—clinical aspects of hyperpituitarism and of hypopituitarism." *Journal of American Medical Association,* 24 July 1909, *53,* 249-255. In Cushing's handwriting on his copy of the reprint is the following: "This was written in a rush the week before the meeting, Simmons having called in vain for it sometime in April. It was brushed up afterward in a confused month of dentistry, brain tumor operations, writing of papers 'for' and with Bordley, struggling over the reports with Crowe and Homans, preparing for Budapest and Liverpool addresses and winding up with a hemorrhoid operation before sailing."

[15] Professor Marburg had used the terms hypo- and hyper-pituitarism the previous year, but he had made his deduction from clinical material without experimental verification. In his copy of Marburg's paper H.C. had written: "We had just 'gotten on' to the 'hypo' manifestations and could find nothing comparable to these suggestions. The whole thing burst on me one day at the laboratory so that the writing was not difficult. I found the note later in *Deutsches Zeitschrift für Nervenheilkunde,* 1908, *36,* p. 114, by Otto Marburg, in which he uses hyper- and hypo-pituitarism though he had no experimental proof."

fat with persistence of infantile sexual characteristics when the process dates from youth, and a tendency toward a loss of the acquired signs of adolescence when it appears in adult life.

Experimental observations show not only that the anterior lobe of the hypophysis is a structure of such importance that a condition of apituitarism is incompatible with the long maintenance of life, but also that its partial removal leads to symptoms comparable to those which we regard as characteristic of lessened secretion (hypopituitarism) in man. A tumor of the gland itself, or one arising in its neighborhood and implicating the gland by pressure, is naturally the lesion to which one or the other of these conditions has heretofore been attributed, though it is probable that over-secretion from simple hypertrophy, or under-secretion from atrophy, will be found to occur irrespective of tumor growth when examination of the pituitary body becomes a routine measure in the postmortem examination of all cases in which the conditions suggest one or the other of the symptoms-complex described. When due to tumor, surgery is the treatment that these conditions demand, and at present there are reasonably satisfactory ways of approaching the gland; but clinicians and surgeons must clearly distinguish between the local manifestations of the neoplasm due to involvement of structures in its neighborhood other than hypophysis, and those of a general character from disturbances of metabolism due to alterations of the hypophysis itself.

The oration on the "Hypophysis cerebri" was scarcely in type before he had submitted another report with Crowe and Homans for Schafer's Journal at Edinburgh. In this were described the restorative effects of transplanting pituitary tissue into hypophysectomized animals[16] which was the next important step in the elucidation of the pituitary problem.

At the combined meeting of the American Physiological Society and the American Association for the Advancement of Science in Boston on 28 December 1909 H.C. gave a general summary of the physiological functions of the pituitary. The paper, published early in 1910,[17] attracted wide attention and his résumé gives a clear picture of the state of knowledge at that time:

. . . Summary. It may be said that the pituitary body is a double organ in the sense that the secretion of its anterior and solidly epithelial portion discharges into the blood sinuses which traverse this part of the gland; whereas the hyaline substance, apparently the product of secretion from the epithelial investment of the posterior lobe, enters the cerebrospinal space by way of channels in the pars nervosa. Though possessing a physiologically active principle, as shown by the results of injections, the secretion of the posterior lobe does not seem to be so vitally essential to physiological equilibrium as that of the anterior lobe, the total removal of which leads to death with a peculiar train of symptoms which set in at an early date in adult and after a longer interval in younger animals.

Alterations in the gland, which often ultimately assume the character of a malignant growth (adenoma) but which presumably, at least in their earlier

[16] "Effects of hypophyseal transplantation following total hypophysectomy in the canine." *Quarterly Journal of Experimental Physiology*, 1909, *2*, 389-400.

[17] "The function of the pituitary body." *American Journal of Medical Science*, April 1910, n.s. *139*, 473-484.

stages, represent an hypertrophy, are common in clinical conditions of overgrowth (acromegaly and gigantism), and certain feeding experiments lend support to the view that these clinical states represent the consequences of hyperactivity of the pars anterior. Partial removals of the anterior lobe usually lead to obvious disturbances of metabolism accompanied oftentimes by adiposity and in the young by a persistence of infantilism, or in adults by a tendency to lose the secondary sexual characteristics already acquired. These experimental conditions are comparable to those which have been recognized clinically as accompaniments likewise of tumors in the hypophyseal region, which under these circumstances can therefore be interpreted as lesions which through pressure have led to lessened glandular activity.

In view of the apparent interrelation of many of the glands of internal secretion it is quite probable that certain of the symptoms known to accompany hypophyseal disease may be consequent upon a secondary change in other glands which follows the primary lesion of the hypophysis. These changes are seemingly more outspoken and more widespread after a lesion of the pituitary body than after a corresponding lesion of any other individual member of the group of ductless glands, and in view of its unusually well-protected position one might have conjectured that it must represent a vitally important organ.

Acromegaly

Acromegaly, first described in 1884 by Fritsche and Edwin Klebs,[18] is a clinical condition characterized by enlargement of the hands, feet, and jaws, thickening and coarsening of the skin of the face, and gross enlargement of the abdominal viscera. The condition was redescribed by Pierre Marie,[19] the French neurologist, in 1886 and he believed it associated with a tumor of the pituitary gland. Although several preliminary attempts had been made to operate on the pituitaries of acromegalic patients, the results had been discouraging, save for one successful case reported by Schloffer in 1907.[20]

Since it was now well known in the profession that Cushing was deeply interested in everything relating to the pituitary, a case of acromegaly, his first to be attacked surgically, was referred to him in 1909. In the letter of 11 April 1909 to his father quoted earlier he refers to the case with great enthusiasm since not only was the operation conspicuously successful as far as relief of symptoms was concerned, but the patient made a surprisingly prompt postoperative recovery and was able to walk into a surgical clinic six days after the procedure (the pituitary had been exposed through the forehead just above the nose). The clinical history of the case is briefly recapitulated:

[18] Fritsche, und Klebs, E. *Ein Beitrag zur Pathologie des Riesenwuches. Klinische und pathologisch-anatomische Untersuchungen.* Leipzig, F. C. W. Vogel, 1884, 89 pages.

[19] Marie, P. "Sur deux cas d'acromégalie; hypertrophie singulière, non congénitale, des extrémités supérieures, inférieures et céphalique." *Revue de Médecine,* 1886, *6,* 297-333.

[20] Schloffer, H. "Erfolgreiche Operation eines Hypophysentumors auf nasalem Wege." *Wiener klinische Wochenschrift,* 1907, *20,* 621-624.

J.H., a South Dakota farmer of Swedish extraction, 38 years of age, had been sent to Cushing by Dr. C. H. Mayo from the Mayo Clinic in Rochester, Minnesota, complaining of headache and photophobia, together with progressive enlargement of the tongue, lips, face, and the four extremities. His history disclosed little of significance beyond the periodic headache from which he had suffered for some eight years. For two years there had also been lassitude, increased fatiguability, and impotence.

Operation. This was performed on 25 March 1909, but owing to the great size of his tongue, the patient was unable to take ether. The windpipe was therefore opened and ether given directly into the trachea; this incidentally permitted Cushing to obtain a specimen of the thyroid which showed evidence of enlargement ("colloid goitre") now known to be commonly associated with acromegaly. The pituitary, being the most difficult of access from a surgical standpoint of any gland in the body, was approached by the route which Schloffer had recommended two years previously, namely, through the middle of the forehead via the frontal sinuses to the base of the skull. On opening the bony cavity (the "sella turcica") in which the pituitary lies, the anterior lobe of the gland was found grossly enlarged and about a third of it was removed—the principle of subtotal removal being similar to that practised by surgeons in dealing with the thyroid in cases of exophthalmic goitre. The patient made a prompt recovery and his headaches and photophobia were immediately relieved. Shortly after the operation the gross thickening of lips, hands, feet, and tongue had also largely subsided. Those changes affecting the bony parts, however, remained, since bone once laid down in the body is not re-absorbed. Cushing kept in touch with *J.H.*, who remained virtually symptom-free for some twenty years. News of his death, following an acute upper respiratory infection, was received in 1930.

Few clinical results could have been more gratifying than this and it naturally whetted Cushing's interest in similar cases. He could not resist making a detailed report of this particular case immediately, and had taken the opportunity of presenting it at the International Medical Congress at Budapest in August of 1909. The report was also promptly published in this country in December of the same year.[21] Between March 1909 and September 1911, when he committed to the press his monograph on the pituitary body, H.C. had forty-six cases involving the pituitary, most of which he had operated upon. Of these nine were acromegalics, three of whom were subjected to operation. Two succumbed to the procedure.

Giants and Dwarfs

When the anterior lobe of the pituitary exhibits excessive activity and enlargement in adults, the bones of the extremities become heavy, as do the viscera, since after adolescence the long bones cannot increase in length, the growing points at the ends of the bones having become fixed and incapable of further growth. If, however, cells in the anterior pituitary become excessively active before the long bones have stopped growing, *i.e.*, before adolescence, then they may become

[21] "Partial hypophysectomy for acromegaly with remarks on the function of the hypophysis." *Annals of Surgery*, December 1909, *50*, 1002-1017.

longer and longer and a human giant may be the result. Gigantism, then, is a condition akin to acromegaly, but the onset occurs earlier in life. Cushing had thus laid hold of a highly important physiological fact: namely, that cells in the anterior part of the pituitary body elaborate a secretion that controls growth, particularly growth of the skeleton. One of his associates of Hopkins days, Herbert M. Evans, later isolated and purified the growth hormone, thus vindicating Cushing's early deductions based upon experimental studies in animals and clinical observations in man. In the pituitary monograph several cases of gigantism were described; one, the case of John Turner, came to autopsy on 14 January 1911 after a thorough-going clinical study in which the sella turcica had been found by X-ray to be grossly enlarged. Cushing records that the autopsy was conducted under "inauspicious circumstances" by Drs. Crowe and Sharpe; specimens were obtained from all major organs.

Cushing was always fascinated by the circus, particularly by the sideshows where he obtained histories of the giants, fat women, and midgets, and any other freak that might happen to be on display. In this way he made friends with many circus personalities and over the years managed to keep in touch with several well-known giants and midgets. Sir Arthur Keith, the distinguished curator of the Hunterian Museum, consented some years ago, on Cushing's insistence, to removing the top of the skull of the famous Irish giant whose skeleton had long been on display in the Museum, in order to ascertain the condition of the sella turcica where the pituitary body would have been. Sure enough, the sella was grossly enlarged and there was evidence that there had been a sizeable intracranial extension of the pituitary tumor.

But H.C. was as much interested in dwarfs as in giants, and many of his friends will remember that during the hot summer of 1929 after the family went to Little Boar's Head he surreptitiously filled the house with dwarfs on whom an attempt was being made to test the efficacy of some growth hormones recently purified by Herbert Evans. One patient in particular, named Edna, so endeared herself to the household that the servants were willing to put up with the hullabaloo which went on from morning till night after H.C. had conveniently departed for the hospital. Mrs. Albert Bigelow, a neighbor in Brookline, recalls that one of his circus patients, an acromegalic English woman, invited him to call on her in the circus car when it came to Boston, adding that all the side-show freaks were living in a sleeping car on the railroad tracks back of the Hotel Lenox.

> She said she would like Harvey to meet "Half-a-Lady," a poor woman with no legs who also had the privilege of having two whole sections in the car as her home. She said the giants and dwarfs had only one section apiece. As the

woman had to be at the circus afternoons and evenings and since of course Harvey could not go there in the morning, it was arranged that there would be someone to meet him at the side of Mechanics Hall after the evening performance. When the appointed evening arrived, one of the dwarfs was waiting there for him. The little creature had a lantern and he dived into an alley leading to the tracks. Since it was a very dark night Harvey said it was an eerie experience as if he were following a hobgoblin or will-o'the-wisp as the lantern jiggled up and down ahead of him, the dwarf hopping over the tracks and in and out among freight cars in a dangerous route which finally led to the sleeping car and home of the Ugliest Lady, where one of the giants was waiting to lift up the dwarf and help Harvey on to the car, for it was too steep a step for anyone except a giant to manage without a platform. In one corner at the end of the car Harvey made his call on his strangely pathetic patient. She had arranged her children's photographs on the walls and had a few little knick-knacks about and had courageously made a semblance of a room of her own. She introduced him to her friends, Half-a-Lady and the giants and dwarfs, before he left, and he said it was all such a strange combination of something slightly comic and yet really so exceedingly tragic that he felt torn between smiles and tears in telling about it.

This same patient was the subject of a letter which H.C. felt impelled to send to *Time* magazine after she had been made the object of ridicule in a previous issue. The letter, which *Time* published under the caption "Skin Deep," ran thus:

Sirs: . . . May I accordingly tell you something of the woman whose picture you published on p. 17 of *Time,* May 2, [1927] under the caption of "Uglies"? This unfortunate woman who sits in the sideshow of Ringling Brothers "between Fat Lady and Armless Wonder" and "affects white lace hats, woolen mittens and high laced shoes" has a story which is far from mirth-provoking. Could it have been written up for you by O. Henry, it would have provoked tears rather than laughter. The facts are as follows: She is, as you say, a peasant of Kent and four times a mother. The father of these four children, a truck gardener, died some years ago and left her their sole support. She, previously a vigorous and good-looking young woman, has become the victim of a disease known as acromegaly. This cruel and deforming malady not only completely transforms the outward appearance of those whom it afflicts but is attended with great suffering and often with loss of vision.

One of Mr. Ringling's agents prevailed upon her to travel with the circus and to pose as the "ugliest woman in the world" as a means of livelihood. Mr. Ringling is kind to his people and she is well cared for. But she suffers from intolerable headaches, has become nearly blind, and permits herself to be laughed at and heckled by an unfeeling people in order to provide the wherewithal to educate her four children. Beauty is but skin deep. Being a physician, I do not like to feel that *Time* can be frivolous over the tragedies of disease.

1910

Anyone who studies the monograph on the pituitary will understand why much of the year 1910 came to be devoted to its preparation. As usual, however, many other things impinged upon him. His last letter to his father mentions an interview with Mr. Taft:

H.C. to H.K.C. *9 January* [*1910*].

. . . The long mislaid photograph of the [Tarbell] portrait turned up today and I am forwarding it to you. On the envelope was simply *The Museum of Fine Arts, Boston* so that I presume it was taken there. I assume they have the negative therefore, and prints can be obtained from them if any of the family want them. I think Kate would like a copy. Would you prefer to have me send for them?

"The Professor," Finney and I went to Washington [5 Jan.] to interview the President about the pending Surgeon Gen'l of the Navy appointment. Rixey wishes a reappointment and we wished to put in a word for Stokes. Mr. Taft was very pleasant and 'smiling'—this was the day before Gifford Pinchot's Explosion, or he might not have been.[22]

The Johns Hopkins Historical Club met on 10 January, and Cushing and Barker gave an account of the Budapest Congress. On the 19th H.C. was in Cleveland for a paper on "The special field of neurological surgery—five years later,"—a sequel[22a] to the one he had presented there in 1905. In the light of his rapidly increasing number of operations he was now able to speak with considerably more assurance:

We have had at this writing about 180 patients suffering from brain tumor, the larger number of them having been admitted during the past two years—namely 64 from October 1908 to October 1909, and nearly an equal number from October 1909 to date. Some 250 operations have been performed on these patients, including such preliminary measures as a subtemporal decompression for the relief of headaches and preservation of vision before localization was possible. . . . In our last 100 cases, over a period of 18 months, there were eight operative fatalities in the first 50 and only three in the second 50; there were only 10 extirpations or six cyst evacuations with practical cures in the first 50, and there have been 20 in the last 50. In the entire 100, therefore, there have been 30 apparent (to all intents and purposes) cures, 13 operative deaths and 57 measures which have been definitely palliative.

In speaking of the training of a neurological surgeon he has this to say:

. . . There is no question but that a training for neurological surgery must come through laboratory experiences, and just as we are indebted to experimentation on the lower animals for almost every fact of importance which has made for the advance of this particular department, so also must we call upon them for the mere practice of hand essential to success in their clinical applications. Those who oppose the employment of animals for such purposes leave us the only alternative of subjecting our fellow man, as a lesser creature, to our first crude manipulations.

His friend, J. K. Mitchell, sent an enthusiastic comment about the paper:

Dear Cushing You are always interesting—& I have been enjoying your Neurologic Surgery paper & differing & agreeing with you in a cheerful & con-

[22] Admiral Stokes received the appointment. The "Pinchot Explosion" had reference to the National Conservation Commission whose corrupt administration Mr. Pinchot, then Chief of the Forestry Service, had exposed, rather inopportunely for the President, who dismissed him on 7 January 1910.

[22a] *Johns Hopkins Hospital Bulletin,* November 1910, *21,* 325-339.

versational fashion. Yes, every surgeon ought to have some general medical training—every internist (all sorts of 'em) ought to have some surgical experience & all the surgical observation he can get. They have to get these experiences either way when young—if they are any good they soon grow too busy.

I count among my best assets ten years of general medical work—for which I am grateful to my wise father—who wouldn't have me with him & turned me on the wide world—and the surgical apprenticeship I gained by being an "office-student" of Keen's & later an unofficial assistant to him & to Goodell. I often wish some of the neurologs whom I meet could have had innere & aussere Medezin in like fashion! Also—the reference to the colour-field changes & inversions remind me to say again how admirable a piece of work you & Dr. Bordley did!

In the midst of the trip to Cleveland Abraham Flexner summoned him abruptly by telegram to New York to discuss "IMPORTANT PROPOSITION MEDICAL EDUCATION." H.C. introduces his dossier of materials about this incident with the following brief note:[23]

These unexpected telegrams came to me in Cleveland Jany 19th and 20th, when I was there reading a paper at the instigation of Ludlow before the Lakeside Alumni. I went [back to New York] on Thursday night [the 20th] and met Abraham Flexner at the Belmont and thence to the Carnegie Foundation where Mr. Brookings [President of Corporation, Washington University], who was on the eve of his departure for a rest in Egypt, unfolded his plans to Johns Hopkinize the Medical Department of the Washington University. He to back the project with his entire fortune. I had no inkling what the meeting was about, thinking it might have something to do with the Research Defense League in view of the recent attack on the Rockefeller Institute and Flexner by the antivivisectionists.

February was a particularly hectic month, for in addition to the proposal from St. Louis, and also one from Harvard, he was faced with the decision whether or not to operate on General Wood; on the heels of this came the illness and death of his father.

Early in February word was received that H.K.C. was poorly. Beginning on the 8th he was confined to his bed by a series of anginal seizures which alternated with cerebral attacks involving transient paralysis of his right hand and loss of speech, and on the 10th a wire summoned H.C. to Cleveland. Henry Kirke recognized him when he arrived on the morning of the 11th and exchanged a few words with him, remarking with characteristic Cushing reserve: "I do not know what will happen, but it is all right for I have already said all that I wished to say about everything." He died shortly after midnight on the morning of the 12th.

In his desk was an envelope addressed to his daughter Alice, dated 29 January 1904, containing a brief handwritten will and several admonitions about business. One sentence in the will reads: "My watch is to go to Harvey, if he desires it, since his own was a some-

[23] See Chapter X, p. 337 for further details.

what less expensive one than those of his brothers. It is, however, so complex that it is a somewhat costly one to keep in repair." Among the admonitions were the following: "Do not lend money. Let the broker whose business it is do that. . . . Do not endorse anybody's note. . . . Do not become bondsman or a surety for any executor or administrator or anyone else. . . . Keep the family property together as long as possible. . . . Very earnestly submitted for the adoption of all concerned. H.K.C. October 8th 1898." In examining their father's wardrobe they found that he had not bought a new suit in ten years, and practically everything that he had was threadbare except for one suit that he had set aside especially for the funeral. In accord with family tradition he had thus "come out even."

H.K.C.'s systematic ways were further exemplified by the fact that he had kept a complete file of all the letters H.C. had written to the members of the Cleveland family since he first went to Yale in 1887—nearly all preserved in their original covers and arranged in strict chronological sequence. And H.C., his father's son, tied them up in bundles, took them back to Baltimore, and put them out of sight on top of one of the church-warden bookcases.[24] There were many letters of sympathy after his father's death but probably none gave H.C. greater solace than those from Welch and Osler:

William H. Welch to H.C. *22 February 1910.*

Dear Cushing, I appreciated very much your letter from Cleveland—you know that you have my sincere sympathy. Your father was the best type of man and physician, and I am glad to have had the privilege of knowing him. His mode of death is the most fortunate one, as was also that of my sister. She died instantaneously while apparently in particularly cheerful mood and good health. . . . I appreciated very much Mrs. Cushing's kind letter of sympathy. . . . With best wishes, Yours ever sincerely, WILLIAM H. WELCH.

William Osler to H.C. *25 February 1910.*

Dear Cushing 'Tis sad to hear of your good father's death, but he had a fine life, with nothing to regret, and he was spared a long illness. You must have been a great joy to him—a son after his own heart. What a remarkable record for so many generations. It is a great thing to come of such good stock. I am rejoiced to hear the good news about Wood—do give him my regards & best wishes. What a fortunate thing that you operated, and took the risk! It is too bad that Edsall is not to go to St. Louis. Look over the ground carefully. You have such a grip on the East that I can understand how loath you must be to go beyond the Mississippi. But there are plenty of good fellows there. . . . Love to Kate & the angels. Yours ever, Wm OSLER.

[24] At least that is where they were found when the house at 691 Whitney Avenue in New Haven was dismantled some months after Dr. Cushing's death in 1939. He had evidently forgotten them, for he did not use them when preparing the Osler biography, and there is no doubt that they would have been of inestimable value to him since the letters from 1901 through 1909 are full of Osler and would have furnished many details not included in the Osler biography.

First Operation on General Wood

The day before Cushing arrived in Cleveland for his father's last illness, H.K.C. had commented upon a newspaper report that his son had successfully operated upon a well-known general of the United States Army. Major General Leonard Wood, Chief of Staff of the Army and later Governor of the Philippines,[25] one of the most influential military figures of his time, had struck his head on a low chandelier in the autumn of 1898 when on shipboard with Major General Frank McCoy. A small growth involving the bone began to appear some years later under the site of the injury;[26] by 1902 there was evidence that an intracranial tumor was developing, causing symptoms of increased intracranial pressure with numbness and weakness of the left side of his body. Then focal seizures occurred in these extremities. H.C. had first seen General Wood a year previously and had advised against immediate operation. Meanwhile the General had become worse and, on 5 February 1910, the first stage of the operation was carried out. On the 9th (two days before his father's death), he removed a large meningeal tumor—the most difficult, because they are generally the most vascular of all the tumors of the intracranial cavity. This was the first time that he had had success with this type of lesion—his first encounter with such a growth [in the case of John Maloney] having been back in his student days at the M.G.H. The details of the story are best told in H.C.'s own words taken from the report of the case in his monograph on the meningiomas (1938). He introduces the case report with the following apology: "The patient was a man accustomed to sacrifice himself for others, first as a doctor

[25] There is no clear evidence to substantiate the contention that the selection of Pershing rather than Wood as supreme commander of the AEF in 1917 was a result of Wood's physical condition. On at least two later occasions he was given a physical clearance by medical authorities: ". . . they tell me I have made a recovery such as is only found in the *very young,* all of which has a very pleasing sound," Wood wrote from Paris to Mrs. Wood on 16 February 1918, after his motor accident. The *New York Sun,* 30 March 1918, reported his thorough examination before the Medical Examining Board in Washington. Among other things he was made to hop about the room, first on one foot and then on the other. "He don't hop the way I do," exclaimed one of the examining surgeons, "but, my God, he *can* hop!" Members of the board remarked that they had never examined a subject of Wood's years and experience who presented so few physical defects, and gave Wood a clean bill of health as physically qualified for active service. The selection of Pershing appears, rather, as another link in the chain of an opposing administration's effort to prevent Wood's rise to greater public favor than he had occasioned by his long and vigorous support of national preparedness. For a thorough treatment of this controversial matter see Hermann Hagedorn, *Leonard Wood. A biography* (New York, 1931).

[26] With regard to his original injury Hagedorn reports (II, 58) that Theodore Roosevelt wrote Wood 4 June 1904: "Word was brought us, that in a fencing bout with McCoy, he did something to you which kept you in bed a week. Root and I thought of getting up a round-robin letter of congratulation to McCoy, but feared that if we did so you might administer the water cure to him! Give him my good wishes instead."

and then as a soldier and administrator; and it is no betrayal of many years of friendship now to tell the heroic story of his malady which ended in an operative fatality from *the fault of having replaced at the first operation an involved dura and bone flap* due to ignorance of the life history of these formidable lesions. Leonard Wood was a man who

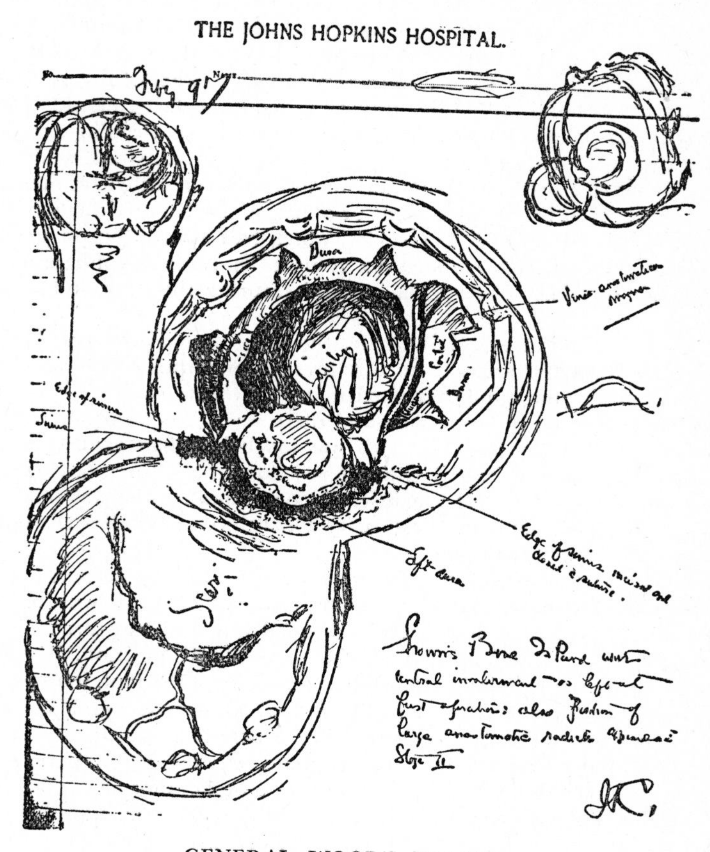

GENERAL WOOD'S TUMOR
Operative sketch showing size and position of the tumor removed from General Wood on 9 February 1910

took the slings of outrageous fortune with gallantry; and could he have been consulted about the propriety of having the case reported at this time without anonymity he might possibly have hesitated, but in order to spare the writer's feelings rather than his own." After giving a detailed clinical history of Wood's illness, he described the second stage of the operation as follows:

Operation II. *February 9, 1910.* Second stage under ether with tumor extirpation. On reelevating the flap and reflecting the dura, a bulging, dry cortex with greatly flattened convolutions and the margin of a parasagittal tumor were exposed. The lesion was at first taken to be a glioma until, by blunt dissection through the thinned crescentic edge of enveloping cortex, the surface of an encapsulated lesion was brought into view. The dura was reflected upward from the surface of the tumor to which it was only slightly adherent, and the lateral incisions were carried to the margins of the sinus. Then by slow dissection and the occasional use of "clips" brain was brushed away from the upper hemisphere of an unexpectedly large but enucleable lesion. Fortunately the two large venae anastomoticae which passed one in front and one behind the growth could be pushed aside and it was unnecessary to ligate either of them.

The growth was finally tilted out leaving a smooth-surfaced mould covered by *apparently intact pia arachnoid.* There was inconsiderable bleeding except at the small area of attachment of the growth at the margin of the sinus, where a sharp venous haemorrhage occurred. This was temporarily controlled by pressure and subsequently checked by the placement of a marginal suture. Ultimately the field was rendered completely dry. The cavity, which had already begun to fill in as the compressed hemisphere tended to resume its normal configuration, was filled with salt solution before replacing and suturing the dura and closing the flap.

The four-hour session was well borne, the pulse rate at the end being only 100. Recovery from the anaesthetic was prompt and quiet with no vomiting. Subjective tingling and numbness particularly in *the ulnar distribution of the arm and hand* followed the operation and there was a temporary increase in the disability of the left arm and leg. This was much less than expected and soon disappeared. The wound healed without reaction, the sutures having been removed on the second day. Not a man easily kept confined, he was soon allowed to be up in a wheel-chair; and on *February 20th,* eleven days after the operation, he began to walk about his room.

He was discharged on *March 5, 1910,* a month after his admission; and as though nothing had happened immediately resumed his work with accustomed vigor. He reported in 1916 that he had remained well and had carried the heavy responsibility, both mental and physical, incidental to his position. His only disability was the persistent limp due to residual spasticity of the foot. There had been no return of the focal seizures. . . . As is well known, General Wood subsequently led a most active and effective life which lies outside this story. His capacity for work and his fondness for strenuous exercise are well remembered. When on a tour of inspection in France in *1918* a Stokes mortar exploded killing several persons and seriously injuring him and two of his aides who were bystanders. He alone of all the survivors curiously showed no effects of "shell shock." Though seen and heard from not infrequently during the ten years following his tumor operation, he made no allusion to it other than briefly to say he never felt in better health. Of his obvious lameness he appeared to be unconscious, and his tireless energy was proverbial among his associates.

It apparently was not until after his return to the Philippines as Governor in *1921* that he began again to have occasional Jacksonian seizures in his foot. He disregarded the signal, said nothing about it to anyone, and went about his business with customary vigor. By *1923* the spasticity in his leg had begun to increase and the left arm again became affected. To conquer this, he would engage daily in target practice with an army pistol, being able to outshoot most of his competitors with his left hand.

He had acquired a *bilateral inguinal hernia* which though large he managed to keep in place with a self-devised strap. First one (in *September 1926*) and then the other (in *January 1927*) became strangulated and were successfully and skilfully operated upon in the emergency by the staff surgeon, Col. L. Z. Fletcher. In *April 1927* he was *thrown from a motor car in an accident,* receiving a severe blow on the right side of his head. Making this an excuse for his crippled condition and increasing lameness, after a final tour of inspection of the southern islands, he came home, made his official report to President Coolidge and on the insistence of his friend Dr. Alexander Lambert was brought to the Brigham Hospital.

READMISSION. *August 4, 1927.* Examination. He had grown exceedingly heavy. He had an almost complete left spastic hemiplegia with considerable contraction

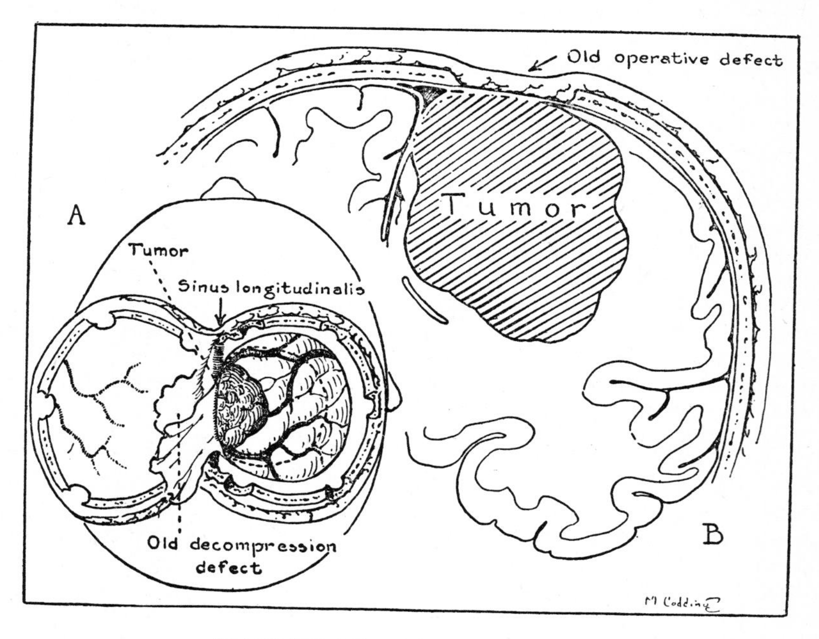

DIAGRAM OF WOOD OPERATION

When H.C. reported General Wood's case he had a diagram prepared from his original operative sketch which illustrates the great value of the drawings made immediately after almost every operation (*Meningiomas,* 1938, Fig. 331)

of the arm, sagging of the left face and ptosis. There was *astereognosis and loss of all sense of position in the left hand and foot* though with an effort he could get out of his chair, stand, and take a few steps with assistance. There was a *complete left homonymous hemianopsia* and loss of reading vision. The eyegrounds were within normal limits. His blood-pressure was only 124/92. There was a definitely *pulsating median protrusion* at the mesial edge of the old flap and the X-ray showed erosion of the bone in this region over an area 5 to 6 cm. in diameter evidently crossing the midline.

There followed an account of another, apparently successful, removal of a huge recurrent meningioma—but an unsuspected hemorrhage had occurred into one of the cerebral ventricles, and the

General died a few hours after the operation had been completed. Few tragedies ever upset Cushing more than this, and for weeks he was inconsolable, for not only had Wood been a close friend, but the original operation he had performed on Wood had been a turning point in his own life, and probably the outstanding event of his surgical career. Arthur Tracy Cabot had come down from Harvard to witness the first operation, in 1910, and H.C. wrote in his volume of Leonard Wood memorabilia: "As matters stood it was good fortune that things went as well as they did in 1910. Arthur Cabot was then on the Corporation at Harvard. He had never seen an operation of the kind—no more had I. But I am quite sure that what he saw was what put me in line as candidate for the Chair of Surgery here." H.C. left an account of another incident in connection with the first operation on Wood:

> The evening after this operation the doorbell rang at our Chase St. house and a man came in saying he was General Scott & that he had been walking the streets all the afternoon and evening and couldn't stand it any longer—he simply *had* to know something of General Wood's condition. I brought him in and when he saw K.C. they nearly fell into each other's arms. It appeared that they had been together with General Miles, Cody (Buffalo Bill) and others on a tour of inspection in the west many years before. It must have been midnight when he left and he spent the whole time talking of Leonard Wood as though he might have been his one and only son. It was very touching.

After a brief trip to Milwaukee, where he had spent a day with Osler's old friend and associate, H. V. Ogden, H.C. worked steadily in his clinic for the remainder of the month. In April Welch celebrated his sixtieth birthday. His birthdays, usually celebrated jointly with H.C., had come to be festive occasions to which their friends always looked forward. Many years later H.C. set down the following notes about the party in 1910: "The [Welch] 60th birthday festivity was on a much larger scale than in 1900. He was that year President of the A.M.A. and there was a great turn-out in the ballroom of the Hotel Belvedere, if I remember right. I had only shortly before operated on General Wood, who, much to my embarrassment and to the astonishment of others, insisted on coming to the dinner with his head closely capped. It was a stirring occasion with 400-500 guests and excellent speeches. All the guests received small copies of Brenner's remarkable bas-relief, and Max Brödel's cartoon of 'Welch rabbits' made a great hit."

During May there was the usual sequence of clinical meetings, a paper on oculomotor palsies at the American Neurological Association on 2 May; another presentation on epilepsy as a manifestation of brain tumors at a meeting of the National Association for the Study of Epilepsy held on 7 May in Baltimore; and the night before there had been a medical alumni reunion of the Johns Hopkins Hospital during which a program of operations had been arranged in the Hunterian Laboratory. But this was not all, for we find him in Washington on the 9th attending a meeting of the American Surgical Association. Some of his younger friends in later life protested because they could not induce him to go to all the meetings at which he would have been welcome. Anyone who looks over his incredible calendar during these years of feverish activity will have greater sympathy with his disinclination to attend meetings during the last fifteen years of his life. His secretaries amused themselves during these years by keeping special folders containing his various invitations to lecture, all filed with his various letters of refusal. Between 1920 and 1939 these folders grew fatter and fatter and one year (1934) he politely turned down thirty-four such proposals. It can be said on his behalf that he never used a form letter for such regrets—no two of them are alike, except for the frequent reference to the sweating and palpitation which invariably came over him before making any kind of public utterance.

Though the month of May was crowded with medical meetings, it was made happy by the arrival on 22 May of a second son, Henry Kirke. In June there were two more papers, one in Washington with Emil Goetsch on the secretion of the posterior lobe of the pituitary,[27] and at Syracuse on 6 June a second rendering of his paper on the special field of neurological surgery. During the summer he went off to England for another meeting of the Society of Clinical Surgery, the first that had been held abroad. Of this he wrote sometime later:[28]

By the time we had completed our second circuit [in the U.S.], the *Wanderlust* got into our blood and at the instigation of Edward Martin it was decided to pay a visit in the summer of 1910 to Great Britain where a society modeled on our own, the Provincial Surgical Society, had been organized by some British surgeons, a few of whom had attended one or two of our meetings. As Mumford was unable to go, Lund as acting secretary in his place took copious notes which were printed and distributed later on.

Twenty-three members including three invited guests—"Honorary Consultants" they were called, *viz.* Frank Billings (Chicago), Samuel Alexander (New York) and John Clark (Philadelphia)—sailed June 22nd on the *Mauretania* and were joined abroad by five other members who had preceded them. Outstanding among the events of that memorable trip which progressed from Liverpool to London to Edinburgh to Newcastle to Leeds were: the afternoon with Robert Jones who with surprising skill and rapidity performed 28 orthopaedic operations; the visit to Kings Hospital where Sir Watson Cheyne with excellent results still conserva-

[27] "Concerning the secretion of the infundibular lobe of the pituitary body and its presence in the cerebrospinal fluid." (With E. Goetsch). *American Journal of Physiology,* 1 November 1910, 27, 60-86. This paper offered evidence that posterior lobe secretion of the pituitary could be detected in the cerebrospinal fluid. H.C. believed that this was its normal mode of egress from the gland.

[28] For some reason there is no diary of this trip—the only one of his trips outside the country which is unrecorded.

tively used Lister's original antiseptic technique (excluding the spray); the Sunday boating party on the Thames; tea on the terrace at the Houses of Parliament; the demonstrations by Sir Victor Horsley at the National Hospital and in his old laboratory at University College; the day passed in Oxford with Osler as both cicerone and host; and the dinner in the Royal College of Surgeons in Edinburgh when pipers in kilts brought in the haggis (a ceremony imitated by the irrepressible Martin at our autumn meeting when Philadelphia scrapple took the place of haggis); and the final day and farewell dinner with Moynihan at Leeds after which most of the party returned the next day on the [later] ill-fated *Lusitania* from Liverpool.

During September he was at Little Boar's Head with the family preparing his well-known paper on the use of silver clips to control bleeding in cerebral operations.[29] And on 5 October the Hanover Surgical Club at Dartmouth induced him to read a paper on brain tumors and their surgical treatment. After this the shadow of the coming Harvey Lecture on 10 December hung over him and it is safe to say that everything else assumed secondary importance as he prepared his paper on disorders of the pituitary—the lecture that formed the basis for his book.

H.C. always prided himself on the fact that he was a physiologist and a member of the American Physiological Society. His paper on sensations evoked from stimulation of the postcentral convolution of the brain of conscious human subjects issued in *Brain* in 1909[30] had attracted wide attention since it established that a mosaic of sensory foci exists in the human brain similar in distribution to that of the motor area which he had helped Sherrington to work out in chimpanzees and gorillas in 1901. On 30 December he wound up the year with another physiological paper with Goetsch and Conrad Jacobson on carbohydrate tolerance in relation to the pituitary presented at New Haven at the annual meeting of the American Physiological Society.

As an investigator Harvey Cushing had conspicuous faults as well as obvious virtues. In the papers on posterior pituitary secretion he had been led astray, but despite an imposing array of evidence to the contrary, he never really admitted that he had been wrong; in addition, he unfortunately caused a number of his junior associates to waste valuable time and effort in attempting to establish his original contention. It was a curious foible in a man who had achieved so much in so many directions. Conrad Jacobson, who was an admirer of Cushing, mentions this, and he writes with feeling since he was one

[29] "The control of bleeding in operations for brain tumors. With the description of silver 'clips' for the occlusion of vessels inaccessible to the ligature." *Annals of Surgery,* July 1911, *54,* 1-19.

[30] "A note upon the faradic stimulation of the post-central gyrus in conscious patients." *Brain,* May 1909, *32,* 44-53.

of those whom H.C. had involved in this manner during his service at the old Hunterian in 1911 and in the Hospital in 1912:

As a research man he was of the deductive type of mind. Some investigators gather their data and try to draw their conclusions from them. He was inclined to have a theory and then use all of his efforts and ingenuity to prove the validity of it. One of the last papers he published while he was at Hopkins was on the blood-pressure-raising effect of spinal fluid. He always had the idea that the pituitary gland secretion found its way into the spinal fluid. By concentrating spinal fluid and injecting the same into animals he obtained certain blood-pressure-raising effects which he concluded were due to the presence of pituitary secretion. This paper encountered some rather destructive criticism by Carlson, the physiologist. He approached the problem from a different angle and could find no hemodynamic reaction. To meet this criticism of Carlson's, my first research in the Hunterian was "to get Carlson," so to speak. Artificial spinal fluid was made according to the chemical composition of spinal fluid. On concentration and injection of these, identical results were obtained. The blood-pressure-raising effect was entirely due to the increased salt content produced by the concentrations. It was difficult for Cushing to believe this, but when confronted with the actual facts, made the remark that "I could make as good spinal fluid as the Good Lord Himself."

But in spite of this, for several years every spinal fluid that was taken in his clinic or operating room in any amount was sent to me for kimograph tracings and many a Saturday afternoon was spent in the laboratory with Dr. Cushing on this problem, he intently looking for something to bear out his theory. He would be quite elated when with a little added force in injecting the fluid, there would be an increased blood-pressure effect and rather crestfallen when the identical result would be obtained by the artificial spinal fluid. It was rather difficult to make Cushing conduct it as a quantitative as well as a qualitative experiment. After a large number of animals had been used, a large number of spinal fluids investigated, and we had over three hundred fifty nicely mounted kimograph tracings, the subject remained fallow for some time. One noon, after lunch, I was summoned to Dr. Cushing's office. Here were Dr. Cushing and Dr. Cannon with this large stack of kimographic tracings before them. Dr. Cushing remarked that Dr. Cannon did see some blood-pressure-raising effect in the tracing he had in his hand. In the characteristic Cushing manner, any detailed discussion or explanation on my part was over-ridden for the moment, so intense was his feeling on this problem. The only reply that I could make was the final one, "It is a question if this one is a normal tracing and the other three hundred forty-nine are abnormal variations, or if the three hundred forty-nine are normal and this one the variation." Dr. Cannon's detailed study of the problem and tracings led him to just one conclusion. In spite of all the experimental work to the contrary, I believe that Cushing to the day of his death still thought there was pituitary extract in the spinal fluid.

Cushing's interpretation of certain facts which were produced experimentally under his direction undoubtedly has been rather too enthusiastic and has been and will be questioned. When he was reminded of these facts by some of his contemporaries, he usually remarked, "I never expected to settle these things; I have set others thinking about them and this is the main purpose, after all." He had the most remarkable power of writing a paper. Quotations from the recesses of the literature as well as experimental facts were used to prove his contention. His papers were all frankly readable. One feels that Cushing's greatness in the research line is due more to his interpretation of clinical findings from his operative cases than to the experimental work on animals.

1911

H.C. was still hard at work on his pituitary monograph. His service at the Hospital was becoming increasingly busy, and the men working with him were pushed to keep up with him. Conrad Jacobson has described the clinic and laboratory during this period with vividness and candor:

While Dr. Cushing was in charge of Neurosurgery at the Johns Hopkins Hospital, the service was conducted by himself and an assistant known throughout the hospital as "Cushing's man." This individual was usually selected from the graduating class. While several men were considered for the position, it was given to the one who possessed what was spoken of as "Geist." This expression was a favorite one of the "Chief's." Such an individual was supposed to have some tendency towards research work, some special ability to work alone and to possess the usual qualifications of a good medical student. The choice was not one limited to scholarship but rather to personal fitness. This man had charge of the Hunterian Laboratory of Surgical Research for a year. During this year he was a free lance devoting himself mainly to research work and occasionally brought into contact with the hospital if his research work was in any way related to the clinical aspects of the patients. It was understood, however, that the research work undertaken should be along neurological lines, both he and Dr. Cushing collaborating in the articles published. After spending a year in the Hunterian Laboratory, he was given the hospital year on Cushing's service. The hospital year was a particularly hard one. At this time, every little detail regarding the patient, concerning the various special examinations and pertaining to new and exacting operations was a personal affair with Dr. Cushing. He was an extremely hard taskmaster and drove his men incessantly, almost to the point of exhaustion. He was an indefatigable worker and expected the same of his assistant. "Cushing's man" was looked upon by the rest of the hospital staff with considerable sympathy for what was ahead of him, as well as respect for the honor associated with this position. . . . Cushing's selections of the first few assistants were, on the whole, harmonious. It soon became evident that "Geist" not only concerned the innate ability of the assistant for work but also concerned a temperament which could meet or put up with the demands of a most exacting taskmaster.

Walter Dandy was selected from the class of 1910 to carry on the work as research assistant in the Hunterian Laboratory for a year and then as "Cushing's man" to take care of the increasing neurosurgical work in the hospital. While in the Hunterian he became interested in the problem of absorption from the pleural cavity. This was not a neurological problem and I believe from this there developed a conflict of personalities which made Dr. Dandy's service extremely arduous and accounts for the personal feeling which existed between these men during Dr. Cushing's life. Dr. Dandy's hospital service was not a very pleasant or agreeable one. Before the clinical year was finished, he was forewarned that he would not be included in the group which Dr. Cushing took with him to Boston.[31] After some months of trying uncertainty for Dr. Dandy, Halsted found

[31] Dr. Dandy recalls (1945) that he and H.C. first came to loggerheads over some experiments on the relation of the sympathetic nervous system to glycosuria; he had

a place for him on his surgical service at Hopkins. This was the beginning of Dr. Dandy's remarkable development in neurosurgery—radical neurosurgery in contrast to Dr. Cushing's conservative surgery. . . .

Cushing's men were, as a rule, extremely loyal to him. They gave him all they had. Some served him perhaps too long and perhaps too faithfully. It could hardly be otherwise, for Dr. Cushing's powers of persuasion were very forceful and convincing when conditions demanded. This loyalty extended to the lower brackets of men also as was so genuinely exemplified by Jimmie. Jimmie was a rather small, wizened-up Welshman who had charge of the animals at the Hunterian Laboratory, this a rather disagreeable, uninviting task as can be easily understood. The Hunterian consisted of two departments, the surgical research side and the pathological research side, each occupying one half of the building. Cushing and his men had charge of the entire building—the general personnel, the upkeep of animals, their distribution to the various departments of the Medical School and so forth. Dr. Cushing gave orders for the building to be closed on a certain holiday. The pathological department desired to do some experimental work on that day and requested some animals from Jimmie. They argued that Cushing had nothing to say about the running of their department. Jimmie's reply was, "Orders is orders, and if Dr. Cushing says that the building should be burned down, in well nigh half an hour there would be little of the building left." There was no work done in the building on that holiday.

Concurrently with his clinical and experimental work there had been in process over many months the negotiations which led to H.C.'s acceptance of the chair of surgery at Harvard (see Ch. X), and during 1911 he was much preoccupied with settling his affairs in Baltimore in preparation for his transfer to Boston. His friends there had written enthusiastically about his coming, and his replies show great warmth and appreciation. More or less out of the blue he wrote to Codman on 3 January:

I have been going over the M.G.H. "Publications" and rereading your duodenal papers. They are simply 'bang up'!—by far the best things that have been written, and written—what's more—in by far the most effective, readable, and telling way. You're a wonder as I've always secretly thought. The only reason they didn't make you the prospective surgeon to the Brigham was that it would have looked like a family affair—architect *et al.* I wish they'd do it now and let me back out. You only have an occasional belly ache while I have perpetual cold feet. Then I've got the dickens of a lot to do here and my head buzzes with hemianopsias, carbohydrate assimilation limits, plasma in which things will grow, dyspituitarism, and pinealismus, not to speak of Willie, Mary, Betsey & Henry. Yours ever admiringly, with love and a Happy New Year to you and Katie, H.C.

When in New Haven in December he had made a new friend in Herbert Thoms, who shortly thereafter wrote to enquire about the mode of anesthesia which H.C. was using for his pituitary cases. Thoms, the well-known Yale obstetrician, who is now one of the

---

obtained results contrary to those that were expected and those about to be reported with Weed and Jacobson (*Johns Hopkins Hospital Bulletin*, February 1913, *24*, 40-52). After the altercation Dandy stated that H.C. then informed him that he would not be taken to Boston.

curators of the Historical Library at Yale, received the following prompt reply:

H.C. to Herbert Thoms *14 January 1911.*

Dear Dr. Thoms: I am glad to have heard from you and to have received your suggestions in regard to the anaesthetization of these pituitary body cases. We have for a year or two employed some such method as you outline, more for the reason of getting the anaesthetist out of the field and to avoid the use of the mask than for any other. Occasionally it is impossible to anaesthetize these patients by mouth, owing to the great hypertrophy of the tongue, which in the state of relaxation closes the glottis, no matter how much drawn forward or hooked up it may be. Hence we have been forced to do a tracheotomy on two or three occasions. Usually, however, after the first anaesthetization in the customary way, a silver tube wrapped with gauze, so that it will serve to hook up and hold down the base of the tongue, is inserted in the corner of the mouth, and warmed vapor anaesthesia is given, and in this way I can get a clear field for the naso-labial approach. However, your experience in these matters is so much greater than our own that I doubt not that you can devise things which will be of help to all those who must practise these difficult measures. It was a great pleasure to see you the other day in New Haven. . . .

In February H.C. appeared before the Academy of Medicine in Toronto with a paper on "Brain tumors and their surgical treatment."[32]

In March he received the distressing news that his favorite brother, Ned, was seriously ill in Cleveland, and it was later learned that he had developed an inoperable carcinoma of the lower bowel. E.F.C. failed rapidly and died on 25 March. His death was a bitter blow for the entire family, but H.C. took it particularly hard. A brief letter from Klebs gave him great comfort:

Montolivet, Ouchy,
A. C. Klebs to H.C. *28 May 1911.*

Dear Cushing Jacobs told me, just before leaving Divonne the other day, of the sad loss that had come to you through the death of your brother. Poor old man, I feel with you and I press your hand through the distance and in silence. "Frater ave atque vale." . . . With warm regards, Most sincerely yours, ARNOLD C. KLEBS.

H.C. replied: "Yes, dear Klebs, it is but too true. It has been a crushing blow to us all and we are as yet too stunned to grasp its full significance. He was far and away the best of the whole tribe and I think the best physician I ever knew. I will send you Mumford's editorial about him." He also wrote as follows to Codman:

H.C. to E. A. Codman *17 April 1911.*

Dear Amory: I am so grateful for your letter. One rather hungers for words from his friends under such circumstances. We are all too stunned as yet to take in the significance of it.

They have been making a strong appeal to get me to go back to Cleveland—as

[32] Abstract in *Canada Lancet*, March 1911, *44*, 507-509.

though I or *anyone* could take his place! I don't believe I ever talked much with you about Ned. He was a great physician—the best I have ever known, I think. I found among father's things a letter which Maurice wrote him while Ned was in the M.G.H. I presume he impressed everyone in the same way. What they will do in Cleveland without him I cannot imagine.

Another communication of this time was a particularly friendly letter from John Collins Warren:

58 Beacon Street, Boston,
24 April 1911.

Dear Dr. Cushing: I was about to write to you upon a matter connected with the old Medical School, when I received the notice (some little time past now) of the death of your brother of Cleveland. Now I find another and more extended account in the *Boston Medical and Surgical Journal.* I have read both of these with great interest, the former showing me how much importance was attached to him as a citizen in his native city, and the latter, his standing in his profession. Of course I remember him well during his hospital days, when I had the privilege of enjoying his services there, and it was a great pleasure to me to see him once more on Ether Day. It seems hard to realize that he had reached an age when one was likely to be exposed to cancer, for I always felt it was his lot to have a long, useful career, following the footsteps of your father.

As I said, I had intended writing about this time to call your attention to the fact that the old Medical School on North Grove St. was being razed to the ground and that we had discovered there the remains of a collection of the Phrenological Society, which was purchased at the time of Spurzheim's death and placed in the building when it was completed. My grandfather bought with it the skull of Spurzheim himself: to this has since been added the skull of Dr. Robertson, his friend and admirer, who left in his will the request that his skull should be placed beside that of Spurzheim.

The collection of casts, about 150 in number, has been transferred to the new Medical School, and Dr. Whitney tells me that he has the original catalogue. As the casts are numbered, this may be of some use, although many of them have been broken and destroyed in the fullness of time. I find considerable literature concerning Spurzheim and the Phrenological Society. It appeared that Mr. George B. Calvert of Baltimore published a book, with illustrations, on Phrenology, etc. in 1832: and I have in my hand a book by Nahum Capen called "Reminiscences of Spurzheim and Coombe." In the Annals of Phrenology I find an interesting article and report on the skull of Spurzheim. It seemed to me that there was material here for an historical study which might throw some light upon our notion of cerebral localization. As you doubtless know, Spurzheim made his home and collection in Boston and died here and was buried in Mt. Auburn.

I shall be glad to get your opinion whether it would be worth while to work up a paper on this subject, or whether you might possibly like to do it yourself. . . . I hear also from Mr. Reynolds encouraging news about the Brigham Hospital and am hoping some day when I go out to the Medical School to rub my eyes and see a man with a spade in his hand. . . .

Cushing's scientific interest during the year had turned to the visual system as a result of his work on the pituitary. He had developed his own dark room for examining the visual fields, and since this was a time-consuming occupation he decided to take on as an associate someone who could carry out these visual examinations;

thus in June he wrote Dr. Howell, the Dean, about Clifford Walker and his other appointees for the following academic year:

H.C. to W. H. Howell *5 June 1911.*

Dear Dr. Howell: Lest Dr. Halsted's expected departure for Europe should cause him to overlook the matter of next year's recommendations I wish to send you the following names which I have already submitted to him: Dr. Conrad Jacobson to succeed Dr. Dandy in the Hunterian Laboratory; Dr. Emil Goetsch to remain as my assistant on Dr. Halsted's service in the Hospital—I believe that he has an official assistantship on the Faculty—Dr. W. E. Dandy to succeed Dr. Sharpe in the hospital. There is, I believe, no official title connected with this position.

I have persuaded Clifford B. Walker, of the present graduating class, to stay and work on ophthalmological problems in the Hunterian Laboratory and in the hospital next year. I hope that he will "make good." . . . If he proves to be a good man, as I trust he will, it is possible that there may be something more for him later on. Very respectfully yours, HARVEY CUSHING.

Papers on visual problems also began to appear during the year,[33] and they aroused much interest and favorable comment among his ophthalmological colleagues who, up to the time of Cushing's work, had been much confused about visual disturbances associated with pituitary tumors. Thus George de Schweinitz, the well-known Philadelphia ophthalmologist, writes (25 Jan. 1914): "If I could manage to slip down to Baltimore some Sunday, would you let me look at the fields of vision of your pituitary body cases? I saw a few that you threw on the screen when you lectured at the College, but I would like to study them a little more in detail, as I have made some observations, not yet published, which I think may have some interest in connection with the visual field phenomena of pituitary body disease, and I would like to see if similar fields occur in your series." In June H.C. journeyed to Los Angeles for a meeting of the American Medical Association to present a paper on distortions of the visual fields.[34] From this point onward the manuscript of the pituitary monograph must have absorbed all of his available time away from the clinic and laboratory, for his bibliography shows that he published no further reports until November 1912 when the third paper in the visual series, this one with Walker, appeared in the *Archives of Ophthalmology*.

The Pituitary Monograph (1912)

Cushing's sixteen years in Baltimore culminated in the publication of a large technical monograph entitled *The pituitary body and its*

[33] "Distortions of the visual fields in cases of brain tumor. Statistical studies." (First paper) (With G. J. Heuer). *Johns Hopkins Hospital Bulletin,* June 1911, *22,* 190-195.

[34] "Distortions of the visual fields in cases of brain tumor." (Second paper) "Dyschromatopsia in relation to stages of choked disk." (With G. J. Heuer). *Journal of the American Medical Association,* 15 July 1911, *57,* 200-208.

disorders, which bore the subtitle "Clinical states produced by disorders of the hypophysis cerebri." The material had originally been presented in December 1910 as a Harvey Lecture in New York, and the book which grew out of the lecture ran to some 350 closely printed pages. His friends abroad joked with him about the length of his lecture, and when the book appeared he had several enquiries about how long he had taken to deliver it. Although it has defects, the monograph stands as a milestone in American medicine, and more particularly in the history of endocrinology, for it introduced a clinical concept of endocrine function which did much to clarify a rapidly growing subject that had not yet taken firm root. With the loss of his father and brother still vividly before him, it was natural that he should inscribe his book: "In loving memory of three physicians: ERASTUS CUSHING (1802-1893)—HENRY K. CUSHING (1827-1910) —EDWARD F. CUSHING (1862-1911)."

The pituitary monograph is based upon a detailed clinical study of fifty cases of endocrine disturbance. All of the things for which Cushing stood in clinical medicine are exemplified in the remarkable case histories of his fifty subjects. The records are full, sometimes almost too full, for a casual reader can easily get lost in the wealth of clinical detail. The book is profusely illustrated (319 figures), and since changes in facial contours constituted an important part of the story he wished to present, photographs of many of his cases are included. Those showing the development of acromegaly in individual cases have become classic and have subsequently been reproduced in many textbooks of endocrinology, physiology, and clinical medicine. There is an almost Germanic thoroughness about the text and an irritating Germanic habit, which he had no doubt picked up in Berne, of letter-spacing words for purposes of emphasis —this, rather than the more usual practice of securing emphasis through the use of italics.

The basic theme of the book and its main contribution have already been outlined in the discussion of acromegaly and gigantism earlier in this chapter. The concept of hypopituitarism is further elaborated, and experience with his nine cases of acromegaly had led him to conclude that the disease tends to be self-limiting in that it starts with a phase of active hyperpituitarism which in the course of time may subside; and with atrophy of the secreting cells of the anterior lobe the patient may pass into a state of *hypo*pituitarism, retaining, however, the features of abnormal bony growth. Since, however, vision may be lost, owing to pressure exerted by the enlarging pituitary gland on the optic nerve, operative relief is generally indicated. Operation thus serves two functions—preservation of vision and conversion of the hyperpituitary state into one of hypopituitarism.

Cushing made a further contribution in that his microscopic studies of the pituitary gland itself, in cases of acromegaly, disclosed a preponderance of cells of a particular type, *i.e.,* cells that stained readily with a dye "eosin" (the cells in question were thus said to exhibit "eosinophilia"). He concluded from this that the growth hormone is elaborated by these eosinophilic cells and that the other cells in the anterior lobe, which are described as "basophilic," probably elaborate some other essential secretion. Cushing's clinical acumen is nowhere better illustrated than in this last conclusion. He did not know what the basophil cells did, but he concluded that they must do something. However, he had to wait twenty years before his ideas crystallized sufficiently for him to recognize the syndrome that now bears his name.

One cannot dismiss the pituitary monograph without brief mention of Cushing's surgical contribution for, until his work appeared, there were few in the surgical world who had the courage to tackle a pituitary operation. After Cushing had shown the way the operation became something of a routine affair which many soon began to undertake. In Cushing's first case the pituitary was approached through the frontal sinuses; but such an approach has two disadvantages—the first being that the frontal sinuses are often infected and meningitis may follow when the cranial cavity is entered through them; the other, that it leaves a cyclopean scar, distasteful especially to women. Cushing found that the pituitary could also be approached satisfactorily by elevating the upper lip and approaching the sphenoidal bone by a submucous dissection of the nasal mucous membrane. This largely removed the hazard of infection and it had the great advantage of leaving no visible scar. In current parlance this operation has come to be known as Cushing's transsphenoidal approach. In cases of marked intracranial extension of the pituitary tumor a more formidable surgical procedure is necessitated, involving a large bone flap similar to that employed for any other brain tumor. Cushing's thinking at this period, as far as pituitary function is concerned, is well summarized in a letter written two years later to a young German medical student, now the distinguished Chicago neuropathologist, Gerhardt von Bonin:

Harvard University,
H.C. to Gerhardt von Bonin *17 February 1913.*

My dear Dr. von Bonin I received your interesting paper a few days ago, and your letter written from Freiburg has followed it. In your letter you express some doubts regarding the explanation of the stages of pituitary disorders. So far as I am aware, the explanation is as follows. There had long been great confusion as to whether acromegaly, Fröhlich's syndrome and so on were expression of over- or of underactivity of the gland. Fröhlich, as you will remember, reported his case as one of *tumor of the pituitary body* without acromegaly, the implication being that it was astonishing that a tumor of the pituitary body could occur without acromegaly, inasmuch as cases of acromegaly were found to be associated with tumor.

The first definite indication of the fact that the syndrome of Fröhlich and other allied syndromes in which adiposity, small stature and so on were due to an hypophysial insufficiency, was furnished by the experiments conducted with Crowe and Homans in the Hunterian Laboratory, which I first mentioned in an address before the American Medical Association at Atlantic City in 1909, under the title of "The Hypophysis Cerebri: Clinical Aspects of Hyperpituitarism and of Hypopituitarism." I cannot believe that before this paper was written anyone had a clear conception of a symptomatology due to hypophysial insufficiency.

Now, in regard to the overlapping of these symptoms—dyspituitarism, in other words—I think that in your paper your meaning is perhaps not quite as clear as it might be, although those who have been working on the subject will understand what you have in mind. I do not feel that hyperpituitarism—that is acromegaly, in its active stages—and hypopituitarism—that is, the expression of hypophysial insufficiency—can go hand in hand, although there may be some symptoms of one or the other condition which are more or less merged as the disorder passes over from glandular overactivity into glandular underactivity. It is in much the same way that hyperthyroidism passes over into hypothyroidism—the patient having some slight manifestations of myxoedema when possibly rapid pulse, exophthalmos and so on are still present.

It is important to remember, of course, that a person who has once become an acromegalic, owing to a glandular hyperplasia (anterior lobe) will always remain an acromegalic, even though the gland, in so far as its activity is concerned, has passed over into a completely inactive condition, so that superimposed on the fixed acromegalic changes in the skeleton there are adiposity, subnormal temperature, high sugar tolerance and so on, characteristic of conditions of glandular insufficiency. In many of our patients with fairly outspoken signs of hypopituitarism by careful skeletal studies we can detect evidences of transient early acromegaly, for these skeletal evidences of course remain fairly fixed [fugitive acromegaly of H.C.'s later papers]. . . . With regards, and trusting that I may have the privilege of meeting you at some time, I am, Very truly yours, HARVEY CUSHING.

To this he received a prompt acknowledgment:

Freiburg [Germany],
Gerhardt von Bonin to H.C. *9 March 1913.*

Dear Professor Cushing Thanks very much for your letter which I got some time ago & which I have read with great interest. I see that my idea about your views was wrong after all, which I had feared already when I read your book on the pituitary, after my paper had gone to the press. But I still think that the theory which I have given in my paper & which was suggested to me mainly by the study of your papers & that of Herring—hence my misrepresentation—will account for the facts, too.

I have just written to Professor [Sir Arthur] Keith who has still another paper of mine in hand, that I should like to work this point out more fully & then publish it somewhere. The main difficulty seems to be that we have not enough accounts of beginning cases of acromegaly. If we should find traces of hypopituitarism there, too, it would be in favour of a "mechanical explanation" (compression of the infundibulum by the growing tumour); if traces of hypopituitarism develop, but *later the acromegalic symptoms became then stationary,* it would speak for your theory. I am unable to get Leonard Mark's autobiography here at Freiburg; he probably gives some data which would be of use in this connection.

The pituitary monograph had an enthusiastic reception, as a result of which Cushing found himself involved in a voluminous correspondence:

981 Madison Avenue, New York,
W. G. MacCallum to H.C. *15 July 1912.*

Dear Harvey Your splendid monograph on Pituitary disorders came today and I've read in it with delight. Accept my very best congratulations. It seems to me quite the most masterly presentation of a medical subject we have had in America. I can't think of anything to compare with it—it is magnificent. I must write to you again about it when I've finished—in the meanwhile my best thanks for it. Sincerely yours, W. G. MacCallum.

Philadelphia,
Weir Mitchell to H.C. *6 November 1912.*

My dear Harvey Cushing: Your book almost persuades me to regret that I have not been a surgeon. I suppose that is the best thing I can say about it, except that as an evidence of regard for me I find it still more valuable. It has one defect in common with a great many other American books. It is printed on paper so heavy that to hold the book long requires previous serious gymnastic training. There is a good deal in it I shall read with care. I see you put three physicians back of you. My son Jack has eight back of him in my family. We have not yet produced a surgeon, but I live in hopes. Yours very truly, Weir Mitchell.

University Club, New York,
M. Allen Starr to H.C. *14 September* [1912].

My dear Dr. Cushing I have spent this morning over your book and I must write and thank you for it—not merely for my copy—but for having worked out the problems and put them so clearly. It is the finest contribution to medical science which has been made in America for many a long year, and will be of service to the world. As I read it several cases occurred to my memory which it explains. Accept my hearty congratulations on it. Sincerely yours, Allen Starr.

Oxford,
Sir William Osler to H.C. *29 July 1912.*

Dear Harvey C. In the first place thanks for your book, which is a *"ripper"* and opens several new chapters in cerebral physiology, to say nothing of metabolism. The figures are excellent. What a lot of work you must have put into it! It is very nice to see the dedication to the three generations but 'tis very sad that poor Ned did not have a chance to live out his days.

I am sending you the three Locke books, the Wotton and the Woolsey; keeping the Sprat and the Napier. They put a *friendly* value on the books—so friendly that I am almost ashamed to take it from them, and quite ashamed to take anything for your share. Don't suppose I would let you have the three Lockes, if I hadn't them! I have heard from Sudhoff that the "Tabulae Sex" is to be reproduced, so that it is not worth while doing anything about it. Sincerely yours, W.O. Love to the darlings, all.

161 Beacon Street [Boston],
John B. Blake to H.C. *26 October 1912.*

My dear Harvey Cushing I have been reading your book about the Pituitary body—and must congratulate you very heartily upon it. One who examines critically medical works, particularly those published in America, cannot fail to be impressed with a lack of literary value which is painful, and an equal lack of system, simplicity and the quality of making new or complicated problems easily understood. On all three of these points your book is a contrast to our familiar text books, for it is logical in arrangement, lucid in exposition, and attractive in literary style. It is a little difficult for some of us to understand how you find time to do so much. Perhaps you intend to show us the method! Sincerely yours, JOHN B. BLAKE.

E. A. Schafer to H.C. *University of Edinburgh, 25 July 1912.*

My dear Harvey Cushing, That is a magnificent book on the Pituitary Body which you have just been good enough to send me. As an amplification of a single lecture it must hold the record! . . . I daresay you are over on this side just now—but as I don't know your whereabouts this must go to America. Why have you never found your way to this place? or to North Berwick? Sincerely yours, E. A. SCHAFER.

1912

Cushing's intellectual curiosity led him into many highways and byways, interesting but unpredictable. His belief that posterior pituitary secretion is discharged into the cerebrospinal fluid led him to study sugar metabolism—a field which he confessed he never fully grasped, even though he and his Harvard classmate Elliott Joslin had frequent discussions about the nature of diabetes. His cases of acromegaly were almost invariably diabetic, and this bothered him not a little, for he never could find an adequate explanation. When Professor Houssay discovered (1933) that an animal could survive the loss of its pancreas if its pituitary gland had previously been removed, H.C. believed the explanation of diabetes in acromegalics was in sight: but he was distressed to think that John Homans, who in 1910 had made an observation similar to that of Houssay's, had evidently just missed the discovery of insulin and also the pituitary pancreatic interrelation. Writing to W. G. MacCallum he recalls Homans' early experiments in this connection:

. . . I am most interested in your case of diabetes which appears to sustain Houssay's experimental findings. You will perhaps recall in the days when Sam Crowe, John Homans and I were working on the pituitary body that we found the animals acquired a marked increase in carbohydrate tolerance (and the same thing was true of patients with pituitary insufficiency) and we began attempting to extirpate the pancreas piece-meal. Unfortunately we never got so far as to attempt a total extirpation for just at this juncture I was transferred to Boston and John Homans went abroad to work with Bayliss and Starling on the pancreas. If he had kept at it I think he might possibly have hit upon insulin for he was pretty close to it. But then, I suppose that was true of many.

Another problem that intrigued him at this time was that of the hibernating animal, and we find him stirring up his friends of the New York Zoological Society by asking that they obtain hibernating rodents for him in the middle of January. W. T. Hornaday, the Director, was somewhat aghast and replied that hibernating animals cannot be caught while they are hibernating because the ground is frozen; they must be trapped when it is warm and be kept until the time for hibernation comes. H.C. and Emil Goetsch became convinced that hibernation had something to do with the pituitary, for a hypophysectomized animal exhibits the type of lethargy displayed by one that is hibernating. They announced their findings in a preliminary note in 1913:[35]

> . . . In a series of hibernating animals (woodchucks) it has been found that during the dormant period the pituitary gland not only diminishes in size but undergoes extreme histological alterations, chiefly evident in the cells of the pars anterior, which completely lose their characteristic differential reactions to acid and basic stains. At the end of the dormant period the gland enlarges and the cells regain their characteristic staining reactions. On the basis of this observation hibernation may be ascribed to a period of physiological inactivity, possibly of the entire ductless gland series, but certainly more especially of the pituitary body, not only for the reason that the changes in this structure are particularly apparent but because deprivation of the secretion of this gland alone of the series produces a train of symptoms comparable to those of hibernation. . . .

H.C.'s excursions into diabetes, hibernation, etc., and his incessant operating caused him to overspend his budget and on being called to account by the Dean he answered with studied naïveté.

H.C. to J. Whitridge Williams *12 January 1912.*

Dear Dr. Williams: I am overwhelmed! We have been doing a lot of work, but I had no idea that we could possibly have run over our allowance, for there has been comparatively little expense connected with the work we are doing, except for stains and things of that kind. Still, there have been half a dozen men working in the laboratory and I suppose they may have cut into the supplies more seriously than usual. However, I should prefer to see the laboratory busy and spending more money than is expected of them than to have no one at work there and keep within the appropriation. I don't see what there is for me to do other than to offer to make up the deficit. We shall certainly need more funds if we are to keep on until next June, and I hereby wish to petition for another five hundred dollars, if this is not out of order. Very truly yours, HARVEY CUSHING.

P.S. Jacobson explains the matter as follows: We pay from our budget for all of the food for *all* of the dogs and even when there is special feeding required. All of the dogs which die before use (and there are many from distemper &c.) are charged to us at 35¢ apiece. There was a $300 hangover from last year's bills recently rendered thro' the office etc. Can we not bring you our books some day at Mr. Coy's office and clarify the situation? H.C.

With the pituitary monograph off his mind and the Harvard decision made, came a general exuberance of spirit which seemed to creep into all of his letters, especially those to Osler. He had decided

[35] "Hibernation and the pituitary body." (With E. Goetsch). *Proceedings of the Society of Experimental Biology, New York,* 1913, *11,* 25-26. Also: "Hibernation and the pituitary body." (With E. Goetsch). *Journal of Experimental Medicine,* 1 July 1915, *22,* 25-47).

to go abroad again with the Society of Clinical Surgery, this time to visit the German clinics, and incidentally to pursue Vesalius in Belgium. He had also received a gratifying invitation to present a major discourse at the International Medical Congress to be held in London in August, 1913. On accepting the invitation he received the following gracious letter from the President of the Congress:[36]

Sir Thomas Barlow to H.C. *10, Wimpole Street, London, 15 January 1912.*

Dear Dr. Cushing I am extremely glad that you can give the address in Surgery at the International in August 1913. Your confrères in Pathology & Medicine respectively will be Ehrlich & Chauffard—a first rate triumvirate! With kind regards, Very truly yours, THOS. BARLOW.

W.O., who no doubt had had a hand in the choice of H.C., wrote (10 Feb.): "As to the Congress, there are only three general addresses —Ehrlich, Chauffard and yourself. You need not be specially alarmed as Chauffard is not so far up the rung as you are—and just about your age. . . . It is a great pity Welch could not be in the Senate; he would own the republican party in about a year!" Another honor which came to H.C. during the year was an invitation to address the National Academy of Sciences on Wednesday, 17 April. He promptly accepted President Remsen's invitation and chose for his topic, "Some observations on the function of the pituitary," in which he once again summarized his latest studies in the field.

The Baltimoreans have always been noted for their epicurean tastes and the group at Hopkins needed only a visitor or an historical meeting as an excuse for arranging a feast. One is surprised that H.C., who cared so little for food, fell in with this custom, but he both gave and attended many of these dinners with apparent enjoyment. Thus in February he arranged a dinner at the Maryland Club in honor of Fielding Garrison, the distinguished medical historian who shared Cushing's literary tastes and with whom through the years he had carried on a voluminous correspondence, principally on historical topics. On 17 February there was a large testimonial dinner at the Hotel Belvedere for Dr. Finney, which H.C. could not forego. He then received these amusing letters from Halsted:

W. S. Halsted to H.C. *16 May 1912.*

Dear Cushing Dr. Welch and I would like to invite some of the members of the Faculty to meet you and McCrae at dinner and had thought of Friday night, the twenty-fourth, as a convenient date if agreeable to both of you. There will be no formalities nor speeches and we shall attempt to be as cheerful as possible under the circumstances. Hoping that you will consent to be our guest and give us the satisfaction of bringing a few of your friends together in this way, I am, Yours as ever, W. S. HALSTED.

[36] Sir Thomas Barlow, who died early in 1945 at the age of 99 years, in addition to his great attainments in clinical medicine had for nearly twenty years the interesting distinction of being the oldest recipient of an honorary degree from Harvard University.

On the next day:

Dear Cushing This will remind you, more or less, of the dinner you have promised to grace at the Maryland Club on Saturday, May the 25th at seven o'clock & thirty minutes. Suicide will not excuse you either for absence or tardiness or unkempt appearance. Yours, W. S. HALSTED.

The farewell dinner for Cushing and McCrae accordingly took place at the Maryland Club on 25 May. McCrae had just accepted the Professorship of Medicine at Jefferson in Philadelphia, and since he and Cushing had originally gone to Baltimore at approximately the same time, their simultaneous departure meant a serious break for the Hopkins faculty. There had been many inducements to remain offered to them, but Osler, always in the background with wise advice, felt that for each one the move was indicated, and he wrote a letter to the effect that a body with no circulation is inevitably dead and he therefore congratulated Hopkins on its revival.

After a paper at Atlantic City in June H.C. was off again for his projected European trip with the Society of Clinical Surgery, a hectic trek through the German clinics. There were seventeen in the party which arrived in Bremen on 18 June, and one wonders how they survived their paralyzing itinerary even though much of it was by motor car:

. . . Hamburg (Kümmell), Berlin (Bier, Körte, *et al.*), Leipzig (Payr), Jena (Lexer), Vienna (von Eiselsberg, Hochenegg, etc.), Munich where in his new Poliklinik we attended one of Friedrich von Müller's famous exercises. From there by train to Tübingen where after a morning with Perthes we proceeded by motor to Stuttgart (Hofmeister), to Heidelberg (Wilms), to Würzburg (Enderlen), Frankfurt (Rehn); and while in Frankfurt we had the unusual privilege of visiting Paul Ehrlich's laboratory and of lunching with him afterward. From Frankfurt we motored down the picturesque Valley of the Rhine to Wiesbaden, stopping on the way at Schwalbach to lunch handsomely with Adolphus Busch and his family; and thus on to Coblenz and finally Bonn to visit Garrè's clinic.

In the midst of this strenuous *Rundreise* he forsook the Society at Berlin to attend on 22 June the *Jubiläum* marking Theodor Kocher's fortieth year as Professor of Surgery at the University of Berne. "A great occasion," he wrote, "music—many tributes—Horsley should have spoken in English, but it was good. . . . The student who presented the great wreath of *Alpenrosen* was particularly thrilling." Leaving Berne, Cushing rejoined the Society the next day at Leipzig.

The 10th of July found H.C. in London on his way to Oxford and the following day a prompt account of the visit was sent from 13 Norham Gardens:

Lady Osler to K.C.

Dearest Kate, Our two Vesalius lunatics are deep in the book shelves in the hall & I must send you a line to tell you how I wish you were here. We were delighted to find Harvey could come today and we hope to keep him until Saturday morning. I have never seen him look so well—he is almost fat—and just as dear as ever. I am so glad to hear about the Brookline house—asparagus bed —toothless chauffeur—and everything. Somehow I feel as though you would be nearer in Boston than in Baltimore. . . .

A few random entries from his diary tell the rest:

July 11th, Oxford. We motored back to Oxford and had a cozy dinner as Mrs. O. had promised—in the open air—light until 9.30—still as a forest, the quiet only accentuated by Big Tom's 101 strokes for Woolsey's 101 scholars at 9 o'clock when Oxford gates are closed. An hour with Dr. O.'s books which I gather he is to give to Montreal. They are being splendidly catalogued—and have burst from the Library into the hall.

A set of old anatomical *Blätter* with superimposed fragments on the body—one the male figures—with the head of Vesalius taken from the Calcar plate. This we took the next day to Horace Hart for a photo. Lang wanted an outrageous price for them. One was a picture of a boy with haemophilia.

July 12th, Oxford. Morning at Bodleian where Dr. O. still retains the Stirling-Maxwell *Tab. Sex.* Some talk of reproducing them again. An adventurous time looking up the Vesal items in the Bodley library—entries pasted in the large vols. of the catalogue. No 1543 *Fabrica.* We called for the volumes containing the *Concilia* of Vesal. . . . Later in an attempt to see the Borgarutius volumes, two of which had been catalogued, I was held up by some species of red tape—Sir Wm. having gone. I had difficulty in explaining my presence in the inner sanctum for readers and my presumption in using Sir Wm. Osler's name in calling for books. [Sir William had been knighted at the time of the coronation in 1911.] . . . However I had the great satisfaction in pointing out to the sub-librarian that their darn catalogue was wrong for the 1st item catalogued as a Borgarutius of 1552 proved to be the pocket edition of Vesal: *Lugduni Ap. Joan Tornaesium* 1552.

. . . Later on I got lost in a crypt of a bookshop behind the Mitre Hotel. . . . Subsequently Dr. O. and I went to the Christ Church Library where we had some discussion about the Vesal portrait. We looked through the Leonardo drawings and to kill time during a shower we went through their quite interesting collection of medical works in the 'Wake' library. There were many 2nd hand duplicates which we looked over—Napier's mathematics &c. [which W.O. later gave to the Yale Elizabethan Club]. Again a delightful dinner in the open air, then I hied me to town [London] at 9.30 heavily laden with books, fishing tackle for Willie and memories of a charming visit.

The next day (13 July) he sailed from Liverpool, much refreshed by his month's holiday, strenuous though it had been; and he was thus ready to cope with all the problems that were sure to beset him in his new post. Before he knew it the goods and chattels at 107 East Chase Street were being packed up, along with four babies and Mrs. Cushing, for the move to Boston where they settled, toward the end of September, at 305 Walnut Street in Brookline near the Sargent estate.

CHAPTER X

Academic Calls. Planning a University Hospital

1902–1912

FOLLOWING Cushing's return from Europe in 1901 he had many opportunities to accept positions in other institutions. His first call had come from the University of Maryland where Dr. L. E. Neale had suggested him for the chair of surgery in June 1902. Bloodgood, his predecessor as Halsted's resident, was first offered the post, but they both declined, and Cushing later explained: "It would have been a good post for either Bloodgood or myself but I presume we both asked for more than they could give." In February 1904 he was approached again—this time by W. W. Keen, the vigorous Professor of Surgery at Jefferson Medical College in Philadelphia, who had collaborated with Weir Mitchell and Morehouse in the well-known study of gunshot wounds in the Civil War, and who was Cushing's principal predecessor in neurosurgery in this country. Since H.C. had been invited to present papers in Philadelphia several times, the local profession was well informed about his work, and Keen was especially impressed by his talents. Cushing was therefore his natural choice for a successor when he reached the statutory age of retirement. H.C. considered the matter for two years, but there is no record of the negotiations since they were evidently carried on by word of mouth or through handwritten letters which were not preserved. The letter tendering his formal regrets was discovered and returned by Miss Florence Keen after her father died in 1933:

H.C. to W. W. Keen *13 March 1906.*

Dear Dr. Keen I have thought the matter over very seriously and though the offer is a most alluring one I think it would be unwise for me to accept it. My admiration for and fondness of you is such that my decision has been especially hard to make and I know of nothing that could have given me greater satisfaction than the feeling that in a measure I was about to succeed one whose record almost more than any other I would like to emulate.

The reasons need not be reviewed and you know me well enough to know that I have not lightly considered the matter. I may be able better to explain the reasons for my determination when next we meet. May it be soon and often. I regard your confidences of course as eminently personal. I have spoken to Dr. Welch, Dr. Osler and Mrs. C. of course, and it should go no further. Ever gratefully and affectionately yours, HARVEY CUSHING.

Keen was much disappointed and the next day replied: "I suppose that your letter must be considered as final though I do so with a great deal of reluctance. You know how warmly I feel about you and how earnestly desirous for you to come here—so much so that I offered . . . to resign if you would come and take my place."

There followed during the years 1906 to 1909 urgent invitations to attractive posts at Charlottesville, Virginia, the New York Hospital, Yale University, New York University (Bellevue Hospital), and Washington University at St. Louis. He refused all of these calls, after due consideration, hesitating the longest over the one from his alma mater, doubtless the most gratifying. In February 1906 Cushing had been invited to speak at New Haven. Mr. Hadley, who had unfortunately been out of town at the time, wrote him that, "All Yale men are proud of the work you are doing: and I only wish that I were able to congratulate you on it in person instead of by letter." On 5 April, President Hadley followed this with a definite proposal:

3 W. Franklin St.
~~1018 North Calvert Street~~

Dear Dr. Keen.

I have thought the matter over very seriously and though the offer is a most alluring one I think it would be unwise for me to accept it. My admiration for and fondness of you is such that my decision

CUSHING TO W. W. KEEN
H.C.'s letter regretting the call to become Dr. Keen's successor at Jefferson

My dear Dr. Cushing: By vote of the Executive Board of the Medical School, I write to ask if you could come on here to talk over the possibility of accepting a professorship of surgery in the Yale Medical School. To put the School on the right level we need above all things else one or two men in surgery and in medicine of just the type that you represent. It is very hard to find such men; and I was greatly pleased when I heard that circumstances were such that we might properly extend an invitation of this kind. I do not know whether we can do the things that are requisite to make the place attractive to you; but I do know that we shall make every effort to bring about this result. . . .

Cushing visited New Haven in response to this letter and after his return to Baltimore complied with Mr. Hadley's request for a statement concerning the Yale Medical School in a rather detailed letter which is of interest, not only to Yale and its alumni, but to those concerned with the larger problems of medical education and the hospital-medical school relationship:

H.C. to President Hadley *30 April 1906.*

Dear Mr. Hadley: I promised to make a statement of my views in regard to the Medical School in so far as the conditions there bear upon the clinical positions which you wish to see filled. In the first place, I see no reason why a School of the first rank in all of its departments should not exist at New Haven. There seems to be an opinion that the city is too small to support with sufficient clinical material the last two years of a large medical school, and that for this reason the main effort should be directed towards perfecting the course in the preclinical years, with the idea that most students are likely to go to larger centres for the completion of their medical course. I think in many respects this view is not well grounded. In my estimation, the day is not far distant when, as is the case in Germany, the small select schools in relatively small cities will become those whose degrees are most sought after by the best class of students. Indeed, were it wise to provide for such a division of a course as has been suggested, it would be better for students to be gathered in large cities for their preclinical years of work, and to scatter in smaller places for their practical work in the clinic. It is not an abundance of patients that makes for the most successful clinical teaching, but the way in which the small number is utilized as a means of instruction. In cities even smaller than New Haven there is plenty of teaching material for the clinical years if only it can be made available.

As a Yale student I would rather see no School of Medicine at New Haven than a half-way one, and I believe furthermore that the aim should be to put the School on such a footing that it will attract students from outside rather than so to modify the course in the undergraduate departments that your own 'Sheff' and academic students will make the chief number of those who are encouraged to take their medical degrees at Yale. It is, in my opinion, the reputation and traditions of a university as a whole which in large measure bring students to its undergraduate departments. It is otherwise in a professional school, where students are likely to be attracted more by the reputation of the individuals who may be teaching than by the School in which they teach.

So far as I could see during my brief visit, the one pressing need of the School is a hospital with a continuous service for those occupying the clinical Chairs. Without a hospital in which they have clinical and teaching privileges *the year round,* clinical professors are as destitute of opportunities for instruction and investigation as a chemist or a physicist would be without a laboratory. And without such a hospital a medical school can hardly expect to develop. Then from a hospital point of view, nothing so certainly assures its growth and reputation as such an alliance, for unless it be primarily a teaching institution and issue publications, it can hardly have more than a local reputation. Whether it will be possible to influence the Directors of the New Haven Hospital to put its wards or a part of them to such use, or whether it will be possible to raise funds to build a University Hospital remains with you to determine. Assuredly here lies the crux of the situation. The present new Dispensary offers excellent opportunities, so far as they go, but a dispensary, aside from the care of minor or 'ambulatory' ailments, is merely a feeder to a hospital, and the patients who go through this dispensary (under the direct control of the School) are, under present conditions, distributed to a hospital and come under the care of physicians and surgeons *not* directly connected with the School and so are lost to the School as teaching material except during a very small part of the year.

A further need is for more mature students with whom to work—students who in their fourth year could safely have the freedom of hospital wards and benefit by the free opportunities of working there. This would mean raising the requirements for admission and would for a time lessen the number in the entering classes. To graduate, each year, a small number—let us say at the outside 25—of well-trained men who could readily secure hospital and teaching positions elsewhere, would soon place the School in a position it could never attain if its energies were expended in handling large classes—so large as to prohibit much personal contact with instructors. This doubtless would be expensive, and whether the university at this time would feel able to afford it, I do not know; but it would certainly not be an experiment.

From the standpoint of a clinical teacher the salary which is proposed for the Professor of Surgery and a teaching assistant would be considered sufficiently generous, but without the assurance of a continuous hospital service with private-ward privileges, in an institution directly under the control of or closely affiliated with the Medical School, much as I would like to accept this position in my own college town, I do not feel that the opportunities for clinical investigation and instruction are at present sufficient to justify my giving up those which I already enjoy in Baltimore. Very respectfully yours, HARVEY CUSHING.

Mr. Hadley did not conclude from this letter that the issue was closed, and further negotiations continued throughout 1906 with many exchanges between H.C., Mr. Hadley, and Professor Herbert E. Smith, then Dean of the Yale Medical Faculty, but in February and March 1907 Mr. Hadley pressed H.C. for a definite reply. Meanwhile his friends at Harvard were beginning to importune him about considering a chair of surgery there and he remembered a hint which he had had in 1903 from Councilman, the pathologist at Harvard Medical School and one of his warmest friends and advocates—"I think that medicine and surgery are going to have an awakening here in a short time and that there will be a chance for outside men." After other, more definite letters from Councilman and encouragement also from J. G. Mumford, who had been a close and loyal friend since their M.G.H. days, he finally wrote Mr. Hadley with mixed feelings. Much as he hated to turn down Yale, which had come to mean so much in his life, he finally did so, largely on the basis of the fact that the New Haven Hospital was not a university hospital, and the Medical School, in consequence, was not in a position to use the clinical material effectively for teaching or research:

H.C. to President Hadley *21 March 1907.*

Dear Mr. Hadley: It has been a very difficult matter for me to decide, and it is with many regrets that, after this long delay, I must finally say that I think it would be unwise for me to accept the position. My feeling of loyalty to my college, your cordial and flattering invitation, the knowledge that you yourself and my many other friends on the faculty would do all in their power to aid Dean Smith and his new associates in an earnest effort to put the school on a better basis, the promise of a new regime at the New Haven Hospital, Blumer's presence, my belief in the advantages to a teacher of a somewhat peripatetic existence, the attraction which living in a place like New Haven holds out to both Mrs. Cushing and myself—all these things and more have influenced me in the desire to ally myself with the Yale Medical School.

On the other hand, I do not feel that the outlook is sufficient to justify me in giving up my present post for the one which is offered at New Haven. As matters stand, I can see that, for some years at least, the incumbent of the chair at Yale, if he does his duty as a university servant, will needs give up his entire time to the reorganization of clinical teaching under circumstances which are as yet unfavorable to the task; in an institution not under the control of the school, with far too few public patients at his disposal, and with students as yet not recognized as a necessary part of a hospital organization.

These things can doubtless be changed in time, but in the interim, which may be long, he must give himself over largely to the impossible methods of teaching clinical medicine by lectures and recitations, and further must devote much of his energies to the extra-mural establishment of an expensive operating plant where he may serve such of the community as wish to consult him privately. To do full duty toward his teaching position the occupant of one of the clinical chairs should have, I think, the privilege of concentrating all his energies under one roof, for only in this way can he add to the repute of his university, his school and his hospital. Under the other, the divided arrangement, his professional duties are almost certain to become subordinated to his outside professional ones.

As I am situated here I can give almost all of my working time to the University as a teacher and investigator, and see my private patients in the same hospital in which I do my clinical teaching. My professional income is made with but slight interruption to my more important duties. Even if it should be possible in a few years to bring about such rearrangements as I think are necessary in order to put the clinical teaching on the plane where we all wish to see it, I would certainly be deprived in the meantime from continuing such investigations as I have been able to make in my especial branch of surgery. After an interruption of a few years, should the local conditions at New Haven so change that I could then carry lightly the responsibilities of the university position and be able to turn much of the routine work over to trained assistants, I would, in all probability, be unable to resume this work, even should I then have the clinical material and the laboratory facilities which are necessary for its furtherance. It is presumably this very work which has given me a professional prominence sufficient to justify you in offering me this important post, and I am loath to give it up entirely. I feel that possibly I can do more good in my profession by a continuance, for the present at least, of this special work than I can by enrolling myself as a teacher of general surgery and by occupying a chair which could be held as well, perhaps better, by many others.

I am confident, as I said before, that if the effort is made in the right direction the school at New Haven may become—as the university medical schools at Madison, Cleveland and Charlottesville are already becoming—one of the choice schools in the country and one which will be greatly preferred not only by students of the highest rank, but by teachers, to any of the institutions in the larger cities. Such a condition has come to pass in Germany, where the better men choose to remain connected with the medical departments of the smaller universities rather than go to schools in metropolitan centers. To accomplish this a strictly university hospital is needed and a large endowment is necessary, for a small school is relatively more expensive than a large one.

I hope that you may be able to bring this about during the time of your presidency, and I deeply regret my inability, under the present circumstances, to be of direct aid to you in such a movement by coming to New Haven. If in any way whatever, by helping you in choosing some other man for the position or by advice of any sort in regard to the clinical work in the school or in the hospital, I may be of any service I sincerely trust that you will call upon me.

I regret very much that it has taken me such a long time to formulate these conclusions, and I hope that the delay will not have inconvenienced you to any great degree. Again thanking you for your kindness and consideration in the matter, I remain, Very respectfully yours, HARVEY CUSHING.

While Cushing had been considering the Yale offer, news had slipped out of Harvard's windfall in gaining control of the estate of Peter Bent Brigham. Brigham, a merchant of Boston born in Bakersfield, Vermont, had risen from peddling fish on the streets of Boston to be a financier of some eminence, leaving a fortune of $1,300,000. His will stipulated that the property should be kept as a trust for twenty-five years and then, after full payment of all of the estate's liabilities, "my said executors shall dispose of said rest and residue of my property and estate and of all the interest and accumulations which have accrued thereon for the purpose of founding of a hospital in said Boston, to be called the Brigham Hospital for the care of sick persons in indigent circumstances residing in the said County of Suffolk." The estate had been placed in the able hands of Mr. Robert Codman and by 1902 it amounted to $4,000,000. Since construction of the hospital did not commence until 1911, the assets were then sufficient to provide a maintenance fund of $5,000,000 after building costs of $1,250,000 had been met. For Harvard the opportunity was ideal—a university hospital which could be placed largely under the control of the Medical School so that all clinical material would be available for teaching. Welch, who evidently knew what was going on behind the scenes, arranged to have H.C. meet with Billings, who was advising the Peter Bent Brigham architects: "This is just to remind you of the dinner at the Maryland Club on Thursday, the 21st, at quarter before eight, when Dr. Billings is coming to discuss the plans of the Brigham Hospital." At the top of the page on which this letter is pasted, H.C. has written: "The plot thickens."

Two weeks later a halting enquiry was sent to Councilman in which mention is made of the rumor that he was about to be considered for the Brigham Hospital. He also stated that Yale had acceded to all his stipulations, "and they have now renewed their advances in a way which I find hard to refuse." Councilman's reply was frank:

Harvard Medical School,
W. T. Councilman to H.C. *7 March 1907.*

My dear Cushing: . . . The Brigham Hospital trustees have bought the land they need. The general plans for the hospital have been agreed upon. An architectural competition will be held and probably building operations will be started this autumn. There is no man here who would be considered for the position of surgeon save possibly Nichols. It would be difficult to have him appointed and the appointment would arouse a storm of opposition. He does not expect the appointment. So far as I know you are the only man who would be considered for the place now. Carrel is nothing but a very expert sew-er.

I have tried to have you appointed so that the Surgical Department of the hospital could be formed by you. But they will not do this. I presume the trustees will be ready to make an appointment in two or possibly three years. Billings is not going to hurry the construction of the hospital and there is a certain advantage in this, for the laboratories here are growing and forming a basis for the hospital. The spirit of the place is admirable and there is a fine body of young men. I never expected again to see the Hopkins enthusiasm and spirit of work repeated but it is here now. "Everybody works but Father" & even he has hardly time for lunch. I do not believe there is any doubt the appointment will be tendered you. Some man might arise but there is no sign of him.

As for your plans I cannot advise. The experience of two or three years at Yale might be good for you & would certainly be good for them. There might be danger for you in it, and it would mean hard work with but little to show for it. I am going to violate your confidence in showing your letter to Dr. Walcott and telling him what I have written you. It will go no further. Sincerely yours, W. T. COUNCILMAN.

Councilman must also have informed Cushing's friend, J. G. Mumford of H.C.'s uncertainties, for on the same day Mumford wrote in a similar vein:

29 Commonwealth Avenue, Boston,
7 March 1907.

Dear Harvey Here's a confidential word regarding plans: It must have been evident to you that your friends here, Dr. Warren, Allie Porter and your humble servant, have long been striving to bring about an arrangement by which you might be called to a Chair of Surgery at Harvard. Various interests and governing bodies have had to be consulted and advised with, and progress has been slow. As you know, the proposition involves, of course, your appointment as Surgeon to the projected Brigham Hospital. Allie and I have worked out a rather simple plan, which is now being considered by the authorities, but before pressing it further I am writing to you, without other authority than my own, to ask your opinion of it. Essentially it is this:

That on Dr. Warren's present retirement, there be continued the three professors, Bradford, Richardson, and Burrell, and that you be added—making four; that the 4 hold equal rank; that they choose from among themselves a Chairman or Dean; that Richardson continue in charge of M.G.H. teaching and Burrell of B.C.H.; that the four reorganize the general teaching scheme—especially the didactic work, laboratory work, animal work, neurological surgery etc., with reference to your interests; that pending the erection of the Brigham, in which you should have a hand, the Brigham people might open a surgical dispensary somewhere; and that you be given beds at the M.G.H. until your own hospital is completed. . . .

Mumford followed with two further letters that shed important light on developments at the Brigham and on the plans and hopes of H.C.'s friends in Boston for his transfer to the Harvard Medical School:

9 March 1907.

Dear Harvey I have your good note, and appreciate keenly the difficulty of your position. I wish I were so placed as to give you definite and final advice, and not to add baseless rumors to your troubles (the younger men here do want you). On Monday, the 11th, the Harvard Corporation will meet. Probably they will take some action. Hadley's ultimatum expires on Wednesday next. Wait until the 18th, at least, before you reply to New Haven. By then I hope to have some news for you—one way or the other. You are a good philosopher, Lad; and I am leaving no stone unturned to bring you to Boston. But who am I? Thine, always aff'y J.G.M.

J. G. Mumford to H.C. *17 March 1907.*

Dear Harvey Here is the situation, so far as I can get at it after some considerable talk with members of the Corporation and others—unofficial talk, be it said. The Corporation cannot be hurried. Mr. Eliot is on the seas. The Hospital Trustees are slow and difficult. All of these folk are thinking, but nothing is doing. Dr. Warren has resigned. No man can say what will be the outcome of it all. The Yale ultimatum of March 20th adds to the difficulties.

I feel therefore that I cannot rightly advise you, but I can add this thought, in which I believe I am not mistaken; if you go to New Haven, or if you do not—the attitude of the Harvard Corporation will not alter as regards yourself. Should they decide to call you they will do so wherever you are. . . .

News of the negotiations with Harvard and Yale had spread, and many Baltimore friends implored him to put aside any thought of leaving Baltimore. Adolf Meyer's letter is typical:

My dear Cushing Do *not* break loose from us! Map out under what conditions you can stay with us in Baltimore in an absolutely well defined and undisturbed sphere which is yours and which can give us an outlook to a truly efficient and determined plan for a school of neurology & psychiatry. The thought of your going away would cut sadly into my hopes. Why load yourself down with a deadly amount of heterogeneous surgery & administrative responsibility when we need you & your work so in the field of your own choice! I know it takes courage to stick to true efficiency and happiness and to turn down the glaring imagery of ever burdensome independence. Make your conditions known to your friends so that we know how to attain our common aim.

In December of 1909 his old friend, I. McD. Garfield, another loyal supporter of the movement to effect his transfer to Boston, was appointed to the Board of Trustees of the as yet nonexistent Peter Bent Brigham Hospital. As the full plans of the Brigham Trustees were disclosed, H.C. became more and more strongly attracted by the opportunity. In the meantime, however, he was beset by another tempting offer—the one from Washington University in St. Louis. With encouragement from the Carnegie Foundation, Washington University had obtained more than $2,000,000 endowment from Messrs. W. K. Bixby, Adolphus Busch, Edward Mallinkrodt, and Robert Brookings for the reorganization of their school on a full-time basis similar to that of Johns Hopkins. They were out for the best, and H.C. was high on their list of choices. The proposal was first made early in January by Abraham Flexner as head of the Carnegie Foundation for the Advancement of Teaching. On 25 January he asked H.C. again "how the St. Louis thing looks." There followed three letters from the Chancellor of Washington University, D. F. Houston, and then a final appeal from Mr. Flexner, who tried personally to induce Cushing to accept. H.C. left things open with St. Louis until sometime between 25 April and 1 May, but evidently he then withdrew, for *Science* for 6 May 1910 announced the new appointments at Washington University as George Dock of Tulane,

John Howland of Bellevue, Eugene Opie of the Rockefeller Institute, and Joseph Erlanger of Wisconsin.

Word of this was also circulated and precipitated a letter from Lowell, the new president of Harvard, the first official letter that had come from the University:

Harvard University,
President Lowell to H.C. *29 March 1910.*

Dear Sir: Hearing that a very tempting invitation has been made to you from Washington University, St. Louis, I write to say that you will probably receive within a few days an invitation to take a professorship at Harvard, and the position of Chief Surgeon in the new Brigham Hospital. This position will give great opportunities of usefulness. Perhaps you may think me indiscreet in writing, before I have a definite offer to make, but I do so in order that you may not accept one offer without knowing of the other. Yours very truly, A. LAWRENCE LOWELL.

The negotiations with the Brigham Trustees and with Mr. Lowell continued in April. Dr. Frederick C. Shattuck put Cushing's mind at ease on the 9th, and on the 12th formal letters came both from Mr. Lowell, as President of Harvard, and from Mr. Alexander Cochrane, President of the Brigham Trustees:

Boston,
Frederick C. Shattuck to H.C. *9 April 1910.*

Dear Cushing There is a good reason why you had not heard officially from Harvard University when I was in Baltimore, namely, that your nomination had to be acted upon by the Overseers and they at that time had had no meeting. I quite forgot that concurrent action on their part was necessary. This is the whole explanation of the delay. The desire that you should come to us is as unanimous as it is strong. Yours sincerely, FRED'K C. SHATTUCK.

President Lowell to H.C. *12 April 1910.*

Dear Dr. Cushing You will, I understand, receive forthwith a communication from the Trustees of the Brigham Hospital, and I write to say that if you accept the place of Chief Surgeon at the Hospital, the Corporation will at the same time appoint you Professor in the Harvard Medical School. Although the two bodies are acting in cooperation, they are acting independently, and the Trustees of the Hospital prefer that my communication to you should be made independently, Yours very truly, A. LAWRENCE LOWELL.

Alexander Cochrane to H.C. *12 April 1910.*

Dear Dr. Cushing At a meeting of the Trustees of the Peter Bent Brigham Hospital held April 11th, it was voted to authorize the President to communicate with you with a view of your appointment as Surgeon-in-Chief of the Peter Bent Brigham Hospital. The Trustees unanimously hope that you will accept and that mutually satisfactory arrangements can be made as to your position. Your active duties will be delayed until the hospital is completed which we hope will be as soon as possible. . . .

Throughout these negotiations there seemed to be uncertainty in everyone's mind concerning the precise relation of the Moseley Professorship of Surgery at Harvard and the Brigham Hospital to the rest of the Surgical Department, in which there were already three full professors and six assistant professors. Mumford had suggested a rotating chairmanship (7 March). John Collins Warren touched upon the subject in a letter written on 14 April, and, although it is not so stated, H.C. was led to believe from Mr. Lowell's letter of the 18th that he was to be head of the department:

President Lowell to H.C. *18 April 1910.*

Dear Dr. Cushing: The professorship would be a professorship of surgery, and would involve surgical teaching in the Medical School. I meant to have said to you the other day that if you accept the position in the Hospital you will be recommended at once for appointment as professor to take effect whenever you are ready to undertake the duties, which will be, of course, when the Brigham Hospital is ready for occupancy, unless you prefer to come sooner. Yours very truly, A. LAWRENCE LOWELL.

The phraseology of this letter, however, left him in doubt, and he accordingly drafted a letter on the 22d putting the question directly, but he eventually decided against it for on the original copy preserved among his papers he has written: "This letter was apparently not sent. It would have been better if it had been."

H.C. to President Lowell *22 April 1910.*

Dear Mr. Lowell Please forgive me for writing again to ask for a little more specific information in regard to the professorship. I do not expect this to be more than a confidential statement, but I shall, of course, wish to know whether the proposed professorship is presumed to indicate the head of the surgical department. Very respectfully yours, HARVEY CUSHING.

Knowing what was going on, Osler cabled on the 20th "DO ACCEPT HARVARD." He received similar advice from many other friends, including "Allie" Porter, his friend of M.G.H. days. Finally, after many further exchanges, he submitted his formal acceptance to Mr. Lowell, evidently on 17 May. Thus at the age of forty-one Cushing was appointed to the senior chair of surgery at Harvard.

A horde of congratulatory letters arrived and the public press for 24 May carried detailed notices. A few excerpts will give some indication of the great spontaneous enthusiasm evinced by some of his closest friends:

From Mumford: Your rejoiceful note about the Brigham has just come, and truly I find it hard to express my satisfaction that my labors of the past six years, at last, have come to fruition. How's that? To the deuce with Christmas and Halley's comet. You know, old man, that I'm a bit of a sentimentalist; so that the fact of my having here in Boston my closest friend in the profession is a very great happiness. You probably know something of the situation here, and of the chill which, in this conventional community, must oppress a man of any sort of vision. Then, you know, there are many sides to the program—the social, as well as the professional—and Helen rejoices with me that Kate and the children, as well as your simple self, are to dwell in our midst. Helen is even now about writing to your dear lady. . . .

From Councilman: I am perfectly delighted. . . . Every one will be glad—there is every disposition here to give you what you want. With you and Christian at the wheel the new hospital should start out under the best conditions. What we particularly need at the school is some influence to bring the clinic and the laboratory classes together and I think you and your work will be that influence. I had just read your splendid hypophysis work when your letter came. . . .

From S. Flexner: What a lucky girl Miss Brigham is! She has my sincerest felicitations. Well, well, so Boston and Harvard are really to have you and a regenerated surgery. It is splendid for you both. You will have a chance for a great work there and I do not see how you could decline the opportunity. . . .

From Codman: I was delighted with your little note. Not only pleased for you, for Boston, and the Harvard Medical School, but inwardly tickled with my own good judgment in picking out the man for the job nearly 20 years ago when I first saw you. . . .

From Hurd: My congratulations on the arrival of the boy [the Cushings' second son, Henry] and my regrets that you are to go away from us! Knowing with what rapidity hospitals are not built I am hoping that the Peter Bent Brigham replica will not be ready for business by 1912 and that we may be called upon "to bear with you" for a longer time.

From Halsted: . . . My sincerest congratulations. I believe you have made the wiser choice.

From Crile: I was delighted today to hear from Ned that you are to go to Boston. Please accept my warmest congratulations. Think of the meeting of the Clinical Society in your brand new workshop—what a house warming we will give you.

From J. C. Warren: I need not say that I was delighted to get your letter. I congratulate Harvard most heartily. I believe that, from your point of view, you have made a very wise decision. Dr. Councilman and I are very optimistic about the future of the Medical School, as the result of the receipt of this news.

From M. H. Richardson: . . . I shall be most happy to see you and to do all I can to help you in starting out. Any changes that you may contemplate when you come you may be desirous of starting early. I may be able to help you by anticipation. There is as much enthusiasm in the Department as has ever been. . . .

From Cannon: Yerkes and I have been rejoicing together over the great news that Dr. Councilman has conveyed to us. I am more happy about your coming here than I can express. It means a new life and a stirring into activity of agencies for medical and surgical improvement that have needed the enthusiasm you can bring. I hope that physiology may help in the rejuvenation and be in turn benefitted by it. . . .

From Dock: I assure you we are all very sorry that Boston is too much for you. I was afraid when I heard the East a-callin' our chance was gone. However, I hoped that the Boston people might not be able to offer you as much freedom as you would have had in St. Louis. . . .

From Welch: My hearty congratulations to you and to Harvard. You know how we all feel about losing you, and how glad we would be to do anything possible to keep you. . . .

From Kelly: My heartfelt congratulations even tho' we must lose you. The Harvard Chair is the position of greatest dignity in the country to say nothing of the unlimited opportunities. I wish I were young enough and you had the chance to say "come go with me and be gynecologist there!" . . .

THE TARBELL PORTRAIT

The inset in the upper left corner is the photograph which the artist had evidently used in lieu of sittings

DR. CUSHING AND BETSEY IN 1910

MRS. CUSHING AND CHILDREN IN 1910

THE 'TABULAE SEX' OF VESALIUS

On his visit to Venice in 1909 H.C. photographed each page of the San Marco copy of Vesalius' first anatomical tables—one of the two copies known to exist

MRS. CUSHING AND SIR HENRY HEAD

One of H.C.'s photographs taken at the Budapest Congress in August 1909

Before onset of disease

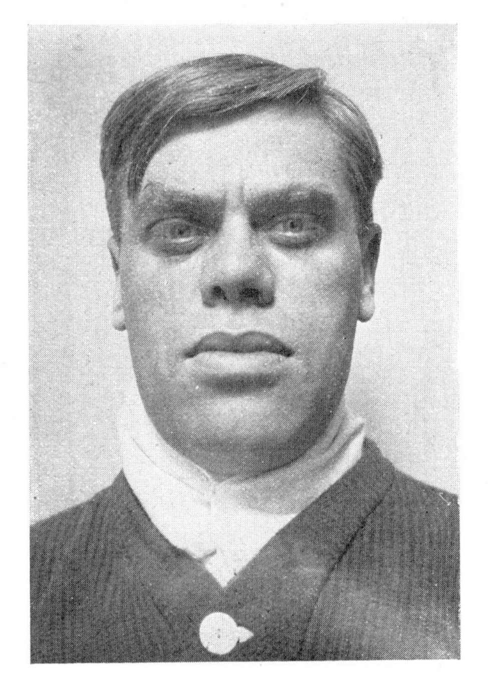

Before operation

After operation

DEVELOPMENT OF ACROMEGALY

From photographs of the first case of acromegaly which Cushing dealt with surgically

From Osler: It is delightful to hear that you have settled upon Boston, where I am sure you and Kate will be very happy. There will be trials and tribulations of course at the medical school; I cannot understand why they should not have made proper arrangements. I am sure all will turn out satisfactorily in the long run. . . .

From Charles Eliot: . . . I think you and Dr. Christian will have a really good chance, under the Brigham Trustees, to conduct a hospital in the best interests, first, of the patients, secondly, of medical teaching, and thirdly, of medical research. To associate successfully these three humane works in eastern Massachusetts will be a great achievement. . . .

When Cushing was first appointed, the Moseley Professorship of Surgery at Harvard Medical School was not vacant. On John Collins Warren's retirement from the Moseley Professorship in 1907, Maurice Richardson had been appointed in his place. A warm friendship had developed out of Cushing's admiration for Richardson in medical school days and on 19 July 1907 Richardson had written: "My appointment to the professorship was a great surprise to me, for I concurred fully with the views of my friends that, with the new Medical School[1] under the control of the faculty, we ought to call to Boston a younger man, and put him in charge of the new hospital. This, I have no doubt, will be done in the near future; but it probably seemed to the corporation that it would be so long before this desirable event could take place that it would be better in the meantime to put in my unworthy self to fill the Moseley Professorship. I cannot see any other reason why they should have done so." Richardson had indicated that he was prepared to resign when H.C. took over. Had he done this, however, there would have been hard feeling in many quarters, as Robert Greenough indicated when writing to congratulate H.C. on his decision to come to Harvard.

377 Beacon Street, Boston,
Robert B. Greenough to H.C. *22 May 1910.*

Dear Harvey I got home safely to my admiring family and found your news had leaked already from Mr. Lowell's letter, and therein there was something of an excitement because I understand you said to Mr. Lowell that you understood that Dr. Richardson was to give up the Moseley Professorship in two years. Perhaps that was not what you said, but Dr. Walcott (and Dr. Richardson) who saw the letter understood it so. As a fact I think I told you in speaking of Dr. Richardson's health that I did not believe he could keep up his school and hospital work for two years more, but his age (57 or 58) will give him four more years if he is able to take them. He has repeatedly threatened to resign and said that he was ready to do so when his resignation was desired, but he apparently does not relish the idea that anyone should think him *obliged* to give up before his time.

I am writing thus fully, as I imagine that something might be said or written

[1] The new Harvard Medical School buildings on Longwood Avenue had been dedicated in September 1906. Plans for the Brigham Hospital developed immediately thereafter.

to you on the subject, and I thought you might be forewarned. One cannot well say to Dr. R. that one does not estimate his chances of being able to do his work for more than two years as good, however much that may be the case. With this exception, everyone is pleased as can be at your decision, and accepts it as a promise of better days to come. . . .

In June H.C. received formal notice of his appointment as University Professor of Surgery:

President Lowell to H.C. *14 June 1910.*

Dear Dr. Cushing . . . At the meeting of the Corporation yesterday you were elected University Professor of Surgery, your salary to begin whenever you take up your duties. As it was your desire to have eventually the Moseley Professorship now held by Dr. Richardson, when he retires, and as in the meanwhile it is thought very desirable that you should hold a Professorship in the School, it was thought wise to elect you at once a University Professor in this way. I hope that this course meets with your approval. It seems to me it carries out your ideas as I understood them the other day. It creates for you an additional place which disappears as soon as you take up the Moseley Professorship.[2] I shall have occasion to consult you later more in detail about appointments in the Surgical Department. Very truly yours,
A. LAWRENCE LOWELL.

Office of the
President and Fellows
of Harvard College.
30 State Street, Boston December 11th, 1912.

Sir

I beg to inform you that on the 7th day of October you were elected by the President and Fellows

Moseley Professor of Surgery

from September 1, 1912 and that this election was duly confirmed by the Board of Overseers at their meeting of December 11th, 1912.

Your obedient servant,
G. Peabody Gardner
Secretary.

Professor Harvey Cushing,

APPOINTMENT AS MOSELEY PROFESSOR

The official notice of appointment to the Moseley Chair as from 1 September 1912

During the summer Mr. Lowell, Dr. Richardson, and H.C. agreed on the plan for a committee administration of the department of surgery during the two-year interval, 1910-1912, while the hospital was being constructed.

The Peter Bent Brigham Hospital

In his letter of instructions to his Trustees, Mr. Johns Hopkins provided that the hospital which he had endowed should be a part of the medical school, as well as of the university which he had also founded. In Boston, prior to Peter Bent Brigham's bequest, the Harvard Medical School, although administered by the University, was without a university hospital as such. For the training of its students it had an informal understanding with the Massachusetts

[2] On account of Dr. Richardson's sudden death on 31 July 1912 (after a heavy day of operating at the M.G.H.), Cushing's University Professorship of Surgery was terminated and at the meeting of the Board of Overseers his election as Moseley Professor of Surgery on 11 December was confirmed as from the date of 1 September 1912.

General Hospital, and later with the Boston City Hospital, whereby students in the Medical School would serve for a period as externes or house pupils (as Cushing had served at the M.G.H. during his third and fourth years). From the standpoint of the M.G.H. it was an enlightened and much more satisfactory hospital-medical school relationship than that existing in many other American schools. In Europe several of the larger teaching hospitals are supported by government in the belief that medical instruction is a function of the state. In Vienna, for example, the Allgemeines Krankenhaus (the large municipal hospital to which students have flocked from all over the world for more than two hundred years) is supported by the state, and the rich clinical material which passes through the hospital is made freely available for teaching purposes, since all who die in this state institution must by law be subjected to a postmortem examination.

The Johns Hopkins Hospital had set a brilliant example and the Peter Bent Brigham was in a position to profit by its experience. In his Founder's Day address at the Brigham in November 1914, Welch remarked: "I consider that the Corporation of the Peter Bent Brigham Hospital, in showing that a recently established hospital can be brought into a close relationship with a great medical school, has not only rendered a very large service to the Harvard Medical School but has made a valuable contribution to medical education in general in this country."

The choice of Henry A. Christian for Physician-in-Chief at the Brigham was a fortunate one for Cushing and also the Brigham Trustees. Christian, who had been trained under Osler, had been graduated from the Hopkins in 1900; some years after settling in Boston he was appointed chief physician of the Carney Hospital where he insisted upon bringing medical students into the hospital wards prior to their interneships in accordance with the Hopkins practice. He had known Cushing while in Baltimore and felt warmly disposed toward him as is indicated in a cordial letter written as soon as Cushing had made the decision to come to the Brigham:

252 Marlborough Street, Boston,
Henry A. Christian to H.C. *22 May 1910.*

I was exceedingly pleased at the news in your note and am looking forward with keenest anticipation to the work to be done in association with you. For a long time some of us have talked about your coming to Boston some day to head a service & be professor of surgery at Harvard. I must confess in the beginning it seemed very much a castle in the air. Still that does not make the materialization of our dreams any the less delightful. . . .

My own cherished desires are realized in this opportunity for work at the Brigham & to have you on the other side of the pole is just as I wished. I think you will enjoy the life in Boston. I very certainly have. Coming here a stranger

I have found many warm friends & a most cordial reception. I am sure you will be equally fortunate. If I can answer any questions as they come up, please call on me. We are all congratulating ourselves on your decision and are very happy at the outcome. Very sincerely, HENRY A. CHRISTIAN.

Fully conscious of their unique opportunity, Harvey Cushing, as Surgeon-in-Chief, and Henry Christian, as Physician-in-Chief, sought to write a charter of organization which would incorporate all of the best features of the Johns Hopkins plan, laying particular emphasis

HARVARD MEDICAL SCHOOL AND THE P.B.B.H.

An architect's drawing of 1911 showing how the projected Peter Bent Brigham Hospital would articulate with the Harvard Medical School and the other hospitals in the area

upon the use of their clinical material for teaching purposes, both for the undergraduate medical student and for the internes and resident staff. Their first difficulty lay in one of the terms of Brigham's will: namely, that the hospital be designed to care for the indigent poor of Suffolk County. This, it was feared, would preclude acceptance of paying patients. Discussion of this problem began early in 1910, shortly after the original Board of Trustees had been appointed. Dr. F. B. Harrington, as Medical Adviser to the Corporation, had sought legal advice from John P. Reynolds, Trustee and Chairman of the Building Committee:

Boston,
John P. Reynolds to F. B. Harrington *17 February 1910.*

My dear Dr. Harrington The title of the Brigham Hospital is the Peter Bent Brigham Hospital, a Massachusetts corporation of which Alexander Cochrane is president, Edmund D. Codman, treasurer and L. H. H. Johnson, secretary, who, together with the following, compose the Board of Trustees:

Walter Hunnewell	Irwin McD. Garfield
Henry S. Howe	John P. Reynolds
Augustus Hemenway	Eben S. Draper

William Ropes Trask

I have reminded Mr. Johnson that he is to send you a copy of the legal opinion in regard to the matter of paying beds, and when I return after the holiday next week, I will try to arrange a time convenient to you when we can take a look, together with Dr. Howard, at the plans now in the hands of the architects. . . . JOHN P. REYNOLDS.

Before Cushing formally accepted the appointment, he insisted that the question of paying beds be settled and he also made a number of other farsighted stipulations indicated in a letter to Mr. Cochrane:

H.C. to Mr. Alexander Cochrane — *Baltimore, 16 April 1910.*

Dear Mr. Cochrane According to your request I shall endeavor to set down as briefly as possible some of the matters which we went over at considerable length Wednesday afternoon. . . . I gathered when the matter was first set before me that this document was explicit in stating that the hospital should be reserved solely for the indigent sick of Suffolk County. If this were actually the case, the possibility of future growth and development of the institution would be so limited and the opportunities of work and of advancing medical knowledge so inferior to those which I at present enjoy that it seemed unnecessary to consider the matter further. However, after reading Mr. Dabney's "opinion" and the copy of the will, which you kindly loaned to me, I am encouraged to think that I had misinterpreted the situation. . . .

Even had Mr. Brigham expressly stated, thirty years ago, that the hospital was to be *exclusively* for the benefit of the indigent sick of a small territory he would have been the first to realize, could he have understood hospital conditions as they exist today, that these very persons are most likely to be benefited by the establishment in their midst of an institution on such broad lines that it will attract not only eminent attendants but also the well-to-do sick from the ends of the country, whose presence there would not only make the donor's name honored throughout the land, but would also make the very individuals for whom the charity is primarily intended far more appreciative of the institution and at the same time more likely to be well served by it.

No hospital can attain anything other than merely local celebrity which is not both a teaching hospital and one from which definite advancement in our knowledge of diseases and their treatment can come. . . . I feel emphatically that the incumbents of the posts which you wish to establish should spend, with their staffs, their entire working time within the walls of the institution, caring for the sick, teaching, and investigating disease. Such a continuous service could hardly be secured for the hospital from any individual who comes to you with a national reputation unless he could care for his well-to-do as well as his charity patients under the same roof, unless his direct recompense from the hospital were in a measure commensurate with his earning capacity under other circumstances—a most desirable arrangement from every point of view.

In brief, a ward for so-called pay patients should in the first place be remunerative from the standpoint of hospital administration; it keeps the attendants at work in the one institution instead of scattering their energies and thus making poor institutional servants of them; it brings a wide reputation to the hospital and makes the indigent sick not only much more appreciative of the charity but the charity much more effective in curing them of their maladies. . . . Had my experience with cases of brain tumor been limited to patients from Baltimore County my knowledge of this group of maladies would be negligible, my medical contributions unimportant, and I would never have been thought of as a candidate for the position you have tendered me. Forgive this personal note.

Through the interest of the Carnegie Foundation, it is on these broad lines that the Barnes Hospital is to be established in St. Louis in affiliation with the remodeled Washington University Medical School. Their object is to make another distinct advance in medical education similar to that which resulted from the establishment of the Johns Hopkins Hospital twenty-five years ago. A notable group of young men has been selected to build up the school and hospital, which in a few years should rank among the foremost in the country. I have been approached as one of this group, and though under no binding agreement, opportunities have been offered on such broad lines and so free from restriction that they have appealed greatly to us all.

Naturally my closer affiliation with the profession in Boston and the cordiality shown by you all makes also a strong appeal, but it would be an injustice to yourselves if after attaching myself I should find that the institution did not offer an equally wide scope for such small powers of usefulness as I may possess for the advancement of American medicine.

I am sorry to have drawn this letter out to such length. The question as to what, in your interpretation of Mr. Brigham's will, the hospital is to stand for seems to me the immediately fundamental one; and this must, I feel, with all apologies, be clearly outlined before such minor matters (as to how the junior staff appointments are to be made or salaries apportioned and the like) need be considered. Very respectfully yours, HARVEY CUSHING.

After careful deliberation the Trustees acceded to all of Cushing's recommendations:

Alexander Cochrane to H.C. *20 June 1910.*

Dear Dr. Cushing . . . I only drop you an additional line before my departure for Europe on the 22nd to say once more how pleased I am, and all my colleagues also, that you are to be the Surgeon-in-Chief of the Peter Bent Brigham Hospital, when the Hospital is ready. We have been unanimous in meeting your views in regard to the management of the Hospital, as covered in your letter [of 16 April] to us.

The salary, as arranged with you, is to be $5,000 per year.

You are expected to have the nomination of your staff but the Trustees, of course, have entire power to reject any or all nominations. Mr. Reynolds, the Chairman of the Building Committee, will be happy to confer with you in regard to getting your advice about the plans. With best wishes, I am, Yours sincerely, ALEXANDER COCHRANE.

On 26 July 1911 came the welcome news from Mr. Reynolds that the contract for the Hospital had been signed and work was to begin immediately: ". . . We trust that the ground will be broken for the new hospital by August 1st. I think there is fair reason to believe that we shall finish it in fifteen months—in other words, have it open and ready for patients by the first of November, 1912." Dr. Howard, the new superintendent of the Hospital, also wrote H.C. and noted with some pride, "We are rather getting ahead of the St. Louis men. I doubt if they get the contract let for their hospital this fall. They have no one whose special business alone is to push along the hospital." Mr. Lowell likewise sent him the glad tidings.

After having agreed on fundamentals, the medical and surgical chiefs began to work out the details. They proceeded slowly and cautiously, and during 1910 and 1911 their plans were carefully developed for the Hospital and the organization of its clinical services. Staff appointments were the subject of lively discussions. H.C. was insistent that the power of appointment of the clinical staff should rest with the Surgeon-in-Chief and Physician-in-Chief respectively, subject to approval by the Trustees through an Executive Committee which would consist of three persons—the heads of the two services and the Superintendent of the Hospital.[3] In November 1911 Cushing and Christian drafted the plan they proposed for the organization of the staff and submitted it for approval to the Board of Trustees. It was an interesting document and was adopted by the Trustees with a few minor verbal changes suggested by the business and legal minds on the Board:

Henry A. Christian and Harvey Cushing *Boston,*
to Alexander Cochrane *6 November 1911.*

Dear Sir In our judgment it seems that it is time now to proceed to the further organization of the Staff of the Peter Bent Brigham Hospital, in order that the services of some of the men whom we believe desirable for that Staff may be secured. Delay in this matter might be the cause of our losing such men owing to their acceptance of positions elsewhere, not knowing of the possibilities in the Peter Bent Brigham Hospital.

Before proceeding to a consideration of individuals for positions, it seems to us desirable that a general plan of Staff organization be determined upon. So far as we know, the only steps so far taken to that end are the appointment of the Physician-in-Chief, the Surgeon-in-Chief, and the Superintendent, and the expression in the letter to us that we should have the privilege of nominating to the Board of Trustees our various assistants. In regard to the general organization of the Hospital Staff, we would advise:

General Staff Organization. (1) That the Staff of the Hospital consist of the Physician-in-Chief, the Surgeon-in-Chief, and their respective assistants, with the exception of the House-officers; the Consulting Pathologist, and the Consulting Physiologist, and the Consulting Chemist, and their assistants; the Superintendent, and such others as may subsequently be added on the recommendation of the Executive Committee of the Staff to the Trustees.

(2) That all Staff appointments shall cease automatically when the encumbent reaches the age of sixty-three years.

(3) That there shall be an Executive Committee of the Staff composed of the Physician-in-Chief, the Surgeon-in-Chief, and the Superintendent.

[3] Later the Pathologist to the Hospital was added to the Executive Committee.

(4) That each member of the Executive Committee shall have the privilege on request of appearing at meetings of the Trustees to present matters immediately concerned with his Department, and that each member of the Executive Committee shall bear identical relations to the Trustees of the Hospital.

(5) That the Physician-in-Chief, the Surgeon-in-Chief, and the Superintendent each shall have the privilege of nominating to the Trustees his assistants, and at any time recommending their dismissal for adequate cause.

(6) That the other members of Staff shall be nominated to the Trustees by the Executive Committee of the Staff.

Medical and Surgical Staff. We submit in connection with the above, the enclosed schedule of Staff positions, which will give some idea of the probable number of men needed when all of the beds of the Hospital are occupied, and when the general work of the Hospital is fully under way. Furthermore, we have appended to this schedule salaries suggested for these various members of the Staff. It is to be realized in this connection that conditions in medicine and in hospitals are very rapidly changing, and that new opportunities with increasing salaries are being offered to young men engaged in such work. Consequently we regard this schedule of Staff positions and of salaries as a tentative one, expressing what in our judgment today are likely to be the needs of the Hospital during its first few years of existence, and what it will be necessary to pay to secure these services. Doubtless later increases will have to be made in many of these.

Consulting Pathologist, Physiologist, Chemist. We believe that at the present time, the best arrangement for the work of the Hospital will be to throw the burden of it on the resident staff, the Physician-in-Chief, and the Surgeon-in-Chief, with the aid of the non-resident assistants appearing in the schedule immediately preceding Physician-in-Chief and Surgeon-in-Chief; that in addition to these there should be a Consulting Pathologist, a Consulting Physiologist, and a Consulting Chemist, with no regularly fixed duties, to be called upon freely for advice, and to have complete freedom of visiting and making suggestions in the aid of the work of all Departments of the Hospital. Furthermore, it is believed that no salaries should be paid to these men until such time as it is evident that such service is making a considerable demand on their time.

Consultants in Specialties. It is furthermore believed that at an early day it will be necessary to secure the services of other consultants covering certain of the specialties, namely, neurology, otology, ophthalmology, dermatology, and laryngology. As far as the wards of the Hospital are concerned, with the beds divided for medical and surgical patients, relatively little demand will be made upon the services of such consultants for the specialties, and consequently they can be secured either without salary, or with small remuneration. In connection with the Out-patient Department probably in a short time larger demands will be made upon the men engaged in these special lines of work, and other arrangements will then have to be made.

In the beginning the Out-patient Department will undoubtedly be small, and it is planned to organize this at the outset for a relatively small number of patients, and to provide ample space for growth. It is believed this Out-patient Department should be open continuously for the treatment of patients, and at first should be operated by the medical and surgical staff as shown in the schedule referred to above. With growth it may be necessary to organize separate departments covering the special lines of work, and then a considerable staff of men for these will be needed. It seems wise to us to postpone such organization until we can determine from the method of development of the Out-patient Department under the plan of having a continuous Out-patient Service what are the immediate and future requirements for such special departments. These requirements will naturally be influenced by the possible development about the Peter Bent Brigham Hospital of various special clinics, to which ambulatory patients advantageously can be referred. Should the Trustees wish to have an estimate of the probable cost of such subsequent developments, we think a tentative figure of $100.00 per month for each man on duty daily in such an Out-patient Department might be given, and that for some time $1200.00 per Department, or $6000.00, if there are five of these Departments, might be considered sufficient.

Roentgenologist. In regard to a Roentgenologist we have put down no salary figure. This Department will probably involve the employment of one or more technical assistants not graduates in medicine, with the probable supervision of a resident or visiting graduate in medicine. The exact organization must depend in large part upon the training and ability of the men whom we can secure to do the technical work. Some idea of the probable cost of such a department, which should be established as early as possible, may be obtained from the figures which we submit of the cost of this department during the past year at two large hospitals, the Boston City Hospital, $4481.29, and the Massachusetts General Hospital, $4663.58, which figures include salaries and the cost of supplies, but not cost of power, light and caretaking of building. From this cost may be subtracted such fees as are paid by patients for Roentgen ray examinations.

Photographer and Artist. In similar way no salary has been named for a photographer and an artist. Both will be needed in the work of the Hospital. The photographic work possibly may be combined with that of the roentgenologist. The personnel of this department will be a determining factor; no definite figure can be set for his salary nor for the cost of his materials. The call for work by an artist is apt to be a varying quantity, and so difficult of estimate. Arrangements may be made for utilizing a portion of the time of artists employed in the Harvard Medical School or other adjacent institutions. Under these circumstances a probable cost cannot be stated until organization has progressed much further.

Autopsies. One other matter we deem of the very greatest importance for the future success of the Peter Bent Brigham Hospital, and we would ask the Trustees of the Hospital to take early action upon it. This matter has reference to the securing of autopsies on patients dying in the Hospital. We believe that the best interests of the development of the scientific work and improvement in our methods of treating patients can only be obtained by the careful post-mortem study of fatal cases. To this end, we would ask the Trustees to adopt a rule that on admission to the general wards of the Hospital each patient, and his nearest relative, as provided by law governing such matters, shall be required to sign an agreement providing that, in case of his or her death, a post-mortem examination of the body shall be made whenever in the judgment of the Staff such an examination is desirable. We feel that this matter cannot be too strongly insisted upon. Such a rule is now established for all of the Government Hospitals (Marine, etc.) in this country, and has long been in existence in all the great German clinics.

The Surgeon-in-Chief and the Physician-in-Chief will separately submit a schedule of what we believe needed in the way of members of the Staff at the time of the actual opening of the Hospital. We would ask that the Board of Trustees indicate to us now the date on which they will require our services, it being understood that on that date our salary payments will begin, in order that we may make the necessary arrangements of our work to meet these engagements with you. We ask that this date be named thus far in advance for the reason that both of us are holding positions and are engaged in work, a certain part of which will need to be discontinued before we begin our service at the Brigham Hospital. It is desirable that ample notice be given to the institutions with which we are at present connected of the time at which our resignations are to take effect. Very truly yours, HENRY A. CHRISTIAN HARVEY CUSHING.

P.S. Dr. Cushing wishes to add that in view of the difficulties of training a new operative staff for responsible surgical work, it will be necessary for him at as early a date as possible, to select and educate for her special duties an operating room head nurse, as well as an anaesthetist. He feels that both of these women should have at least six months of special training, and should visit other large clinics before undertaking their work at the Brigham Hospital; and that their salaries—or such proportion of their future salaries as may seem reasonable—should begin as soon as the proper individuals for these tasks can be selected, and an agreement made with them for a certain term of service after the opening of the Hospital.

Cushing had brought sound judgment and foresight to the working out of his plans for organization of the staff, but when he came to work on the architects' drawings, he showed a curious inability to visualize the detail of a building from the plans or even from an elevation.[4] Thus he made little attempt to plan his surgical wards at the Brigham beyond the stipulation that there be plenty of light in the operating room and that it should come from behind him so that it fell over his shoulder without casting a shadow. The result was that he had a well-lighted operating room, but many changes had to be made after the building was completed because he had given too little attention to essential services such as electric outlets for burrs, heaters, head lights, etc. And since he had left things largely to Christian, the surgical wards were built essentially as replicas of the well-planned medical wards.

Although he was not temperamental with the architects, he had begun early to worry the life out of the Brigham Trustees about the progress of the building. In December 1911 he wrote a long and, on the face of it, most unreasonable letter to Alexander Cochrane, stating that unless Mr. Cochrane could promise absolutely that a surgical ward and the operating unit would be ready in October, or at the latest by 1 November 1912, he saw no point in coming up from Baltimore until the autumn of 1913—that he had responsibilities to the junior staff which he was bringing with him, and unless they could begin to operate at once, they would all go sour. Mrs. Cushing

[4] In 1938 and 1939 in New Haven when the plans for the new Yale Medical Library were under consideration, he proved equally oblivious to the meaning of drawings. He insisted only that the old books be as accessible to the students as the modern books; how this was to be achieved, he left entirely to the architect.

fortunately saw the letter before it was sent and persuaded him to modify it, but Mr. Cochrane was much disturbed by even the softened form of the letter, and he went to Christian asking what manner of man they were getting to head their surgical service. Christian poured oil on the troubled waters and told H.C. politely but firmly that he had made a mistake and that he must at once write a more reasonable letter to the Board. H.C. took this meekly and forthwith sent a most brief and businesslike note to Mr. Cochrane:

H.C. to Alexander Cochrane *10 January 1912.*

Dear Mr. Cochrane: I understand that you wish a specific statement from me in regard to the appointments which will in all probability be desirable on the surgical service at the opening of the Brigham Hospital.

A sufficient working staff, I judge, would be as follows: (a) the surgeon-in-chief; (b) an associate or visiting surgeon, salary $2,000; (c) a resident surgeon, salary $1,000; (d) an assistant resident surgeon, salary $500; (e) half the surgical house officers without salary, as outlined in the schedule appended to the joint letter of Dr. Christian and myself, with a plan of promotion and increase of staff, in accord with Dr. Christian's plan concerning the medical house officers; (f) a stenographer; (g) a possible sojourn abroad for some of these individuals. Very sincerely yours, HARVEY CUSHING.

H.C. evidently sent another demanding letter to Mr. Cochrane about the time of completion of the surgical unit, asking him once more to commit himself, and Henry Christian this time wrote H.C. much more sternly (27 Jan.):

I do not believe that you at all understand Mr. Cochrane's make-up. He is, I think, that type of business man who considers his promise as good as his bond. Consequently he makes no statements he is not absolutely sure of. This is his attitude in regard to the opening of the Brigham Hospital. The Building Committee have told him that they expect to have the building completed and ready to open sometime during the month of October. . . . You say "I should very much rather make the transfer to Boston six months after the shop is ready than six months before." I am very certain that you do not wish to do either one of these things, but of the two, it would be distinctly preferable for you to be ahead of the opening rather than after. This is a shop in which you will probably work the rest of your active life-time.

H.C. apologized, and once more Christian succeeded in smoothing Mr. Cochrane's ruffled feathers.

Another detail which H.C. and Christian settled in the months before H.C. arrived was the matter of the retirement age for the attending surgeon and physician. H.C. wrote to Christian:

20 November 1911.

Dear Henry Why not put the surgical age of retirement for the attending surgeon at sixty and the physician at sixty-three or sixty-five, as you think best? I have an idea that the surgeon's fingers are apt to get a little stiff and thus make him less competent before the physician's cerebral vessels do. However, as I told you, I would like to see the day when somebody would be appointed surgeon somewhere who had no hands, for the operative part is the least part of the work. Then, of course, many of us may get, vascularly speaking, a little inelastic well on this side of sixty, or may remain in this respect as youthful at seventy as are others at fifty. This is all a lottery of inheritance and habits, and I shall be very glad, for one, to have it legislated to stop active work at sixty. Ever yours, H.C.

After further discussion, sixty-three was settled upon. When the year 1932 came around, Cushing fretted at the retirement age which he himself had set, but he did not ask for special consideration.

The building of the Hospital progressed quite satisfactorily during the summer, but when H.C. arrived in September he was indignant that he could not do a craniotomy at once amidst the bricks and plaster. The long period of transition had not been easy for a person of his impatient nature, and he was not one to stand by silently if his plans were thwarted. Then, too, as his assistants well knew, cases always appeared more urgent when obstacles were encountered, whether they were contractors or holidays.

CHAPTER XI

Settling in Boston

1912–1914

IN February 1937 Cushing wrote to George R. Minot: ". . . When I first went to Boston there were three things I wanted to see done: one, to have a common instead of departmental source of animals for experimental use; another, to fuse into one the separate departmental libraries; and the third, to have a School publication like the *Johns Hopkins Hospital Bulletin* to which the younger folks could have ready access for their early papers when they were trying their wings. The present library at the Harvard Medical School is the one of these three most nearly consummated; but even so, it was a long struggle and in the end some of the departments refused to come in. . . ." His interest in the Library explains a reference in a letter which he received in August 1912 from his colleague in the Department of Surgery, Professor Edward H. Bradford (with whom he had worked as a medical student): "I am glad," Bradford said, "you feel as you do in regard to the Library and the need of a Journal." Bradford also thought that the Harvard Medical Alumni Association should purchase the *Boston Medical and Surgical Journal* and that the School should subsidize it; but this was not to happen and H.C., unfortunately for the School, never succeeded in establishing a journal. In a letter of 14 August Bradford wrote about H.C.'s temporary office, stating that there would be room for his books and a secretary in the surgical department. He added: "The arrangements for the teaching in the autumn will not be materially changed by Dr. Richardson's death [on 31 July]. Plans for the future are held in abeyance."

Urgent as were the many problems of organization in the School and Hospital, it was characteristic of H.C. to be just as vitally interested in the welfare of the medical students. The crying need at Harvard, as in most medical schools in the country, was for a dormitory where under one roof students could have adequate food and decent living quarters. Even before H.C. arrived in Boston he began to discuss with John Collins Warren the idea of such a dormitory as a memorial to Maurice Richardson and to offer his active support and encouragement.

J. Collins Warren to H.C. *Pride's Crossing, Mass., 19 August 1912.*

Dear Dr. Cushing: Many thanks for your kind and generous acknowledgement of my little reprint.[1] . . . Since your letter was received however I have been asked what was going to be done about a memorial for Maurice Richardson. He had a long list of millionaire G.P.'s [grateful patients] among whom there may be one or two who might be pleased to help such a project. The land will cost $200,000—there are 4 acres. If that could be obtained I think the building part could be solved either by the Corporation putting some money in as an investment, or on some business basis by selling bonds or stock. All this I am planning to study out in the autumn. I think a Club House with memorial halls to medical worthies, such as Porter, Richardson, etc. would be a taking proposition.

I showed the ground to J. P. Morgan Jr. this spring and he thought it most important for the school to get control of it. It seems as if the time had come when the medical student should be placed upon an equality socially with the other students in the University. Your letter gives me much encouragement. I shall not open a subscription list just yet but will try to develop a plan of campaign first.[2] Sincerely yours, J. COLLINS WARREN.

During August and September 1912 H.C. came to Boston several times to confer with the Building Committee at the Hospital and to see the Trustees. Evidently he bothered the Trustees to such an extent that on 15 August they voted funds to send him back again to Europe where he might remain until the Hospital was completed.[3] At the same time funds were also appropriated for his first Brigham appointees, Emil Goetsch and Conrad Jacobson, to go abroad for a period of study (in accordance with an item (g) in the letter of 10 January 1912 to Mr. Cochrane [p. 351]). On 5 September Cushing wrote indignantly to Christian (who was in Wales) about the slow progress: "I returned a few days ago, and find that practically nothing has been done since my departure [for Europe] in the way of making the changes we asked for. Dr. Howard has been away for six weeks and has just returned today. Your last letter evidently held up the amphitheatre, and as they are planning to let out their various bids in one lot the other things have consequently not been done." Cables were exchanged and Howard retorted to Christian: "Your telegram of September 8th and letter both received. I cannot see why you should be surprised that nothing was done on the Amphitheatre. You had better reread your letter to me, dropping out absolutely from under what Cushing and I had agreed to, and you had agreed

[1] "The social side of student life." *Boston Medical and Surgical Journal,* 13 June 1912, *166,* 875-876, 895-896.

[2] The war came, and the medical students at Harvard did not have decent living quarters until Vanderbilt Hall was opened 4 October 1927.

[3] Since H.C. had returned from his tour with the Society of Clinical Surgery on 20 July, he did not feel disposed to accept the Trustees' proposal that he return at once to Europe.

to in the telegram. The arrival of that letter stopped everything. Reread it and see if you would have wanted to have done anything if you had been in my place."

On 3 October 1912, writing on a Brigham Hospital letterhead, H.C. remarked to Simon Flexner: "I have just come to town, and the family have gotten under our roof at 305 Walnut Street, Brookline. . . . Everything looks most promising, and the people are cordial to a degree. The hospital is not ready as yet, alas! but we are sailing into the surgical laboratory. We have more room than we had at the Hunterian and I hope we will be able to do at least as much work as we did there." Three days later he wrote to Klebs from 305 Walnut Street: "We are struggling to get settled, and it's hades—with a capital H. Wish we could have you here, but the plumbers and paperers are camped in the house and will not be out of *your* future room for a month."

In those days H.C. had begun to drive an automobile, but a few weeks after he arrived in Boston he had an unhappy motor accident (in which he was not at fault) that resulted in the death of an elderly female pedestrian. Thereafter, he employed an ever-faithful Austrian named Gus, who drove him at any time of the day or night to and from the Hospital. Gus was also man-of-all-work who looked after the garden at 305 Walnut Street and acted as general handy man around the house. He gave wholehearted devotion to the "Doctor" but his unconventional behavior was as often a source of embarrassment to the family as it was of amusement to their friends. He took all rebukes with silent (or almost silent) stoicism but there is no doubt that he had his moments. H.C. often recounted with great glee the story of a morning when he was feeling irritable and distracted after a late night with an emergency operation and took occasion to give Gus 'what-to' for his sins of omission in the garden, not washing the car, etc., etc. Gus listened patiently and when it was all over said stonily: "Doctor, you got egg on your chin."

The discouragements of these early days in Boston were somewhat mitigated by the many warmhearted expressions of friendship and appreciation which came from Baltimore. Halsted wrote: "We are trying to reconcile ourselves to the loss of yourself and family and to regard it as an inevitable phenological incident. Our attempts to give the dog course would make you smile." And from Welch: "You have left a yawning chasm but a happier thought is of all the good things you have done for us, and which will never be forgotten." Howell added: "There is no one in sight who can begin to take your place."

Cushing entered into his activities at Boston with much enthusiasm and he and Mrs. Cushing were received with the greatest cordiality. H.C., however, strongly disliked formal social functions and only with the greatest difficulty was Mrs. Cushing able to get him into proper evening attire for a Boston banquet. One night in October he disgraced himself by forgetting a dinner being given in his honor by Dr. George H. Monks at 51 Commonwealth Avenue for the surgical department. Lewis Weed recalls that he was having a quiet supper with the Cushings at 305 Walnut Street when shortly after eight his host telephoned in great perturbation of spirit, with the result that H.C. dashed out the door and appeared in an old gray suit at the large festive gathering where everyone else was in tails and white tie. On another occasion some years later, when Mrs. Cushing had induced him to attend a coming-out ball for the daughter of one of their friends, H.C. pulled himself together to the extent of getting on a white tie and a smoking jacket. He attended the dinner, but when he had ushered his ladies through the revolving door of the Copley Plaza Hotel, they were startled to discover that he had stayed in the door and had disappeared rapidly down the street.

Cushing enjoyed good conversation, and when he found himself in company that he respected, he was a good listener; in other circumstances he could himself be garrulous. If one measures a man by the company he keeps, then it must be said of Harvey Cushing that he attracted the brighter minds for he was on terms of intimacy with the best intellects of his time; they sought him out and all but demanded his presence. In Boston one of the first to welcome him was Henry Lee Higginson (1834-1919), the distinguished public servant and financier. Of him H.C. has written:

> . . . "The Major" was the most beloved of men and what I with countless others owe to him is more than I can set down. From the time when we came to Boston till the afternoon when K.C., Susan Chapin and I saw him in his bedroom for a visit just before he was taken to the M.G.H. for his fatal operation, his acts of friendship to us were unbounded. Being strangers in a foreign land we loved him for this as for himself perhaps more and in a different way than did his own people.

Another who became one of his intimates was James Ford Rhodes, the well-known historian who, like H.C., had grown up in Cleveland. In November Rhodes took him to the Tavern Club to meet the Governor-General of the Philippines, William Cameron Forbes. His subsequent association with Rhodes led to his being taken into the two most select dining clubs in Boston—"The Club" and "The Saturday Club." In 1927 at the time of Rhodes' death H.C. described his contacts with him:

> I owed much to James Rhodes—the very membership in the Saturday Club indeed was due to him, I am sure. Also my election to "The (Friday) Club"

and a proposal from the Wintersnight Club. He chided me for not joining the latter but the meetings came on Tuesdays which would, I feared, collide with the Hospital meetings we were planning to hold weekly at the P.B.B.H.

The dinners of "The Club" with Henry L. Higginson, John T. Morse, Jr., Moorfield Storey, George F. Moore, Bliss Perry, Sturgis Bigelow, Lord Camperdown, Tom Perry, occasionally Mr. Pompelli [*sic*] and others have been the most enjoyable things I have participated in here. Such good talk! Even if the Civil War did largely figure. Many times I have heard the bloody fence corner at Gettysburg fought over again. I was the last person elected to "The Club." They possibly did not want to experiment further. But I never missed a meeting and truly loved these old men who treated me like one of their contemporaries tho' (Bliss Perry excepted) they were old enough to be my parents. James Rhodes always stopped for me the winter he was living here in Brookline. And when he came back from his long sojourn in the Riviera and took the Seeley house overlooking our tennis court I hoped for some years of neighborly association with him. But he was a broken man. Only once did he manage to get to the Saturday Club. And his brief remarks on Chas. Eliot before the Historical Society constituted his last public utterance—made with an effort. With his death and with that of another neighbor Charles Sargent, who has been my "Summer Club" friend, Brookline will seem empty to me.

Further details concerning his dining clubs can be gleaned from letters received by H.C. at the time:

James F. Rhodes to H.C. *392 Beacon Street,*
8 November 1913.

Dear Doctor Cushing, You made a good speech the other evening at the Tavern and, as a brother Clevelander, I was proud of you. I wish you might have a glimpse at two of our Boston Clubs. I would like very much to have you come to the Wednesday Evening Club which meets at my house on Nov. 19. We gather sometime between 9.30 and 10. Supper is served at 10 and the party breaks up at 12 but one may leave before that hour if he so desires or indeed, as I do frequently, come at 9. . . . With kind regards to Mrs. Cushing, I am, Very truly yours, JAMES F. RHODES.

13 December 1913.

Dear Harvey, For so I must address you and you must call me James or Jim. I will tell you why. When Mr. Pritchett first came here he felt that he was a little "out of it" as the men called one another by their Christian names, Fred, Henry, John, Jim, etc. and he said that to "keep our end up" as we were from the West, we must do likewise: hence Harvey and James. It is a good example to follow.

Will you take dinner with The Club as my guest on Friday, January 2d? If you can come will you meet me in the reception room of the Algonquin Club at five minutes before 7? We dine at seven and the party generally breaks up at 10 or 10.30. The Club is small. We were six at the December dinner, about ten in November. With kind regards and hoping that you can come, Very truly yours, JAMES F. RHODES. Henry L. Higginson & Moorfield Storey are members of the Club and generally come.

30 December 1913.

Dear Harvey, It may interest you to know the members of the Club with whom you will dine on Friday:

John T. Morse
Henry L. Higginson
James Crafts
Tom Perry
Charles Grinnell
John C. Gray
W. D. Howells
Bliss Perry
Professor Pumpelly
Dr. Walcott
Hon. George Duncan

There may be others who do not occur to me. We have no printed list and no rules. There are some members who are never here like Justice Holmes, Henry Pritchett & (I think) Henry James. I shall await you in the reception room of the Algonquin Club next Friday at five minutes before 7. With kind regards Very truly yours, JAMES F. RHODES.

P.S. We are rarely less than 6, almost never more than 10.

31 January 1914

Dear Harvey, You were today admitted as a member of the Saturday Club and if my note is in advance of the official notification of the Secretary it is simply to advise you as an Ohioan, having lived longer in Boston than you have, to accept all memberships offered you (unless there be a good reason for declining) and afterwards to weed out the different societies & clubs. At any time that I could be of help to you in the literary societies or social clubs, command me. I know nothing about the scientific or medical societies and clubs.

The Saturday Club you will enjoy, if you can get to it the last Saturday of the month. The luncheon is at 1.30 and we generally leave at 3.30 or 4. I hope you will be able to come. Curiously enough the Club is endowed and our meat and drink cost us nothing. Mr. Howells said today that in this respect, so far as his experience went, it is a unique club. With kind regards, Very truly yours, JAMES F. RHODES.

The society is good at the club and the talk excellent. President Eliot, who was really your sponsor, will be disappointed if you are not able to come to our luncheons. But accept whether or not you think you can come.

16 Fairfield Street,
John T. Morse, Jr. to H.C. *13 February 1914.*

My dear Dr. Cushing: I have the pleasure of notifying you that you have been elected a member of *"The Club."* This somewhat egotistical name is borne by a dinner-club which has been in existence for nearly a generation, & which those who have belonged to it have found extremely pleasant. You were proposed by your friend, Dr. James Ford Rhodes, who will doubtless give you full information concerning it. We meet on the first Friday in each month, & I sincerely hope that you have not consecrated that evening to any other fixed engagement, & that you will do us the honor of joining us. I am, Very sincerely yours, JOHN T. MORSE, JR.

James F. Rhodes to H.C. *14 February 1914.*

Dear Harvey, Before you receive this, you will have had the word from John T. Morse, announcing your election to "The Club." Henry L. Higginson avers that this is the choicest dining club in Boston as it is certainly the most difficult to get into. I send to you a list of members marking with an X those who are apt to come. Some, like Morse, Tom Perry, Henry L. Higginson and I, never miss a dinner on any account. When you have looked over the list will you kindly return it, as it is the only one that I possess.

. . . I hear on all sides that you are the greatest brain surgeon in the world. I know well what I should do were I that and only 45 years old. I should make everything subservient to my operating work. I should do as little administrative work as possible. I should leave the history of medicine to others. Administrators and historians are plenty. A truly great operative surgeon is rare. And think of it to have the brain for your province! When next I see you I want to add a word to this and I promise you never to recur to the subject again & I will illustrate it by my own experience if I did not tell it to you a year ago. This is what I do. I have reduced my dining clubs to two: The Club and one other. When I come back in the autumn I enter on my engagement book the days of these dinners from Nov. to May and I tell my good wife these are sacred engagements with which nothing must interfere. The Tavern, the Wednesday, the Thursday (when I went to it) will yield to anything you may want to do, but not these. Do likewise with The Club and I am sure that the pleasure you there receive will make your work lighter and do a little toward keeping you young. With kind regards to Mrs. Cushing, Very truly yrs, JAMES F. RHODES.

The Saturday Club is not "in it" with The Club. Always neglect the former for the latter but don't tell President Eliot I said so.

The Club flourished for several years more and H.C. attended many of the meetings. That it finally ceased to exist is indicated in a much later letter from Morse:

John T. Morse, Jr. to H.C. *19 November 1927.*

Dear Dr. Cushing: At last I send you herewith a list of the members of THE CLUB, from its birth to the present day. I am ashamed to have been so tardy in replying to you; but I am living, as it were, astride of two places, Boston and Needham, and the consequences are a shocking disorganization. It has been about as cozy a little club as could be built up in Boston. To let it die seems a great pity. I wish you would try to keep the first Friday in December free; I think we may then gather the remnants and talk matters over, and at worst have one more pleasant meeting. Very sincerely yours, JOHN T. MORSE, JR.

THE CLUB

Henry Adams
Alexander Agassiz
Thomas B. Aldrich
Wm. Sturgis Bigelow
James M. Crafts
Thomas B. Curtis
Harvey Cushing
J. R. Dennett
George A. Duncan (Lord Camperdown)
John Fiske
John C. Gray
Charles E. Grinnell
Charles Hale
Henry L. Higginson
Oliver Wendell Holmes (the younger)
Edward S. Hooper
W. D. Howells
Henry James
William James
George F. Moore
John T. Morse, Jr.
Baron Osten-Sacken
Francis Parkman
Charles E. Perkins
William Perkins
Bliss Perry
Thomas S. Perry
H. S. Pritchett
Raphael Pumpelly
Henry H. Richardson
James Ford Rhodes
Arthur G. Sedgwick
Moorfield Storey
Henry P. Walcott
W. P. Walley
J. Collins Warren
Charles A. Whittier
Theodore W. Richards

Despite increasing clinical responsibilities H.C. was surprisingly regular in his attendance at the Saturday Club and also at The Club. The Saturday Club at the time of Cushing's election had a membership of 43 and included personalities such as W. T. Councilman, M. A. DeWolfe Howe, Theodore Richards, Lawrence J. Henderson, Charles Sprague Sargent, A. Lawrence Lowell, Moorfield Storey and William Sturgis Bigelow[4]—to mention only a few. The Club, as already indicated, was much smaller. Bliss Perry, the well-known Professor of English at Harvard, had this to say of H.C. and his three dining clubs (14 March 1940):

. . . As I jot down a few dates for you I am rebellious at the futility of trying to indicate the real personality of any Club member by means of dates and anecdotes. Harvey was a radiant person in any company, as you know, but when I try to focus him as one of a group, I am at a loss. I can see his face and his wonderful eyes through any cloud of cigarette smoke, and hear his laugh, but the shifting circles of men around him elude me.

I find that he was elected to the Tavern Club in 1912 . . . but I have no very clear recollection of him as a Taverner. My impression is that his surgical work did not allow him time to lunch frequently at the Club, and the special dinners there are usually so largely attended that any individual is lost in the crowd unless he happens to make a speech. . . .

I remember him more vividly at the Saturday Club, which he joined in 1914, but as you know, he was greatly preoccupied with World War problems for the next five years and could not be a very regular attendant at the monthly luncheons. I should say that Councilman and Rhodes and Richard Strong (after 1922) were the men by whom he most often sat. President Eliot admired him greatly. I remember one Saturday when Eliot and Harvey were at the Peter Bent Brigham Hospital together, and arrived at the Club forty-five minutes late. It appeared that they had started on time, but that a boy had darted in front of Harvey's car on Huntington Avenue, and that the chauffeur had driven straight over him. There was a bad scalp wound, and an indentation in the boy's skull deep enough, Harvey said, to hide a pigeon's egg. They rushed him back to the Hospital and Harvey got him on to the operating table, only to find that the indentation was merely a curious malformation due to an accident in childhood, and that aside from the scalp wound the boy was all right. . . .

My recollection is that Harvey rarely talked medical or surgical "shop" at the Saturday Club, but he was quick to catch up any chance remark about a new or an old book—in fact the older the better. When he was writing Osler's

[4] William Sturgis Bigelow, son of Henry Jacob, had an unusual personality which fascinated Cushing. On an old piece of yellow paper he had scratched the following notes about him (found in *The early years of the Saturday Club*): "Sturgis Bigelow had astasia abasia and was confined to his bed for the last three years of his life. After the Saturday Club meetings I used to go in to see him with James Rhodes in the old residence, 56 Beacon Street, just up the hill from 'Col' Warren's. We would find him sitting up in bed in his 3rd floor front room looking out on the Common, in his dressing gown with a radio at his elbow. He would smile and listen to our talk but I was not sure how much he enjoyed it or how much he took in. One can't be confined to a single room for 3 years at 76 years of age and be very lively. Over his bed hung the picture of the Buddhist Priest who had befriended (converted?) him.

"A strange man. I rowed with him once over the Base Hospital on the Common episode—the day when it was ventilated at the Saturday Club—ending with Gorgas' telephone message to report at Washington to go abroad. He bore no grudge. He always chipped in with me to support the Surgical Laboratory in the School which the School treated so shabbily—a thousand each. This he did for several years without a question. One night when the old boys had been talking about the Civil War he said, "Does anyone know how to get an ink stain off from a Panama straw hat? I was putting my initials in my hat today and they show through." Nobody knew. His last appearance in public I believe was when they gave Will Mayo the first Henry Jacob Bigelow Medal."

life he used to talk with me a good deal about the technique of writing biography. One remark of his about the Osler book impressed me particularly. He said that he thought many of the best passages had leaped into his mind after he had dressed for an operation, and that he would then summon his secretary and dictate a memorandum, to be elaborated later. His theory was that the cerebral excitement just preceding an operation stimulated the brain in other fields than that of surgery. I think a stranger lunching at the Saturday Club and wholly ignorant of the various members would have classified Harvey Cushing at once as a book-lover rather than as a famous surgeon. . . . In my own opinion he was really happier at the monthly evening dinners of "The" Club (Friday) than he was at either the Tavern Club or the Saturday Club. I have given some account of this Club in my *And Gladly Teach,* pp. 288-290. "The" Club never kept any written records and I do not remember when Harvey was elected to it, but I know that he enjoyed it greatly. His work for the day was done, and as there were rarely more than eight or ten men at the dinners, we had real "general conversation" in which H.C. excelled. His friends Rhodes and J. T. Morse were always present, and he took especial delight in the talk of Major Higginson, Dr. Sturgis Bigelow and Thomas Sergeant ("Tom") Perry. Harvey and I were the last survivors of this group, which dissolved in 1928....

At the end of his first year in Boston Osler cheered H.C. with a characteristic letter announcing plans for his Silliman Lectures at Yale and his willingness subsequently to pay a visit to Boston:

Oxford,
Sir William Osler to H.C. *31 December 1912.*

Dear Harvey C.: I hope you have had a good Christmas—the first of many at Harvard. What a good time you must have with the children! Congratulate Bill on the captaincy of his football team; he will be in the same position soon at Yale! . . .

About my visit—I shall go first to the opening [of the Phipps Clinic] at the Hopkins, which is fixed for April 16th. I begin my Yale lectures on the 20th and shall stay at New Haven for 10 days. After that I am free. I should be delighted to give an informal talk at the opening of the Brigham—not, please, a set address, as I shall be pumped out. Nothing would give me more pleasure than to give a lecture on the Clarendon Press with lantern slides. I think I could make it interesting and instructive, and Hart would help me to get a set of new pictures. . . . As I think I told you I missed the Pagel library, which I thought had gone to St. Louis, but Dock tells me that he has not yet made final arrangements. Fock has offered to duplicate all the important items, and my brother E. B. has sent the necessary cash, so that will make a great addition to the historical side of my collection. I have had a very good haul this year in many ways, and have picked up some gems and jewels—the last an exceptionally fine 12th century manuscript of Constantinus Africanus. We had a houseful for Christmas, and a very happy time. Sincerely yours, W.O.

1913

One reason for H.C.'s impatience with the progress of the Hospital building was the fact that he had brought with him from Baltimore a group of able house officers and research men who for the first four months had very little to do, save for Lewis H. Weed and Emil Goetsch who were organizing the experimental laboratory in the Medical School and were getting on with their research. Such operating as there was for the others on the team had to be done at the Corey Hill Hospital. The initial team included: Lewis Weed, who later succeeded Mall as Professor of Anatomy at Johns Hopkins; Conrad Jacobson, who settled in Seattle as neurologist and neurosurgeon; Emil Goetsch, now well-known as a neurosurgeon and a professor of surgery at the Long Island College Hospital. On 1 November they were joined by Ernest G. Grey and Paul Wegefarth.[5] John Homans, who had worked with him in Baltimore two years earlier, and David Cheever, son of David Williams Cheever, H.C.'s preceptor in surgery during his medical school days, were both made permanent members of the Brigham surgical staff. David Cheever, who had been a member of the surgical staff of the Boston City Hospital, was also actively associated with the Department of Anatomy at Harvard and was a distinguished teacher of surgical anatomy. For twenty years Homans and Cheever formed the bulwark of Cushing's general surgical team, serving loyally and maintaining a firm *esprit de corps* in their department. They were joined in 1916 by William C. Quinby, the eminent urological surgeon. It was thus a strong group and all were fired by the new venture and much stimulated by Cushing's driving enthusiasm.

The new Hospital was also fortunate in its choice of a superintendent of nurses, for Miss Carrie M. Hall not only developed an effective nursing service for the Hospital, but a school of nursing with high academic standing that soon gained international prominence. Miss Hall also organized the nursing unit for Base Hospital No. 5 when it went to France in 1917.

There are many anecdotes from the early members of the Brigham surgical staff, none more vivid than John Morton's account of the house officers' early struggles with a penurious Superintendent:

> He was determined not to give the internes a night lunch. In consequence, the internes raided the private wards' ice boxes every night, taking the food that had been prepared for the next day. This started a feud between the administration and the internes which was finally resolved by Dr. Cushing saying that men who worked as hard as internes did needed nourishment and that the hospital should put out a night lunch of some kind. By this time the internes had been accustomed to high living so that when crackers, milk and cheese were put out, it did not compare with the roast chicken, ice cream, etc. of the free-raiding days. However, it was finally resolved correctly for everybody.

[5] Later appointments in the early group included: 1 January 1913, Charles Bagley, Jr.; 1 March 1913, Stephen A. Cobb, Jr. and John J. Morton; 1 July 1913, Edward B. Towne and Gilbert Horrax; 1 October 1913, Carl W. Rand; 1 November 1913, Elliott C. Cutler and Samuel H. Hurwitz; 11 December 1913, Walter M. Boothby; 1 March 1914, Stanley Cobb and Edwin P. Lehman.

Morton also alludes to the impact of Cushing and the resident system upon the medical profession in Boston. The other hospitals had junior and senior interneships but under this system the men obtained only minimal surgical training and had little opportunity to carry out major surgical procedures themselves. "Cushing men made the decisions as to the people in the ward services, and they were quite accomplished surgeons when they came to Boston. I don't know who was most active in leading the opposition to the resident system, but I presume the M.G.H. group. I remember distinctly that there was great surprise at the appointments of John Homans and David Cheever as attending men to the surgical staff. I consider that this was a great diplomatic stroke.'

Although Cushing continued to fret during his first three months in Boston about delays on the part of the Brigham architects and builders, there had been substantial progress, and he had plenty to occupy him meanwhile in the surgical laboratory and in preparing for press several papers that he had brought up with him from Baltimore. On 30 December 1912 he had gone to Cleveland to present a paper with Lewis H. Weed and Conrad Jacobson before the American Physiological Society on the nervous control of the pituitary.[6] This is one of Cushing's most important papers, since it gives indication of the large extent to which metabolic functions of the body as a whole are under nervous control.

In his First Annual Report as Surgeon-in-Chief of the Brigham Hospital H.C. records: "Our first patient, a woman with varicose veins of the legs, entered the hospital on January 27, 1913. In the twenty-four succeeding months to January 1, 1915 there were 2,184 admissions, the average of the last three months being about 150 patients a month which is approaching the present limits of our 110 beds." Cushing's annual reports were unusual documents and any one of them can be read with pleasure and profit, for they disclose a kind of vigor and originality which one seldom encounters in such administrative papers. When this first annual report, covering the years 1913-1914, was issued, many were surprised by the detailed appendix in which every fatality which had occurred in the hospital was described in detail. The causes of death were fully indicated, even when they involved bad clinical judgment, faulty anesthesia, or a mistake in diagnosis—and special attention was given to all cases falling into these three categories.

Throughout his clinical career Cushing stressed the imperative importance of autopsy examination. Christian was of the same mind

[6] "Further studies on the rôle of the hypophysis in the metabolism of carbohydrates. The autonomic control of the pituitary gland." (With L. H. Weed and C. Jacobson). *Johns Hopkins Hospital Bulletin,* February 1913, *24,* 40-52.

and had urged in 1911 that no patient be admitted to the Brigham whose family would not sign an autopsy release beforehand, but Cushing feared that this was too drastic and that they would in consequence be faced with the uncomfortable prospect of having certain patients rushed out of the hospital when death was imminent. He chose the more realistic compromise of bringing pressure to bear upon those families who were reluctant to grant permission for autopsies. In using the word "pressure," one is perhaps guilty of understatement, for H.C. with his important or unusual cases was capable of going to great lengths for his necropsies, even to paying funeral expenses. And when news of a patient's death came only after burial, hope was even then not abandoned, and on several such occasions the interests of science were ultimately served. Members of his house staff more than once packed their bags at midnight to go anywhere from northern Maine to South Carolina, and even, on one occasion, by plane to Florida to carry out an examination. Dr. Eisenhardt, his pathologist, has estimated that over the years he obtained autopsies on more than ninety per cent of his patients with brain tumor who had died either before or after operation.

During 1913, when he was organizing his operating service, he refused nearly all invitations, social and scientific. One exception was the Society of Clinical Surgery, to which he was always devoted. The meeting that year took him in March to New Orleans, where the group visited the clinic of Rudolph Matas. He broke away again to attend the opening exercises of the Phipps Clinic in Baltimore and to present a paper on psychiatric disturbances in patients with intracranial tumor (18 April).[7]

In the house officers' dining room at the Brigham Hospital hangs a group photograph taken on 30 April 1913 of the original group which constituted the professional, nursing, and administrative staff of the hospital. "In the group," wrote H.C. in his Sixth Annual Report, "are a few guests and the two central figures are John Collins Warren and William Osler [in derby hats]. . . . I have always thought of these two men as our guardian spirits of medicine and surgery—the Cosmas and Damian of the institution." Cushing continued:

> It happened that Sir William Osler was in this country on a visit and though we were in no condition to have a formal opening his presence forced the occasion, for we wished his baptism even though the hospital, with the exception of a single ward which was given over to House Officers, patients, operating plant, and kitchen, was still in the stage of scaffolding and plaster. His influence, indeed, even without this early blessing of our venture, was strong among us. Councilman was an old friend and colleague of the early days at

[7] "Psychic disturbances associated with disorders of the ductless glands." *American Journal of Insanity*, 1913, *69*, 965-990.

Johns Hopkins, Christian was a pupil, and the writer had been for many years a junior colleague, though not on his own service.

His address to us, which was taken down at the time, was informal and not given with any expectation of publication, though it deserves reprinting in full. What he said was usually wise, and as he gave us some admonitions and wise counsel it is perhaps fitting at this time to recall some of his words. "I have seen today what I have always wished would come here in Boston, what I have always thought would come: I have seen a new and perfectly striking departure in hospital growth. When I first became connected with the Toronto General Hospital it was organized according to the old plan, under which services were not divided and a man took three months at a time in medicine and surgery. This meant of course an extremely mixed service—the attendant might operate for a compound fracture and the next thing on his hands be a case of pneumonia. And perhaps it was but natural that there should be a great deal of opposition when medicine and surgery were divided, for nearly every physician, when he sees an operation going on, feels he could do it much better himself, and there is scarcely a surgeon who has not aspirations towards the treatment of pneumonia. Even today this old-fashioned system still prevails in a number of our large teaching hospitals, and in many of them the House Physician stays only six months.

"At the Johns Hopkins Hospital we made a new departure in hospital management—that is, a new departure in this country, but by no means in medical education, for we simply adopted a combination of German and English methods. In the first place we were paid officials of the hospital. We followed the German system of organization in appointing a head of the service, with a group of house physicians and a group of subordinates and with proper clinical laboratories. And we adopted the English plan of regarding the student as a part of the hospital organization—as large a part as an interne or nurse—of making him feel that he was not in the ward simply as a matter of granting him certain rights but that he was there to get his education as a clinical clerk or surgical dresser. I have always felt that as soon as a student enters the hospital he should begin to get his information just as he gets it when he goes out into practice, by daily contact with patients in the Out-Patient Department and wards. . . ."

In May H.C. managed to attend the meeting of the American Neurological Association in Washington, where he and Clifford Walker presented a paper on visual disturbances in cases of brain tumor.[8] In June his only public appearance was for his Shattuck Lecture before the Massachusetts Medical Society on diabetes insipidus,[9] a condition often encountered with tumors of the pituitary,

[8] "The perimetric deviations accompanying pituitary lesions (preliminary note)." *Journal of Nervous and Mental Diseases,* 1913, *40,* 793-794.

[9] "Concerning diabetes insipidus and the polyurias of hypophysial origin." *Boston Medical and Surgical Journal,* 19 June 1913, *168,* 901-910. The material for this lecture was largely based on the experimental work of Goetsch and Jacobson carried out in the Hunterian Laboratory before they went to Boston. Dr. Howard Naffziger who had been on service as Assistant Resident during 1911-1912 (in succession to Goetsch) had worked up such data on diabetes insipidus as were available from the Hopkins pituitary cases. Although the material was not used as such in the Shattuck Lecture, Cushing makes reference to their clinical experience. "It was my intention, in conjunction with

in which patients develop undue thirst and have a correspondingly large output of urine. This, as it happened, was a theme on which Cushing in the early days went somewhat off the track. Some of his friends suggested that he had become too "pituitary-minded," and that he was inclined to attribute every exotic new clinical entity to pituitary malfunction. Actually, he was not far wrong about diabetes insipidus. He was, however, disturbed a few years later when his associates, Percival Bailey and Frédéric Bremer, discovered that diabetes insipidus could be induced in animals by making small lesions at the base of the brain that did not encroach upon the pituitary. Cushing had believed that the condition resulted from injury to the posterior part of the pituitary gland. It turned out that both were right, for the area of the base of the brain which Bailey and Bremer had injured contains nerve cells that control the secretory cells in the posterior pituitary; the secretion elaborated by these cells regulates the kidney tubules and when the secretion is short, the kidney tubules fail to conserve the body's water—hence a disturbance either of these nerve cells or of the pituitary's secretory cells can cause diabetes insipidus. This stands as a further instance of highly productive research which Cushing stimulated by directing attention to a problem that he did not actually solve.

Later in June Yale University, wishing to recognize the distinguished appointment that had come to one of her sons, elected on the 18th to confer an honorary M.A. degree. It might seem that his Alma Mater would have given him higher academic recognition than this; actually, however, the honorary M.A. at Yale is seldom given except to younger alumni who have made contributions of unusual distinction. On this occasion other honorary degrees had been given to John G. Hibben, the President of Princeton, and Alfred Noyes, the British poet. William Howard Taft, who had become a professor at Yale, gave the Phi Beta Kappa address.

The 17th International Medical Congress

For Cushing the principal event of the year was the International Medical Congress held at London during the early days of August. Shortly before the Congress opened, he had word from the President of the Royal College of Surgeons in England (Sir Rickman Godlee,

---

one of my assistants, Dr. Howard C. Naffziger, to make a detailed report of our personal experiences in this direction during the past few years at the Johns Hopkins Hospital and to assemble the past clinical observations which had a bearing on the subject. This intent has been anticipated in large part by the publication, from Minkowski's clinic in Breslau, of an excellent article by E. Frank, in the *Berliner klinische Wochenschrift*." Naffziger had been invited to go to Boston with the original Brigham group and had accepted, but the illness of his mother in July 1912 prevented him from going.

nephew of Lord Lister) that he had been elected to Honorary Fellowship in the College. Now, at the age of forty-four, he also had the unusual distinction of giving one of the three principal addresses at the Congress.[10] The British had planned the Congress in "the grand manner," and it is doubtful whether the medical profession will ever again witness an international gathering of such pomp and circumstance. Referring to the Congress in the Osler biography, H.C. writes:

. . . Thirty-two years before, in 1881, another of these great congresses had been held in London, which Palmer Howard of McGill and his protégé William Osler had attended, and which was graced by "the presence of the Prince of Wales and the Crown Prince of Prussia." Both were now in their graves, and so also were all the great figures that made notable a congress at which Pasteur and Bastian had tilted over spontaneous generation, and at which Huxley, Lister, Virchow, and Koch had all spoken. Comparable to these, there were no outstanding figures at this second London congress, whose transactions, comprising a staggering list of subjects, may be said to have been based almost entirely on the further development of the researches of those giants. There was one exception perhaps, the most picturesque figure of the congress, a German from Frankfurt, Paul Ehrlich, the discoverer of salvarsan, whose brilliant career was to end just two years later, and after only twelve months of war, believing to the end that his Kaiser was an upholder of peace. . . .

It was a brilliant and memorable scene when, on the morning of August 6th, in the Albert Hall, packed to the doors and ceiling, Prince Arthur of Connaught, speaking for the King, formally opened the congress. He was followed by Sir Edward Grey, who spoke for the Government; and then came addresses from twenty-five or more official delegates from several countries, picturesque in uniform or academic gown. If nothing more, it showed what a vast labour of organization in providing for 7,000 participants had been put on the shoulders of practically one man, Dr. [later Sir] Wilmot P. Herringham. The whole congress was on such a scale as to make any subsequent attempt to rival it appear hopeless. Indeed, Professor von Müller, who, with his wife and daughter, was among Osler's special guests at Brown's, and who was chosen President of the succeeding congress (which, but for a cataclysm unforeseen, would have been held in Munich in 1917) expressed himself despairingly in regard to the possibility of competing with it. . . .

But, like all other gatherings of the sort, the congress was chiefly interesting on its social side. There were magnificent dinners—one of 500 guests at the Hotel Cecil given by the Government, and at which John Morley, Lord President of the Council, presided—and another at the Savoy, given by the President of the Congress. There were conversaziones at the South Kensington Museum, and by the Corporation of London at the Guildhall. There were receptions at Windsor Castle, at Lambeth Palace, at Strawberry Hill, and at all the London Hospitals. On Sunday there were excursions to Oxford, to Cambridge, and on the river, and, for the more pious who remained, a special service at St. Paul's and another at the Abbey. But perhaps the most picturesque of all the entertainments was the evening fête on August 11th given by Lord

[10] The other addresses were given by Paul Ehrlich (the discoverer of salvarsan, who was responsible for founding modern work in the field of chemotherapy), and by A. M. E. Chauffard, a well-known French clinician.

and Lady Strathcona in the Botanical Gardens at Regent's Park, which were decorated like fairyland by Japanese lanterns pendant from long bamboo poles, and where there was music from the Royal Artillery band, and where the pipers of the Scots Guards played, and a folk-song quartette provided entertainment. There a wonderful old man just approaching his ninety-third year stood under a marquee at the head of the receiving line, prepared to shake hands with approximately 5,000 people who approached in a sinuous queue without apparent end, until Osler in desperation, after this had gone on for more than an hour, entered into a conspiracy with his wife, who sent word to their host that she wished to speak to him. . . . Another aftermath was a letter in *The Times* of August 13th in which Sir Henry Morris expostulated against some statements expressed by speakers [Harvey Cushing] at the congress concerning the development leading towards whole-time professional services in hospitals and medical schools. . . .

The Oslers had taken a large suite (engaged a year in advance) at Brown's, their favorite hotel in London, and there they entertained for ten days at lunch, tea, and dinner. At the formal dinners and banquets H.C. consented to appear in full dress and decorations. The following week he had a sympathetic letter from Lewis Weed, who had also been present, expressing the hope "that Mrs. Cushing and you are recuperating rapidly from the effects of the 'gastronomic congress.' "

Cushing's discourse at the Congress attracted wide notice and also stirred up controversy—rather more than he had anticipated. The address bore the title, "Realignments in greater medicine: Their effect upon surgery and the influence of surgery upon them," and was presented at a plenary session in the Albert Hall on Thursday, 7 August, with Sir Thomas Barlow presiding. It was an energetic plea for reform in medical education, and for recognition of the rôle surgery had come to play in general medicine. He struck fearlessly at many of the outmoded practices of the British schools: "The more difficult and complicated problems of disease," he said, "will thus gravitate to large institutions where no longer 'visiting' appointees but directors of hospital units in continuous service, aided by a correspondingly adapted hospital administration, can uninterruptedly devote themselves to their work without entering into competition for practice beyond the walls of the institution. . . . After all, is not the essential thing to inculcate in the student's mind the habit of acquiring clinical knowledge for himself? And there is no possible way of doing this except by bringing him into immediate touch with the sick-bed. This, in the terms of Huxley, makes for centrifugal education, whereas our customary methods are centripetal in direction, with the effort to drive formulas into the student's head rather than to teach him how to produce ideas of his own."

This amounted to a frontal attack upon vested interests of the British hospital system, and particularly British custom with regard to training in surgery. It was true then that a student could pass an examination in surgery from knowledge gained in the dissecting room without ever having entered a surgical operating theatre. Cushing had also been actively interested in the antivivisection controversy for many years and he elected to take issue with the British antivivisection laws. Next morning *The Times* carried a detailed résumé of the address with the comment: "The audience seemed to expect that Professor Harvey Cushing would seize the opportunity to expound some of his own original work in brain surgery. The orator's emphatic protest against the antivivisection movement and his exposition of the broadening of the basis of scientific medicine, and the conversion of the family doctor into a scientific member of a hospital system were received with the keenest interest."

Cushing made the assertion, and this also caused trouble with some of his British colleagues, that the decline in productivity of the British hospitals since the time of John Hunter was no doubt due to the fact that animal experimentation had been curtailed. In *The Times* for 13 August Sir Henry Morris took vigorous exception to Cushing's deduction, and he proceeded to hurl Flexner's report on American medical education at Cushing's head. "It must, however, be, not the medical schools of Great Britain, but the deplorable history and discreditable condition of the medical schools in the United States, so vividly described by Mr. Abraham Flexner, which have inspired Professor Cushing with the forecast of what is to happen to hospitals, medical education, and the family doctors in the immediate future." To this Osler promptly replied in *The Times* for 14 August:

> Sir Henry Morris's opinion carries the weight of his distinguished position and long experience as a teacher, but I am afraid he does not realize the changed and changing conditions—certainly in medicine—or he would not speak of the head of a modern clinic as a 'Jack-of-all-trades.' Let him visit Krehl at Heidelberg, Kraus or His at Berlin, von Müller at Munich or, should he prefer a surgical clinic, that of the Mayo brothers at Rochester, Minnesota, and he will understand what organization under a 'Jack-of-all-trades' means. In the rearrangements of London University it is very important to have the active cooperation of such men as Sir Henry Morris; and of this I am sure—that a visit of a week or two to any one of the clinics I have mentioned would make of him a strong convert to the scheme suggested by the Royal Commission, so far as the hospital work is concerned.

The correspondence in *The Times* concerning the training of doctors went on for several weeks. Sir Henry Morris fulminated on three successive days (14, 15, and 16 Aug.) but on the 18th Sir Charles A. Ballance, the well-known British neurosurgeon, rose in Cushing's defense as had Osler. On the 23rd one W. H. Clayton Greene made another plea for the so-called "practical" doctor; he doubted "if the most erudite professors are going to instill scientific craving into the bulk of our students." This was too much for W.O. and from the Culag Hotel in Lochinver where he had gone with Lady Osler and the Cushings for a rest following the Congress he penned the following, somewhat acidulous response which he evidently thought better of and never sent:

> I have waited for a teacher more familiar with London students to protest against the Philistinism of Mr. C. G. whose letter appeared in your issue of August 23rd. As the London hospitals train our students, Oxford & Cambridge teachers have a direct interest in the problems of medical education in the metropolis. From my point of view there is only one intellectual infection of any permanent value to the medical student—the scientific spirit, & outlook, & attitude of mind, which he gets, often unconsciously, from his teachers and fellows. If good, it leavens his life's work. That he may be steeped in it and be at the same time thoroughly practical is the experience of scores of teachers & of scores of pupils, of men of the type of Bowman & Paget. The practical man [whom Mr. C. G. had lauded] was well defined by a general practitioner in my company a few moments ago as one who never learns anything after leaving his hospital. I should be precious sorry to have any student in whom I was interested come under the influence of a man who in these days could say that "scientific education may be excellent as an ideal but I doubt if it materially assists the average practitioner in the treatment of disease." Mr. G. represents a type—the men who jeered at Harvey, scoffed at Pasteur & scorned Lister—the carpenters in surgery and the pill-mongers in medicine, without vision beyond the bench or the counter. The tragedy is that the type persists.

On the whole, however, the address was well received, and H.C. had a large number of congratulatory letters from discriminating persons. The summary to the address deserves quotation:

> These, then, are some of the transformations and realignments which are taking place in medicine, and which, directly or indirectly, have come through the great contributions made a generation ago by those with whose names this address was introduced: the public, not only awake to the great developments in medicine which animal experimentation has made possible, but ready to participate in their application for the general welfare; the physician at large, the valued family adviser, reaching out toward the important problems of hygiene and prevention of disease, while the individual patient, as the complexities of disease unravel, needing more and more specialized and more and more surgicalized treatment, gravitates toward the modern hospital; the preclinical science departments, which formerly existed in splendid isolation, with their fences down, owing to the levelling influence of experimental pathology; hospital organizations undergoing changes which will ultimately require the full time and continuous activity of those who serve them for the benefit alike of student, of science, and of patient.
>
> The kaleidoscope of medicine is turning. These are merely some of the present rearrangements of the images as I see them—new patterns from original fragments—for "Is there anything whereof it may be said: See, this is new? It hath been already of old time, which was before us."

It has been intimated that H.C. had a busy week during the Congress. Not only did he attend the opening banquet given by Lord Beauchamp to meet the Lord President of the Council on 5 August, but he was admitted on the 6th to Honorary Fellowship in the Royal College of Surgeons,[11] and attended the dinner for the Honorary Fellows that evening; on the 7th came his major address on "Realignments," and on the 8th a paper on the organs of internal secretion which was published promptly in the *Lancet* for 23 August; on the 9th he gave a third paper on "Affections of the pituitary body" which was likewise published in the *Lancet* for the 23d; finally on the 11th came a fourth paper on tumors of the brain, also issued in the *Lancet*.[12]

Following the Congress the Cushings went north for a quiet week with the Oslers at Lochinver, after which the Oslers proceeded to Inverness to be with the Strathconas for a week-end at Glencoe and the Cushings made their way to Liverpool to sail on the *Lusitania*. The children had been at Little Boar's Head for the summer and Mrs. Cushing joined them on her arrival. H.C. remained in Boston, where he set out with high spirits to put into effect some of the things that he had so energetically recommended in his "Realignments" address in London. It must have given him some satisfaction to read in the *Journal of the American Medical Association* for 30 August a generous allusion to his address. Sir Edward Schafer had drafted a resolution in support of animal experimentation, which had been adopted unanimously at the closing meeting of the Congress. "Not only this," the editorial goes on to say, "but Harvey Cushing's brilliant address in surgery contained a well-reasoned and vividly illustrated argument and an emphatic protest against restrictive legislation which would seriously impede, if it did not entirely arrest, the progress of medical knowledge."

The hospital wards at the Brigham were now largely completed and his operating unit had been satisfactorily equipped. The amphitheater, to his annoyance, had not yet been finished, but much refreshed by his trip, he plunged into clinical work with his usual vigor; now that he could do all of his operating at the Brigham, he refused to work elsewhere.

Cushing's daily routine varied little. After he had shaved with an open-edged razor, he usually breakfasted just before eight; then Gus, the chauffeur, drove him down to the hospital, which was only five

[11] It was remarked by a British friend that Cushing shared with King Edward VII alone the distinction of being an Honorary Fellow of both the Royal College of Surgeons and the Royal College of Physicians (see p. 710).

[12] "The correlation of the organs of internal secretion and their disturbances." *Lancet*, 23 August 1913, 2, 546-547; "The treatment of tumours of the brain and the indications for operation." *Lancet*, 23 August, 6 September 1913, 2, 552, 739; "Affections of the pituitary body." *Lancet*, 23 August 1913, 2, 565.

or six minutes away at the rate Gus drove, so that he was regularly at his desk before eight-thirty. He first went through the morning mail and then he dictated for at least two hours. If an operation were scheduled—and he averaged about four a week throughout his years at the Brigham—the middle of the day was completely occupied with the operation and a long operative note. The latter was always a detailed affair, generally accompanied by a sketch, which for some reason he usually made while his rubber gloves were still on. Then came the dressings of those who had had operations during the preceding week, and after that new cases were looked at and the next operation decided upon. By that time it was often five o'clock and he frequently returned to his office to find a group of prospective patients waiting to see him after having been examined by one of his assistants. His secretarial staff were apt to be a little frantic by this time in the afternoon, his mail not having been signed and they having been left with the somewhat wearing task of keeping the 'three o'clock appointment' from becoming too restless.

Sandwiched into this busy daily routine would be frequent visits from his house staff, from his associates in medicine, and from groups in the surgical laboratory. Postmortem studies always interested him, and while he came in later years to leave the removal of the brain to his colleagues, the task of sectioning it was rarely delegated but was always undertaken with lively curiosity, for therein lay the final answer to his uncertainties. The ever-patient Gus, at the door by five-thirty, seldom drove H.C. home before seven.

Although Cushing always ate sparingly, he had a particular fondness for hot toast drenched in butter. He always had several slices at breakfast and in the late afternoon after operating he would often make more toast, which he would munch in his dressing room while dictating his operative notes. He seldom ate lunch except when attending a meeting of the Saturday Club, and even then his friends noticed that he was likely to become so interested in general conversation that he forgot to eat.

This apparent unawareness of food was the despair of his surgical assistants. He seldom got around to operating before eleven, and the operations frequently lasted four or five hours. Therefore, since his assistants had generally begun to do the preliminaries by 10.00 a.m., it was a long, empty stretch before anyone on the team had food. Many times operations that had commenced at 10.00 or 10.30 were not completed until 4.00 or 5.00. Later on, following the introduction of the electrical cautery and other more adequate methods of hemostasis, the operations became shorter; but even then a craniotomy averaged two and a half to three hours and a cerebellar exploration, because of the meticulous closure, at least four hours.

NO. 305 WALNUT STREET, BROOKLINE, MASSACHUSETTS

The house in Brookline which the Cushings occupied from the time of their arrival in Boston in October 1912 until they departed for New Haven in October 1933

SOME MEMBERS OF THE SATURDAY CLUB

Charles Sprague Sargent James Ford Rhodes
Henry Lee Higginson Harvey Cushing
Charcoal drawings by John Singer Sargent

UNOFFICIAL OPENING OF P.B.B.H. 30 APRIL 1913

The group photograph of the original staff of the Peter Bent Brigham Hospital taken scarcely two months after the first patients had been received; the ceremony had been arranged on the occasion of Sir William Osler's visit to Boston. Seated in the center row are: Charles Sedgwick Minot, W. T. Councilman, H. A. Christian, Sir William Osler, John Collins Warren, H.C., H. B. Howard, L. H. Burlingham, W. B. Cannon. Miss Carrie M. Hall, first Superintendent of Nurses, stands immediately behind Dr. Warren

SURGICAL STAFF OF P.B.B.H. 1914

The original surgical house staff of the Peter Bent Brigham Hospital in the spring of 1914. *Standing:* E. C. Cutler, Gilbert Horrax, L. H. Weed, E. B. Towne, J. J. Morton, S. H. Hurwitz. *Seated:* C. W. Rand, Emil Goetsch, H.C., John Homans, Conrad Jacobson. *Front:* E. P. Lehman, Stanley Cobb. [Paul Wegefarth and E. G. Grey are missing.]

Having survived the day on toast and two eggs in the morning, with more toast and a cup of tea at four, he usually ate quite heartily in the evening, but not enough to make him sleepy, for he was at his desk with the greatest regularity from eight until midnight. If the family had guests for dinner, he was a most gracious host—if the day had not been too exacting at the hospital—but he had cultivated the Oslerian habit of disappearing promptly the meal was over. And if a guest happened to be a medical student or a house officer, he was backed out of the front door half an hour after dinner and was on his way down the street before he quite realized what had happened to him.

During his active years Cushing was as a rule most abstemious as far as alcoholic beverages were concerned. When travelling, particularly with epicurean friends such as William Welch and Arnold Klebs, he made merry with them, but he often complained that his gastric capacity could not compete with that of his high-living friends. However, he was an inveterate smoker and, on days on which he did not operate, he was capable of going through two or more packets of cigarettes. Occasionally he tried to break himself of the habit on a corncob pipe, but he usually became so irritable during these periods of good intentions that his family and staff were glad to see the cigarettes come out again. During the last few years of his life, when it became evident that tobacco was impairing his health, he made a number of heroic attempts on denicotinized cigarettes, but he never succeeded in weaning himself from tobacco. At this time he began to take cocktails and wine more freely and when his medical advisers tried to be stern with him about using his denicotinized cigarettes, he responded with a look of sardonic impatience, "Damn it, do you like a cocktail without alcohol?"

Cushing's capacity for sustained work was truly remarkable and many have wondered why he did not go stale. After 1901 he practically never took a vacation except when ill and once commented drily that the one time he was wheedled into going fishing, the European war broke out. It was no doubt the variety in Cushing's existence that kept him at the top of his form for such long stretches; for he could turn quickly from a heavy day of operating to Vesalius or to a laboratory problem. His dining clubs also helped to divert his mind into other channels of thought and were a further source of relaxation. Mrs. Albert Bigelow, a near neighbor, gives a vivid picture of the Cushing household at this time:

It was probably about 1912 when we first began to see the Cushings. They asked us to play tennis with them and we went there often for a set of doubles with Kate and Harvey, or sometimes for an afternoon of cutting in, when young doctors and their wives and other friends of theirs were there too. The Cushing children nearly matched our children as to ages and all went to the same private school, close to the Cushings' house. Betsey and our Gwladys became close friends from the age of five or so and have always kept up that warm friendship. Bill, Mary, and our eldest daughter and two sons all went to the same dancing class, and Bill and our Bert sometimes went pheasant shooting together. All these things drew our two families together and soon it became our custom to drop in at the Cushings' at their hospitable tea hour once or twice a week. . . .

Albert and I and our youngest daughter Gwladys, who went there more than any of our other children on account of her close attachment to Betsey, will never forget the tea hour at that house. Kate created there a remarkable atmosphere of hospitality. Just as Harvey was a genius in his profession, so was she a genius in managing the perfect home for such a man. He could always come back from the terrific strain of his work at the hospital to a peaceful home and a serene wife who had intelligent understanding, a grand sense of humor, and who supplied the creature comforts which only a good housekeeper can provide. . . .

Albert and Harvey spent several summers in Brookline when Kate and her children had left for Little Boar's Head and I was away for part of the summer with our family. One year I was there through July and we often played tennis with Harvey on his court, some of the other doctors and their wives making up the right number for doubles. Harvey always had tea before we started to play and he sat behind the urn and was most particular about making the tea in a preheated earthenware teapot and letting it simmer the proper length of time, telling amusing and interesting stories as he poured it. . . .

At first both Harvey and Albert strongly disliked to see women smoking. Later Albert got entirely over this point of view and I think Harvey kept up his attitude largely as part of a game with Kate and his daughters, for there was always whispering and giggling when they heard him coming if they were smoking, and they quickly put out their cigarettes. Of course he knew all about it, and I think he just kept up his insistence that he didn't want to see them smoking as a kind of joke, or to tease them a little.

This side of Harvey's character reminds me that he told us that at the first meeting of the Saturday Club which he attended after the war, he wondered whether the conversation would be as good as usual without any wine or liquor to stimulate the flow of words, and he was delighted to find that the talk was as witty and bright as ever, and the group sat about longer and broke up later than in the days before prohibition, which the Club had decided to observe.

* * * * *

During his first two years at Boston Cushing had a particularly resourceful group of young investigators. One of them, Lewis Weed, had started his work during 1913 on cerebrospinal fluid and its pathways. A series of nine papers on this subject were subsequently issued from the surgical laboratory—the introductory paper being written by Cushing himself.[13] But the administrative load of organizing the new hospital, his teaching, and his mounting clinical burden,

[13] "Studies on the cerebro-spinal fluid and its pathway. I. Introduction." *Journal of Medical Research,* September 1914, n.s. *26,* 1-19.

most of which he was carrying personally, drew him more and more away from the experimental laboratory. Nevertheless, he had a deft way of keeping in touch with the experiments and was a stern task-master when a manuscript prepared by one of his assistants was being made ready for publication. He was especially particular about details of illustrations and bibliography, and he also insisted that a scientific paper should have histrionic qualities, that the reader's attention should be engaged from the outset by having the problem presented in an interesting manner. Frequently this brought him into conflict with journal editors, especially those of the American Medical Association who, he felt, had little imagination about writing; he said that after a paper had gone through their editorial mill, it came back sounding as though it had been written by a high school boy from the backwoods—in fact, all their papers, he insisted, might have come from the same uninspired source.

There is no doubt that Cushing, despite the attractiveness of many of his scientific presentations, tended at times to overdramatize, particularly his clinical reports, in an effort to make them interesting. In later life he gradually learned that his best men—those who had views of their own and who had cultivated their own literary style—often did not see eye-to-eye with him about scientific writing, and he came more and more to allow them their own preferences—even as he had forced Kocher and Kronecker to do.

During the late months of 1913 and the whole year of 1914 he continued as far as possible to avoid outside commitments. In October 1913 the decennial meeting of the Society of Clinical Surgery was held at Rochester, with the Mayos their hosts once again.

> . . . Our Autumn meeting of that, our decennial year, held at the Mayo Clinic was memorable not only for its demonstration of the remarkable growth that had taken place since the time of our first visit eight years before but also for the delightful two-day excursion down the Mississippi from Red Wing to Dubuque on the steamer Oronoco which Richard Harte, to demonstrate his training as a pilot, steered safely through the shoals of the river the better part of one afternoon. Another happy memory lies in the fact that Mumford was well enough to be with us and was elected President of the Society at this meeting, which was his last. He died at Clifton Springs a year later from complications of a long-standing mitral stenosis, and Crile's fine tribute to him appears in the minutes of the 22d meeting held in Boston November 13, 1914.

On 12 November Osler's old friend, H. V. Ogden, lured H.C. once again to Milwaukee for a medical meeting; later (25 February 1914), he gave the Weir Mitchell Lecture at Philadelphia, describing his most recent experiences in pituitary surgery. In the monograph on the pituitary, which had gone to press in the spring of 1911, he had recorded the results of 61 operations on 43 patients. He was now able to report upon 114 cases, in which 125 operations had been performed with only 10 fatalities, or a mortality of 8 per cent (case mortality of 10.5 per cent).[14] Fifty of these operations had been performed in Boston with a mortality rate of only 4 per cent.

The result was both gratifying and impressive, and it incidentally indicates that between the time that the hospital was first opened at the end of January 1913 and February 1914—12 months—he had operated on 50 pituitary patients; during the same period he had undertaken at least 150 other major procedures. These latter were reported upon at a meeting of the American Medical Association held at Atlantic City on 23 June. In the 149 craniotomies he had had a case mortality of 7.3 per cent. He pointed out that the operative mortality for 265 consecutive cases at the National Hospital at Queen Square, London, had been 53.3 per cent.[15]

1914

In August, Elliott Cutler, who was then a surgical house officer, took Cushing on a fishing trip in the Canadian woods and, as previously mentioned, it was while there that H.C. received the first news of the declaration of war. During the autumn of 1914 Cushing occupied himself with "preparedness" agitation, but he also found time on 5 October to attend the twenty-fifth anniversary celebration of the Johns Hopkins Hospital. On 3 November the Harvard Medical Society, which was now well-established, had arranged a memorial meeting for H.C.'s warm friend, James G. Mumford, who had died on 16 October. On this occasion H.C. read an appreciation which was never published.

On the 12th the Peter Bent Brigham Hospital held a Founder's Day celebration at which Edmund D. Codman gave an account of his trusteeship of the Brigham estate, and Welch delivered the principal address, dwelling upon his favorite theme—the position and importance of a university hospital in medical education. H.C. followed appropriately on much the same theme, elaborating what he had said in London about the centripetal versus the centrifugal hospital service. There were also brief addresses by John Collins Warren and Frank Billings. On Henry Barton Jacobs' copy of the Founder's Day program, which H.C. had evidently filched, one finds the following frank comment set down in pencil in Jacobs' hand: "Very stupid speeches by Welch and Billings. Harvey Cushing made a fine presentation for the staff." Welch's speech, to be sure, was not his most inspired—perhaps he had prepared it beforehand instead of writing

[14] "Surgical experiences with pituitary disorders." *Journal of the American Medical Association,* 31 October 1914, *63,* 1515-1525.

[15] "Concerning the results of operations for brain tumor." *Journal of the American Medical Association,* 16 January 1915, *64,* 189-195.

it the night before on the Federal Express, where, in 1908, he had acquitted himself brilliantly in preparing his Ether Day Address.

On the 18th we find H.C. attending a large dinner at the Copley Plaza held in honor of the 80th birthday of his warm friend and admirer, Major Henry Lee Higginson, at which Higginson made his *confessio fidei:* ". . . from my boyhood I have had a deep and passionate wish that we should live according to our highest ideals, that we should live the higher life, that we should remember the creed of our nation, that we should try to make others happier in order that our country should be prosperous in the highest sense of the word, and that our country's people should be happy. There are many things in this life which are hard to bear, and if any man can make the path of anybody else happier, he is a fortunate man."

The Full-time Plan

Within a year of the opening of the Brigham Hospital Cushing and Christian found themselves plunged into a controversy over the full-time plan for clinical instruction—which caused Cushing to submit his resignation to Mr. Lowell and forced Harvard to decline a gift of a million and a half dollars from the General Education Board. The story turns on Cushing's long-time convictions about medical education, on the basic issues of which he would accept no compromise.

Cushing had entered Harvard shortly after the Medical School curriculum had been drastically revised, he having been in one of the earliest classes to have the privilege of laboratory experimentation in the preclinical years, and also to have the option of a four-year rather than a three-year course of study. He came to feel, however, that important as laboratory experimentation is, preclinical departments had become overspecialized to the detriment of a student's ultimate clinical training. "Here we are," he said later to Abraham Flexner in 1921, "struggling to preserve a race of pure preclinical scientists who are unable to reproduce their own species unless we incubate them. I begin to think they waste an immense amount of the student's time and it would be infinitely better if the students began their first two years with clinical work and supplemented it by such laboratory exercises as their clinical work indicated the necessity of. I think in this way you will probably get more men interested in science than we do now. . . . I told Cannon the other day that we ought to give up the course in physiology and that he had better come into the clinic as a Professor of Medicine and teach a little physiology on the side; of course he had a fit."

H.C. was probably only half serious about giving up physiology as a formal part of the curriculum, but he was in deadly earnest in suggesting that students should be brought into contact with clinical problems at the earliest possible moment in their career in medical school. At the Harvard Medical School in 1925 he inaugurated Saturday morning clinics on a purely voluntary basis for first-year students. They attended in great numbers and second-year men often turned up to repeat this elective opportunity. Cushing was also scornful of preclinical teachers who lived in an ivory tower and refused to make reference to possible clinical applications of the material which they were presenting to their students. He would have been the first to recognize the contribution of laboratory men to the advancement of medical science, and there were many of his Ph.D. colleagues without clinical training for whom he had profound admiration. But he was equally firm in his conviction that a man who lacked clinical experience was inevitably handicapped if called upon to teach students of medicine, and there were many of his junior colleagues with Ph.D.'s whom he browbeat into completing their clinical training.

The full-time controversy in which Cushing became so heavily involved had an important historical background. During the 19th century a medical student received his training largely through associating himself with a man already in practice. The better schools offered pre-clinical training, but until the last quarter of the 19th century, clinical opportunities were usually limited. There were lectures on clinical subjects, but the students in this country seldom saw a patient until after they had been graduated, for the clinical clerkships of the British schools had not been adopted here until the end of the century. Surgeons in Britain, however, had to get their training the hard way for in England primary emphasis had always been, and to a certain extent continues to be, placed on anatomy. Dissection became the cornerstone of British medical education, and while John Hunter, at the end of the 18th century, had attempted to liberalize the curriculum, in 1914 it still remained true, as mentioned earlier, that a man wishing to go into surgery could pass examinations qualifying him to practise without ever having himself performed a surgical operation, the examination questions being almost wholly anatomical.

It was the special contribution of the Johns Hopkins Medical School to medical education that students were brought into the wards, as H.C.'s dedication of the 'Osler' significantly indicates:

TO MEDICAL STUDENTS

> In the hope that something of Osler's spirit may be conveyed to those of a generation that has not known him; and particularly to those in America, lest it be forgotten who it was that made it possible for them to work at the bedside in the wards.

In 1900 medical schools throughout the United States had few common standards. There were fly-by-night schools that gave degrees for a consideration, and there were others that pretended to give a well-rounded course such as those in New York where the students were obliged to supplement their information through attendance at special "quiz" classes like those with which Dr. Welch had become involved in the early days.

Although much of the credit for the vast reform in medical education during the early years of the twentieth century must be given to Mr. Abraham Flexner for his report on *Medical education in the United States and Canada,* issued in 1910, one should recall that the Committee on Medical Education and especially the Council on Medical Education (created in 1904) of the American Medical Association were largely responsible for initiating the movement and for implementing the recommendations of the Flexner report. Arthur Dean Bevan, Chairman of the A.M.A. Council on Medical Education from 1904 to 1928, wrote with pardonable pride in 1932: "As a matter of fact the American Medical Association deserved practically all of the credit for the reorganization of medical education in this country. It was at our request that Pritchett of the Carnegie Foundation agreed to make a report of our work as a special report of the Carnegie Foundation. Eighty per cent of the Flexner report was taken from the work of the Council on Medical Education. We were, of course, very grateful to Pritchett and to Flexner for this work as it enabled us to put out of business the twenty-two homeopathic schools and twelve eclectic schools which were running at that time." In regard to "full-time"[16] Dr. Bevan adds: "I was at New Haven at the meeting of the American Surgical Association and had the opportunity of looking over and talking over the Medical School at Yale. I cannot help but feel that they would be very much stronger if they were on the Harvard scheme of organization rather than the full-time scheme." The background of the Harvard controversy and compromise, for which Harvey Cushing and Henry Christian are principally responsible, is indicated in the following exchange:

Boston,
H.C. to President Lowell *30 March 1914.*

Dear Mr. Lowell It is my impression that the reasons for the adoption in Baltimore of the proposal from the General Education Board were based upon the feeling, chiefly on the part of the heads of the preclinical departments, that the school was getting into a rut, from which it should be extricated no

[16] The "full-time" plan was originally proposed in 1902 by Lewellys Barker who, as a teacher of anatomy in Chicago, felt that medical standards would be improved if a certain proportion of teachers in clinical years could be paid sufficiently by the universities so that it would be unnecessary for them to have the burden of private practice, and if they did see private cases, the fees for such consultations should accrue to the universities.

matter how seriously the method adopted might temporarily wrench their machine. Unquestionably this feeling would not have arisen had the heads of the clinical departments been given the opportunity some years ago voluntarily to place themselves on a whole-service basis similar to that on which my colleague and myself now serve at the Brigham Hospital.

It seems to me that the clinical departments of the Harvard Medical School, on the other hand, by their own initiative give promise of getting out of the rut into which they had fallen, and the injection at this time of a new element into the situation might seriously complicate it. Were we at a standstill or in financial straits we might have to ask others to help pull our load, and to accept their terms no matter how experimental they might appear to be. On the other hand, were our engine moving more smoothly than it is, we might otherwise be justified in venturing to test it on an unbroken road.

Not without various difficulties we are slowly working out our own problems at the Brigham Hospital—problems which concern the continuous whole-time service of the clinical chiefs—problems therefore which are somewhat idealistic and which moreover are novel to those who are concerned with the hospital administration. The difficulties are gradually being smoothed out, but the experiment, from all points of view, cannot as yet be deemed a complete success. Before we have quite found ourselves, on this basis, it is proposed that we make a still more radical experiment in so far as our relation to the institution is concerned. . . . You have had the assurance of my interest in and sympathy with the essential features of the proposal from the General Education Board. You have had the assurance also of my complete readiness to withdraw from my interlocked university and hospital position in favor of anyone whom you may wish to appoint on the new basis if you are convinced not only that the step should be taken but that it should be taken at this time, lest the opportunity be lost; for I am unwilling that my tenure of office should block the movement if it is the consensus of opinion that our more rapid advancement as a medical institution lies urgently in this direction.

To this President Lowell replied on 4 April:

. . . I understand your position perfectly. It is, substantially, that we have made a real innovation, which promises to be a great improvement in clinical teaching, in connection with the Brigham Hospital; and that it is unwise, at present, to complicate this with further experiment, the results of which must necessarily be uncertain. Your position seems to me perfectly reasonable; and while it will prevent our applying to the General Education Board now for a gift for full-time clinical professors, it may not prevent our doing so at some future time, in case the experiment as now tried at Johns Hopkins proves successful.

This letter seemed to close the subject temporarily, but Mr. Flexner was not discouraged and three months later was still asking that final action be postponed until all aspects of the full-time plan for the Brigham Hospital had been explored. President Lowell, however, was anxious to have the matter settled.

President Lowell to H.C. *10 July 1914.*

Dear Dr. Cushing I have received a letter from Mr. Flexner of which I enclose a copy. We ought to make up our minds very quickly whether we can or cannot present a plan for full-time professors in connection with the Brigham, which will be satisfactory to the General Education Board; and the suggestion made—I suppose with your approval—is that you should become Visiting Surgeon, or a special member of the Staff at the Brigham, and that the Surgical Chief should be some younger man. This is very much in accord with what you have said to me, but I had not supposed it would be accepted. It seems, however, that Mr. Flexner might do so. . . .

H.C. to President Lowell *Circa July 1914.*

Dear Mr. Lowell . . . Mr. Flexner came in to see me after their meeting and we talked the matter over afresh. I took the liberty of letting him read a copy of my letter to you of March 30 and I think he fully understands my reasons for what was there expressed. So far as I can see, the situation has not in any way altered in the succeeding three months. I would be glad to see you and Dr. Bradford here at any time convenient to you, but I can hardly believe there will be anything more for me to say other than what I have already said: namely, that if you are convinced not only that the step should be taken but that it should be taken at this time, I will gladly withdraw in favour of anyone whom the Brigham Hospital and the School may wish to appoint in my place so soon as they let me know that the change is for the best.

Christian was of the same mind and wrote Mr. Lowell in like vein. After eight months of further negotiations Mr. Lowell made a more definite proposal just as H.C. was leaving for Paris:

President Lowell to H.C. *6 March 1915.*

Dear Dr. Cushing . . . If I were in your position, I should be unwilling to accept a full-time professorship. On the other hand, if I were (as I believe you are) probably the first brain surgeon in the world, I should—if I were wise—not want to have my contributions to surgery impaired by the routine and fret incident to managing a clinic, for I know by experience how difficult it is to do original work and administer anything at the same time. One always thinks that it will take very little time, and practically it eats up a great amount of energy.

I should not write this letter now, had you not told me that you would be perfectly satisfied to give up the position of chief of the clinic, and devote yourself to your surgery. Now, what I have to suggest for your consideration is that you should retain the Moseley Professorship of Surgery, have control of as many beds at the Brigham as are necessary for cerebral and such other surgery as you desire to practice, but that you pass over the position of surgeon-in-chief and control of the clinic to the holder of a new professor's chair, on the full-time basis. I know you will answer this letter frankly, for if the suggestion does not appeal to you, I shall drop it. If it does appeal to you I shall expect you to tell the Trustees of the Hospital so.

To this H.C. responded with a disarming grace which under the circumstances was unexpected:

H.C. to President Lowell *7 March 1915.*

Dear Mr. Lowell I have assured you before that any plan which you may think feasible in bringing about the establishment of full-time positions in the School on the General Education Board basis, will receive my support and cooperation. As I see the matter there are three alternatives: (1) for me to accept a position on exactly the same basis as that occupied by the Professor of Surgery at Johns Hopkins; (2) for me to step aside and serve the School and Hospital under the individual whom we may all agree upon as the best available appointee for the position; (3) for me to accept the proposal which you make in your letter of yesterday, though it is one which I fear the General Education Board will not look favorably upon.

The first of these alternatives is one, we agree, that I should not be expected to accept. Either of the latter alternatives I will promptly and gladly accept whenever you are prepared for the move. I will send a copy of this note to Mr. Cochrane as you request, with the hope that some agreement may be come to between yourselves and the General Education Board. I appreciate greatly your friendly and sympathetic letter.

The affair was finally settled by the hard-headed business instincts of the Brigham Trustees while H.C. was in Paris. Harvard turned down the offer of $1,500,000 from the General Education Board.

Boston,
Alexander Cochrane to President Lowell *15 April 1915.*

Dear President Lowell When the Committee on Whole-time met with you at Mr. Howe's office, it was suggested that the Committee might consult to advantage with our Medical Adviser Dr. F. C. Shattuck and also with Dr. Henry P. Walcott. The Committee had a most interesting meeting with these two gentlemen on Monday evening, March 22nd, at the Somerset Club. I think, perhaps, it is only necessary to sum up the result of a long and most earnest talk which, of course, only took the form of opinions and advice.

The opinions and advice were unanimous that it was not advisable for the Peter Bent Brigham Hospital to make any changes in the Staff, having in mind introducing Whole-time in the Hospital. It was felt that this experiment on Whole-time was being tried out elsewhere. It was thought by some of us that there would be certain well-defined risks of friction in the Staff if we introduced a new Chief Surgeon. While coming to this conclusion, we had fully in mind the fact that our present Chief Surgeon had written to you that he was quite willing to make the change. It was felt that the system now being apparently successfully worked in our Hospital might ultimately prove to be the better way and be a Whole-time that would commend itself to all in the future.

I wish to convey the idea to you that there was no dogmatizing and that we all felt experience might modify the view of any of the gentlemen taking part in the meeting. Our decision was come to with the united regret of the Committee and also of the two gentlemen who took part in the discussion for the reason that we all should be glad if the benefaction from the General Education Board could come to Harvard College. If you think it is desirable, I shall be glad to have the Committee meet you or I will meet you myself.

In H.C.'s next to the last Annual Report he writes of all this in retrospect, and since this represents his final and most considered statement on the full-time scheme, it is quoted in full:

Our American medical schools at that time [1904], mostly proprietary in character, were unnecessarily numerous and most of them of an inferior type. The American Medical Association after an elaborate survey had already succeeded in a quiet way in closing the doors of some of the least worthy schools when in 1910 there appeared Mr. Abraham Flexner's elaborate report to the

Carnegie Foundation for the Advancement of Teaching on "Medical Education in the United States and Canada." This sensational publication served to call public attention to the deplorable conditions that prevailed and had a profoundly beneficial effect not only in accelerating the elimination of many poorly equipped and conducted medical schools but at the same time in raising the standards of the survivors. While in this monumental report the Johns Hopkins was singled out and held up to view as approaching the ideal, only two years elapsed before the clinical departments of this particular school came privately, by the same virile pen, to be severely criticized. To correct what were regarded as abuses of their academic positions a full-time service for the chiefs of the clinics was proposed and though there were differences of opinion, the program, financed by the General Education Board, was finally adopted and, with Dr. Barker's resignation, in January, 1914, put in full operation.

Meanwhile, in 1912 Dr. Christian and I, in full accord with the general principles of a whole-time service, were in the process of coming to a working arrangement with the Board of Incorporators of the Brigham Hospital. Their original proposal, that we give half-time to the hospital and half-time elsewhere to our private practice, was looked upon as an arrangement unfavorable to the future development and reputation of the hospital on which we hoped to concentrate our energies. This implied some provision, however modest, for the reception of private patients. While the sick poor of Suffolk County had been uppermost in the testator's mind, he could scarcely have foreseen in 1870 that they would fare better in a teaching hospital with a university connection, where no distinction would be drawn in the matter of care between the indigent and those able to pay their way. And after an opinion favorable to this view had been legally handed down, the cautious administrators of the fund finally acceded to our alternative proposal and I trust have had no reason to regret it.

So it came about that we were the first clinical teachers, so far as I know, who desired and were permitted to give their undivided attention to the work of a teaching hospital and to confine their professional activities within its walls. In so doing we were to have the privilege of accepting fees from patients who might consult us during such hours as we felt justified in setting aside for this purpose. It was foreseen that the privilege of thus supplementing a meagre hospital salary was one which might come to be abused, but experience proves that with the increasing growth of the hospital we tend from year to year to give less rather than more time to our private affairs.

Subsequently, through funds provided by the General Education Board, of which Mr. Flexner by now had become the Director, the major clinical departments at Johns Hopkins, as already stated, were put upon a full-time clinical basis which differed from our own in a single respect—and this, be it said, was regarded by the sponsors of the plan as an all-important difference—namely, that the institution rather than the attendants was to collect and utilize the fees from private patients. Here, then, appeared to be an opportunity to put to the test of time a controlled experiment regarding a new and revolutionary academic policy. Would the holders of full-time clinical chairs on a larger and fixed salary prove in the long run to be more stimulating teachers, more productive investigators, and better hospital servants than would those who are at liberty to supplement a smaller salary through personal dealings with their private patients? The answer might then have been foreseen, namely, that the personal characteristics of those chiefly concerned will determine whether they will be happier and, therefore, accomplish more on one or the other basis.

Our self-imposed program, however, was not permitted to stand unchallenged for in October, 1913, after some overtures, the General Education Board offered to give the Harvard Medical School a million and a half dollars provided the chiefs-of-clinic at the Brigham Hospital would agree to serve as full-time officers on the same financial basis as that about to be instituted in Baltimore. The Medical School was then in debt and the promised financial relief would have been a veritable windfall; but I never could convince myself that those here who pressed us to accept the restrictions imposed by the gift (apart from several of our preclinical colleagues) were interested as much in the principle involved as in securing the gift. On my own part, a term of service limited to twenty years with an academic salary on which a family of children were to be educated and no pension in sight in case of accident or ill health seemed a dubious proposition. I doubted, moreover, whether such an arrangement would in any way activate me and feared, indeed, that it might encourage indolence. If the purpose of the plan was to prevent the attendants in university hospitals from exploiting their position for their personal ends, there was just as much reason to fear, human nature being what it is, that hospital superintendents and trustees might be tempted in a pinch to exploit their salaried professional attendants. With no pretense to be anything more than an amateur investigator, I could not see that a fixed salary would either improve my status in this respect or give me any more freedom for such researches as I was capable of directing or undertaking. And coming of a race of general practitioners, the intimate and confidential relation between doctor and patient—one of the most precious things in Medicine—was in my blood and I could not look upon the cold institutional program with any great enthusiasm, much less with any expectation that it would serve to make something out of me that I was not already.

To make the story short, more or less active negotiations regarding this highly disconcerting proposal were on foot from October, 1913 until March, 1915 when the first Harvard Medical Unit sailed for France. At this time pressure upon me had become such that I felt obliged to put my resignation in the hands of the University to act upon during my absence as they saw fit. I did not feel justified in longer blocking the project and was quite willing to relinquish my chair in favor of some younger man who had come to assume fewer responsibilities and obligations. On my return three months later, it was learned that conferences had been held and the proposal found to be unacceptable to the Hospital Trustees. So, after this prolonged distraction at the very outset, we started in once more to see what might be done on our originally planned basis.

* * * * *

Following his call to Yale in 1906 Cushing never lost an opportunity to lend a helping hand to its School of Medicine. If Yale was to have a university hospital as a part of the Medical School, it needed fresh endowment. Sporadic attempts had been made to obtain funds after Joseph Marshall Flint had been appointed Professor of Surgery in 1907, and a number of teaching beds in the New Haven Hospital had been endowed, but no substantial general endowment was obtained until 1914. The General Education Board had, as just mentioned, launched its campaign to establish full-time clinical teaching in a number of carefully selected centers. The Johns Hopkins had accepted the plan, Harvard had turned it down, and in March 1914 Yale was confronted with an opportunity to obtain $600,000 from the General Education Board provided they could secure an equivalent sum from other sources prior to 1 July of that year. Anson Phelps Stokes, Secretary of Yale, and George Parmly Day, the Treasurer, set out energetically to raise the necessary funds, and they turned at once to Cushing for aid. He in turn addressed a letter to the Treasurer in which he referred to the Yale Medical School and "its golden opportunity." This letter was used in the appeal for funds, and by 30 May Mr. Day was able to report that their goal had been reached. He added, "Your letter to me did more for us than any other one thing. I told you if we got our start we'd owe it to you." And on 16 June, after the results of the drive had been announced at Commencement, Day reiterated: "To you, for all you have done to make possible these great pledges of support, we are all more grateful than I can tell you. Your letter to me about the importance to the University and to the community of the proposed alliance between the hospital and the Medical School was the one thing above all others which led to the gifts. . . . The end is not yet, in fact I feel we have only begun."

In attempting to match the sum from the General Education Board, Yale had secured an outright gift of $500,000 from the Trustees of Anthony N. Brady, and a further sum of $125,000 from the same source for building a memorial laboratory of pathology. Mr. Charles W. Harkness had pledged $100,000, and an unnamed alumnus an equivalent amount, so that when the drive was closed nearly $2,000,000 had been raised.

On 15 June 1914 the Yale School of Medicine celebrated its Centennial with appropriate exercises, during which Walter R. Steiner of Hartford described the evolution of medicine in Connecticut, including an account of the founding of the Medical School. William H. Howell of Baltimore discussed premedical studies in their relation to professional training. The success of the endowment was announced, and the exercises terminated to the strains of "Pomp and Circumstance."[17] The war, however, retarded developments and the general reorganization of the School did not begin until Milton Winternitz was appointed Dean and Professor of Pathology in 1917.

The year 1914 marked the four hundredth anniversary of the birth of H.C.'s patron saint, Andreas Vesalius. Cushing and Osler had been in correspondence about the possibility of attending the elaborate celebrations which were being planned at Brussels and

[17] *Memorial of the centennial of the Yale Medical School 1814-1914.* Yale University Press, 1915, 60 pp.

Louvain to mark the occasion. But the Germans intervened, and, instead, the Louvain Library was destroyed and with it all of the Vesalian relics, including the unique copy of the *Fabrica* printed on vellum which H.C. had seen in 1912. Despite the war he felt that some effort should be made to observe the quatercentenary of Vesalius, and a meeting was accordingly arranged on 8 December for the Harvard Medical Society. The session was opened by H.C., who gave a brief account of the life and work of Vesalius. There followed papers on Louvain and its university by Robert M. Green, and the principal address, entitled "The Vesalian spirit," was given by Lewis Pilcher.[18]

H.C. had indeed brought to Boston something of the spirit of the Johns Hopkins Historical Club, which he had fostered for so many years at Baltimore; but as Alan Gregg testifies he had also brought much else: "I was a witness, callow and superficial and peripheral withal but nonetheless a witness, of the remarkable leaven which Cushing's yeasty mind brought to the Boston of 1912 or 1913. Boston then was able to recognize a scholarly and radiant mind though I think such recognition would have come hard for a surgeon triply handicapped with origins marked Cleveland, Yale, and Johns Hopkins. Three factors saved the day: H.C. had been a house pupil at the Massachusetts General Hospital, he was a brain surgeon with no competitors in Boston, and after all the Brigham as a new hospital should be accorded at least the chance of taking an outsider. Standing on this narrow step of Athene's temple, Cushing's sheer devotion to what Boston wanted or wanted to be thought as wanting, carried, and at times swept, men into a new and gusty atmosphere of pleased delight in the wealth that History and Tradition held for medical men. It was a new day and I remember it vividly."

[18] The papers read on this occasion were appropriately published on the last day of the year ("The quatercentenary of Andreas Vesalius. 1514—December 31—1914." *Boston Medical and Surgical Journal,* 31 December 1914, *171,* 995-1002)—good planning, for Vesalius' mother had not kept track of time at his birth and no one was certain whether the great anatomist came into the world before midnight on the 31st or after midnight on the first day of the new year 1515. At the meeting of the American Medical Association in June H.C. and Edward Streeter presented a Vesalius exhibit and distributed a pamphlet issued especially for the occasion. The preface states that "the purpose of the present exhibit is to bring together the various editions of Vesalius and to follow for a space of two centuries the fortunes of his plates." They had found the exhibit rather exhausting and at the end were somewhat disillusioned when a nearsighted old practitioner, after inspecting the placard over their booth, asked for samples—having misinterpreted "Vesalius" as "vaseline"!

CHAPTER XII

The Harvard Unit in Paris and After

1915–1917

LONG before the war broke out Harvey Cushing had been aware, partly through his association with Leonard Wood, of the need for greater military strength in the United States, and particularly for larger numbers of well-trained medical and hospital personnel in the armed forces. General Wood, who had been in Germany in 1902 (when he was received by the Kaiser), had had access to intelligence reports from diplomatic sources and was keenly aware of the dangers of a German war. However, the country at large was strongly isolationistic, and Wood had lost favor, both in the public eye and more particularly in the unrealistic eye of Woodrow Wilson, because of his "Preparedness" agitation. Cushing, like Wood, had also seen at close range something of the Prussian character and, unlike most Americans, was more fully prepared to appreciate the significance of the Herculean attempts which Wood was making to prepare the nation for war.

When news of the war interrupted H.C.'s fishing trip in August 1914 he returned immediately to Boston. He had been disappointed not to have had opportunity to take a more active part in the Spanish War, but through his contacts with men such as Walter Reed, Gorgas, Wood, and others in the Surgeon General's Office, he had become familiar with the Medical Department of the Army; also his advice had been sought in connection with the appointment of several Surgeons General both of the Army and Navy. He was therefore well informed and ready to serve at the earliest possible moment.

Late in August he had word that a group of Americans, resident in Paris, had undertaken the organization of a military hospital and motor ambulance service sponsored by the American ambassador, Robert Bacon (and later by his successor, Myron T. Herrick), under the auspices of the American Hospital at Neuilly-sur-Seine, then directed by Dr. G. W. du Bouchet and Dr. E. L. Gros. The French Government had also placed at their disposal the *Lycée Pasteur,* a school closely adjacent to the hospital, which was altered and equipped to receive some 600 beds. The new unit was designated the "Ambulance Américaine"—*ambulance* being the usual French term for a military hospital. The Ambulance, which was staffed at first by a rotation of medical personnel (principally from the College of Physicians and Surgeons in New York), was at the outset largely financed by Mrs. Harry Payne Whitney. It received its first wounded on 7 September 1914.

Soon after Cushing had news of this he began to correspond with Osler about the possibility of going over for a period of time on an unofficial basis, but when the Ambulance Américaine at Neuilly urged a number of American universities to form units which would assume responsibility for three-month periods in rotation he began (early in December) to think of organizing a Harvard unit. George Crile had started to assemble his unit in Cleveland in November and was able to sail with a fully equipped group on 1 January. Before Crile's departure H.C. wrote to him of his plans:

H.C. to George W. Crile *24 December 1914.*

My dear George: . . . I think it is safe to say that Harvard University, through its Surgical Department, can prepare to send a contingent to take hold after yours has taken its turn, or to overlap upon them if necessary. Dr. Bradford [the Dean] was under the impression that you would like before you sail to get some word in regard to the number and character of the men who would be likely to volunteer, but it seems to me that all you need is the assurance that we shall be glad to do our part. My own suggestion is that you give us before you leave some idea of the amount of money which you think will have to be raised to cover the expenses of our contingent, giving us perhaps the figures that have been raised for your own party. Then, when you have reached Paris and are under way, you can send us full details of the work so that we can fill in any possible gaps you may find in your own organization. I have no doubt that there will be a great number of volunteers and the difficulty will be in picking just the right people out of the number.

I should of course be glad to go, not only for the reasons that you give, but with an idea of service. As a matter of fact, I have already had some little correspondence with Sir William Osler with regard to the possibility of going to England, though this has been on a purely personal basis as yet and there has been no formal proposition, and perhaps after all he is not very serious about it. The American Ambulance proposal naturally is a much more important one, for it comes on a university basis.

I think we shall have no difficulty in raising the money for such a cause, but I should like to get from you some idea of what you think would cover a three months' sojourn, for you have looked into that, I doubt not, with care. Whether I personally shall be able to go, for reasons I will explain later, I cannot tell, but I certainly hope I may. Being by accident the head of the department, it might mean more if I should go than if one of my associates should have charge of the contingent. I am sure that each one of them would be eager to do so, should I not be able to go. . . .

Crile's unit had scarcely arrived in Paris when H.C. made a formal proposal to Mr. Cochrane. In due course Cushing's proposal (which had already been approved by Harvard University) was authorized somewhat cautiously by formal vote of the Brigham Trustees:

VOTED, that the invitation to the Peter Bent Brigham Hospital to take charge of one third of the Ambulance Hospital in Paris, France for a period of three months as outlined in the letter of Dr. Cushing under date of January 8, 1915 be accepted, provided that such action be considered by counsel within the powers of the Corporation and legally proper, and further that the Members of the Staff make it clear that such action would benefit the work and add to the efficiency of our own Hospital.

Exchanges about the undertaking now became frequent, and H.C. sent several letters asking for details about staff and equipment. Thus on 14 January he wrote Crile:

Dear George: We are a good deal at sea in regard to the contingent from here. In the first place, whether or not we are to come, and in the second place, whether or not it is to be for April if we are to come. . . . I hope you will write just as soon as you can in regard to the work; whether it is worth while; whether you are actually needed; whether there is great cordiality about these University representations, whether your equipment is satisfactory and so on. Do try to get hold of a secretary and send me a long and full missive as soon as you can. . . . The money has already been promised by one individual here. I am to meet him tomorrow at lunch, and shall try to interest him so that he will agree to cover all possible expenditures. Whether or not it is best to have one man do this or whether it would increase local interest in the expedition if there are a number of contributors, I am not sure. . . . Ever yours, H.C.

P.S. How about the nursing equipment? Do we need any nurses except for the operating room? Do we need any special supplies or apparatus? Blood pressure apparatus, gauze, etc? Is there much neurological material? What particular problems may we fit ourselves to undertake? How many may we expect to keep at work? . . .

Meanwhile Crile was unconsciously answering many of the queries in an enthusiastic report written to his Cleveland associate, a copy of which went to H.C.:

The American Hospital of Paris,
G. W. Crile to W. E. Lower *15 January 1915.*

This institution is a corker. We have a splendid operating room and a research room next door, both large and well lighted; we have an entire floor composed of 19 wards of 8 beds each. The cooking is good, service excellent; nursing good. As a military hospital, it is surprisingly good. Every variety of wound comes in. There is just now no tetanus. All cases receive an immunizing dose of antitoxin on admission. The service consists of every variety of penetrating and infected wounds. Many nerve lesions, many head and face injuries and especially a great variety of compound fractures. Some gas gangrene. I hope you will arrange to come as it rounds out an experience unfamiliar to our general work at home. I am intensely interested in it all.

As to the Personnel and practical management, I would make the following suggestions: (a) Do not attempt to bring any supplies; they are furnished here. (b) Do not bring trunks, only hand luggage; and should you bring either trunks or supplies in cases, they must be personally attended throughout. We have been all through that experience and know. (c) I brought two operating room nurses, two anesthetists and four members of my hospital staff; but one anesthetist is needed. A stenographer is a great help. The operating room end is of least importance. The most important thing is the judgment—difficult to make—

as to the management of the many complications of infection, penetration, etc. (d) The nurses and entire staff are given quarters and meals in the house. (e) All workers on your staff will be offered luncheon and dinner in the hospital. (f) The expense is therefore light. The White Star gave first class tickets on the *Adriatic* at about $65.00. Thus, you see with no living expenses here and an extremely low rate of passage, the entire cost is small. . . . Sincerely yours, G. W. Crile.

During February feverish preparations were made. On 21 January the Ambulance had written officially to Harvard confirming that it would accept the Harvard Unit on 1 April 1915, and on 30 January Crile wrote H.C. giving full recommendations concerning equipment, staff, and probable costs. Robert Greenough, executive officer of the Unit, then sent an official communication which may be quoted in part:

R. B. Greenough to G. W. du Bouchet *8 February 1915.*

Dear Dr. du Bouchet: You will have received, some time since, from Dr. Bradford, the Dean of the Harvard Medical School, his cable accepting the offer of the service from April 1st to July 1st, 1915, by the Harvard Unit. I may say that we were very grateful for the early assignment, and we appreciate very much the opportunity which you offer to us.

I think you will be interested to know how far our preparations have been made, and any suggestions which you may have to offer with regard to the personnel of the expedition will be very acceptable. Dr. Cushing will go as leader of the expedition. Dr. Cushing's interest being neurological surgery, he has asked me to go as surgeon and executive officer of the expedition, and to take charge of the general organization. We have been so fortunate as to secure the assistance of Dr. Richard P. Strong, the Professor of Tropical Medicine in the Harvard Medical School, as bacteriologist. We have also got Dr. Osgood, an orthopedic surgeon, as one of our group, and Dr. Vincent, a junior surgeon, who has been interested in transfusion and blood-vessel surgery. These gentlemen, together with a group of house-surgeons, graduates of the Massachusetts General and Brigham Hospitals, and a competent anaesthetist, Dr. Boothby, make up our Harvard Unit.

If any criticism or suggestions occur to you with regard to the propriety of including these individuals, or substituting others, I shall appreciate it if you will let me know. Dr. Cushing is, of course, anxious as far as possible to turn his time to good advantage, and he will probably not be able to stay more than six weeks in Paris. Dr. Blake has already offered to Dr. Cushing the neurological cases in his service. We are planning to bring for Dr. Cushing the necessary assistants, nurses, and apparatus for his particular work, and I shall be interested to know if you think there is likely to be sufficient neurological material to justify this special preparation. . . .

Then followed a series of detailed questions concerning records, nurses and orderlies, lodgings, operating gowns, etc. The personnel was thus settled upon, and by the middle of March everything was in readiness, Mr. William Lindsey of Boston having agreed to finance the undertaking. There were six senior surgeons, seven house officers, and four nurses, the complete roster including:

Senior Staff: Walter M. Boothby, Harvey Cushing, Robert B. Greenough, Robert B. Osgood, Richard P. Strong, Beth Vincent.

House Officers: Lyman G. Barton, Jr., George Benet, Fred A. Coller, Elliott C. Cutler, Orville F. Rogers, Jr., M. N. Smith-Petersen, Philip D. Wilson.

Nurses: Edith J. Cox, Geraldine K. Martin, Helen Parks, and Marion Wilson.

Before leaving H.C. received two most gratifying letters, one from the Brigham Trustees and the other from Mr. Higginson:

Alexander Cochrane to H.C. *11 March 1915.*

Dear Dr. Cushing: The Trustees of the Peter Bent Brigham Hospital desire to place at your disposal a gift of one thousand dollars with which we have purchased a draft on Messrs. Hottinguer and Co., Paris, for 5,250 francs which please find enclosed. This sum is, of course, to be entirely at your personal disposition to spend for the benefit of medical service in France in any way you see fit—either by a gift from you to the Hospital where you intend to work or in any other way that seems best. . . . Yours very sincerely, ALEXANDER COCHRANE, For the Trustees of the Peter Bent Brigham Hospital.

Henry L. Higginson to H.C. *44 State Street, Boston, 6 March 1915.*

Dear Doctor Cushing: I have instructed our people to send you a letter of credit for £1,000, which you will use if you wish, repaying us at your leisure. If you prefer to leave money or securities here before going, do so; but in that matter please suit yourself. Can I do anything more in this line? I shall send to you a note to our people in London, which is to be used if you like, and also a letter to Mr. Herman Harjes, who is of the firm of Morgan, Harjes & Company, to whom you will go in Paris for money. His father was born in Philadelphia, and was a fine old gentleman who died a year ago; and Herman Harjes is perhaps a French citizen or perhaps an American citizen, but at any rate he is a very agreeable and excellent gentleman. Your errand is so fine that everybody will be glad to help you.

Now, may I ask if you would like to have a letter from Governor Herrick to this or that man in Paris? I do not see that you will want anything, but such letters, even if not used, may be a comfort, and if used, are certainly a comfort. . . . With kindest wishes, I am, Yours truly, H. L. HIGGINSON.

And again on 22 March Higginson wrote: "If you have a chance to say any pleasant word to the French or English people, I hope you will explain to them how we sympathize with them and admire their courage and tenacity. (By 'we' I mean the people generally whom you and I know.) As I may have told you, having on my hands a lot of musicians of all nationalities [in the Boston Symphony Orchestra], I 'sit on the fence' in public. In private you know all about me." Cushing also took the precaution to write to Alexis Carrel, who had gone to Paris at the outbreak of the war, to ask how French surgeons would react to an American contingent:

8 March 1915.

Dear Carrel: I have long wanted to write you but have only just heard from Flexner where you are to be reached. Crile may possibly have told you that I am coming over with a contingent from Harvard to be at the American Ambulance

Hospital for the three months after April first. I shall probably be able to stay only a part of the time, but I am planning to go over to help get the group established. Of just how much use we shall be, I cannot tell; I fear not very much. I have some little apprehension in regard to the way in which the American Ambulance Hospital may be looked upon by the French surgeons. But however this may be, we are coming merely with the idea of being of some help to the cause of the Allies and however neutral we may presumably be, one cannot help being partisan; and almost everyone here, with the exception of those of German extraction, is in sympathy with the cause of the Allies. . . .

The unit sailed on Thursday, 18 March, on the old *Canopic* and landed in sight of Gibraltar at Algeciras on the 28th. En route hidden talent had been discovered, for Richard Strong distinguished himself by playing the steward's mandolin and Robert Osgood added to the music by converting a rum barrel into a base drum. H.C., who had no musical gifts, sketched and scribbled. After a brief inspection of Algeciras, they went on to Madrid where H.C. found the rare first Spanish edition of the Valverde Vesalius (Rome, 1556).[1] Then there were two dreary, sleepless nights on trains to Paris, with stops en route at Hendaye and Bordeaux. Passages from his Journal tell the rest of the story.[2]

A MEMBER OF THE UNIT
Sketch made on shipboard of Richard Pearson Strong

1 April, Paris. It was a poor night, and a most bedraggled group of people made some tea in one of our baskets about 6 a.m. But despite the cold, our first bright clear day brought us cheer; and we finally slid into the Gare d'Orléans, where was breakfast, and a chance to pull ourselves together. Very exciting to look out on the streets of war-time Paris—officers speeding by in motor cars—an armored car with machine guns—ambulances and all else—all in gray war paint except for the red crosses and the red splashes of the old French uniforms.

Greenough commandeered three big buses into which we clambered, bag and baggage, and set out across the river, through the Place de la Concorde, where Alsace and Lorraine are still draped in black, out along the Élysées, past the Arc to the Porte Maillot, and through it into Neuilly. A very interesting ride on a crisp, clear, spring morning. But the streets seemed very empty for Paris—children playing whip top on the Élysées paths as usual, showing that it was

[1] Cushing, H. *A bio-bibliography of Andreas Vesalius.* N.Y., Schuman's, 1943, p. 146.

[2] Cushing kept a highly illustrated, handwritten diary record of his first trip in 1915 which was subsequently bound up in four small quarto volumes. A transcription of these notes together with further correspondence and other memorabilia brought together while he was in Paris represents Vol. I of the nine huge volumes of his war diary, only a small fraction of which was actually used in *From a surgeon's journal,* published in 1936. Excerpts are therefore given both from the original diary as well as from the published version.

really not Sunday, though it looked it. Everyone not in uniform seems to be garbed in black.

The converted Lycée Pasteur, now the Ambulance Américaine, is not far from the Porte Maillot, and as we approached it along the Boulevard d'Inkermann it was immediately recognizable: the handsome school building with its courtyard full of Ford motor ambulances, over which a bevy of uniformed drivers—youngsters from home, for the most part—were tinkering, some freshly arrived *châssis* being newly assembled. A row of patients and nurses waved a welcome from the upper terraces; Blake and others of the permanent staff, most of them in khaki, greeted us below.

The hospital was quite a revelation, and we met so many people and saw so many familiar faces it's impossible to set it all down. They have admitted no new cases to our 164 beds—indeed, have emptied them as far as they were able, so that we may have a fairly fresh start. The first man we saw had a dreadful paraplegia, with a huge bedsore, due to a section of the spinal cord. He'd been shot in the back by a pointed French bullet—recognizable in the X-ray. *In* a Frenchman, too! So war is doubly dangerous for the soldier—from behind as well as before. Many other minor cases—none of them very bad—we hurriedly glanced at as we were ushered through the several rooms. No Germans. They would require a guard, and the few they have had in the past did not make them very popular.

2 *April, Good Friday.* It is difficult to say just what are one's most vivid impressions: the amazing patience of the seriously wounded, some of them hanging on for months; the dreadful deformities (not so much in the way of amputations, but broken jaws and twisted, scarred faces); the tedious healing of the infected wounds, with discharging sinuses, tubes, irrigations, and repeated dressings—so much so that grating and painful fractures are simply abandoned to wait for wounds to heal, which they don't seem to do; the risks under apparently favorable circumstances of attempting clean operations, most of which seem to have broken down—a varicocele, an appendix, and worst of all, a thoracotomy for a bullet in the pericardium which apparently was doing no harm.

Some of this miscellaneous work savors of "souvenir surgery," and doubtless pressure may oftentimes be brought to bear by the wounded, for they are very proud of these trophies. From the man in question the unoffending bullet, which he wanted as an exhibit to show his visitors, was removed from the pericardial sac; but he got a collapsed left lung, a right pneumonia, then in turn a left pneumonia, and now a bad empyema, with a tube in his side which may or may not close some day. Still he seemed very proud and happy.

The histories are all interesting, citing, as they do, the man's name, regiment, the place where he received the injury and under what circumstances, how long he had had on his clothes without changing them, where he got his first, second, and possibly third dressing before reaching our ambulance, and so on—each item full of horrible, though fascinating, possibilities. No doubt this will all seem very commonplace after we have been here a few days.

I was going over a man this afternoon with a facial paralysis from a bullet wound in the mastoid. He got hit during an engagement on September 7 at a place called Croult, and, with a field full of other wounded, was left for dead. The enemy came over them a day or so later; a soldier poked at him and, finding him alive, swung at his head with the butt end of his musket, breaking his jaw. He was finally picked up during a counter-attack and, after a bad otitis media and erysipelas, is now ready—after seven months!—for a nerve anastomosis. It seems hardly worth while, under present circumstances, to attempt cosmetic operations. What's a simple facial paralysis, after all? . . . Many of the men have deformed toes (possibly from *sabots?*) and they complain that their military shoes are bad, though those we saw seemed sensible enough. But there are other bizarre troubles with the men's feet of really serious nature. There are erythromelalgia-like feet—painful, blue, cold, macerated-looking extremities; and indeed the whole circulatory condition of many of the *blessés* is very bad. It is presumable that the worst of this is over, with the return of not only dry but warm weather. The standing in cold water, even though above the freezing point—one cause of the so-called water-bite—is as bad as frostbite itself, especially when helped by the too-tight application of puttees which may shrink. Some of these poor devils must have so stood for days in hastily dug trenches without a chance of getting off their boots.

Almost from the start, the majority of the men have been admitted with bronchitis, and many with influenza-like colds. Then, too, the African troops may have brought with them underlying tropical disorders of which we know little. One of them was a fine Turco in a gay Zouave uniform, with a through-and-through thoracic wound made by a German "ball," the wound of entrance so small it could hardly be found. Can you picture him, with no one around he can understand or who can understand him, industriously putting together the biggest and the most intricate jig-saw puzzle "made in America" you ever saw, on a table in an American hospital in France, with Americans taking care of him? What can his thoughts of us be? They tell us the Germans don't take the blacks prisoners; but then, what may or may not we believe about all this business? Here we are as near the worst affair in history as Boston is to Worcester, and everyone appears to take it as though it had always been so, and always would be, and meanwhile goes about his own little business unconcernedly.

3 April. A continuous rain. Morning passed at the Ambulance combing out and indexing the neurological cases. As a matter of fact, few of the wounded escape from a nerve lesion of one sort or another. . . .

All the wounded from the S.E. part of the lines supposedly routed to Lyon and the South of France—those from the centre come here; those from the North, including the British, go to Dunkerque, etc. There are very few Tommies in our wards. One of them today was playing checkers with a Turco and said his black friend had learned the game so quickly he could now almost always beat him—but he thought he had him this time.

One of the hospital attendants told me at lunch that on passing the Invalides the other day he saw an old veteran of 1870 in his long blue coat balancing on his two wooden pegs with the aid of two crutches, in order to salute a victim of the present war—45 years younger, but in the same condition.

Cushing continued at Neuilly for ten days, and from this initial experience he was better able to visualize what equipment and personnel our forces would need when we entered the conflict—for there was no shadow of doubt in his mind that the United States would soon be in the war and that active preparations for this eventuality should begin at once. It was one reason why he decided to return home before the end of the group's three-month term of service. Meanwhile, in order that he might gain further knowledge of the medical situation as a whole, he was taken about on various tours of inspection. All these experiences he records in some detail. Among other things he was shocked by the way the wounded were moved. Thus on the 5th he notes:

In the early days things were badly disorganized, and the conditions were shocking. The wounded were all rushed south as rapidly as possible and the more seriously ill were put off whenever and wherever trains stopped. They were picked up in any way chance might favor—luckily if by an ambulance, but more often by a cattle or provision train returning from the Front. One of these trains had dumped about five hundred badly wounded men and left them lying between the tracks in the rain, with no cover whatsoever. Blake spoke of one English officer who had been six days thus in transport, with a musket for a splint tied to a compound fracture of the femur, no dressing whatsoever, almost no food or drink; he was in delirium when he arrived. Fortunately the wounded were young and in the pink of physical condition; few would otherwise have pulled through.

Again on the 8th and 9th:

. . . Everyone, of course, tells us that we know nothing yet of what it can really be like. After the battle of the Marne the wounded came in sixty at a time, with the operating room in continuous performance and not enough beds to go around. One comes upon many examples of hairbreadth escapes. In our wards is a man who got off with a slight burn of the forearm when a German contact shell exploded near him, and yet many of his companions were killed. Another man had both bones of his forearm broken in similar fashion without being actually hit, and yet his more distant companions suffered heavily from shrapnel. One man was blown into a tree and hung there for a long time by his trouser leg. Another was blown out of a trench and found the timing piece (*fusée*) of a shell in the seat of his trousers. Many have barely escaped because they happened to be stooping when a shell exploded near by. One artillery officer was knocked down three times in succession by shells landing only a metre or two away from him; he suffers from a severe nervous concussion—what the British call "shell shock."

On the 11th he and Richard Strong paid a visit to the French Second Army front where H.C. with his forbidden camera managed to photograph almost every important landmark; maps were also obtained, and his notebook bulged with details concerning the German advance from 20 August to 3 September 1914 when von Kluck reached Senlis within sight of the Eiffel Tower (about 60 kilometers distant). During lunch in Amiens Cushing and his party were "informed that the medical situation which had promised to be most serious was rapidly improving."

They returned from Amiens by Montdidier and Chantilly to Paris, arriving at the Crillon toward midnight—a round trip of 260 miles. On the 12th H.C. lunched with the Carrels, and on the same day Richard Strong set off on his typhoid mission to Serbia. On the 13th and 14th Carrel had arranged another trip to see a large base hospital at Compiègne.

And so we . . . turned back via Gournay and Monchy to Compiègne again, reaching our destination fully two hours late—an embarrassment, as it proved, for Carrel had expected us by 10 o'clock and, cherishing an idea that my transfer to Compiègne for some work might be requisitioned, had asked Gen. Nimier to meet us at that hour. We repaired to lunch promptly and I did the best I could to be polite to *M. le Médecin Inspecteur Général de la Sixième Armée* and his five colonels and to thank him for the inscribed copy of his *Blessures du Crâne et de l'Encéphale* which he presented to me. Having arrived two hours late and by mischance having excused myself for a moment to say goodbye to Mr. Carroll, which moment happened to coincide with the General's own departure, I could not have impressed him favorably. We then paid a visit to the large ward where Dr. D——— did a number of dressings—very badly I thought—unnecessary pain and bleeding from the extraction of adherent gauze. It was awful—wicked indeed—to see the poor devils, one of whom chewed a hole in his coverlet rather than utter a groan. The time will come when they will learn better methods, but meanwhile there will be much needless suffering.

What is known as *Hôpital Complémentaire 21* is in a once fashionable hotel —the Rond Royal—on the very edge of the Forêt de Compiègne—an ideal spot and one which Carrel chose for his purposes on careful survey after he got free from his miserable detail, first in the Lyon hospital and then at the War Office. Here, backed by Rockefeller money and with an admirable staff, a great opportunity lies open for special studies of wound treatment. The lines along which they have started to work include the suction treatment of suppurating wounds without dressings; the employment of irrigation with bactericidal fluids which are being worked out by Henry Dakin; methods of increasing resistance to pathogenic organisms by turpentine injections, etc., etc.

There are at present 51 beds with 86 attendants, including slaveys of all kinds—11 scientific, medical, and administrative officers; 13 experienced Swiss nurses supplied by Theodor Kocher; numerous secretaries, laboratory technicians, linen-room people, scrub women, ambulance men; and 47 soldier orderlies who do everything from boots to waiting on table and keeping up the gardens. It is indeed a research hospital *de luxe* with running water in all the rooms, which are large, most of them having baths, comfortable beds, electricity, and all modern improvements. Over the *dramatis personae* Madame Carrel rules as housekeeper and "general tyrant," according to her husband.

There are also stables and four chauffeurs whom I had forgotten to mention —one of them a professional racing driver who has figured in international events—another Sarah Bernhardt's leading man on her last tour of the U.S.A.—the third an equally celebrated actor from the Odéon—the fourth an underling. These deserve special mention because late in the afternoon behind chauffeurs 1 and 4 in an open car we went on an expedition, meanwhile clutching everything that was detachable and only coming up for breath when stopped by a sentry, gun on high. Thus for some 10 km. to the west, where, in the château of the Duchesse de Quelquechose, an English lady of title has well-meaningly established an Ambulance under the direction of a most unprepossessing English surgeon with a rachitic build and bad teeth, who has a single amateur nurse to help him—neither of them speaks a word of French, and they appear to have a comparable familiarity with surgery. We are plied with tea and English marmalade while he bitterly complains that the French don't send him the kind of wounded that make it worth while for him to remain—only minor injuries and few of those. In short, *M. l'Inspecteur* had sized up the situation.

14 April. 2nd day at Compiègne. A beautiful warm spring morning, buds swelling perceptibly, birds singing melodiously, artillery horses exercising in the open space in the *forêt* outside my window. Meanwhile distant cannonading recalls the more serious matters of the day and place. From the experience of yesterday afternoon it is apparent that society dotes on the excitement of the war and loves to provide—however badly—for the wounded, particularly if they are presentable and can be wheeled in to afternoon tea—neither of which they ordinarily are.

Several other hospitals in the area were visited on this trip, and the evening of the 19th found him back in Neuilly where he spent the remainder of the month of April operating with his unit. On the 24th he and Walter Boothby were called to La Chapelle—the Paris station for distributing the wounded—where they saw the first gas casualties of the war.

. . . It has been only two days since these fellows were hit, and many of them, regarded as sitting cases, have stuck it out believing they could walk off the train. But not all could. One poor boy, who collapsed before us, they put on a stretcher and took to the emergency booth. Others had to be helped as they walked on between the two rows of booths to the farther end of the building, where were two large squares of benches arranged in a double row about an iron brazier in which a warm charcoal fire was glowing; for it was a cold, raw, and drizzly afternoon. There was a separate place for the slightly wounded officers, of whom there were some six or eight. . . . It was soon whispered about that this lot had come from Ypres and that they had all suffered greatly from some German *gaz asphyxiant;* but I hardly believed the tale, or thought I had misunderstood, until this evening's *communiqué* bears it out. Many of them were coughing; but then, as I've said, most of the wounded still come in with a bronchitis. We have heard rumors for some days of a movement of German troops in the direction of Ypres, and this attack is apparently the result.

. . . When we got back to the Ambulance, the air was full of tales of the asphyxiating gas which the Germans had turned loose on Thursday—but it is difficult to get a straight story. A huge, low-lying greenish cloud of smoke with a yellowish top began to roll down from the German trenches, fanned by a steady easterly wind. At the same time there was a terrifically heavy bombardment. The smoke was suffocating and smelled to some like ether and sulphur, to another like a thousand sulphur matches, to still another like burning rosin. One man said that there were about a thousand Zouaves of the *Bataillon d'Afrique* in the lines and only sixty got back—either suffocated or shot as they clambered out of the trenches to escape. Another of the men was *en repos* five kilometres away and says he could smell the gas there. . . .

Sunday, 25 April. It has apparently been a large affair at Ypres, with the Germans the aggressors. Several hundred more wounded at La Chappelle this morning—all the ambulance men out—all our beds full. . . . We fluoroscoped two of yesterday's head cases this morning and operated on one of them—a young lieutenant named Daumale who was looking through his field glasses when a Mauser bullet made a direct hit of the lens in front of his right eye, exploding the cylinder and producing an ugly wound not only of his hand but of his right orbital region and cheek. Some metal fragments could be seen by X-ray, driven back into the base of the skull. The eye had been immediately enucleated by the regimental surgeon, but the whole region had become badly infected—an ugly affair. It was necessary to open and drain the antrum. The other man proved to have a fragment of *obus* deep down in his right hemisphere. . . .

There followed a brilliant description of Cushing's first use of the magnet in combination with a nail for extraction of shell fragments from the interior of the brain:

Wednesday, 28 April. Still very busy and the hospital is crowded. I had a strange time operating for du Bouchet on one of his patients—Lafourcode in No. 77—supposed to have a *gouttière* bullet wound of the skull, which I did not question, though murmuring something about the desirability of an X-ray.

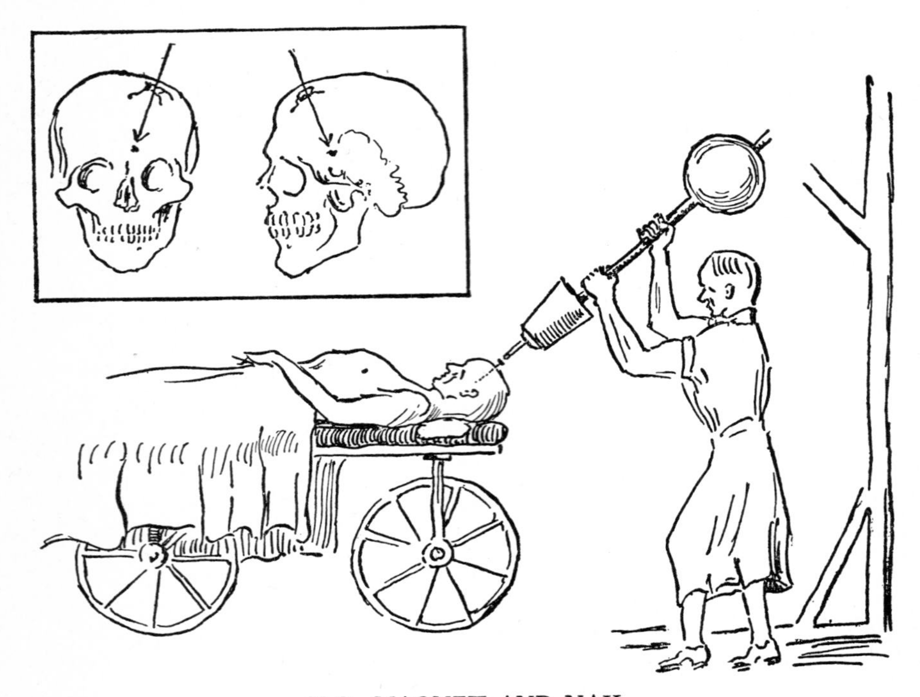

H.C., MAGNET AND NAIL

Inset at upper left: Skull diagram showing position of shell fragments at the base of the brain

At all events, I was persuaded to take the case in hand and it proved to be not a gutter wound at all, the presumed wound of exit being merely where the man had fallen and cut his head on some sharp object. The track of the missile, along which an aluminum probe could be passed, led directly downward toward the base of the brain. This afternoon an X-ray showed a fragment of *obus* just over the sella—not a bullet at all. . . .

Thursday, 29 April. Several unsuccessful trials this morning to extract the shell fragment by the aid of the magnet from the brain of poor Lafourcode. I was afraid to use the huge probe which they have and so determined to make, or have made, another—of which later. We had tried every possible thing in our own cabinet and in those on the lower floors without success. Finally, while I was at lunch, Boothby hit upon precisely what was needed in the shape of a large wire nail about six inches long, the point of which he had carefully rounded off.

Well, there was the usual crowd in the X-ray room and approaching corridor, and much excitement when we let the nail slide by gravity into the central mechanism of smiling Lafourcode; for at no time did he have any pressure symptoms, and all of these procedures were of course without an anaesthetic. While the X-ray plate was being developed to see whether the nail and missile were in contact, who should drop in but Albert Kocher with a friend from Berne; and then shortly a card was sent in by Tom Perry's friend, Salomon Reinach, *Membre de l'Institut,* author of the *History of Religions,* and much else. So all together we finally traipsed into the first-floor operating room, where Cutler mightily brings up the magnet and slowly we extract the nail—and—there was nothing on it! Suppressed sighs and groans. I tried again, very carefully—with the same result. More sighs, and people began to go out. A third time—nothing. By this time I began to grumble: "Never saw anything of this kind pulled off with such a crowd. Hoodooed ourselves from the start. Should have had an X-ray made when the man first entered the hospital." The usual thing, as when one begins to scold his golf ball.

I had taken off my gloves and put the nail down; but then—let's try just once more! So I slipped the brutal thing again down the track, 3½ inches to the base of the brain, and again Cutler gingerly swung the big magnet down and made contact. The current was switched on and as before we slowly drew out the nail—and there it was, the little fragment of rough steel hanging on to its tip! Much emotion on all sides—especially on the part of A. Kocher and Salomon Reinach, both of whom could hardly bear it. . . .

Cushing departed from the Ambulance Américaine on 3 May, proceeding by motor to Boulogne. Here he encountered several of his neurological colleagues from Britain, including Gordon Holmes and Percy Sargent; also his old friend, Cuthbert Wallace, the surgeon. Holmes and Sargent, as neurologist and neurosurgeon respectively, had charge of cases of injury of the brain and spinal cord. Holmes at this time was commencing his important studies upon cerebellar and spinal injuries. Cushing was especially interested in their cases of spinal transection—also in the many "gutter" wounds in the heads of soldiers who had unwarily emerged above the top of a trench.

. . . After tea, Holmes and Sargent took me back to No. 13, where I saw an amazing number of head and spinal wounds, for they often receive daily convoys of 300 recently wounded. With the proper backing these two men have an unparalleled opportunity, not only to be of service to the individual wounded, but, when this is all over, to make a contribution to physiology, neurology, and surgery which will be epochal. The things chiefly dwelt upon this afternoon were the group of longitudinal-sinus injuries, mostly from gutter wounds across the vault of the skull which are characterized by a striking rigidity of all four extremities. The condition resembles the spastic paraplegia following birth injuries, and they attribute the clinical picture to a vascular injury of the sinus. However this may be, the condition is quite recoverable spontaneously, and they therefore no longer operate on wounds of this type unless there are some complications compelling them to do so. Though recognized and described in isolated cases, as in Osler's recent report, nowhere, so far as I am aware, has anyone observed and studied such a large group as these men have had. We must have seen ten or twelve examples this very afternoon, all of whom will be evacuated in a day or two, for these hospitals must endeavor to keep empty.

Another group of injuries that were new to me were the transections of the spinal cord in the lower neck, which show, in addition to the total paralysis, an extraordinary lowering of body temperature—sometimes as low as 93°F.—with suppression of urine and death in two or three days, consciousness being retained to the end. They already have full notes of one or more spinal transections for every segment of the cord, with the specimens preserved for future study—a life's work. Such of the cases as recover sufficiently to be evacuated are sent to Henry Head at the London Hospital, by whom they are subsequently followed.

On the whole, I take No. 13 to be a good example of the large overseas hospitals of the R.A.M.C. The comforts are slight, the attendance insufficient, the work, though it naturally varies, is simply overwhelming—perhaps as many admissions a day as the American Ambulance might get in a month. And the wounded, bear in mind, are seriously and acutely hit, rushed on from one and all of the casualty clearing stations a few miles behind the lines as soon as transportation is possible. Records, if kept at all, must necessarily be utterly inadequate, so that such clinical notes as Holmes manages to jot down are purely personal ones. Indeed, in rushes no notes whatever can be made, and the wretched tags, insecurely attached to a button of the wounded soldier's uniform, are often lost or become rumpled and completely illegible—far less practical than the French tags with which we have become so familiar. There were two poor aphasic chaps from some Scottish regiment who were necessarily listed as "unknown" since all identification marks had been lost in transit.

The wounded to-day at the Casino number 520, not counting the 200 who are under canvas; but occasionally in active times they run up to 900, with an attending staff which varies in number from ten to sixteen. There was none but very ill men, all bed patients, and in the huge restaurants of the building, which contained about 200 closely packed cots, there may have been three or four nurses and as many orderlies. Compared with this our leisurely job at Neuilly with 162 beds filled with subacute or chronic *blessés* and an *auxiliaire* or orderly for every 10 to 12 patients seems child's play. This is truly a man-sized job, in the midst of which the Britisher stops for tea, and everyone—even down to the Tommy—has time to shave; and it's taking-it-quietly that possibly enables them to see things through with some measure of composure.

And so, at seven, back to dinner at the château, where there was a pleasant mess with pleasant guests, among them Sir Almroth Wright, as amusing and chatty as he was iconoclastic. A good deal about wounds, antiseptics, infections, and several digs at Wright, which he parried with his customary cleverness. . . .

On the 5th Sir George Makins and Sir Anthony Bowlby took Cushing to see the shelling of Ypres from Scherpenberg Hill. With German planes overhead and heavy shelling not far distant, they inspected front line casualty clearing stations, and, in the course of the tour, H.C. met other friends, including Cuthbert Bazett, the coming young British physiologist of Magdalen College, Oxford.

. . . It's getting on toward three o'clock and, Bowlby taking Col. Atkins and me in his car while Sir George [Makins] and Mr. Bacon [the American ambassador] follow, we proceed through Locre with windmills and hop fields on all sides. Dodging lorries and ambulances, and with the sound of continuous gunfire constantly drawing nearer, we finally reach No. 8 Field Ambulance at la Clytte, where I'm surprised to find Bazett the physiologist in charge. Almost as we dismount, an aeroplane circles up from this side of the line, and as it rises—we judge to about 5000 feet—it sails out to the eastward in the direction of the Ypres salient, and we hear the guns and see the white puffs of German shrapnel, all of the shells appearing to explode behind and below. And then another machine—a Taube—ascends from far beyond, and it looks like an engagement; but the Britisher appears satisfied with his reconnaissance and sails away to the north to disappear from sight.

The abandoned house serving as an Ambulance is about three miles from Ypres at the foot of a low hill near Mt. Kemmel. There were a number of desperately ill men, mostly with abdominal and cranial wounds, too ill to be evacuated; and we were shown some adjoining sheds where were other equally bad cases; but we do not care to examine them in any detail—it's too harrowing.

And so we finally leave friend Bazett to his forlorn job and take our way to the bottom of the hill, where we are to get a glimpse of Ypres and its surroundings, whence all the sounds of firing emanate. Up a short winding road, past a line of newly made English trenches, and then out on to a little cleared space. It would have been interesting enough as a simple, lovely, pastoral view across Belgian countryside; but here we were watching a distant struggle for a city—one of the most desperate as yet in this world's war. Col. Atkins says that from this same point on Scherpenberg Hill, King George, when here, watched the bombardment of Ypres—happening to have a cloudless day.

Despite delays and difficulties they arrived back at Boulogne in time to see Percy Sargent's final operation of the day.

After a pick-up supper, learning that Sargent was winding up a busy operative day at No. 13, Holmes guides me down there—literally so, for it is black as tar and he has to count the steps as we descend the twisting path down the hillside. And we are in time to see his final case, a bad shell wound of the right parietal region with a big piece of *obus* and countless fragments of bone, and a definite though well-localized infection. It was a very careful, neat, and expeditious performance. And so back again through the pitch-black town we grope our way up to our lodgings; and this was plenty enough for the day, and making these heavy-eyed notes before turning in has been an effort.

On the 6th H.C. crossed to England and, as one would anticipate, went immediately to Oxford.

A warm greeting at 13 Norham Gardens, where Lady Osler's sister is staying, and a quiet family dinner, after which delightful glimpses of Sir William's wonderful collection of books and manuscripts, for which he is planning to have a new sort of catalogue made. Also talk of Revere's growing interest in bibliography and the recent hoax which he, with his friend Bobby Emmons as an accomplice, played on his father—the fictitious sale of a valuable library in the hands of a hermit book collector in Norwich.

W.O. finally turns in, only to be aroused by news that Poynton's son has been killed—news which he must transmit to the family. And then Lady O. and her sister and I sit up long, talking the sort of gossip of the war to which W.O. will never listen, for he hears all he can bear during the day, being perforce in London most of the time. Also talk of the Belgians and their enormous families quartered in Oxford—Lady Osler's original scheme which has brought with it so many difficulties. So different, France and England! In Paris, everyone who has the remotest excuse wears black; in London, a ban has been put on the exhibition of any evidences of mourning.

The next day he was in London picking up his boat ticket.

. . . Then lunch at the Automobile Club with Sir William and Walter Morley Fletcher, the physiologist. He is secretary of the Medical Research Committee and has been appointed, in conjunction with Osler and Adami, to make preparations for a Medical History of the War. A colossal undertaking it will be, unless records can be more carefully kept than seems possible under the present circumstances in France. This they hope to rectify.

Fletcher has been looking into the psychopathic ("shell shock") cases, of which there must be many—as I gathered from Pierre Janet to be true also in France—men who have broken down nervously under the terrific strain of trench warfare and the frightful bombardments. One story he told of an officer who, following the near-by explosion of a shell which did not injure him, has now a completely changed personality. He is at a hospital somewhere in Wiltshire, I believe, and has had to be reëducated to read and write and speak; he now uses a Wiltshire dialect whereas he came from an educated class in another part of England. He has absolutely no recollection of a previous existence, but when put in an hypnotic state he is his former self in every respect and perfectly clear on all events up to the moment of the explosion of the shell.

At 3 p.m. an appointment with Sir Alfred Keogh at the War Office, where a pink pass must be filled out to explain my business. An interesting and rather prolonged visit, with much about the American university project; and he has to-day received an acceptance from Rush for July 1st, I believe, with 33 surgeons and 75 nurses. Then about my views of the *Service de Santé* and how it compares with the R.A.M.C. I feebly criticized the flimsy tags such as I had seen Bazett hooking on to men's buttons; whereupon he produces this new one with an envelope, which does not seem so very practical either. He points out on the huge map hanging on the wall where all the hospitals—military and Red Cross, both at home and overseas—are located. . . .

. . . While making some purchases in the Burlington Arcade, an agitated bobby pokes his head in the door and loudly announces: "They've got the Lusitania!" There can be no doubt about it, for by the time I get back to Trafalgar Square sandwich men appear bearing the news—nothing more than the bare fact, however, and there is a huge crowd gathered before the Cunard office with policemen holding them back. "Wot'll they do next?" says my taxi man. "When will England wake up?" say I. This may arouse them—and us! A few hours later I stop again at the Cunard office. On the street there is the same gathering craning to read the bulletin boards, which give no additional news other than that some of the survivors are being taken to Queenstown and that lists will be published later. The office evidently will remain open all night; within is another crowd, with haggard, anxious and tear-stained faces—waiting.

Saturday, 8 May. There is little to be learned from the morning papers except the simple announcement—the Lusitania has been sunk. Boothby and I take the train from Euston at 10.30 and share a compartment with a lady who is traveling with a parrot in a huge cage; the bird tries vainly to sleep and can't. About three we pull into Liverpool and are packed, bird cage and all, into a bus and have a long rattly ride to some remote wharf far up the Mersey where lies the *St. Paul,* and there we find many people in trouble. . . . We and the parrot were almost at the end of the long line of prospective passengers, all of whom, one by one, were obliged to produce passports properly viséd before they could go aboard. . . . Doubtless the *Lusitania* was a little on everyone's nerves. And doubtless, too, there had been a great many shifts of plans in the past twelve hours, both to go and not to go—and the "to go's" have had scant time to get their papers in order.

Well, we finally left some fifty despairing people on the dock and pulled out into the stream. We were locked down the Mersey and there, at the last stage, pulled up alongside of the mammoth Mauretania, in gray and black as though in mourning for her sister whose dangerous place she now must take. Some hours late, we are at last moving out into the Irish Sea between long rows of floating red and white flash buoys which mew at us disconsolately.

Sunday, May 9, 11 a.m. . . . Most of the passengers were at morning service and I was writing here when Boothby looked in and said I had better come on the forward deck. This I did, but rather wish I had not. We were going through the *Lusitania* wreckage—had been, indeed, for the past half hour. Steamer chairs, oars, boxes, overturned boats—and bodies. As I came out we passed quite near a collapsible boat which was bottom side up, with the body of a woman and a child floating alongside; they must have been tied to it in some way, else with the easterly wind the boat would have drifted from them.

All told, I believe some fifteen bodies were counted, and this was only in our immediate lane; the wreckage must have been strewn for some twenty miles or more—we at least were passing through it for considerably over an hour. Once we veered off to get a nearer view of the only boat which was seen to be right side up; but the officers, all of whom were on the bridge scrutinizing everything with their glasses, appeared satisfied and we went back on our course.

That was about all. No, there was something else: a single little trawler a long way off on our port quarter, evidently patrolling for corpses—at a guinea each—on this sunny Sabbath morning.

On reaching the United States H.C. found the eastern seaboard seething with indignation over the *Lusitania,* but official Washington, at least as far as the White House was concerned, was making an ostrich-like pretense of insisting upon technical neutrality. Medical officers were not permitted to go either to Britain or France as observers; liaison was poor, and even the State Department had difficulty in obtaining intelligence reports of any significance. Meanwhile in our very midst, von Bernstorff and von Papen were giving military information about shipping, about our strength—or rather the lack of it—and, along with prominent German-Americans such as Hugo Münsterberg of Harvard, were doing everything in their power to encourage isolationist sentiment in the country at large. Societies and pressure groups had sprung up all over the country, some shouting for peace at any price, such as the Women's Peace Party headed by Jane Addams who dispatched herself to Europe with a group who sought to stop the war. Henry Ford sent his good ship *Oscar II* in the interests of peace, and the more powerful League to Enforce Peace, incorporated on 7 June 1915, was headed by ex-President William Howard Taft who led his Republican followers in the same isolationist channels that his son followed twenty-five years later. Cushing, from his glimpse of the battlefields with the appalling losses of men and material and his knowledge of the lack of preparedness on the part both of Britain and France, was aware that if Britain and France went down, our military position would be precarious to a degree.

He must have been heartened, however, to discover that the country at large was not as blind as Miss Addams, Mr. Ford, or Mr. Taft for other organizations had sprung up, such as the National Security League, and the American Defense Society, the latter having been founded in August 1915 by a Democratic minority which had broken with the policies of Mr. Wilson's administration. Theodore Roosevelt fulminated to Julian Street on 23 June 1915: "Wilson is the one man now alive most responsible for our present unpreparedness." And again on 8 July in less restrained language: "Wilson's constituents who have been most active in speaking about preparedness have been the German-Americans, the other hyphenated Americans, the professional pacifists, the flubdubs, and the molly-coddles all of whom have united in screaming against preparedness and in applauding him [Wilson]." When Wood proposed a training camp at Plattsburg, Wilson saw to it that no financial support was available for the camp; such training units as were established in 1915 and 1916 were sponsored largely by private enterprise.

1915-1917

The return to Boston on 17 May 1915 brought a prompt resumption of hospital and school responsibilities. But much more demanding on head and heart was a fervent desire to break down the unawareness of war's imminence and make people in general and his medical colleagues in particular see the necessity of formulating plans and methods of procedure against the time when all their resources would have to be actively mobilized to meet a world crisis. His convictions were such that he could not be silent. This led to writing papers and delivering speeches, all of which he did in his stride. Thus on the 25th, only a week after his return, he gave an account at a meeting of the Harvard Medical Society of his experiences which one of his audience, Mr. M. A. DeWolfe Howe, described in a note next day as a "most interesting and memorable meeting." He also issued a brief letter about the American Ambulance in the *Boston Medical and Surgical Journal.*[3]

A week later he received a group of doctors on their way to the Pan-American Medical Congress in San Francisco, but the invitation to give a paper at their meeting (17-21 June) was refused on the

[3] "The Harvard Unit at the American Ambulance in Neuilly, Paris." *Boston Medical and Surgical Journal,* 27 May 1915, *172,* 801-803. Later he published an account of his days with the R.A.M.C.: "With the British Medical Corps in France." *Yale Review,* April 1916, *5,* 523-539.

grounds of previous absence from his clinic. Early in June he was off to Cleveland for the annual meeting of the American Surgical Association which moved on to Chicago for a further session. From there he went to St. Louis on 10 June to attend the Commencement celebration at Washington University and to receive an honorary Sc.D. The citation ran:

> Professor of Surgery at Harvard University. A brilliant practical surgeon, whose success has been reached through the study of the underlying sciences, anatomy, physiology, and pathology; who devised methods of operations through scientific experiments. A man who wrote an entire book upon a single diminutive gland and thereby made an invaluable contribution to surgery. A specialist of world-wide reputation in the most delicate of all fields—the brain and spinal cord. With great results already to his credit, even greater things are promised by his prospective years of applied scientific investigations and skillful manipulations.

In the midst of all this activity Barbara, the Cushings' fifth and last child, made her appearance (15 July 1915). She shortly thereafter accompanied her mother to Little Boar's Head where she spent her first summer "getting away from it all."

During the months following his return from France, the work of the American Ambulance was naturally uppermost in H.C.'s mind. The organization had come in for public criticism even while he had been abroad and, curiously enough, there had been pressure against it even from the Red Cross which had intimated that the Ambulance was poaching on its preserve. Accordingly in October 1915 he prepared a brief, eight-page pamphlet outlining the major objectives of the Neuilly group. This statement stands as one of the most effective of any of the public utterances issued at this time on the subject of medical preparedness:

> The generous, prompt and sympathetic response from all true Americans in their non-partisan efforts to alleviate the suffering of the nations now engaged in the misery of war has served to brighten the edge of the heavy cloud which has so long darkened and hung over Europe. Every individual has doubtless felt this appeal more or less strongly, from the child who learns to roll a bandage to the mother with her knitting and the father who finds he can give where he was little accustomed to give before. But owing to the colossal nature of the struggle and the unparalleled number of wounded, individual efforts at succor, however fine the spirit may be, are but the proverbial drop in the bucket and it is possible to cope with the situation, and in a measure meet its needs, only through powerful organizations like the Red Cross Society and the Rockefeller Foundation or through the concerted action of groups of intelligent and self-sacrificing people who submerge their individuality in a cooperative labor.
>
> One of the first of such groups, encouraged by the American Ambassador, came together in Paris soon after the outbreak of war and had the imagination to formulate and energy to establish an Ambulance in conjunction with the existent American Hospital. A large school building in Neuilly-sur-Seine, designated the Lycée Pasteur, which they were permitted by the French Govern-

ment to use, though still under construction, was miraculously transformed and adapted to the purposes of a hospital. Volunteers, trained and untrained, appeared from every walk in life and out of such beginnings there has grown an institution, which in all unpreparedness played an effective rôle as a first line hospital during the tragic September days of the Marne, and, after the withdrawal of the western lines to their present intrenched position, has progressively developed into the most efficient and best equipped of all the base hospitals caring for the French wounded, its present capacity being nearly 600 beds.

Of the more picturesque activities of the volunteers constituting the mobile Ambulance corps connected with the hospital, others will speak—activities often exhausting, often so dangerous that they have been rewarded in the case of some of the drivers by the prized *Croix de Guerre* for heroism under fire; but it is of the institution as a military base hospital and the recognition it has won and respect it holds in French opinion, popular, military, and governmental, that I shall venture to say a few words based on the experience of my all too brief service there.

In the first place, be it remembered, the American Ambulance is a militarized hospital under the direction of the Minister of War and though employing the emblem of the Geneva Convention, as do all institutions and individuals engaged in the care of the wounded, it is not a so-called Red Cross Hospital. There have been two small hospitals of the latter type in France, supported by the funds and under the control of trained officers and nurses furnished by the parent American society and both have done admirable work. No institution, however, manned and financed by foreigners has performed work of the scope and on an equal scale with that at the American Ambulance, and the withdrawal, owing to lack of sufficient funds to continue them, of the Red Cross Hospitals at Pau and Yvetot, is a sufficient reason, if there were no others, for further generous support to the Ambulance at Neuilly, so that it may continue to represent in France the practical quality of American generosity for the sufferers throughout the war on its present level of excellence; unless we are willing to admit that our early outpouring of sympathy was a spasmodic impulse which is now waning. . . .

When an offer came from the Ambulance committee to certain American Universities, asking that they participate in the Service in successive periods of three months each, there was a prompt acceptance, and the Western Reserve University and Harvard have already served their terms and have been succeeded by a contingent from the University of Pennsylvania, which in October will be followed by the University of Minnesota and in turn by others. My association with the Ambulance was in connection with one of these contingents and I have never worked in a hospital at home where the combination of capacity and willingness on the part of the attendants, and of appreciation and gratitude on the part of the patients, was equally apparent. And they were most of them—attendants and patients alike—amateurs at the business, never having seen the inside of a hospital before. We have had a recent example in the Plattsburg and other training camps of what rapid progress toward learning a profession can be made by intelligent people whose heart is in it—and so it has happened among the volunteer amateur nurses, auxiliaries and orderlies at the American Ambulance. One amazing result of this voluntary system has been the low unit cost of care for the wounded. The cost-sheets of the hospital show that the cost per patient is below that in any American hospital, which is a gratifying assurance that good value is received for every dollar given to this merciful work.

The hospital has been visited and highly recommended by practically all the French officials from the President down, and it is so well known throughout the army that happy is the wounded soldier whose tag from the distributing station reads "Ambulance Américaine." The French soldier, probably more than the soldier of any other nation, has aroused the sympathy and admiration of the world. Someone has said that his apparent gaiety is but the sister of anguish and the first cousin to tears, but he approaches the war with the crusaders' spirit of faith, and endures its wounds with a cheerful fortitude whose appeal is irresistible. . . . The work of the American Ambulance should be coupled with that of the Belgian Relief and the Servian Commission in having served to offset the feeling that tends to prevail abroad, whether or not it is justified, that the American people have not played a wholly unselfish rôle in their attitude toward this far-reaching conflict.

During the meetings in the autumn of 1915 and the spring of 1916 H.C. had taken every opportunity available to urge medical preparedness upon his colleagues; but although heart and soul in this "cause," he did not neglect historical interests. He arranged a meeting of the Harvard Medical Society in January 1916 devoted to Jenner, Waterhouse, and the history of inoculation. And in February, when his friend Arnold Klebs arrived from Switzerland, he induced him to give a paper before the Society on Leonardo da Vinci. On 23 February he went to New Haven to address the local Red Cross chapter on the work of the Red Cross in war, and in May he attended meetings of the American Philosophical Society and American Neurological Association.

National Research Council

During these crowded years Cushing became actively interested in the work of yet another organization. On 3 March 1863 Abraham Lincoln, feeling the need for advice in scientific matters, had created the National Academy of Sciences and conferred upon it an official charter authorized by the Congress. The original members of the National Academy aided Mr. Lincoln in mobilizing the scientific talent of the North to assist the government in the prosecution of the Civil War. In peacetime the Academy was to promote the best interests of science in the country at large and it was also called upon to foster research in the national interest. The National Academy thus became the recognized scientific agency of the federal government, but its functions, as far as the government was concerned, were purely advisory in nature and no provision was made for the appropriation of federal funds for its support. This was to be derived from private sources so as to be wholly free of political influence. The Academy celebrated its fiftieth anniversary in 1913 and the history of its activities written at that time was an impressive record of services rendered to the people of the United States during the first half century of its existence.

Early in 1916 President Wilson, who publicly had been loath to lend any support to the "preparedness" agitation, became aware that both the War and Navy Departments must enlist the aid of the nation's scientists. At the spring meeting of the Academy in 1916 (17-19 April) William Welch, then its president, was authorized to offer the services of the Academy to the government "in the interests of national security and welfare and preparedness for the emergency which it was then seen to be facing with respect to the World War." The offer was accepted by the President who promptly asked the Academy to prepare a plan of procedure. At a special meeting held in New York on 19 June the Academy, in view of the advanced age of the majority of its members, had recommended that a National Research Council be formed whose purpose would be to enlist younger scientific talent in the interests of national defense, to bring into cooperation existing governmental and other research organizations, and to employ "scientific methods in strengthening the national defense and such other applications of science as will promote the national security and welfare." The Council was to be composed of leading American investigators both from civil life and from the armed services. The plan was approved by President Wilson on 24 July and the Council had its first meeting on 20 September 1916. Mr. Wilson's letter authorizing the formation of the Council is little known:

Washington, D.C.,
President Wilson to William Welch *24 July 1916.*

My dear Dr. Welch: I want to tell you with what gratification I have received the preliminary report of the National Research Council, which was formed at my request under the National Academy of Sciences. The outline of work there set forth and the evidences of remarkable progress towards the accomplishment of the object of the Council are indeed gratifying. May I not take this occasion to say that the Departments of the Government are ready to co-operate in every way that may be required, and that the heads of the Departments most immediately concerned are now, at my request, actively engaged in considering the best methods of co-operation? Representatives of Government Bureaus will be appointed as members of the Research Council as the Council desires. Cordially and sincerely yours, WOODROW WILSON.

W. W. Keen had been called by the newly formed National Research Council as one of the senior advisers in surgery and on 26 October he turned to Cushing for assistance:

Philadelphia,
W. W. Keen to H.C. *26 October 1916.*

Dear Dr. Cushing: I have been asked by the National Research Council, of which I am a member, to draw up a report on "The new discoveries and their application in the treatment of wounds in the present war." I take it that it means not only in the treatment of wounds, but any improvement in surgical treatment, and also in feeding, transportation, etc. I shall be very much obliged to you if you will give me from your very wide experience your view on the various matters which will naturally suggest themselves to your mind. Especially important, of course, is the question of treatment in infection. I do not just know how to appreciate the value, for instance, of Dakin's chloramine-T, Sir Almroth Wright's method, or various other methods which have been suggested.

I should like to know your views as to the best treatment of gas gangrene; of the value of preventive treatment of tetanus; of the treatment of burns by the preparation which Dr. Barthe calls ambrine. I have seen some very remarkable photographs of cases treated by this preparation, which I understand is resin, wax, and paraffine, but I have seen also some very absurd descriptions of the impossibilities it was said to accomplish. I should like to find out what the real truth is. Any other observations as to questions of transportation, feeding, housing, etc. would be very much appreciated and I would be glad to embody them in my report. Our reports are for national use.

H.C. replied promptly and with the thought and thoroughness which characterized all his responses to such appeals:

H.C. to W. W. Keen *28 October 1916.*

Dear Dr. Keen: . . . My own experience was largely limited to the treatment of cranial injuries, and it was not a particularly large one. I am sending you a reprint in which I have stated my feelings in the matter. . . . Although the metal helmets have lessened the number of small penetrating wounds which we saw, there are, nevertheless, of course, still a great number of them. One thing that will confront your committee, of course, is the question of protection, and it looks as though we were going back by gradations to the armor of the Middle Ages. Another very important thing is protection against gas attacks, and I am sorry you were not here Wednesday to hear Haldane speak on the subject, for gas masks of one type or another will unquestionably have to be prepared for.

I hardly know what to say in answer to your questions in regard to the treatment of infection. Dakin's solution is still being used with apparently very good results, and the same is true of Wright's hypertonic saline. All these things, as is true of the treatment of wounds in general, come down to the basis, more or less, of a personal equation with the individual surgeon, and there has been a very extensive controversy, particularly in England, between those who regard themselves representatives of Lister, versus those who are opposed to the use of any antiseptics, and Wright is their very capable leader. . . . Carrel, as you know, is endeavoring to shorten the life of wound-healing by radical excision of tissue after primary partial sterilization with Dakin's fluid.

There seems to me no 'best treatment' for gas gangrene, for when gangrene has set in, it necessarily means amputation. I presume that your question really means gas infection, which is not such a dread condition as it was thought to be, and although amputations for gas infection were performed during the first part of the war, they very soon learned that gas infection, short of gas gangrene, was a very recoverable type of infection.

Tetanus has absolutely disappeared, owing to the immediate injections which are given at the first aid stations, a very serious blow to the antivivisectionists. . . . Transportation you will find a very serious problem, particularly as our day coaches—unless holes can be cut in the sides—are absolutely unfit for the carrying of wounded, and the only cars which have side openings are freight cars, with impossible springs. . . .

The year 1916 found H.C. deeply involved in another technical monograph. Early in his work in neurological surgery he had become interested in tumors affecting the cerebellum, puzzled by the variable results of operation. It so happens that many of the growths arising in this part of the cranial cavity, since they develop slowly from cells that make up the supporting framework of the brain, are singularly favorable and, if successfully removed, tend not to recur.[4] He had encountered a number of tumors in this region, and it led him to ask why it was that some tumors are favorable and fail to return once they are removed, while others tend to come back with discouraging rapidity and frequency. To obtain an answer, a microscopical study of the different types of growth was necessary.

Although his training had been broad, he had not drilled himself in the special techniques for microscopical study of the brain and its abnormal growths. Beginning in 1914 W. T. Councilman had studied and described many of the tumors encountered during H.C.'s early years at the Brigham Hospital; some of his Johns Hopkins Hospital specimens and a few of those from the Peter Bent Brigham series had also been sent to F. B. Mallory of the Boston City Hospital for sectioning and diagnosis. Later under the stimulus of H.C.'s assistant, Percival Bailey, a systematic microscopical study was made of all the different types of tumor which had come under Cushing's observation.

During 1916 Miss Louise Eisenhardt, a talented woman who had come into the office in 1915, assisted him in the preparation for press of the acoustic monograph.[5] This treatise was an outgrowth of a chapter on "endotheliomas" of the cerebellopontile angle which had been intended for the monograph on meningiomas (not completed until 1938). He had given an abstract of this monograph on 5 February in Baltimore at a meeting of the Johns Hopkins Medical Society. He had succeeded in completing the manuscript of the acoustic monograph by the first week in May (1917) and he left it in the hands of Miss Eisenhardt to see through the press while he was in France. The monograph was important for several reasons. It was the first detailed account that he had given of a special group of intracranial tumors other than the pituitary, and it also recorded the progress that had occurred in neurosurgical technique since 1908 when he wrote the monograph for W. W. Keen. The book was received almost as enthusiastically as had been the pituitary monograph. One British review may be cited:

[4] Cushing's patient with the longest survival period is one Milton W. Ferguson who was first operated upon for a cerebellar tumor in July 1908 and who is still leading a useful life thirty-seven years later.

[5] *Tumors of the nervus acusticus and the syndrome of the cerebellopontile angle.* Philadelphia and London, W. B. Saunders Co., 1917, 296 pp.

Professor Harvey Cushing's book is both a record of a great surgical advance and a model of how such a record should be made. Since the beginning of this century a miasma of depression has settled upon the field of neurological surgery, originating from an honest and fearless recognition of the fact that the end-results in the mass are bad. Nor is there any ray of hope for the victims of most intracranial tumours from an alternative method of treatment. The patient and splendid work of Cushing during the last fifteen years, as revealed in this book, has dispelled at least some portion of the cloud. It is not only the practical achievement of the reduction of an operative mortality from an average elsewhere and everywhere of 70 per cent to under 14 per cent in his own clinic that compels admiration; but, further, it is the picture presented of vision and courage in the face of overwhelming difficulties and disappointments, recognizing failures with fearless honesty, rectifying them with consummate judgement and skill, and finally achieving the triumph so modestly set forth in these pages.[6]

The book was subsequently translated into French by H.C.'s good friend, Thierry de Martel[7] whom he was presently to see once again in Paris.

[6] *The British Journal of Surgery*, 1918-1919, *6*, 472-473.

[7] *Les tumeurs du nerf auditif et le syndrome de l'angle ponto-cérébelleux*. Traduction française par les Docteurs Michel Deniker et Thierry de Martel. Paris, Librairie Octave Doin, Gaston Doin, Éditeur, 1924, 429 pp.

CHAPTER XIII

Base Hospital Number 5

1915–1918

WHEN King George V decorated Major General W. C. Gorgas as Knight Commander of St. Michael and St. George in June 1920, he thanked him "for all the help which he had given the British Army in sending medical officers and nurses to work for the British forces," and assured him that "this help had been of immense value." The honor came to Gorgas as he lay, very ill, in a nursing home in London, having suffered a cerebral hemorrhage while en route to North Africa on a yellow fever mission for the United States Government. Four weeks later at his funeral "the crowds of bared people," H.C. wrote, "behaved in the same silent, reverent, British way as when their beloved 'Jackie' Fisher [Lord Fisher, Admiral of the Fleet] was carried by." Thus did the British nation express gratitude and respect to a man who, in serving his own country, had likewise served its allies. His appointment as Surgeon General of the United States Army on 1 January 1914 was one of the wisest appointments of President Wilson's administration, albeit a natural one in view of his having made possible the building of the Panama Canal, this despite Goethals' interference and other seemingly unsurmountable administrative difficulties.

Gorgas and Leonard Wood had been of a single mind on the question of preparedness and immediately the war broke out in Europe Gorgas began to think of ways and means of training personnel for the Medical Department of the Army since he knew their services would inevitably be required. Resources, however, were minimal, and President Wilson's insistence on technical neutrality made it impossible for Gorgas to move. After a year of more or less futile efforts the Surgeon General (in August 1915) turned in desperation to university groups such as those at Western Reserve and at Harvard which had already had some experience in the war and were therefore better prepared to give their personnel such training that in the event of war (then threatening with Mexico) they could serve as the nucleus of a group of base hospitals. On 18 September Gorgas asked Cushing personally whether he could organize such a unit, adding that he planned to develop about forty similar units throughout the country. He also asked Cushing, as one who had seen war problems at first hand, to give a lecture to his medical officers in Washington. Gorgas received a prompt reply to the request concerning the unit with several constructive suggestions:

H.C. to Major General W. C. Gorgas *21 September 1915.*

My dear General Gorgas: I am obliged for your letter of Sept. 18th which puts me at ease. There can be no question but that we could organize here just such a unit. If you can send me the necessary data I will see that the matter is put through, and the contingent can be put on the Surgical Department basis, or the Medical School basis, or the University basis, as you desire. It is an admirable idea.

There is one thing that I feel like emphasizing and that is the great desirability of having provision made for Base Hospitals devoted to special lines of work, where, for example, the neurological, dental, orthopaedic and other special things can be well taken care of. The general surgeon is pretty apt to think that he can satisfactorily cover the whole ground, and the results in France, and I presume elsewhere, were pretty bad until they began to appreciate the need and the economy of concentrating as many particular kinds of wounds as they could in special hands. All this hails back to the Mitchell, Morehouse and Keen work in the sixties, which I suppose was one of the first similar Base Hospitals ever established. Then, too, the psychiatrists and internists of various kinds must, of course, be included. All of this, I doubt not, you have fully in mind.

Gorgas' open-minded reply was characteristic of the man:

Surgeon General Gorgas to H.C. *25 September 1915.*

Dear Dr. Cushing Yours of September the 21st is acknowledged. I would suggest, to begin with, that you get such professional men as you think best for the purpose, send me their names, and I will arrange to have them enter the Medical Reserve Corps if they are not already in. I think it would be well for you to select your staff as you think best. For instance, in case your Unit is ordered to a General Hospital at San Antonio in time of war you would go down there and have charge of the operating and surgical wards; it would therefore be advantageous for you to take with you all the personnel to which you are accustomed. I think your idea of a special hospital is excellent. But I presume that at the beginning of a war we could not do much specializing. For instance, at San Antonio you would probably at first have to receive all the severely wounded sent there; but we could soon concentrate all head injuries, and our General Hospitals would gradually become specialized in this line. The whole thing is new and we shall no doubt make improvements as we go along. With kindest regards, I remain, Yours very sincerely, W. C. GORGAS.

During the next month letters went back and forth between Cushing, Gorgas, and President Lowell, to whom H.C. had written on 30 September: "I feel that the enclosed letter [of 25 September from General Gorgas] possibly concerns a matter that should be brought to your attention. General Gorgas has spoken to me once or twice on the subject, and finally wrote to ask if I thought it was possible in the various Universities to have a group of men organized on some such basis as that of the American Ambulance in Paris, so that in the event of their being needed they could be called without the delay which would be incidental to having them enrolled in the Medical Reserve Corps in case they were not previously members of that Corps. I told him that I was quite sure that it would be possible and ventured to say that it would probably meet with the approval of those in authority. . . ."

While President Lowell approved in principle, he and his advisers envisaged a more ambitious plan which would involve departments of the Medical School other than those of Surgery. He accordingly wrote to Gorgas (2 Oct.): The plan "seems to me an object of great importance, which the authorities of the Medical School would no doubt be glad to assist. It would be best, I suppose, to have such an organization so prepared that it could furnish the staff of a complete field hospital, with the appropriate number of surgeons, physicians, dentists, specialists and pathologists; keeping its lists full so that when any man desired to retire from the liability of being called into service, some younger man could be placed on the list instead. Before submitting such a plan to the Medical School, I should like to hear more in detail what you have in mind." Gorgas, somewhat taken aback to have a university president—and a layman at that—draw up an over-all plan for a Utopian military hospital, nevertheless replied patiently that he wanted Cushing to organize a surgical unit on the lines originally proposed. Mr. Lowell again objected (23 Oct.), but Gorgas held his ground and H.C. was then authorized to proceed.

These negotiations which, despite Mr. Lowell's alternatives, had seemed at first so promising, soon ran afoul of isolationistic sentiment. In the prefatory note to the second volume of his original war diary Cushing describes the many difficulties encountered while attempting to stir the country into some semblance of preparedness:

. . . The letters herein are samples of the correspondence that passed over my desk subsequent to our return from Paris in 1915 and until we left for France again two years later. Largely through Leonard Wood's herculean efforts, "Preparedness" came to be a national issue, the Plattsburg Officers' Training Camps were established, and our reluctant President and his Cabinet had to take cognizance of the movement, though Mr. Wilson was re-elected in the autumn of 1916 largely on the platform of his having kept us out of war.

Even though the government would not permit any Army Medical Officers to go abroad to gain experience, some steps toward medical preparedness were being taken. In September 1915 General Gorgas proposed to Crile and me that we set about recruiting from the Medical Reserve Corps two surgical units similar to those we had taken to Neuilly. He suggested that such units might be useful—say at San Antonio—in case of war with Mexico. This plan was soon expanded into the idea of our enrolling the officers and personnel for two Army Base Hospitals to be called No. 1 and No. 2—each with a university-medical-school background.

How these plans were frustrated by objections from the Red Cross officials will appear in the letters here selected for preservation. They also indicate some of the difficulties subsequently experienced in organizing these units under any auspices whatsoever. A university president [Lowell] who did not wish to be dictated to by Washington, who preferred an army to a Red Cross organization and expected to make his own appointments—Brigham Hospital trustees who could not see why, if the Massachusetts General and the City Hospital were to have the credit of a Base Hospital Unit, they could not have one as well—the want of any definite plan of organization other than that based upon our brief experience abroad—the great difficulty of getting the requisite number of persons to enroll in the so-called minor personnel: These were but a few of the unexpected obstacles encountered.

We unfortunately in the end were not permitted to take undergraduate medical students, as did the Johns Hopkins Unit and one or two others. Fifty students had at one time been enrolled, but most of them were scared off by the University Committee when our probable entry into the war was threatened. The Hopkins students who went over as orderlies, after a profitable service under their accredited teachers, were graduated at Bazoilles, received commissions, and had the great satisfaction of seeing foreign service.

New England, from the time of the torpedoing of the *Lusitania,* had been in a more or less bellicose mood, with a strong undercurrent of insistence upon war. But the country as a whole showed small interest in the conflict, neutrality and pacifism representing the general attitude. This was partly traceable to the Bernstorffs, von Papens, and others, who openly preached the gospel of peace while secretly subsidizing plots to embroil us with Mexico and to undermine our legitimate commerce with the Allies. So at least it was generally believed.

In unofficial ways, meanwhile, noncombatant aid was being given to the Allied cause. Along the lines proposed by Sir Wm. Osler and Robert Bacon, a few medical units had gone to take charge of hospitals in France under the R.A.M.C. The service was not wholly satisfactory for a number of reasons. The rotation was too rapid, and with all good will on both sides unforeseen difficulties arose when a group of noncommissioned Americans attempted to work under a retired British Army officer as C.O. with British nurses and orderlies in the wards. . . . The New England Surgical Dressings Committee under Mrs. Mead's leadership, from its small beginnings in the Infants' Hospital, whence sterilized supplies were forwarded to Neuilly for us in 1915, had grown to a large organization that sent out millions of carefully prepared and sterilized dressings sealed in tins, which were distributed widely over France. This work ere long was transferred to a room in the Brigham Hospital, and though efforts were made from time to time to oust the committee from these quarters, the hospital superintendent finally came to appreciate and sympathize with the work whose good repute more than repaid the institution for the space given up to it.

Unfortunately this splendid pre-war organization, whose history should be written, was finally broken up and disbanded by the American Red Cross; there may possibly have been faults of misunderstanding on both sides. However this may be, No. 22 General, as well as Base Hospital No. 5, throughout their period with the R.A.M.C. relied entirely on these incomparable dressings, and without the "Boston tins" Horrax and I could have done little during our long stay at No. 46 C.C.S. in 1917. . . . In looking back on this period through the light of these letters it is interesting to see how far short of the final actualities we fell in our imaginings of any possible service our Base Hospital might render. They amounted to nothing more than a possible call to duty for a time on "the Border." References to San Antonio kept cropping up, and that we should ever come to work under canvas, rather than in an old building of some sort, was smiled upon when we attempted to inject life into our organization by an actual trial mobilization on the Common: this, it was believed, would not only lay bare our weak spots, but would give us some experience with army forms and incidentally arouse local interest and support in the general preparedness movement. . . .

At the present day, June 29th, 1919, when I have been sorting over these papers, the Peace Treaty is being signed by unwilling frock-coated representatives of the unscrupulous Prussian swashbucklers who, under other circumstances—and it was unquestionably a close call—would have had the upper hand. In this case our fat country would have had to pay the piper in full.

The Battle of Boston Common

The negotiations for bringing together a base hospital unit continued during 1916 and 1917 and ended in a struggle which Cushing picturesquely termed "the battle of Boston Common." By way of impressing upon the public the importance of hospital units to the fighting forces, H.C., perhaps with more naïveté than realism, proposed that a typical base hospital unit be set up on Boston Common where the working of such a military unit might be seen at first hand by all passers-by who would thus have before them a daily reminder of the need, not only for trained personnel, but for medical supplies of every description. From his contacts with friends in The Club and the Saturday Club he should have known his Boston well enough to have anticipated the determined opposition that he encountered in full measure. The idea was excellent, or it would have been in any place but in a New England town where the green, or common as the case may be, is sacred. Had Cushing settled a little earlier in Boston he might have known better than to waste his energy; but in the fervor of his patriotic zeal, he was instead spurred on to more radical effort by the conservative, and to him narrow-minded, opposition. The outcome of the Battle for the Common is told in a diary entry for 28 April:

Saturday, 28 April 1917. My dander has been up like Dr. John Brown's little mongrel when a bigger dog exhumed his buried bone, and I've been hitting out at these stand-pat Bostonians and their Common. A Mid-Westerner's traditions of the old parade ground and its noble history need be no less patriotic than theirs. Boston for two years past has been 75 per cent talk and kick, and 25 per cent action. Massachusetts is the thirty-third state to complete her quota of militia, instead of the first—as she once would have been. Curiously enough, they don't seem disturbed about it.

A busy morning; started a pituitary transfrontal operation an hour late. Good case—congenital suprasellar cyst—best operation of the kind I have ever done. Councilman joins me, and so to the Saturday Club luncheon—for more work as a publicity agent. On the way let off some steam on him and easily aroused his indignation at the opposition. An unusually large gathering—Haskins, William Thayer, Mark Howe, Ellery Sedgwick, Pickering, Dr. Walcott, President Lowell, Dr. Emerson, Sturgis Bigelow, Richards, and several more, with one or two guests—one of them Major Azan in his *horizon-bleu* uniform, a fine type of young French officer such as I remember two years ago. Before we took our places Mr. Eliot quite unexpectedly said, "I should like to have you sit by me today." This I did—where some guest usually sits. We began with the oysters, when he turned saying: "A friend telephoned to me this morning to use my influence to have this hospital of yours kept off the Common."

With that I was off with the familiar story. "Have as much respect for the Common as anyone—the Harvard Regiment parades down the principal streets behind a band—if they mean business a good many of them are going to get hurt, and someone had better begin to learn how to take care of them in an army hospital under something like field conditions—hospitals as necessary in war as troops—we don't propose to be put somewhere on a back street—deserve the

PROPOSED HOSPITAL ON BOSTON COMMON

most prominent place for the mobilization that the city can find—seeing some people in uniform actually at work will increase Red Cross subscriptions and encourage enlistments. More important than all, will give us invaluable training with army procedures and forms. Anyhow it's only for a matter of six weeks, even should the other two hospitals join in." Well, he got interested and finally indignant. . . .

Too bad I could not have finished the above while I was warmed up to it. It was an extraordinary occasion. I saw no food after the oysters—only something red. Told them I thought little of their regard for an historically dead instead of a living Boston Common. Got Major Azan with his splinted arm to explain what military hospitals were for, which he did movingly; slammed out at someone who wanted to bet there would be a stone annex of the City Hospital on the Common before the summer was over; chided Henry Higginson and Dr. Walcott for not having stood by me at the Corporation meeting.

Jim Curtis, who has been in Washington long enough to understand that we are supposedly at war, quietly remarked, "Funny, when I got to New York this morning the first thing I heard was: 'Boston has the jump on us at last; they are going to get one of their base hospitals out on Boston Common, and we are only talking about ours.' " This provided a glimmer of hope. But someone [Bigelow] bustled up saying he would personally defend the parade ground (on which his bedroom windows look down) against this sacrilege; and I, that he typified those who, to protect a plot of grass, would ignore the country's unpreparedness—the Common could be reseeded.

Well, in the midst of it all—getting more and more 'het up'—I was called downstairs to the telephone: telegram from War Department, Washington—"WIRE THIS OFFICE EARLIEST POSSIBLE DATE YOUR UNIT CAN BE MOBILIZED FOR DUTY ABROAD. ALL EXPENSES BORNE BY GOVERNMENT. (Signed) GORGAS." . . .

The details of the Boston Common episode are amusing in retrospect, but the feelings of Cushing and also of his opponents had risen at the time to a high pitch. Cushing was impatient not only with New England conservatism, but with the flagrant tardiness of our entry into the war—for he had felt since 1915 that the issues were crystal clear, and that the country as a whole was dangerously exposing itself by not taking an aggressive stand. Many of the letters from the voluminous files of correspondence covering this period were far more outspoken than anything he later committed to press in the *Atlantic Monthly* or in the *Surgeon's journal.* One of these letters, to Mr. Ripley, his German teacher at Yale in 1887, written just before his unit sailed for France, shows how intensely he felt:

H.C. to Alfred L. Ripley *4 May 1917.*

My dear Rip Alas, I have no time to look over the plan, nor to help you about it. As you may imagine, we are simply swamped with detail work in our preparations to get off Saturday. At least, we have promised to be ready Saturday. It seems years ago since I dined with you and Fred at the club. People here in Boston don't seem to realize that we are going in answer to an urgent call, just about like the few marines that Winston Churchill threw into Antwerp. You know how people felt about them—and when they see our army uniforms they will be saying abroad, "At last they are coming." I hear people here still grumbling about the grass on Boston Common.

H.C. clearly lost the Battle of the Common. After eighteen years, when in New Haven and at a safe distance from Boston, he enjoyed telling about it in the *Atlantic Monthly.*[1] He took particular delight in the discovery that his friends in Boston saw no more humor in the idea then than they had in 1915. He could not seem to appreciate that to a Bostonian his proposal about the Common was somewhat akin to suggesting to an archbishop the desecration of his high altar. Throughout the entire "battle" Cushing exhibited two conspicuous characteristics: an intense and deep-rooted patriotism and a restrained indifference to the use of accepted channels. Red tape made

[1] "From a surgeon's journal. I. The Harvard Unit and the Ambulance Américaine. II. The battle of Boston Common. III. With the B.E.F. in France. IV. With the A.E.F." *Atlantic Monthly,* October-December 1934, *154,* 385-399; 590-601; 696-707; January 1935, *155,* 102-116.

him aggressive, and army procedure was to prove a trial to one of his individualistic tendencies.

Base Hospital No. 5 Overseas[2]

On 29 April 1917, the day after he had had word at the Saturday Club that his unit was being mobilized, Cushing wrote:

> Yesterday afternoon and evening a whirlwind trying to get in touch with members of the Unit scattered for the week-end. At it again all today in the endeavor to complete our enrollment. Many changes necessary. Frequent exchange of telegrams with Washington. Wonder what they will say about these eleventh-hour withdrawals. May lose us our chance. Decide to go on tonight with Cutler for inside information and authority to advertise for personnel. Visit in p.m. with General Edwards for a few minutes. Will do anything—everything—for us. "First thing Leonard Wood told me was to get behind your base-hospital mobilization." He and Mrs. Edwards both very cordial—very cosmopolitan—very unprovincial. Just what is it? They will shock Boston. Fine to see him in his uniform, though he is not to be officially in charge till Tuesday a.m. Encounter Mr. Storrow on the train—much interest. Offers us, from the Committee of Public Safety, $5000 for incidental expenses.
>
> *Monday eve, 30 April, Federal Express.* A good thing to be "Johnny on the spot." After a snatch at breakfast we got to the Red Cross Building about 8.30, before anyone was there. As we were planning our campaign and reviewing the countless questions we wished to ask, Eliot Wadsworth came in and, knowing our mission, planted us in Colonel Kean's office. There we overheard much telephoning from all parts of the country, though the Washington exchange is poor and the lines overbusy—people wanting to know if they can be guaranteed against submarines, and so forth.

While in Washington on 30 April to make final arrangements with Gorgas about Base Hospital No. 5, H.C. was surprised to find Welch in Gorgas' office. Welch had been one of Gorgas' teachers in New York in the early days, and had offered his services to the Surgeon General's Office when war was declared. H.C. found him answering the telephone and helping in other ways to handle the mounting volume of correspondence. He records that before his interview with Gorgas was finished, "Welch appeared, took off his coat, lit a cigar, and began to answer Gorgas' mail for him."

The unit received its sailing orders on 5 May and boarded the *SS. Saxonia* Friday, 11 May, at 4 p.m. with 26 officers, 185 enlisted men, 81 nurses, 1 dietitian, and 3 secretaries included in its personnel. Cushing records:

> Aboard *SS. Saxonia,* waiting at anchor in the Narrows while some new firemen are secured to take the places of six who vanished shortly before we left the dock—evidently preferring none to a salt-water job now. It has been a hectic week. . . . Getting accustomed to a uniform easier than expected. Cannon

[2] Since the war years have been covered so thoroughly in the 'Surgeon's Journal,' they will be mentioned here but briefly.

says when he first appeared in one his small boy called out: 'Mamma, look, here comes Father dressed up like a Boy Scout!' One of Peabody's parishioners congratulated him on his 'union suit'—indicating some confusion between the advertisements for underwear in the backs of magazines, 'The Union forever,' and *E pluribus unum*. Getting accustomed to army ways less easy. Was informed yesterday that I must go ('proceed' is the word) to Governor's Island for my 'ordnance'—not quite sure what that meant or how to get there, but saluted and obeyed. . . . Our sailing was supposed to be 'secret'; yet everyone in N.Y. Harbor must have known the *Saxonia* was loaded with ammunition, have seen us go aboard, and have heard our whistles blowing when we left the dock.

Saturday, 12 May. We passed out of the Narrows last evening with searchlights wigwagging and boring into the clouds. Patterson [the C.O. of the unit] called a meeting in the saloon and introduced himself to officers and nurses, and this morning we started on a purely military basis with 'Orders of the Day' posted—an office set up in the library—men on guard mount in the passageways, over the ammunition, etc. . . . First boat drill this p.m.—rather a gruesome performance—all kinds of life preservers hanging on all kinds of people in all sorts of ways. The Captain, being the proud possessor of an inflatable waistcoat, finally appears and blows himself up for us. His name is Vennison, a bantam Englishman recently on the *Alaunia,* which was torpedoed in the Channel. . . . An extraordinary monochrome evening, all bluish-gray—the ship, the sea, the clouds. . . .

Falmouth, 22 May, 10 p.m. Waiting in a cold station for our train to start, with good prospect of sitting up all night. Enlisted men are to go to the R.A.M.C. training centre at Blackpool—officers and nurses to London. It's been a long day. Aroused early, we passed the Scilly Islands at 6 a.m. and soon ran into a cold fog. In the late afternoon picked our way slowly through mine fields into Falmouth Harbor, passing tankers, trawlers, destroyers, a Dane painted white with big red polka dots, two Dutchmen—tramps—with "Rotterdam" painted on their sides in letters six feet high and the alternate eight-foot-wide red and white stripes prescribed by the Germans at the time we were told we might send one ship a week to Falmouth. . . .

London, 30 May. To the War Office with the C.O. for an appointment with the two D.G.'s—Keogh and Sloggett. Very much disturbed at our prospect—a down-at-the-heels hospital at Camiers under canvas. A most undesirable and badly drained camp, according to Strong, who has just been there with the U.S.A. Sanitary Commission. . . . Then a hurried lunch and we depart from Charing Cross at 1.30, together with a solemn crowd of British officers returning to the Front. A gloomy crossing on the packet from Folkestone to Boulogne—cold, foggy, crowded. In life belts again and most everyone standing. We were surrounded by destroyers, which in the fog were invisible, but which growled and screamed and scolded at one another with their sirens all the way across. On disembarking our kodaks were taken from us and, packed in huge charabanc affairs, we were carried some 15 miles down the coast to our destination. A late frugal supper in a cold mess hall, and now to bed on a cot in a small conical tent, without undressing.

Thursday, 31 May. Camiers. Beginning to take over. A shockingly dirty, unkempt camp. Luckily about half of the patients have been evacuated before our arrival, leaving only 600 or so. Our first convoy of 200 wounded at 1 a.m., half of them 'sitters' and half 'stretchers'—systematically disposed of by members of the outgoing unit, with whom, naturally, we are not very popular. Each of our officers will have charge of about 100 beds. What can they possibly do with daily notes of the cases?

Sunday, 4 June. I have just parted from young Graham, pathologist of the group we are supplanting, who is going to turn over his tent to me. He hates to leave this place—forlorn as it is and though he is going to a new billet where there is a good laboratory—chiefly because he has planted a few pitiful flowers in the hard-baked clay on the border of the drainage ditch about his tent and some of them are coming up. There are to be some Scotch marigolds, D.V., and in the corners are some ragged bamboo poles on which a little cluster of sweet peas may some day climb. Graham has been in since Mons, was wounded, has a shortened arm, and wears a D.S.O. ribbon.

We are having glorious weather—the first, according to all accounts, since last year. Lucky for us, as this particular 'No. 11 General' is under water in wet weather. We are effectually swallowed up in the British Army Machine, and already Base Hospital No. 5 has completely lost its identity. Communication anywhere is nearly impossible: succeeded three days ago in sending home a cable requesting supplies and asking for an acknowledgement. None has come and there seems to be no way to get anything done—even to buy food for the mess—except through cumbersome channels. Little wonder people become inert and careless. . . .

This was his introduction to No. 11 General where for six months he served as an operating surgeon with the British Expeditionary Force, being detached from the Unit for special duty during the battles for the Messines and Passchendaele ridges. "An unexpected order came last evening [5 June] to report to the D.M.S. of the 2nd Army at Hazebrouck. No explanation accompanied it and our C.O. was somewhat peeved thereby—'dictating to a United States Army Officer,' etc. It was stated that a car would call for me at 9 a.m. and sure enough it did, in the shape of a large ambulance for four lying cases, as usual driven by two females. No knowledge of what to take, or for how long, but a compromise was made with a bedding roll—which was not needed—and a few instruments, which distinctly were." Two days later [7 June] he writes of some of the medical and surgical problems encountered:

. . . Crile arrives from his base at Rouen and we learn that some of the great problems of the war are lice and scabies, which a bath and disinfection every ten days keep only moderately down. Mumps and measles too have been serious among the newcomers, especially the New Zealanders. Then, too, forms of albuminuria occur, and there are many fevers like trench fever that are poorly understood, together with a variety of febrile disorders commonly designated 'Pyrexia of uncertain origin' for want of a more precise designation. . . .

The wounds in most cases of course are multiple. 'Multiple' indeed may hardly convey the impression. Most shell explosion effects—very few bullet wounds in a game like yesterday's. Indeed the more trifling the wound appears to be, the more serious it may prove on investigation. Or the reverse may be true—an ugly-looking wound that proves relatively trifling. One boy had a small temporal wound and stated that there was a hole in his tin hat. The operation showed that a strip of his helmet about two inches long and half an inch wide had been cut out as though by a can opener. This metal sliver had curled in through the temporal bone over his ear, passed through the brain, and its point emerged just behind the external angular process. Not a pleasant thing to dislodge, particularly as it had divided his meningeal artery, which began to bleed after the bone was removed and the missile loosened. . . .

He also described the fighting:

. . . And before long there's a bang! and black earth is thrown up like a geyser 200 yards away and another one nearer—in short, just like the picture post-cards. And the savage in you makes you adore it with its squalor and wastefulness and danger and strife and glorious noise. You feel that, after all, this is what men were intended for rather than to sit in easy chairs with a cigarette and whiskey, the evening paper or the best-seller, and to pretend that such a veneer means civilization and that there is no barbarian behind your starched and studded shirtfront. . . . There was little if any appreciable artillery firing in our direction and, as a contrast to what at the moment was going on across the exposed valley to which the British have tenaciously clung so long, not ten yards from us on the slope below was a little old man in a sort of garden, busily mending two long brown windmill sails which were spread out on the grass—either uninterested or unaware. . . .

The Air Raid of 4 September. . . . Whether or not it was an established policy of the enemy to bomb hospitals, whether it was a matter of presumed reprisals, whether the hospitals, as was more or less inevitable, were placed too near troop encampments and military stores, railroad sidings and ammunition dumps, whether bombing of hospitals was consequently accidental or an expression of personal "hate" on the part of some individual avions, need not now be discussed. The Casualty Clearing Stations in forward areas were of course continually subjected to nocturnal bombing raids, and few of the fifteen or more of these stations behind the British Vth Army during the early Passchendaele operation had escaped fatalities from those horrible nightmare experiences.

But the Base had so far been exempt until on the night of September 4, 1917, without warning other than the extinguishing of lights in the area a few moments before, a Gotha swept over the Camiers area and dropped a succession of seven bombs, five of them being direct hits in Base Hospital No. 5's compound. The first two hits were close together among the tents of the recently attached officers. Lieutenant Fitzsimons when last seen was standing at the opening of his tent and was literally blown to pieces by a bomb which fell at his feet. Lieutenants McGuire, Whidden, and Smith occupying adjoining tents which were literally riddled—someone counted four hundred holes in McGuire's tent—had providential escapes, though all were more or less seriously wounded. The third and fourth bombs struck one of the large marquees full of patients, killing Private Tugo on orderly duty and slightly wounding Miss Parmelee, the nurse who was standing beside him. Twenty-two bed patients in this and the adjacent marquee were more or less seriously rewounded. The last hit, a few seconds later, was in the reception tent, where two regulars, Private Rubino and Private Woods our bugler, together with Private McLeod and Sergeant English, were on duty. Woods and Rubino were killed, McLeod so seriously mutilated that both legs had to be amputated at the mid-thigh. Sloan, Mason, and Stanion were also wounded, and English had a serious "shell shock" from which he was long in recovering. There were, needless to say, many narrow escapes, with not a few acts of heroism, and it was an experience for those who participated in it that gave a profound distaste for the many subsequent air raids the Unit had to live through during its year in Boulogne, where it was in a most exposed position to the Gothas coming in, as they usually did, from the sea.

On September 8 the bodies of Lieutenant Fitzsimons, with Privates Tugo, Woods, and Rubino, were interred in the great military cemetery in the sand dunes between Camiers and Etaples, the first of any of the American Expeditionary Forces to have made the great sacrifice, the more tragic for its having occurred at the hands of an unseen enemy far from the line of battle. Six months later other victims—nurses, officers and men—of far worse raids over hospitals in the vicinity came to lie beside them in that huge field of many thousands of wooden crosses, which lay in plain sight of the great training ground. . . .

Base Hospital No. 5 was assigned to the British (No. 11 General Hospital) at Camiers from May until November 1917 when it was transferred to Boulogne to No. 13 General Hospital.[3] Through the services of Miss Julia Shepley, his personal secretary at the Brigham and now one of three secretaries attached to the Unit, he was able not only to keep the detailed day-to-day record of events (both military and medical), but he also kept for his own files detailed case histories of each of the thousands of wounded men on whom he had personally operated.

These case histories were to be used again many years later—in a way Cushing could never have foreseen when he kept them so painstakingly. In May 1942 Brigadier Hugh Cairns, who had spent a year with Cushing in 1926-1927 and who was in charge of neurosurgery for the R.A.M.C. during the Second World War, cabled the Yale Historical Library for any possible information that would aid in locating the 119 cases with wounds involving the brain and its enveloping structures on which Cushing had reported in his important paper published in the *British Journal of Surgery* during the summer of 1918.[4] Cairns wished to trace these cases since they represented the only series of such wounds from the last war that had been described in detail. But since Cushing's histories which had been carefully packed were lost en route to this country, it seemed highly improbable that the desired information was available. However, on turning to H.C.'s bound copy of this classic paper, there was found, in Miss Shepley's hand, the full names of every case, together with serial numbers, home addresses, and regimental attachments. On the basis of this information Cairns was able, through the Ministry of Pensions, to trace many of the living cases and to have them examined.[5] With many of these patients Cushing had kept in personal touch. Of one of them he wrote in his diary:

[3] Although formally at Camiers until November, Cushing with one of his neurosurgical teams went forward in July to 46 C.C.S. where he remained until 31 October. Here he did some of the most strenuous operating of the entire war period.

[4] "A study of a series of wounds involving the brain and its enveloping structures." *British Journal of Surgery*, April 1918, *5*, 558-684.

[5] Cairns, H. "Head injuries in war, with especial reference to gunshot wounds, including a report on the late results in some of Harvey Cushing's cases of 1917," *War Medicine*, September 1942, 2, 772-785.

There is a nice fellow from Devonshire named Killick, a subaltern of the 6th London Regiment (174th Brigade and so the 58th Division) with about ten wounds, who is doing well enough to evacuate to-night. His objective was Wurst Farm and he is cheered to learn that it was gained and hopes his platoon got through the German barrage which caught him about at the concrete emplacements west of Hoppner Farm, quite early in the morning. He says that they were swinging around from the north, through the "triangle": Hoppner, von Tirpitz, to Wurst Farm, and were to meet the 55th Division coming up from the south to catch the place like a pair of nippers. Judging from the objective map for the 55th, I rather doubt this.

At the time of Cushing's death Mrs. Cushing received this letter:

Peacehaven, England,
H. A. Killick to K.C. *10 October 1939.*

Dear Mrs. Cushing, . . . In 1917—at "Mendinghem" (No. 46 C.C.S.) I was a patient of the professor's—and had it not been for his skill and attention, I don't suppose I should be here to write this. (You will find my name mentioned on p. 210 of his "From a Surgeon's Journal.") Moreover, although he was undoubtedly the leader and teacher in his branch of surgery, he was still human, and I can remember how he told me you had "packed his grip" and bidden him go to France in 1915 to do what he could to help. Twenty-two years have passed since he saved my life and now I have a son of 20 who is a pilot in the Royal Air Force—should he be unlucky enough to be wounded as I was in 1917 I could wish him no better fate than to fall into hands as capable and kindly as those of your husband. Yours very sincerely, H. A. KILLICK.

Revere Osler

For Cushing one of the saddest experiences of the war was the death of Revere Osler which he touches upon but briefly in the Osler biography, giving no indication of the part he himself played in bringing comfort to the boy's father and mother. The diary entry gives the principal details:

Thursday, 30 August 1917. . . . Rather used up, I was preparing to turn in at 10 last night, when came this shocking message: "Sir Wm. Osler's son seriously wounded at 47 C.C.S. Can Major Cushing come immediately?" The C.O. let me have an ambulance, and in a pouring rain we reached Dosinghem in about half an hour. It could not have been much worse, though there was a bare chance—one traversing through the upper abdomen, another penetrating the chest just above the heart, two others in the thigh, fortunately without a fracture. The local C.O. would not let me cable, and I finally insisted on phoning G.H.Q.—got General Macpherson on the wire and persuaded him to send to Oxford via the London War Office: "Revere seriously wounded: not hopelessly: conscious: comfortable."

Crile came over from Rémy with Eisenbrey, and after a transfusion, Darrach, assisted by Brewer, opened the abdomen about midnight. There had been bleeding from two holes—in the upper colon and the mesenteric vessels. His condition remained unaltered, and about seven this morning the world lost this fine boy, as it does many others every day.

We saw him buried in the early morning. A soggy Flanders field beside a little oak grove to the rear of the Dosinghem group—an overcast, windy, autumnal day—the long rows of simple wooden crosses—the new ditches half full of water being dug by Chinese coolies wearing tin helmets—the boy wrapped in an army blanket and covered by a weather-worn Union Jack, carried on their shoulders by four slipping stretcher-bearers. A strange scene—the great-great-grandson of Paul Revere under a British flag, and awaiting him a group of some six or eight American Army medical officers—saddened with the thoughts of his father.

But the extent of the tragedy so far as Sir William and Lady Osler were concerned, can only be gleaned from the painful messages from 13 Norham Gardens. First came a telegram and a letter: "THANK GOD YOU ARE WITH HIM TANTE GRACE OSLER."

Lady Osler to H.C. *31 August 1917.*

Dearest Harvey, Our one comfort is that you were with him—No one in the world could have done as much and no one been fonder of him—I can only think what an agony it was to you when you saw him come in. You will tell us *Everything* I know. Dear Revere, he was living for his leave—a letter last evening told what we would do—I hope he knew you and could talk to you. It is very hard—and we are getting old. There was a fine life in store for the boy—but it couldn't be. I always expected this to happen—but I never could be ready. Our love, TANTE GRACE.

Revere had recognized H.C. and with his leave in mind had smiled, saying, "Surely this will take me home."

Sir William Osler to H.C. *31 August 1917.*

Dear Harvey What a comfort to feel that you were with the laddie at the end and that some one who loved him and that he loved was near. We are heart-broken but shall face the ordeal bravely. With deepest gratitude, Yours affect'ly WM. OSLER.

Sir William Osler to K.C. *31 August 1917.*

Dear Kate The sole comfort in our sorrow is that Harvey was with the dear laddie at the end. Was there ever anything more fortunate! Of all men he is the one we should have chosen to be near Revere at the end. We cannot tell you what a consolation it is to us. Grace keeps up bravely and we are going to bear our sorrow with patience, but we are just heartbroken as you may suppose. He had grown more and more lovable as the years passed and he and I had so much in common. Blessings on you all, Yours affectionately, WM. OSLER.

Lady Osler to K.C. *1 September 1917.*

Oh Kate, dear Kate My darling fair baby has gone—just laid in that wet, cold Belgium, but thank God for two things—your Harvey was with him and he has gone to a peaceful spot. I feel sure of that—and we are rather old and may go too, very soon. Just fancy Harvey being with him. We are waiting and waiting for his letter and I am sure he will come here on his first leave—and perhaps bring some messages he couldn't even write. I can only see Revere lying on his stretcher with Harvey holding his dear, dirty hand. It is our comfort—our only comfort today to think Harvey was there and you'll be glad too. . . .

My poor man is heartbroken. I feel very anxious for him. He puts up a bluff in the daytime but the nights—three nights—have been torture—and I am watching near his door now in case he needs me. Sue is such a blessing—but must go soon to you all and help—at home. We can look after each other and she knows so well now what is needed. This letter is from my poor old heart. Good night.

TANTE GRACE.

* * * * *

At Boulogne during the winter of 1917-1918 H.C. operated almost incessantly, particularly during the German spring offensive which began with the advance on Amiens in March. In May, however, his surgical endeavors were interrupted. Keeping a diary in war time, especially when stationed close to an active battlefront, is fraught with difficulty because of security regulations; in most military organizations diary keeping is strictly prohibited except for the commanding officers who are obliged to keep official records. Cushing, being the man he was, could no more have gone through the war without recording the epic events in the midst of which he found himself than he could have performed a surgical operation without describing it immediately after. A physician of the written word, he was impelled to set everything down with unconscious disregard for military regulations. He ignored many a rule and when he finally ran afoul of the censors, they would certainly have made serious trouble for him had they known of all the photographs and verbal accounts of battles included in his voluminous diary.

He was first put on the carpet for the seemingly trivial offense of quoting in a letter to his wife a remark culled from a letter of a British Tommy which he (H.C.) had censored. Quoting anything from a document which one has read as a censor is strictly forbidden; Cushing, however, had merely lifted the remark as a *bon mot* and he protested that he was being tripped up on a minor technicality. He was warned and the case was dismissed. In May 1918 a more serious charge was preferred against him. On the 8th, out of a clear sky, he was ordered to report to the Commanding General at Tours. H.C. still had the rank of major and he imagined that he was being summoned in connection with his long overdue promotion. However, on reaching Tours on the 9th he was informed that court martial proceedings were likely to be instituted because he had enclosed in a letter home a paper written by a member of his unit offering harsh criticism of a British surgeon. The document in question had, according to H.C., been caught up inadvertently.

How I came to do so I do not recall; but we were expecting orders to close up any day and all of us were sending home whatever lay loose on our desks. It's one of the reasons why it's dangerous out here to put one's thoughts too much on paper along with the things one hears. I have written a letter of apology and explanation and can but await the verdict with the greatest possible humiliation. Being my second offense with the British Censor makes matters worse; and they have passed the matter on to our Adjutant General. It took most of this afternoon to find out what my summons was for: no one had any record of it; and when the blow came I should have been glad to be "spurlos versenkt." . . .

On the 11th he wrote: "Col. McCaw, who is in charge here as Acting Chief Surgeon in the absence of both Bradley and Ireland, though very friendly, shakes his head over my sorry case and says: 'Come in again to-morrow.' I therefore sport no chevrons and keep as inconspicuous as possible." And again on the 13th: "Col. McCaw says so far as he can see I too will be sent home—though for different reasons. I go about with my tail between my legs and humbly report once a day to ask if there are any orders for me. None." Cushing was kept in suspense for ten days, during which time he stayed with an old friend of college days, Colonel Hugh Bayne. Another friend, recalling the incident years later, writes:

In the Autumn of 1918 I was a Red Cross commissioner living at the Bernerhof when a joint American-German commission for the exchange of prisoners met in Berne. Maj. Gen. [X.] (Judge-Advocate on Pershing's staff) was one of them. We saw much of each other. One day he asked if I knew Harvey Cushing—adding that he hoped I was no friend of his. I said we were good friends, and asked what he had against Dr. Cushing. He then told me that had his advice been taken Dr. Cushing would have been sent to Leavenworth prison and that such would have been ordered by a court martial had not many American doctors in France petitioned Pershing in Cushing's behalf. The charge against him was that in a letter to his wife, which was intercepted by French censors and sent to the British Government, Cushing had [included a paper which] severely criticised a British surgeon. The British War Office had demanded that Cushing should be court martialed. His defence was that he had never meant to send the offending paper, but had mistakenly gathered up this sheet of memoranda together with what he sent to his wife. General [X.] was bitterly opposed to the acceptance of such an excuse and very critical of Pershing's granting of the petition.

This, however, may well be the exaggeration of a hazy memory. One in authority who was in a position to know the facts had no recollection of a proposed court martial, nor of the petition, nor of the affair having reached the Judge Advocate. The outcome, which H.C.'s diary fails to mention, would appear to have been his transfer from No. 13, which was under the offended British, to American Headquarters. While waiting in suspense he managed to escape boredom by negotiating his first flight in an airplane.

Wednesday, 15 May. Memorable for my first flight. . . . After my usual morning disappointment, and having been refused a movement order to spend the day in Blois, I wandered out to the Pont de Tours, sat in a park at the foot of a statue of Rabelais, played with some French children there, and finally, seeing some young flying men standing on the bridge, asked them how to get to the aerodrome. They were going that way themselves—indeed were waiting for a bus, and would I not go along; only about 7 kilometres on the Route Nationale to Paris. Thus it happened; and I found Raymond Noyes, an instructor in the local flying school, who is in charge of the Observation School in this the 2nd Am. Aviation Centre. We had lunch, made an inspection, looked at photographs, and about 4 p.m., weather conditions being perfect, he asked: "Would I care to go up?" Of course. So I am put in appropriate togs, a pilot named Taylor appears, and in a Sopworth Type I A2 with the ominous number 13 on its side we are off before there is time to reconsider.

We were up an hour and flew over the beautiful country down the right bank at an average height of 1100 metres—almost down to where the Vienne empties into the Loire—then across the river, with Chinon in the distance; over the Forêt de Chinon, Azay-le-Rideau, then directly over Tours and so back to the camp. It was what Taylor called a bit bumpy in spots, but on the whole much the gentlest and most comfortable form of transport imaginable, and I came down tingling as though I'd had a glass of champagne. One experiences no sense of height at all and practically none of leaving the ground. The only moment of what might be called surprise was when we began to spiral down over the camp, but Captain Taylor, I'm glad to say, is not a stunting pilot. . . .

By the 16th Cushing had received permission to attend a meeting of the Medical Research Committee in Paris.

Thursday, 16 May, Tours. While at headquarters as usual the first thing this a.m., McKernon turns up en route to Paris with a blanket movement-order covering all Consultants. Though I have officially received no such appointment, on the basis of this order Col. McCaw gives me permission to accompany McKernon; and to atone, I presume, for having kept me on the rack these past two weeks, he invites me to lunch with other regulars of the Medical Corps at a luxurious billet hung with tapestries and with an outlying garden.

Friday evening. Paris. To-day's open meetings were held in the Hotel Continental as were those of a month ago when I was too busy at Pernes to attend. Morning sessions were given over to military orthopaedics (Goldthwait and Osgood and two French Médecins Majors).

At our committee meeting in the p.m., Rose Bradford, T. R. Elliott, and Cummins represented the B.E.F. No report from the "wound closure" subcommittee which, alas, had never been called together owing to some mix-up between ourselves and the British. I urged that the policy of the organization be formulated, for it has never been set down and there has been a good deal of misunderstanding about it; then, too, the antivivisectionists have openly protested against the prostitution of Red Cross funds for animal experimentation under such "celebrated vivisectors" as Crile, Cannon, and myself.

Saturday, the 18th. The "medical aspects of aviation" in the morning with papers by Col. Birley and Major Flack of the R.F.C., and remarks by Barcroft on polycythaemia—all very interesting. At noon Cannon, Taylor, Elliott, and I had a confab, as a result of which I missed not only lunch but most of the afternoon session in an effort to draw up a statement of the original unwritten policy of our meetings, from which we seem to be slipping away. Participants in the gas session of the afternoon were Cols. Elliott, Herringham, Barcroft, and Meakins, representing the British; then a French Colonel and Col. Fries of our Engineer Corps in charge of the Gas Service. Col. Fries indiscreetly described our losses at Seicheprey—indiscreetly, at least, from the British point of view, for all matters relating to gas warfare are "confidential" with the B.E.F. Barcroft, who I believe is a Quaker, appeared comfortably in civies; and though he may be a conscientious objector, he certainly, as contributor to the chemistry of gas warfare, is in a position to concoct more devilish ways of killing Boches than if he were actually in service.

There are, in Elliott's opinion, good reasons for military secrecy regarding gas. For example, the enemy sends over his gas in shells marked with a yellow (mustard gas), blue (the arsenical compounds), or green (phosgene) cross, as told by the investigation of duds. The British learned that after shelling with mustard gas the enemy never attacked for a few days because the gas lingers and his own troops would consequently suffer. Hence after a bombardment of yellow-cross shells the British used to move out their holding troops and substitute reserves in small numbers.

If British officials had tried to have Cushing court martialed, the Irish atoned for the indignity by haling him to Dublin where in a spirited Gaelic ritual he was made an Honorary Fellow of the Royal College of Surgeons in Ireland.[6] His diary gives a vivid description of the colorful ceremony:

. . . The ceremony in the afternoon was most elaborate, and amusingly disproportionate to the occasion—*viz.*, me. There was a guard of honor drawn up in the lower hall—the students' O.T.C., which I had to inspect. Then tea in the council room for the elect, and Viscount French appears with his Staff—very fine. He reminded me of a small edition of a much-decorated Leonard Wood. . . . I sank alongside of the Field Marshal, Lord Lieutenant, Viscount, and Viceroy rolled into one—sank, I say, into a large carved chair in which, as I was told later, Daniel O'Connell once died or did something equally foolish. As a matter of fact, I should have stood, but too late now. Then they began tormenting me—the Vice President read slowly the names of former Honorary Fellows—66 I believe—Abernethy, Benjamin Brodie, Syme, Pott, Astley Cooper, John Hunter, Lister, Huxley, Jonathan Hutchinson, Paget, Helmholtz, John Billings (this made me feel a little more at home), Robert Jones, Moynihan, Keogh, Sir Almroth Wright—perfectly at home. They then told other things about the College and finally, coming to me, read dates out of an ancient *Who's Who* about someone I vaguely recognized as having met.

Then I arose and stood back to the audience before a large and threatening mace, while the President, between me and a background of intertwined American and Irish flags, uttered other things about painting the lily and such sentiments. Finally I was permitted to sit again in the lap of Daniel O'Connell's chair and wished I too might also die there—but no, I had to sign the roll—a slippery parchment containing signatures if anything less legible than mine—then was given a green box with a diploma, a book in green vellum containing the roll of honor of the College in this war, and Lord French was given a duplicate of it, which he will doubtless prize. Then, horrors! I was given the opportunity of making a public acceptance!! It was pretty bad, but they cheered me along and I got through somehow with a kind of after-dinner-speech effect. . . .

[6] Cushing was still serving under the British Army and Lt. General Sir Arthur Sloggett, Director General of the British Army Medical Service, had been consulted about granting Cushing leave. On 14 April he readily assented, adding "It will be a very nice compliment to the U.S. Army." When H.C. was ordered to Tours on 9 May, Roger I. Lee, the C.O. of No. 13 General Hospital, wired to Dublin that Cushing could not be present to receive the fellowship. Leave, however, was finally granted after he had left Tours.

Sunday, 26 May. Dublin. The morning paper says that with my most "pronounced American accent," I addressed the gathering, etc.

A full account of his speech appeared in the Dublin morning paper for Monday, the 27th. How well he knew the Irish factions is not clear but his courage was probably greater than his judgment, for the account of what he said runs thus:

> . . . "We are in [the war] as a country; our neighbour, Canada, is now in as a country. You here in this beautiful land are the next people to us, and we expect you to be in as a country (hear, hear, and applause), and you certainly will. We know the Irish; there are more Irish in America than there are here. I think there are more Irish in Boston than in Ireland, and the Irish everywhere are usually on top. Someone has made the amusing statement that Ireland is the only place in the world that is not governed by Irishmen (laughter); but if there is any trouble, if anyone needs support or counsel, or to be aided in a good cause, you are pretty sure to find an Irishman at your left and at your right hand." Proceeding, Major Cushing said he knew very well what Ireland had already done in the present war; and nothing finer, perhaps, was done in the war than what was done by the Dublin Fusiliers and the Munster Fusiliers (applause) at Gallipoli. All last summer he was at the back of an Army in which the 16th and 36th Divisions were fighting side by side; and he didn't believe there was anything better done than was done by men from the North and from the South of Ireland (applause). . . .

While in Dublin H.C. renewed his acquaintance with the animals at the Royal Zoological Society, some of whom he had seen on his previous visit to Dublin in 1904: "Then we saw our friends the lions and other big cats again and made them roar and play as long ago when I first met them. When a house full of lions roar something peculiar happens to one's diaphragm which vibrates as though tuned to their vocal message. The same old attendant and breeder of lions was there—has been there in fact for 38 years."

By the end of May, Cushing was back at No. 13 General Hospital at Boulogne dealing with the casualties of the Second Battle of the Marne. In June 1918 he was transferred to the Medical Headquarters of the A.E.F. at Neufchâteau in the Vosges as Senior Consultant in Neurosurgery and was promoted to the rank of Lt. Colonel. Here he participated in the major engagements at Château-Thierry, St. Mihiel, and the Argonne. Between the offensives he visited other hospitals, attended medical conferences in Paris, crossed the Channel to confer with physicians at Oxford and London, and visited the front lines many times investigating conditions, care of the wounded in the casualty clearing stations, etc. During the major battles he and his team often operated for sixteen to eighteen hours at a stretch.

Throughout these periods of intense activity and strain H.C. rarely failed to record the happenings of the day—bits of comedy, pathos, and philosophy, acts of heroism, snatches of history, sketches of the Flanders countryside along with notes of operations, impressions of people, conflict of nationalities—all the hurly-burly of war as seen through his keen and sensitive eye. When one peruses his war diary, which extends in the original to nearly a million words (the equivalent of four printed volumes the size of this biography), all profusely illustrated with photographs, maps, and memorabilia of every description, and when one appreciates the exhausting clinical load he was carrying during the entire period, one finds the diversity of the two years' record almost unbelievable. With the calm detachment of an historian and the acute perception of an artist, he sketched the human, homely incidents of his days against the grim background of war.

Sunday, 4 June 1917 [*Wimereux*]. . . . There was a large gathering of officers from everywhere, and Sargent, promising to bring me back in the morning, persuaded me to stay and dine at the Australian mess and spend the night with him at No. 32 Stationary. . . . It is a famous mess in what was the Wimereux Golf Club. From the porch one can see the cliffs of Dover on a clear day, and alongshore the point of Ambleteuse projects out into the sea. This was Napoleon's naval base for his planned invasion of England—the old supports for the piers still visible. . . . The most striking figure of all [at dinner] was a Captain (Sir Beachcroft) Towse, wearing the uniform of the Gordon Highlanders with a V.C. ribbon—slim, dapper, erect, precise—and blind! One of the most promising officers of the regular army, a great polo player, shot through both orbits in the Boer War. He is now writing letters home for Tommies on a typewriter, and spends his days in the hospitals, . . . and entertaining people at mess. . . .

Wednesday, 13 June. . . . We then went through Arras itself—more badly damaged than one would surmise from a distance, though the massive cathedral with its collapsed roof and ruined tower—little more than a great mound of rubble—can be seen for miles. Heaven only knows how often Arras-on-the-Scarpe has been laid waste and ravaged by vandals in bygone times, or how many treaties have been signed here or how many elaborate tapestries—perhaps after Jean Foucquet's actual designs—were woven here in the fifteenth century and scattered throughout Europe. Certainly it could never have been so hard hit before, yet I suppose a new Arras will inevitably arise on the ruins and that these two recent years of incessant bombardment will fade into past history. . . .

Thursday, 14 June. In the little town itself [Crécy] we saw the old unexplained Spanish monument and one or two newer shafts; and finally . . . we drove off to the south for a kilometre or so and found the old weather-beaten granite cross with some lines from Froissart cut in below, and this inscription:

Cette Croix rappelle la fin héroique de Jean
de Luxembourg Roi de Bohème mort pour
la France. Le 26 Août 1346

The blind John of Bohemia was one of eleven princes killed on that day, and it was his feathers that Edward the Black Prince, who commanded a division of the English, adopted as the Prince of Wales' emblem. . . .

Sunday, 1 July. . . . Our flags, so movingly consecrated by Bishop Lawrence, have scarcely been out of their rubber cases since we left Fort Totten. I wish the nurses and men were equally well protected from the cold and wet.

Tuesday, 3 July. George Denny, Chairman of the Laundry Committee, squares himself by pinning notices on our bulletin board. . . . Today as follows—with an empty match box tacked on below:

"Laundry. Persons receiving articles in their wash of unknown origin will kindly place them in this box. Honesty is the best policy, and by means of the box method all hard feelings will be wiped out and each can receive his own goods through an excellent clearing house system. I am counting on the purity of soul of the command to make the idea efficient. G. P. Denny, L.C." Tonight a sock with many holes was draped over the box. . . .

TENT AT MENDINGHEM
With 46 C.C.S. in July 1917

4 July 1917. Vive l'Amérique! An historic day to have arrived in Paris. . . . After a real bath at the Crillon, I met the Strongs hustling about—must go immediately to Les Invalides—they have tickets—special seats—Pershing—American troops—Fourth of July . . . and so forth. [Later] some American Ambulance people were encountered . . . who insisted that I go with them to the ceremony at the Picpus, the cemetery where Lafayette is buried, in a remote part of Paris. . . . Many dignitaries were grouped about the tomb. . . . Brand Whitlock read at length many pages about civilization and humanity—very immaculate . . . both the speech and B.W. . . .

Wednesday, 15 August [46 C.C.S., Mendinghem]. We nearly "busted" on six cases in the twenty-four hours since yesterday's note. We began at 8 p.m. . . . crawled home for some eggs in the mess and to bed at 2.30 a.m. . . . [One case] this man "Chave"—queer name—when roused from his semiconsciousness made it known that he had some precious false teeth. They were removed, somewhat more easily than was his broken frontal bone. They must have been on his mind, for I remember when rongeuring out fragments of his skull he kept muttering that I was breaking his teeth. . . .

Friday, 17 August. We beat our record to-day with eight cases—all serious ones. A prompt start at 9 a.m. with two cases always in waiting—notes made, X-rays taken, and heads shaved. It's amusing to think that at home I used to regard a single major cranial operation as a day's work. These eight averaged two hours apiece—one or two very interesting ones. . . . Tonight while operating on a Boche prisoner . . . about 11 p.m.—our seventh case—some Fritz planes came over on a bombing raid, as they do almost every night nowadays. . . . Of course all our lights were switched off, and we had to finish with candles. . . . The case in waiting was a little eighteen-year-old Tommy from East London —scared, peaked, underfed, underdeveloped. He had been in training six months and was in the trenches for the first time during the present show—*just ten minutes* when he was hit.

Sunday, 19 August. . . . Someone leaning out of the window cried out: "There's a falling plane. Nose down, spinning, wings laid back, like a dead bird. He fell just beyond No. 64, and the familiar, irresistible impulse made everyone run toward the spot—I too as soon as I could leave. I got across the track, past the post-mortem tent, as far as the rapidly growing cemetery on the other side of No. 64. Here were about a hundred grinning Chinese coolies, in their blue tunics—though some were stripped to the waist—digging two fresh ditches, about six by twenty feet. The Far East digging in the upstart West with its boasted civilization! This held me up, and I refrained from crossing the road to see the mangled machine and the dead thing under it. . . .

Camiers. Saturday, 8 September. . . . Yellowlees proceeded to show us some crazy men who thought there were bombs under their beds. . . . Then to see Miss Parmelee, our nurse, who had the closest kind of call; rather used up to-day after her antitoxin, but she deserves a Military Cross or whatever women are given for presence of mind, neglect of self, and thought of others, in time of possible panic. She had been standing at the entrance of C-V, not twenty-five feet from the third bomb. She's rather frail and it knocked her down, but she heard the cries and groans of the patients, got right to work and stayed on duty all night. In the morning she turned up in the operating room, where had been a mêlée all night, to get Morton to take a tiny shell fragment out of her eyelid. Her sweater had six good-sized holes in it and her heavy outer coat about as many. Her watch was picked off by a piece of the shell, leaving only the strap, and it has not yet been found. . . .

Sunday, 21 Oct. A beautiful autumnal Sunday. Clopton over in the morning from Rémy to look on at our dressings. In the afternoon to Dosinghem to see Revere's grave and meet the new sergeant who is caring for it. It's dreadful to see that place grow—a thousand burials in the past three weeks. A service going on—a Padre, a Tommy at attention at the foot of the grave, a body in a blanket barely showing above the surface of the muddy water in the bottom of the ditch. . . .

Wednesday, 14 November. . . . Meanwhile the Flemish farmer on whose land No. 46 C.C.S. was laid out—and I presume it's true of other farmers elsewhere—doesn't really care. He philosophizes that he and his forbears long before him have tilled the same acres, as will his progeny long after him. It has not made much difference to any of them, what governments have come and gone—now Roman, now Spanish, now French, now German, now Belgian, now English—nor what wars brought them; and for that matter he usually manages to make a little more money at such times—as in the case of the pigs at No. 46 fattening on crusts from the officers' mess. Is his the *vox populi?* . . . Julius Caesar said the Belgae are by far the bravest because they are most distant from the culture and civilization of Rome—furthermore they are neighbors to the Germans across the Rhine with whom they constantly wage war. . . .

Sunday, 16 December. Boulogne. . . . Robby thinks we are pessimistic at the Base. We are. From my small experience there is less grousing at the Front than the rear—the less perspective you have of the whole situation and the more you are concentrated on your own little job, the better for you. And people talk too much, particularly the pessimistic ones. . . . During war time only optimists like Bowlby should have the privilege of speech. . . .

Sunday evening, 2 June 1918. . . . Another gorgeous day. Col. Webb-Johnson took me to Calais to see some spinal cases, and we made a day of it. To Audreselles, cutting across Cap Gris-Nez to Wissant—the villagers in their Sunday best; the villages decorated with gaudy bunting and flowers and the streets strewn with greens—the *Fête Dieu,* which, according to my *Histoire de France,* goes back to 1246 and was inaugurated in Liège. But far more gorgeous were the hillsides with their rectangles of bright yellow mustard, others of brilliant scarlet—*luzerne,* I presume—and still others with a pinkish vetch, sewed in on the quilt of varied greens. The road bordered by a profusion of wild flowers, thrift and buttercups and the first of the red poppies, with other things I did not know. Across the bridge with its line of trenches dating back to 1915—then Sangatte, where stand the partly demolished brick buildings which some 15 years ago were erected by the company organized to tunnel under the English Channel—a project which was abandoned, alas! . . .

On 28 January 1918 we find Cushing writing of the death of the brother of his old and dear friend, Thomas McCrae:

I saw poor Jack McCrae with Elder at No. 14 General last night—the last time. A bright flame rapidly burning out. He died early this morning. Just made Consulting Physician to the 1st Army—the only Canadian so far to be thus honored. Never strong, he gave his all with the Canadian Artillery during the prolonged second battle of Ypres and after, at which time he wrote his imperishable verses [*In Flanders Fields*]. Since those frightful days he has never been his old gay and companionable self, but has rather sought solitude. A soldier from top to toe—how he would have hated to die in bed. . . . Was anyone ever more respected and loved than he? Someone has said that "children and animals followed him as shadows follow other men."

In the diary entry for 6 August 1918, after his transfer to the Headquarters of the Medical and Surgical Consultants at Neufchâteau, we find the first mention of ill health. "Here after three days in bed with a not-yet-diagnosed malady which I regarded as the Spanish flu—three days' grippe—or what you will. This came on top of two rackety days around Château-Thierry, getting back home supperless, cold, and wet, in an open Dodge at 1 a.m. I had suddenly aged and our driver had to help me upstairs—teeth chattering and done in. . . ." There followed two months of intense activity—visiting hospital after hospital to expedite the work of the various neurosurgical teams and operating steadily after the battle of St. Mihiel. On 8 October en route to Paris he writes:

> The last four days passed with the kindly Strongs, who are much concerned about my health and, though poorly themselves, they nevertheless have made their apartment a hospital for me. Something has happened to my hind legs and I wobble like a tabetic and can't feel the floor when I unsteadily get up in the morning. Bastianelli, who has a ready thermometer, has taken my temperature every time he's seen me and finds I have fever; Thayer caught me defenseless last night and couldn't elicit my deep reflexes and mumbled something about extrasystoles. They all insist on my going away—the Riviera, Rome, Oxford, all suggested. These places all sound to me like going to the moon. So this is the sequence of the grippe. We may perhaps thank it for helping us win the war if it really hit the German Army thus hard in February last. . . .

On 17 October he writes again: "Too poor on my pins to go to Vichy as planned. Marked increase of numbness and unsteadiness with a good deal of involvement of my hands. Schwab comes to the rescue, takes me to his hospital at Priez-la-Fauche as 'a guest,' and gives up his room to me." The next day: "Very kind people here. I am being kept in bed, having little use of my lean and shrunk shanks. Schwab shakes his head and talks about a multiple toxic neuritis with leucopenia. A new set of visitors and acquaintances—notably a vociferous militia colonel who occupies the room next to mine and is strong on things to eat and drink at bizarre hours." He remained more or less in bed during the last three weeks of October with bouts of headache, double vision, and numbness of both lower extremities. No one felt able to make a diagnosis, least of all H.C. himself. It was possibly an obscure virus infection of the nervous system (encephalitis), but the major blood vessels of his lower extremities had become thrombosed and occluded. On 31 October he writes:

> A "guest" here, a fortnight now—unfortunately missing the last act of the drama. It's a curious business—unquestionably still progressing—purely a sensory affair, fortunately without pain, though with considerable muscular wasting. The paresthesias are chiefly in soles and palms and I have a vague sense of

familiarity with the sensation—as though I had met it somewhere in a dream. Like stepping barefoot on a very stiff and prickly doormat—a feeling, too, as though the plantar and palmar fascias had shrunk in the wash and were drawn taut. As Gowers used to say, our sensations transcend our vocabularies. But it's so characteristic someone who has it ought to describe it—preferably a doctor. . . .

Writing in 1924 to S. Burt Wolbach, Councilman's successor in the chair of pathology at Harvard, about a hospital patient with an undiagnosed malady, H.C. commented incidentally on his own illness in 1918: "I do not know what to say about this case. It sounds very much as though he actually had trench fever. . . . Reading this man's history makes me feel that I must have had trench fever, and that that accounts for the disabilities of my own hind legs. I am glad to say I have so far largely escaped the neurasthenia this poor fellow suffers from. . . ." Since H.C. never gave in to any ailment, he continued to keep his diary, answer his mail, and to enjoy his fellow patients and visits from friends:

Sunday, 3 November. My hands now have caught up with my feet—so numb and clumsy that shaving's a danger and buttoning laborious. When the periphery is thus affected the brain too is benumbed and awkward. Still, there are bright spots. A visit from Kerr this morning with documents from the office—also McLean, with a new novel and the news. This grows more and more amazing every day—the collapse one by one of the props on which Germany has built up her dreams of world domination—Mittel-Europa and the East.

For the first time since Wednesday from my chair laboriously to one of our Dodge cars. Soft air—soft smoky colors—the foliage almost more beautiful than in its earlier stages of ripening. As far as Reynel and back—the old peasants in their white caps—church bells ringing—even the cows idled about the village with the air of *permissionnaires,* as though taking a deserved Sunday afternoon off. The French gardener here is planting pansies along the south wall of the L—— "so the Americans can send blossoms home in envelopes to their sweethearts."

As soon as possible he insisted on daily exercise and massage. Sidney I. Schwab, writing to Cushing many years later, said, "I was thinking . . . of the therapeutic side of your case and I believe the effort we made to get you up and about, to do everything, to make you ambulatory rather than to keep you in bed was good therapy in spite of the conventional ideas against it. As I get more intimately acquainted with sick people rather than diseases, I am impressed with the necessity of keeping the human being in action as long as it is possible to do so without injury. That was apparently what happened in your case and there was perhaps behind it the same logic that influences me now."

During the first two weeks of November Cushing's malady began to lift, but he continued to be a semi-invalid until the 15th when he felt well enough to attend a meeting at the La Fouche hospital of the

LEAVING WITH THE UNIT
9 May 1917

OFFICERS OF THE UNIT, MAY 1917

Top row: F. R. Ober, T. R. Goethals, E. B. Towne, A. V. Bock, H. Forbes, O. H. Robertson, J. J. Morton. *Second row:* G. P. Denny, P. Brown, W. B. Cannon, E. C. Cutler, J. L. Stoddard, G. Horrax. *Third row:* Villaret, R. Fitz, G. S. Derby, W. M. Boothby, M. E. Peabody, H. Lyman, H. Binney. *Fourth row:* A. G. Reynolds, H. Cushing, R. U. Patterson, R. I. Lee, R. B. Osgood

JOHN McCRAE AND "BONNEAU"
At No. 3 Canadian General in Flanders

Reclassification Board on disposition of patients. On the 11th he had written:

La dynastie des Hohenzollern a été balayée; but in this process some twenty millions of human beings have perished or been mutilated, and who is to be held responsible for this? The terms of the armistice were signed early this morning, though the signal to "cease fire" was not given until the 72 hours were up, *viz.,* at 11 a.m. In these last few hours many poor fellows must have needlessly fallen. Thus the Great War ends at the eleventh hour on this eleventh day of the eleventh month of 1918; and the Kaiser awakes from his forty years' dream of world dominion. It's a piteous spectacle. . . . He came so very near to fulfilling his ambition—the Hohenzollern rule of a Prussianized world. *Weltmacht oder Niedergang.* He gambled and lost, so it is to be downfall.

The past few days have been comparable to the last few minutes of a decisive intercollegiate football game at the end of a season. On one side of the field, alive with color and excitement, an exultant crowd, touched by the last rays of a November sun—an unexpected victory within their grasp through an unlooked-for collapse of the visiting team. Across, on the other side of the darkening field, tense, colorless, shivering, and still, sit the defeated, watching their opponents roll up goal after goal as they smash through an ever-weakening line that shortly before seemed impregnable.

Just so, till the whistle blew, the Allies plunged ahead on the five-yard line of the Western Front. The Americans pushed over at Sedan—a mass play carried the French beyond the Mézières-Hirson line—and the British Guards Division on the left centre went through to Mauberge and Mons, where early in the game they so desperately and hopelessly resisted an apparently unconquerable foe. Surely the Bowmen of Agincourt, the Angel of Mons, and Saint George himself must have appeared yesterday, even as they are said to have appeared in those tragic days of August 1914. It's a trivial comparison—a world war and a football game—but when something is so colossal as to transcend comprehension one must reduce it to the simple terms of familiar things. . . .

And again on the 16th:

7 p.m. Adieu, La Fauche. Four weeks there were somehow passed, under the kind attention of Schwab and his people. So in the old Dodge back to the attic of 57 rue Gohier in Neufchâteau, with its smells and draughts and flapping paper partitions. We huddle about a cylindrical iron stove and envy the deaf Duncan, the mangy "Gamin," and the slatternly Henriette, who together occupy the warm box of a kitchen. Too tired, squalid, and uncomfortable to talk to one another, we scarcely need to do so while familiar shibboleths resound in our ears—that this was to be a war to end all wars, and that the world from now will be made safe for democracy. We wonder. We shall at least see what democracy can make of it—and after all this destruction there is certainly much remaking to be done.

And these shall be no easy idle years,
For only by the toil of stubborn men,
Of women toiling stubbornly with men,
Shall earth attain her heritage of dreams.

On Thanksgiving Day:

Neufchâteau, 28 November. Rainy season in earnest. All day in the office filing peripheral nerve literature and keeping close to a stove. Found in the enemy literature (*Deutsche medicinische Wochenschrift,* 1918, p. 854) an article on *Polyneuritis ambulatoria*—"in young and otherwise healthy individuals, with loss of deep reflexes and without signs of cortical disease." So I am not the only one. . . . All are wondering now that Mr. Wilson—or Mrs. Wilson?—has decided to come over, what particular claim we have to a prominent seat at the Peace Table. Our total casualties are some 326,000, only a little more than half of them representing battle casualties, *viz.,* 179,625. The few thousand American dead are tabulated as follows:

Killed or died of wounds	36,164
Died of disease	14,601
Died unspecified	2,604
	53,369

Unofficial reports credit the French (excluding the Colonials) with 1,700,000 dead and casualties untold, a large percentage of the *poilus* having of course been wounded more than once. This far exceeds the losses of the British, who have had only 658,704 dead out of something over three and a half million casualties. Indeed someone has stated that the total number of cases (mostly British) treated by each of our six original Base Hospital Units serving with the B.E.F. exceeds the total casualties of the A.E.F. B.H. No. 4, for example, had 67,591 patients.

What an insignificant toll we have paid after all! It is illuminating to compare the Canadian and American lists and to find the figures practically identical. The Canadian Corps with its total of *ca.* 400,000 volunteer troops have been in the thick of it since the second Ypres, while we with something like five times that number in the A.E.F. have had battalions in the line for only a few paltry months.

	Canadian	*American*
Wounded	152,779	179,635
Prisoners	2,860	2,163
Missing	5,394	11,600
Dead	50,334	53,369
Total	211,367	246,767

While we have been prodigal of our regulars and marines, a very small proportion of our *ca.* two million men have been in contact with the enemy; the Canadians, on the other hand, from the outset have been regarded as essentially a fighting corps. To put it another way, approximately two out of every four Canadians who have served in the B.E.F. have been killed or wounded, whereas something less than two out of every sixteen Americans who embarked to the tune of "Over There" were booked for casualties.

An Amsterdam report of the German losses shows that during the past few weeks they have rapidly risen, almost to the level of the French figures, which, as a matter of fact, may never be precisely made known.

	Up to Oct. 31	*Up to Nov. 10*
Germans killed	1,580,000	1,600,000
Germans missing	260,000	103,000 (?)
German prisoners	290,000	618,000
Germans wounded	4,000,000	4,064,000
Total	6,130,000	6,385,000

At the close of hostilities nearly 18,000 wounded Americans were occupying beds in overcrowded hospitals officered and manned by war-weary people, most of whom were looking for any kind of excuse to get leave and go sightseeing along with the Army of Occupation. Since many of the wounded were still in need of serious secondary operations, the problem was one for which G.H.Q. scarcely knew the answer. It was at first decided that they were to be rushed home; but soon after this programme was set in operation, the ports of embarkation became so jammed that at Savenay, for example, 10,000 patients in 8,000 beds, mostly under canvas, were despondently awaiting the long-overdue transports. Ere long came word from Washington that since no more hospital beds were available at home, the remainder must stay in France until provision could be made to receive them. As no one had had any experience with demobilization on a large scale, there were orders and counter orders and unbelievable confusion.

Meanwhile, final meetings were being held in Paris of the R.C. Research Committee; also of the *Conférence Chirurgicale Interalliée* in which British, French, Belgian, Italian, Portuguese, Japanese, Serbian, and American doctors compared notes. It was even thought that further sessions might profitably be held and plans were laid accordingly; but these things required constructive efforts for which there was no longer either enthusiasm or leadership.

To add to the rich detail in the diary concerning H.C.'s activities during the war, there are many anecdotes and recollections prompted by the vividness of the impression he made on the large number of people he encountered during these years. A few may be cited:

From Cary B. Gamble (8 March 1940). I did not come in contact with Dr. Cushing from the time he left Baltimore until during the war in France. One night in September 1918, I took dinner with him at the Consultants' Headquarters at Neufchâteau. There were two very distinguished eye specialists of the English Army there and one or two other of our friends. The two Englishmen were on a tour of inspection. Dr. Cushing came in late, and something brought up the question of Vauban. Immediately we heard from Dr. Cushing a most enlightening talk concerning the great engineer. He told us more than we could have found in any book; described his life, his work at Ypres, the forts at Verdun and at Belfort; and, in addition, Vauban's career as a financier for which Louis XIV punished him severely.

The whole talk was given in his usual brilliant style and was most fascinating. One of the Englishmen, a Colonel, asked me afterwards who that remarkable man was. It was this side of Dr. Cushing that must have appealed to Dr. Osler as it did to most of us.

From S. B. Herdman (12 March 1940). Dr. Cushing gave me but a kind word and in such a way that it did constitute one moment of glory in the dreadful months I spent operating upon the nontransportable wounded of the Second Division during the campaign of 1918. After the battle of St. Mihiel, my good friend Colonel Burton J. Lee—of tender memory—took me to Neufchâteau to meet General John Finney, then head of the Section of Surgery of the American Expeditionary Forces. That is another story. However, as we approached General Finney's office, we met Colonel Cushing, to whom I was introduced by Colonel Lee. Dr. Cushing merely stated: "Herdman, I have heard of you and your work, and I congratulate you." What he said and the manner of his saying it were compensation for the many heartbreaking weeks I had spent in doing the best I could under adverse conditions. . . .

From C. W. Rand (March 1940).[7] His methods of treating head wounds at the front had proved revolutionary and many lives were thereby saved. I think he took deep satisfaction in visiting his various 'teams' who were carrying out his operative technique. On one round of inspection he happened into a tent hospital and found me in the act of removing a piece of shrapnel from a soldier's brain. I became aware of him standing behind me and felt a good deal as I had when he watched me trying to anaesthetize the dog, years before. I even wondered about my 'golf-balls,' but peering over my shoulder he said quietly 'Good work,' thus dispelling my apprehensions.

From George Crile (21 March 1940). The most striking memory I have of Cushing's work at Neufchâteau is his incessant activity for improvement of the handling of brain cases—of which we had such a large number. He gave to this task, an almost impossible task, every minute care and technically perfected detail which he had used in his Clinic in Boston. General Bowlby one day commented to me on the long time required for Cushing to perform an operation, thus making it necessary to schedule fewer operations; but the influence of Cushing's masterly technique on the other surgeons in the B.E.F. was a model of excellence, counterbalancing the long time required for the technical execution. He was always a perfectionist. His authority and reputation in this field made him a most valuable person in the field of brain injury for both the B.E.F. and the A.E.F.

Cushing published four papers which represent the sum and substance of his technical contribution to wartime surgery. The first was issued shortly after his return from Paris in 1915 and was based on his experience in Paris and with the British at Boulogne.[8] In this report he gives a detailed description of the magnet-nail technique for withdrawing deep-lying metal fragments. In February 1918 he also published a brief paper on penetrating wounds of the brain;[9] but his most important paper on wartime injuries of the brain appeared in April 1918.[10] In November 1919 he published a fourth paper on "Neurological surgery and the war."[11]

Although these four papers constitute his published contribution, the advance that he had made through insistence upon detailed study of a few cases proved to be enormous. It should be pointed out, furthermore, that throughout 1918 he was under a constant barrage of criticism, both from the British and from our own Surgeon General's Office, for refusing to evacuate his cases with sufficient rapidity.

[7] Rand, C. W. "Doctor Cushing as I knew him." *Bulletin of the Los Angeles Neurological Society,* March, 1940, *5,* 1-8.

[8] "Concerning operations for the cranio-cerebral wounds of modern warfare." *Military Surgeon,* June 1916, *38,* 601-615; July 1916, *39,* 22-30.

[9] "Notes on penetrating wounds of the brain." *British Medical Journal,* 23 February 1918, *1,* 221-226.

[10] "A study of a series of wounds involving the brain and its enveloping structures." *British Journal of Surgery,* April 1918, *5,* 558-684.

[11] *Boston Medical and Surgical Journal,* 6 November 1919, *181,* 549-552. In 1927 he also contributed a brief chapter on "Organization and activities of the neurosurgical service, A.E.F." In: *Medical Department of the U.S. Army in the World War,* vol. XI (Surgery), Part 1, 749-758. Washington, Govt. Printing Office, 1927.

During some of the major battles many cases of head wounds succumbed in H.C.'s anterooms while awaiting operation. In these periods of stress when Cushing and his team operated continuously for long hours, he sometimes handled as many as eight or ten cases of major injury. Some of his other colleagues in a similar stretch might have patched up fifteen or twenty, but Cushing took the view that unless some semblance of adequate surgery were possible, the case were better left untouched. At this distance it would be difficult to pass judgment on his underlying policy or the basis of his decision in individual cases. Perhaps he did operate slowly, and more slowly than might have been regarded necessary in the circumstances, but his patients were more likely to emerge from the war as useful citizens, and he himself emerged with the major neurosurgical contribution of the war to his credit. The paper in the *British Journal of Surgery* of 1918 has done much to influence the thinking of the younger generation of neurosurgeons who have been called upon to deal with even vaster numbers of similar injuries in the Second World War.

When the "Surgeon's Journal"[12] was published in 1936 the reviews were legion and the response almost uniformly enthusiastic. One reviewer wrote:

> . . . In its pages we find a distinguished surgeon describing with grim fidelity a syndrome of gigantic proportions, at times in almost poetic language; and one lives again through those days of restrained emotion in a tale told "in vibrating strophes attuned to the actuality." To a surgeon the book will have perennial interest because it is written by Harvey Cushing, but the book has a far wider appeal: humor, pathos, extraordinary versatility of interest in botany, architecture, ballistics make it a rich and most unusual human document, and it will undoubtedly stand as one of the significant records of the war period. . . . There have been published few diaries of the Great War written by physicians or surgeons, and the present lucid record comes at a most appropriate moment when a reminder is clearly needed—and let those in high places not forget Walt Whitman's remark which the diarist quotes on his flyleaf: "The marrow of the tragedy is concentrated in the hospitals. Well it is their mothers and sisters cannot see them—cannot conceive and never conceived these things." . . .

One of the most thoughtful estimates both of the book and of Cushing's part in the war is found in a letter from his friend, Sidney I. Schwab:

St. Louis, Missouri,
Sidney I. Schwab to H.C. *25 April 1936.*

Dear Harvey: Thanks so much for the presentation copy of your book. Your little note on the frontispage touched me very much. . . . I have of course read many war books, not so many in the last few years as before that time, but I think yours, to me at least, has the most personal touch and gives

[12] *From a surgeon's journal 1915-1918.* Boston, Little, Brown and Co., 1936, 534 pp.

the most vivid impressions of any that I have yet read. I think somehow you have gotten into your book the atmosphere of war, its rush, resiliency, its strangeness, its foolishness, stupidities, its heroism and its wastefulness. I know of no stronger argument against war than reading your pages. The waste of intelligence, human fineness, all the delicacies, gentle intuitions, are shown nakedly in your vividly written pages. I wondered over and over again as I read your book how in the world you have done all this. How you could have had the patience to have set down, almost every day I imagine, what that day's events and experiences were and how you had the industry and the energy to get the details, the names, regiments, and places and all the rest.

In thinking over this it occurred to me that you were the same kind of person in the war that you were in your own hospital, in your private work and in your laboratory, and that perhaps is the most illuminating thing that I got out of your book in regard to your own self. I think that you have the unique distinction of having acted in the war just exactly as you have acted all through your professional life as far as I know that life. Most of us who went to war were different people, influenced by surroundings and changing atmosphere, leading, without knowing it perhaps, a sort of artificial and false life, trying to reach standards that were beyond us or sinking to standards that were below us. You seem to be one of the few men I have known in the war who was the same person all through it. I do not say this to you in any flattering way, but rather to point out the peculiar characteristic influence of your book on me. . . . Wishing you the greatest of good luck, I am, Gratefully yours, SIDNEY I. SCHWAB.

Armistice stopped the guns; for the surgeons there was no armistice. Cushing's mind kept looking forward. "The war's over—people are tired, God knows—the Army will not listen to any new constructive schemes—sick and wounded will be shoved home immediately at the rate of 10,000 a week. . . ." Within a week after his return he began to take stock of his war experience and on the basis of it quickly and constructively laid plans for the future, for he felt that the lessons learned had significance both for medicine and for the nation.

CHAPTER XIV

Postwar Problems: The Institute of Neurology

1919

IN 1934, shortly before the dedication of the Montreal Neurological Institute, Cushing wrote Alan Gregg of the Rockefeller Foundation asking whether the proposal made in 1919 for the establishment of a national institute of neurology had had anything to do with the Foundation's decision to sponsor Dr. Penfield's Institute at Montreal. His letter runs:

H.C. to Alan Gregg — *New Haven, Connecticut, 2 August 1934.*

Dear Alan: I wonder if I ever told you, as a matter of history, that Tom Salmon, S. I. Schwab, D. J. McCarthy, L. H. Weed and I representing our several departments of clinical psychiatry, neurology, neurosurgery and experimental neuropathology agreed after the war to relinquish our professorial posts and to start a National Institute of Neurology, preferably at Washington, with two objects. One of them was to continue with our supervision of the nervous and mental disorders, both organic and functional, that had occurred in the army; and the other was to establish an institute thereby which could be continued in peace times as a National Institute of Neurology. It was a large programme and we thought we needed an endowment of about ten million for it. This would have meant nothing to the Government which has since squandered hundreds of millions on these same patients over whom we had agreed to take supervision.

The Government, in spite of their talk of reconstruction, couldn't see it, but Dr. Welch did and he thought the Rockefeller Foundation might do it—he even went so far as to say that considering the urgency he would have felt that this was more important for the country at large than the hygiene programme into which the Foundation had decided to launch. . . .

To this enquiry Gregg replied:

Alan Gregg to H.C. — *Southold, New York, 8 August 1934.*

Dear Dr. Cushing: Your letter of August 2 came last night. Your account of the project to start a National Institute of Neurology was new to me and, so far as I know, did not have a traceable connection with the development at Montreal. . . . Perhaps you'll let me add a bit to this answer to your question? The more I see of men and things, the more I think causes are but rarely single and simple. Thus it was not merely a request from Penfield and Martin coinciding with a special desire on our part to help neurology which decided the matter: there was a conviction that it is men that matter, especially in a new undertaking. I thought Penfield a good bet (and I think so now) and my colleagues agreed. I could wish that the end-result of your address would be a heightened appreciation of the meaning of persons:—of the importance of finding them, training them thoroughly, and backing them generously and thus liberating their energies. When institutions in this country hold these things to be their job I shall be in favor of institutions wholeheartedly.

On 9 May 1917, two days before Base Hospital No. 5 left for Europe, H.C. had sounded out Abraham Flexner about support for an institute: "I want very much to know whether there is any possibility that the General Education Board would be interested in the establishment of an institute for the study of nervous and mental diseases, which might save neurology and psychiatry from their present rather isolated and stagnant position, and which would bring in clinical psychiatry, neurology and surgery with experimental neurology and physiology and with the pathology and embryology of the nervous system." He added that he thought Sherrington, the British physiologist, might be induced to join such an institute after the war. Mr. Flexner had no opportunity to reply to this enquiry since Cushing had already sailed when he received the letter, but his ultimate reaction to the proposal was indicated by the later developments.

As the war cases accumulated and as Cushing came to appreciate more clearly the potential value and interest attaching to the varied clinical material which had been under his care, he was convinced that something should be done on a national scale to take advantage of such a unique opportunity to advance scientific medicine. It stimulated him to keep his own case records in far greater detail than was possible on the small Army record forms; he also made a particular point of recording the home addresses of his patients so that they could be followed after demobilization. The problems which interested him were legion: the regeneration of cut nerves, reflex reactions in man after the spinal cord had been severed, and questions of functional localization in different parts of the brain. Early in November 1918, when at Neufchâteau, he outlined plans in some detail to Weed, who was then in Baltimore in charge of a War Department laboratory for study of injuries to the nervous system.

H.C. to Capt. Lewis H. Weed *10 November 1918.*

My dear Lew: . . . The war is apparently so nearly over [24 hours before the Armistice] that the plans which we had made out here to build up a Neurological Institute are likely to fall short of their consummation, and I want to give you a little idea of what I have in mind so that you can do what you can toward it from your side. It seems a pity to let all this good work which has been done on the war neuroses by the neuro-psychiatrists, by the young neurologists out here, and by our neuro-surgical teams, go by the board as soon as these people get home. For the first time in our medical history all these people have been working more or less together and I think it is most important that the best of them should be held together.

What I want to see is an American Institute of Neurology which will be made up of the best of these younger men and which of course will include such groups as those in your own laboratory. It will be useful not only for the sake of clearing up the cases which we have been sending home and are going to send home now in large numbers, that will need after-care, but more important still, it ought to serve as the nucleus of a future Institute where neurological pathology, anatomy, psychiatry, organic neurology, and neurosurgery can have a home—in short, a great School of Neurology so that we can have something comparable to or better than the National Hospital at Queen Square or the Salpêtrière. Do you get me? I think it is quite probable that the General Education Board would look favorably upon such a scheme. Of course the Directors and Associates should be full-time people, and some day we can have an American School of Neurology of which we can be proud. Ever yours, HARVEY CUSHING.

Weed responded enthusiastically, indicating that he would be willing to give up his post in Baltimore and join the staff of the proposed institute on a full-time basis. Cushing likewise was prepared to give up his Moseley Professorship at Harvard if the institute plan materialized. Shortly after arriving home on 19 February 1919 he laid his plans before the General Education Board. He was still recuperating from the attack of polyneuritis but his enthusiasm for the project was undimmed. On 1 March he wrote to Welch: "If I can get leave (for I am still in service), I would like to talk to you about this matter of a neurological institute. If there is any possibility of such a thing becoming established and if the project would be looked upon favorably, I would be glad to devote what time is left to me to foster it, though the directorship of such an institution as I have in mind would much better fall into the hands of someone like Salmon. Men like McCarthy, Schwab, and others with whom I have talked are most enthusiastic and I think would join forces and give their full time. . . . I doubt very much whether the New York people will look favorably upon it for I think Dana and others feel that the [New York] Neurological Institute already represents such a movement." During the next few days, Cushing occupied himself preparing a memorandum (dated 9 March) for presentation to the General Education Board. A few paragraphs may be quoted:

PROJECT FOR THE ESTABLISHMENT OF A NATIONAL INSTITUTE FOR THE INVESTIGATION OF DISORDERS OF THE NERVOUS SYSTEM

The Need: There is no centralization of the many existing activities devoted, either from a sociological, investigative or therapeutic aspect, to the study of the nervous system and its disorders. There is no institution in the country for the training of those interested in these subjects where a graduate student can at present get other than a narrow instruction merely in one direction. We do not even have an institution comparable to the National Hospital for Nervous Diseases in London, or the Salpêtrière in Paris.

The psychiatrist, the neurologist, the neuro-surgical specialist, the experimental pathologist with an interest in neurological problems, as well as the sociologist, are working apart in unco-ordinated direction; and there is little to attract the more capable medical students to take up these admittedly important subjects. In short, we have no great "School" (in its broad sense) of Neurology. . . .

The Opportunity: This arises through the extraordinary condition of the moment, for: A nucleus of trained men is now available—men who have been more or less pried away from their institutional associations for the purposes of war work; in the course of a few months these men are likely to become unavailable. The immense wealth of material immediately at hand, both of functional and organic cases, the result of the war neuroses and wounds, represents material for study never again to be available unless after a similar great war. The lessons to be drawn from these accidental experiments are to be learned now or not at all. . . .

The Urgency: These various sources of supply, professional and clinical, will soon cease to exist. The medical officers concerned will have withdrawn from the service to take up their former positions, and they can hardly be gathered again. The material, moreover, is gradually being lost and scattered, for much of it is seeking private professional aid. . . .

The Program: For the next six or eight months, a selected group of men should continue in active supervision of the neurological cases resulting from the war, either under the Surgeon-General of the Army or the War Risk Bureau. This would not only be a national service and furnish the best care to the damaged soldiers but would save for future investigation and study a large amount of this valuable and irreplaceable material. At the expiration of this period, selected members from this group, or the entire group if it is wisely chosen, should pass over as the staff of the permanent institution on a peace basis. . . .

Suggested Plan of Organization: An ex-officio governing board with a representative of the Surgeon-General of the Army, of the Public Health Service, of the American Neurological Association, of the National Committee for Mental Hygiene, etc.

A chief executive.

Directors of clinical and technical departments.

The departments should comprise: 1) Neurology in its sociological aspects (mental hygiene; criminology; care of the insane and epileptic, etc.); 2) Psychiatry, with a hospital ward of perhaps 60 beds; 3) Neurology, again with 60 beds; 4) Neuro-surgery, also with 60 beds; 5) Neuro-pathology, with a central laboratory, and representation for the other departments. These are very broad outlines. There should be statistical studies, a library, a publication department, an out-patient clinic, possibly a laboratory representation for anatomical, physiological and embryological studies. There should be an assistant in psychology in the department of psychiatry, etc. The organization should be very elastic, in short.

Cost: With possibly 200 hospital beds, laboratories, salaries and such an organization as is suggested, it is estimated that an endowment of $10,000,000 would be necessary, if the proposed institution is to become influential and play a national rôle in public welfare.

Mr. Embree of the General Education Board handed the memorandum on the same day to Welch for an opinion. Welch wrote H.C. that "it looks most attractive." On 11 March H.C. acknowledged Welch's letter and again mentioned the great urgency of the project and that now "is the moment to take advantage of the opportunity of getting proper personnel and of profiting by all the material which can never be duplicated." Welch had also indicated that the new Surgeon General, M. W. Ireland, was interested in the proposal. On learning of this H.C. promptly wrote to Colonel Frank Billings in the S.G.O. to enlist his interest and support. Brigadier General Finney wrote to H.C. on the 12th reiterating that Ireland was interested, that he [Finney] was prepared to push it, and that the Army would support it. On the 14th an enthusiastic note went off to Lewis Weed: "Everyone is crazy about the idea and the only thing is —where will the money come from. I saw George Vincent [President of the Rockefeller Foundation] who took to it like a hot cake but he said the Rockefeller Foundation was poor. He figured out we might do it for seven million, but I told him to call it ten, but I wish now I had said twenty. Meanwhile, hang on to your group and keep your important studies going."

Cushing now began to think about additional personnel and we find him scribbling on preliminary drafts names such as Dakin, Stanley Cobb, Horrax, Weed, Wislocki, Viets, etc. On 20 March he pressed Mr. Vincent for a decision saying, "I feel that our great opportunity is gradually slipping by, as the men we would want are getting out of the Army and digging into their former positions." No definite word came, but on the 29th H.C. arranged a dinner in New York for those who had expressed an interest in the project. Among others he included Henry S. Pritchett, President of the Carnegie Foundation for the Advancement of Teaching.

On 1 April General Ireland requested a full report concerning the proposed institute. H.C. forwarded his memorandum and in a letter of the 2d stated: "I put the matter up to the Rockefeller Foundation and I think President Vincent is interested, and have put it up to Mr. Pritchett of the Carnegie Foundation . . . but both Foundations plead poverty." On the 3d, H.C., now feeling frustrated, wrote to Weed that Simon Flexner was unwilling to support the institute proposal, probably because he felt it would be running in competition with the Rockefeller Institute, and that Dr. Flexner could not conceive of any problems in neurology that could not be worked upon in existing research foundations.[1]

Meanwhile E. E. Southard, Sidney I. Schwab, and Thomas W. Salmon wrote expressing their endorsement of the undertaking, but on 8 April, Cushing's birthday, he received official regrets from President Pritchett. On the 16th Vincent asked for further information. In his reply H.C. went out of his way to take issue with Simon Flexner from whom he felt the Foundation was receiving bad advice.

[1] H.C. in this letter indiscreetly "let the cat out of the bag" by congratulating Lewis Weed on being chosen to succeed Mall as Professor of Anatomy at Johns Hopkins. This was before Weed had heard of the appointment which was not made until 11 May.

H.C. to George Vincent *17 April 1919.*

Dear Dr. Vincent: Thanks much for your letter of April 16th. We had a meeting in New York about two weeks ago of certain men whose interest in the proposed Institute we hoped to enlist. They were not men whom we thought of as possible candidates for positions, but men whose relation to neurology in the country was such that their opinions regarding a National Neurological Institute were sought. Col. Salmon, who engineered the meeting, asked Simon Flexner to be present, and I did not feel that Flexner was very much impressed, however, by our unanimity of opinion or by the prospects that such an Institute would be of great service. As Flexner naturally would be the one to represent us before the Rockefeller Foundation, I felt rather hopeless of seeing the project go through, and have consequently secured my discharge from the Army, and have gone back to my University work.

Dr. Flexner's attitude regarding the Institute was rather that of the experimental pathologist, and he said that he did not believe that we would be able to find sufficiently profitable problems to work upon or to justify the expenditure of so large a sum as had been looked for. Personally, I feel that there are innumerable problems of importance along neurological lines, even from the one point of view of the experimental pathologist. However, I was confronted by the necessity of making a decision of throwing my energies into the building up of such an Institute as was proposed, in collaboration with others, or to get back into my former position. I did not feel that I could very well keep on the fence any longer, for in the event of an early alliance with an Institute of Neurology, in all justice to the school here, I should have had to hand in my resignation.

I have written to Salmon to this effect, and believe that he has some plan worked out whereby a start may be made, which is less ambitious than the original project laid before you. I shall, of course, be only too eager to help him in any way, but anything short of the original plan will result I fear in the loss of the active participation of those who would make the movement a great success. I am hugely obliged to you for at least giving me a hearing.

A few days later H.C. received other letters—one from Adolf Meyer urging that plans for psychiatry be carefully reviewed, another from Lewis Weed, who was outspokenly enthusiastic:

Baltimore, Maryland,
Adolf Meyer to H.C. *26 April 1919.*

My dear Cushing: . . . Dr. Salmon had told me that Dr. Southard was going to formulate a more definite plan with regard to the things we discussed. I had in mind to write to you right after the meeting. The greatest difficulty undoubtedly is the fact that the Welch school of medicine in this country has not the slightest sympathy for anything that goes outside of what can be handled with their usual methods, namely, those of studying outside factors. After all, there is a field of pathology in which outside factors are not as tangible and manageable, and it seems to me that unless one is willing to pay a great deal of attention to the machinery and to the individual, one will not go very far with a conception of neuropsychiatry. The lack of a philosophical background and the lack of experience will have to be counteracted by clearness on our own side. I cannot help regretting that there was not a very carefully worked out plan instead of the somewhat hasty and too personal sketch the adjustment of which in the presence of Flexner was somewhat unfortunate. I wrote yesterday to Dr. Orton:

"Neuropsychiatry has rendered to the Nation a service which might properly be rewarded by a wholehearted financial and organizatory support either of one or a few principal research and training stations with ample means comparable to those at the disposal of the European research institutes. Through the endowment of professorships and fellowships and appropriate means of publication and reasonable facilities for teaching in medical schools and post-graduate work, the conditions for institutional and non-institutional neuropsychiatry would be furnished with facilities made systematically accessible for the younger physicians to gather experience in the various places offering the facts and the teachers, where to-day the initiative and financial support has to be carried altogether by the student or at least too exclusively."

I cannot help but feel that a single institute, unless it is on a much more liberal and broad basis than you outlined, would tend to put into cold storage some very essential and important starts in various places. To say that your central institute could train the men for us is all right if I know who is going to train them on the psychiatric side and if I have an idea of who is going to pay the salaries of those trained men when they come to me. This puts bluntly the crux of the difficulty that I see, as far as my own outlook on future psychiatric work is concerned. A general research institute such as the Rockefeller Institute is not by any means such an unquestionable boon. In reality, I do believe that it was possible only on account of the fact that there were so many perfectly satisfactory departments scattered over the country and capable of keeping a certain balance in the system. It would be most deplorable if we had to think that the Rockefeller Institute point of view were the only one in the country, unless it is really going to broaden out so as to include our field, so important to the race. . . . Most sincerely yours, ADOLF MEYER.

Baltimore, Maryland,
Lewis H. Weed to H.C. *21 April 1919.*

Dear Dr. Cushing, On my return this morning from my first leave in twenty months I found your letters awaiting me. I am greatly disappointed that the prospects for the national institute are not immediately promising for the opportunities such an organization would have are tremendous. Of course, I realize that this is a tremendously hard time to get the funds but I had hoped that it could go through. I am still hoping that, as you indicate, there is yet some chance of its happening. There is nothing that I would rather do than go into such an institute and I am living in the belief that some time soon we are all going to have the chance to show what can be done in Neurology. . . .

I hope then to get out of the Army, as there will be no further work for me. I am still quite undecided as to what to do next year; I am still Associate Professor in Anatomy but there is no chief in the department. No one knows whether Harrison is coming but I think the chance is remote. Both Dr. Meyer and Dr. MacCallum want me to develop neurology in their departments but I am not yet sure that the opportunity is all that one might desire in either laboratory. I only wish that there was a real chance for experimental neurology somewhere. . . . Do let me know if anything more turns up about the institute. And please remember that, no matter what job I am holding, I will be ready always to consider the opportunity for real experimental neurology. Yours as ever, LEWIS H. WEED.

Unhappily the proposal drifted and gradually died of inanition. The Surgeon General encountered difficulties in a higher echelon of the War Department, and he and his advisers, although enthusiastic, were soon hampered by the economies of a reactionary Congress. In October, when it was announced that Mr. Rockefeller had made a further gift for the benefit of medicine in general to the Rockefeller Foundation, H.C., with his ancestral persistence, again approached one of the Flexner family:

H.C. to Abraham Flexner *30 October 1919.*

Dear Mr. Flexner: There are many ways of improving the situation of Medicine in the country, one by working through the Medical Schools themselves, and the other by concentrating on special subjects like public health, and I think, as you know, that Neurology in its broad aspects needs attention, not only for the benefit of Neurology but for the benefit of Medicine in general and indeed for the benefit of the entire country. In view of the recent large gift from Mr. Rockefeller I wonder whether it would be wise to reopen again the Neurological Institute matter of which I spoke to you some months ago.

But the die was cast—neurology was not a branch of medicine which the philanthropic foundations were at that time disposed to support; and so a brilliant opportunity lapsed. The vast material which might have been studied was lost track of in the files of the Veterans Bureau. There was virtually no follow-up on cases of nerve injury—or for that matter on anything else. The Medical Department of the Army wrote its imposing seventeen-volume history with scant knowledge of what had become of individual cases, and it therefore had little scientific basis for appraising different forms of therapy that had been used in the various theaters; and when the Second World War was upon us twenty years later the lessons which might have been learned from the last war had to be learned again—the hard way.[2]

In retrospect it seems probable that Cushing might have secured support from the Foundations if he had been a little more subtle in his approach and less personal. There is no doubt that he was desperately fatigued after his two years of incessant activity, and his polyneuritis had not increased his patience. He had in the past also affronted those who were holding out for the unmodified Hopkins full-time plan for clinical teachers. For this reason, it is not surprising

[2] Cushing had made a formal presentation of his project in an address before the American Medico-Psychological Association held at Philadelphia 18 June 1919; the paper was published the following October: "Concerning the establishment of a National Institute of Neurology." *American Journal of Insanity*, October 1919, *76*, 113-129. Also *Transactions of the American Medico-Psychological Association*, 1919, *26*, 167-183. A similar paper was presented on 16 June before the Congress of American Physicians and Surgeons in which further recommendations were made concerning the rehabilitation of neurological cases: "Some neurological aspects of reconstruction." *Archives of Neurology and Psychiatry, Chicago*, November 1919, *2*, 493-504. Also: *Transactions of the American Neurological Association*, 1919, 24-35; *Transactions of the Congress of American Physicians and Surgeons*, 1919, *11*, 23-41.

that the powers in both the Rockefeller and the Carnegie Foundations tended to be somewhat uneasy about anything that Cushing might propose.

Fortunately Cushing had other things on his mind when he returned from Europe; the first was a permanent record of U. S. Army Base Hospital No. 5. Between the time of his arrival home at the end of February and the following November he managed to put together and publish anonymously a detailed history of Base Hospital No. 5.[3] It was based of course upon his war diary, and the story is told in a most interesting manner with photographs, maps, and running textual narrative. The ten who lost their lives while in Europe are listed in the appendix, and there is a roster of officers, nurses, and enlisted men for each of whom the military history is meticulously set down. Cushing made a point of keeping in touch with members of the Unit, and he preserved letters which he had received from a large proportion of them. The volume was published promptly at the Harvard University Press and circulated to individual members of the Unit as a Christmas present.

Despite the agitation for the neurological institute and the time and effort that went into compiling the history of the Base Hospital, H.C. managed during the year to attend a large number of meetings, for in addition to those already mentioned, we find him at the National Academy of Sciences in April. On 4 June he read a paper to the Massachusetts Medical Society on "Neurological surgery and the war";[4] in October a paper on "Brain tumor statistics"[5] for the American College of Surgeons. In November the National Academy of Sciences again met at New Haven, and the American Academy of Arts and Sciences in Boston. In December he went to Philadelphia to give the Hatfield Lecture on trigeminal neuralgia,[6] a theme which he had first developed in Philadelphia twenty years earlier.

The year 1919 was filled with lights and shadows, for on 26 May he was obliged to go to Cleveland in connection with the most tragic death of his brilliant nephew, Kirke Cushing, son of his brother Harry. On finishing his work at the Harvard Medical School and before starting his interneship, Kirke had gone off on a canoe trip down the Connecticut River and had been drowned when his craft was caught in an eddy. H.C. had taken a particular interest in his career both at Yale and in the Medical School, and it must have

[3] *The story of U.S. Army Base Hospital No. 5.* By a member of the Unit. Cambridge, Mass., University Press, 1919, 118 pp.

[4] *Boston Medical and Surgical Journal,* 6 November 1919, *181,* 549-552.

[5] *Medical Record,* New York, 6 March 1920, *97,* 417-418.

[6] "The major trigeminal neuralgias and their surgical treatment based on experiences with 332 Gasserian operations. First paper. The varieties of facial neuralgia." *American Journal of the Medical Sciences,* August 1920, *160,* 157-184.

caused him particular grief to add to the family bookplate the initials and graduation date of this young nephew whose future had seemed so full of promise.

Shortly after H.C.'s return from Europe Major General Ireland wrote a cordial letter of appreciation which ended: "Don't talk about anything that the Army has done for you. You can not imagine how much we all appreciate the work you have done for the Army during

George R.I.

George the Fifth by the Grace of God of the United Kingdom of Great Britain and Ireland, and of the British Dominions beyond the Seas, King Defender of the Faith, Emperor of India and Sovereign of the Most Honourable Order of the Bath, To Colonel Harvey Cushing, United States Army.

Greeting Whereas We have thought fit to nominate and appoint you to be an Honorary Member of the Military division of the Third Class, or Companions of Our said Most Honourable Order of the Bath. We do by these Presents grant unto you the dignity of a Companion of Our said Order and hereby authorise you to have hold and enjoy the said dignity and rank as an Honorary Member of the Military division of the Third Class or Companions of Our aforesaid Order, together with all and singular the privileges thereunto belonging or appertaining.

Given at Our Court at Saint James's under Our Sign Manual and the Seal of Our said Order this Twenty seventh day of March 1919, in the Ninth year of Our Reign

By the Sovereign's Command

Great Master

Grant of the dignity of a Companion (Military division) of the Order of the Bath to Colonel Harvey Cushing.

COMPANION OF THE BATH

the past two years." The British Government in recognition of Cushing's services had conferred upon him the order of the Companion of the Bath (C.B.) in March 1919. In April came word of his citation by General Pershing "For exceptionally meritorious and conspicuous services as Director of Base Hospital No. 5." In June two honorary degrees were conferred upon him in recognition of his war work, one on 12 June at Western Reserve (Doctor of Laws), and the second at Yale on 19 June (Doctor of Science).

During the year H.C. served on a committee that issued two large birthday volumes for his friend and mentor, William Osler. H.C. did not himself contribute to the volume, because of his late return after the war and probably for other reasons. He had been much concerned about W.O.'s health, for Lady Osler reported that since Revere's death he had been sleeping badly and losing weight. W.O., moreover, continued to have a distressing series of upper respiratory infections, accompanied by paroxysms of coughing. An empyema was drained on 15 December. A cable arrived announcing his death at 4.30 p.m. on 29 December 1919. Throughout the year H.C., fearing that Osler would not long survive, wrote him frequently and added many important books to his library, including the first edition of Galvani on animal electricity (1791) and Clemenceau's M.D. thesis. With the latter went a characteristic note:

H.C. to W.O. *20 May 1919.*

Dear Sir William I am sending you a birthday present—Clemenceau's thesis for his doctorate in Medicine. Most people have forgotten that his varied career began in Medicine. *You* of course have not, and very probably have a copy already among those in your Bibliotheca curiosa (?) section. If so you know how to hand it on. It at least will let you know that I am thinking of you even though I could not manage to put my mind on anything suitable for the anniversary volumes. Nor could I write anything for the J. H. Bulletin, though I made a start under *"No 3 West Franklin St"* for I think—well I needn't say what I think. It became a little too intimate for anyone to see but you and Lady O., so I tore it up. You will understand. I will write soon about the Vesal. picture. I fear I did not send enough money and will supplement it by £10.

P.S. I wish it was the Ed. princeps but even these are difficult to find. I got this from Robert Bliss of our Embassy via the old *Tigre* himself. H.C.

On returning to Boston in February 1919, Cushing had been faced with the problems of reorganizing not only his neurological service but also the general surgical service which had been ably looked after during his absence by Dr. David Cheever, but which had been seriously weakened by the loss of younger men to the war. Conrad Jacobson was Resident in charge of the surgical service while H.C. was in France but he withdrew to go to the University of Minnesota shortly after H.C.'s return.

From April 1919 much of the operative burden on the neurological service was shared with his loyal pupil of Hopkins days, Gilbert Horrax, aided by a series of neurological residents beginning with Howard Fleming (1919-1920), Charles E. Locke, Jr. (1920-1921), Daniel W. Wheeler (1921-1922), Kenneth McKenzie (1922-1923), and others to be mentioned later. After graduating from Johns Hopkins, Horrax in 1913 interned at the Brigham, and in 1914 Cushing appointed him to the Arthur Tracy Cabot Fellowship in the Surgical Laboratory at Harvard. He became Assistant Resident in Neurosurgery in 1915-1916 and accompanied Cushing to France with Base Hospital No. 5 in 1917. Selfless in his devotion to his Chief, Horrax came to be regarded as the one who had gained more complete mastery of Cushing's fastidious surgical technique than any other pupil. The operating room had been ably organized by Miss

Geraldine Martin (later Mrs. Horrax), the talented nurse whom H.C. had brought from Baltimore to be in charge of the Brigham operating room in the hope of instilling Hopkins standards in Boston. Miss Gerrard, the anesthetist of the team, also rendered invaluable service. These three understanding members of his staff had meant everything to him and had done much to carry the service over the ups and downs inevitable in the formative years of a young hospital.

In spite of the polyneuritis which had made H.C. fear, while in France, that he would never be able to operate again, he returned to his operating room within a few days after arriving from Europe and began to assume as heavy a load as before the war. During the first weeks his hands bothered him and he often finished an operation in a state bordering upon complete physical collapse. His improvement was rapid, however, and by April he was able to send an encouraging report to Sidney Schwab:

> . . . I am really doing surprisingly well, and except for a little remnant of trouble in my legs which prevents my walking any great distance, and some little cardiac irregularity, which is apparently so common in these cases, I am in good form. I have been operating and aside from the difficulties of getting my staff organization swinging smoothly, I find that things go about as usual. I am not below par in manual facility I find, except for a little tendency to tire, which of course may affect my judgment somewhat, but even these things are doubtless improving. My knee kicks are back, normally active. For all this I owe you my undying gratitude. . . .

One of the well-laid plans for his neurological clinic, which had been largely held in abeyance on account of the war, had been a program for thorough histological study of his tumors, the importance of which had become increasingly apparent. Therefore, when in February an application was received from a man who had had unusual training in the techniques for microscopic study of the nervous system, the candidate was quickly accepted. This was Percival Bailey of Chicago who, after receiving his M.D., had taken his Ph.D. under Professor Bensley of Chicago. Bailey arrived in March and Cushing made him at once his first postwar Assistant Resident in Neurological Surgery. He immediately started his microscopic studies of Cushing's various tumors, and so began the fruitful association which was to continue for ten years, at the end of which time Bailey accepted the chair of neurology at the University of Chicago.

The Society of Neurological Surgeons

Since Cushing was an ardent believer in the value of meetings, it is not surprising to find him sponsoring a society which aimed to foster his specialty. Dr. Ernest Sachs recalls that after H.C. had delivered "a memorable address [on brain tumor statistics] before the American College of Surgeons at its New York meeting [21 October 1919] . . . Dr. W. J. Mayo, who had presided that year, said that a new surgical specialty of neurological surgery had now been founded." At this time Cushing suggested the formation of a society so that neurosurgeons might come together once or twice a year to discuss problems of mutual interest and to see one another at work, much as had the members of the Society of Clinical Surgery. The idea evoked great enthusiasm, and presently H.C. received a gracious letter of enquiry from one of those to whom the suggestion had originally been broached:

Alfred W. Adson to H.C. — *Rochester, Minnesota, 18 November 1919.*

Dear Dr. Cushing: Have you made any progress with reference to the Society of Neurological Surgeons? My short visit with you in Boston has, I think, inspired me more than any other clinical trip I have ever taken. It has caused me to return to Rochester with renewed energy and a determination to work harder than ever on the neurosurgical cases coming through our clinic.

I wish to express my sincere appreciation of the time and attention you so kindly devoted to me while there, and to thank you for the many courtesies you extended to me. I shall look forward with pleasure to seeing you again on my next trip East. Sincerely, A. W. ADSON.

In the early correspondence the new group, which had ten charter members,[7] designated itself "The Neurosurgical Club." The first meeting was held at the Brigham Hospital in March 1920, at which time the Club incorporated as the Society of Neurological Surgeons and voted to hold the first formal meeting on 26 and 27 November 1920. This meeting was evidently a great success; cases were shown and operations staged for the group. A few days later Sachs wrote: "I am still under the spell of the wonderful meeting we had in Boston," and he asked for information about the cerebellar retractor that he had seen used. On 4 December H.C. sent him, as secretary of the new Society, follow-up reports on the cases that had been presented. The woman with the pituitary adenoma "has done well and there is a rapid and early return of vision, with light perception on the third day in her previously blind eye," etc.

Thereafter the Society had one and sometimes two meetings a year. Although its membership is now relatively senior, it continues to flourish, but since it has taken in few new members in recent years, its functions have been to some extent assumed by the Harvey Cushing Society founded in 1932.

[7] A. W. Adson, Charles Bagley, Jr., Harvey Cushing, Charles E. Dowman, Charles A. Elsberg, Charles H. Frazier, Samuel C. Harvey, Gilbert Horrax, Dean Lewis, Ernest Sachs.

CHAPTER XV

Literary Pursuits: The Osler Biography

1920–1924

CUSHING'S early letters and his initial scientific papers do not suggest that he was born with a natural flair for writing. His family epistles from Yale and the Harvard Medical School are immature and often awkward in expression, and if it were not for the fact that they nearly all had an undercurrent of humor, many would be put down as dull and unsophisticated. Despite the artlessness of much of his early prose, he sometimes rose to considerable heights in narrative writing—his account of the blizzard of 1888 being a case in point, and some of his early travel diaries are comparable with the best descriptive prose of any physician-traveller. Cushing's early scientific reports also tend to be labored; clinical details are well described, but the papers as a whole are heavy. This is notably true of his first report on gunshot wounds of the spine and his typhoid papers. H.C.'s initial excursion into historical writing (1901), a paper written at Berne entitled "Haller and his native town," has general interest,[1] but one could not foresee in its involved germanic sentences the pen that later wrote:

> . . . So they—the living—left him overnight; alone in the Lady Chapel beside the famous 'watching-chamber' which overlooks the shrine of the Saint, and with the quaint effigy of his beloved Robert Burton near by—lying in the scarlet gown of Oxford, his bier covered with a plain velvet pall on which lay a single sheaf of lilies and his favourite copy of the 'Religio', *comes viæ vitæque.*
>
> And perhaps the New Year night saw, led by Revere, another procession pass by the 'watching-chamber'—the spirits of many, old and young—of former and modern times—of Linacre, Harvey, and Sydenham; of John Locke, Gesner, and Louis; of Bartlett, Beaumont, and Bassett; of Johnson, Bovell, and Howard; of Mitchell, Leidy, and Stillé; of Gilman, Billings, and Trudeau; of Hutchinson, Horsley, and Payne; of the younger men his pupils who had gone before—Jack Hewetson, MacCallum, and McCrae; and in still greater number those youths bearing scars of wounds who more recently had known and felt the affection and warmth of the 'Open Arms'—doubly dead in that they died so young.

H.C. had achieved his mastery of English prose by dint of hard work, wide reading, and constant practice. It has been estimated that during his last twelve years at the Brigham Hospital he committed to paper between 5,000 and 10,000 words a day. After 1913 his letters

[1] *American Medicine,* 1901, 2, 542-544; 580-582.

were in most instances dictated, but until the end of his life he also wrote many by hand, and a communication to which he attached special importance would often go through four or five drafts before it met with his satisfaction. The same was true of all his scientific papers, the first drafts of which were always handwritten as was practically the entire MS of the Osler biography. His briefer addresses, particularly those on ceremonial occasions, were sometimes written and rewritten a dozen times. A well-remembered example is his "Emancipators" given at the Lister Centenary Celebration in July 1927, which his secretary recalls was copied a dozen times. A few paragraphs give indication of its force:

> . . . On a May morning a few weeks ago, I stood at the portal of the Lincoln Memorial in Washington and with the depth of emotion the spot engenders gazed upon that marvelous seated figure of the Emancipator there enshrined. And as I read again those familiar phrases spoken at Gettysburg, there came to mind how comparable were he and Lister in their dedication to the proposition that all men are created equal. Lister freed man from the shackles of sepsis; Lincoln, a race from those of slavery. Yet how different the men, their medium of service, and the manner by which the seemingly inevitable was thrust upon them. . . .
>
> The act on which Lincoln's life centres itself is not that for which an adoring nation has put a halo round his memory. Rather have a people once divided come to look upon him as expressing what they would wish to have represent them before the world. He thereby has become a symbol from which his countrymen reap a harvest of precious associations. So may our profession reap from Lister's life something far more precious than pride in his accomplishment and the satisfaction of claiming him as our own, namely, that spiritual harvest which comes from the example of an unblemished character, for kindness, meekness and comfort were in his tongue.
>
> Though lives die, the life is not dead; and the memory of lives such as these will be reverently and forever shared not by a profession alone, not by a nation alone, but by the universal brotherhood of man.

After Sir William Osler's death, Lady Osler had sent a touching letter to H.C. "It has been such a long and trying illness," she wrote, "October 13th he told me how it would end, and I believed every word he ever said seriously. I have never changed my opinion although the doctors said I was too depressed. Revere's death killed him, hastened on by the loving birthday friends. I told you last February . . . that he couldn't stand it . . . although perhaps I should not say it. He never saw the completed volumes, they arrived on the 26th and 27th and he was not fit for the excitement, and then it was too late."

Lady Osler first thought that William S. Thayer, one of Osler's successors in the chair of medicine at the Hopkins, was the logical person to write the Life, but as soon as she received the *Boston Evening Transcript* (of 3 Jan. 1920) and read H.C.'s "Sir William

Osler: the man," she was convinced that he was the only one to be entrusted with it. The appreciation began:

> In the first shock of grief at the news of Sir William Osler's death it is difficult for anyone who felt close to him to say what is in his heart. And the strange thing about this unusually gifted and versatile man is that everyone fortunate enough to have been brought in contact with him shares in this feeling of devotion, for he gave of himself much to all. This was true of his patients as might be expected, and he was sought far and wide not only because of his wide knowledge of medicine and great wisdom, but because of his generosity, sympathy and great personal charm. It was true also—and this is more rare—of the members of his profession for whom, high or low, he showed a spirit of brotherly helpfulness untinctured by those petty jealousies which sometimes mar their relationships. "Never believe what a patient may tell you to the detriment of another physician—even though you may fear it is true," was one of his sayings to students, and he was preëminently the physician to physicians and their families, and would go out of his way unsolicited and unsparingly to help them when he learned that they were ill or in distress of any kind. . . .

So Lady Osler promptly put the direct question: "Sir William has left no autobiography, there is the preface to the catalogue—unfinished, and many, many things unfinished, and all the little red books full of wonderful things. Tom [McCrae] looked at some of them and will tell you. There is one vital question—who shall write the memoir. I know of only one man worthy and able to do it and that is *you,* and printed by the [Oxford] Press—I can say no more. I leave the answer to you. There is no one here who knows everything—medicine, brain, home, friends, heart, endurance, in fact all that he was—you know all." The next day she wrote again saying that she had consulted Sir Humphry Rolleston, and when he was told that she had approached H.C., Sir Humphrey had responded "Wonderful, wonderful. Can he, will he do it?" She continued: "I have come home with my mind and heart full of it and am sending this second note to you to ask if you will think seriously of it. I am convinced there is no one else who understands as you do."

Clearly this was a request which H.C. could not decline. Osler had meant everything to him for twenty years. He had been a spiritual father and had had a keener understanding of Cushing's own restless nature than almost anyone, and had done much to inculcate in H.C. his love of literature and history and his undying interest in Vesalius. So Cushing, who was frantically eager to get back to his clinic after nearly four years' interruption of war, committed himself to the formidable undertaking; and it proved much more so than he had surmised. His reply to Lady Osler's letters was somewhat delayed, owing to his having been away, but he accepted without question.

H.C. to Lady Osler *13 March 1920.*

Dear Lady Osler: I have just come back from two weeks in the South with

Kate. . . . I am thrilled at the thought that you should want me to undertake the biography and that you should feel that I am capable of it. I have many misgivings on this latter score; however, anything that you want or that you think he would have liked I shall of course try to do. At least there would be no harm in getting a start and gathering material, and if I should fall by the wayside it could be used by someone else.

I have no delusions regarding the importance of the task nor the amount of time it will take, and I have talked with some of my biographer friends here, *e.g.*, Bliss Perry, who is undertaking Mr. Higginson's life, and Mark Howe, who has just finished one of George Meyer. It means about a year's work, and about six months of uninterrupted study and writing, and I suppose that a good deal of this latter time would have to be in Oxford, which of course would be a great joy.

You will have to help me, of course, . . . in getting letters, for unquestionably the easiest thing to do would be to make him tell his own story so far as possible. Most of the letters I know were mere scraps, but even so they were often illuminating and always interesting. One great difficulty, as I found in looking over my own things, is that he rarely dated the letters except to give the day, so that it will be necessary to ask people so far as possible to supply the dates. I have already written to a few people—to de Schweinitz, who, I understand, is going to write Weir Mitchell's life [never completed], and I hope he may find among the Mitchell papers some of Sir William's letters. I have written also to Dr. Hurd as a starter for the Baltimore group, and will try to take up a few people each day, for I think personal appeals will amount to more than a published appeal, though the day will doubtless come when this will have to be done and a note asking for letters put, for example, in the *Johns Hopkins Bulletin* and in the *Journal* of the A.M.A. The Baltimore period I can of course cover more easily, and will be able probably to get most of the material here. . . . Do you suppose that any of the various secretaries that he has had in Oxford kept duplicate carbon copies of such letters as he dictated—I mean letters more than merely professional notes?

Other letters followed:

H.C. to Lady Osler *31 March 1920.*

Dear Tanta Grace: . . . Do please ask Miss Smart to go through her stenographic note-books and pick out any letters that are important or interesting which he may have sent during her year with him, and make copies of them for me unless she by chance took carbon copies. If so, please have her keep all carbon copies. It is possible, too, that some of the note-books of her predecessors may be there, and please don't let her throw them out if this is the case. The more interesting letters he probably wrote longhand, but still there is likely to be some important information in the dictated ones, and I shall hope to have hundreds of them before I get very far. . . .

21 April 1920.

Dear Tanta Grace: . . . I am a little uncertain as to plans, but I shall hope to get over as soon as I can get things straightened out here, say the 1st of July, for a month or six weeks, and will put in hard licks at the material that you may have. I suppose I shall have to go through all the books for his personal notes in them. Perhaps Archie [Malloch] will jot down on a piece of paper such things as he encounters from time to time that may be useful.

What shall I do about a secretary? I may need one or two when I am there. I wish that I might send Julia Shepley over beforehand so that she can get a start. I shall need someone of course who is familiar with his handwriting and knows more or less about his topics, and she has been giving most of her time to this, here. I see that Miss Smart is still staying on, though you indicated that she might wish to seek another post. . . .

8 May 1920.

Dear Tanta Grace: . . . I shall hope to hear from you soon about the secretary matter. It is going to be awfully difficult, I find, to get steamer accommodations. I shall unquestionably have loads of things to copy and I am not sure but that I shall need two people for this. I suppose Miss Smart's time is fully occupied with other work. Would it be possible to get anyone in Oxford? I know that Sir William had great difficulty getting medical secretaries, and the sort of things I shall need to have copied will take not only some familiarity with his handwriting but also with medical and medical-historical names and places. . . .

Most revealing of his early plans for organizing the biography are those found in a letter written to Mrs. Cushing from 13 Norham Gardens during the summer of 1920 when he made his first visit to Oxford after Sir William's death:

H.C. to K.C. (on blue paper) *15 July 1920.*

This is the kind of stuff we're working on—blue for biog. notes, yellow for book notes, pink for varia, white for letters. It's getting to be a complicated job and my folders which used to sit on the desk have grown to about a yard in thickness. There's little variety in the life—get to work about 9 and finish about midnight—meals and tea are interspersed with an occasional trip to Bodley's, the Press, Ch[rist] Ch[urch] or somewhere else for information. I really should take six months [!] at it and have 4 hustling secs. like mine at home. Two here now—W.O.'s Miss Smart and a new one who cannot take shorthand. Lady O. cabled for Julia Shepley and then yesterday we called it off again. I found it might complicate the household here, but it would have helped matters along greatly if I could have given a lot of this material by dictation to someone who could have written it up at leisure next winter when I shall be at other things. It's a big task—six months would be none too long to give it right now. But that would eliminate me from my proper job. The Howards come today. Archie Malloch comes every week-end.

Cushing had grossly underestimated the time that would be required for the completion of the task. By the end of the first year, he had many of the early chapters in rough draft, but there were numerous gaps and he was tireless in his efforts to fill them. He proceeded in a strictly chronological manner, arranging letters and anecdotes by year, month, day, and occasionally almost by hours. At the outset, as is indicated in his letter of July 1920 to Mrs. Cushing, he had systematized his source material. Once his chapter numbers had been settled upon, he sent out his enquiries with the chapter number at the head of the letter, and sufficient space was generally left at the bottom of the letter for the reply. When the reply arrived it was filed under the appropriate chapter; as soon as the information had been incorporated in the text, the letter was dropped into an author file. For four years he directed these missives of enquiry to Lady Osler who was at times much amused by the thoroughness of his search, but she had moments of being somewhat irked by his persistence. Thus on 17 August 1922 he had written with 'Chapter XI; p. 4' at the top, "Here's a funny question which I hope you can answer: What church did old Dr. D. H. Agnew attend? He was of Scotch-Irish ancestry and I assume some Presbyterian Church." Lady Osler replied on the bottom of this note in longhand, "I haven't the slightest idea," and "You old goose. Please tell me something.

PETER BENT BRIGHAM HOSPITAL

JOSEPH B. HOWLAND, M. D. SUPERINTENDENT · 721 HUNTINGTON AVENUE · HARVEY CUSHING, M. D. SURGEON-IN-CHIEF

HENRY A. CHRISTIAN, M. D. PHYSICIAN-IN-CHIEF · BOSTON 17, MASS. · S. BURT WOLBACH, M. D. PATHOLOGIST

(Chapter XI; p. 4)

August 17, 1922.

Lady Osler,
13 Norham Gardens,
Oxford, England.

Dear Tanta Grace: - Here's a funny question which I hope you can answer:

What church did old Dr. D. H. Agnew attend? He was of Scotch-Irish ancestry and I assume some Presbyterian church.

Dear Harvey
I havent the slightest idea. Tanta Grace

You old Goose. Please tell me something
Who was that old man with green hair who went to the 11 o'ck service at the Unitarian Church across the way?

COLLECTING INFORMATION
One of H.C.'s notes to Lady Osler and her peppery reply

Who was that old man with green hair who went to the 11 o'clock service at the Unitarian Church across the way?"

During the summer he spread his materials on long, improvised tables at 305 Walnut Street, insisting that there was nothing so important in writing a biography as elbow room. In the course of the first year he read a great many biographies and discussed the technique of biographical writing with his friends at the Saturday Club, particularly Bliss Perry. During his last illness Sir William had read Henry Festing Jones' recent life of Samuel Butler and had expressed admiration for it as a biography although he thought Butler himself a "pig." H.C. read the two-volume Butler going over on the boat in July 1920 and in later years frequently mentioned that Jones' 'Butler' influenced him more than any other biography. He had also read and expressed admiration for Lockhart's 'Scott.' Mrs. Cushing had long been a Johnson enthusiast and knowing her Boswell intimately, she was therefore a competent critic, and the Osler biography benefited at many points from her sound literary judgment. She also guided H.C. in matters of taste, and there were evidently serious differences from time to time as to what could or could not be included. Lady Osler occasionally protested about the inclusion of details that she regarded as essentially private, and she at times abused "Harvey" in her frank, goodnatured way about using her letters and leaving so little to the imagination. In one letter she expostulated "Harvey, you are writing Willie's life, not mine." Actually Lady Osler's letters, which were ever direct and vivid, proved of inestimable value even though they were seldom dated.

H.C. was particularly fortunate in having throughout the preparation of the biography the services of Miss Julia Shepley of Brookline, Massachusetts, who had been with the U. S. Base Hospital No. 5 throughout its time in France, and who had been at Oxford and knew the Osler family and many of their connections. During the first year there were others who had assisted with the transcription of letters and source material, but throughout the final three years Miss Shepley handled the entire correspondence and prepared final copy for press. The manuscript, as orginally submitted, ran to nearly a million words but at the urgent insistence of various readers in Britain, particularly those of the Oxford Press, he curtailed the manuscript during 1924 by one third, *i.e.*, to about 650,000 words. Miss Shepley remained in Oxford while the book was passing through the press and attended to the proofs. The remarkably full index was compiled by Mr. Reginald H. Hill, then of the Bodleian Library, and one of the editors of the Osler catalogue.

H.C. spent the first part of the summer of 1924 at Oxford getting the book started through the press. Lady Osler received her first bound copy on 29 March 1925 and the book was officially published on 16 April. "I had a vague idea," he said, "that with the 'Osler' published my troubles would be over, whether or not the book should prove to be a success. From the time I left England until April 1925, when the book finally came out, there had been a good deal of correspondence with Oxford but I was busily trying to get back into my professional stride after four years of 'biographying.' . . . I was sadly mistaken about my troubles being over, for about the first of May letters began to pour in and for the next six months they came by every mail till I began to dread the postman." At first he started to keep all the correspondence, but after he was awarded the Pulitzer Prize for the biography in 1926 a second wave of letters started, so on a Sunday afternoon in September 1926 he consigned two-thirds of his correspondence about the biography to the wastebasket and had the remaining letters and reviews bound up in three fat volumes.

To say that the book had an enthusiastic reception would be a gross understatement. Osler's friends, almost to a man (and certainly to a woman), were wholehearted in their praise. Few books can have been read with more meticulous care, for there is scarcely a page in the entire two volumes which did not come in for comment. Although the proofs had been read most closely and the manuscript itself had been perused by some of the most eagle-eyed critics of this country and England, a number of minor errors had crept in, all of which H.C. systematically recorded. In August 1936 he issued an eight-page brochure of *corrigenda* and *addenda*. The errors thus set down were none of them serious and, recognizing human frailty, one is amazed that more mistakes were not found in a work of such magnitude.

The book had been admirably designed, by the best talent the Oxford Press could offer, much after the style of the Jones' 'Butler.' R. W. Chapman had attended to the business arrangements on behalf of the Clarendon Press, and John Johnson, Printer to Oxford University, had designed the page. Especially useful were the systematic running heads giving over-all dates on the left-hand page and Osler's age on the right. When the book went into page form the Oxford Press had routinely used the chapter title as the center running head for each page. Cushing decided that this would never do, and he thereupon sat down and wrote running heads for every odd-numbered page in the book, adapting the running head to the context of the page in question. Thus on page 25 of Volume I one finds " 'Barrie's Bad Boys' " as the running head; on page 43, "Grinding Bones and Teeth"; page 53, "Theology Abandoned"; page 527, "Immersed in Bunyan"; in Volume II, page 9, "Osler's Protective Colouring"; and on page 15, "With Iz. Walton, jr. in Scotland," and so it went throughout the book. Lady Osler, unlike H.C., was averse to illustrations. Out of a large mass of material he finally got forty-five past her censorship, but only on the condition that they be executed by Emery Walker, the well-known London engraver, at her expense if necessary, and his skilful reproduction added much to the quality of the book as a whole.

It was this attention to detail that gave the Osler biography an intimate touch of Cushing himself. Many of the reviewers, however, drew attention to the fact that he had otherwise left himself out of the book completely, and while the name of almost every important medical personage of Osler's lifetime is found in the index, Cushing's name is significantly absent, even though he had been on terms of intimacy with W.O. for many years. The subterfuges which he used to avoid direct quotation from his own letters or diaries are amusing. Dr. W. W. Francis states that the term "latchkeyer" had been little used in the Baltimore days, but that it had been revived by H.C. to conceal his own identity when writing the 'Osler.' Another instance is found in the account of the International Congress in 1913 in which he alludes to Sir Henry Morris's expostulation against statements of certain speakers [*sic*] at the Congress. Sir Henry's explosion was directed not against "speakers," but against one speaker in particular, namely, Harvey Cushing. Some of Cushing's friends felt that he had gone to wholly unnecessary lengths in the direction of anonymity, and that the completeness of the record suffered in consequence. Certainly any friend of the Oslers would have derived satisfaction from knowing that Harvey Cushing had himself attended Revere Osler when he was so severely wounded in Flanders. He was not given to such extremes of modesty in his professional writing, and no one would have taken it amiss had he permitted his name to appear in places other than the title-page. In reading the Jones 'Butler' he had been irritated by the way in which Jones had brought himself into the story, and no doubt this circumstance settled him in his determination to efface himself from the 'Osler.'

As intimated earlier, the reviews were almost uniformly enthusiastic, as were the many letters which he received. There were several serious criticisms, one of which came from his devoted friend, William H. Welch. Welch wrote a detailed review for the *Saturday Review of Literature* (21 Nov. 1925) which subsequently was reprinted in full as a twenty-six-page pamphlet. In this, after praising the book's many virtues, he accused Cushing of unduly emphasizing Osler's distrust of the full-time plan. For Welch, "full-time" was something of a banner and an oriflamme, and to have Osler portrayed as one who opposed the greatest development (as Welch thought) in the history of American medicine was more than he could endure without protest. Welch also viewed it as an open criticism of the policies of the Rockefeller Foundation and the General Education Board. So fearful was he that Cushing's biography would create a false impression that he had some two thousand copies of his review printed and widely circulated by the Rockefeller Foundation. In writing to H.C., Welch says (4 December 1925), "I never discussed 'full-time' very much with Osler and I was much distressed when I learned later about some of the letters which had been written him from here on the subject, and which I fear put the idea in his head that our action somehow reflected on him. Of course nothing could be farther from the truth." Specifically Welch felt that Cushing had failed to indicate that Osler was fully aware of the benefits that had come of full-time medicine and that he should have included Osler's appeal to McGill to adopt full-time. The review continues:

> . . . He was not in sympathy with the introduction later at the Johns Hopkins of the so-called "full-time" system, intended to relieve the heads of the major clinics and some of their assistants from the necessity of engaging in private practice for a livelihood. Dr. Cushing has introduced in the second volume several passages expressive of Osler's opinions on this much discussed subject, which, by the way, should not be called, as is done by the author, "the Rockefeller programme," for it did not originate with any Rockefeller Board. Although Osler expressed himself generally in opposition, "he hedged a good deal," as the author remarks, and was evidently perplexed, as appears from a sentence following an expression of disapproval of full-time teaching in an address in 1913: "At the same time let me frankly confess that I mistrust my own judgment, as this is a problem for young men and for the future." A correction should be made at the end of the footnote in Vol. II, p. 420, for Osler's final expression on this subject was not in the paper of 1915 there referred to, but in the opening letter to the Dean of the Medical Faculty of McGill University, his own alma mater, written in August, 1919, only a few weeks before the onset of his last illness, from which a few phrases are quoted later in the volume, but with regrettable omission, in view of what had appeared in previous pages, of the essential part of the letter urging the appointment of "whole-time (or if thought wiser largely so)" heads of clinics, and of assistants, "whole and part time."

Welch also believed that Cushing had overemphasized the importance of Osler's public health propaganda. "I think," Welch said, "you can readily correct the statement about propaganda being as important as scientific discovery, which is doubtless inadvertent." He continued:

> . . . One, however, pauses when in another connection the feeling is expressed "that Osler's greatest professional service was that of a propagandist of public health measures," and is frankly startled when the Philistinic remark follows that this is "a rôle as important as that of the laboratory scientist whose cloistered studies supplied the knowledge on which our whole public health movement is based"—that is to say of a Pasteur or a Koch. There might possibly be acquiescence in the former statement in England where Osler had no real clinic nor opportunity for important clinical teaching, but after all he was a clinician, not a sanitarian, and as already indicated won his brightest laurels in the field which he cultivated so assiduously and successfully and where his professional ambitions lay. It is not necessary to shift these laurels in order to appreciate properly the aid which he rendered to the movements of public health, in which he was deeply interested. Less frequently the originator than the animator of these movements, he was always ready to respond to appeals to address public meetings and to participate effectively in other ways. No other voice was so powerful in arousing the interest and action of the public and the profession. He had the "daemonic" faculty, the faculty which awakens intelligent enthusiasm in others. . . .

Welch made one other significant critical comment:

> Osler was personally familiar not only with the system of teaching in the English hospitals but also with the organization and spirit of the German medical clinics. In an article published as early as 1884 immediately after a visit to the Berlin clinics he says: "The advanced position of German medicine and the reputation of the schools as teaching centres are largely fruits of this system."

Osler left no doubt of the nature of his professional ambitions, which he summarized in an address at a farewell dinner given by the profession of the United States and Canada in 1905, as being first "to make of myself a good clinical physician," to rank with eminent physicians of the past whom he names, an ambition more than fulfilled, and second "to build up a great clinic on Teutonic lines, not on those previously followed here and in England, but on lines which have placed the scientific medicine of Germany in the forefront of the world. And if I have done anything to promote the growth of clinical medicine, it has been in this direction, in the formation of a large clinic with a well organized series of assistants and house physicians and with proper laboratories in which to work at the intricate problems that confront us in internal medicine. For the opportunities which I have had at Johns Hopkins Hospital to carry out these ideas I am truly thankful."

On 23 November H.C. acknowledged Welch's criticism:

H.C. to William H. Welch *23 November 1925.*

Dear Dr. Welch: . . . I am glad of your criticisms because, after all, I don't think the book has been criticised enough for its own good. I shall be glad to have the list of errata. Not many people have taken the trouble to send me any corrections, Garrison a few and Thayer a few, and Barker has pointed out a split infinitive. I am quite ashamed of myself for not having split more, for I have no objection whatever to split infinitives and in fact rather like them. There are a few glaring breaks, like *John* for *James* in the case of the Cardinal [Gibbons]. I hope you haven't found many more. The book has had a most amazing sale, far and away above anything that I could have imagined, and mostly in this country where it costs a third again the price that they put on it in England. They have just printed a third five thousand, and Humphrey Milford told me in London that they had sold nine thousand of the first ten here in the States. I am very glad that Joslin prevailed upon the Press to let the medical students have them at something like nine dollars, and I judge that they must have sold a good many of them at that price, for I have been kept busy inscribing volumes.

Cushing received a specific criticism from another source. His friends in Philadelphia felt that he had been particularly unfair in his statements regarding William Pepper, W.O.'s associate during his years in Philadelphia, and it is doubtful whether the open antagonism implied in Cushing's account of Pepper and Osler actually existed. The statement concerning Pepper which particularly rankled was that he was capable of bringing a case of jaundice out of the wards to illustrate a lecture on pernicious anemia. Also that "Pepper . . . would enter the classroom while taking off gloves and coat and immediately begin a brilliant discourse on some topic, not always related to his prescribed subject. Osler, on the other hand, could be dignified enough and serious, but playfulness and gaiety were always ready to break through the mask. Moreover, anything suggesting the *poseur* was foreign to his make-up, and there was no concealment of the fact that he felt the need of elaborate preparations for his more formal student exercises." The Pepper family and Pepper's friends were naturally indignant at this implication which, as far as Cushing was concerned, must have been inadvertent. His intention had been to contrast two very different personalities, and it is clear that he did not intend the unpleasant innuendo. In writing to his friend A. C. Abbott (21 May 1925), he said: "It looks as though you had just reached the Philadelphia period and do not fully approve of it. The sections were read by two or three Philadelphia men before I let them go to press and no one suggested that I had been unfair about Pepper. No, I never saw Pepper and had no contacts with him whatsoever and am quite aware that he was a great man; but I did not realize that I had in any way failed to make this apparent nor that he and W.O. were ever on anything more than the most friendly terms. Please read this part over some day or read over the parts in which you will find the index 'Peppered,' and let me know if you still hold the same opinion." Several others in Philadelphia abused Cushing roundly, but the error had been made, and although H.C. regretted it, he felt that anything in the way of a public correction would do more harm than good, so the matter was dropped.

The letters which H.C. received about the biography are too numerous to quote. He was especially pleased, however, by the following from his and Osler's old friend, Walter Morley Fletcher:

Sir Walter Morley Fletcher to H.C. *27 April 1925.*

Dear Cushing, I have just returned from a ten days' holiday in France to find the two attractive volumes of your 'Osler' on my table at home. I want to tell you at once what pleasure they will now be giving to thousands of others. Just before Easter I had a week-end with Lady Osler at Oxford, and saw the first copy of both volumes which had just reached her from the Press. After a tête-à-tête dinner with her and a delightful talk, I sat in front of a wood fire in that blessed library with your two volumes on my knee, and I browsed in them till the early hours of the morning. I could not have wished a more perfect setting for my first reading of them. You can easily guess how I felt as I sat in that room, among all those books, and with countless memories of his ways and sayings and kindnesses. I meant to write at once to thank you for your part in this, but I was dashing from place to place, and never seemed to have the right chance.

Do let me now warmly congratulate you. I admire very greatly indeed the skill with which you have got so much material into so small a space, while keeping right proportions of perspective. You have done the most difficult thing of all; you have not allowed detail to obscure the general sense of narrative and progress, and yet you have given abundantly the small details without which no portrait could have been given or any effective tale told. This particular difficulty is one common to all biographers, but in your case it was specially great because of Osler's multifarious interests. Above all, I think you have succeeded in showing his beauty as a human being and a moral teacher, without letting that be submerged in his distinction as a physician or an educationalist, or an antiquarian, or an official. I think you must be pleased with the form of the book. I think the type and page and general make-up are all quite excellent. The illustrations are all very precious possessions.

I had better chances than any but very few of your readers of knowing what work you had to give to the book, and under what embarrassments. Of course I know that this was completely a labour of love for you, but it must have been very hard for you very often. I am sure you must now look back upon the work with great satisfaction and the proper pride that comes from giving the best you can to a job. I feel almost envious of you to have been able to pay such a tribute to such a friend. Like very many others, I owe you a real debt of gratitude for what you have done. . . .

A long, handwritten letter from a non-medical Yale man must also have given H.C. much satisfaction:

Supreme Court of the United States,
Mr. Justice Taft to H.C. *Washington, D.C., 14 December 1926.*

My dear Dr. Cushing, I have had a warning in my work in the Supreme Court. I have overdone matters resulting in heart fibrillation and have had Dr. W. S. Thayer's examination and advice. I have slowed up and am leading a very quiet life trying to continue to pull my weight in the boat in the court. As a consequence I do not work between supper and bedtime at 9.30 P.M. So it is that I have been devoting an hour and a half an evening to reading and have been able to read carefully your life of Sir Wm. Osler. I finished it last night with moist eyes. I have rarely read a work which has given more pleasure and awakened more interest. I say pleasure. It was pleasure to think that so great a man could unite with his supreme usefulness so noble and attractive a character. I had known of his high standing in his profession and his work at Johns Hopkins but it needed your two volumes to bring out his remarkable qualities and the proportions of his achievements.

The union in him of profound medical knowledge and indomitable effort at research on the one hand and his literary and classical and historical culture make him one of a century. To read of what he wrote and what he must have read and made part of him gives to one like me a humiliating sense of intense ignorance. His broad catholic attitude toward all men, whether Germans or not, his intense enthusiasms in bettering conditions, his admiration for men of all ages before him whose useful assistance in advancing the medical art and science and whose worth he was acutely joyful to disclose and thereby to render delayed reward are inspiring to read of. The preparation of such a biography must have involved the greatest labor, much as you were assisted by your medical knowledge and by Dr. Osler's wonderful correspondence, and by that wonderful woman, Lady Osler. Your self suppression I regretted because I longed for your personal expression of view. You have created a monumental work of highest value and I could not refrain from writing to you to express my personal gratitude for what you have done for me in it. The tragedy in the loss of Revere which the Oslers, father and mother, suffered and the noble way in which they bore up under it illumines the story as of epic character. I hope that the plans of Sir William in respect to his library and his other projects are working as he would have them.

I have not seen you for many a year but I follow you and your work as well as I can, *i.e.* as well as I can that of a Yale man at Harvard. My deepest sympathy in the blinding sorrow of the loss of your boy went to you when I heard of it. Nothing can take away the lifelong effect of such a blow and only hard work can mitigate it. I am proud as a Yale man of the position and influence you

SIR WILLIAM OSLER, Bart.
H.C.'s favorite photograph of Osler in later life, taken in Baltimore
7 May 1913 by Lawrence Reynolds of Detroit

WALTER E. DANDY AND H.C.
After a game of tennis at Jekyl Island, Georgia, February 1921. From a photograph by Mrs. Harry R. Slack, Jr.

FAMILY GROUP AT LITTLE BOAR'S HEAD
From a photograph taken in the summer of 1921. Mrs. Crowell, K.C.'s mother, in rear at left. *Back row:* William, Betsey, Mary, H.C.
Front row: Henry, K.C., Barbara

wield in your profession and of the debt you have put all under to you for this life of your leader. Sincerely yours, WM. H. TAFT.

Give my love and congratulations to Lawrence Lowell when you see him. Tell him that Justice Holmes thinks one at 70 is just beginning middle age.

Cushing's acknowledgements of the various letters received about the 'Osler' are interesting but are also far too numerous for extensive quotation. One to a bookseller friend is particularly illuminating:

H.C. to Edgar H. Wells *12 May 1926.*

Dear Wells, Thanks for your note which is much appreciated. My chief satisfaction in having written the 'Osler' was in the hope that it might prove to offset and be a sort of antidote to 'Arrowsmith,' a book the spirit of which I despise. It's funny that we should have both been 'Pulitzerized.' I have swallowed the dose without turning a hair, but it seems to have nauseated Brother Sinclair. They are very clever, these Lewis, de Kruif, Mencken fellows, and I confess to reading them. Even so, one has to contemplate with amusement mingled with disapproval modern art, jazz and bobbed hair.

I have always been promising myself a visit to your shop and I groan when I see your catalogues. Sometime if you, in turn, will run up a signal when you are in Boston and will at least come and have tea with us, you will see why. Books are already all over the house, and they propagate themselves, like rabbits, with little encouragement. Always sincerely yours, HARVEY CUSHING.

Lady Osler, too, was inundated with letters about the biography, but since she did not have the squirrel tendencies of the Cushing family, she preserved almost nothing. At the time of her death (in August 1928), three letters about the biography (which had evidently brought her particular satisfaction) were found in her desk. From Arnold Muirhead who later wrote Lady Osler's biography:

Bexhill-on-Sea, Sussex,
Arnold M. Muirhead to Lady Osler *24 May 1925.*

Dear Lady Osler: I feel that I didn't thank you half enough for giving me the Biography. They are two wonderful volumes and I have enjoyed every page. But they've done something more for me than that. I don't think anyone can read the story of all Sir William accomplished during his waking hours each day, without feeling ashamed of all the time one fritters away and loses. I made a terrible mess of last term. I just idled away valuable hours and let myself sink under the depressing atmosphere which pervaded the school owing to the continual illness and bad weather. But the Biography has changed all that. When I wake in the morning I seize pencil and paper or a book and I continue during the day to seize and make use of all the odd five minutes of leisure which I get. It's amazing how much more I accomplish: those odd moments when added up make quite a respectable total. Of course I have occasional lapses from grace but they are getting fewer!

I've never read a biography more full of wit and fun: Sir William's joy in and zest for life just sparkle from the pages. There are pages also which make me brush the tears from my eyes but they make the book a human document. What *is* life but a mingling of laughter and tears? Every man worth his salt has a strain of hero-worship in him. Sir William had it, and he in turn became an object of worship. I don't wonder because few men seem to have understood "youth" better than he. So many men of mature years are ready to scoff at youth instead of encouraging. Sir William realised that the future of medicine was with the rising generation and he always seemed ready with a helping, advising and encouraging hand. Youth—I know—*is* extravagant in opinions but generally from an excess of keenness. . . .

From one of the most erudite scholars of Oxford:

Norham End, Oxford,
C. R. L. Fletcher to Lady Osler *24 April 1925.*

Dear Lady Osler: I have just finished THE BOOK. When you hear people say (as you will) that it is too long, you may, if you please, reply "Well, the Senior Survivor of the Delegates of the C. Press from that glorious and tragic time has just written to me to say that he would not have missed a word of it for anything."

In truth, I could not lay it down, and luckily I had an idle week in which to read and, I hope, digest it. It is the record of a most lovely and most noble life—we knew it would be that. But we did not know how good, how artistic and how simple, that record would be made. Mr. Cushing must be not only a man of letters and a man of Science of a very high order, but he must have also the capacity for appreciating a great man in quite an unusual degree. I suspect, however, that all the best parts of the life were contributed by yourself and only filtered through Mr. Cushing.

This is not to say that I am wholly pleased with all Mr. Cushing's 'language' and I am surprised that the Bishop of Ripon [a reader for The Clarendon Press] left in some American words and phrases which Sir William (often as he might use them in his playful letters) would have been the first to repudiate in a serious text. He was himself a perfect stylist, a pure 'classic', as great as a man of letters as he was as a man of science; and I think he would have been horrified to see such a word as 'boost' in a grave text on a grave subject. There are several other things of this sort but I won't worry you with them. I have made out a list of a few slips and sent to the Bishop for him to send on to our Secretary for correction in a Second edition, but to you I only subjoin such as will interest yourself. . . . But no words of mine can convey adequately the pleasure that I have derived from reading the book. It would be difficult to say which parts of it were the most delightful. Utterly ignorant as I am of medicine and science I took an almost equal delight in Sir William's scientific papers as in his literary. Here was a man who could explain and glorify these things to the lay mind—and how wonderfully he did it. Believe me, Very sincerely yours, C. R. L. FLETCHER.

From P. S. Allen, the Erasmus scholar:

Corpus Christi College, Oxford,
26 April 1925.

Dear Lady Osler: It is bountiful of you to give us these splendid volumes. I have wanted many times to write to you, since they came, but each time I sit down, I take them up and go on reading till the time is gone, and I must wait another opportunity. We are most grateful for such detail about every one of you: and are greedy to know as much as possible. It is good to have so many pictures. I turn from one to another, and can't decide which I like best—from the Prefect in the wonderful top-hat, to the Regius in his infinite tenderness.

I have told you before what an inspiration his life has given me; and what it has been to me, it must be to countless others. Such lives are a revelation of

God; and his is one that I always have in mind when I am trying to hold on to the Divine. My faith is that life on such a plane has attained to immortality, and that tho' it seems for the time severed from us, we may hope some day to enjoy definite contact again, if we can struggle up to the same level, or within reach of those who are there. It is a continual source of thankfulness to us to have been given the friendship of him and you; and we thank you for letting us know more, thro' these volumes, of what lies behind. Yours sincerely, P. S. ALLEN.

1920

The foregoing account of the writing of the Osler biography might convey the impression that Cushing had accomplished little else during that period; this, however, is far from the truth. His clinic was growing and doctors as well as patients had begun to come to him from great distances. Between January of 1920 and the end of December 1924, when the last chapters of the Osler biography were committed to the press, Cushing had published fifty major papers and reports—an average of one a month. Many of these were lengthy contributions, such as the highly illustrated chapter entitled "The purpose and technical steps of a subtemporal decompression," which appeared in Ochsner's *Surgical diagnosis and treatment,* 1920. There were also important papers from men who had come to work in Cushing's clinic. Frederick Foley, following up Weed's work on hypertonic solutions, published four papers on the reduction of intracranial tension by intravenous injection of strong salt solution—the salt through its osmotic pressure withdrawing fluid from the brain tissue into the blood stream.[2] This turned out to be an important technical procedure for tiding patients over an acute bout of increased intracranial pressure.

Cushing continued to make his five-year progress reports on the special field of neurological surgery, the fourth such having been delivered on 7 October 1920 in Iowa (Waterloo) before the Tri-State Medical Society and on 8 October before the Cleveland Academy of Medicine.[3] He records that in 1910 his series of cases of brain tumor had run to 180 and that by the time he left Baltimore (in 1912) the number had risen to 330. Despite his absences during the war he had had an additional 735 cases to his credit at the Brigham Hospital between its opening and September 1920. Thus, with

[2] Preliminary results were announced by Cushing and Foley in "Alterations of intracranial tension by salt solutions in the alimentary canal." *Proceedings of the Society for Experimental Biology, N.Y.*, 22 May 1920, *17*, 217-218.

[3] "The special field of neurological surgery after another interval." *Archives of Neurology and Psychiatry, Chicago*, 1920, *4*, 603-637. Also: *Illinois Medical Journal*, 1921, *39*, 133-141, 185-195; *Wisconsin Medical Journal*, 1921, *19*, 501-520; *Journal of Iowa State Medical Society*, 1921, *11*, 337-342, 385-394, 426-430; *Ohio State Medical Journal*, 1921, *17*, 293-302, 373-380.

well over a thousand cases, he was able to offer a statistically significant classification of his brain tumors and in this way laid the foundation for his major contribution to neurology: namely, the analysis of the life history and symptomatology of each specific type of brain tumor. Of the 1,072 cases in his series in 1920, 604, or 60 per cent, had been verified by microscopic study of tissue obtained either at autopsy or operation. Other cases of obvious brain tumor in which operation or autopsy had been denied were classified as "brain tumor unverified." In this 1920 tumor report he once again made a plea for a national institute of neurology where his broadly conceived program for study of the life history of brain lesions might be established. Cushing's Sixth Annual P.B.B.H. Report published early in 1920 shows the same vigor and originality as his earlier reports and the same attention to detail. In 1919, 198 operations were performed on the neurosurgical service with 18 fatalities, a mortality rate of 9.1 per cent. Each fatality was, as usual, duly abstracted. In 1921, however, he gave up publishing abstracts of postoperative fatalities, adding that the object of publicizing these data was "to make a clean breast of all of our more serious errors of judgment; as a matter of fact so few avoidable errors are disclosed in this way that it hardly seems worth while to continue with this custom, particularly in view of the labor [required] to compile this part of our formal reports and of the desire to lessen the expense of their publication."

During 1920 the Harvard Medical Society took on a new lease of life, largely as a result of Cushing's initiative. On 20 January there was a special Osler memorial meeting at which Drs. Councilman, Edward Streeter, Joseph Pratt, and H.C. all spoke—H.C. giving his stirring paper entitled "William Osler, the man,"[4] which as mentioned earlier, had originally been published anonymously in the *Boston Evening Transcript* a week after Sir William's death. On 15 February H.C. arranged a dinner for the Drinker family prior to an interesting session at which the Drinkers (Drs. Cecil K. and Katherine R.) presented an account of their study of medicine in colonial Philadelphia as depicted in the Diary of Elizabeth Drinker 1749-1807, later to be issued in book form.[5]

The Surgeon-in-Chief 'pro tempore'

A unique custom instituted by Christian in 1915 at the Brigham Hospital was that of appointing each year a Surgeon-in-Chief and a Physician-in-Chief *pro tempore*. H.C. had tried to induce Halsted

[4] *Annals of Medical History*, 1920, 2, 157-167.

[5] Drinker, C. K. *Not so long ago. A chronicle of medicine and doctors in colonial Philadelphia*. New York, Oxford University Press, 1937, 183 pp.

to come in December 1915, but his health had not permitted. In July 1919 he approached Dean Lewis, who had just been appointed Surgeon-in-Chief to the University Hospital in Chicago:

H.C. to Dean Lewis *3 July 1919.*

My dear Dean: . . . There is one thing more I shall hold you up to, and that is that some time next winter when you can make plans to do so you will come up here and spend two weeks with us in the hospital as the exchange visiting surgeon. Frank Billings was here, as you may remember, one year, with Christian in the same capacity. I have never ventured to have anyone in surgery—I made some advances once to Halsted but he failed me at the last moment. We would have great fun playing together in the clinic and you could do what you chose and take what occasional exercises you cared to take with the material at hand. It would be a great thing for us to have you here. The medical incumbents of the position in the past have been W. S. Thayer, Warfield Longcope, A. W. Hewlett, Frank Billings, and Thomas Lewis, the heart man from London. I hope that we may come to have an equally notable list and I want to start with you. You would have to get leave of absence of course, and any time that would suit you would be quite agreeable to me.

Accordingly, during the third week in March, Lewis took over the surgical service at the Brigham and ran it according to his own lights. "His stay," Cushing writes, "was an inspiration to us all, and if he took away as a result of his visit a fraction of the inspiration he left with us—staff, house officers, and students alike—he must have felt repaid." Lewis wrote after his departure: "I cannot tell you how much I appreciate being asked to come to your clinic and the many kindnesses shown me while there. It was one of the most stimulating experiences that I have ever had. In some ways, however, the experience was somewhat discouraging, for one realizes what a high standard you have set and how difficult it will be to even approach it."

Lewis' sojourn at the Brigham left such an impression that Cushing never again missed the opportunity of making an annual appointment during his remaining years at the Brigham. He had a succession of distinguished men, sometimes two in a year. The full roster follows:

DR. DEAN D. LEWIS, Rush Medical College, Chicago, 15-24 March 1920.
MR. G. E. GASK, St. Bartholomew's Hospital, London, 20 March-3 April 1921.
SIR CUTHBERT WALLACE, St. Thomas's Hospital, London, 24 April-8 May 1922.
SIR HAROLD STILES, Royal Hospital for Children, Edinburgh, 8-21 April 1923.
DR. CHARLES F. HOOVER, Lakeside Hospital, Cleveland, 3-9 February 1924.
SIR D'ARCY POWER, St. Bartholomew's Hospital, London, 20 April-5 May 1924.
DR. EVARTS A. GRAHAM, Washington University, St. Louis, 26 April-3 May 1925.
DR. CLARENCE L. STARR, Toronto General Hospital, Toronto, 7-16 March 1926.
DR. EMMET RIXFORD, Stanford University, California, 25 April-9 May 1927.
SIR CHARLES BALLANCE, St. Thomas's Hospital, London, 15-25 October 1928.
PROF. RENÉ LERICHE, University of Lyons, France, 12-20 June 1929.
PROF. D. P. D. WILKIE, Royal Infirmary, Edinburgh, 7-14 October 1929.

PROF. GUNNAR NYSTRÖM, University of Upsala, Sweden, 23-26 May 1930.
PROF. OTFRID FOERSTER, University of Breslau, Germany, 1-14 October 1930.
PROF. VITTORIO PUTTI, University of Bologna, Italy, 30 May-6 June 1932.
DR. GEORGE J. HEUER, New York Hospital, 12-16 July 1932.

While Dean Lewis had been directing his service for him, H.C. had relaxed and given a paper on 22 March entitled "Doctor poets," in 'Copey's room' at Harvard. Professor Copeland had written him a disarming letter containing a request he could not turn down:

15 Hollis Hall, Cambridge,
Prof. C. T. Copeland to H.C. *8 March 1920.*

Dear Harvey: In despair of falling in with you at our Frat, I take at last to the difficult and delicate art of writing to remind you of your years-long promise. The war, if you remember, got in the way of your coming to my room to talk to my young men. The occasion is of such long duration—I've been doing this sort of thing for 27 years—that it has come to have a ritual. We dine at the Tavern Club with selected youths, and about nine come out to Cambridge. Here, beginning promptly at ten o'clock, you talk a monologue for half an hour or so, not much longer because the audience have to sit on the floor. After the monologue we give a chance to ask questions, and that is all there is to it. I think you will enjoy it all, though I know it will mean some strain and sacrifice. . . . Don't try to telephone to me, because it is two flights down in a noisy entry. Let me have a line by return of post—a special delivery stamp appreciated—saying that you will talk for me on Monday, the twenty-second of this month. If the fifteenth would be better I can easily make it the fifteenth.

Don't you ever lunch at the Tavern Club on Wednesday? Yours very truly, C. T. COPELAND.

On the 27th he went to the 38th annual jamboree of the McGill medical students as their guest of honor, his purpose in going to Montreal having been to get some McGill atmosphere and source material for the Osler biography—and a McGill medical student dinner has unforgettable atmosphere. In the midst of all this he made a point of attending his usual run of meetings—the Boston Surgical Society on 5 April, the American Academy of Arts and Sciences on 14 April, and he was scheduled for a meeting of the American Medical Association at New Orleans on 26 April, but, on arriving at Worcester, he changed his mind and returned to Boston—to find that his staff had all taken a holiday in the belief that he was safely on his way to New Orleans. In May there were five more meetings (at three of which he read papers); a session with Richard Pearce about Rockefeller fellows from abroad; and a British-French medical mission on 14 May headed by Sir Humphry Rolleston and Professor Roussy of Paris. Over the week-end of the 20th he repaired to New Haven for a dinner in Professor Chittenden's honor and stayed over to see the Yale-Harvard baseball game on the 22d. A week later he was in Cleveland for a meeting of the Society of Clinical Surgery.

These first months of 1920 are typical of what followed during the ensuing four years, and one stands in admiration of Cushing for the fact that he was able to keep his standards, both literary and surgical, as high as they obviously were and at the same time create a literary document requiring as much detailed research as the Osler biography. His calendar for the month of June was similarly crowded and, as we have already seen, July found him at Oxford plunging into preliminary work for the 'Osler.' On 29 July he received an honorary LL.D. at Cambridge University. During this visit to Cambridge he had stayed with Sir Arthur Shipley who had then just unearthed from among the beams in the roof of his lodge at Christ's a number of beautifully preserved sixteenth century rats' nests made up principally of leaves from a hitherto unknown Caxton, a find which gave Cushing something of a biologico-bibliographic thrill.

On returning to Boston early in August, work on the Osler biography was begun in earnest. In October he presided at the opening meeting of the Harvard Medical Society which was marked by a notable paper by a young member of the staff of the Rockefeller Institute, Francis Gilman Blake, who described his studies on experimental pneumonia—this a few months before his appointment as Professor of Medicine at the Yale University School of Medicine.

During November H.C. was able to withdraw somewhat from public commitments. He found time, however, to arrange a meeting on 16 November of the Harvard Medical Society at which President Eliot, along with Drs. F. C. Shattuck, William F. Whitney, and Edward C. Streeter spoke on Oliver Wendell Holmes.[6] Dr. Warren had been unable to attend; H.C. accordingly sent him an account made amusing by his Victorian reaction to an O.W.H. poem with obstetrical leanings:

H.C. to J. Collins Warren *17 November 1920.*

Dear 'Col': . . . We had the meeting last night; and I don't think you missed very much, though I was delighted to see such a large turnout even with such a bad storm. The room was packed, whether from interest in medical history or through the lure of Mr. Eliot, I am not quite sure. Mr. Eliot gave a dignified and unexciting account of his relation to the development of the school in the sixties and seventies, but did not say very much about O.W.H.

Fred Shattuck followed and, to my great discomfiture, read at length one of those lurid, fugitive Holmes poems intended solely for the ears of obstetricians. Someone should have expurgated it for him. Dr. Whitney had an interesting display, and spoke well; but Streeter carried off the honors with his display of books and the way he presented them. We missed you very much.

On 19 and 20 November he had another New Haven week-end

[6] In 1923 (at Cushing's instigation), Mr. Eliot's comments were published in the *Harvard Graduates Magazine.*

on the occasion of the Harvard-Yale football game. He also gave a clinic at the New Haven Hospital for Joseph Marshall Flint, the Professor of Surgery.

An interesting episode, most characteristic of Cushing, occurred late in October following a football game between Harvard and Centre, a small college in Kentucky. Since Centre was a complete unknown in the annals of Harvard football, the whole of Greater Boston seems to have turned out for the game, with the result that the gate receipts were far more than anticipated and about ten times the $4,000 Harvard had guaranteed Centre to cover the expenses of the team. H.C. felt that some degree of largesse was indicated and accordingly addressed himself to Mr. Lowell on the subject, and later to Dean LeBaron Briggs: "I feel equally sure that an unsolicited gift from Harvard University to Centre College (not the Centre College Athletic Committee) would put Harvard on such a footing throughout the entire South as, for example, the return of the Chinese indemnity put the United States in relation with the Orient. It was a generous act, not at all a necessary one." This suggestion was carried out.

The year ended with a dinner for Walter Camp, long the football coach at Yale. H.C. retained his active interest in sport of all types throughout his life, and especially in college athletics and all those associated with these activities. Thus it is natural to find Mr. Camp staying with the Cushings in Brookline and incidentally putting the entire family through his system of morning calisthenics so popular at the time.

1921

The year 1920 had been particularly hectic because prior to Osler's death H.C. had many commitments, but in 1921 his calendar was very different—less travel, fewer meetings, and (his files reveal) seventeen written regrets to invitations to speak. January was almost completely quiet. In February the Boston Surgical Society, of which H.C. was president, had a meeting at the Harvard Club, and a chapter from the Osler biography evidently went with him to the meeting since the notice records that Cushing presented "Some notes on William Osler's boyhood."

At the end of February H.C. took two weeks off for a trip South to Jekyl Island (Georgia) with Mrs. Cushing, the Robert Lovetts of Boston, and the Howard Elliotts of New York. There he had much-needed rest and relaxation with long hours out of doors playing tennis, ever one of his favorite games. Finding his former Baltimore assistant, Dr. Walter Dandy, also on the Island, he took delight in challenging him once again on the court.

In March Mr. George E. Gask, Professor of Surgery at the University of London and Surgeon to St. Bartholomew's Hospital did a tour of duty as Surgeon-in-Chief *pro tem.* Gask's sojourn, like that of Dean Lewis, proved eminently successful and afforded a welcome opportunity for an exchange of points of view on surgical problems between Great Britain and the United States. "Bringing with him," Cushing wrote in his Annual Report, "the traditions of that ancient foundation, famous for its succession of eminent surgical teachers, we learned much from him of the methods there so long and so successfully pursued. Living as he did in the Resident's room, on intimate terms with the house staff, they in particular profited by his presence and example. His visit will be long remembered, for it made a bright spot in the year's work and was a stimulus to us all."

In May two of H.C.'s warmest friends from Britain arrived on a medical mission—Sir Walter Morley Fletcher, Secretary of the Medical Research Council, and Sir Wilmot Herringham, who had organized the International Medical Congress in 1913. A letter to Fletcher after he returned to England discloses much about the writer as well as the recipient, for H.C. and Sir Walter—a Cambridge "blue"—had both been ardent followers of sport:

H.C. to Sir Walter Fletcher *28 June 1921.*

My dear Fletcher: I am so pleased to have had your little essay written years ago on Harvard and Yale. It is a very fair appraisal of the two places and comparison of their characteristics with those of Oxford and Cambridge. However, I think you would hardly know Yale if you saw it again today, as indeed you did, I believe. We are so young over here that like the children we appear to grow up overnight, and many of the foolish characteristics of Yale College of the nineties have long since disappeared. I think that the athletics, too, are on a far better basis; and though sports are taken a little too seriously, there is a constant trend toward sport for sport's sake rather than for championship trophies. . . .

I fear that we sent you and Herringham away completely exhausted. You do not mention your ruptured tendon which in itself was enough, and I suppose poor Herringham with his herpes was to be sympathized with still more. I hope you will both have recovered fully ere this. You left an indelible impression upon the family, one and all, and "hey what what" is the byword of the household. With affectionate regards, I am, Always yours, HARVEY CUSHING.

P.S. Do send some Osler notes, if you can get around to it.

In 1933, after Fletcher's death, H.C. addressed the Oxford and Cambridge Track and Field Team at Harvard and spoke of Fletcher as one whom athletics had prepared for life—one who knew how to accept victory or defeat, without taking either too seriously.

Following Fletcher's visit, H.C. and his friends Malcolm Storer and Edward C. Streeter called, on 31 May, a general meeting "of physicians in New England who are interested in the historical and cultural aspects of medicine," with the end in view of organizing the Boston Medical History Club. A small but enthusiastic group gathered at the Boston Medical Library and laid plans for a series of meetings to begin in October 1921. They did not worry about a constitution and there were no formal publications. The history of the club (which is still in existence) during the period from 1921 to 1933 can be reconstructed from the printed notices of meetings and the carefully preserved correspondence about them in H.C.'s files.[7]

BOSTON
MEDICAL HISTORY CLUB

A MEETING of physicians of New England who are interested in the historical and cultural aspects of Medicine has been called for the purpose of organizing a Medico-Historical Club in Boston.

THIS MEETING will be held at the Boston Medical Library, No. 8 The Fenway, Tuesday, May thirty-first, at 3.30 P.M.

YOU ARE INVITED to be present at this time to consider brief preliminaries of organization and programme. If you find it impossible to attend, please signify on the enclosed form your approval of the plan and desire to join. Dues will be nominal or nil. Four or five programme meetings a year are contemplated.

HARVEY CUSHING
MALCOLM STORER
EDWARD C STREETER

BOSTON MEDICAL HISTORY CLUB

In June 1921 the American Medical Association met in Boston and, since H.C. was president of the Association for the Study of Internal Secretions which met at the same time, he took an active part. His presidential address put forth a devastating allegory in which he excoriated those who had come to exploit endocrinology uncritically and for their own dubious ends. "Endocrinology as a special subject," he writes, "if it wishes to survive and come to be a factor in medical practice, must look out for the character of its clinical advance agents, lest it come to be utterly discredited. We have nothing as yet in the treatment of pituitary insufficiency comparable to what Victor Horsley and his pupil Murray accomplished for myxoedema, and we are still further behind in the case of the other glands. Indeed, no Magellan or Balboa for ductless gland therapeutics has yet appeared . . . meanwhile there is many an imitator of Cortez and Pizzaro to trade on the superstitious awe of the natives who will soon come to be fully disillusioned."[8]

[7] Cushing was the first president of the club and Edward C. Streeter the original secretary-treasurer. The first regular meeting was held on 20 October 1921 with the following members in attendance: J. F. Ballard, J. W. Bartol, Harold Bowditch, David Cheever, A. L. Chute, I. H. Coriat, W. P. Coues, J. W. Cummin, Harvey Cushing, J. E. Donley, J. W. Farlow, R. M. Green, Reid Hunt, Timothy Leary, J. H. Pratt, Lawrence Reynolds, George Sarton, M. C. Smith, H. R. Stedman, Malcolm Storer, E. C. Streeter, E. W. Taylor, P. E. Truesdale, H. R. Viets.

[8] "Disorders of the pituitary gland. Retrospective and prophetic." *Journal of the American Medical Association,* 18 June 1921, *76,* 1721-1726.

A notable event of the A.M.A. meeting was the bestowal on William J. Mayo of the first Henry Jacob Bigelow Medal. The Boston Surgical Society, which had been founded in February 1915, was the recipient at the time of its foundation of a sum of money presented by William Sturgis Bigelow (1850-1926), one of H.C.'s Saturday Club friends. Bigelow stipulated that the interest from the fund should from time to time be used for the presentation of a medal in honor of his father, Henry Jacob Bigelow (1818-1890), to one chosen for his "contribution to the advancement of surgery." Owing to the war, no presentation was made until 1921, and it was highly fitting that one of the brothers Mayo should have been first to be designated. Cushing was chairman of the committee that made the selection and he insisted that it be looked upon as a national rather than a local event. For this reason the ceremony was arranged as part of the program of the A.M.A. meeting. In writing to Mayo in September 1920, H.C. expresses himself on the subject of the medal and the presentation:

H.C. to W. J. Mayo *13 September 1920.*

Dear Will: . . . I should like to see this Bigelow Medal given as a sort of annual blue ribbon to men who have contributed largely to surgery. *You* of course are in a class by yourself and it is eminently fitting that you should be the first recipient. In your private ear I may say that some of the members of the Society, though not all, would like to have it a purely local and private affair, but I am dead set against this. I feel, myself, that there could be no more appropriate occasion than in connection with the A.M.A. meeting here next June, but whether I can swing this I do not know. . . .

P.S. An address from you would make the A.M.A. meeting a great success here, and I feel, too, that an address from you in which appropriate things are said about Henry J. Bigelow, who was really a great figure in surgery, may serve completely to bury the hatchet. For, as you know, during his time New England was a little loath to accept the A.M.A. at what you and I and most others know to be its real worth.

Subsequent recipients of the Bigelow Medal were W. W. Keen of Philadelphia (1922); Rudolph Matas, New Orleans (1926); Chevalier Jackson, Philadelphia (1928); George Grey Turner, Newcastle-upon-Tyne (1931); J. M. T. Finney, Baltimore (1932), and Cushing himself who received it in 1933 after he had retired from Harvard.

On 11 June 1921 a dinner was held in New Haven in honor of Joseph Marshall Flint who, because of ill health, was retiring from the chair of surgery at Yale to live in Switzerland. Cushing's continued interest in and affection for Yale were very evident in his painstaking arrangements for this function. In April Milton C. Winternitz, the new dean, had invited him to be toastmaster and to arrange for the speakers. He had accepted promptly and a few days later Simon Flexner, Ross G. Harrison, William H. Welch, William H. Carmalt, and others received personal letters from H.C.

inviting them to attend. To James Rowland Angell, who had just been designated successor to Arthur T. Hadley as president of the University, he addressed himself as follows:

H.C. to James R. Angell *23 May 1921.*

My dear Mr. Angell: May I introduce myself to you as a Yale man of ancient vintage who has been called upon to preside at a dinner to be given in New Haven for Dr. Joseph M. Flint on the evening of June eleventh. I feel that there is a very great opportunity offered on this occasion, not only to do a pleasant thing for Flint on his retirement, but also to give the Yale Medical School a real boost which they need very much just at this time. If the two young men, Dr. Blake and Dr. Harvey, who are to take charge of the Medical and Surgical Departments, can be made to feel that the Yale alumni in medicine are really behind them, and the same thing is even more true of the hard-working and enthusiastic Dean, Dr. Winternitz, the occasion will be more than worth while. I have asked a few men to come and speak, among them Dr. Welch, Secretary Stokes, R. G. Harrison, and Simon Flexner. If you could by any possibility be present, it would insure the success of the occasion.

I know that you will accept if you possibly can. I have always felt that a small, well-organized medical school at New Haven might come to be one of the foremost schools of the country, with all the advantages possessed by such schools as those in the smaller German University centers in the heyday of German medicine. Anything we can do to bring this about will be very well worth while.

Mr. Angell's reply disclosed his concern for the Medical School:

James R. Angell to H.C. *25 May 1921.*

Dear Dr. Cushing: . . . I may say that the Medical School is one of the great divisions of Yale in which I feel a most vital interest. I am sure that it contains possibilities of the greatest usefulness and I am very eager that it should be given every opportunity to demonstrate its possibilities.

Should I finally find it impossible to be present, I shall appreciate it if you will express my high regard for Dr. Flint, my sincere regret that I cannot join in this farewell to him and my most earnest hopes for the success of the Medical School. Yours very truly, JAMES R. ANGELL.

William Welch, who was unable to be present, sent a message:

Baltimore,
William Welch to H.C. *25 May 1921.*

Dear Cushing I am so glad that there is to be a dinner for Flint in New Haven and that you are to preside. I agree it is also a good opportunity to express our interest in the Medical School and the gratification which we feel in the fine development of opportunities there, which promise a bright future.

Flint deserves such a recognition as this will be for all that he has stood for and accomplished for the School and for surgery under rather difficult conditions. I hope that his retirement from the chair at Yale does not mean his withdrawal from active professional studies and work. He is too vigorous mentally and physically and too fine a character to make such a renunciation easy to contemplate. . . . Ever sincerely yours, WILLIAM H. WELCH.

Flint was deeply moved by the dinner, partly on account of what was said of him, but more particularly because he knew that one of his own dreams for Yale was about to come true. With Winternitz as the energetic dean and Samuel C. Harvey and Francis G. Blake placed in charge respectively of the departments of surgery and medicine, the great transformation of the Medical School, which Cushing had envisaged in 1906, was soon to be realized through the cooperation of a wise and forthright president.

After trips to Atlantic City and Toronto, H.C. was back again in New Haven for his thirtieth reunion from the 18th to the 23d, and gave the principal address at the Yale alumni luncheon. His feeling for his alma mater was never more forcibly expressed:

Though we older boys find our familiar Yale still here, it is at the same time a different Yale—at once new and old. Thirty years ago our life here centered about the Old Fence, flanked by the Brick Row and shaded by magnificent elms. It was a homely setting, though our affections made it seem lovely beyond expression. Today the Class is quartered on the top of an outlying building from which we get a view of the existent Yale far more beautiful than anything we could have pictured in our time. One evening last summer, from the upper common room in Queen's College, I looked out at the spires of Oxford—St. Mary's, the Radcliffe Camera, the towers of All Souls and the Bodleian—silhouetted against the afterglow in the western sky. I knew by their silence what effect it had upon my companions. It was graven on their very souls through years of association. In the past three evenings my classmates have looked out from our point of vantage as the setting sun lit up the new towers of Yale. For beauty of scene nothing, not even Oxford, could be more inspiring. If there are sermons in stones, certainly Gamble Rogers has put them into these glorious buildings as a heritage for all future generations of Yale men. That incomparable tower will forever stand as a symbol of youth's eternal dream. . . .

In closing this meeting, Mr. Hadley will not take it amiss if in the name of the alumni I refer to two others who bore no small share in the success of his administration. The first of them was Mrs. Hadley, unrivaled as the ideal of a university president's wife. The other has been the Secretary of the University. How even an Angell is going to conduct the affairs of this great University without such a consummate stage manager as Anson Stokes to abet him remains to be seen. The name of this Galahad will forever be coupled with the Arthurian legend. To him has been due among other things the perfection of the setting of our Yale academic functions. I would have wished to call upon him on this occasion but it is characteristic that he is busily preparing for tomorrow's ceremonies, and has thereby dodged the tribute we, the alumni, would all have been glad to pay him here.

During the summer he retired to 305 Walnut Street and there at his long, improvised tables he spent three months working on the 'Osler,' uninterrupted save for the preparation of his Ether Day Address. In 1921 the physicians at the M.G.H. suddenly realized that this was not only their centenary year, but the seventy-fifth anniversary of the discovery of ether anesthesia, and Ether Day being 16 October, there would be little time to plan an appropriate celebration. Frederic Washburn, Superintendent of the M.G.H., on 28 July wrote a somewhat casual letter to H.C. saying that he would be one of five speakers on Ether Day and that he must confine his remarks to twenty minutes—Dr. Balch having mentioned the plan to H.C. earlier in the month. To this H.C. replied "I . . . am rather staggered because I really made no definite agreement and my mind is on something quite different from preparing an address. . . . Do let me know who the other speakers are and what they are supposed to talk about. . . . Perhaps after hearing more definitely from you I may be able to adjust myself to the possibility of participating."

At this juncture Washburn disappeared on his holiday, and nothing further happened until the end of September when we find H.C. in correspondence with the older janitors, nurses, and operating room attendants at the hospital—the surgeons go hang, he wanted real source material! Thus on 6 October he wrote: "Dear Nellie Skillen—I am writing the Ether Day Address and wish to say something about your father [janitor in the anatomy laboratory] and the important part he played in the history of the medical school. Have you the exact dates of when he first went to the M.G.H. and the old North Grove Street School? . . . I saw him shortly before [his death] at the M.G.H. and he was facing his end with the philosophy and courage which I would have expected from him. I was most devoted to him . . . and always hoped that he had some feeling for me in return."

Having brought material together from the greatest variety of sources, H.C. prepared an address which turned out to be one of the most remarkable of his career. It was designated "The personality of a hospital," and although four speakers had preceded him (Henry P. Walcott, Surgeon General M. W. Ireland, Frederick C. Shattuck, and C. Macfie Campbell), the address held the attention of a large Bostonian audience for at least forty-five minutes, H.C. having coolly ignored the twenty-minute stipulation. Shortly thereafter he had a dozen or more letters, the most amusing and outspoken being those of Councilman and Streeter:

W. T. Councilman to H.C. [*Postmarked 19 October 1921*].

My dear Cushing, Two or three times in my life when I thought a man had written a very pleasing book or said something very well I have told him so and been glad to have done it. So now I want to tell you how very good your address at the M.G.H. was. That you should have been able to pay such a tribute to the really fine old institution without further glorifying a few individuals who have already received too much—I think it was the best address of its kind I ever heard and it made me feel that I possibly may be regarded as an inconspicuous brick in a good building. I thought the addresses too numerous and too fulsome—I am always amused when I go there—it is so d——ed respectable and the audience seems to compliment itself in being for a time in the effulgent glory. I sometimes now in my old age get so tired of the Back Bay as to be willing to die to escape it.

Edward C. Streeter to H.C. *3 November 1921.*

Dear Harvey: I have just read your Ether Day address. A joy, a veritable *coup,* and I would to God you had invited me to hear it delivered. Institution, town and profession are deeply beholden to you for this; if I may gauge values, far and away the best etherial discourse pronounced under the old dome in many a moon. The man who could remain unawed and unmoved by your words is a rotter and does not "belong." Magisterial, believe me. Yours ever, EDW. C. STREETER.

Something of the spirit of the address can be gleaned from a few random passages:

. . . Raiment counts for little and the humblest may cover a personality capable of permanently influencing the motives, the ideals and actions of countless others. So also, many of us have known hospitals under perishable and tattered canvas which possessed an individuality, character and spirit often found lacking in others encased in a more enduring shell of brick and mortar. . . .

I think the faithful Hugh McGee has the record for service, fifty years in fact, but James Mains with his Parkinsonian tremor was the mainstay of the Bigelow amphitheatre for nearly as long. Then there were Barry, inimitable mimic of surgeons who had gone before, Piper the night orderly, "Out-Patient" John, and Louis Brown, who first came a boy with osteomyelitis and died here thirty years later, from complications of his old malady, meanwhile having become, as a photomicrographic expert, a most useful and loyal servant of the Hospital. Strongly represented, too, is the personality of that beloved Walter Dodd, who grew from an apothecary clerk to have charge of one of the first and best X-ray departments in the country and, like the soldier he was, stood by his guns in the service of the Hospital to the end—"doubly dead in that he died so young." All these are represented no less than, perhaps even more than, those of greater fame who were given more prominent rôles and received the plaudits, but gave far less time to the performance.

Nor need the list be so restricted, for women—many of them—have done their part, even Nellie and Ellen in the Flat, dear old Maggie, the waitress, Bridget Gibbon in the laundry, who for thirty-four years has known better than any-one else which of the surgeons and their pupils, East or West, was the least tidy. Then, too, there have been women higher up who for hours have stood wearily handing things to imperious and impatient surgeons, or have for so many years spent unselfish hours, like Miss McCrae, in giving nurses the distinctive stamp of the Massachusetts General Hospital Training School. A woman, indeed, with vision and opportunity, may even be one of the outstanding figures, as has been true of St. Thomas's Hospital, in whose annals Florence Nightingale shares the honors with, if she does not even outshine, such as Mead and Cheselden, whom Alexander Pope immortalized.

So let us remember that someone other than a visiting physician or surgeon may indelibly stamp his personality on the hospital he serves. In the old Blockley Hospital in Philadelphia a tablet has been erected to Thomas Owen, who for some thirty years as head nurse of the men's medical floor was known to successive generations of attendants and residents, most of whom are forgotten or at least their association with that picturesque old hospital has been, while his will remain for all time. And why? Because he gave all that he had to the institution and it left him famous, whereas the others, a good many of them, used the old Philadelphia Hospital not infrequently for political or private ends and are buried in oblivion. Such a one as this Owen was Jim Skillen, originally a Massachusetts General Hospital ward tender, who came back here to die of an incurable malady after passing uncountable years as janitor of the Medical School. There he probably meant more to more students than did any individual teacher, for he at least knew us all by name and had very clear and forcefully expressed notions as to our individual worth, as well as to the worth of our many instructors.[9]

Another occasion, and one to which he had given careful thought and preparation, claimed Cushing's attention on 18 October. At noon a simple ceremony was held at Louis Pasteur and Longwood Avenues, just in front of the Harvard Medical School, at which the members of Base Hospital No. 5 met to dedicate a memorial, the Oscar C. Tugo Circle, in memory of their comrade, the first enlisted man in the American Expeditionary Force to be killed in the great war. President Lowell presided, Bishop Lawrence led the religious preliminaries, the principal address was given by Surgeon General Ireland, and there followed remarks by Andrew Peters, then Mayor of Boston, and General Edwards. President Harding had sent a letter of greeting and regret. H.C. subsequently brought together and had published a full account of the proceedings with a suitable prefatory note.[10]

Two days later the Boston Medical History Club, which H.C. had a hand in organizing and of which he was president, had its first meeting with a paper by Henry Viets on Nicolaus of Cusa and the discussion was opened by the distinguished young Belgian historian, George Sarton. H.C.'s guiding influence in the new society can be inferred from a letter to Streeter:

H.C. to Edward C. Streeter *7 October 1921.*

Dear Ned: I have yours of October sixth, and the Cusanus program will be O.K. I wonder if it would not be a good thing to have either at the beginning or at the end of each meeting an informal "Exhibition of books and papers relating to the history of medicine," and have as many people as desire bring in things which they would briefly like to show, and take possibly a half hour for this sort of thing. This would be of interest and get a good many men on their feet who otherwise might not have any special paper worthy of a place on a printed program. Indeed, it might possibly act as a spur to do something more with their material.

During the last week of October the American College of Surgeons,

[9] In 1930 Mrs. William W. Vaughan, daughter of Dr. and Mrs. Samuel Parkman, asked for and was granted permission to reprint the address in memory of her parents to give the internes and nurses "as they leave the hospital during the next ten years."

[10] "Dedication exercises of the Oscar C. Tugo Circle, Pasteur and Longwood Avenues, Boston, October 18, 1921, in memory of the first enlisted man in the American Expeditionary Force to be killed in the Great War." *Boston Medical and Surgical Journal,* 22 December 1921, *185,* 739-746. This was subsequently printed by the Merrymount Press and issued in book form the following year.

under the leadership of Franklin Martin, its energetic secretary-general, held its first large-scale, postwar meeting in Philadelphia. At a special convocation on the 28th, opened by Cardinal Dougherty, Archbishop of Philadelphia, there was an unusual ceremony in which official delegates of the Royal College of Surgeons in Ireland, as a gesture of international goodwill, conferred honorary fellowships of their College on eight American surgeons. At that time Cushing, the only American who held honorary Fellowship in the Irish College, was chosen to introduce the distinguished guests. His speech of welcome was particularly felicitous:

On March 2nd of 1784 the Royal College of Surgeons in Ireland came into the world, as was quite fitting, in a Maternity Hospital. This was none other than the famous Dublin Rotunda founded long before by Surgeon Bartholomew Moss, but the event of which I speak took place not in a ward but in the Board Room and by Royal proclamation. To the country of Jonathan Swift, of Oliver Goldsmith and of Edmund Burke the world owes a great debt. But in medicine no less than in literature and public affairs have Irishmen stood high in the English-speaking world. The medical history of ancient Erin reaches back to times prehistoric when Druids were priests and physicians. She had in Thomas Molyneux in the 17th century a figure likened to the English Sydenham, and the following two centuries produced Irishmen whose names are permanently enrolled among the leaders of our profession. . . .

In the winter of 1917-18, the Base Hospital to which I was attached had as its neighbor in Wimereux a hospital set up on the site where, 100 years before, Napoleon had gathered his legions for an invasion of England. This was No. 83 Dublin General Hospital, the Chief Surgeon and organizer of which was Colonel Sir William Taylor, President of the Irish College; and we learned to love and respect the members of his Unit, not only for their personal qualities but for the stand they had taken in regard to the war. At that time, in May of 1918, there had been something over 1000 persons holding degrees of the Irish College who had been in service; 35 of them had been killed in action or had died in service; 36 had received the Military Cross; 45 the Distinguished Service Order; and 173 had been "mentioned in despatches." I may give a single instance of what it may mean for an Irish doctor to be mentioned in despatches:

"Captain Henry James Burke, R.A.M.C., for conspicuous gallantry on 8th November, 1915, near Turco Farm. A sergeant in the front line had his leg crushed by the blowing in of a dug-out, and Captain Burke found immediate amputation necessary. In order to save time he crawled across the open to get his instruments, while the enemy turned a machine gun on him. In spite of their fire he returned the same way, and coolly performed the operation in the trench while the enemy were shelling it heavily."

Irishmen do not do things according to precedent. Chary of its honorary degrees, the Irish College, though it has been known to give its honors *in absentia*, has never before, so far as I am aware, sent delegates to another country to confer them. . . . It is my privilege to introduce to you Sir William Taylor and Sir Robert Woods, of the Royal College of Surgeons in Ireland.

Sir William Taylor then asked that Sir Robert Woods be permitted to take the chair that he might confer fellowships upon George

E. Brewer (New York), George W. Crile (Cleveland), John M. T. Finney (Baltimore), Richard H. Harte (Philadelphia), William W. Keen (Philadelphia), Charles H. Mayo and William J. Mayo (Rochester, Minn.), and Albert J. Ochsner (Chicago). "It is only right and proper," Sir Robert said, "that nations which have a common heritage in language, institutions, customs, and sympathies, and which are actuated by the same high ideals of love of liberty and justice should do honor to each other and I do not believe there is a place on the habitable surface of the globe so appropriate for such a function as this city of Philadelphia."[11] It was a stirring occasion and Cushing's remarks evidently made a deep impression, for he was promptly elected president of the American College of Surgeons for the following year.

The remainder of 1921 was largely given over to operating by day and writing the 'Osler' by night.

1922

During 1922 Cushing avoided public appearances almost as conscientiously as he had the preceding year. Again he declined some sixteen invitations to speak before various medical societies and he devoted at least half of his time to the 'Osler.' He had spent a few days at New Year's with Mrs. Cushing visiting friends at Williamstown. Apart from this his calendar for January and February was almost fully clear, and his Osler file reveals that he had sent out dozens of letters enquiring about the later period of Osler's life. The manuscript of the biography was well blocked out, and he had by now settled on the major chapter subdivisions.

Gask's sojourn in 1921 as Surgeon-in-Chief *pro tem* had been so successful that another distinguished English surgeon, Sir Cuthbert Wallace, was invited this year, and once again the staff was immensely stimulated by a fresh and original approach to surgical problems. When inviting Sir Cuthbert, H.C. remarked, "Mind you, there are no great professors over here; we are all students, and trying to learn together, and you will see many bad things and possibly a few good things about our system."

Sir Cuthbert, Professor of Surgery and Dean at St. Thomas's Hospital Medical School in London, was another friend of the war years who represented the best traditions of British medicine. Like Gask he was an excellent diagnostician, and it was most healthy for American medical students and house officers to have brought home to them the importance of depending upon their five physical senses in arriving at a diagnosis rather than upon X-rays and clinical

[11] "Remarks at conferring of honorary fellowships in the Royal College of Surgeons in Ireland." *Surgery, Gynecology and Obstetrics*, December 1921, *33*, 707-708.

technicians. Sir Cuthbert was a man of great directness and he took the view that our students were coddled into intellectual lethargy by instruments of precision. When he left, he presented the Brigham surgical staff with a silver cup which came to be known as the Sir Cuthbert Wallace Interhospital Tennis Trophy. In 1926 Clarence Bird, the Surgical Resident, reported:

> While preparing this season's schedule for the Interhospital Tennis Matches, it occurred to me that you would be pleased to know just what you "started" when you gave the "Sir Cuthbert Wallace Interhospital Tennis Trophy" in 1922. The competition is now a yearly fixture and never fails to arouse much interest. The Brigham won in 1922, 1923, and 1924. It then became a question as to whether or not the hospital had earned permanent possession; whether, if not, the cup should be perpetual; and, if another hospital won, whether or not they should be allowed to take it away for a year to grace their table. There were strong voices on both sides of these questions. Finally Dr. Cushing came to the rescue by providing a *new* cup exactly like the original. We called it "The Sir Cuthbert Wallace Interhospital Tennis Trophy, No. 2" and put it up for competition last summer. The Massachusetts General Hospital won the first leg and is in possession of the new trophy for the present, while we keep the first cup. We are planning, of course, to have *both* for our use next winter!

During the winter two most attractive invitations had come to give lectures abroad and, since a trip to Europe would afford further opportunity for collection of Osler material, he promptly accepted, and he and Mrs. Cushing crossed on the *Mauretania,* leaving New York on 20 May. These trips abroad, which from now on were made almost every year, provided an escape from the incessant demands made on him. He was not, however, one who relaxed on a boat, especially when lectures were to be given on arrival in Europe; but the trip enabled him to work without interruption. This year his first commitment was a lecture in Paris on the syndromes of the pituitary which was presented for him in French by Percival Bailey at the *IIIe Réunion Neurologique Internationale.* It was an elaborate paper which had been translated for him by Paul Martin, the young Belgian neurosurgeon who had spent the winter as a Rockefeller Fellow in Cushing's clinic.

Once again he presented the statistics of his brain tumor series. To May 1922 he had had 780 cases of verified tumor, of which 154 were pituitary adenomas, *i.e.,* approximately 20 per cent. He listed the congenital cysts of the pituitary separately; of these he had had 35 cases, which brought the total of pituitary lesions to 25 per cent. From now on, through his associate, Louise Eisenhardt, Cushing kept his tumor figures up to date so that at any given time he was able to ascertain quickly how his percentages were running and what his mortality rates were for any given type of lesion. For the next ten years he occupied himself with trying to beat his own score. His over-all mortality rate for every type of tumor was still between 9 and 10 per cent. By 1931 he had reduced it to 6.8 per cent.

His paper had been presented on 3 June. That evening a large banquet was given at Restaurant Marguery which brought together many outstanding students of the nervous system: Joseph Babinski, one of the foremost French neurologists, Monrad-Krohn of Oslo, Viggo Christiansen from Copenhagen, and Percival Bailey, Cushing's brilliant young assistant who was spending a year in the clinic of Pierre Marie.

The Cushings crossed a day or two later to London, where H.C. was made a "Perpetual Student" of St. Bartholomew's Hospital and reciprocated by taking over the surgical service at Bart's for a fortnight for Mr. Gask who had been his guest the year before. When H.C. received the invitation he had written: "Coming as I do, from one of the newest hospitals in this country to one of the oldest in England, I look forward with the greatest interest and pleasure to my sojourn with you." *The Lancet* took cognizance of the appointment in the following comment:

> Professor G. E. Gask deputised at Harvard in the spring of 1921, and Sir Cuthbert Wallace has just returned from filling a similar office. Although recognized as the leading neurological surgeon in the world, Professor Cushing did not operate while he was in this country but spent his time in observing methods of instruction, talking to students, and teaching in the out-patient and casualty departments of the hospital. His association with British surgeons during the war and the knowledge then acquired of the ways and manners of British sick and wounded made it possible for him to enter at once fully into the life of an English hospital. . . . It would be interesting to know what impression the great American surgeon formed from his intimate visit here. At all events he has left a pleasant impression behind him.

The Lancet in its report of the dinner of the West London Medico-Chirurgical Society on 7 June given in Cushing's honor says: "The health of the Cavendish lecturer, Prof. Harvey Cushing, was proposed by Sir Arthur Keith in a brilliant dinner speech. No man, he said, was better fitted to cement the brotherhood of the medical professions in the two great English-speaking countries than Prof. Cushing."

Cushing was at his best the night of the Cavendish Lecture. Lady Osler and Mrs. Cushing had come up from Oxford for the occasion, and Mr. Donald Armour, the well-known London neurosurgeon, gave a small dinner beforehand. H.C., who had at long last learned the ways of the British as far as formal dress was concerned, made a concession and appeared immaculately clad in 'tails' and a white tie—Lady Osler's influence no doubt, for Mrs. Cushing had long since despaired of ever persuading him to dress properly for a ceremonial occasion.

The meningiomas are a special group of tumors which had engaged Cushing's interest since 1895. His early success in removing such a tumor from General Wood had stirred him, and he had planned, prior to the war, to bring out a monograph on this group of tumors. But from a pathological standpoint they proved to be confusing and he did not bring himself to make a general presentation on the subject until 1922. The Cavendish Lecture, which was enthusiastically received in the British medical press, introduced the term 'meningioma' (formerly 'dural endothelioma') and the term has had almost universal adoption. As was usual with Cushing's papers, the manuscript was profusely illustrated and the journal *Brain,* in which it was published (and which was still suffering from wartime shortages), omitted a number of his figures (and, in H.C.'s opinion, reproduced the others badly), with the result that he had the paper entirely reprinted on his return. H.C. was ever the despair of journal editors and printers; he insisted on using his own conventions and was impatient to a degree if for any reason his preferences were not followed. He was especially fastidious about illustrative matter and few engravers were able to satisfy him.

Following Cushing's example, several of his pupils had begun to publish their operative statistics on brain tumors. The first report of this character, from Heuer and Dandy, appeared in 1916;[12] 62 of their 70 cases were operated upon with a case mortality of 12.8 per cent, but none of the tumors had been removed in its entirety, and only 24 of the 62 were listed as having been improved by the procedure. This was a candid report, and since Cushing followed the publications of his pupils with close scrutiny, he promptly wrote Heuer (10 Aug. 1916) a friendly letter. With his pupils he was quick to praise when he felt that it was due and at times was even overgenerous; but he did not hesitate to criticize, or even to rebuke if he thought someone had strayed or had not given due credit to those who had preceded him. At times H.C. seemed jealous of his own priority, and several who had had difficulties while on his service have insisted that he could not face serious competition. This contention perhaps had a basis, since in his younger days he had candidly stated that he had set out to lead the field of brain surgery. Now and again he offered brusque criticism when it would have been wiser and more dignified to remain quiet. Such is an unfortunate letter written to Walter Dandy in 1922 commenting on a preliminary report on total extirpation of acoustic nerve tumors.[13] Cushing

[12] Heuer, G. J. and Dandy, W. E. "A report of seventy cases of brain tumor." *Johns Hopkins Hospital Bulletin,* 1916, *27,* 224-237.

[13] Dandy, W. E. "An operation for the total extirpation of tumors in the cerebellopontine angle. A preliminary report." *Johns Hopkins Hospital Bulletin,* September 1922, *33,* 344.

fancied that Dandy had deliberately avoided mention of the acoustic nerve monograph published in 1917 and that he was claiming for himself credit for an operative approach which H.C. had first fully described in 1917. Dandy was naturally much offended by the accusation and took the reasonable position that in a preliminary note it was not customary to cite the literature and that he had merely wished to emphasize that total extirpation of acoustic nerve tumors was possible by the Cushing approach (up to that time Cushing and his followers had not attempted anything beyond a subtotal intracapsular extirpation). Dandy subsequently reported upon his individual cases[14] in detail, but he never forgave his preceptor for this unexpected rebuke.[15]

It is regrettable that such a feeling of bitterness should have grown up between these two distinguished contributors to the advancement of neurosurgery. Dandy at this time had introduced the useful diagnostic procedure of ventriculography, which for many years Cushing was loath to adopt because he felt that it would discourage neurosurgeons from becoming adequately trained as neurologists and from doing their own neurological examinations.[16] Dandy has also been responsible for other innovations. Whereas Cushing was always conservative, as far as brain tumor removals were concerned, Dandy believed that more radical measures could be safely undertaken, as is exemplified by his attempts at total removal of acoustic nerve tumors. Dandy also developed, in 1928, a lateral approach for acoustic nerve tumors which was quicker and much less arduous than H.C.'s bilateral cerebellar approach.

[14] Dandy, Walter E. "An operation for the total removal of cerebellopontile angle (acoustic) tumors." *Surgery, Gynecology and Obstetrics,* August 1925, *41,* 129-148.

[15] There can be no doubt that Cushing's reproach of Dr. Dandy was uncalled for, but it had been carefully considered since the files disclose an unsent letter of 13 September 1922 in which H.C. wrote: "I think there is only one possible way to justify yourself . . . and that is to publish in the *Bulletin* your complete series of acoustic tumors and to give your operative results." On the 25th he eventually sent to Dandy direct a letter he had intended for the Editor of the *Bulletin* to which he appended a handwritten note to Dandy making reference to bad taste, bad manners, and the importance of a "high plane of professional ethics." Dandy in a letter of 29 September (also unsent) wrote: "Doubtless I should feel a keen resentment, but I do not; I feel very sorry for one who is laboring under such an obsession, and particularly since it is one to whom I should now be feeling the deepest debt of gratitude and upon whom I should look with the greatest adoration and should consider my friend, guide, and master." Eventually, on 20 October, Dr. Dandy sent a restrained acknowledgment expressing regret that Dr. Cushing felt as he did. [Prior to his death on 19 April 1946 Dr. Dandy had read this section of the manuscript and had made available his complete file of letters from Dr. Cushing.]

[16] On 12 May 1922 Cushing wrote Dandy: "I was glad that you brought the ventriculography matter before the Neurological Association, and hope you didn't feel that we were too critical. It has been an important contribution, but you must be very careful not to overdo it, lest you make people expect too much of it, for under these circumstances it is likely to get a black eye. With this friendly advice, I remain, Always most sincerely yours."

Although Cushing was regarded as conservative by many of his colleagues, one finds that there was usually good reason for many of his cautious tendencies. One of his earliest complete removals had been the tumor of General Wood, but many other similar successes followed, as described in the Cavendish Lecture. Horrax writes: "It is likewise true that such tumors as the astrocytomatous cyst and the hemangiomatous cyst of the cerebellum, which we now take out completely by removing the mural nodule as well as evacuating the fluid from the cyst, were not tackled radically in those years [1911-1912] whereas subsequent to 1920 or thereabouts they were shown by Dr. Cushing to be capable of complete removal. On the other hand, at the Peter Bent Brigham Hospital from June of 1913 up to the time of the first World War, I can remember the complete extirpation of many meningiomas, particularly those, of course, which involved the motor area and gave rise to Jacksonian convulsions." As far as acoustic tumors go, Horrax adds: "Certainly after coming to Boston he very soon began to do extremely radical intracapsular extirpations, much more so, in fact, than any neurological surgeons elsewhere were doing at that time and with infinitely better results."

After the Cavendish Lecture the Cushings sailed the 14th of June on the *Samaria,* but the ship broke down two days out of Liverpool and they were obliged to return to port. After a few days at Oxford they sailed again, this time on the *Laconia,* and arrived in Boston on 30 June. Mrs. Cushing, as usual, spent the summer at Little Boar's Head, and H.C. had three months, almost without interruption, to work on the biography.

In October we find him again at Montreal, this time to help dedicate the new biological building at McGill. It proved a particularly pleasant occasion, for the other principal speaker was Sir Charles Sherrington. H.C. reminisced in some detail about Osler's years at McGill and his insistence upon the development of both preclinical and clinical laboratories. "Osler," he said, "pleaded for the introduction into the hospital of methods comparable to those so rapidly coming into use in most preclinical laboratories—of practical work at the bedside to replace the time-honored system of lectures. He had inaugurated this program at the Johns Hopkins where the students had been put intimately to work on the wards, and he was vigorously urging the same revolutionary procedure upon the New York Hospital. What he accomplished in this direction is well enough known, but that he had previously and for the first time here at McGill striven to give the undergraduate students an equally intimate first-hand knowledge of medical sciences . . . has been largely forgotten." Sir Charles, who was then president of the Royal Society of London, brought greetings from Burlington House; he also went out of his way to make gracious reference to Cushing. "I cannot," he said, "avoid envisaging these biological sciences . . . from the aspect of their bearing upon medicine, . . . including under that comprehensive term surgery and all branches of the healing art—medicine as it is represented by its eminent exponent Dr. Harvey Cushing . . . in whom we recognize a great surgeon and, at the same time, a physician unsurpassed in his own field."

At the end of the month H.C. was involved for nearly a week in a meeting of the American College of Surgeons, of which he was president. This entailed two addresses; the first his presidential discourse, "The physician and the surgeon," in which he expanded upon the old theme originally developed in his "Realignments" address in 1913. He opened his speech with an apt paragraph from Gilbertus Anglicus beginning, "Why, in God's name, in our days is there such a great difference between the physician and surgeon?" Cushing then proceeded to shake a metaphorical finger at his audience—the substance of his theme might be paraphrased: 'Be not carpenters and barbers doing the bidding of other men (the physicians), be a physician in your own right, make your own diagnoses. Any surgeon who operates on the basis of another man's diagnosis has no claim to be a practitioner of the healing art.' He ended this spirited address with a brief passage from the 13th century surgeon, Lanfranc: "No one can be a good physician who has no idea of surgical operation, and the surgeon is nothing if ignorant of medicine. In a word, one must be familiar with both departments of Medicine."[17] In his second paper, on surgical end-results,[18] a vigorous plea was made for an adequate system of follow-up, so that statistics concerning the effectiveness of any particular procedure might be comparable from one clinic to another.

In the course of the meetings H.C. again had occasion, on behalf of the Boston Surgical Society, to present the Bigelow Medal, this time to his old friend, W. W. Keen, who was then in his eighty-fifth year. He described Keen as "an institution," and continued:

> The institution to which I refer has been distinguished from the outset for its patriotism; and its first official act as long ago as 1861 was the loan to the Fifth Massachusetts Regiment, and so to the Nation, of an assistant surgeon. Soon after it came into existence, the same institution established an editorial and publishing bureau, and since the first appearance in print in 1864 of a medical classic entitled 'Gunshot wounds and other injuries of the nerves,' there has followed a series of essays, monographs and volumes of no less interest and importance. It has given to the profession a succession of teachers in anatomy and surgery in more than one school of medicine—demonstrators, lecturers,

[17] "The physician and the surgeon." *Boston Medical and Surgical Journal,* 2 November, 1922, *187,* 623-630. Also: *Surgery, Gynecology, and Obstetrics,* December 1922, *35,* 701-710.

[18] "Surgical end-results in general, with a case of cavernous haemangioma of the skull in particular." *Surgery, Gynecology, and Obstetrics,* March 1923, *36,* 303-308.

professors, and even a professor emeritus—so that its pupils have been legion. When that most unpromising of all specialties, the surgery of the nervous system, needed an optimistic pioneer, it was called upon to furnish one. . . . Accordingly to you, Sir, to you as an American institution, to you who already stand knee-deep in honors, in all affection and with all humbleness, in the name of the Boston Surgical Society, and by its direction, I present still another award, the Henry Jacob Bigelow Medal, highly deserved not only for your accomplishments and services to medicine, but for that which means more than these—for that more enduring quality—your professional character.

By way of winding up his week, H.C. took Keen as his guest to the Saturday Club.

It had been a strenuous week, but his efforts did not pass unappreciated as a letter a few days later from Franklin H. Martin, director of the College, indicated:

I cannot allow another day to pass without thanking you from the bottom of my heart for your aid in making the Clinical Congress of the American College of Surgeons the high-water-mark success which it proved to be. . . . I have heard many very commendatory remarks about the smoothness and artistic beauty of the Convocation program on Friday evening. Of course I am aware what a strain it was for you to have upon your shoulders the distraction of the Presidency of this meeting while playing the stellar role in the clinical program, delivering three public addresses at the evening sessions, and being generally responsible for a great congress. However, I cannot regret that it was as it was, and I thank you for your generous aid in our work. . . .

Earlier in the month William Halsted had died in Baltimore, and H.C. had gone down to be of any possible help to those who, like himself, had become very devoted to the shy, withdrawn "Professor." On his return he wrote a discerning appreciation[19] which he sent to *Science* with characteristic promptness. It is clear that after ten years Cushing had come to appreciate Halsted much more than he had during his years under him in Baltimore.

On 16 November 1922 H.C. was called upon to officiate at the opening of the Nurses' Home at the University of Maryland. On this ceremonial occasion he paid tribute to a gallant woman, Louisa Parsons, first superintendent of nurses in the University of Maryland Hospital.

. . . Those who remember her say that she was a woman who would immediately be singled out as a person of distinction, a woman of charming manner, with a pleasant voice and the brilliant complexion of a gipsy, a woman who loved animals, who was always found doing something for someone else; but a woman of determination, prompt of action, knowing no indecision; a woman, moreover, who appears to have been capable of instilling in others because of her unselfishness, modesty, and charm, such a devotion toward herself as she in turn gave to those in need of her professional care. Of such a disciple Florence Nightingale

[19] "William Stewart Halsted, 1852-1922." *Science*, 27 October 1922, *56*, 461-464. Also: *Proceedings of the American Academy of Arts and Sciences*, September 1923, *58*, 599-604.

might well have been proud, and of her as well as of her famous prototype Longfellow's lines might have been written:

As if a door in heaven should be
Opened and then closed suddenly,
The vision came and went,
The light shone and was spent.

A Lady with a Lamp shall stand
In the great history of the land,
A noble type of good,
Heroic womanhood.

* * * * *

The end of the month found him in New Haven as usual for the Harvard-Yale game. In December he went out to St. Louis for a meeting of the Society of Neurological Surgeons, and on returning, on 19 December, he presided at a meeting of the Harvard Medical Society. In November, he had written a characteristic note to Henry R. Viets: "Let's get up a Gasserian meeting with your paper as a leader, to be followed by someone else on herpes and encephalitis, and perhaps thirdly, a Gasserian operation and its end-result talk. What do you say?" Jonas Friedenwald of Baltimore spoke on herpes, and the meeting was evidently a great success.

In Baltimore there had been much agitation about a successor to Halsted. On 7 December 1922 Lewis Weed telephoned to Cushing to say that a Hopkins committee, consisting of W. G. MacCallum, Warfield T. Longcope, J. M. T. Finney, and himself, had voted unanimously to nominate H.C. as Halsted's successor. There was to have been a faculty meeting the following day and Cushing, with greater promptness than usual in such circumstances, wired immediately that he could not possibly face another transplantation. There were a number of letters exchanged, but his decision was final. The war had prevented him from getting his clinic into full swing and he now had his opportunity to develop the Brigham surgical service as he wished.

1923

The centenary of Louis Pasteur's birth fell on 27 December 1922. The turn of the year was therefore a period in which Pasteur celebrations were held throughout the world, and nowhere did the great French savant appear to be more keenly appreciated than in the United States. On 18 December 1922 Cushing had spoken on Pasteur, along with L. J. Henderson and M. J. Rosenau, at a meeting of the Boston Medical History Club. On this occasion Malcolm Storer exhibited his remarkable collection of Pasteur medals. The principal celebration, however, was held by the Harvard Medical Society on 8 January 1923, and Cushing had gone to great trouble in arranging it. Charles Eliot, who was then in his ninetieth year, was to have attended but inclement weather prevented, and his challenging paper entitled "Pasteur as a democrat" was read in his absence by Cushing and was later published.[20] This, the last published work of the great American educator, concluded:

> Pasteur was an intense patriot. To have added something to the honor and wealth of his country through his successful researches was his chief reward. He never forgave the Germans for cutting off Alsace and part of Lorraine from France. He declined a degree from Bonn University, and refused to become a member of the Berlin Academy. In him love of country and love of family and friends were so commingled that they seemed one. Together they supplied the leading motives of a consecrated life.

Other details of the meeting are given in the same issue of the *Journal:*

> . . . On this occasion Dr. Harvey Cushing delivered an address in which matters of interest relating to Pasteur's forebears and the region of Franche Comté, where Pasteur was born, were spoken of, and showed pictures of Salins, Besançon, Arbois, Dôle and other places which were associated with the Pasteurs. Dr. Simon Flexner of New York gave a review of Pasteur's more important scientific contributions to the knowledge of fermentation, infectious diseases and immunity. Dr. Lawrence Henderson spoke of Pasteur as a chemist and Dr. S. B. Wolbach showed some original glassware such as that which Pasteur had used in his earlier experiments disproving spontaneous generation. This glassware had been brought from France by Dr. Sturgis Bigelow, an early pupil of this great scientist who had become an expert glass-blower, this technique of Dr. Bigelow being one of the factors which gave him entrée into Pasteur's laboratory.

The reference to Sturgis Bigelow and Pasteur is of great interest and deserves to be more widely known. Bigelow had told Cushing that when he first went to Pasteur's laboratory, Pasteur asked him what he could do and he modestly said that he had no special skills, that he was merely a graduate of the Harvard Medical School. Pasteur declined to receive him. Bigelow had noticed during his long wait to see Pasteur that his assistants were making miserable work of their glass blowing. Bigelow thereupon apprenticed himself to a glass blower and returned to Pasteur a few months later saying, "Now, Monsieur, I can blow glass," and Pasteur promptly accepted him. When Bigelow returned to Boston he found that his father, Henry Jacob, was so opposed to the new teaching of Pasteur and Lister that there was no opportunity to develop antiseptic surgery. After persevering for a year at the M.G.H., he gave up and went to Japan where he remained for seven years, meanwhile being converted to northern Buddhism. Such was the conservatism of Boston and the M.G.H. in the 1870's—and with strange irony Sturgis Bigelow in 1915 established a medal in honor of a father for whom he could have had little professional respect.

There was another interesting facet to the Pasteur celebrations.

[20] *Boston Medical and Surgical Journal,* 1923, *188,* 138-140.

In preparing his paper Mr. Eliot had found a statement of H.C.'s to which he took exception in a letter of 10 January 1923: "I have just read," Eliot wrote, "an alleged quotation from an address by you before the American College of Surgeons last October—'and after all the strength of a profession, as of a nation, is represented by its average product.' I think I agree with Pasteur rather than with you on that subject. He said that it was the élite of a nation which determined its present status and its place in history. See, for example, the leaders of the Pilgrim Fathers, Benjamin Franklin and the patriot leaders of the American Revolution, Abraham Lincoln, and U. S. Grant in the Civil War, and the solitary Woodrow Wilson in the Great War." This evoked one of the most interesting and significant letters in Cushing's voluminous files; it is a genuine *confessio fidei,* illustrating not only his basic faith in the democratic way of life, but also his idealism, which was combined with an undercurrent of cynicism—"the doctor of the old school is largely replaced by the chiropractor, and our average citizen hardly knows the difference."

H.C. to Charles W. Eliot *13 January 1923.*

Dear Mr. Eliot: Thank you so much for your letter of January 10th. I will send it to the *Journal* and will ask them to send you the galley proof. It is the best picture of the man that I have read among the many things that have been recently published concerning him. . . . Lawrence Henderson, as you know, is not a great admirer of what seemed to have been Pasteur's kind of mind. However, he had put a great deal of thought upon his paper, and I shall look forward to seeing it when it is published, for he gave merely an abstract of what he had already presented before the Philosophical Society, I believe, in Philadelphia. . . . I have just returned from a meeting in New York at which Chittenden, Welch, Biggs, Flexner and W. W. Keen all spoke, and the New York Academy had collected a most interesting lot of Pasteuriana, among them his medals and many of his original color sketches, including those of his father and mother. They are really admirable—much better than I had supposed they would be in view of his youth at the time they were made. I think his artistic bent must have had a good deal to do with his imagination in research as well. The ability to pictorialize often, I think, goes hand in hand with research imagination.

Of all the speakers in New York, no doubt Dr. Keen took the palm, for though Welch was more eloquent than I have heard him for some time, nevertheless Dr. Keen did better I think than any of them. His address I presume will be published, for most of the others spoke more or less extemporaneously. There was a representative from the Pasteur Institute there and one of Pasteur's old pupils, Laplace of Philadelphia, had a flask containing bouillon which Pasteur himself had sealed forty years ago, and which was as clear today as when it had been originally sealed. There were some amusing incidents too. Dr. Keen, the last speaker, related that he had already attended four Pasteur meetings at which a number of people had spoken, and he was now so thoroughly 'Pasteurized' that he felt he would last a good while.

You have spoken about something you saw in the *Harvard Alumni Bulletin* which was quoted from me. I am sending you a copy of the original address, and though I am not particularly proud of it, I don't wish to be misquoted. Certainly as far as Pasteur is concerned, he stands, as you say, easily first as a contributor to the progress of medicine, and I know full well that he himself was an admirer of great men, as I think perhaps all of us are. Still, you will see from the context of the address just what I was driving at, namely that without the Jean Josephs, which constitute France to my thinking, the Louis Pasteurs would not be possible, nor would they be appreciated. So the patriot leaders of the American Revolution were made possible by the character of the people behind them—so, too, the leaders in the Civil War. And I fear that possibly the average American today is not quite of the same fine quality as in those times, for otherwise the solitary Mr. Wilson, as you call him, might have had a greater following—that is all I meant. In medicine we have a few really eminent men—Theobald Smith is one, for example, but the average product in spite of our efforts is low. The doctor of the old school is largely replaced by the chiropractor, and our average citizen hardly knows the difference.

Pasteur of course was fortunate in his biographer, and that has made him widely known, but this is by no means the chief reason why he is the idol of France, and I doubt very much whether in this country we would have discovered him so quickly as the French did. . . .

Mr. Eliot, in a three-page reply, avoided the point at issue—whether the élite or the quality of the common man determined the greatness of a nation—and launched into a most interesting discussion of the future of medical education, arising out of his perusal of H.C.'s address, "The physician and the surgeon." Two significant paragraphs may be quoted:

. . . Now I entirely agree with you that the first two years need more clinical teaching over the sick and wounded, and that the ordinary practitioner should be able to make all of the common diagnostic examinations himself in independence of hospitals, dispensaries, or commercial laboratories; but it does seem to me absolutely necessary that the medical school should also somehow train men of highest skill in all the diagnostic processes including many which the ordinary practitioner cannot be expected to perform. I see no way to make the School train these two different sorts of graduates without increasing largely the total outlay on the Medical School. Individual instruction is already carried to an extreme in the School and this teaching of the individual has increased enormously the cost of conducting the Medical School during the last twenty-five years. Massachusetts is not ready to make large annual appropriations of money raised by taxation for the support of any professional school, least of all, of the Harvard Medical School.

In your address you showed how hard it is in these times for a man to be really familiar with both medicine and surgery. It is even harder to plan the programs of a medical school so that it can produce both physicians who are well acquainted with surgical operations, and surgeons who have a thorough knowledge of medicine. Yet the school of the future ought to be so conducted that the highly trained young physician, whom you mention on page 12 [of the address], would not be able to say after his summer's experience on an island where there was no local physician, "Never before had his powers of observation and his common sense been so thoroughly exercised." Sincerely yours, CHARLES W. ELIOT.[21]

[21] Mr. Eliot died on 22 August 1926 in the ninety-third year of his age.

Again in 1923 Cushing managed to keep his slate clear, and since it had become known that he would not commit himself to speaking engagements, fewer invitations came, and this year we find record of only fourteen refusals. He was also tending to devote more time to the students, as is indicated by the introduction in 1922-1923 of the Saturday morning clinics for first-year students. Students and house officers of that vintage have recalled many episodes that illustrate both his capacities as a teacher and the preëminently human qualities which characterized his relations with patients, particularly the indigent. Arthur W. Wright recalls:

The same great simplicity which made Dr. Cushing so beloved by all of us was manifested again during the time I was on his service as a fourth-year student in surgery. A young Jewish school teacher was brought to the Peter Bent Brigham Hospital by her mother and brother. She had a cerebellar tumor. The family could not afford a private room for the patient and she was placed in a ward. There she was assigned to me for the usual student clinical work-up. In those days Dr. Cushing had a young assistant who was the very essence of impersonal efficiency. He was cold, stern, rather quick-tempered, and lacked that sympathetic understanding of patients which his chief had. One day, the last which her family could spend in Boston, the patient's brother asked the assistant if he could meet and talk briefly to Dr. Cushing about his sister before he left for home. "Oh, no," said the young doctor. "Your sister, you know, is only a ward patient and Dr. Cushing is much too busy to give you any time."

The mother and brother, sentimental Hebrew folk, were in despair. They came to me, the junior doctor, to talk tearfully about the necessity of leaving before their loved one was operated upon and without seeing Dr. Cushing. I was so disturbed that, rather boldly I suppose, I went directly to Dr. Cushing who happened to be in his office. He received me as if I were a colleague on his staff, listened to what I had to say and replied, "Why, Wright, I am never too busy to see members of a patient's family, no matter who the patient is. Tell her brother *and* her mother to come down here immediately and I will be glad to see them now." They came into his office quite overcome by the promptness with which he was willing to see them. Dr. Cushing talked with them, quietly, sympathetically, and hopefully. It was a study to watch them. As he talked I could see the look of despair vanish and one of hopefulness take its place. They left greatly encouraged and so full of wholehearted affection for the great surgeon that they could find no words to express their feelings.

Wright also tells of another incident:

During my third year my father happened to pass through Boston and came out to the medical school to visit me. He arrived just before I was to go to a surgical clinic in the amphitheatre at the Peter Bent Brigham Hospital. On the spur of the moment I asked him to go with me. Father is not a physician but had always been interested in medicine, so I gave little thought to the possibility that he might be upset by what he saw.

Into the amphitheatre he went, apparently not disturbed at the prospect of hearing a surgeon discuss his cases. The first patient to be shown, however, was a man whose leg had recently been amputated at the knee. Dr. Cushing, to show the operative result, exposed the healing stump to the class. The sight proved too much for Father and he promptly fainted. Some of my classmates and I brought him to very quickly but Dr. Cushing, noticing the little commotion in his audience, came up immediately to see if Father were seriously ill. I naturally was embarrassed and apologized for unwittingly being responsible for the disturbance which had upset his clinic. But Dr. Cushing made light of the interruption, took Father gently and sympathetically by the arm, helped him down the aisle and out of the amphitheatre to his office which was not far away. There he was most considerate. He examined Father briefly and, finding nothing seriously wrong, had him lie down on a couch in his office and bade me keep him there until he returned.

Father's indisposition fortunately was very temporary and he was soon quite normal but we waited for Dr. Cushing. When he returned he was again the same sympathetic, very genuine, hospitable person who made Father, naturally a retiring and diffident man, feel very much at home. We then had a brief, informal, and long-to-be-remembered visit with that great surgeon. My father has never forgotten Dr. Cushing. Today he recalls with pleasure and a certain understandable embarrassment his own visit with a sympathetic, understanding, and very human man.

H.C. remarked repeatedly that he considered the third-year students a most critical audience and he felt he must take great pains over the planning of the clinical exercise. This is borne out by W. M. Wishard, Jr., a third-year student at this time, who kept a notebook of "personal touches" in Cushing's clinics.

3 October 1923. Try to recall the patient's face in every instance and a general picture of the case.

[In case of popliteal aneurysm—referring to attempt to feel the post-tibial artery]: Try it on yourself so you will know where to find the artery.

[*Re* blood-vessel surgery]: Mistakes are often made . . . a house doctor ligated the femoral vein without killing the patient.

10 October. [*Re* diseases of the endocrine organs] The country is all excited over the latest fad and many of the physicians are as bad as the laity. . . . Voilà "The Gland Stealers." . . . it is for the medical student of today to keep his feet upon the ground (and to see that his teacher does the same) and calmly view the facts of this study.

21 November. [*Re* patient with gastric ulcer] Hard-working, law-abiding, porridge-eating, God-fearing Scot. . . . Good fellow and we want to help him. Fifty per cent of diagnosis in G-I disease lies in the history so get a good one.

19 December. [*Re* patient shown with varicose veins] This all reminds me of the recent examination in which a lady was asked to describe the circulation. She said that it 'consisted of two parts—the arterial and the venereal.' Never touch anything on an extremity until you see if there is any metastasis elsewhere.

[*Re* Case No. 3 shown] She is emaciated, pale, and looks ill. Hippocrates would have said she looked after his nomenclature. . . . What does Osler say about the limits of the abdomen? 'It is between wind and water, extending from the neck to the knees.' . . . Here is one of the trials and sorrows of Medicine. I do not know of anything that can be done.

21 January 1924. [*Re* Case 1 shown. Speaking of headaches] You can treat a large number of cases in a purely hygienic way. Have a little system of your own and tell your patients of it. They will often know these things without your telling them but the added weight of authority vested in you makes your advice then much more important.

23 January. This little case should show you the importance of little things; always investigate your colds. Never operate in the face of a coryza. Cure it first and find its cause.

28 January. As the opportunities for seeing fractures in this clinic are small I should advise you to look at the anatomical studies of fractured skulls in the Warren Museum. Whenever visiting other schools go through their museums; and when in Washington go through the Surgeon General's Museum.

30 January. Always remember the surgeon is responsible for what his assistants and nurses do [referring to a hot water bottle burn]. If a patient complains of pain from a dressing, remove it. Never give drugs for such pain.

20 February. The study of neurological cases is the same as any other: dig out the facts; be sure they are right; then assemble them. History is important toward diagnosis. After the diagnosis is made, try to visualize the lesion. In testing the sense of smell, don't use such things as vanilla, but test the patient with his own toilet articles with which he is familiar. [In another instance Dr. Cushing had explained: "Vanilla is good, but strong and may be unknown to that patient. Try them with familiar things such as their toothpaste or toilet soap. Test for both nostrils."]

The Harvard Medical Society had a particularly active year with meetings each month, all of them arranged personally by H.C., but he had now seen to it that a secretary was appointed each year and many of his junior house staff sought this privilege because, as Samuel A. Levine recalls, it gave the incumbent much more in the way of personal contact with "the Chief."

During the second week in April Sir Harold Stiles came from Edinburgh to serve as Surgeon-in-Chief *pro tem* at the same time that Dr. Lewis A. Conner of Columbia was serving as Physician-in-Chief. On 12 April a large dinner was arranged for the two honorary chiefs. Sir Harold's visit was pleasantly recalled in H.C.'s Annual Report several months later: "Sir Harold brought to us and implanted here some of the superb traditions of the Edinburgh School, in which he holds what may be regarded as the blue-ribbon position in British surgery—a post held before him in sequence by James Russell, Syme, Lister, and others. This visit established a bond between the Edinburgh School and our own which I trust will never be loosened; and Dr. [Francis] Newton on leaving for abroad carried with him to Edinburgh to present to Sir Harold a suitably inscribed piece of silver bearing the names of the devoted house officers who had served under him in Boston."

In many of Cushing's letters to junior staff members there are references to the importance of maintaining an *esprit de corps,* and in this connection he always stressed the value of attending reunions and of keeping up with the members of one's academic group, be it college, medical school, or hospital. It is not surprising, therefore, that he and Christian went to great trouble at the end of May 1923 to celebrate the tenth anniversary of the Brigham Hospital. Every staff member, past and present, was invited to attend, and a formidable three-day program of papers was arranged—the titles of which brought in almost every branch of clinical medicine and surgery. During the Brigham Decennial H.C. arranged for the unveiling of a tablet in commemoration of the work, in a wing of the Hospital, of the New England Surgical Dressings Committee. His address, "The Boston tins," recalled the gallant work in 1917 of a group of Boston women, headed by Mrs. Frederick S. Mead, in packing sterilized surgical dressings in tins at a time when supplies from the Red Cross and other sources were desperately short. He recalled also the difficulties which were encountered at the hands of the Red Cross, which fancied that the Boston committee was usurping its prerogatives. He might have recalled that New England women had done the same thing in the Civil War; indeed, the United States Sanitary Commission, established within a few days of Mr. Lincoln's first call for volunteers in 1861, was in large measure the result of the spontaneous response of the Mrs. Meads of 1861 in Massachusetts, Rhode Island, and Connecticut (incidentally the United States Sanitary Commission helped pave the way for the Red Cross movement). Cushing concluded his address:

> . . . A tablet cannot tell all, and it is to be hoped that some day the full story will come to be told in print, and the more precious of the documents relating to your organization filed where they can be accessible to the future historian of the Great War; for without reference to the part played by women, and by none more effectively and with finer *esprit* than by this group of some six thousand women of New England, who under the auspices of the National Civic Federation, worked to fill the Boston tins—a significant detail of such a history will be wanting.

Cushing had been elected president of the American Neurological Association in 1923 and he was obliged to give his presidential address in Boston a few days after the Brigham reunion. The Neurological Association had been made up largely of clinical neurologists and, while Cushing could hold his own in any branch of clinical neurology, the "old guard" in the Association tended to look upon neurosurgeons as interlopers, and the more senior neurologists had only just come to realize that neurosurgery had not only invaded the sacred precincts of clinical neurology, but had already begun to dominate it. Cushing was naïvely conscious of the fact that in large measure he was personally responsible for the ascendency of neurosurgery, and he took an autobiographical turn (from which earlier chapters of this biography have profited) by addressing the gathering on "Neurological surgeons: with the report of one case"[22]—himself.

[22] *Archives of Neurology and Psychiatry, Chicago,* October 1923, *10,* 381-390. Also: *Transactions of the American Neurological Association,* 1923, 1-10.

Before describing his own clinical history, however, he could not resist the following:

. . . That surgeons should have been admitted into this intimate guild now nearing its half-century of existence speaks well for the open-mindedness of its members. And if any of you had misgivings as to our acceptability here, on the basis that metaphysicians and artisans make an impossible social mixture, we can only hope that time will justify your action by our becoming through this contact better neurologists and your becoming more familiar than before with the possibility of handicraft as an increasingly dependable therapeutic measure for certain otherwise hopeless maladies. The fusion will be of benefit if for no other reason than that the balance sheets of surgery should periodically be audited by those not actually engaged in its practice.

He then went on with his reminiscences:

. . . The medical traditions of my forebears inclined me to the abnegating life of a family practitioner. To this I looked forward during my medical course in the early nineties; and I still think there is no more satisfactory or higher calling in medicine. But providence willed otherwise. As an undergraduate I had attended with no especial thrill what for the time must have been an excellent series of clinical exercises in neurology. I can recall, strangely enough, that in this course I saw for the first time a case of exophthalmic goiter, and another of acromegaly, and heard leontiasis ossea and sporadic cretinism discussed. But on the whole, the impression was gained that the diseases of the nervous system were obscure and included chiefly those maladies for which little could be done—maladies, in short, in which the profession as a whole showed little interest.

I had, to be sure, used as a text-book that admirable small treatise on nervous diseases written by Christiàn A. Herter, himself a victim of one of them; but this book was devoted purely to diagnosis and we students were given no opportunity to study thoroughly for ourselves and to examine from day to day an individual patient with a nervous disorder. Furthermore, we gathered from our remote position on the benches that treatment could be summed up under bromids, iodids, electricity, and the asylum.

Such minor operations as were recommended were largely orthopedic in nature, and though the skull might often enough be trephined for fractures, I saw as a hospital intern in surgery only one operation that I remember for an organic lesion of the brain. A patient with Jacksonian epilepsy having a "march" involving the upper extremity was sent into the hospital for operation, by the professor of neurology. After repeated craniocerebral measurements the situation of the chief fissures was marked with an indelible pencil on the shaven scalp, the precise spot overlying the center whence movements of the thumb were presumed to originate being indicated by a cross. At this spot the surgeon, into whose service the case had come, was expected to trephine, and on the eventful day, through a stellate incision he removed a button of bone about an inch in diameter. A discussion ensued as to whether the tense dura which had been exposed should be incised, a step which was finally taken without disclosing a recognizable lesion. This negative finding was looked on as rather a joke on the neurologist, who, poor man, had assumed the entire responsibility, and there seemed no reason for any further surgical interest in the matter.

This was a typical example of surgery made to order, a relic of medievalism in medicine brought down to the end of the nineteenth century. To every onlooker the only way to avoid such an impasse must have been obvious. Either the surgeon would have to take greater interest in the problem through familiarizing himself with the brain and its diseases, or the neurologist would have to learn enough surgery to do the operation himself. It is not entirely clear which of these eventualities has been responsible for the changes time has brought about.

H.C. had many reactions to his address; Weisenburg and others grumbled, but Frederick Tilney, a neurologist of the old school who had broader vision than most, wrote him a few days later in most enthusiastic terms:

Now that the meeting is so successfully over and one can view it all in retrospect, I think it can be said in all honesty that it was the best meeting of the American Neurological Association in many a long year. I am not at all sure that it was not the most successful in the history of the Association, at least in many respects. Of the long past meetings, I cannot speak from experience, but certainly within my memory we never gathered under more pleasant circumstances, we never were treated with more gracious hospitality, and there never has been that pervading sense of unity and good fellowship which you instilled into our gathering. If a humble secretary is entitled to express an opinion, I would say that you were, far and away, the best presiding officer who has crossed my path.

And now that you have had your hand upon the helm in directing the fortunes of this important society, I sincerely trust that your interest will continue to direct its activities to the even higher possibilities which, it seems to me, lie before it. Not a few men have expressed the view that the American Neurological Association should in time become one of the great leaders in fostering the public health, in supervising education and in giving guidance in all those matters which pertain so intimately to human development and a more profitable kind of human existence. . . .

In July the Committee seeking a successor for the chair of surgery in Cleveland which Crile was relinquishing wrote to say that H.C. would be nominated for the post unanimously if he would name the conditions under which he would accept. This was the third invitation he had had to return to Cleveland (and there was to be one more), and it evoked a carefully worded reply, only a brief portion of which is given herewith:

H.C. to Charles F. Hoover *25 July 1923.*

. . . It is a wrench at my heart strings to have to say no, particularly as I would rejoice to be again in the home of my forebears, working as Father and Ned did, for the welfare of the Western Reserve School, but there is an old adage that it is easier to refuse in the beginning than in the end, so I shall have to beg of you not to press me in this proposal.

I need not say that nothing could have pleased me more than that you should have expressed a wish for me to come, but I know far better than you what are my present limitations. Leaving everything else aside, my age is a chief barrier, for at fifty-four I am pretty well set in my ways, and I do not believe that I would stand a transplantation at all well. . . .

I have watched this business of filling chairs now for many years, and am fully aware not only that people hold on to their posts longer than they should, but also that when new appointments are made it is a mistake to select anyone from the generation of the outgoing Chief. . . .

Look at what happened at the Hopkins in 1889—Welch, Osler, Halsted and Kelly, all under forty. It takes young men to do these things, and a faculty is apt to pull together best and longest when the men in the senior posts are all of approximately the same age. . . .

Could I only dispense with my spectacles and my gray hairs and my poor hind legs, the result of my polyneuritis in France, and thereby persuade myself that I was fifteen years younger, I would have wired you my acceptance on reading your letter this morning, instead of dictating to you this long screed of regret and explanation.

Three months later (18 Oct. 1923) the welfare of medicine in the Western Reserve was still engaging his interest, and his comments on the situation stand as a revealing and forthright statement of his own convictions:

I was perfectly staggered when Cutler told me that you were building a 1000-bed hospital. If that is the case, I would advise him strongly not to go near Cleveland, much as I would like to see him there on the job. What you want is a good 300-bed university hospital. Possibly 150 beds for medicine and another 150 for surgery are 25 too many, but still you could use these for the specialties and then have a big Out-Door Department as a feeder. If you do this, you will make a great name for yourselves and for Cleveland. If you have a whale of a hospital with a great private ward, you may do some good work for a lot of people, but as an academic institution nobody will ever hear anything of you. The other big hospitals would have to do the rest of the work, but it cannot be thrust on the shoulders of your teaching staff.

We have done pretty well here by the Brigham in ten years and I think already have an international reputation—that is, the *hospital* has the reputation, not Christian and myself, though of course we share in it. The hospital goes on forever, and we are only here for a few moments as far as the duration of its life is concerned. . . .

I may add for your information that we have a private ward of 38 rooms and there are at least 12 of us who do all of our private work there. I may perhaps have as many as ten private cases at a time, which is as many as I ought to have. I am not making a fortune out of it as I could if I went outside and catered to a big private clinic, but I am doing other things which I think are more important and far more interesting.

The remainder of the year slipped away with his chief occupation still being the 'Osler.' His literary pursuits were interrupted on 16 August by a formal decoration (Chevalier, Légion d'Honneur) which General Gouraud conferred upon him on behalf of the French government. H.C., who found humor in the serious occasion, describes the ceremony amusingly in a note the next day to Mr. Lowell:

It was a simple, brief and interesting ceremony. . . . There were some amusing episodes relating to my family. I had used Mrs. Cushing as a hatrack, as you may have observed, and meanwhile she had been called upon to produce a safety pin, an act she was endeavoring to perform when, much to her embarrassment, you called for her. I meanwhile was concentrating upon the General, wondering how with one hand the ribbon could be pinned on a coat—particularly when there was no pin. His resourceful aide called upon General Riley, who had a concealed safety pin put to an important use—namely, in lieu of a suspender button. Unabashed, the grave General produced it, and promptly ordered his own aide to get another (what we call 'passing the buck' in army language), and this aide in turn appealed to Mrs. Cushing. She was engaged in coming to his aid (aide) when you called her by name. (But all this was unobserved by me and I hope by the General and you.) . . .

Since his son Bill had entered Yale this year, H.C. made a particular point of attending the Harvard-Yale game in order to meet some of Bill's college friends. Another instance of Cushing's interest in Yale is found in a letter at this time addressed to a member of the medical faculty in response to a request for advice over differences that had arisen concerning an appointment. H.C. usually avoided being drawn into controversies in other schools but when Yale was involved he had no reluctance about speaking his mind.

. . . Your group I think has had the greatest opportunity in the country of doing again and perhaps better what was done in the 90's in Baltimore. But what was done there was only done because of mutual charity and sympathy and understanding and making the most of the men who were chosen. Even my lamented Chief, Dr. Halsted, with all his failings and peculiarities was made the most of and came out of it a great figure in the history of medicine. . . . My advice to you as a friend, as a Yale man, and as one who has the welfare of the Yale Medical School greatly at heart is that the best thing that you can do for the school and to put yourselves right in the eyes of the country who expect great things of you, is to see that [your candidate] is promptly given the position to which his work, personality, attainments, and academic instincts fully entitle him. . . .

None of us can find all the qualities we would like even in our best and most intimate friends and colleagues. I belong to a very intimate club here in Boston which has gone on for half a century. The club, as so many clubs do, has had difficulty in agreeing upon new members. Someone remarked the other day that he wondered how many present members of the club would be re-elected if we should all resign. What I think you fellows need at New Haven is to have an occasional love feast with a drink or two under your skins and a little more of patting one another on the back with words of encouragement such as used to be the custom in the heyday of the Johns Hopkins. If you can't do a little of this sort of thing, you will neither be able to retain and get the best out of the men you have nor to secure others.

1924

Early in 1924 John Singer Sargent, who was then living in the Copley Plaza Hotel in Boston, was approached concerning a crayon of H.C.—one of those quick sketches which Sargent himself ineptly referred to as "mugs" and which had caught the imagination of lovers of art throughout the world. Cushing's friends in the Saturday Club had had their "mugs" scattered throughout Boston—Major Higginson, Charles S. Sargent, and James Ford Rhodes among others;[23] and H.C., who could scarcely be ranked as a good sitter, finally consented. He and Sargent, however, did not seem to understand one another—or, as someone suggested, they perhaps understood one another too well. At all events, after the first rather uncomfortable sitting, H.C. brought along Barbara, aged nine, to keep him distracted. He complained, when the sketch was finished, that Sargent had made him look scornful or, as he put it more bluntly to his friends, as though he'd been 'weaned on a pickle.' However, he had evidently met his match, as notes from Sargent suggest:

> You take it like a man, for whom operations have no terror. Any morning at 10 o'clock next week—room 601 Copley Plaza, will suit me with a day or two's notice. So take your choice—and bring your anesthetist [Barbara]. . . .
>
> Bayley sent me the drawing and I confess I did not see the slightest scornfulness to the expression or anything to change in the face. I did lighten a dark [shadow] under the nose a trifle, but without cosmetics, and I shortened and thickened the neck a little. I am returning the drawing to Bayley's and I hope you will be satisfied. If you are not, I assume that I am not the right man to do you, and I had rather return the charge and keep the drawing myself. I don't often have such a good head to draw.

Cushing dutifully paid his $1,000 for the portrait; in later years the family concluded that the experience had probably been worth the price since he so often made a good story of it.

H.C. was now on the final stretch of the Osler biography but, despite the fact that he "regretted" nineteen invitations to speak, he had more commitments than in the previous three years. On 3 March he addressed the Annual Congress on Medical Education on a subject close to his heart: namely, "The clinical teacher and the medical curriculum," in which he reiterated his conviction that students should begin to see patients as soon as they enter medical school.

The Harvard Medical Society had a series of lively meetings during the winter, one of the most interesting having been in March when Chevalier Jackson, the distinguished Philadelphia bronchoscopist, gave the principal address. The occasion served to illustrate the fact that Cushing's assistants never knew what they might be called upon to do, and Tracy Putnam, then on the service, tells of H.C.'s unusual request at this time:

> Jackson had been invited to come to Boston to speak at a meeting of the Harvard Medical Society, and the Chief had arranged a dinner for him beforehand, inviting Ally Porter, David Cheever, John Homans, Mosher and Crockett, among others. The train from Philadelphia arrived that noon and there was no word from Jackson. Finally Miss Stanton ran him down at the Copley Plaza and received the reply that never, in any circumstances, would he think of going out to dinner before delivering an address. He always went to bed and had

[23] See Chapter XI.

bread and milk or something of the sort. He was immovable in this decision and yet the dinner was already arranged. Dr. Cushing, with his characteristic resourcefulness, called in his resident and informed him that he was to be Chevalier Jackson for that evening. The fact that there was a disparity in stature between the two and also that Jackson had a beard while the resident did not, did not stand in the way for a moment. A beard was improvised and Mosher and Crockett, who knew Jackson, were tipped off. It was arranged that Jackson should arrive late at the Harvard Club. There the Chief met him and they encountered Samuel Levine who was duly introduced and who asked after a patient they had treated together. I do not know that he got a very definite reply. Jackson then arrived in a dimly lighted room and was introduced all around. Exactly what the other guests thought I do not know, but it appeared that some of them at least felt they had met a celebrity. Only David Cheever maintained that he had guessed the identity of the distinguished visitor, but had dismissed the idea from his mind as altogether fantastic. I believe that there were even those who, after hearing the evening's address, felt it better to disbelieve their own eyes than the Chief's introduction.

Many have elaborated on this amusing episode and Levine remembered the following additional details:

... We all met Dr. Jackson, chatted with him, dined with him and then went on up to the School. About nine o'clock that evening while Dr. Jackson was giving his talk, it first dawned on Chan Frothingham that the man who was talking was not the same person that we had dined with. It seems that when Dr. Cushing learned at noon that Dr. Jackson could not attend the dinner, he asked Tracy Putnam to dress up as Dr. Jackson and take his part at the Harvard Club. This Tracy did with complete success, so much so that some of the men who knew Dr. Jackson very well, were taken in. I, who ought to have known Tracy very well, talked to him about a rather important and famous patient whom I had sent to Philadelphia. He made some noncommittal monosyllabic replies, but I never for a moment recognized Tracy in his assumed rôle. I think it was one of the cleverest "plays" of this sort that I remember.

Dr. Levine relates several other stories of Cushing at this time:

During the years 1924 to 1926 he was president of the Harvard Medical Society while I was secretary which entailed sending out notices and helping to conduct meetings every other Tuesday night. One day I was to meet him around one o'clock to talk over one of the coming meetings but Miss Stanton told me he had suddenly taken the 1:00 o'clock train for New York. This was an unusual and unexpected interruption in his schedule. An artist who had previously been operated on by Dr. Cushing and had become ambulatory had suddenly gone into coma that morning. She had previously been, as I remember it, in a two-bed room on "A" but because of her disability had become impoverished and now belonged to the group of ward cases. Despite this, when the Chief learned of the sudden turn, he jumped on the train, hurried to see her in New York and brought her back to the Peter Bent Brigham Hospital. I thought that was an extremely decent thing for him to have done, especially when it was said that he refused to go to New York to see H. P. Davison, the financier of the House of Morgan, because he believed he would do better if he came to the Brigham Hospital under his care. This illustrates well how the financial reward never influenced the Chief's judgment about medical matters.

There were other such instances. One very hot Saturday afternoon during the summer of 1924 or 1925 I was working in the laboratory all alone on some paper I was publishing. When I finished, I walked to the front through the operating room. It was about five o'clock and everything was quiet as it is on a midsummer's Saturday afternoon. None of the visiting men were around—they were either vacationing or taking the week-end off—but there was the Chief working on a dressing of a little Italian child from ward C main. I never forgot that experience.

In April Sir D'Arcy Power (1855-1941), historian, scholar, and one of the senior surgeons of Great Britain, came for two weeks as Surgeon-in-Chief *pro tem.* Sir D'Arcy, a most gracious and kindly man, had been away from active surgical practice for some years and at his age he was scarcely qualified to take over an active surgical service. There were many amusing stories about getting him scrubbed up, keeping him sterile, etc., but, once he became accustomed to the paraphernalia of an American operating room, it was clear that his hand had not lost its deftness, and his well-stocked brain proved a source of unending stimulation and delight to the entire staff. Incidentally, he read and criticized, while in Boston, the MS of the entire second volume of the Osler biography covering the English period. After Sir D'Arcy departed H.C. received a characteristic letter:

Chateau Frontenac, Quebec,
Sir D'Arcy Power to H.C. *6 May 1924.*

My dear Cushing, This you will call a bread & butter letter although we call it a "Collins" after Jane Austen's character in *Pride & Prejudice.* At any rate it brings to you my heartiest thanks for all the kindness & care which I have had from yourself & from all the staff, senior as well as junior, of the hospital. I have been perfectly overwhelmed by it & also a little ashamed that there was so little to be given in return. You have acted very wisely in introducing such a system of visiting for the spoken word is much stronger than the written one & to me personally it has been an intense pleasure to see representatives of the great medical families who made Boston famous in history.

I am so glad to hear you say that you are coming over to England in June. You will stay with me whilst you are in London, so consider it settled & tell me the approximate day when you know it yourself.

Quite an easy journey, but snow lying everywhere. No summer time here, no buds, no nothing but hot rooms, so I have opened the window and upset the whole heating economy. With best wishes to Mrs. Cushing & yourself & love to Barbara. Yrs ever, D'ARCY POWER.

Between 1922 and 1924 Percival Bailey had spent a year abroad in France. On returning he at once commenced his elaborate long-range program of microscopic study of all the brain tumors in Cushing's collection, classifying them on an embryological basis. Tumors of the brain, and indeed of any other part of the body, arise from growing cells, normal at an early stage of embryological development, but abnormal in the mature organism. It so happens that clusters of primitive cells are sometimes found in the part of the brain known as the cerebellum (and in a particular part of the cerebellum, the "nodulus," which lies in the roof of the fourth ventricle). For reasons as yet undisclosed these primitive cells, or "rests," as they are sometimes called, may begin subdividing with abnormal rapidity and in that way start a malignant growth. Such tumors are prone to occur in young children, and unfortunately they belong to the group of tumors that grow rapidly and, when removed, tend quickly to recur. Prior to the work of Cushing and Bailey, these growths had not been recognized as a pathological entity distinct from other tumors of the cerebellum (*e.g.*, those which form cysts and grow much less rapidly). Their paper describing this neoplasm (which they named "medulloblastoma") was presented before the A.N.A. at Philadelphia in June.[24] H.C. found this group of tumors particularly challenging and once he had become aware that the outlook for such cases was bad, instead of refusing operation when these children returned with recurrences, he would often operate again and again in order to give anxious parents the satisfaction of having the child remain alive for a few more months. In the back of his mind there was also the hope that if the part of the brain from which these cells originated could be removed, he might one day effect a complete cure. One child went for eleven years without a recurrence and Cushing's hopes were high, but they were dashed at the end of the twelfth year when the boy came back with a massive recurrence.

Two days after the meeting of the American Neurological Association H.C. acted as toastmaster at a testimonial dinner given for Dr. George H. Simmons, Editor of the *Journal of the American Medical Association*. Simmons, then in his seventy-third year, had acted as editor of the *Journal* of the A.M.A. for forty years and had brought not only this weekly, but also a group of specialist A.M.A. journals into a position of world prominence. To be sure, he had been something of a martinet, and Cushing himself had frequently chafed when made to conform with the unbending editorial conventions, particularly Simmons' arbitrary midwestern spelling rules (which continue to offend the literary sensibilities of many medical men throughout the world). But Cushing was not a person who would permit a petty annoyance of this character to blind him to the larger achievement of a man such as Simmons. Thus he wrote to Matas: "I think we all have very much the same feeling about Simmons and the A.M.A., and I confess that I never send a paper

[24] "Medulloblastoma cerebelli: a common type of mid-cerebellar glioma of childhood." *Transactions of the American Neurological Association*, 1924, 89-121. Also: *Archives of Neurology and Psychiatry, Chicago*, August 1925, *14*, 192-223.

to the Journal without swearing I will never send another, for it comes back with modified spelling which horrifies me and with all my carefully studied expressions turned into Simmonesque phrases. But nevertheless, I choose to overlook these things and think it would be a good thing for the A.M.A. and all the special societies if they could get together and pay him a tribute for the good things he has done and to forget the others." His speech at the dinner began:

> . . . Given a frictionless pulley over which passes a weightless rope with a ten-pound monkey on one end evenly balanced by a ten-pound weight on the other: Should the monkey climb the rope, what will happen to the ten-pound weight? Will it remain stationary or will it go up or go down as the monkey ascends? It is a matter on which eminent scientists appear to disagree.
>
> Now our friend, George H. Simmons, in whose honor we have gathered here this evening, must have felt many times during the past twenty-five years that this was the problem he was trying to solve. The frictionless pulley is represented by the organization at 535 North Dearborn Street which he had perfected. At one end of the rope was the ponderous American medical profession ready to drop with a thud should he let go, whereas he was the monkey hanging on without cessation at the other. . . . Simmons did the impossible. He climbed the rope, and on the other side of his perfected pulley the entire profession of the country has gone up with him. Some have seen this and wondered.

Cushing's comparison of Simmons to a monkey climbing on a rope confused his audience slightly, but Simmons evidently took it in the spirit intended, for he wrote:

> The strenuous conditions that accompany the Annual Session of the "Greatest medical organization in the world" are over. (This is the twenty-sixth that has come under my supervision and, thank Heaven, the last.) This gives me the first opportunity I have had to tell you how much I appreciate the sacrifices you made to attend the presentation dinner; also, to thank you for presiding. I refer to the sacrifices because I know that you had made all arrangements to go to England, and that you cancelled them solely to be present that night. Further, I know that you must have devoted considerable time and thought to the task to have done so well as Toastmaster, especially in the introductory remarks.
>
> I felt especially proud that night of the character of the men who so kindly responded to the toasts. It was the great day—or night—of my life, and you were one of the chief "instigators." . . .

Cushing's willingness to act as toastmaster did much to unify professional sentiment in the country with regard to the A.M.A., there having always been sectional feeling, and certain medical schools on the eastern seaboard, resenting what they looked upon as Chicago domination, had threatened to withdraw their support.

Following a farewell dinner for Elliott Cutler on the 13th (Cutler had just been appointed to the chair of surgery at Western Reserve), and a Harvard Commencement on 19 June at which H.C. sponsored his friend, W. J. Mayo, for an honorary degree, he sailed on the 21st on the *Scythia* for England, where, as recorded earlier in this chapter, he started the Osler biography through the press. His journey over was filled with anxiety for his close friend, Robert Lovett, who was aboard with his wife, fell desperately ill and died shortly after their arrival in Liverpool. With his usual promptness H.C. set down a heartfelt appreciation which reached the Boston Surgical Society in time for its July meeting.[25]

In London H.C. met Sir Walter Morley Fletcher who took him to an auction at Sotheby's where he impoverished himself bidding on some incunabula; but apart from this one day in "town" he spent eighteen hours a day for six weeks, first on the manuscript and later on the galleys of the 'Osler.'

As if not content with having finished one large literary venture, immediately on his return he settled down to the preparation of an address (which turned into a small book) for the dedication of the new medical building at Western Reserve in Cleveland on 5 October. He entitled it "The Western Reserve and its medical traditions."[26] The essay shows evidence of much patient research, but as with the 'Osler' it was obviously a labor of love, since there was nothing that stirred him more than the stories of his pioneering forebears on both sides of the family who, discontented with their lot in New England journeyed to the Western Reserve where they set up their own vigorous way of life, their schools, and their traditions in medicine. He spoke of Jared Potter Kirtland, eminent physician and horticulturalist, who had founded the Cleveland Academy of Natural Sciences (1845), of John Delamater (1787-1867), teacher and general practitioner, "the most beloved and honored physician of all time in the community." He concluded with a particularly forceful paragraph:

> Out of esteem for your traditions I have endeavored in this address to recall how this Western Reserve, this City of Cleveland, this University and this Medical School, came to be what and where they are. In so doing mention has been made of some few of those who have contributed to your local and institutional history, but more particularly of those who have been benefactors in the upbuilding of the medical department. But, after all, it is men and not buildings—brains and not bricks—that make a great school. Hence it is incumbent upon us to hold in grateful remembrance those who have unselfishly given of their knowledge and skill—of their heart, head and hands—as teachers, thinkers, and investigators, no less than those who have given of their substance. For in the last analysis it is the teacher and worker on whom the reputation of a school must rest—on such faithful servants, to pick types, as were Kirtland and Delamater in their day in the Medical School; Seymour and Morley in their day in the College—men who loom large at a distance though they pass unnoticed on the streets at home—men whose influence and example carry on through gener-

[25] "Robert Williamson Lovett, 1859-1924." *Boston Medical and Surgical Journal,* 19 February 1925, *192,* 374-375.

[26] *Cleveland: Privately printed* [1924], 33 pp.

ations of pupils though their names be all too soon forgotten by the people among whom they have lived.

There were many enthusiastic letters about the Western Reserve address. His friends in Cleveland were immensely pleased and Lewis Weed, an old Clevelander, wrote: "My mother also read the paper with the greatest pleasure. . . . I was transported back to my boyhood, surrounded by all the old families, and somehow your words gave me the feeling that here in Baltimore I was far from home and I somehow felt that I belonged out there in Cleveland. When I read one of your papers or addresses, I think that you should do nothing but write; when I see you operate, I think you should do nothing but that; and when I see you experiment, I feel that you should do nothing else but experiment."

From Frederick Shattuck, "I have just read, at one lick, your deeply interesting and well-executed address in Cleveland. It is a remarkable story, remarkably well told." Dr. Shattuck carried the note to H.C. by hand, bursting into his office one Saturday afternoon to congratulate him personally and also to expostulate with the Moseley Professor of Surgery for having spelt the great Indian offensive weapon "tommyhawk." There were also letters about the address from men such as George F. Moore, who had one time been invited to the presidency of Adelbert College at Cleveland. Another particularly pleasant friendship which two years later grew out of the Western Reserve address was that with Lucien Price, better known to Bostonians as "Uncle Dudley" of the *Boston Globe*. In 1926 Mr. Price published in the April *Atlantic Monthly* a remarkable article entitled "Olympians in homespun," in which he described the vigorous faculty in an Ohio academy, recognized at once by H.C. as Hudson School at Kent where many of the Cushing family had been educated. A reprint of his Western Reserve address went promptly to Mr. Price with the following note:

H.C. to Lucien Price *7 April 1926.*

Dear Mr. Price: I can't tell you with what solid gratification I read the leading article in this month's *Atlantic*. I do not have much time for general reading but Mrs. Cushing insisted on my perusal of "Olympians in Homespun," whatever else went by the board. And she was quite right about it. All I could say when I finished was 'Amen.' Here is a man who has served up a proper antidote for Arrowsmith, doctor, Main Street and all.

This happened Sunday night and the next morning I wrote Ellery Sedgwick to commend the article and to ask for your address. Meanwhile, I have discovered you in another way. I have long been addicted to the morning *Herald* at breakfast, but when the [Colonel] House papers began to come out I subscribed to the *Globe* and incidentally discovered Uncle Dudley whom I enjoy even more and in quite another way than the Colonel's disclosures. Sedgwick tells me that you are Uncle Dudley, or at least half of him. Hence this letter addressed to the

Globe to thank you for an article which I wish might be read in every household in the country.

Incidentally I discover that you are of Western Reserve parentage, at least I take it that the allusion to the firelands and all indicates the Western Reserve. I consequently am taking the liberty of sending you a skit on this subject which, though in no way to be classed with your "Olympians in Homespun," nevertheless may interest you.

Mr. Price was delighted and replied enthusiastically on a scrap of orange copy paper:

Grateful as I am for your letter, and a most gracious one it is, what gave me equal pleasure was the reprint of your Medical School address at Cleveland. Let me confess: I did not know one-half of this history: and what is more, I doubt if it has ever anywhere been more entertainingly told. The personal anecdotes and family history are just what it wanted to take the starch out of it and limber it up. I regularly roared over that episode of your brother absentmindedly getting off the train at Hudson, and also your childhood theory of heaven and peppermints. Kent, where they were going to the wedding, is my home town—"Woolwick." And Dr. Dudley Allen, who heads your bibliography, came and went in our house continually on surgical errands with my father. But what I want to know is: how does a surgeon find time to beat journalists at their own game? Have you more copies of this address? . . .

Further anecdotes of early days in Cleveland followed from H.C.:

Thanks for your letter. Of course you shall have more of those Western Reserve addresses. I distributed a few among some old-time Clevelanders but for the most part they are sitting here on my shelves. Many a happy day I spent in Kent as a boy. Two of my uncles, Edward Day and Charles Williams, ran a glass factory there which broke up as soon as the government shut down on their importing Belgian glass blowers. I of course knew Dudley Allen well. . . . My grandfather gave him a start in Cleveland and I am glad to know that he and your father came in touch with one another. . . .

In February 1927, possibly under the stimulus of Cushing's interest, Mr. Price had a sequel in the *Atlantic* entitled "Hardscrabble Hellas" —describing how the boys at the Academy had Latin, Greek, mathematics, philosophy, and history all poured into them in the rugged surroundings of a snow-smothered Ohio River valley. "Sleep with windows open you determinedly would, but on zero nights the only efficient heating was to pool quilts and blankets and sleep three in a bed. On rising you broke the ice in your water jug and built a fire to thaw out the face cloth. . . . Shower baths? On the old campus there was not so much as one stationary tub. . . . If the windy plains of Troy were much windier than these bedrooms on a January night, Helen showed poor judgment in ever leaving home." This was the Spartan background that Cushing knew and loved and he could not resist sending dozens of copies of Price's paper to his friends in Ohio and elsewhere—for it depicted the intellectual soil from which he himself had sprung.

CHAPTER XVI

Growth of a Clinic

The Life History of Brain Tumors and Electrosurgery

1925–1928

WITH the publication of the Osler biography Cushing became one of the most talked-of men in medicine, and in Europe he was looked upon as our foremost surgeon. He could now relax from the biography and the exigencies of war, and was able to give more attention to his family and to his clinic. In the latter, his energies were largely expended in two principal directions: first, in the extension of knowledge of life expectancy of patients having various types of brain tumor—the program, mentioned earlier, of histological study inaugurated by Percival Bailey who was later joined by Louise Eisenhardt; secondly, in the improvement of his surgical technique through the development of electrosurgical methods for the control of hemorrhage.

At home his growing family had made itself very much a part of the community in Brookline and Boston. The five children were now reaching maturity and, since each one had inherited his parents' lively interest in things and people, each had begun to make demands upon his father's attention. They all had hospitable tendencies and had they followed their instincts there would have been a houseful of guests continuously.

In January 1925 William, the eldest, having completed his studies at Andover, was then a sophomore at Yale at the age of 21. Mary was turning 19, Betsey 16, Henry 14, and Barbara 9. The two eldest girls attended Miss May's School in Boston and Barbara, first the Park School and later Miss Winsor's. During these years they would pile into the back seat of the car with their father each morning shortly after eight, and Gus would whisk them off, first to the hospital and then to school. They were thus at home in the evenings and were obliged to entertain their friends more or less under their father's nose, for after dinner he was almost invariably at work in his study just off the drawing room. His Victorian tendencies restricted their freedom to some extent, which for the most part they took goodnaturedly except when occasionally "Va," as they called him, attempted to expedite the departure of some young hopeful who had outstayed the bedtime hour. H.C.'s notions of domestic discipline were to some extent dictated by his rather impatient temperament and his own convenience, for the hours from ten to midnight were for him the most productive of the day—particularly when there was no din in the next room.

Bill was a typical Cushing with much of his father's reserve and independence of mind, but he had not yet developed his father's powers of application and, being of closely similar temperament, the two had occasional clashes—very much as H.C. and H.K.C. had had their differences over expense accounts and college sports. Like H.C., Bill had the usual undergraduate escapades (which he was somewhat less successful in concealing than H.C. had been), but his record at Yale, as far as academic work was concerned, was quite as creditable as his father's. He showed a keen interest in books and his book bills at one time were so considerable that his father commented indulgently when he saw one of the unitemized accounts that he must be buying either false teeth or a library. H.C.'s letters to Bill and also to Henry, who followed Bill at Yale, were strikingly similar to those of H.K.C. to H.C. in college, but gayer and more tolerant, and college athletics, now energetically encouraged, were not in this generation a bone of contention.

H.C. to W.H.C. *13 February 1924.*

Dear Bill: Golly, what a tough lot of examination papers! 'Avogadro's Law'—who in the dickens was this old bird? Still, I suppose you encountered him in your Chemistry course and I may have done so once and forgotten who he was. I am glad I got through college in the early '90's though I suppose the exams of those days would have looked about as severe to your grandfather as these of yours do to me.

Glad you pulled through without a condition. It must have meant hard grinding, but the thing of course is to peg away faithfully from day to day, nuisance though it is, and to keep brushing up a bit on a review. I think that is really the way to do it and then examinations don't seem so mountainous. It will be a Utopian time when there are no such things, and we are struggling to introduce the custom in the Medical School. As a matter of fact, we know pretty well who ought to get through and who ought not to get through without subjecting the men to a written test. . . . I do not wonder you rebel at Carlyle. He is a tough nut. Carlyle is bad enough himself but Carlyle plus a sore-headed Prof. must be worse. But after all, what you had better do is to get interested in the old man himself. You remember the Whistler picture of him over the bookshelves. And then have you met Jane? She was a queer bird and looked like an old horse. If you will pick up a short biography about them and read it before you read his stuff, you will find it easier, I think. I am sending a check which will reach the Bursar's Office in time.

5 April 1924.

Dear Bill: So glad to have had your good letter. I wish you would write oftener. It must be a great relief to have got your exams off. I judge from what you say to your mother that you will not be home and are going off with the team for your vacation. . . . I hope you can hold down your short-stop job. It is where I first started myself, but I didn't have quite good enough a wing for the post and so got shunted to the out-field in time. Still, I believe I played short-stop through Freshman year.

1 May 1924.

Dear Bill: . . . You say that you are sitting up until 3 A.M. revising a composition—not a good preparation for good reflexes on the diamond. It's a good thing to keep early hours if you are going to keep perfectly fit. But do let me hear something about the trip. I have had a report from the Registrar showing that you got through your half term O.K., though you dropped off a little below the class average. Don't get into a slump, old man, about your lessons.

14 September 1925.

Dear Bill: I am glad to see that you are getting to be a bloated bond holder. There are only two ways to become one in the end though I don't think it's a particularly desirable ambition. These two ways are to pay your bills promptly and never to take a chance on any wild-cat speculation. . . .

15 February 1926.

Dear Bill: Delighted with your letter! You must be quite set up, and I certainly am. After all, it's rather good fun going out for a score, whether it's a low score in golf or a high score in school. Life all round is a kind of sporting event and the best any of us can do is to try continually to improve our game. I hope you have fixed it up with that dentigerous cuss. I wrote him a polite note. I am sending your tuition check direct to F. B. Johnson to save you trouble.

H.C. was much more generous from a financial standpoint than H.K.C. had been, and instead of causing the boys to make pleas for additional funds whenever they ran short, he placed them on a regular allowance of $100 a month over and above their immediate expenses of tuition, board, and lodging. H.C. no doubt had never forgotten the unpleasantness of having to request over a period of ten years almost every penny that H.K.C. ever sent him. Both sons were to some extent handicapped at Yale by the prominence of their father, and this no doubt accounts for the fact that neither one was initially drawn to the study of medicine.

In some ways Cushing was more austere with his daughters than with his sons. He continued in his unyielding prejudice against smoking or drinking as far as the distaff side of the house was concerned, and he became so aggressively unpleasant if the girls attempted to smoke in public that they were obliged to enjoy their cigarettes in private. For many years he also strongly disapproved of cocktails, at least for Mrs. Cushing and the girls, but on this point he gave in after settling in New Haven. Despite these interesting old-fashioned traits which at times made for minor domestic difficulty, H.C. could be generous, thoughtful, and fatherly in the highest sense. He enjoyed nothing so much as bringing home presents for the children when he had been on his travels. He wrote them many amusing letters, sometimes accompanied by lively sketches. Several letters to Barbara while at Westover School illustrate his capacity for affectionate whimsey.

H.C. to Barbara—aged 15 *2 November 1930.*

How's the sweet and beautiful darling? Having a good time I judge from your letter which filled me with joy. We have been having a Hungarian here for lunch who has kissed Mother's and Sis Cow's [Mary's] and Mrs. Jas. Roosevelt's hands and is now paying them compliments in the front room which they are lapping up. Don't you wish you were here? I'm glad you've got a nice room and nice roommates and nice everything. That means you are having fun—and after all life is what one makes of it. Some people always enjoy it and some never do and it's a great thing to belong in the former class—don't you think so? I'm sure you do.

Jimmy [Roosevelt] has been making many political speeches the past week. Nevertheless *de Gustibus* and I will probably vote the Republican ticket just the same. I must go and attend the Hungarian now that I've given the others a chance at him. . . .

16 February [1933].

Oh, my soul, body and whiskers! A note from Laura Dillingham this A.M. giving your school marks! There must be some mistake. No Cushing ever did anything like this. I'm bursting with pride. If I were near I'd give you a big hug and all the rest in sight—including Laura and the one with a bun.

[Postscript] That Miami episode [referring to the attempt on Mr. Roosevelt's life] was a blessing in disguise. The country needed a shaking up. And the R[oosevelt]s have behaved marvellously—so unperturbed. Just what we'd expect.

New Haven, 19 May 1934.

How *is* the darling? And in view of her fine record at School how would she like to be rewarded by a little runabout all her own? And would she like one just like Betsey's or some other kind? Please let me know quick.

Developments at Yale

Behind the scenes Cushing continued to work actively in promoting the best interests of the Yale School of Medicine. In 1920 Milton C. Winternitz, a dynamic young pathologist from William Welch's laboratory at the Hopkins, was made dean of the School in succession to Cushing's friend of Hopkins days, Dr. George Blumer. In Winternitz's Second Annual Report of the School of Medicine for 1921-1922 he records that in July of 1921 the Sterling trustees had granted a sum of $1,320,000 for the erection of a Sterling Hall of Medicine, opposite the New Haven Hospital, which would provide space for modern preclinical laboratories of anatomy, physiology, and pharmacology; other funds from the Anthony N. Brady trustees would make possible a suitable building attached to the hospital for the laboratories of pathology and bacteriology. The blueprint for the reorganization of the School was thus well in hand by July 1922. Cushing and Welch followed these developments with eager interest, for they believed that a second Johns Hopkins might spring up in New Haven if proper conditions could be created to attract men of the first rank.

There were delays in the erection of Sterling Hall, but it was made ready for occupancy in the late autumn of 1924, and in December Mr. Angell invited both Cushing and Welch to take part in the dedication exercises on Alumni Day, 23 February 1925. They both accepted with alacrity, and Cushing came forward with a challenging and, as it turned out, much discussed address to which he gave the Hippocratic title: *"Experimentum periculosum: Judicium difficile."* He had gone to some trouble to acquaint himself with the early history of medicine at Yale, and he spoke once again about his Cleveland worthy, Jared Potter Kirtland who, as it happened, was the fifth graduate of the Yale Medical Institution, having entered the year it was founded (1812) and been graduated in 1815. He also referred to the Rev. Peter Parker, M.D., who, after graduation from Yale in 1834, had founded at Canton, as a medical missionary, the first modern hospital in China. But the basic theme of his address was perhaps a little surprising for the dedication of preclinical laboratories. He enquired whether we were not overdoing preclinical work in the medical students' curriculum. "Can there be such a thing," he asked, "as too good a preparation for medicine?" He had recently seen the massive foundations of a great cathedral in which, funds having run short, the roof and the tower were left unbuilt. "Are we not perhaps doing this sort of thing in the case of our medical students, many of whom will be incapable of erecting much of anything on the expensive, reinforced foundation. . . . Better, you will say, than to build on foundations of rubble a top-heavy clinical superstructure which must be continually shored up in later years lest it collapse." He then went on to remind his listeners that many of the great discoveries in medicine had been made, not by laboratory men, but by busy practitioners, men such as Harvey, Hunter, Jenner, Koch, and Lister. He then playfully suggested that more men might go into scientific medicine if they had their clinical years first and returned in their third and fourth years to the basic preclinical sciences.

There can be little doubt that Cushing's emphasis was deliberate, for he still felt that the real need of the Yale Medical School had not been fully appreciated, either by its faculty or by Mr. Angell—the need which he had been stressing for a full twenty years, namely, that of a properly endowed university hospital. He suggested to Winternitz that too much emphasis was being placed upon the preclinical sciences and too little upon building up the clinical departments and the hospital.

When Welch was called upon, he pulled, as usual, a few blank pages of a would-be manuscript from his pocket and proceeded to offer a devastating extemporaneous rebuttal of virtually everything that Cushing had said. Recalling the incident, H.C. wrote:

Twelve years ago [23 February 1925] when the new Sterling Hall of Medicine at Yale was dedicated, both Dr. Welch and I, as graduates of the College, were asked to make addresses. I being the younger spoke first and offered the suggestion that if they planned to turn out good practitioners in the rejuvenated School, medicine be taught in terms of the patient from the outset instead of only in the last two years.

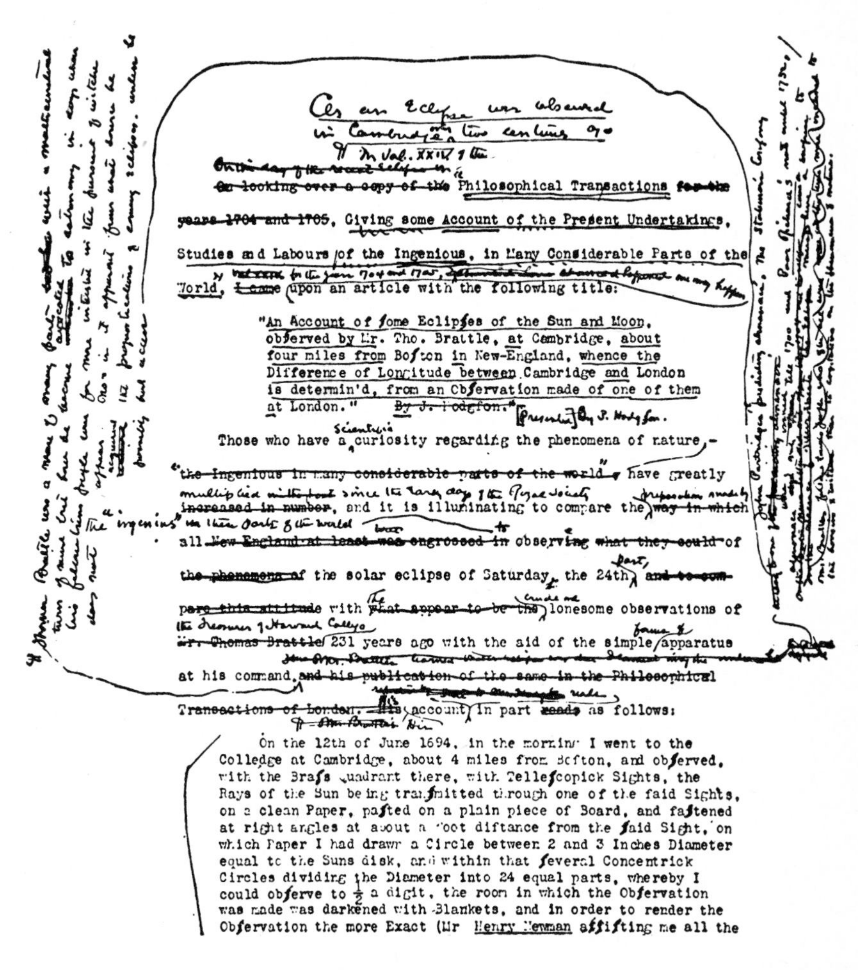

~~On looking over a copy of the~~ Philosophical Transactions ~~for the years 1704 and 1705~~, Giving some Account of the Present Undertakings, Studies and Labours of the Ingenious, in Many Considerable Parts of the World, ~~I came~~ upon an article with the following title:

"An Account of ſome Eclipſes of the Sun and Moon, obſerved by Mr. Tho. Brattle, at Cambridge, about four miles from Boſton in New-England, whence the Difference of Longitude between Cambridge and London is determin'd, from an Obſervation made of one of them at London." ~~By J. Hodgſon.~~

Those who have a curiosity regarding the phenomena of nature ~~the Ingenious in many considerable parts of the world~~ have greatly ~~increased in number~~, and it is illuminating to compare the ~~way in which~~ all ~~New England at least was engrossed in~~ observing ~~what they could of the phenomena of~~ the solar eclipse of Saturday, the 24th ~~and to compare this attitude~~ with ~~what appear to be the~~ lonesome observations of ~~Mr. Thomas Brattle~~ 231 years ago with the aid of the simple apparatus at his command ~~and his publication of the same in the Philosophical Transactions of London. His~~ account in part ~~reads~~ as follows:

On the 12th of June 1694, in the morning I went to the Colledge at Cambridge, about 4 miles from Boſton, and obſerved, with the Braſs Quadrant there, with Telleſcopick Sights, the Rays of the Sun being tranſmitted through one of the ſaid Sights, on a clean Paper, paſted on a plain piece of Board, and faſtened at right angles at about a foot diſtance from the ſaid Sight, on which Paper I had drawn a Circle between 2 and 3 Inches Diameter equal to the Suns disk, and within that ſeveral Concentrick Circles dividing the Diameter into 24 equal parts, whereby I could obſerve to ½ a digit, the room in which the Obſervation was made was darkened with Blankets, and in order to render the Obſervation the more Exact (Mr Henry Newman aſſiſting me all the

A TYPICAL MANUSCRIPT PAGE

The first page of Cushing's note on the eclipse described by Thomas Brattle on 12 June 1694

Dr. Welch then arose and tore my proposal to bits, stating in effect that the kind of doctor I had in mind was going out—that henceforth, with a public health officer in every community, people would be *prevented* from getting ill, leaving the old-time practitioner twiddling his thumbs. We then went to a reception where over a cup of tea I mildly protested, reminding him of his own forebears who were that happy conjunction of country doctor and self-appointed health officer. With that well-known twinkle in his eye he replied: "I know as well as you do that with our present educational system doctors comparable to Osler and Janeway are not likely to be seen again." And to my query, "Why didn't you say so?" he rejoined, "Because I'm now a Professor of Public Health."

During January and February of 1925 Cushing's insatiable curiosity led him into an astronomical byway. There had been a total eclipse in Boston on 24 January and two days later H.C., quite by accident, encountered in an early volume of the *Philosophical Transactions* of the Royal Society (which he had borrowed in another connection) an account of Thomas Brattle's description of the eclipse observed in Cambridge, Massachusetts, on 12 June 1694. Much impressed by the coincidence and also by the accuracy of Brattle's observation, H.C. set his friend Professor Harlow Shapley to work looking up information for him about the colonial astronomer. The result was a paper, over which he had taken considerable trouble, issued in March in the *Harvard Alumni Bulletin*.[1]

Ever since Cushing's debilitating attack of vascular polyneuritis in the autumn of 1918 he had been physically below par. During 1919 and 1920 any ordeal in the operating room proved extremely fatiguing and owing to the fact that the main arteries (the femorals) to both of his legs had become permanently occluded by an ascending thrombosis, it was no longer possible for him to indulge in strenuous physical exercise; indeed from 1920 on he could not walk for more than a block or two without stopping to rest. Those who were aware of his difficulty recognized his clever manoeuvres to rest his legs—a passing airplane, a bird, the species of a tree or flower would quickly engage his attention and he would stop to inspect; or if walking the long trek from his office to Ward A at the Brigham Hospital, he would stop suddenly along the corridor to talk about a patient. Despite this physical handicap, he still played at horseshoes, from time to time frequently also at croquet, and until 1930 he even played a conservative but, to most of his opponents, a rather devastating game of tennis. With seemingly little effort he placed his shots with diabolical accuracy and managed to return his opponent's best plays without appearing to move more than a few slow steps.

The Osler biography, with its long hours of sustained work and incessant smoking (in the manuscript and the proof sheets one often found cigarette burns), had further encroached upon his health, and a lingering bronchitis which began in January 1925 finally culminated in a sharp attack of "grippe," which took him for two weeks at the end of March to Thomasville, Georgia, with his "horsey" Cleveland friends. He managed to get back to Baltimore, however,

[1] "An eclipse observed over two centuries ago." *Harvard Alumni Bulletin,* 5 March 1925, 27, 669-671.

on 8 April in time to celebrate Dr. Welch's seventy-fifth birthday and to present him with the first volume of the 'Osler.'

This of course was a delightful occasion—Dr. Welch in great form, reciting poetry, telling stories, etc. Each of us brought a small present—I the first volume from the press of Osler's biography which I had wangled from the Oxford Press office in New York that morning where it had just arrived. It was Chapman's personal copy but I insisted on having it. There were some old bottles produced and Thayer read a poem.

We broke up about 11.30 and F. C. Walcott and I went to the station and boarded the night train for New York. Dr. Welch had left us at the club saying that he wished to go to his rooms for a few minutes. There he acknowledged telegrams and letters until 2.30 and caught the train just as it pulled out. My surprise was great the next morning early when I was awakened by the porter and on parting my curtains looked directly in the face of Dr. Welch sitting on the edge of his berth with next to nothing on and as cheerful as though he had had eight hours' sleep instead of about four. We breakfasted in the station but he had to hurry off for a 9 o'clock appointment at the Rockefeller Institute or somewhere.

After the birthday party H.C. returned to Boston much refreshed from his holiday in Georgia. The last week in April his friend, Evarts A. Graham, arrived from St. Louis for a tour of duty as Surgeon-in-Chief *pro tem.* H.C. had watched the development of the Barnes Hospital with more than passing interest, for it had grown to full stature over the same period of time as had the Brigham Hospital whose surgical direction he had finally chosen to undertake. In addition, much of the recent experimental work in the Surgical Laboratory had centered around the use of various substances for visualizing the gall bladder in X-ray and as this was a field in which Dr. Graham had long worked Cushing's invitation to him had been greeted with enthusiasm by the junior staff.

There were the usual meetings in May and June, but H.C. this year seems to have missed most of them except for the Congress of American Physicians and Surgeons on 5 May in which he took part in a general discussion on the ductless glands.[2]

Brain Tumor Classification

Percival Bailey had continued to work feverishly upon brain tumor classification. The paper on the medulloblastomas in 1924 had created a very considerable stir and at a meeting of the Harvard Medical Society on 24 March 1925 Bailey read a general paper on the classification of tumors of the glioma group. It will be recalled that three of the primary categories of brain tumor are: those arising from glands within the head (pituitary and pineal); tumors growing from the coverings of the brain (meningiomas); and finally the

[2] "Ductless glands (discussion)." *Transactions of the Congress of American Physicians and Surgeons,* 1925, *13,* 61-64.

"gliomas"—tumors of the glial cells which form the supporting matrix of the brain and spinal cord. In the adult brain there are many different types of these supporting glial cells and each type may develop tumor growth. In Bailey's view, however, all originate from a common cellular ancestor. Through patient study of Cushing's vast material Bailey was able to arrange the different types of glial tumors in an evolutionary tree, indicating their interrelations and embryological origin. With full clinical records at their disposal, it was possible for the two men to correlate the life history of each tumor with its histological type. H.C. had arranged to have Bailey take another year off in Europe; before his departure in the summer of 1925 he and Cushing had made the manuscript on the classification of gliomas ready for press.[3]

After the family were safely at Little Boar's Head for the summer Cushing devoted himself to putting the finishing touches on the glioma monograph and to the preparation of another detailed work for the Cameron Prize Lectures to be presented in October.[4] In January 1924 he had received a cordial letter from Arthur R. Cushny, the Professor of Pharmacology at Edinburgh, notifying him that he had been nominated for the Cameron Prize for 1924-1925. The Prize was founded in 1878 by Dr. Andrew R. Cameron of New South Wales, and was regarded as an honor of considerable historical importance, involving the delivery of three lectures and an honorarium of £200. Among previous recipients had been Pasteur (1889), Lister (1890), Ferrier (1891), and Horsley (1893); the only American having been Simon Flexner (1911). The Foundation stipulated that the lectures should incorporate the results of research with which the Prizeman himself had been intimately associated. Cushing accordingly settled upon the three subjects to which he had devoted primary attention during the previous twenty-five years; in a sense, therefore, the Cameron Lectures may be looked upon as Cushing's scientific autobiography up to 1925.

The first lecture was entitled "The third circulation and its channels." In preparing for it he had consulted his colleagues in physiology—Sherrington, Howell, and others—and he complained that none of the existing textbooks of physiology had an adequate account of the cerebrospinal fluid and its movements. In the brief space of fifty pages Cushing summarized seventy published papers issued on the subject by himself and his pupils since 1901. The bibliography is

[3] *A classification of the tumors of the glioma group on a histogenetic basis with a correlated study of prognosis.* (With P. Bailey). Philadelphia, London, and Montreal, J. B. Lippincott Co., 1926. 175 pp.

[4] *Studies in intracranial physiology and surgery. The third circulation. The hypophysis. The gliomas.* London, Humphrey Milford, Oxford University Press, 1926, 146 pp.

arranged chronologically, ending with Tracy Putnam's important paper on "Chronic subdural haematoma" which had appeared in September 1925.[5] The lecture began appropriately with a reference to Robert Whytt, the Edinburgh neurologist and neurophysiologist of the 18th century who in 1768 first described tuberculous meningitis. He then told how he and Lewis H. Weed in 1912 had posed the problem of the origin of the cerebrospinal fluid and the channels of its escape back into the venous side of the circulation. The details are too technical for inclusion here, but for students of medicine the first Cameron Lecture can be recommended as a model of scientific exposition.

The second lecture, "The pituitary gland as now known," told the story of how, under the stimulus of Edward Sharpey-Schafer, a group of men early in the century had come to study the functions of the pituitary, and how he (H.C.) and Reford in 1907 had come to repeat Paulesco's studies on hypophysectomy. He then summarized developments that had occurred since the publication of the pituitary monograph in 1912. Although this lecture lacks the clarity of that on the cerebrospinal fluid, it is valuable in tracing historical developments in the field. Appended to it is a bibliography of forty-nine papers emanating from his laboratories and clinic.

The third Cameron Lecture, "Intracranial tumours and the surgeon," opened with appreciative allusion to Sir William Macewen, the celebrated Scottish neurosurgeon, and after presenting the historical backgrounds Cushing launched into the subject of tumor classification, giving data on his 1146 verified cases (to 1 September 1925), and then summarized his and Bailey's forthcoming monograph on the gliomas, based on 492 individually studied cases. This lecture has a list of sixty-two papers originating in his clinic.

The reaction of Cushing's friends, known and unknown, to the Cameron Lectures was almost as enthusiastic as it had been for the 'Osler,' and since the new work came so soon on the heels of the biography his productivity seemed to many almost incredible. One editorial comment may be cited as typical of many (*London Hospital Gazette*, September 1926):

> There can be few more interesting figures in the surgical world of today than Professor Harvey Cushing. Starting out some twenty-five years ago to specialise in the surgery of the brain Dr. Cushing rapidly attained a position of great distinction. The way in which it was done can be gathered from a study of his Cameron Lectures, now issued in book form. . . . His distinction is—and it is a distinction which places him for all time in the front rank of scientific investigators, and his almost unique position among surgical specialists—

[5] Putnam, T. J. "Chronic subdural haematoma: its pathology, its relation to pachymeningitis haemorrhagica and its surgical treatment." *Archives of Surgery, Chicago*, September 1925, 2, 329-393.

his distinction is that he has regarded and studied his specialty from every conceivable angle. . . . Here is the right kind of specialist fit to join such former Cameron Prizemen as Pasteur, Lister, Horsley. *Si sic omnes!*

He also heard from many of his friends. From Asher, "You show yourself not alone as a master of surgery but also of experimental medicine." The lectures had been dedicated to his Fellows and Assistant Residents in Baltimore and Boston, and Samuel Harvey wrote, "It was a very gracious thing for you to remember your previous incumbents in the dedication. The debt is in the reverse direction of course." From T. R. Elliott in London, "Nothing that you have ever written, not even your life of Osler, gave me greater pleasure than your Edinburgh lectures. . . . It was so delightful to read the tale of the ever-running current of your thought throughout all the years, and to see it passing by the channels you had made in the hands of your many pupils." From a student, "Your example will, I am sure, spur each one of us on to try and emulate your careful, painstaking manner of research." The letters from Lewis Weed and Evarts Graham may be quoted in greater detail.

Baltimore,
Lewis H. Weed to H.C. *9 June 1926.*

Your new book "Studies in Intracranial Physiology and Surgery" came to me two days ago and as you probably will suspect, I dropped all my work in order to read it from cover to cover. May I tell you that the Lectures form a perfectly charming volume, so interesting and so suggestive of new lines of work? You surely should take satisfaction in the great development of these neurological problems in the hands of the groups around you. The volume shows more graphically than ever the influence of one person in the growth of knowledge of one little corner in medicine. Many, many thanks for the book: I shall prize it greatly as a real contribution. . . .

St. Louis,
Evarts A. Graham to H.C. *2 October 1926.*

When I came home from Europe recently I found a copy of your Cameron Lectures which you so kindly had sent to me. I have read them, not once but twice, and have been thrilled not only by the usual entrancing style which we always expect in products of your pen, but also by the amazing amount of work which your fertile brain has stimulated. I say amazing merely because when one sees a person's work collected in this form it makes an impression of its tremendous volume in a way which is different from that experienced by merely reading the articles as they come out in the current journals.

H.C. had sailed for England on 3 October 1925 and, after a day or two at Brown's Hotel in London, he spent a week with Lady Osler at Oxford going over the voluminous correspondence about the biography. He then proceeded to North Berwick in Scotland where he spent the week-end of 17 October with his friend Sir Edward Sharpey-Schafer, who at the age of seventy-five still occupied the chair of physiology at Edinburgh.[6] The balance of the week he spent *en famille* with the Cushnys at Peffermill House[7] in Craigmillar, a village near Edinburgh. James Slater, one of the younger surgeons at Edinburgh, recalls dining with Cushing at the Infirmary Mess.

> . . . He dined in the Residency and spent an evening in the Mess on the occasion of his Cameron Lectureship. I happened to sit next him and remember his vivacity and fund of stories and the obvious enjoyment he derived as the guest of a lot of young and somewhat boisterous people and the fun with which he entered into choruses which somebody played. However, I recall quite vividly that he left the Mess at a respectable hour in the company of Norman Dott with whom he was staying. One little personal reminiscence of Cushing which impressed me greatly was the fact that after that evening in the Mess I saw nothing of him for some eighteen months and on the next occasion he not only recognised me but was actually able to name me.

The Cameron Lectures were given on the 19th, 20th, and 22d. With typical Scottish thoughtfulness it was arranged so that he was not obliged to lecture the day after Professor Cushny's elaborate dinner for the Cameron Prize Lecturer given the night of the 20th. On the 23d H.C. paid a visit to Sir James Mackenzie's Institute at St. Andrew's and gave an informal lecture to the staff.[8] On the 24th he sailed for New York, and early in November he was once more surrounded by work—proof sheets of two monographs and a large volume of correspondence and clinical work which had accumulated in his absence.

His staff, which had now grown considerably, was eagerly awaiting him. Bailey was still in France but Gilbert Horrax had been in charge of the neurological service during his absence. Leo M. Davidoff had come as Assistant Resident, and Tracy J. Putnam was industriously feeding purified growth hormone of the anterior pituitary to one of two Boston bull terrier litter-mates, Putnam being the Arthur Tracy Cabot Fellow for the year in charge of the Laboratory of Surgical Research.

Voluntary Graduate Assistants

Cushing at this time had begun to encourage men to come to his clinic as voluntary graduate assistants. Charles P. Symonds of London had initiated the custom in 1920 when he had come for four months from June through September. He was followed in October 1920 by Frédéric Bremer of Brussels, who spent the winter of 1920-1921 working with Percival Bailey on the problem of experimental dia-

[6] The last time he had stayed with Schafer (1901) H.C. had caught the mumps!

[7] This historic manor house will be known to readers of Scott as the 'Dumbiedikes' of *The Heart of Midlothian.* Cushny died of a stroke in February 1926.

[8] Sir James had died the preceding January.

betes insipidus.[9] During the spring of 1925 Arthur Van Dessel of Louvain had served as a voluntary assistant, and when Cushing arrived from Europe, Jean Morelle, also from Louvain, was awaiting him, as was Francis C. Grant of Philadelphia who remained from October until May. Boris M. Fried, the Russian pathologist, also attached himself to Cushing's clinic at this time and remained there for seven years. During the winter of 1925-1926 two others arrived, Walter Lehmann from Göttingen, who spent three months, and Edgar F. Fincher, Jr., from Atlanta.

From 1925 until Cushing's resignation in 1932 the voluntary assistants added much to the life of the clinic. After they had become acclimated Cushing often gave them very considerable responsibility. To each one on arrival he assigned a problem, and while he usually delegated one of his staff members to supervise the arbeit so assigned, he himself generally kept in close touch and always gave painstaking attention to any paper that might result. After his own experience with Kocher and Kronecker, he never attempted in the first instance to write a paper for one of his pupils, but his revisions now and again were tantamount to primary composition.

1926

At the beginning of each year, usually in the first week, Cushing spent a day interviewing prospective house officers. It was a responsibility that he took most seriously and a man was seldom accepted whom he had not personally examined; notes were made on each candidate and he often drew sketches of the men to help his memory. This year he met a group of some thirty hopeful applicants on 12 January and he and his senior associates selected for 1927 Cobb Pilcher, William J. German, Trygve Gunderson, Cameron L. Haight, Joseph Barr, and Richard H. Meagher, among others. Franc D. Ingraham, who had just had a year in surgical research at Johns Hopkins, was chosen as Assistant Resident.

Cushing's first appearance outside Boston during the year was in Baltimore on 22 January when he attended the unveiling ceremony for the portrait of Revere Osler at the newly founded Tudor and Stuart Club, an initial gift of money together with Revere's books having been presented by his parents to the Johns Hopkins University in his memory. Following the unveiling a dinner had been arranged for Dr. Dean Lewis, the recently appointed Professor of Surgery. Those who arranged the latter occasion had inadvertently caused Cushing considerable annoyance, for if there was anything that

[9] Bailey, P., and Bremer, F. "Experimental diabetes insipidus." *Archives of Internal Medicine,* December 1921, *28,* 773-803.

made him "see red," it was to be asked in advance of a meeting for a "news release." To him it savored of commercialism, and when such a request for the Lewis dinner arrived by telegram from the hallowed precincts of the Johns Hopkins Hospital he concluded that they were all on the road to perdition. Hence the following amusing (but unsent) protest dated 16 January 1926 to Lewis H. Weed:

What in the world has got into you people? Here I am, an unoffending person still loyal to the J.H.H. and its traditions. I had a note from Bloodgood some months ago saying that they were going to give a dinner for Dean Lewis and establish a Johns Hopkins Surgical Society. We are already surfeited with surgical societies, but if they want to establish one at the J.H.H., all right, and I thought I would come to pay my respects to my friend Dean. Shortly after, I received a notice, from Bloodgood I believe, already printed, stating that I was going to make a speech and represent the Alumni at said dinner. I don't do this sort of thing at all well, but there was nothing for it but to let the matter go and I thought my friends of the Surgical Department would make allowances.

But now comes a telegram from Walter Hughson, saying: "Please send as soon as possible the abstract of your speech at the Lewis dinner." What in thunder do you fellows think I am doing; sitting up nights writing a speech? I thought that I would appear at the dinner, and if the spirit moved me I would say how pleasant it was to welcome Dean Lewis into our J.H.H. ranks. But *this* simply terrifies me. If there are to be reporters present and if speeches made at this dinner are to appear in the press, this is the kind of spirit I don't like to see at the J.H.H. or anywhere in medical circles. It certainly is not the kind of dinner I have been accustomed to attend in days gone by in Baltimore.

If H.C. had felt that his colleagues at Hopkins were slipping from grace he could not have been annoyed with them long for he shortly made anonymously an outright gift of $25,000 to establish a fellowship in the old Hunterian; this he announced in a letter of 27 March to President Goodnow:

As our contribution to the Johns Hopkins Endowment Fund, Mrs. Cushing and I wish to give the University the sum of twenty-five thousand dollars, the income of which we would like to have used to provide a salary for the Fellow in charge of the Hunterian Laboratory at the Medical School. The reasons for wishing to establish this fellowship are purely sentimental ones. I feel under great obligation to the University for having permitted me, some twenty and more years ago, together with Dr. W. G. MacCallum, to organize the original Hunterian Laboratory in which I subsequently passed some most happy and profitable years. During that period, I was permitted to appoint each year a recent graduate into whose hands the general supervision of the laboratory was put. There exists somewhere in its archives a bound volume of reprints of papers which were written therefrom, together with a letter telling something of how the laboratory came to be established and of the early workers there.

Since my transfer to Boston, I have had the privilege of conducting a similar laboratory and of appointing annually the Fellow in charge, and regard it as one of the great assets of my position here. Hence it is my desire that the selection of the incumbent for this proposed Hunterian Fellowship should be in the hands of the Professor of Surgery at the Johns Hopkins, or of the Senior

Professor of Surgery, should the department ever grow to be of such a size that it comes to be under two heads.

I have had some correspondence with Dean Weed on this subject and now wish to bring the matter to your personal attention. I trust that it will not make the gift less acceptable to have us designate the purpose for which we desire to have it used. I am aware that universities prefer unrestricted gifts and it is perhaps not the thing for us to specify the disposition of a contribution under the circumstances of your present campaign. May I request further that the names of the donors be not made public, at least until I shall have retired from my present academic post?

A handwritten note from Lewis Weed to Mrs. Cushing expressed the feeling at the Hopkins:

. . . I have told Dr. Cushing by letter how much good this endowment will do in the training of young men but I wish also to tell you of my personal appreciation of this very generous gift.

All that I can really say is that I think that this gift of yours and Dr. Cushing's is just like you both. Both of you have always been so wonderfully good to the young people around you: you have so markedly broadened the viewpoint, the horizon of so many of us. And now this personal influence of you both is going to be continued permanently! It is really a fine thing for the medical school, and I, like all who know of your intention, am elated. If only you and Dr. Cushing were here in Baltimore to add a personal hand to the training of these young men, I should be more than happy—I should be content. So please let me thank you and Dr. Cushing. I should like to see the Fellowship named at once the "Harvey Cushing Fellowship," but I realize that you do not want it so.

To H.C. Weed wrote, "Under Dean Lewis and Ferdinand Lee the Hunterian is coming back into its own. There is tremendous activity in the old building and it calls to my mind the type of work carried out when I was there with you. I miss, however, in that laboratory only one thing: there is no longer the group of happy people around Joe seated at a microtome."

In March, somewhat to H.C.'s surprise, the War Department buried the hatchet and awarded him the Distinguished Service Medal "for exceptionally meritorious and distinguished services in the performance of duties of great responsibility as Colonel, Medical Corps, United States Army, Senior Consultant of Neurological Surgery, A.E.F., and in direct charge of the treatment of gunshot wounds of the head in hospitals of the 1st Army, American Expeditionary Forces."

Cushing's interest in medical history had not lapsed in the course of the war years and during the writing of the 'Osler' it had been greatly stimulated; he had had little opportunity, however, to study the catalogues, and the inroads which the war and a rapidly growing family had made on his income did not permit him to buy as freely as he would have in other circumstances. About 1926 he once again became an avid student of old book catalogues, and the more scholarly men in the trade, such as Wilfred Voynich and E. P. Goldschmidt of London, were frequent visitors. They had studied Cushing's tastes and interests and knew his susceptibilities. He had commenced to acquire a number of medical incunabula and an occasional early manuscript. Major purchases in this sphere were generally referred to Arnold Klebs for advice, or to Edward C. Streeter, who was then living nearby at 280 Beacon Street. During

THE UNITED STATES OF AMERICA

TO ALL WHO SHALL SEE THESE PRESENTS, GREETING:
THIS IS TO CERTIFY THAT
THE PRESIDENT OF THE UNITED STATES OF AMERICA
PURSUANT TO ACT OF CONGRESS APPROVED JULY 9, 1918.
HAS AWARDED TO
Harvey Cushing
THE DISTINGUISHED SERVICE MEDAL
FOR
EXCEPTIONALLY MERITORIOUS AND DISTINGUISHED SERVICES
IN THE PERFORMANCE OF DUTIES OF GREAT RESPONSIBILITY AS
Colonel, Medical Corps, United States Army, Senior Consultant of Neurological Surgery, A. E. F., and in direct charge of the treatment of gunshot wounds of the head in hospitals of the 1st Army, American Expeditionary Forces.
GIVEN UNDER MY HAND AT THE CITY OF WASHINGTON
THIS *fourth* DAY OF *March*, 19*26*.

Dwight F. Davis
SECRETARY OF WAR

RECORDED IN THE OFFICE OF
THE ADJUTANT GENERAL
Robert C. Davis
THE ADJUTANT GENERAL

THE DIPLOMA OF THE D.S.M.

these years Streeter had weekly meetings at his house, usually on Sunday evenings, of a small group of students (of all ages) interested in medical history when he went to great trouble to put out books from his own remarkable collection. On Sunday, 7 January, H.C. attended one of these sessions and the next morning he sent Streeter a copy of the newly published *Iconography of Andreas Vesalius* by Spielmann with a note, "I enjoyed the 'class' enormously last night and am always delighted to have a glimpse of your treasures. I don't know whether I should have permitted myself to let you make that addition to my collection last night, but I could not resist the temptation." H.C. had purloined a Vesalian item from Streeter to fill a gap in his own collection. Whenever he found something he did not possess relating to Vesalius in the hands of another private collector he took it for granted that the volume in question was his birthright; in fact there was never a question. However, he always cleared his conscience by being overgenerous in making amends for his bibliophilic larceny.

The iconography of Vesalius was one of his own particular passions and he had been in correspondence on the subject with Spielmann and others since 1907; it is not surprising therefore that he contributed a foreword to the Spielmann monograph. "In no country," he wrote, "will this volume be more welcome than in the United States—a country which, even in Vesalius' latter days, was nothing more than a wilderness of immeasurable extent. . . . But Vesalius' life shows that medical science then as now knew no bounds and its historical figures are nowhere more appreciated and honoured than by those who endeavour to emulate them in a part of the world unmapped and unknown in the days when the *Fabrica* was written." In his much grangerized copy of Spielmann's book is a large collection of letters from Vesalian scholars, including Osler, Garrison, and many others, and to these letters he has appended a note describing how he obtained the large portrait of Vesalius that was later left with his books to the Yale Medical Library: "On my return from France in 1919, rather the worse for wear, I saw the Ryman portrait with W.O. in Oxford. This was on January 20th, as told in my diary. I subsequently saw Spielmann in London on the 31st, and he assured me that the picture which Ryman had secured must surely be the Donaldson portrait, and he showed me a photograph of it, but I was sure he was mistaken. Spielmann subsequently went to Oxford, as these letters show, and, as his Iconography explains, found it was still another 'copy' [?] of the Louvre portrait."

Vesalius was much on his mind during the spring of 1926, and on 27 April he read a paper on the Vesalian portraits to the Harvard Medical Society. His renewed interest in books and medical libraries was no doubt also stimulated by Lewis Weed's activities in Baltimore in planning the Welch Library. Edward L. Tilton, the architect, had come to Boston on Monday 26 April to show H.C. the plans, and the next day the following significant letter went off to Weed—significant in the light of the plans which he ultimately drew up for the Yale Medical Library, where there are no flights of steps to deter a student from entering:

Thanks for sending Mr. Tilton on. I had him for dinner last night and he showed us the plans. I was delighted to see them and haven't a thing to criticise. What a monument to Popsy this library will be! It ought to become the most important in the country next to the Surgeon General's.

If I had been making the plans, I think I would have put the main students' reading room on the ground floor so that they wouldn't even have to go up a step to drift in. Even a single flight of steps may be a deterent; but then, that is a small matter and after all, it's a very low climb. And there is only one thing to consider, that books breed books, and so soon as there is a noble home for them they multiply beyond all expectations, so that I estimate that in twenty years your apparently abundant stacks will be over-crowded. I would have liked therefore to see the stacks in the basement floor compact sliding stacks like those in the Bodleian where the less important and infrequently consulted old files of big journals could be stored without necessarily having space between the files for standing room. But this too is a small matter, and I think that the entire outlay is ideal.

In reply Weed gave interesting details concerning their plans for future expansion and added that he hoped H.C.'s prediction of over-crowded stacks in twenty years would be fulfilled, although they now had only 50,000 books with space for 400,000, as well as provision for future expansion if necessary.

At this time one of H.C.'s former pupils, who had become dean in a leading medical school and had served for three years in that capacity, requested his advice about accepting a threatened re-appointment to the deanship. H.C.'s reply is characteristic, since deans as deans were a race of men for whom he had little sympathy:

H.C. to a former pupil *10 June 1926.*

. . . Now for your other project. I should be perfectly emphatic about it if I were you. You would make a great dean or a great anything else that you cared to put your hand to, but an administrative capacity is not such a rare thing in this world as a research capacity. I am quite sure that the deanship cut in on Howell's work even in days when the school was much simpler. You had better ask him if that wasn't so. What I recall of research in the occasional few years when I was fortunate enough to be able to do nothing else is an all-engrossing job, and you can't divide it with anything else. Then, there is such a thing as a school being over-deaned, as I think ours is. If you really want my advice, therefore, I would get out when your three years are up and let someone else take it on. But it's a matter about which you will have to make up your own mind, of course, and whatever your decision you will have my best wishes.

Cushing's attention to detail is well illustrated in the time and trouble he took in planning testimonial dinners. In April he had learned that his old friend and teacher of M.G.H. days, E. Wyllys Taylor, then in charge of neurology at Harvard, was to have his sixtieth birthday on 7 May. A dinner was of course indicated and funds were promptly raised for a portrait. Letters went flying in all directions—to Shattuck, Richardson, Sears, Derby, Zinsser, Peabody, Christian, and many others. Henry Viets was asked to send out a more general notice to Taylor's former pupils and by 3 May he reported seventy-nine acceptances. Viets had received the following specific instructions. "One thing I think is very important, namely, that place cards should be put at the tables. Nothing is more confusing when there is a large dinner than for people to be scrambling for seats. There ought to be place cards with a schema in the outer hall so that people may know where they are to sit." Stanley Cobb and Tracy Putnam were assigned the responsibility of preparing a masque to brighten up the occasion; this turned out to be a slight boomerang as far as H.C. was concerned, for the masque consisted of a mock honorary degree ceremony with Bronson Crothers, "Sir" Henry Viets, Harvey Cushing, and James Ayer as the victims. Cushing's citation ran as follows:

Dean: Bring Professor Cushing to the throne!
(Music begins slowly as before, then—)
Executioner: (sings—to the tune of "Anna Held" B^b)
Neurology, Surgery—
No one mixes them so well—
With his scalpel he beats hell,
But Biography is his "Forté,"
Two thousand pages never phases
Our Harvey!
Dean: I, by the authority vested in me,
present you with the degree of
H.C.
which, being interpreted, means
Harvey Cushing
or
Human Cocktail
the ingredients of which are
Art, Letters, Surgery, Neurology
and
Charming Personality
May you live long and prosper!

Sometime later Stanley Cobb explained: "The Dean in this scene was Tracy and the Executioner was myself and I sang the verse, which I am also guilty of having written. In spite of the fact that he was momentarily annoyed at the degree, he relaxed after the meaning of the initials was elucidated and that evening he wrote me an extremely nice and characteristic note."

Cushing himself presided at the dinner. He recalled the case of the meningiomatous John Maloney, which he and Taylor had seen at the M.G.H. in 1895, and added "It made a great impression on me and started my interest in neurosurgery." In referring to Taylor he said, "This unconscious influence of a teacher on a pupil is the most effective kind of teaching." He ended by telling one of his better stories—about Henry Head and the peephole in a girls' school.

. . . One may never tell what a small episode will lead to. Henry Head the neurologist once explained to me fully how it was that the Great War would not have occurred had he not on an occasion looked through a peephole in a door in a girls' school. He happened to be making a visit with the Superintendent and they passed one of the classroom doors, all of which were provided with peepholes for the convenience of the supervisor. He was asked if he cared to take a look. He did, and his eye lighted on a person conducting the class with whom he promptly became enamoured. They went in. He was introduced. She ultimately became his wife. They were polylinguists and travelled much when he was not writing books. Once when they were bicycling in France, he with his strongly Teutonic cast of countenance and VanDyke beard was heard talking German to his wife in an out-of-the-way countryside where there were military stores. The murder of the Austrian Crown Prince had recently taken place. The French were uneasy. He was arrested; a camera was found in their duffel bag. Explanations were useless. Complications ensued which reached international proportions. So the war was precipitated all because of a look through a peephole. There were innumerable other details which I must omit just as I must omit many details of what has happened since Wyllys Taylor and I met over that man with a lump on his head who came to the M.G.H. some years ago and the climax of this present moment.

On 21 and 22 May the Society of Clinical Surgery held its annual meeting in Boston, and H.C. arranged an elaborate program of clinics, operations, and papers. During May he had also been at work on a commencement address to be given on 5 June at Jefferson Medical College in Philadelphia. Thomas McCrae had induced him to accept this responsibility, and in the course of the exercises he was awarded an honorary Litt.D.

His address, 'Consecratio medici,' although it dealt with an old theme, namely, the iniquities of too much science and too little clinical training in the medical students' curriculum, was probably more widely quoted than any of Cushing's general addresses, and he chose it as the title for his first collected volume of addresses which appeared in 1928.[10] Before permitting publication of the address originally he wrote to his trusted adviser, Professor F. T. Lewis, scholarly Harvard anatomist, asking him to read the manuscript and saying, "What I want to know is whether there is anything in it which could possibly hurt the feelings of a devoted laboratory worker like yourself, for if there is, I would not care to publish it. I set much store by your opinion." Lewis returned some grammatical corrections but expressed great enthusiasm about the general theme, and there were many other enthusiastic letters, including one from William Lyon Phelps who added "I am glad that you mentioned 'Bonny Brier Bush' for those last chapters ought not to perish."

There were also those who disagreed with his general theme, as the following letter from Dr. Drinker indicates:

Cecil K. Drinker to H.C. *Boston, 16 June 1926.*

Dear Dr. Cushing: I have read your paper with a great deal of interest and

[10] *Consecratio medici and other papers.* Boston, Little, Brown, and Company 1928, 276 pp.

as you no doubt expected, I disagree with certain parts of it. I am one of the few men teaching in a fundamental department who has had a medical internship and a general residency in medicine, and who has eventually been on the visiting staff of the Brigham, the General and the City Hospital in charge of a ward of patients at each place. I have taught fourth year students on the wards in clinical medicine and I have taught first year students as they come to us quite raw here in the laboratories. I am inclined to believe that it is a mistake to distract the students from the difficult things which are given them in the first two years for the incomplete and vague attractions of the clinic. I know that it seems a hard baptism to think of coming into medicine and spending two years without seeing anything of it, but our students are picked from a large group and certainly they ought to be able to stand such an apprenticeship without being stultified by it.

I wonder what real evidence there is that the average medical student is less adept in the art of medicine today than was the student seventy-five years ago. It was no real loss in artistry when Sanctorius first used Galileo's pulsilogia, when the clinical thermometer and the stethoscope came along. Is it so necessary to feel that the X-ray, the chemical test and the electrocardiogram take away from the art of the profession?

Since the war Cushing's life had, despite his intense activity, sloped on the whole toward the sunny side. His efforts in the fields of medicine, surgery, and writing had brought him wide recognition and many honors; and his children, now grown up and with strong personalities in their own right, were an ever-increasing source of pleasure and pride. On the morning of 12 June, while preparing to operate on a woman who had gone blind the preceding day because of pressure from a brain tumor, word came to him by telephone from New Haven that Bill, his eldest son, had been killed early that morning in a motor crash near Guilford, Connecticut. With extraordinary control Cushing gave the necessary instructions to the authorities in New Haven and proceeded with the scheduled operation. His team were not informed of what had happened until the operation had been completed. The blow was particularly bitter, for Bill, after some academic floundering when he first went to Yale, had learned how to work and had become a student of considerable promise. Fortunately for Cushing his grief could be assuaged by his work and his innumerable distractions: after a brief period with the family at Little Boar's Head, he plunged into a summer of almost incessant operating.

His rapidly increasing clinical burdens were to a great extent lightened by the devotion of his loyal assistant, Gilbert Horrax, whom H.C. regarded as the most steady and reliable of all the men he had trained. Horrax frequently "opened," *i.e.*, started the operation and exposed the tumor, after which Cushing would take over. Horrax might then return an hour or so later to do the closure. Basically, however, H.C. disliked making such demands upon his assistants, since one of his *dicta* was that a successful operation should be carried through from beginning to end by a single person.

Those who were close to him at this time recall his extraordinary ability to refresh himself by a brief nap. After long operations he would go down to the examining room next to his office and lie down for a short time after having given instructions to his secretary to awaken him in fifteen minutes. In this way he was able to recuperate quickly from the fatigue entailed by his exacting surgical procedures.

During 1926 he seldom missed an operation any week-day, and his assistants recall with some grief that he had a particular fondness for scheduling "double-headers" on Saturday afternoons and holidays, usually on the pretext of their being acute emergencies—at least so it seemed. His surgical technique was growing increasingly fastidious and until the introduction of electrosurgery, it appeared to his staff that operations had become correspondingly long. Cerebellar explorations, which usually required a minimum of two hours for the closure alone, often occupied a stretch of five or six hours between the initial incision and the final stages of the dressing. The reason for these slower procedures probably stemmed from the fact that Cushing was now teaching men from abroad in ever-increasing numbers. There was seldom an operation, after 1925, that was not witnessed by a group of onlookers, often men who had come from great distances to see him operate. His first and second assistants might also have come from afar—such men as Paul Martin of Brussels, Norman Dott of Edinburgh, Hugh Cairns of London, not to mention the large group of voluntary graduate assistants described earlier in this chapter. Each operation, accordingly, became in a sense a teaching exercise. On the rare occasions when he operated alone with his immediate team, consisting of Gilbert Horrax and one of his American assistant residents, he might take short cuts and speed up the procedure, but whenever there was an audience, particularly a foreign audience, he operated in the Halsted manner with the greatest deliberation, often carrying through the entire procedure himself, even to the last stitch and the last fold of the dressing. Ordinarily, however, after he had gained confidence in his Assistant Resident or when Horrax's services were available, Cushing would withdraw and leave the closure to the team. Toward the end of an assistant resident's term of appointment, he might play the rôle of first assistant himself and allow the resident to carry out the craniotomy, but most of his staff agreed that H.C. was not a particularly restful first assistant. Unconsciously, when things became tense, he seemed to take the instruments out of the operator's hands and proceed to deal with the crisis himself.

Many experienced surgeons who came to Cushing's clinic were

surprised that he assumed so much of the detail himself. Abdominal surgeons who were accustomed to circulate from one operation to the next, leaving openings and closures to assistants, and who through such organization were able to assume responsibility for fifteen or twenty operations a day, expressed surprise that Cushing seldom undertook more than one major procedure a day—the double-headers were rare, and a third operation would be undertaken only in the case of an extreme emergency.

Arrest of hemorrhage had always been the main cause of delay in neurosurgical procedures and from his first experience back in M.G.H. days, Cushing began to exercise his ingenuity in devising ways and means of securing hemostasis. The scalp is itself a highly vascular tissue, and one of the reasons why surgeons were loath to operate on the brain was the difficulty in controlling hemorrhage from the skin, let alone that from underlying muscle, bone, and cerebral tissue. As we have seen, Cushing started logically by introducing the head tourniquet; this was abandoned when he found that surface bleeding could be controlled by injecting the skin with the blood-vessel constrictor, adrenalin. This, added to the light tension of the pendant hemostats on the skin edges, completely prevented serious bleeding from this source. To deal with bone Victor Horsley's sterile bone wax sufficed and having once entered the skull, where bleeding might be particularly serious and awkward to handle, he used the small silver clip, developed in 1910, which could be applied to vessels that were out of reach of the ligature. Pieces of fresh muscle were used to stop capillary bleeding. Suction was introduced to deal with gross hemorrhage, especially when occurring in deep cavities. He also considered the use of fibrin, the normal constituent of a blood clot, and started Ernest Grey on the problem of developing a fibrin preparation that might be used to promote clotting.[11] But hemorrhage, even with all these ingenious devices, continued to be a serious problem and there were many types of tumor that he dared not touch because of their vascularity.[12]

Electrosurgical Procedures

The use of high-frequency currents in surgery did not originate with Cushing, but their value in neurological surgery was first estab-

[11] Grey, E. "Fibrin as a haemostatic in cerebral surgery." *Surgery, Gynecology, and Obstetrics,* October 1915, *21,* 452-454. Since they lacked "thrombin," the clotting enzyme, Grey's fibrin preparation proved relatively ineffective as did Harvey's fibrin paper (Harvey, S.C. "Fibrin paper as an haemostatic agent," *Annals of Surgery,* 1918, *68,* 66-70).

[12] Attention must be directed to the valuable historical résumé on "Hemostasis in neurosurgery," by Richard Upjohn Light which has lately been published under the auspices of the Harvey Cushing Society in the September number of the *Journal of Neurosurgery,* 1945, *2,* 414-434.

lished by him. The genito-urinary surgeons had tried various forms of high-frequency current in dealing with benign enlargements of the prostate, strictures, and other conditions of urinary tract obstruction and as early as 1911 W. L. Clark had used them in general surgery, particularly for dealing with malignant growths such as cancer of the breast.[13]

Sometime in the spring or summer of 1926[14] Cushing's interest was drawn to the possibilities of using high-frequency currents to assist with the more vascular tumors and in July he consulted the physicist attached to the Harvard Cancer Commission, Dr. W. T. Bovie, who had developed two separate high-frequency circuits to aid in removing cancerous growths, one designed to cut tissue without bleeding, and the other to coagulate, for example, a vein that had to be severed or a vessel already open and bleeding. Cushing and Bovie experimented with these currents and they developed various loops, balls, and steel points which could be attached to a sterilizable handle for use in applying the current to cerebral tissue. The first surgical trials in the operating room took place on 1 October. H.C.'s operative note states:

> This operation was a perfect circus—many ringed. The New England Surgical Association was here and almost every hand was occupied with them. I had persuaded Dr. Bovie to bring his electrosurgical unit over here to let me see what I could do with his cutting loop. This had necessitated re-electrifying the operating room. Dr. Greenough appeared with four or five coughing Frenchmen with colds in their heads, the student who was acting as possible donor fainted and fell off the seat. It was a little too much for Davidoff's successor [Cairns] who has been here only 2-3 days so that I finally had to call in Horrax. The patient, what is more, began to show marked falling off in r.b.c. and hemoglobin

[13] Clark, W. L. "Oscillatory desiccation in the treatment of accessible malignant growth and minor surgical conditions. A new electrical effect." *Journal of Advanced Therapy*, 1911, *29*, 169-180.

[14] Dr. Samuel Harvey suggests that it may have been earlier than this. Writing to Dr. Light he states: "John Morton and I were attending a session of the American Medical Association in Atlantic City in June 1925, and were watching a demonstration of the use of a desiccating and cutting diathermy machine on a big block of beef, such as is regrettably unobtainable these days! Dr. Cushing came along, stopped to speak to us, and in a purely jocular fashion, one of us, I am not sure which, said, 'Here's something you ought to use on the brain!' Not that we had any idea it was applicable there, but I think with the mischievous purpose of stirring Cushing up at the thought of employing such a gross and disgusting procedure as was evidenced in the demonstration. We did not get the reaction we expected from him. He seemed rather thoughtful, and we separated after a time, with no further thought about the incident. He apparently returned to Boston, and being aware that they were trying out Clark's method of removing malignancies at the Huntington, established contact there. Bovie of course was the physicist, and was working at the time on improving the high frequency apparatus and was in the process of developing a better machine than had been manufactured before. It may have been that Cushing had this in the works before he went to Atlantic City, but he gave no evidence of it at the time, and I cite it as evidence—scarcely necessary—of his alertness and aggressiveness in picking up a new idea."

which had progressively dropped after his primary operation to this morning when his blood was only 2,800,000. In spite of all this, and more, things went surprisingly well. . . . Under novocain a flap was this time turned down with base well in the temporal region so that the scalp could be entirely removed over the situation of the growth, something I should have done at the previous operation. On elevating the flap a large clot was disclosed which was removed by the sucker and a considerable amount of bleeding was started up afresh. I then roughly outlined the remaining extracranial crescent of tumor in the lower part of the field and in order to do so had to go through temporal muscle to get down to temporal bone. This was somewhat difficult.

Then with Dr. Bovie's help I proceeded to take off most satisfactorily the remaining portion of tumor with practically none of the bleeding which was occasioned in the preceding operation. The loop acted perfectly and blood stilling was almost complete but whether we would venture to use anything of this kind in the brain tissue itself I am at a loss to know for almost certainly it would cause convulsions.

The next day H.C. wrote to Bovie, "In spite of the confusion of our many-ringed circus I was delighted to see how well the loop worked. If I could have had it at the first stage, I would have got along as far as I have now in this stage." The case in question was one of a highly vascular myeloma. After several months' further trial with the unit which Bovie had devised, the circuits were submitted to the Liebel Flarsheim Company for commercial construction. Mr. Liebel, the head of the firm, took a personal interest in the development and as a pilot in his own right he flew his plane back and forth to Boston on many occasions while the new equipment was being perfected, and presented H.C. with the first unit.

Cushing, meanwhile, was so much encouraged by the success of the new procedure that he called back all of his patients with supposedly inoperable meningiomas, especially those of the olfactory groove and also the highly vascular blood-vessel tumors (hemangiomas), and proceeded to try out the new electrosurgical procedure. Although his mortality rate increased somewhat during 1927 as a result of attempting tumor removals that he would not have dreamed of approaching without electrosurgery, his success with the new technique was almost phenomenal. During the second half of 1926 and all of 1927 he spent much more time than usual in the operating room and his literary productivity for a time diminished in consequence. In 1926 there were only three published papers, one of them an annual report. His first detailed reports on electrosurgery appeared in 1927 and 1928.[15]

[15] "The meningiomas arising from the olfactory groove and their removal by the aid of electrosurgery." Glasgow, Jackson, Wylie & Co., Publishers to the University, 1927, 53 pp. Also (in part): *Lancet,* 25 June 1927, *1,* 1329-1339. "Electro-surgery as an aid to the removal of intracranial tumors. With a preliminary note on a new surgical-current generator by W. T. Bovie, Ph.D., Chicago." *Surgery, Gynecology, and Obstetrics,* December 1928, *47,* 751-784.

Leo Davidoff had completed his year as Assistant Resident in September and on 25 September a vigorous Oxford rowing "blue," who had gone originally to the University as a Rhodes Scholar from Australia, arrived in Boston to take Davidoff's place. Hugh Cairns had met Cushing in London the year before, and he came to the Brigham prepared for a year of heavy responsibility. His initial assignment was the patient on whom H.C. first used the electro-surgical cutting knife, and the hurly-burly of that operation gave Cairns a taste of what the rest of the year was going to be like. He had fought as a private with the Australians in Gallipoli, and he later served in France as a junior medical officer; he thrived on work and long hours, but he later confessed that Gallipoli and the Battle of the Marne were as nothing compared with the physical stress of a year as Cushing's neurological resident. He operated all day and in the evenings did dressings, examined patients, and dictated detailed histories; if four or five hours of uninterrupted sleep were obtained in a night, he counted himself fortunate. As a matter of self-protection Cushing had come to delegate more and more responsibility to his resident and since Cairns had come to the clinic when it was at its height, he was obliged to carry the brunt of the responsibility. To survive, he also learned the gentle art of delegating responsibility, as many of the voluntary assistants then in the clinic will remember.

For Cairns the experience proved invaluable and within a year or two of his return he had established himself as one of the leading neurosurgeons in London. In 1935 he was called to Oxford to the newly created Nuffield Professorship of Surgery. A few years later he found himself, as had H.C. after his transfer to Boston, immersed in preparations for a world war. As Chief Neurosurgical Consultant to the R.A.M.C. he became responsible for assembling and training all the mobile neurosurgical units which were to render such conspicuous service throughout the war. When the Surgeon General of the United States Army came to organize our neurosurgical units in World War II, it was natural that he should turn to Cairns for advice concerning British experience.

On the completion of his service in Boston in the autumn of 1927, Cairns received a spirited letter of counsel from his chief:

> Herewith my parting advice. Don't imagine that you can learn everything about the surgery of intracranial tumours in a twelve-month, and from having had a hand in dealing with one or two hundred cases. I have been in this business myself for a long time. After my first year or two, I thought I knew much more about the subject than I now do after twenty-five years. Each year the character of the work changes more than you can possibly imagine. Almost every case brings up new problems or modifies one's impressions of old ones presumably solved. Few things are so permanently settled that one can speak about

them with any degree of finality. That of course is one reason why the work is so engrossing.

Don't rag the general practitioner for sending you cases too late. He is improving in this respect. That he has the possibility of brain tumour on his conscience you may have gathered from the number of "suspects" you have seen on the wards during your year. Even though it is our business to keep ahead of him, we too can make mistakes a-plenty as you have had occasion to learn.

If you find you have a hopeless case and can't benefit the patient, don't at least leave him worse off than he was before. And endeavour to keep your mortality low. Your generation will see an improvement on the 10 per cent mortality for which we have striven, which is considerably better than the *circa* 40 per cent acknowledged by those who engaged in this work a generation ago.

Above all, don't fail to make your own diagnostic commitments; and don't fail in case of a fatality to make your own postmortem examination of the brain and histological studies of the tissues if pathological confrères will permit. The operation itself is only a small part of the work if you are going to try and see all round the subject.

Cushing also reported candidly to Sir Walter Morley Fletcher who had sponsored Cairns' sojourn in Boston (23 Sept.):

A group of us from the hospital have just been down to see Cairns off for his boat as he is sailing tomorrow. He has done excellent work and has made himself much beloved and respected on all sides. I think he has a real future ahead of him if he can be given opportunity really to go ahead with the surgery of the nervous system. He of course has much to learn for though he has been intimately in contact with several hundred cases, the surgery of the nervous system is a complicated and difficult business. However, he has made an admirable start and has great promise.

Now I fear that when he gets home the difficulty will be that he will have to help carry the load of general surgery at the London and may be given very little opportunity to profit by the start he has made here. I think he has the right idea and would like to go down and live near the hospital and merge himself in the activities and forego any outside practice. This is the only way really for him to come out on top and he, I think, sees the point. If he has to go and scrabble for work in a nursing home, his interests will be divided and he will end up where most men of the sort end up, on the usual level. It is too bad that they could not have a few private beds at a place like the London, as we have here, so that a man can receive an occasional surgical fee and thereby eke out his living without having to take his mind off his major problem. But this some day will be arranged, I am sure. Meanwhile, it's possible that you might be able to do something to keep him going.

I would appreciate it greatly if you would perhaps send for him and, if you can spare the time, have a talk with him and find out in what way he thinks he has profited by his sojourn here and what he would like to do in the future. Meanwhile, my affectionate greetings to you and your family.

In October 1935 Cairns made a follow-up study of the end results on all patients who had been operated upon during the twelve months from September 1926 to September 1927.[16] Three hundred

[16] "The ultimate results of operations for intracranial tumors." *Yale Journal of Biology and Medicine*, May 1936, *8*, 421-492.

and sixty-nine patients had been admitted to the neurological service during that period with symptoms of intracranial tumor. Of these, 157 cases were verified, either at operation or autopsy; 22 had died in hospital; and 135 had been discharged alive following operation. Thanks to the highly effective system of follow-up developed by Dr. Louise Eisenhardt in Cushing's Brain Tumor Registry each of the 135 cases was traced and a large proportion of those still alive were personally examined by Mr. Cairns. Sixty-three were still alive eight years after their operation and 37 were wage earners. Careful correlation was made between the type of tumor and the duration of survival, the best late results having been seen in the pituitary tumors, the meningiomas, and the slow-growing gliomas of the cerebellum (astrocytomas). A similar study of end results was made in 1934 by W. P. Van Wagenen, Assistant Resident in 1924-1925.

For some months Cushing had been following with deep interest plans for the new School of Medicine and Dentistry at Rochester, New York. His advice had been sought concerning staff, and he had been greatly pleased to learn that John J. Morton, one of his first pupils at the Brigham, had been appointed to the chair of surgery. The associated Strong Memorial Hospital had been planned on a broadly conceived university basis; and when the dedication exercises were held on 25 October, H.C. not only attended but had consented to give a clinic on acromegaly for which his old patients from all over Monroe County were brought in. His efforts were appreciated, for Dr. Whipple, the Dean, later wrote that this, their first surgical clinic, had been a great inspiration.

In November 1926 when Cairns was well in his stride, H.C. turned from his clinical tasks to prepare an address which was delivered at the opening of the Dudley P. Allen Memorial Medical Library in Cleveland—an address that represents Cushing at his literary best.

Great benefactions . . . start with a gift of a handful of books. Some of our great universities have come from equally modest beginnings, books having proved a surer way of making a start than a gift of money. So Yale, for example, was founded.

Each member brought a number of books and presented them to the body; and laying them on the table said these words, or to this effect: 'I give these books for the founding of a College in this Colony.'

Books are tangible property and their sponsors must not only provide for them but make it possible for others to use them. Money gets dissipated and committees disagree as to how it had best be invested or expended. No such question arises when books are concerned; and the soul of an institution that has any pretense to learning comes to reside in its library, no less than does the soul of a profession or of an individual. . . .

If you are to infect the young with the reading-habit, you must set a trap for them, so baited that they will walk into it unawares. Books must be made accessible. It is someone's business in every medical school to teach laboratory methods to the students but it is no one's particular business to teach them how to use medical literature, which to the majority in the long run will be definitely more useful than an experience with smoked paper and Ludwig's drum.

Cushing's avidity in seeking out bookish information is particularly well illustrated by another passage:

. . . A friend has been staying with me whose metabolism and pulse rate in the presence of other people's books run high. He grows exophthalmic with hyperbiblioism. So while you endeavor to concentrate upon your proper tasks he exclaims, "Where did you get this Dolet?" holding up a vaguely remembered calf of a book in his hand. "Oh, I don't remember; someone may have left it at the door, but I always thought it came into being on the bottom shelf of that case in the corner." "Are you aware," says he, ignoring my trivialities, "that Christie knew of only one other copy?" You begin to take interest. "Perhaps someone gave it to me for Christmas. But what about Dolet? Let me see the book; it's only just grown up."

And there it was, sure enough—*A Lyon. Chez Etienne Dolet.* 1542. *Auec priuileige pour dix ans.* And, what is more, with two other Dolet imprints, 'Des tumeurs' and Galen's 'De la raison pour evacuation de sang' newly translated from the Latin into French by a friend of the printer—a veritable triplet.

This is enough; you are lost. The attack is on. Influenza in its abruptness is nothing to it, and days elapse before you are fit to resume your legitimate job. Your fever leads you first to Richard Copley Christie's life of the unfortunate Etienne Dolet, the young Renaissance scholar and printer, contemporary and one-time friend of such as Erasmus and Rabelais, who lived in Lyons when Lyons was a place to live in, and who in the Place Maubert in Paris for his religious opinions, when only thirty-seven, suffered the fate of Servetus and was burned with his books. He had printed possibly eighty pamphlets, which are among the *rares rarissimes* of the collector. In one of them, when translating Plato's Dialogues and quoting Socrates on the immortality of the soul, he had added three words which left the meaning dubious and for this he went to the stake.

And this leaves you anxious to know about Christie, whose chapters, on Rabelais, on Padua, on the trial and the scene at the Place Maubert, give one a vivid picture of the time when printers issued books at the risk of their lives—Christie who worked eight years on his "Dolet" and hints in his preface at a long and continuing illness—but after all, there is this address to write and much time has been lost. Beware the book.[17]

Another responsibility which fell to Cushing in 1926 was a request from students to sponsor their class album. He prepared a preface to the volume in which he addressed himself to the students in ringing language:

Fellow Students of 1926: . . . It is thirty years since the class with which I graduated in the old school on Boylston Street was in your present mood, no less uneasy than you may be about the future and its unknown responsibilities. We still meet occasionally, as I trust you will come to do, for class reunions serve to show in most cases the truth of the poet's saying, that "Success lies in the silence, though fame be in the song." Those of whom perhaps least was expected and of whom least is still heard, in many instances have gained the

[17] *The doctor and his books.* Cleveland, Ohio, privately printed, 1927, 26 pp. Also: *American Journal of Surgery,* January 1928, *4,* 100-110.

greatest happiness in their professional life, in which there can be no finer reward than to deserve the confidence and earn the gratitude of one's patients. Contentment, after all, consists merely in doing the best you can, with what you've got, wherever you may happen to land. . . .

However much the curriculum may change, one generation of medical students differs little from another, and what has happened to us will happen to you, each in his appointed place making what he can of his opportunities. Some of you, whether in laboratory or clinic, will find yourselves the teachers here, thirty years hence, and may, likely enough, be called upon in your turn to supply to some younger men a benediction. Mine to you is in the form of a motto, as old as the Latin tongue whence it is transcribed: "Learn as to live forever; live as to die tomorrow."

1927

In following Cushing's career as a surgeon there has been little occasion thus far to speak of his immediate associates at the Peter Bent Brigham Hospital in the postwar years. The surgical services under Cushing had worked in close cooperation (and nearly always in harmony) with the medical services under Henry Christian. There was healthy rivalry, but there was also a relatively free exchange of consultations and of facilities. Before the war Cushing had set up an anesthesia and metabolism laboratory under Walter Boothby's direction which had served both the medical and surgical services. The large X-ray department, which had gone forward after the war under Lawrence Reynolds and continues to flourish under the able direction of Merrill Sosman, also served both medicine and surgery. Sosman collaborated with Cushing in much of his work and was largely responsible for evolving the details of X-ray therapy for the several groups of radio-sensitive tumors which were being studied microscopically by Percival Bailey.[18] Indeed, the Brigham Hospital showed almost as much leadership in the field of X-ray therapy of cerebral tumors as it had in the surgical handling of these lesions.

Although Cushing himself concentrated heavily on neurological cases the general surgical service at the Brigham Hospital did a large volume of work under the direction of Cushing's three principal associates, John Homans, David Cheever, and William C. Quinby. Homans, whose general textbook of surgery[19] epitomized the teachings of the Harvard Medical School and more particularly the Brigham surgical service, specialized in the surgery of blood vessels and thyroid. Cheever devoted himself in the first instance to abdominal surgery but he, like Homans, touched nearly all branches of

[18] Sosman, M. C. and Putnam, T. J. "Roentgenological aspects of brain tumors—meningiomas." *American Journal of Roentgenology*, January 1925, *13*, 1-12.

[19] Homans, J. *A textbook of surgery*. Springfield, Illinois, Charles C Thomas, 1931. The preface to the first edition begins: "The aim of this book, for which Dr. Harvey Cushing supplied the inspiration, is to record and amplify lectures now given by members of the surgical department of the Harvard Medical School." The 6th edition was published in 1945.

surgery, while Quinby restricted his interests to the genito-urinary field. During these years Francis and Harlan Newton also held appointments on the general surgical service and did much to maintain its high quality. Under Cushing's stimulating direction the general service came to be almost as productive as the neurological. Papers flowed in profusion each year; and with John Homans' 'Textbook,' which has influenced surgical thinking in the country for fifteen years, it is probable that the Brigham became for a time the most influential surgical center in the United States.

During the early months of 1927 Cushing operated steadily and made few public appearances. On 28 January he arranged a meeting held in the Warren Museum at the Harvard Medical School on the history of phrenology, at which Dr. Coues spoke on Spurzheim[20] and a medical student read a paper on the early phrenological societies and their journals.

During the first part of the winter Mrs. Cushing, Barbara, and Betsey were vacationing in the South, and Mary was at home keeping house for her father. There seemed always to be a procession of interesting people in and out of the house; thus on 27 January an old friend of the Cushings, Mrs. William Hooper of Manchester—a remarkable woman who was as quick and amusing in repartee as Cushing himself—brought Mr. and Mrs. A. Edward Newton to tea. Conversation was very spirited and H.C., knowing E.N.'s reputation as a talker, started in on Horace Walpole, Dr. Johnson, and a number of other eighteenth century figures, and talked at such a rate that Mr. Newton had no opportunity to get off on one of his long harangues. This incident illustrates one of Cushing's more interesting characteristics, that of putting in the first word when meeting or greeting anyone, so that he might have command of the situation and direct conversation into channels of his own choosing. This was particularly true when he was dealing with bores or with people who had come to him with a complaint.

In the evening of the day he outtalked Mr. Newton a friend recalls having found him reading Lucien Price's "Hardscrabble Hellas" in the February *Atlantic*. Not wishing to be interrupted by the caller, Cushing promptly read the article aloud to him from beginning to end.

Cushing was very fond of pets, of which there was the usual procession. In the evenings he often turned his attention to Barbara's cocker spaniel, "Red Pepper," and in moments of relaxation from work on the Osler biography he had taught the dog to "play the piano," even as his father before him had taught "Jack." In response

[20] Coues, W. P. "The Spurzheim collection of phrenological casts." *Boston Medical and Surgical Journal,* 1927, *196,* 400-403.

to a quiet question, "Mr. Paderewski, don't you think we might have a little music?" the cocker would trot out of the study across the hall to the drawing room, jump up on the bench, and strike several notes. Then, on hearing the clapping of hands, he would quickly return for his reward. A letter to Lady Osler gives a humorous account of the importance Red Pepper assumed in the family circle: "Kate and Mary got back ten days ago looking very fit, but they spent only one night in Brookline and were more interested in seeing the puppy playing the piano than they were in any tricks which I had acquired during the summer. As a matter of fact, I think I am better as a music teacher for domestic animals than I am as a biographer."

On 16 February H.C. took some of his friends to the Club of Odd Volumes to hear a most scholarly presentation by Edward Streeter on "The French barber surgeons" and the part they had played in spreading the use of the vernacular tongue in medicine. Arnold Klebs had come up from New York to hear the paper, and he and H.C. led a lively discussion afterwards which amused the assembled company, as did Professor Kittredge's learned irrelevancies.

A few days later Cushing was deep in the preparation of an obituary of his friend and near neighbor, James Ford Rhodes, the distinguished American historian, who had done so much during H.C.'s early days in Boston to bring him in touch with many people outside the field of medicine. The appreciation of Rhodes is one of Cushing's more interesting literary pieces since it illustrates his breadth of interest and his capacity to deal with a subject unrelated to medicine.

. . . Largely a self-taught man, and fully aware of the defects of his early schooling, James Rhodes was possibly almost as much surprised as his former Cleveland associates at the reception accorded his first two volumes[21] on their appearance. The chances had been a hundred to one against him. But what is regarded as 'adequate preparation' for a given task may inhibit rather than stimulate productiveness; and with no pretensions to fine writing he had come in due course to engage in his researches with a fresh mind, an exceptional memory, a capacity for sustained literary effort, and a passion for historical truth which more than atoned for any presumed educational deficiencies. He had studied thoroughly the best of his predecessors, ancient and modern, and was not staggered by the accomplishment even of those he felt were the four greatest, Thucydides, Tacitus, Herodotus, and Gibbon—with Tacitus at the top. To preserve from decay the remembrance of what men have done' was, after all, but a modest enterprise in Rhodes's estimation, and he went about his task in his own independent and original way, with candor, sincerity, and thoroughness. Literary style alone never gave any one a niche in the temple of history.

. . . James Rhodes was a modest, unselfish, courteous gentleman to all he met,

[21] Rhodes, J. F. *History of the United States from the compromise of 1850.* New York, Harper & Brothers, Vols. I and II, 1893.

high or low. He could with equal grace and charm of manner hold the affection and esteem of those statesmen and scholars counted among the leaders of his time; or set up a negro barber in business and remain for forty years, in spite of their opposed political views, his undeviating friend and correspondent. But beyond his capacity for and tenacity of friendships, patriotism was his outstanding quality. The sympathies of a true patriot are human, not partisan, and no one in the least blinded by prejudice could have produced those singularly impartial records of that controversial period from 1850 to 1860 which almost overnight raised him from obscurity to a permanent place among our foremost historians.

In March Cushing was found one evening reading proof in his study, talking loudly to himself and gesticulating, completely oblivious that anyone had entered the room. It turned out that he was hurling imprecations at the editorial offices of the A.M.A.—they had changed his English, his spelling, and his punctuation, and Hell would be too kind a fate for the blankety-blank so-and-so's who had wrecked his manuscript. He later cooled off by reading a life of John Coakley Lettsom in preparation for his oration in June before the Medical Society of London where his literary preferences would be respected. This he used to good advantage, as the opening paragraph of that address illustrates:

> One of the tiniest of the Virgin Islands, a speck named Little Vandyke, almost too small to be designated on a map, was once given over—and may still be, for all that is known—to the growing of cotton. On this plantation there happened to be born on November 22, 1744, of Quaker parents, a boy who six years later was sent to England to get his education. His chief asset appears to have been a negro "shuffle," which he had learned from his father's slaves; and without this chance accomplishment, so the story goes, the attention of the Reverend Samuel Fothergill of Warrington would probably not have been drawn to the inconspicuous lad. As it was, he gave him a halfpenny, ere long became his guardian, and in course of time recommended him to the consideration of his brother, Dr. John Fothergill of London, whose protégé he was destined to become. This, in small compass, was the early story of John Coakley Lettsom, the founder and chief benefactor of the venerable society I have the privilege of addressing.

While working on this and the other lectures he was scheduled to give in Britain during the summer he had only one serious interruption when he was obliged to go to Richmond, Virginia, to the American Surgical Association, to present a technical paper on bony tumors of the orbit.[22] His trips abroad had now become yearly events but they were scarcely of the "brain-dusting" variety so often mentioned by Osler; and the summer of 1927 must have been more of a strain than usual since three major addresses were involved. He also had the responsibility, to which he was unaccustomed, of taking with

[22] "Experiences with orbito-ethmoidal osteomata having intracranial complications. With the report of four cases." *Surgery, Gynecology, and Obstetrics,* June 1927, *44,* 721-742.

him his daughter Betsey, aged 18, who decided at the last moment that she would like to accompany her father on a trip to Europe. The services of Miss Stanton, Dr. Cushing's secretary, were promptly enlisted to help out in the crisis. Her responsibilities, however, extended beyond the chaperonage of Betsey, for when they sailed on 4 June on the *SS. Paris,* no one of the three addresses was as yet complete. On arriving they proceeded at once to Lady Osler's at Oxford. The Medical Society address on acromegaly[23] was given on the 13th, after an elaborate dinner arranged by the Fellows of the Society. Sir D'Arcy Power had been careful to instruct Cushing beforehand that because of its great age "The Medical Society of London is the Medical Society of London, not the London Medical Society." As usual, he had gone to great trouble to look into the historical background of the Society and his references to Lettsom were looked upon as particularly happy, especially those at the end.

> . . . I have attempted in this address to bring some order out of the therapeutic chaos which envelops the subject of the pituitary disorders. Whether I have succeeded does not particularly matter. Order will some day come, and the best that can be done in the circumstances is to give hints in that direction. Hints, after all, may serve a useful purpose. Did not Lettsom so entitle as "Hints, designed to promote beneficence, temperance and medical science," a three-volume series of his suggestive articles? I was encouraged in the preparation of this address by one of his paragraphs, written on June 23, 1773, proposing the establishment of this Medical Society. "Many useful facts [he says] are lost from the want of a proper opportunity of conveying them to the world; and though, when considered separately, they might not be of sufficient importance to claim the attention of the publick; yet when a number of them may be collected together, they may become highly deserving of notice. To such facts, when properly authenticated, the Society will always be particularly attentive." And so, in respect to the memory of that industrious, successful, and many-sided man, your founder, if I shall have given for your guidance the latitude and longitude of this "Little Vandyke" of Medicine, the pituitary body, somewhat more precisely, I shall be well content.

Sir Humphry Rolleston, in recalling the Medical Society Lecture, wrote:

> One incident struck me when Cushing gave his lecture on acromegaly at the Medical Society of London on June 13, 1927; before the lecture there was an informal reception and one man after another came to be announced and meet Cushing. Among them was Sir David Ferrier [1843-1929]; Cushing evidently did not catch his name or recognise him. That it was Ferrier was conveyed to him, and it was wonderful to see his pleasure and surprise, as if one had risen from the dead to do honour to him.

The paper was printed with the usual British promptness and before long letters began to come in, one from W. W. Keen: "The

[23] "Acromegaly from a surgical standpoint." *British Medical Journal,* 2, 9 July 1927, 2, 1-9; 48-55.

very first sentence," he wrote, "catches the imagination and one must read it all through with ever-engrossing interest. It is a masterpiece, the best thing you have ever done, not excepting the Cameron Lecture. . . . I am plodding along, more than halfway in my ninety-first [year], which I find a bit better than my ninetieth, and I thought that was pretty good."[24]

The next day H.C. was back at 13 Norham Gardens putting the finishing touches on his Macewen Memorial Lecture. This was a somewhat formidable responsibility, since the new lectureship was being inaugurated by Cushing and he had had indication from Archibald Young, the Professor of Surgery, that elaborate preparations were being made, both for the lecture and for his entertainment in connection with the granting of an LL.D. by the University.

The Macewen Lecture is prefaced by an eight-page historical essay which would warm the heart of any Scot: "Should you scratch deeply enough a man of pioneering spirit, the chances are that you will draw Scottish blood. But one need not go to a distance to blaze a new trail; one may show, as did Macewen, the spirit of a pioneer in his work at home, for not all Scotsmen migrate sooner or later, despite the impression outside Scotland that they so do. The earth may be peopled with Thomsons who have got their education here, yet a sufficient number remain for you to fill with distinction five professorial chairs in your several faculties at one and the same time." He continued:

> It was primarily to see William Hunter's varied collections, scarcely less worthy of a pilgrimage than those of his brother John in London, that, in company with my medical colleague, Thomas McCrae, my first visit to Glasgow was paid just twenty-seven years ago. We had three objects in view: to browse in the Hunterian Museum, to visit Lister's one-time wards, and to see Macewen at work. A memorable visit it was! I recall exclaiming with delight over Calcar's portrait of Vesalius when a voice from an inner room was heard to say, 'Who may that be who offends my ear with a Northumbrian accent?' and out stumped no less a one than the Keeper of the Museum, John Young of blessed memory. I said it was McCrae, a 'Hieland mon,' whom he had overheard; but he would have none of it, and accused me of what he said was a villainous burred tongue.
>
> Atonement was quickly made for this rude greeting, and so it is that I have a copy of Professor Young's delightful account of the Hunterian Library prepared for the ninth jubilee of your University. And nearby are other cherished reminders of that visit, among them John H. Teacher's catalogue of the museum specimens, and photographic copies of those precious sheets supposed to carry Calcar's original drawings for the illustrations in Vesal's *Fabrica*. These memorabilia are no less prized and take up far less room than does the Baskerville edition of William Hunter's *magnum opus*.

The address itself must be put down as a landmark in the history of neurosurgery, since it is the first account of the use of electro-

[24] Dr. Keen died in 1932 at the age of ninety-five.

surgical methods in the removal of brain tumors. He chose for consideration a particular group of meningiomas, namely, those which arise in the region of the olfactory groove. The tumors in this area tend to be large and vascular and before the advent of electrosurgery Cushing had had indifferent success and many fatalities in attempting to remove them. He tried the electric loop for the first time on 1 October 1926 but did not really have the new technique under control until January. Some idea of his own enthusiasm about the new development can be gleaned from the closing passages of the address:

> . . . In this field of neurosurgery a technique utterly different from that which is usually employed by the general surgeon is essential for success, and one promising addition to this technique which is unquestionably capable of enormous development I have ventured to describe at this time. And it gives me special satisfaction to realize how delighted those masters of technique, Theodor Kocher and W. S. Halsted, who laid such stress on the importance of painstaking haemostasis in surgical work, would have been to have seen some of this new surgery, which is so bloodless compared to that of their contemporaries and predecessors.
>
> Electrosurgery at least permits us today to remove certain brain tumours from situations and under circumstances which a year ago—indeed six months ago—I would not have thought possible. In illustration of this I have described a single operation, upon one patient, and have contrasted it with the trials and tribulations of a series of operations conducted only three years ago on another patient for a similar lesion. The electrophysical principles involved are highly technical and are hardly as yet in more than an experimental stage. It will take a combination of physicist and surgeon and electrical technician working together to perfect the apparatus and to develop its future possibilities for surgery in general.
>
> Could such a triumvirate, for example, as Kelvin, whose undergraduate publication, you may recall, was on *The uniform motion of heat in homogeneous solid bodies, and its connection with the mathematical theory of electricity*—could a Kelvin, I say, in combination with a Macewen and a reborn James Watt as their technical assistant, be resurrected to put their fertile minds and dextrous hands to the problems involved, a second revolution in surgical technique, no less startling and significant than that we owe to Lister, might well enough take place.

As relaxation from these formal responsibilities, there was a two-day visit to Manchester to see Mr. and Mrs. Geoffrey Jefferson and the John Rylands Library, and to attend a meeting of the Society of British Neurological Surgeons on 24-25 June. In May H.C. had written to Jefferson: "I want greatly to visit the home of Trotula [Osler's nickname for Mrs. Jefferson, herself an M.D.], Thomas Percival, and others." Jefferson, who seldom nods, proceeded to look up Thomas Percival in the telephone book! H.C., much delighted, wrote to him from Oxford: "Thomas Percival, he of the Code, I may have to leave undisturbed in his tomb. If you had asked Trotula about him, she would have told you who he was."

Sunday, 26 June, found them in Dublin. On Monday, the 27th, the Royal Academy of Medicine of Ireland made Cushing an Honorary Fellow, and he was presented to the Academy by the general secretary in the following words:

> Sir President, Ladies, and Gentlemen,—I have the honour to present to you one who does not need any introduction to this Academy. I rejoice that this is so, for indeed I should be at a loss to describe him fittingly. Eminent as a physician, as a surgeon, and as a physiologist, he has taken the whole realm of medicine as his province, and in that realm all acknowledge him as a chief. Intellectually he towers among his fellows, as those of whom he has written tower physically among ordinary mortals. His brilliant work commands our admiration, but he has won our love and gratitude by enshrining for us in two noble volumes the memory of his greater master, so dear to us all. Let us then, as a fellow-worshipper at the same shrine as ourselves, receive him gladly; let us honour our Academy by enrolling him a Fellow, and let us for himself receive him with our loudest plaudits. Harvey Cushing!

After returning thanks for his election he made a brief address telling of his recent experiences in electrosurgery. On the evening of the same day a public meeting to inaugurate the National Cancer Campaign in Ireland was held in the Royal College of Surgeons with the Marquis of Dufferin and Ava, Speaker of the Senate of Northern Ireland, in the chair—the first occasion in many a troubled year of Irish history when men from the North and South of Ireland had joined together in a common cause. H.C. had evidently overlooked the fact that he was expected to sit on the platform and make a speech, and his remarks on the occasion were wholly extemporaneous.[25]

On Tuesday, the 28th, Trinity College conferred upon him the degree of Honorary Master of Chirurgery in a colorful ceremony. Meanwhile, in keeping with traditions of Irish hospitality, there were luncheons and dinners, the renewal of acquaintances and friendships of long standing (not forgetting his friends in the Zoo), visits to bookshops and libraries until his departure for London toward the end of the week, with a day's motor trip through North Wales to show Betsey the beautiful city of Chester on the river whose name he insisted should be called the "LLDee." There followed a week in Paris in search of sunshine and warmth, among other things, and then on to Edinburgh in time for the Lister Centenary exercises on 20 July and H.C.'s third honorary degree of the summer, an LL.D. from Edinburgh. His citation ran:

> Dr. Harvey Cushing, Professor of Surgery in the University of Harvard, and Surgeon-in-Chief to the Peter Bent Brigham Hospital, has devoted himself to the surgery of the brain and nervous system. He has overcome the baffling difficulties which the worker in this field encounters by a combination of the highest

[25] They were reported briefly by the *Lancet's* Irish correspondent (see *Lancet,* 2 July 1927, p. 43).

technical skill with a profound knowledge of physiology and pathology. Disciples from Medical Schools all over the world flock to sit at his feet. Nor can we forget that he is a collector of rare medical books, who unfolds from the records of the past the origin of conceptions which have subsequently ripened with the development of knowledge. By his invaluable contribution to the history of contemporary medicine in his *Biography of Sir William Osler,* if it stood alone, Professor Cushing has amply earned Apollo's bay.

The Lister Centenary exercises had long been planned, and H.C. appeared to have been more worried over his brief address, "Emancipators," than almost anything he had undertaken. The function was held in the huge McEwan Hall and, because of his particular aversion to microphones, H.C. refused politely but firmly to use the one which was suddenly placed before him without warning, being certain that he would never be able to deliver his address into this new modern contraption, and believing that he could make himself heard without it. Whether the audience did hear him or not is unknown, but he felt the address had been a failure and was extremely sensitive about it, even as was Mr. Lincoln after his Gettysburg Address.

Before leaving Britain he was notified of his election to Honorary Fellowship in the Royal Society of Medicine, and a short time later the Society of British Neurological Surgeons made him an honorary member. He could not have felt that his labors were unappreciated, for he had received three honorary degrees and four honorary memberships all in the space of a month.

But his honors were dimmed when, a few days after his return to his clinic, he lost on the operating table his most celebrated patient, General Leonard Wood. His mood of deep dejection and self-criticism still hung over him a few weeks later when he put together all his letters and memorabilia of General Wood and prefixed them with a long handwritten note which ended: "On my return we were not yet in full swing. Nor were my surgical reflexes and judgment at their best. He was a great man. I've never lost a patient after operation that so upset me. It was *so* near to success. The autopsy showed that there had been some blood forced into the ventricle at the time I temporarily closed and packed the wound. If I had used better judgment he would certainly have been saved and no one the wiser. He could easily enough have had another 15 years as good as the last."

Following General Wood's death Cushing could not bring himself to operate again for nearly two weeks. He slept badly and complained that he had been repeating the operation on the General every night for a week or more. Mrs. Wood had been left in straitened circumstances and toward the end of the month Cushing addressed a letter to Senator Frederick H. Gillett recommending that a pension be granted General Wood's widow by Act of Congress. He pointed out that General Wood, through his service to his country in the Philippines, had been unable to make financial provision for his wife and that in consequence she was now almost destitute. The proposal had the endorsement of General Clarence Edwards of the First Service Command. Senator Gillett replied politely but the Congress failed to act.

September found Cushing getting back into his usual routine. The Medical School opened at the end of the month and he presently discovered to his great consternation that during the summer, unknown to him, the Library Committee of the Medical School had moved the main medical library from the first to the second floor in the Administration Building to make room for the dean's offices. Reginald Fitz, who was chairman of the Library Committee, relates that when Cushing discovered what had happened "he came over to the Peter Bent Brigham Hospital, took the top of my head off, saying that of all the damnably stupid things, the most stupid was to build a library that students had to make an effort to get to." He went on to say that there was no sense in having administrative quarters in a medical school anyway, that deans should be in the cellar, and the more prison-like the quarters, the more satisfactory to all concerned. After this burst H.C. had qualms of conscience and he promptly sent his apologies to Fitz and a bunch of roses to his wife.

H.C. to Reginald Fitz [*late 1927*].

Dear Reg That was most silly and unfeeling of me to have stormed this noon about the giving up of that ground floor library room at the School. You have been giving time to the library problem and I have not. Your ideas are just as likely to be good as are mine—better indeed for you are younger. So please dismiss my explosion from your mind. I'm glad to learn (what I did not know) that you are Chairman of the library committee. Just such a man as you is needed in that position. Good luck to you. I'll back any of your projects. Yours, H.C.

Pleasant happenings more often than expostulations were the occasion for handwritten notes. In October news came from a former member of the surgical staff of the arrival of his first-born son. The father had added much colour to the scene during his two years at the Brigham, and H.C. was quick to welcome the newcomer whom he doubtless promptly regarded as a future candidate for Yale, 'Keys,' and much else.

H.C. to Dan Collier Elkin, Jr. (aged 2 days) *22 October 1927.*

Dear little Dan Jr. This is just a note of greeting and to congratulate you on your choice of parents. But I think you might have chosen to be born in this part of the world so that I might hope to see something of you. If your father ever spanks you, let me know and I will call him down. It will not be the first time. Here in Boston children don't get spanked enough and that is why they are so haughty and haughtonish and go to harvard college.

But then in Georgia it is different. Remember me to Bobby Jones should he go putting past your house; and also remember me kindly to your pa and ma. Affy., HARVEY CUSHING.

Too little has been said about the meetings of the Harvard Medical Society. They had been modelled after those of the Johns Hopkins Medical Society and they ordinarily began with the presentation of two or three interesting cases. An account of one of the meetings from a medical student's diary of this period will give some idea of the interest attaching to such meetings and the part which H.C. generally played in directing them.

11 October 1927. Three cases were presented by various of the house-officers; the first, Crean, a spinal-cord case, exhibiting marked stretch reflexes and involuntary flexor reflexes; it seemed appropriate to show them at this time because they illustrated in a striking way the application of the facts set forth on the previous day by Professor Sherrington in the Dunham Lecture on stretch reflexes. Miss Jabaut was the next shown as an example of one who had these involuntary reflexes and who, following operation, had recovered from them. She walked into the amphitheatre without difficulty whereas four weeks previously she had been completely paralyzed in all four extremities on account of a spinal cord cyst. Finally the patient Krueger was presented, and the fact that the bruit in his left occipital lobe increased in intensity during visual effort was pointed out. Dr. Cobb mentioned his recent studies upon localized increased vascularity of the olfactory bulb following olfactory stimulation. Dr. Cushing then spoke upon the general aspects of brain tumors, and told how in the course of the past twenty years it has been necessary first to improve technique, then diagnosis, and later attempts had been made to extend the pathological knowledge of intracranial tumors; now physiological studies were being made with great profit. Finally Tracy Putnam presented a brilliant paper on the effects of his recent anterior pituitary extract upon the growth of rats and dogs; he showed two dogs, one of which had been injected regularly and one of which had not. The injected dog showed obvious acromegaly and was much heavier than the control.

Sir Charles and Lady Sherrington arrived in Boston on 7 October for a fortnight's visit during which Sir Charles gave the Dunham Lectures at the Medical School.[26] He took a lively part in every phase of the School's activity, and H.C. made a point of showing him the many physiological problems which he was encountering almost daily in his cases. Sir Charles had not previously seen Cushing operate—at least not since 1901 when he had performed the craniotomies at Liverpool on several chimpanzees, the orang, and the gorilla. He was greatly interested in the clinical problems and he stimulated the students and staff not only by his lectures but by freely mixing with them in the clinic and in various laboratories. After the

[26] The Edward K. Dunham Lectureship, founded in 1923, makes it possible for the Harvard Medical School yearly to honor a distinguished contributor in some branch of the medical sciences. The guest delivers three lectures but their publication is not obligatory.

last Dunham Lecture Cushing arranged a dinner for Sherrington's former pupils, among others Alexander Forbes, Cuthbert Bazett, Grayson McCouch, Henry Viets, Stanley Cobb. Any conversation led by Sherrington and Cushing was inevitably bright. They reminisced about the various continental laboratories in which they had worked and later exchanged stories of men who had performed great intellectual feats, Sir Charles remarking that Isaac Newton often worked thirty-six hours at a stretch without nourishment while writing the *Principia*. H.C. added that Poincaré had solved several of his most celebrated mathematical problems while riding in Paris taxicabs—the sound of the horn no doubt assisting his integrations.

During the Sherringtons' visit the Society of Neurological Surgeons assembled at Cushing's clinic (13-15 October), and H.C. operated for them three days in succession. On the 14th he had a most dramatic case of spinal cord tumor, in which a man who had been completely paralyzed in both lower extremities gained sufficient control to walk within twelve hours of the time of the operation. This led Sir Charles into ruminations about the physiology of spinal compression.

Cushing took particular satisfaction in another event which coincided with Sherrington's visit. On the afternoon of 4 October Vanderbilt Hall, the new student dormitory of the Harvard Medical School, was dedicated. With John Collins Warren, H.C. had begun to agitate for adequate student dormitories in the summer of 1912 when he first came to Boston, and it had taken fifteen years for the powers-that-be at Harvard to do for the Medical School what they had long since done for the College. Opening exercises, rather elaborate for Boston, had been arranged with a series of unexciting introductory speeches after which the audience was electrified by forty minutes of George Vincent's torrential oratory.

The Sherringtons departed on the 24th. Meanwhile a group of distinguished French surgeons had come to the clinic, among them Thierry de Martel and Clovis Vincent. On Thursday, the 27th, Mrs. Cushing invited a few friends to meet their French guests at tea. Later, while Cushing stood under a picture of Rheims Cathedral, Thierry de Martel announced in English that he had a pleasant duty to perform, adding that although he spoke English fluently he could not adequately express the depth of his admiration and affection for Cushing in any but his native tongue. He then referred to Cushing as the most distinguished surgeon in this country, if not in the world, who through matchless courage and energy had created a new field of surgical endeavor which had proved a boon to mankind. He mentioned his unrivaled technical skill, his fingers that were deft as those of a Japanese juggler, his attention to detail in all things, and his innate capacity to inspire his students. At the end of the speech H.C. was kissed on both cheeks and the latest decoration from France was pinned upon his lapel, and he thus became an *Officier* of the *Légion d'Honneur.*

November and December were crowded with clinical work. The electrosurgical cutting knife was being used as standard equipment for almost every procedure, and H.C. had become increasingly bold in attacking large and highly vascular lesions until in early November he had a series of unexpected misfortunes. It had been years since he had worried about postoperative sepsis, and now out of the blue came a series of virulent streptococcal infections developing in each instance within a day or two of operation. It reminded one of the old days that Holmes described in his essay on puerperal fever, when nine out of ten patients delivered by a certain midwife would develop childbed fever. After four such episodes Cushing closed down his operating room and re-examined every step in the somewhat involved procedure for sterilization of drapes, instruments, saline, bone wax, and his new electrosurgical knife; he also had the scrubbing ritual for his assistants closely looked into. No basic fault was discovered. Finally, somewhat in desperation, he had the throats of all his team swabbed and cultured, and he discovered, to his deep chagrin, that he himself was carrying a most virulent streptococcus in his own throat, bacteriologically identical with those taken from his infected cases. He thereupon instituted a series of bacteriological tests which involved speaking through a gauze mask with an open Petri dish held some fourteen inches in front of his mouth. To his consternation he found that colonies of pathogenic bacteria were deposited on the dish. Thereafter pieces of discarded X-ray film were inserted in all Brigham masks, and it was found that this prevented oral transmission of mouth organisms during ordinary speech. Reassured, he started once again to operate and there were no further postoperative infections. After this discomforting episode had cleared up, he commented with his usual generosity that he was glad he had been responsible and not someone on his team.

The charter which Cushing and Christian had drawn up for the Brigham in 1911 had worked out well and in operation few modifications were required. Both services were at liberty to have private patients on Ward A and to derive financial benefit from such fees as were charged the private patients. Cushing's fees were moderate to a degree in view of the world-wide reputation which he had now acquired. His usual fee for a craniotomy was $250 during the Hopkins period, provided the patient was able to pay, and $250 to $500 after 1920. As part of his history-taking procedure he always insisted on obtaining personally from his patients or their relatives a statement of their financial position. If, as not infrequently happened, he felt that the added burden of professional fees was more than they should undertake, his usual advice was to save their money for their convalescence; with this went the assurance that he was no more likely to turn the operation over to his assistant in the case of a ward patient than for one on the private service. Occasionally Cushing asked large fees from well-to-do patients, but these sums were turned over directly to one or the other of the two laboratories he in large measure supported. When importuned to do some simple procedure that could be done as well by a junior, he sometimes yielded with the understanding that one of his laboratories would benefit thereby. In one instance the removal of a small wen from a friend's neck made the laboratory budget the richer by five thousand dollars. For several years, as the staff of his surgical laboratories grew, he came to depend on these occasional patients to keep them solvent.

During Cushing's years at Hopkins and Harvard he had come to appreciate the value of graduate fellowships, both for research and for teaching, and it is significant that, as soon as his income had become sufficiently secure, instead of changing his manner of living he presented to various institutions a series of fellowships, the first of which went to the old Hunterian at Hopkins. Now, in December 1927, a year and a half later, he established a similar fellowship in the Department of Surgery at Yale through an outright gift of $25,000 in memory of his son Bill. The William Harvey Cushing Research Fellowship in Surgery continues to flourish, and during the eighteen years since it was created has been held by a series of distinguished young surgical investigators. Appointment is made on the recommendation of the Professor of Surgery.

Cushing's generosity was not, however, restricted to Hopkins and Yale, for he had also established a "Surgeon-in-Chief Fund" at the Peter Bent Brigham Hospital created to send men from his staff abroad for a period of study. He constantly referred to the broadening influence of his own year in Europe, and he aimed to make it possible for members of his staff to have similar opportunity. In October 1921 he had turned over to the Brigham Trustees a check for $5,000 received from a grateful patient. Other contributions followed in 1923, by which time the fund had grown to nearly $18,000. Percival Bailey was the first Fellow to receive support from the fund (1924). In 1926 Cushing wrote the Trustees requesting that the Surgeon-in-Chief Fund be used to establish a Brigham Hospital Travelling Fellowship in Surgery, and Leo Davidoff was designated the first Travelling Fellow. Mr. E. D. Codman, Treasurer of the Brigham Trustees, wrote that the fund "represents the finest spirit of loyalty to the Hospital, the staff and its future beyond any gift the Hospital has received." Other Travelling Fellows who benefited were Harlan F. Newton (1927), Franc D. Ingraham (1928), and William deG. Mahoney (1932).[27] At the time of Cushing's retirement in 1933 the Trustees voted to designate the fund, which had now increased to nearly $35,000, the Harvey Cushing Fellowship Fund, "the interest only to be used, and to be applied in payment of the salary of a Fellow in Surgery to be called the Harvey Cushing Fellow." The appointment was to be made annually and the donor expressed his preference "that a period of study and research be passed by such Fellows in Surgery in some clinic or laboratory in a foreign country, or if deemed wise, in another American institution." Kenneth Wade Thompson was the first Harvey Cushing Fellow, having held the appointment from March to July 1933. Cushing had thus implemented his convictions concerning the value of fellowship opportunity.

His own surgical laboratory had been run, so to speak, on a "shoestring," Cushing himself largely supplementing its budget until 1923, when the Philip Gray Fund was established in memory of a well-to-do patient from Detroit who had had a malignant glioma. His widow requested that $10,000 a year be paid to Cushing for a period of ten years, the money to be used for study of tumors similar to that to which her husband had succumbed. This was supplemented in 1928 by Mr. Chester C. Bolton of Cleveland in gratitude for the treatment which his son Charles had received after his diving accident in June 1927. Cushing's research budget[28] from the Medical School

[27] Cushing's belief in the value of travel is further indicated by his part in securing the George Gorham Peters Travelling Fellowship. In September 1929 Mr. Peters of Boston wrote that he had made provision in his will for a scholarship that would make it possible for a member of the Brigham staff to travel around the world to extend his education, and he had decided to make the scholarship fund available prior to his death. A check for $5,000 was received as the initial installment and A. J. McLean was the first of the globe-circling fellows to be appointed (1929). Eric Oldberg was appointed in 1930, and Frank N. Glenn in 1931. Provision was made for Louise Eisenhardt to make a similar trip, she being the final recipient of the fellowship during Cushing's term as Surgeon-in-Chief.

[28] The Brigham Hospital contributed nothing to Cushing's budget beyond his salary of $5,000, some office supplies from the Hospital store, and lunches for one secretary whose salary was paid by Cushing personally. The penny-wise, pound-foolish economies practised by certain New England hospital superintendents sometimes reached surprising lengths. When H.C. was obliged to take on an artist, a technician, and a photographer (whose salaries he at first paid personally), these people were not even accorded the usual privilege of hospital lunches granted other hospital employees although they did work for the whole hospital staff. The Harvard Medical School, in 1931, contributed $11,600 to Cushing's budget, of which $4,000 was spent in maintaining the Arthur Tracy Cabot Fellow and the general expenses of the surgical laboratory. Cushing's annual expenditure to keep his photographic service, artists, and pathological laboratory going in the postwar years amounted to somewhat over $35,000, so that he was obliged to raise or pay from his own pocket a total of $30,000 each year. At no time did the Dean of the Harvard Medical School or the President of Harvard University raise a hand to lighten this burden.

and the Hospital was not materially increased after 1912 beyond a few hundred dollars assigned for office expenses.

1928

The visit of the French delegation in October gave indication of what was to follow during Cushing's remaining years at the Brigham. Europe was gradually recovering from the World War, restrictions upon travel had largely disappeared, and Welch's prediction that there would be a swing in medicine from the old world to the new was richly vindicated. Through Cushing's acceptance of many invitations to speak before representative gatherings in Europe, his clinic had gained an international flavor and continued to attract visitors from almost every country. As mentioned earlier, Symonds, Dott, and Cairns had set the pace for Britain, Bremer, Martin, and Morelle for Belgium, de Martel and Vincent for France. In November 1927 Sven Ingvar, the distinguished Swedish neurologist, had paid him a visit and a few weeks later came the outstanding authority on the postural reflexes, Rudolf Magnus (who had introduced H.C. to Swedish punch in Heidelberg in 1901), now the Director of the Pharmacological Institute at Utrecht. In March Professor Barger, Cushny's successor in the chair of pharmacology in Edinburgh, came to the clinic and incidentally helped to make preparations for the International Physiological Congress which was to be held in Boston the next year and at which he was to make announcements in six languages (including Russian), without a trace of Scottish accent, at the opening plenary session.

In March Sir Humphry Rolleston appeared at the Brigham to act as Physician-in-Chief *pro tem* on Dr. Christian's service. On ward rounds the students were impressed by his remarkable memory and his unfailing familiarity with literature past and present. Without any apparent effort he seemed able to recall full clinical details of patients he had seen as a house officer fifty years before in the London hospitals, and at the same time could cite the page and volume of a recent paper relevant to a clinical case under discussion in the wards. The students were also impressed by the astonishing ease with which Rolleston seemed to cover the entire realm of clinical medicine and were especially struck by his wide vocabulary and seemingly effortless command of the English language.

The year 1928 marked the 300th anniversary of the publication of William Harvey's book, *De motu cordis,* announcing the discovery of the circulation. As with the Pasteur centenary, this was a thing which Cushing could not possibly overlook; not only did he collect Harvey items with great diligence throughout the year, acquiring a copy of the celebrated first edition (another copy of which he had

had to turn down at $200 twenty years previously), but he also arranged a Harvey meeting for the Harvard Medical Society. A creditable exhibit of Harveian items, made up of his own possessions and others that he had begged or borrowed from his friends, was arranged in the amphitheatre, and Archibald Malloch, Librarian of the New York Academy of Medicine, read a detailed paper on Harvey which was subsequently published in monographic form. Cushing, as one might have anticipated, insisted that his house officers present a number of cases of circulatory aberration, which, like some of the books, had been borrowed for the occasion.

And there were other commemorations. On 26 April there began a three-day celebration of the Brigham's fifteenth anniversary, for which, as with the tenth birthday, a formidable program of fifteen-minute presentations by staff members, past and present, was arranged. In the evenings they made merry and reminisced about old times. Stanley Cobb, who had always been most faithful in helping to provide suitable entertainment for dinners, reunions, and other festive occasions, was travelling in Germany at the time and H.C., not wishing to have him left out, described the goings on (in part) in a characteristic letter:

> . . . We had a most amazingly good time at the reunion. . . . The program went off admirably. I think on the whole the papers were better than anything that I heard subsequently at the Congress in Washington. . . . Perhaps the best part of the whole meeting was the show which was staged. Tracy, I judge, was the stage manager and it was altogether A-1. The nurses gave a minstrel show and subsequently there was a play which concerned the admission of one Lena Rabinowitz (e.g. T.J.P.) into the hospital, with a subsequent abdominal operation by John Homans. In the course of this I appeared and ruthlessly pressing John aside opened Lena's head with some most formidable tools. All of the old-timers in the course of this got most outrageously ragged and the crowd which jammed the amphitheatre was in an uproar. I wish you . . . and others who are abroad might have been there.

He might have added that his cognomen for this skit was "Carvey Pushing" which, perchance, he may not have fully appreciated. Another contemporary account of the reunion gives further details:

> *Thursday, 26 April.* Two hundred former house officers and 200 nurses appeared for the reunion and a three-day program of papers and various festivities had been arranged. There was an amusing take-off on the Chief doing an operation during which he was represented as commandeering at least fifty people into the operating room to do one odd job or another connected with the operation. He seemed to be much entertained at this exposition of his little failing.
>
> *Friday, 27 April.* At 4:30 Dr. Cushing read the closing paper of the day on electrosurgical methods in cerebral operations. He was about to adjourn the meeting when Elliott Cutler came forward saying that he had a small matter to bring before the meeting and proceeded to make a most charming short

speech about the inspiration which the younger members of the Brigham staff had received from their elders and that he wished to take this opportunity to present on behalf of former members of the surgical staff a silver inkstand to the Chief as an expression of their admiration and affection. The Chief became very red and was evidently deeply stirred. When called on for a speech there was an awkward silence and he seemed to have lost his tongue, then suddenly his face brightened and he said that he was quite overwhelmed and that this generous gift made him feel somewhat like a squid who, as he progresses backwards, leaves a trail of ink in his path—which brought down the house. . . . Mrs. Cushing was also in the audience and Dr. Horrax, after a most happy speech, presented her with an enormous bouquet of roses.

Saturday, 28 April. Another day of papers and then the Chief made a farewell address to the reunion in which he referred to the small size of the hospital, and how by virtue of its limited capacity they had been able to raise the standard of clinical studies and achievements. He hoped that the hospital would never succumb to the American tendency to build Gargantuan organizations of unwieldy size whose effectiveness diminishes in geometric proportion to their breadth. He talked to the group as though he were speaking to members of his own family, and one somehow carried away the feeling of being in a happy family group. This, I think, is the secret of the delightful spirit of cooperation which pervades all departments of the Brigham Hospital, and I somehow feel that when the Chief's accomplishments come eventually to be enumerated the spirit of cooperation and friendship which he, in some inexplicable way, had inculcated into the Brigham group will be looked upon as one of his great achievements.

Ever faithful to his neurological and surgical gatherings, H.C. started the month of May by attending a series of meetings in Washington (the American Neurological Association, the American Surgical, and the American Ophthalmological). Between times he paid a visit to Fielding Garrison, who was found in a dingy little room of the Army Medical Library, surrounded by bookshelves with volumes placed helter-skelter on the shelves and great piles of recent journals which he was reading for the *Index catalogue*. Proof sheets were everywhere, since he was also deep in the revision of the fourth edition of his *History of medicine*. At Cushing's request some of the Library's rare Vesalian items were produced, and Garrison then took him to lunch at the Smithsonian with Paul Hoeber, the New York publisher, who insisted upon talking about Cushing's pet aversion, psychoanalysis. H.C. attempted to shift the conversation, and finally he did it successfully by relating how a follower of Freud had psychoanalyzed *Mother Goose:* "Little Jack Horner sat in the corner—naughty, naughty, naughty." Dr. Garrison's lunch was made up principally of such intellectual delicacies along with a cheese sandwich and coffee.

Afterwards they visited the Vollbehr collection of incunabula at the Library of Congress; later Lowdermilk's bookshop, where one of H.C.'s friends found a copy of the first edition of William Beaumont's book on gastric juice (Plattsburgh, 1833). This occasioned some discussion of the appropriateness of reprinting the Beaumont for members of the Physiological Congress the next year, since it obviously represented the most striking single contribution to physiology that had been made in the United States. As it turned out, this was also the considered opinion of William Howell, President of the Congress, and of Walter Cannon who was arranging many of the details.

On the evening of 2 May Cushing attended a meeting of the American Association of the History of Medicine at which Garrison presided. After a presidential discourse on recent excavations in Asia Minor, H.C. presented for the second time a paper he had given in February before the Club of Odd Volumes in Boston entitled, "Who put the fox in foxglove?"—an historical whimsy in which he attempted to establish that the name of Fuchs, the Swiss botanist who was responsible for the term *Digitalis* (from the German *Fingerhut*), had unwittingly been corrupted and introduced into the popular term "foxglove." His quest for confirmation revealed the early use of the Anglo-Saxon term Foxes-glofa, so he abandoned his thesis and never published the paper.

In June he went to Minneapolis to attend a meeting of the American Medical Association where he presented a detailed paper on visual disturbances resulting from meningiomatous tumors at the base of the brain,[29] and on the basis of this report he was awarded the next year the Herman Knapp Prize in Ophthalmology. On his way out he stopped in Chicago for an overnight visit with Dr. Irving Cutter, Dean of Northwestern Medical School, a fellow collector with whom he had much in common.

The summer was largely occupied with drafting papers. As a result of the enlargement of his clinic and the increasing numbers of voluntary assistants he had fallen seriously behind with his manuscripts. There were eighteen published papers that year, nearly all of which were of considerable length, whereas in 1926 he had published only three papers and in 1927 fourteen.

During the summer of 1928 he also brought together his first volume of collected essays which M. A. DeWolfe Howe of the Atlantic Monthly Press had prevailed upon him to undertake. As intimated earlier, he had selected as the first address *Consecratio medici*. By the end of the summer he had re-edited fourteen of his more general addresses and the volume eventually appeared late in

[29] "Meningiomas arising from the tuberculum sellae: with the syndrome of primary optic atrophy and bitemporal field defects combined with a normal sella turcica in a middle-aged person," (With L. Eisenhardt). *Transactions of the Section on Ophthalmology, American Medical Association*, 1928, 322-408.

November—in time to solve many of his worrisome Christmas problems. Many enthusiastic letters were received, the reviews were outspokenly favorable, and the book has had four printings. A letter from Ralph Major exemplifies the general reaction:

Kansas City, Missouri,
Ralph H. Major to H.C. *13 February 1930.*

My dear Dr. Cushing: Yesterday I travelled all day out to a small town in Kansas and before leaving dropped your "Consecratio Medici" into my bag. The ride that I had dreaded passed all too quickly. This was not, of course, my first acquaintance with this volume but I liked it even better on re-reading. I got the same thrill from it that I got once before, rather a number of years back when as a student I read [Osler's] "Aequanimitas."

I hope you will continue to publish such essays as those in the volume "Consecratio Medici." I think the influence of Osler's addresses is far-reaching but it is a voice from the past, the present generation craves also voices from the present—like yours. I liked all the papers, particularly perhaps Consecratio Medici, William Osler the Man, the Clinical Teacher, and the Doctor and His Books. I was surprised to learn that you did not succumb to bibliomania until Dr. MacCallum brought you a copy of the 1543 Fabrica. That must have been in your Baltimore days. I became infected while a student when I picked up in a Baltimore bookshop Henry Baker's "The Microscope Made Easy" 1743 and "Religio Medici" by Sir Tho. Browne, Knt. M.D., London, J. Torbuck M,DCC,XXXVI" both of which books seemed to me at the time to be fabulously ancient. My collection is very small but I enjoy it. I was interested in your prevarications about the books coming to your door, in packages with foreign stamps. Haven't I done the same and also have purchased a large ulster in which I can hide books and introduce them into the house by stealth—probably an old dodge.

I have often wondered whether Dr. Osler was fond of music. I have read how he loved the old hymn "O Quanta Qualia" but I have often had a curiosity to know if he attended many symphony concerts, whether he liked Bach, Beethoven or Tschaikowsky or whether he had any patience with Debussy or Stravinsky, etc. etc.

Lucien Price's review in the *Boston Globe* is headed as follows: "Harvey Cushing, fourth in line of distinguished doctors—once again he wields the pen that commemorated Osler—in *Consecratio Medici* he takes lay readers on an enchanting stroll through the humanism of a noble profession—essays and addresses which are a mosaic of medical history, reminiscence, humor and serene philosophy." The review continues:

. . . This hand, which can wield both scalpel and pen, can make the reader forget the doctor in the man of letters. The essay on "The Western Reserve" . . . is an historical study of that "first footprint in the march of New England westward," written with a grace, an animation and a wit which the average historian would emulate if he knew how. Again, in "Dr. Garth, the Kit-Kat Poet," we are in early 18th century England with Addison, Steele, Pope, Bolingbroke, Sir Joshua, Dr. Johnson and that constellation of statesmen, poets, artists, scholars and philosophers who dined well, drank deep and laughed mightily in what seems to us now an enviable Age of Leisure. In that age this modern surgeon moves about perfectly at home. Had he walked into the tavern near Temple Bar, "At the Sign of the Cat and Fiddle," one can fancy him cracking Latin jokes with the formidable Dr. Johnson and capping epigrams with Pope. Or, being asked to speak at the dedication of a medical library, he produces a disquisition on "The Doctor and His Books," so full of whimsey, so packed with erudition that you think Anatole France's good "Sylvestre Bonnard" has been reincarnated as a bibliophile physician.

During 1928 a cordial relationship developed between Cushing and Charles C Thomas who early in that year had set himself up in Springfield, Illinois, as a medical publisher. On 28 November 1927 Thomas had called and let it be known that he would like to publish Cushing's next book. H.C. was struck by his directness and by his knowledge and driving interest in the craft of publishing and printing, and envisaged the possibility of developing something akin to the intimate writer-publisher relationship that had existed in years past, no doubt having in his mind's eye the type of association which Vesalius had enjoyed with his scholar-printer, Oporinus of Basel.

Much to Thomas' gratification, Cushing without hesitation pointed to an unfinished and highly illustrated monograph on blood-vessel tumors of the brain which he and Percival Bailey were in process of bringing to completion. Thomas accordingly arranged that this monograph would be the first book issued from his newly founded publishing house. He gave the manuscript infinite personal attention, as did the Donnelley Company of Chicago, which did the printing. On 24 March 1928 Cushing wrote: "I am astonished to see what a lot of important things you have already accumulated for publication. We are just about ready with the blood-vessel tumor paper and are in the course of putting together the illustrations with the legends. . . . It is very good of Mr. Donnelley to take it on, but there won't be any sale for it. You will perhaps make up for it by the textbook when it gets ready." Thomas was thus already negotiating for John Homans' 'Surgery,' which Homans readily gave him after seeing what had been done with the blood-vessel tumor monograph. After its appearance in November 1928 Cushing committed three other important technical monographs to Thomas, including his great treatise on the meningiomas (1938). The Harvey Cushing Society also placed in Thomas' sympathetic hands the bibliography of H.C.'s writings, issued in 1939 at the time of his seventieth birthday; likewise the birthday volume which followed the celebration. All of the later works were printed by the George Banta Publishing Company in Menasha, Wisconsin, and Cushing came to be on intimate terms with Cyril Peerenboom, the secretary of that company, and Reinhold Gehner of New York, their resourceful book designer. In some of his previous printing ventures Cushing had not had direct contact with the composing room and he felt a little as though he were dealing with the fourth dimension. Since he could not quite set the type himself, he would have sat directly behind the compositor and the engraver, had he had his way, to see that everything was being done in accordance with his perfectionist concept of the printer's art. When the Osler biography was going through the press he had all but set the running heads himself, much to the consternation of the Oxford Press. The Thomas-Banta combination was the first that had given him the sense of intimate personal relationship with the publisher-printer that he had always so much desired.

With the summer passed, much began to impinge upon Cushing and the clinic. The American College of Surgeons had elected to meet in Boston from 8-12 October and H.C. was obliged to put on the usual series of clinics and operations. The award of the Bigelow Medal to Chevalier Jackson had been arranged on the 10th to coincide with the meeting of the College, and as usual H.C. made the presentation with a few well-chosen lines which seem even more eloquent than those which he had used two years earlier in the presentation to W. W. Keen. They were typed on small cards which he could hold somewhat surreptitiously in the palm of his hand.

> Merit cannot be made greater by calling it to public notice. Virtue lies in the struggle, not in the prize. And the members of this society are fully aware that in conferring this medal they give prominence to themselves rather than to the object of their attentions. For he, in the natural course of things, will already stand high in the esteem and affection of the profession and be one who seeks no other reward. Nor would he so stand did he not look with modesty upon his attainments, be unconscious of the fact that he is a celebrity, and instinctively shun the light of public acclaim.
>
> The works of a sculptor or painter or architect endure for posterity to appraise. The art of surgery in which you so excel calls for gifts no less rare, for perseverance and training no less arduous, for craftsmanship no less artistic and painstaking. But the material on which the surgeon does his work is like himself in the end perishable, and the fact that here was a man whose manual skill and deftness in his chosen field surpassed that of all others of his time becomes soon a fading memory.
>
> But the Recording Angel knows how few there be among us who day after day, year on end, sacrifice themselves as you have done to be continuously at the sudden call principally of stricken children who by your unique talent are literally snatched from the very crossing of the river. For one who can thus spectacularly transmute agony and grief to health and happiness, the blessings of patient and parents are recompense enough, and what posterity may say matters little in comparison.

Writing of the College of Surgeons meeting, H.C. also mentions the dedication on 11 October of the Harvard Medical School parapet, a memorial wall for Base Hospital No. 5, and the dinner which he gave to the group known as the "Lost Legion"—the medical officers who had been dragged out of their quiet lives as country doctors by

H.C. VIEWING AN X-RAY FILM
In his dressing room after an operation (1928).
From a photograph by Walter Willard Boyd

SURGEON AND PATIENT
Examining a young patient a few days after removal of a cerebellar tumor.
From a photograph by Thomas W. Dixon

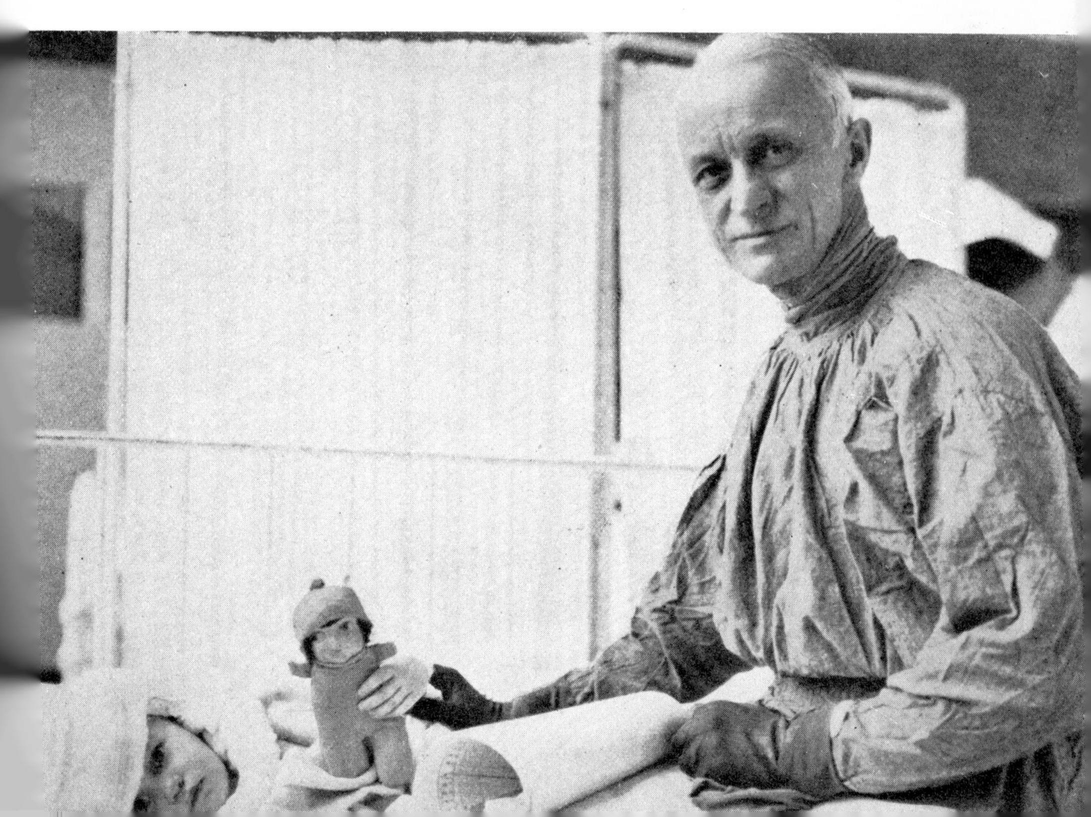

THREE SURGEONS
David Cheever, H.C., René Leriche. From a photograph by Walter Boyd, June 1929

SWEDISH VISITORS
Miss Alma Hedin, H.C., Dr. Sven Hedin. From a photograph by Walter Boyd, June 1929

THE INSTRUMENT TABLE
From a photograph by Walter Boyd

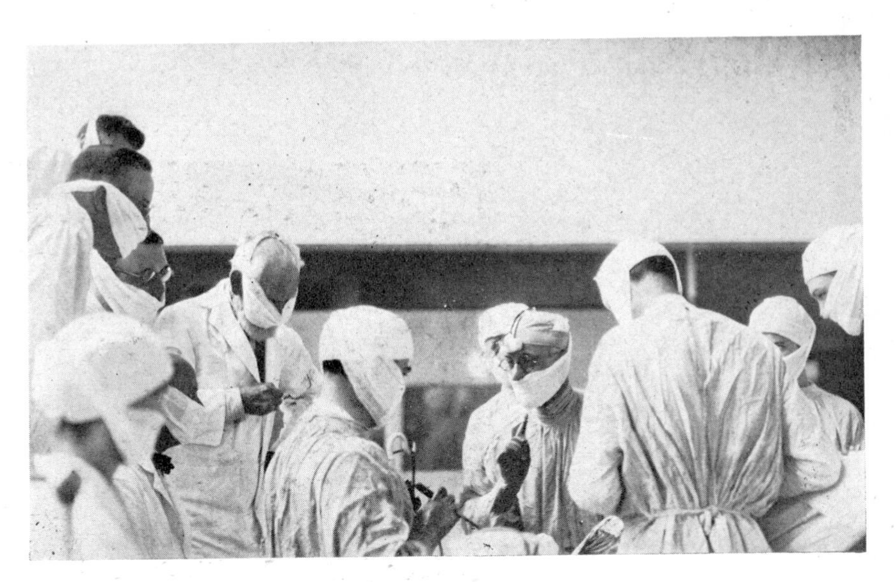

STUDENT AND TEACHER
In the stand, holding his glasses, Prof. I. P. Pavlov. Richard Meagher and Gilbert Horrax assisting. From a photograph by Walter Boyd 21 August 1929

TWO PHYSIOLOGISTS
H.C. *aet.* 60; Pavlov *aet.* 80. From a photograph by Walter Boyd 21 August 1929

the war, dropped into the line without even knowing how to salute and sent over the top the next day with a British battalion. Cushing took a great personal interest in these men and kept in close touch with many of them as he did with the members of Base Hospital No. 5. His remarks at the dedication of the parapet offer another example of his staunch patriotism:

> . . . Not all of us returned. Cut in one of the tablets before you are the names of four whom we saw buried with military honours in that vast harvest of crosses on the dunes of Étaples. They gave their lives in what was thought to be a war to end wars. To those the inscription refers to as once the enemy, we now hold out the hand of reconciliation; and let us hope that between us we may at least make a repetition of such a war unlikely. But should it ever come, there will, we may rest assured, be a no less prompt response for service and readiness for sacrifice on the part of our children than that which was so willingly made by the members of our Unit, and of which this wall and its inscriptions will be an enduring reminder.

The meeting of the College was no sooner over than Sir Charles Ballance, the senior neurosurgeon of Britain, arrived to serve as Surgeon-in-Chief *pro tem.* Ballance had historical and literary interests and had recently published a book on the early history of brain surgery. While he was at the Brigham H.C. arranged for meetings of the Boston Medical History Club on the 22d and of the Harvard Medical Society on the 23d. On the latter occasion Ballance spoke on "Illustrations of brain disease from the great morbid anatomists"—a theme that fascinated Cushing. H.C. and Tracy Putnam then gave an account of their work on the growth hormones of the pituitary.

In the midst of this difficult month there were fifty new admissions on the neurological service and John E. Scarff and Frederic Schreiber, the two Assistant Residents on the neurological service, thought themselves unduly pressed. To remind Cairns of what was going on, H.C. on the 29th sent their admissions list of the week and inscribed on the top in red ink "Help!!"

November was largely devoted to operating and to preparing one of his most attractive general addresses entitled "The medical career," which he presented at Dartmouth College on the 20th of the month. The address bears the subtitle "The ideals, opportunities, and difficulties of the medical profession including a tribute to Dr. Nathan Smith, founder of the Dartmouth Medical School." The blood of the country doctor still flowed forcefully in Cushing's veins and since Ian Maclaren's *Doctor of the old school* was a particular favorite, he recommended that every prospective medical student should read it "if he wishes to know what may be the reward of the country doctor in the love and affection of his patients." He also recommended other books relating to the medical profession:

> And if you would read something about Medicine, I would suggest this

order. You might begin with Ian Maclaren's story of the doctor in *Beside the Bonnie Brier Bush;* and then perhaps Robert Herrick's *Master of the Inn* for a picture of quite another kind of doctor; and then Dr. John Brown's *Rab and His Friends.* Should these stories arouse your interest and sympathy, try some other of John Brown's essays in the "Spare Hours" series, and Weir Mitchell's *Characteristics,* and Osler's '*Æquanimitas* and Stephen Paget's *Confessio Medici*—good things to read whatever you may come to do. And then some medical biographies, preferably by persons who had the gifts to write short ones: Howard Kelly's *Walter Reed,* Agnes Repplier's account of J. William White, for example; Grenfell's autobiography; Trudeau's.

And from this, pass on to some of the books that have been written especially for young men in your position of uncertainty, such as Richard Cabot's *Training and Rewards of the Physician,* published by Lippincott ten years ago, or L. F. Barker's *The Young Man in Medicine* in Sneath's Vocational Series, just issued by Macmillan. And then it may be safe for you to read a cynical and callous novel about a disappointed doctor named Arrowsmith who dabbled ineffectively in medical science, for which piece of fiction the *Life of Pasteur* by Vallery-Radot will serve as an effective antidote.

He also could not refrain from quoting the prayer uttered by President Wheelock of Dartmouth in 1798, which ran: "O Lord, we thank Thee for the Oxygen Gas; we thank Thee for the Hydrogen Gas; and for all the gasses. We thank Thee for the Cerebrum; we thank Thee for the Cerebellum; and for the Medulla Oblongata. Amen!"

The address ends with a forceful quotation from an article in *The American Mercury* by a country doctor about "The Country Doctor":[30]

. . . If [he says], among the medical students and recent graduates of today there should chance to be a man without either scientific or mercenary ambition; who feels no itch for immortal fame, no need for riches or taste for luxury; who lacks the American instinct to do Big Things in a Big Way; whom a modest competence will suffice, with the opportunity to help those who so sorely need the skill of a competent physician; who loves the country and would rather watch the sun setting behind the wooded hills than see the electric signs light up, and prefers clean, clear air to soot and filth; who hates to be jostled by the crowd and to bruise his feet on hard pavements—if such there be, let him go to the country to practice. I can assure him he will be welcomed with open arms, and that—if he behaves himself—he will be happy, as I have been.

A few months later President Hopkins called H.C. back to Dartmouth to receive an honorary Litt.D. Malloch wrote of the address:

Archibald Malloch to H.C. *25 November 1930.*

Dear 'Hardie,' I have just read your little book *The Medical Career* and liked it very much. I have always thought that the Law was not charitable enough. Pres. Wheelock's prayer reminds me of that of the 'minister of the

[30] This address, which was reprinted in book form in 1929 and again in 1930, also served as the first of another group of essays which he was preparing for publication at the time of his death in 1939—*The medical career and other papers.* (Boston, Little, Brown and Company, 1940, 302 pp.).

kirk' after he had heard a philosophical discussion by our Prof. John Watson (Queen's Univ., Kingston, Ont.) on one of his return visits to Scotland: 'Oh Lord, we thank Thee for the Categorical Imperative.' Now we thank you for the picture of Nathan Smith. Dr. Klebs will enter the room at any minute. He arrived yesterday, so I shall be kept busy. . . .

Cushing seemed indefatigable in his zeal for observing centenaries. The year 1928 not only marked the third centenary of the *De motu cordis* and the birth of Malpighi who discovered the capillaries, but it was also the bicentenary of John Hunter's birth. Since H.C. had recently paid a visit to the farm at Long Calderwood in East Kilbride, a parish near Glasgow where in a small roadside cottage John Hunter had first seen the light of day in December 1728, it was of course essential that something be done to celebrate the anniversary of the great physiologist-surgeon. Accordingly, an elaborate program on Hunter was planned[31] for the Harvard Medical Society on 11 December and H.C. arranged a pleasant dinner beforehand. The speakers were Drs. LeRoy M. S. Miner, William Pearce Coues, Arlie V. Bock, Frederic T. Lewis, and Professor William M. Wheeler, with H.C. presiding. Henry Viets had put out a display of Hunteriana, including portraits, medals, and all the extant editions of his various writings. The proceedings of this interesting meeting were published.[32] In closing the meeting H.C. gave a perfect vignette of Hunter: "Hunter was the first to teach the *Science* of Surgery as Paré two hundred years before had advanced the *Art*. But as has been said, he made his name immortal by the labour of his own hands outside the sphere of his vocation. He did not travel by the ordinary road and it is impossible to measure him by the standards of other men."

Not content with having a Hunter celebration, the Harvard Medical Society had still another meeting at which Francis G. Benedict, Director of the Carnegie Nutrition Laboratory in Boston, spoke on the respiratory quotient and its significance.[33] In discussing one of the cases presented before Benedict's paper, Cushing pointed out

[31] Cushing's letter to Viets of 16 August 1928 illustrates how he was continuously stirring up his junior associates to historical writing: "Dear Henry: Don't you think we ought to get up a Hunter celebration for some meeting this next autumn in view of the fact that it is his bi-centenary year? How would you like to tackle the bibliography? I don't think it has ever been gotten together. Most of it of course would be found in the Index Catalogue. And we ought to have some dentist and a geologist and a comparative physiologist, and much else. It's almost like tackling Galen himself. Perhaps you could do the portraits as well as the bibliography. How about it?"

[32] "Exercises in celebration of the bicentenary of the birth of John Hunter." *New England Journal of Medicine,* 18 April 1929, *200,* 810-823.

[33] This meeting was fully covered in the *New England Journal of Medicine* for 27 December 1928, *199,* 1348-1349.

that when the pituitary is removed, the thyroid undergoes atrophy and the metabolic rate falls, but removal of the thyroid is not followed by corresponding changes in the pituitary. For this reason Cushing had concluded that the body's metabolic rate normally is regulated by the pituitary, and that the other endocrines are subservient to it.

The close personal relationship which Harvey Cushing so frequently established with patients and the feeling of personal confidence which he almost invariably inspired has led to a vast outpouring of anecdote and personal recollection from his patients. Since they were all asked to report on the anniversary of their operation and since Cushing nearly always acknowledged these reports personally (or wrote a letter if the reports failed to come on time), his files became filled with a wealth of material describing reactions to the clinic, to the various men on service, and particularly to Cushing himself. One such letter from a New York patient emphasized that despite Cushing's absorption in research problems and the physically exhausting routine of daily operating, and despite the many honors he received as a result of his success therein, he remained to the end (and prided himself upon it) a good physician.

New York,
Max Roesler to H.C. *4 December 1928.*

My dear Dr. Cushing: . . . When I came to the operating table you were not a very clear figure to me. I had been so busy with my own affairs that you were just a nice person I had met—kindly, more human than the god that the Peter Bent staff seemed to think you, and undoubtedly clever.

But to the abnormally acute perceptions of the patient on the table you were very different. In fact there were three of you. There was the doctor talking to assistants or asking for things in a rather low assured voice that was not intelligible to the patient. There was a very wrathy human who made me chuckle to myself when he showed that he did not "suffer fools gladly" when a cold electrode was shoved under my chest. But the important you was the voice that at times spoke to me. It was most startlingly different from the casual you. It was so completely laden with sympathy and understanding that the memory thereof is ineffaceable, and this patient felt that if the time had come for his Fates to cut the thread, it was very good to go with such a voice in his ear. . . .

CHAPTER XVII

Final Years at Harvard: Beating His Own Score

1929-1933

IN 1929 Cushing's clinic had reached the height of its prestige and he held sway over it much as would a commanding general. An ever-increasing number of men from home and abroad were coming to study under him and his contacts with them are interesting in the light of his own youthful experiences. A new man was generally treated with greatest cordiality the first day, but for the next month or two he might find himself wholly neglected except for an occasional rap on the knuckles at an operation (should he by chance be permitted so soon to assist at one). Frederic Schreiber's amusing description of his first months at the Brigham is a case in point:

> The first day I reported to Dr. Cushing's clinic he was most cordial, put his arm about my shoulders and talked to me like a son. Then he did not speak to me again for the next three months except on occasions to tell me to get out of the [observation] stands and disappear somewhere. I was rather mystified and disconcerted by this treatment until the Chief again became very cordial and our relationship was most pleasant until the end of my stay. I did not know his reasons until I heard his speech at the Neurological Conference in Berne in 1931. At that time he said that Kocher would not speak to him for "six" weeks, during which time he "found himself" in the laboratory and decided to stick it out in spite of such treatment. Dr. Cushing explained later that he did this to all men who came to him because he felt that those who did not like the work well enough to stay in spite of his treatment were not suitable to stand the rigors of surgery in later years.

Cushing may have treated his men casually at first, as he did Schreiber, he may have been short with them at operations and critical of their clinical histories, but few went out from the Brigham Hospital without a profound sense of loyalty to him and to his clinic; indeed, one of Cushing's outstanding characteristics was his ability to inspire loyalty in the men who served him. This feeling persisted through the years and whenever occasion arose, his former pupils rallied round to do him honor.

In April 1929 Cushing was to reach his sixtieth birthday. As early as February 1927 Elliott Cutler had addressed letters to Cushing's older pupils, suggesting the idea of a birthday volume and asking for advice about its development; and a year later formal invitations to contribute to a *Festschrift* were sent to all of H.C.'s former pupils, a large majority of whom promptly accepted. The American Medical Association cooperated by permitting the tribute to appear as a special number of the *Archives of Surgery,* and the deadline for manuscripts was set for 1 February 1929. A substantial volume resulted, which had caused Cutler's staff and the editorial offices of the A.M.A. not a little grief. An orthopedic contributor submitted a manuscript with a hundred illustrations of children in braces; Bagley's paper had a huge chart showing three weeks of normal temperatures. In Ross's paper the A.M.A. office arbitrarily changed the name "Barber's Hall" to "Barber Surgeons Hall," which was wholly erroneous; and there was great gnashing of teeth over Locke's colored illustrations and Viets' negative photostats. H.C. had had several recent skirmishes with the A.M.A. office over their cavalier treatment of several Brigham manuscripts, but when he saw the birthday volume and heard something of Cutler's trials and tribulations, he promptly wrote a warmhearted letter to the Editor of the *Journal.*

H.C. to Morris Fishbein (by hand) *9 April 1929.*

Dear Brother Fishbein I am simply bowled over, flabbergasted, dumbfounded, by that Birthday Book you have seen fit to publish. I suppose you must have thought: now the only way to get rid of, to wholly and effectually eliminate, that pestiferous Cushing who behaves as though he was in the manor (Boston) born but wasn't, is to allow his cubs to get out this book after which the only decent thing he can do is to resign and I'll no longer be troubled by his hyphens, dyphthongs [*sic*], P.B.B.H. surgical numbers, his Oljenicks (Ign.) and other crotchets. . . .

Anyhow I am much beholden to you for the trouble you must have taken over this book. . . . I am enclosing a sketch which I am sure represents, in the foreground, a meeting between you and E.C.C.[1]

To this letter Fishbein replied:

Dear Dr. Cushing: I am placing your note of April 9 among my highly prized personal documents. Who knows, some day it may enter into a history of American Medicine. My unbounded respect for your position in your chosen field, and for the unusual number and the quality of your students and assistants, as well as for your literary attainments, made me assent without a moment's hesitation to the suggestion of a birthday volume. I am not going so far as to say that every moment of the process was a pleasure, but it was indeed highly instructive. I have seldom met so delightful and accomplished a personality as E. C. Cutler.

Elliott Cutler then wrote to H.C.: "I am getting a great kick out of the Birthday Book. Thanks for this note from Fishbein which I am

[1] Comic sketch entitled "The Head Proofreader in the Educator Cracker Factory Discovers a Typographical Error"—one of the holes in the cracker is found to be missing.

returning. I did not know before I started—and this opinion is not constructed since seeing his letter—that Fishbein really had such high ideals. Of his intelligence I was long ago assured but the constant turmoil of this recent publication led me to respect his ideals, his generosity, his patience and his ability. . . ." H.C. sent this letter to Fishbein with the following note written across the top: "Dear Fishbein—In these fallen times when more brickbats than bouquets are handed out, it is sometimes consoling to learn, even if indirectly, of the commendation of occasional people. You will therefore not take it amiss if I send you this letter of Cutler's which has just come over my desk."

Although the preparation of the volume had been kept something of a secret, H.C. seems to have had a number of inadvertent fore-warnings, but he had no notion of its size or scope until Saturday, 6 April, when after his usual Saturday operation, which ran well into the afternoon, the clans forgathered in the surgical laboratory at the Medical School, nearly a hundred in number (including members of his family and James Roosevelt, who was about to enter the fold). H.C. was accompanied to the laboratory immediately after he had finished dictating his operative note. When they had all assembled Cutler made the presentation. "Most of us," he said, "are old enough to have become philosophical about the special birthday when we became of age; but only one of us today can view with equanimity the accomplishments of a long enough period of life and work to feel that the future is secure. You, Sir, have given to all of us here an intangible stimulus which we hold amongst our most prized possessions. . . . As a small token of our gratitude and affection . . . we present you with this volume containing articles by a large number of your disciples."

H.C. showed his emotion as he stumbled at first in attempting to reply. He mentioned the *Amenities of sixty* and types of remembrance: the things one regretted, the sorrows, and the causes of happiness. The regrets were past and were best forgotten; the sorrows one did not mention; but the many sources of happiness came from joyous work with other people and the sense of sharing in their accomplishments. At this juncture there was a loud noise and Kenneth McKenzie, a former Assistant Resident, climbed on to a table to offer a touch of comic relief. He had come down from Toronto, he said, to discover, if he could, who selected H.C.'s neckties. They had always interested him and he was sure they had aroused the research instincts of others. In the name of Canada, therefore, he was presenting him with a tie that would outdazzle his bright orange favorite.[2]

[2] At the American College of Surgeons' meeting H.C. had appeared on the platform in a gorgeous orange tie that transfixed the audience.

While delivering his gift, McKenzie read a long-forgotten ditty entitled "The tie that blinds:"

Some may long for the soothing touch
  Of lavender, cream and mauve,
But the ties I wear must possess the glare
  Of a red hot kitchen stove.
The books I read and the life I lead,
  Are sensible, sane and mild
I like calm hats and I don't wear spats,
  But I want my neckties wild.

  Give me a wild tie, brother,
  One with a cosmic urge,
  A tie that will swear, and rip and tear,
  When it sees my old blue serge.

Oh, some will say that a gent's cravat
  Should only be seen, not heard,
But I want a tie that will make men cry
  And render their vision blurred.
I yearn, I long, for a tie so strong
  It will take two men to tie it.
If such there be, just show it to me—
  Whatever the price, I'll buy it!

  Give me a wild tie, brother,
  One with a lot of sins,
  A tie that will blaze in a hectic gaze
  Down where the vest begins.

H.C. disappeared for a moment and returned wearing an apoplectic cravat of enormous dimensions which he confessed had given him horizontal nystagmus; and he added, to satisfy McKenzie's curiosity, that his array of neckties had come to him from grateful patients in lieu of more customary forms of remuneration. Mrs. Cushing, who fortunately had been forewarned, had arranged a buffet supper at their house, and the festive crowd soon gathered at 305 Walnut Street, not, however, before they had managed to dissolve most of the varnish off Miss Stanton's desk, for McKenzie, it seems, had more in his luggage than loud neckties.

The next day, Sunday, Cushing began the rather appalling task of sending handwritten notes of appreciation to each one of the eighty-two contributors, notes that often ran to three pages. He attempted to finish them all on the 7th but probably had an attack of writer's cramp for a few of the notes carried dates later in the week.[3] He did not forget Cutler's secretary, Miss Blake, who had edited the manuscripts and attended to the correspondence:

H.C. to Miss Mildred E. Blake *25 April 1929.*

Dear Miss Blake I understand that you are one of the arch-conspirators in calling to the attention of so many people that I have reached the altogether appalling age of three score. And also that you wrote most of the papers and did most of the correspondence and kept Dr. Cutler and Dr. Fishbein from a duel over hyphens—or was it diphthongs?—or possibly the use of latin in these fallen times. If all this, and more, is true I should think you would need a vacation of about a month on full pay + 10% for you must be about exhausted. Or perhaps on the whole he should reduce your salary as I have done with Miss Stanton—your criminal co-partner—for being so secretive. I have consequently docked her a month's service and diminished her salary. So warn all secy[s] of your acquaintance against Birthday Volumes. Sincerely yours THE VICTIM.

[3] His birthday fell on the 8th, but the considerations of the week-end and the fact that Dr. Welch was having a birthday party in Baltimore on the 8th led Cutler to choose the 6th.

On Sunday night H.C. boarded the "Federal" for Baltimore and spent all day Monday with Welch who was then preparing to move from his quarters in the School of Hygiene to the Library bearing his name which was approaching completion. Welch had just returned from a year's orgy of book buying in Europe and he tried to show H.C. each volume. A letter to Klebs tells the story:

. . . Then I went to Baltimore for Popsy's birthday party—very pleasant. And we spent the greater part of one morning together in the W.H.W. Library. Popsy said we will start at the top and work our way down. We started at the top all right enough, but we never got out of the first alcove in the top stack, Popsy so enthusiastic about every one of his purchases—in Spanish, Czecho-slovakian etc.—saying over each one, "Now don't you think this is just the sort of a collection I should have begun for you?" There was of course nothing to do but smile and say "Yes, just the kind of books for a proper background." Of course I couldn't read a word in any of them.

In addition to the personal notes to the contributors to his birthday volume, H.C. later in the month wrote detailed typed letters to many, especially those who had been unable to attend the party. Two of his resident staff, Richard Meagher and Franc Ingraham, who were in Oxford studying with Sherrington, received a spirited account of the party, for there were no two people who would have enjoyed that festive occasion more than they.

April was a busy month, for scarcely were the birthday parties over when Betsey's engagement to James Roosevelt, a junior at Harvard and eldest son of Franklin D. Roosevelt, then Governor of New York State, was announced at a tea attended by the immediate members of both families. This first meeting of the Cushings and the Roosevelts marked the beginning of a warm and understanding friendship between H.C. and F.D.R.

In May came the distressing news of the Cleveland Clinic disaster. Without waiting to be called H.C. took a night train to Cleveland to see what he could do to help an old friend. He wrote to a former pupil:

. . . Your letter of May 6th is at hand, but it finds me very panicky on account of the shocking news of the explosion in the Crile Clinic which seems to have wiped out one hundred doctors and nurses and patients. I am going out this afternoon, not that I think I can do anything other than as a gesture of sympathy and friendship. Poor Crile has been on the top of the wave all his life, and to have this sudden blow like a bolt from the blue is horrifying. Whether or not we have all of us been able to subscribe to his physiological and biophysical ruminations has nothing to do with the fact that he is a friend in trouble. Apparently there was an explosion in the X-ray room with subsequent conflagration of the films which generated something like phosgene which simply wiped people out. It occurred at the height of a busy morning with the Clinic full of outpatients. Fortunately the Hospital in a separate building seems to have escaped. Crile himself was operating there, but whether he too got gassed subsequently I do not know. John Phillips who was my brother Ned's one-time assistant is one of the victims, and also Locke [who had contributed to H.C.'s birthday volume].

The next day from Cleveland he sent further details to Klebs in Switzerland:

Cleveland, Ohio,
H.C. to A. C. Klebs (by hand) *17 May 1929.*

Dear Arnold, The above will show you where I am and the papers will explain why, viz. the tragic episode in Crile's clinic. The very height of the morning's work at 11.30 with every examination room in a 4-story building occupied by patients, doctors, nurses, employees, etc. A sudden explosion from gas generated in the storage room for the X-ray films, with a burst of gas fumes into practically every room. A lot of heroism on the part of everyone for a few hours and then people getting blue and dropping dead—120 at the last report. I came out last night to see if I could be of any comfort or use. Crile has taken it with amazing equanimity—externally at least. It happened Wednesday morning (15 May). Today is Friday and Crile was operating this morning. Whether this was wise, I don't know, but it was a fine example of poise. City and State and Government officers and gas experts and all the rest can investigate and see that such a horror doesn't happen again. Meanwhile "carry on"—keep at work—do what you can with what you've got left, seems to be the spirit.

The lethal fumes had found their way into the main ventilating ducts of the hospital; in this way they were promptly disseminated throughout the entire building with the result that some 200 people were seriously gassed, 125 fatally. Writing later, Crile said: "Regarding Cushing's visit to the Clinic following our catastrophe, I cannot say too much for his helpfulness at such a time of distress. He interested himself in every detail of the disaster and did everything he possibly could to aid us."

On 29 May Cushing attended the dedication of the Osler Library at Montreal, a ceremony close to his heart at which, much to his delight, he had been asked to represent the Osler Club of London. The preparation of the catalogue of Osler's library had taken far longer than had been anticipated. At the outset the editors had hoped to publish it in 1923, but the revision of Osler's cards had been so painstakingly carried out by his nephew, W. W. Francis, that nine years had been spent in preparing copy and seeing the book through the Oxford Press. (Incidentally, H.C. was the only one concerned who had urged the editors *not* to hurry.) Early in August Lady Osler had instructed that the books at 13 Norham Gardens be packed and shipped to McGill University. The empty packing cases arrived, but a fatal heart attack on 31 August 1928 mercifully spared her from having to part with the books in her lifetime. Dr. Francis took over the task of preparing the library for shipment to Montreal, where the volumes were arranged on the shelves at McGill in a special room set aside and furnished to receive them. The *Bibliotheca Osleriana* was issued on 3 May 1929 just in time for the formal opening of the Library. H.C. wrote of the occasion to Klebs: ". . . And now I'm just back from Montreal. It was hotter than the hinges of Hades—in the 90's. But Thayer was simply inspired—the best thing I have ever heard him give. (They gave him an LL.D. which was much deserved.) It included a perfect tribute to Bill Francis which was timely and what I particularly went up to hear. The library room is most attractive with alcoves, oak wainscoting, rugs, etc. and the books would furnish any, even a poorer room."

Shortly after his return from Montreal H.C. received as a patient in his clinic the prominent Swedish explorer, Sven Hedin, who had been referred from Peiping by Cushing's former pupil, Georges Schaltenbrand. He was accompanied by his public-spirited sister, Alma Hedin, and an attending Stockholm physician, David Hummel. Hedin stayed in the hospital for only five days, after which Schaltenbrand received a cable that there was no present indication for operation. H.C. and the Hedins immediately found much in common, and when it was ascertained that his distinguished patient was not seriously ill, H.C. entertained him and introduced him to many of the brighter groups in Greater Boston. It was found wise, however, to avoid discussion of politics for Hedin had certain political sympathies that his host could not appreciate. But he found Hedin, with his literary gifts and wide interest in literature, art, and exploration, one of the most stimulating men whom he had ever encountered. The Hedins remained in Boston for another week, and by the time of their departure notes were being exchanged between "Alma" and "Sven" and "Harvey," and H.C. had agreed to visit them in Stockholm toward the end of the summer.

After the Hedins' departure, René Leriche of Lyons and Strasburg served for a week as Surgeon-in-Chief *pro tempore*. "To this already famous clinic [at Strasburg] he has added new laurels through his contributions to the surgery of the autonomic nervous system. A friend of many years' acquaintanceship, advantage in our favor was taken of the fact that he had been invited to this country to attend a surgical congress and to receive a degree at Harvard. During his all too brief sojourn from June 13 to June 20, he entered with great spirit into the institutional life of the hospital internes and it is most pleasant to feel that we have established contact with the celebrated Alsatian clinic which our graduates during their travels abroad will be certain to visit in years to come."

This was the summer when Cushing had filled his house with a group of dwarfs (p. 303) who were being treated with a new purified growth hormone which had been under study in animals by Tracy

Putnam. Visitors found him in fine fettle. A contemporary diary gives a few details of his activities at this time:

13 July 1929. Dr. Cushing . . . seemed in excellent spirits and alert, interested and as full of energy as ever. He has filled his house full of pituitary dwarfs as he finds them somewhat temperamental and difficult to keep in hospital during a prolonged series of observations on the effect of extracts of the anterior lobe of the pituitary body given in the hope of making them grow.

17 August. Dined late . . . and returned to the hospital at 10 p.m. in order to finish off some odds and ends. . . . I found that Dr. Cushing had just come from his house to look at a young Dutch boy who is not doing well after his operation. Preparations were made hurriedly for a second operation. It was begun about 10.30 p.m. and I stayed to help. . . . At 1.00 a.m. acted as chauffeur to Dr. Cushing, who by that time had forgotten all about the operation and was waxing most enthusiastic about the coming International Physiological Congress. He told some amusing anecdotes concerning early Congresses which he had attended at the turn of the century.

The more I see of him the more I marvel at his vitality and energy. When I left him he invited me to breakfast the next morning (Sunday) in order to go over a manuscript with him. It being 2 a.m., I asked what time he had breakfast on Sunday and received the curt reply: '8.00 o'clock sharp.'

18 August. Arrived at 8.00 sharp but it was rather an effort. He was already down with the newspaper, a heap of manuscript and a half-finished bowl of porridge in front of him, looking fresh and thoroughly rested, his eyes sparkling. I mentioned Halsted and it started him on an entertaining series of reminiscences about Halsted and his relations with him while he was his Resident Surgeon. He said that Halsted was a man who never set down rules, he was one of those rare spirits who believed that no rule, however detailed or extensive, could ever meet all possible cases; consequently his surgical staff were always left to use their own judgment and were never told what must or must not be done. He said that this was one of the things which he learned from Halsted and had never forgotten. He contrasted the Medical Service of the Brigham Hospital, where everything was run by a book of rules, with his own Surgical Service in which no one had ever seen a printed instruction. . . . He remarked that even in later life, though Halsted was a complete recluse, he was ever quick-witted. He recalled one occasion on which a Southern general in rather rude good humour announced to Halsted over the dinner table that his ears were too big, whereupon Halsted without a moment's hesitation replied, "The better to hear you, my dear general."

The International Physiological Congress

Throughout the summer of 1929 the faculty at the Harvard Medical School were deeply involved in preparations for the 13th International Physiological Congress which was to be held during the week of 19 August. Members began to arrive on Saturday, the 17th, and on the 18th the *SS. Minnekahda,* carrying some 400 European physiologists, docked in the port of Boston at 1.00 p.m.

The Congress was one of the largest international gatherings of scientific men ever held in the United States; it proved to be not only a great success from the scientific standpoint, but something of a triumph of organizational planning, thanks largely to the efforts of Dr. and Mrs. Edwin Cohn (who had acted as general secretaries), their able henchmen, Drs. Alfred Redfield and Hallowell Davis, and many others. The opening ceremony on Monday evening was somewhat unfortunate but thereafter everything went smoothly. Cushing recorded:

> The opening meeting at Sanders Theatre was too absolutely *gauche* for expression. A government representative who talked about nothing but the United States and gas warfare, a representative of the Commonwealth of Massachusetts who, with a military salute many times repeated, said 'Gentlemen, in the name of the Commonwealth, I salute you, coming as you do from all parts of Europe, including China, Japan, and Korea,' and then the president of the University, far from his best, followed by August Krogh, whom nobody could understand and fewer hear. The only moment of enthusiasm was when Pavlov walked on to the platform, when everybody got up and applauded.

During the Congress the Cushings entertained Sir Walter Morley Fletcher, Professor Bottazzi from Naples, Professor and Mrs. Leon Asher from Berne, and Dr. Frédéric Bremer of Brussels. One of his guests recorded:

> Dr. Cushing took all his houseful to Mrs. [Henry B.] Chapin's for tea, she too having a houseful. We had a very entertaining tea party that rather reminded one of 13 Norham Gardens. Dr. Cushing was witty and amusing and most affable to everyone. . . . Afterwards there was a very entertaining supper at which Sir Walter Fletcher and Dr. Cushing regaled the company with stories about disinterring royal tombs; how Halford had run off with the fourth cervical vertebra of Charles I and had subsequently presented it to Queen Victoria, and how many years later there was a service at Windsor Castle, at which said fourth vertebra was re-interred with due pomp and ceremony at Her Majesty's special request. Sir Walter told also how John Hunter, when he was moved from St. Martins-in-the-Fields to Westminster Abbey, had Ben Jonson's skull with red hair still attached, fall on his coffin. Several guests seemed somewhat shocked at the rather casual way in which Englishmen disturb the remains of their distinguished dead.
>
> After dinner Dr. Cushing tried to get Professor Bottazzi to identify the landscape which formed the background of the series of Vesalius' anatomical plates. . . .

On Wednesday Cushing arranged to perform an operation for Professor I. P. Pavlov. The case was unusually interesting, since the patient, in spite of a large tumor of the left hemisphere, had no symptoms of aphasia because he was left-handed. Pavlov was particularly interested in the clinical details of the case because he, too, was left-handed, as all of his family had been for many generations. During the operation, performed under local anesthesia, the patient talked from time to time, much to the surprise of the onlookers. A large bone flap was turned down. As soon as the brain was exposed, it proved fluctuant, and when the postcentral region was incised, a large cyst wall came into view. It gradually bulged forth through the cortical incision and the tumor almost literally fell out like a small ostrich egg into Cushing's hands. The forty or fifty onlookers were much impressed, and the patient not in the least disturbed by the procedure.[4] Pavlov was so much interested that he all but put his prominent whiskers into the operative field. After the operation was ended, he made enquiries about the electrosurgical knife, whereupon H.C. produced a large slab of beef and had Pavlov inscribe his name with the cutting current (specimen now preserved in the Brain Tumor Registry).

Two hundred members of the Congress had been invited to the Brigham for lunch and Pavlov came from the operating room at 2.00 p.m. to join the group. Though lame, he was as lively as a cricket and moved with all the energy of a youth of fifteen. He was to celebrate his eightieth birthday on 14 September, having been born in Riasan, Russia, in 1849. Another episode which particularly interested H.C. was a private meeting with Pavlov in Dr. Cannon's laboratory during which Pavlov delivered an animated lecture on the effects of bromides on experimental neuroses. H.C. gives a colorful description of this session:

> . . . Such a vivid, alert, gesticulating old man you can hardly imagine. Directing his attention to Anrep [the Russian-born physiologist then in the chair at Cairo] who sat calmly alongside, smoking innumerable cigarettes, Pavlov would suddenly stop gesticulating and talking rapidly in Russian, and would then point menacingly to Anrep who possibly asked him a question or two to make sure of his ground, whereupon Pavlov would move his watch and chain, which lay on the table in front of him, along about six inches farther, would then slump down in his chair, shifting his ischial tuberosities to one side or the other—whether because the chair was hard or because this was one of his reflexes I am not sure.
>
> Anrep would then composedly give a most brilliant, concise, clear presentation in English of what had gone before. Pavlov would then pick up the thread again and continue. This went on for an hour and, except for the intrusion of a

[4] The patient on whom Cushing had operated for Pavlov is a well-educated Pittsburgh business executive who has reported with great regularity for sixteen years on the anniversary of his operation. The tumor, though large, turned out to be benign and H.C. looked upon the surgical result as most gratifying. The well-known journalist, Harry Hansen, when reviewing *From a Surgeon's Journal,* mentioned Cushing's operation for Pavlov. The patient in question, reading the review, promptly wrote Mr. Hansen as follows: "Although I was in a very feeble condition, I well remember Professor Pavlov, because when Dr. Cushing introduced me to him he said, 'You are now shaking hands with the world's greatest living physiologist.' . . . The operation lasted four and one-half hours, and I believe them to be the longest hours I have ever put in. One of the secrets of Dr. Cushing's success is that he uses nothing except a local anesthetic which permits the normal functioning of the heart and other organs during the operation. He was lecturing all the time he was working, and would stop occasionally to reassure me that everything was fine or to tell me at different times that the pain would be most severe in order to prepare me so that I would not move. . . ."

few belated guests who crowded into the room, you could have heard a pin drop.
The only grievance I have against my friends, the physiologists in general, is that they have no histrionic sense. The inaugural meeting which I have just spoken of might have been made a thrilling occasion worth perpetuating. This particular episode this morning should at least have been perpetuated by having some good stenographer present in the room, and could there have been a motion picture camera to take Pavlov in action at least once, it would have been memorable. I asked Anrep afterward if he could write it all out *à froid* and he said not by any possibility would he be able to do it again—that he was acting under the hypnotic influence of the old man.

* * * * *

A young Swedish pathologist named Arvid Lindau had attracted Cushing's attention in 1927 through his description of an important new disease entity, designated "hemangiomatosis," which Cushing appropriately christened "Lindau's disease"—a familial condition characterized by tumors of the blood vessels in the retina and also in the central nervous system, sometimes accompanied by cystic degeneration of various internal organs such as the pancreas and the kidney. Blood-vessel tumors of the retina had been described by the Viennese ophthalmologist, von Hippel, but he had not appreciated that the retinal hemangioma was likely to indicate the existence of similar tumors elsewhere in the central nervous system, especially in the cerebellum. A case of Lindau's disease appeared in Cushing's clinic in 1927, and he and Bailey published a detailed report concerning it the following year.[5] Consequently, when H.C. received an invitation from young Lindau to give a lecture at Lund in Sweden, he accepted with alacrity, choosing as his subject the cerebellar medulloblastomas.[6]

Having had little opportunity during the Congress to put his paper in final form, he worked industriously on the *Gripsholm* going over. When he landed at Göteborg, he was met by Dr. Erik Waller, who motored him across Sweden to Lidköping, where a late dinner had been arranged in his honor. There to his great delight H.C. was first introduced to the finest privately owned collection of medical books in Europe. Waller, a busy country surgeon despite his scholarly preoccupation with books, was then performing some 2,000 operations a year in his rural hospital at Lidköping—a scholar-physician and clearly a man after H.C.'s own heart. A brief note to Klebs tells of his reactions: "I am this far on the way. A most delightful spot and this man Waller has such books as you never saw!!! I have almost

[5] "Hemangiomas of cerebellum and retina (Lindau's disease). With the report of a case." (With P. Bailey). *Archives of Ophthalmology, New York,* September 1928, 57, 447-463.

[6] "Experiences with the cerebellar medulloblastomas. A critical review." *Acta Pathologica et Microbiologica Scandinavica,* 1930, 7, 1-86.

decided to remain here a full month some day—perhaps with you." On the bottom of the postcard Waller had penned, "Lidköping Sept. 3d, *3 a.m.*!!! Cordial greetings from Yours sincerely ERIK WALLER."

Cushing's lecture at Lund before the local medical society on 4 September was enthusiastically received. It was followed by an elaborate dinner similar to the one he had experienced the night before in Lidköping, and he soon learned that there is no country on earth where entertainment is more sumptuous than in Sweden. The host in the course of an evening makes several speeches about the distinguished guest, and the guest in turn is expected to make an appropriate rejoinder about his host, his vis-à-vis, and those sitting on either side; and, if the guest is an American, suitable references to the Vikings' early explorations are usually indicated. From Lund, H.C. proceeded on 5 September to Stockholm, where he was the guest of the Hedins at the Grand Hotel. Miss Alma Hedin writes amusingly of his visit:

> . . . Dr. David Hummel was the doctor of Sven's expedition and came with Sven to Boston from Peking in 1929. When Harvey visited us in Stockholm in the fall of the same year Dr. Hummel was his A.D.C. He met Harvey at his arrival and took him to Grand Hotel, where we had ordered the best room and instructed the director that Dr. Cushing should be treated as a royal person. We were therefore much perplexed when Dr. Hummel telephoned us that there was not one room free in the whole place. The excuse was that a Professor Bushing had arrived and had got mixed up with Dr. Cushing and he had been given the best room.
>
> Harvey and Hummel had only time for a light breakfast. Then they attended some operations carried out by Prof. Einar Key, and after that we met at Prof. Key's house for luncheon. The first thing I said to Harvey was of course that I was so sorry because of the horrible mistake. He answered quite seriously but with that little something you know so well in the corner of his eye: "Yes, it is quite dreadful. But this Bushing is always making so much trouble for me." And then he made up a long story about it all. Our chagrin because of his bad reception he changed to a subject for jest which made us roar with laughter. And during the few days of his stay we often returned to his great enemy Bushing and he played a great part in our correspondence.
>
> Dr. Hummel had to go with Harvey to all the libraries, hospitals, sightseeing visits, etc. and as the time for everything was limited, Hummel often had to remind him that they had to break up, which Harvey did not like. Therefore he invented the word "hummelism" because he found him very tyrannical. In our home Harvey met Sven's five sisters, a niece, and several lady-friends. Thereafter he persisted in declaring that Sven had sixteen sisters. The short visit he paid us in September 1929 belongs to the very brightest of all bright memories of our family history. He had the rare gift of putting everybody at ease and of making everybody feel that after all they were somebody and had perhaps accomplished something when so famous and charming a person had spoken so approvingly. . . .

His four days in Stockholm were indeed memorable, for not only had he seen old friends such as Key, Jacobaeus, Nyström, Olivecrona, and the Hedins, but on Sunday he had been presented to the King of Sweden. Later he was motored to Skokloster and to Upsala where he saw the Linné manuscripts and their celebrated silver Bible (Codex argenteus). When he went to the train Monday morning his many friends were there to give him a royal send-off. A few days later bread-and-butter letters were dispatched:

Palace Hotel, Scheveningen,
H.C. to Miss Alma Hedin *13 September 1929.*

Dear Alma: Holland is a very nice country but I left my heart in Sweden. Never did I have such a good time before in my life. Not even Bushing, in spite of all his efforts, was able to spoil it in the slightest. I have been trying to find time to write you a long, long letter but the opportunity never seems to come and just now I am waiting to be taken to the Theatre S (?) to give my lecture. I hope it will come up to the expectations of my ophthalmological friends. But what can I do with a lecture when I am thinking of Gripsholm, of Stockholm, Tycho Brahe, of Charles XII, of Hjalmar Hammarskjöld and more especially of his wife, and Codex argenteus and Henning Haslund, lucky fellow! and of Oscar II and Mammie Lindström and Gustav V and Flower foundation and Hummelism, and best of all, Hedins—many Hedins—each better than the last. Best love to you all, H.C.

P.S. A slogan for the antihummelism society: "We demand 10 minutes instead of 5."

Les Terrasses, Nyon en Suisse,
H.C. to Sven Hedin *15 September 1929.*

Dear Sven I've touched Holland, Belgium, France, and Switzerland since leaving you last Monday morning. They are all very pleasant places and I have seen many agreeable people but none so much as the Swedes. Never did I have such a delightful four days!!—and it was solely due to you that my way was so smoothed from my first setting foot on the gangplank of the *Gripsholm.* I should not have permitted you to pay my hotel bills but I was helpless in the hands of David Hummel. I'm only afraid that Prof. Bushing also had his bills paid from the same source. It would have been just like him. I have not seen him lately. . . .

During his visit H.C. had shown particular interest in one of the treasures of the Royal Library at Stockholm—an early fifteenth century surgical manuscript by John of Arderne. This beautifully illuminated parchment roll, seventeen feet in length, was copied with great fidelity by the Swedish artist, Carl Olausson, and presented by Hedin to H.C. the following Christmas. Cushing's pleasure in this princely gift was unbounded.

H.C. to Miss Alma Hedin *19 December 1929.*

Dear Alma: The copy of that precious Arderne MS. has come safely through the kind intermediation of the Consul-General in New York. I cannot possibly tell you how thrilled and excited I am to possess it. It is truly a marvelous facsimile. I can hardly imagine how it could have been so perfectly done. It will make the most precious item in my medico-historical collection. I shall write to Sven to express my great appreciation. It is so like him to have thought of it. I would much rather have it than a lama temple. . . .

H.C. to Sven Hedin *23 December 1929.*

Dear Sven: The marvelous copy of the Arderne MS. that you have had made for me in celebration, I presume, of the operation I did *not* perform on your spinal marrow has come just in time for Christmas. And such a present! It is an absolutely perfect facsimile of the original—indeed, I am not quite sure but that they have made a mistake and sent me the original. But I will keep mum about this. I will also keep mum about the fact that Hummel and not I really deserved this reward. For it was he that turned the trick and cured you en route to America and not I.

Words fail me to tell you what store I set upon this MS. which will always remain far the most precious item in my library—doubly precious not only in its intrinsic value but because of its association for me with you and your sisters. I have been keeping in touch with you here and there. The postcards which you and Dick Hummel sent me from somewhere on the way to the East reached me safely. Then Alma writes occasionally, giving me word about you, and Schaltenbrand wrote to say that you had reached Peiping though he had not as yet seen you.

By this time I suppose you are undulating in that favourite position of yours, ensconced between the humps of a dromedary while you are writing your notes and sketching the wonders of creation. . . .

Having survived (only just) his six days of Swedish hospitality, Cushing flew on the 9th via Copenhagen to Amsterdam, where Arnold Klebs, who had motored from Nyon in Switzerland, was awaiting him with Oljenick at the airfield. After dining with bibliophilic friends, Bierens de Haan and Nuyens, they proceeded the next day via Volendam and Haarlem to attend the 13th International Ophthalmological Congress at Scheveningen, where H.C. read another major paper, this one on blindness caused by brain tumors which impinge on the optic nerve.[7] Klebs records that Cushing also made a most graceful after-dinner speech at the final banquet on the 12th. The next morning Klebs gathered in Arvid Lindau, and they motored via Delft and Dordrecht to Antwerp where, much to everyone's annoyance, they found the Musée Plantin closed, so they took solace in having lunch at the Zoo. On the 14th they went on through Givet, Dinant, Rheims, and Troyes to Dijon, where Klebs had arranged a dinner at the Faisan d'Or.

By noon of the 15th they had reached Nyon and Klebs' villa, Les Terrasses. After a day's rest they set off on the 17th over the Simplon Pass to Baveno and Milan to attend an auction at Hoepli's, which left Cushing considerably out of pocket with eighteen particularly fine early printed works, several of them incunabula. From Milan they proceeded to Bologna, where they descended upon the distinguished orthopedic surgeon and book collector, Vittorio Putti, and stayed at his house at San Michele in Bosco. On their journey back

[7] "The chiasmal syndrome of primary optic atrophy and bitemporal field defects in adult patients with a normal sella turcica." *Transactions XIIIth International Ophthalmological Congress,* Amsterdam, 1929, 97-184.

they saw the d'Este Library at Modena, and by the 19th they were again in Milan, returning the next day to Switzerland by St. Gotthard and the Axenstrasse, where Klebs took the well-known photograph of Cushing which forms the frontispiece of this biography. Stopping in Zurich at the Baur au Lac on the 21st, they lunched with Felix R. Nager, the eminent Swiss otolaryngologist, after which Cushing "sanctified" a number of his larger fees by acquiring the oldest and probably the most valuable incunabulum in his library, Hartmann Schedel's copy of Pietro d'Abano's *Conciliator* (Mantua 1472), which he had missed earlier that year at an auction (Graupe's). Late in the afternoon of the 21st Klebs, as though he had been born on a Swiss mountain pass, negotiated all the hairpin turns between Zurich and Nyon and deposited H.C. and the *Conciliator* safely at Les Terrasses at midnight. Marcel, the butler, was patiently awaiting them with some cognac, which by this time they no doubt needed. After four days' "rest" with Klebs, H.C. on the 24th took the train to Paris and sailed the following noon on the *Majestic* from Cherbourg.

On his arrival in Boston things had accumulated—books from all over Europe, letters, patients, and Professor D. P. D. Wilkie from Edinburgh, who from 7 to 14 October acted as Surgeon-in-Chief *pro tempore*. H.C. had a great fondness as well as admiration for Scottish medicine, and Wilkie's visit increased this esteem. The staff and students rallied round him perhaps more than they had about any other incumbent from overseas. Of his visit Cushing writes:

> . . . Mr. Wilkie exemplifies at their best the traditions of a famous anatomical School of Surgery and it was a great stimulus to us all to have had this intimate and delightful contact with him. In Colonial days and long afterward, such American medical students as could afford to leave this part of the world flocked to Edinburgh to supplement their meagre training acquired here solely in the process of apprenticeship. That a large number of them received their medical degrees in Edinburgh is a debt the American profession never can fully repay, but it is one we nevertheless need not forget. The visits here of Sir Harold Stiles and of Mr. Wilkie have merely served to increase our local obligations to Scottish medicine, for these gentlemen taught us far more than they learned.
>
> Only in the case of younger men who come here to study can we possibly make some partial repayment of this long-standing indebtedness. It is a great satisfaction, therefore, that Mr. Norman M. Dott of Edinburgh was an Assistant Resident Surgeon here in 1923-1924 and that his assistant, Mr. W. R. Henderson, is at the present time a volunteer worker on the staff. Mr. Dott, moreover, returned to the clinic last August for a period of a few weeks just before the meeting of the International Physiological Congress, and as his visit happened to coincide with Doctor Horrax's vacation, he volunteered to act as his substitute.

Almost before he knew it Cushing was obliged to attend the dedication ceremonies of the Welch Library. His address was evidently written under some pressure, and it does not rank with his other utterances prepared for ceremonial occasions. It had been started on shipboard, and H.C. was heard to remark that it was second-class, like the accommodations in which it was begun. It carried the somewhat unfortunate title, "The binding influence of a Library on a subdividing profession." Medical students, being what they are, were soon off in the corridors whispering among themselves about the evils of bibliographical constipation.

After the Baltimore address, he settled down at the Brigham and made a determined effort to catch up with the summer's accumulation: patients to be operated upon, manuscripts to be read, and a large group of younger men on his clinical staff waiting to air their various problems. At the beginning of the school year H.C. records:

> The following persons, all of them holding travelling fellowships, were appointed as voluntary assistants: Dr. Attracta Halpenny, a graduate of the Royal College of Physicians and Surgeons at Dublin and pathologist to the Richmond Hospital, Dublin, here as Purefoy Memorial Scholar from the College of Surgeons, Dublin; Mr. F. A. R. Stammers, a graduate in medicine of the University of Birmingham who had also served at the London Hospital and had recently been appointed Assistant Surgeon at the Birmingham General Hospital, here on a Rockefeller Fellowship; Mr. William R. Henderson, graduate of the University of Edinburgh and recent House Surgeon in the Royal Infirmary, also here on a Rockefeller Fellowship on the recommendation of the Medical Research Council; Mr. George Armitage, a graduate of Leeds, 1921, recommended by Lord Moynihan, here on a Rockefeller Fellowship; Dr. Gaston De Coppet, a medical graduate, 1924, of the University of Berne and now *Chef de clinique* in Professor de Quervain's surgical service at the Inselspital, likewise holding a Rockefeller Fellowship. This last appointment has given the writer particular gratification for the reason that he owes so much to the clinic in Berne where thirty years ago he spent a happy and most profitable year as a student under Theodor Kocher who was also Professor de Quervain's teacher; he feels therefore that his professional relation to Doctor De Coppet is that of uncle to nephew. . . .

1930

Early in 1930 Cushing's friends in Baltimore and New Haven, realizing that he must retire from the Brigham in two years' time, sought to attract him either to Hopkins or to Yale; his admirers at Western Reserve likewise were making overtures in the hope of persuading him to return to Cleveland. At the time of the dedication of the Welch Library in October 1929, Welch had suggested that Cushing would live longer if he retired and became Professor of the History of Medicine at the Hopkins as successor to the first incumbent (Welch) of that chair. He broached the subject again when he came to Boston for two days in February to give an address at the Boston Medical Library on "Medical libraries and their aims." The visit was evidently much enjoyed by all concerned, and H.C. wrote a detailed account of it in his voluminous Welch memorabilia:

They had been trying without success to raise money in Boston to renovate and increase the stack-room in the Boston Medical Library. Quinby, who was on the Committee, dropped into my dressing room one morning and said he had run across Dr. Welch at a meeting somewhere and the idea occurred to him that possibly Dr. Welch might be persuaded to come on and give a talk about medical libraries and their purposes. This would draw a crowd and possibly increase the number of contributions. Dr. Welch had said of course he would be glad to come.

To ask an outside physician to come and help the Boston profession out of their financial difficulties was bad enough, but Dr. Welch of all people with his 80th birthday in the offing and the date set for the meeting in midwinter. "You don't for a moment expect that even if he meant it he will remember to come or remember what other engagements he may have made for the same evening," I remarked. "Oh yes," said Quinby confidently, "I saw him write it down in his little book." "What arrangements are you going to make for him?" I asked. "That's where you come in," he replied. "Can't you put him up?" So I wrote, knowing that he always preferred to go to a hotel rather than a private home, and he promptly accepted. It is just possible, as he hints in the note that soon followed, his real motive in accepting was to give the Boston Library a good looking over in preparation for what was soon coming in Baltimore.

Wednesday, February 5th, was a cold raw morning with two or three inches of wet snow on the ground. The Federal Express got to the Back Bay at something like 6.50, and Gus and I were just a minute late and saw no sign of Dr. Welch in the dark downstairs platform. Luckily, however, we captured him just as he was boarding a taxi carrying a little light overcoat on his arm and standing in thin shoes in two inches of snow. We went to the house and had breakfast before an open fire so he could warm up though he seemed to have no concern about wet feet. He was full of talk and we sat about for some time until he finally said there were many people he wanted to see and would I just let him order a taxi and go about his calls. I said if he would drop me at the hospital he could have the car to himself and do what he chose but before he went out would he mind being sponged off. His waistcoat, and where this and his trousers met, was simply covered with the most peculiar material, some of which might have been food. I can't imagine what he had run into. It was extraordinarily difficult, for I encountered no resistance whatever to sponging and I had to insert my hand between the spots and Popsy in order to get anything to rub against. Anyhow, I found he wasn't ticklish. The faithful Nellie, who was assisting me and who provided the spot remover, nearly had an apoplexy. Then we stopped at the tailor's on the way to the hospital so that he might remove some peculiar and numerous spots that had been too much for Nellie, me, and the spot remover. This necessitated the temporary separation of Popsy and his outer garments. We meanwhile sat in the window at Bergstein's in Brookline Village while the deed was accomplished, and Popsy remarked that we were extraordinarily particular people here in Boston about our guests and their appearance—that he had bought this suit in Paris only eighteen months ago and he didn't see why it wasn't good enough for Boston.

. . . After all, the aim of this recital was not to point out Popsy's indifference to his personal appearance, for he was naturally tidy. It was rather to emphasize his disregard of himself in coming to Boston in midwinter at eighty years of age to make a speech in behalf of the Boston Library and to help it to raise some funds.

Not long after Welch had started to agitate for H.C. as his successor in the chair of the history of medicine, James Rowland Angell and Milton C. Winternitz, President of Yale and Dean of the Medical School respectively, began to sound out Cushing about coming to New Haven as Professor of Neurology or Neurosurgery, whichever he might prefer. They were aware that he was still at the height of his powers as a surgeon, and it was felt in many quarters that it would be most unfortunate if he were obliged at this juncture to give up surgery entirely. He himself said he would like twenty-five years more, because there were still so many unsolved problems. Many exchanges between the three men followed during the summer of 1930. Yerkes (who was now at Yale) and others also made their attempt at persuasion. After some delay H.C. replied on 2 October: "I have two years more here . . . meanwhile I have many things to do and much uncompleted work to wind up. What will happen then, I don't know. . . . Whether two years hence I will be the person you will want for the purposes you suggest is perhaps open to doubt." To his friends in Boston at this time he waxed hot and cold about moving. He had no idea what provision, if any, Harvard might make for his retirement and the completion of his work; accordingly he was impelled to leave everything entirely open in regard to both Hopkins and Yale. In 1931 both Dean Edsall and Mr. Lowell asked H.C. to remain as Professor of the History of Medicine, but he deferred final decision until 1933.

During the winter there had been fewer major distractions than usual. Faithful always to Yale, he had taken the trouble in January to attend Mr. Altschul's annual dinner for the Yale Library Committee, in that way keeping up with Mr. Keogh, the Librarian, with Chauncey Brewster Tinker, Wilmarth Lewis, and other ardent supporters of the Yale Library, and incidentally enjoying a feast reminiscent of those of Lucullus. Cushing had watched the Yale Library closely for a long time. Two years earlier when the announcement about the new building was made, he had written promptly to Andrew Keogh, the Librarian:

H.C. to Andrew Keogh (by hand) *25 February 1928.*

Dear Keogh: Hail! I've read your report with profit. Also the account in the Alumni Bulletin. Excellent!! I envy you your job, and the pleasure you are to have in the next few years making the Sterling Library the focal point of the University.

And again the next year (also by hand):

10 July 1929.

If Osler didn't put in writing "The library is the heart of the university" he believed it and I've often heard him say as much—possibly in the same words. But I have not been able to locate it. I looked for it in the "Library

School and the College"—an address given in Aberdeen published in the Library Assoc^{n}. Record Aug-Sept. 1917. There are some good things in this, viz. "A collection of books is a university and a custodian of books is necessarily a teacher." Also: "The main business of the college is not vocational but cultural, not final but initiative."

Ever on the alert for men doing interesting things, Cushing discovered that George W. Corner was reading a paper before the Medical History Club of the University of Rochester with the intriguing title, "The rise of medicine at Salerno in the XIIth century," and 'the flighty purpose' was o'ertook, for he immediately wrote: "I wish I could be in Rochester to hear your paper next Monday on Salerno! Don't you think you can squeeze in a day and give it here at the Brigham?" Corner, much pleased, agreed to come on 25 March. When H.C. asked whether an exhibit covering the substance of his lecture might not be in order, the erudite Rochester Professor of Anatomy submitted a list of somewhat occult titles that drew Cushing into correspondence for the next month with medical librarians. He eventually managed to secure, mostly on loan, nearly every item, including *Opera Constantini,* 1536-1539, and the *Opera Ysaac,* 1515. Cushing with his omnivorous interests had always had a lurking desire to learn more about Salerno, and Corner presented the obscure subject with the greatest lucidity and with little evidence of the laborious task he had had in bringing the materials together.

A fortnight later H.C. was off on a pleasant errand. Celebrating Welch's birthday had become an annual and more or less intimate event, but the party held on his eightieth birthday was a more formal occasion, sponsored by President Hoover and held in Washington with much official fanfare. For the birthday brochure that was issued Cushing wrote (anonymously) one of his finest pieces of prose:

> To have stepped, in the prime of life, into a position of acknowledged intellectual leadership in the profession of his choice; to have occupied that position, albeit unconsciously, for those forty years which have seen the most rapid strides in medical progress of all time; to have had such influence in the furtherance of the medical sciences in this country as to turn the tide of students seeking opportunities for higher education from the Old World to the New; to have been as ready in countless unrecorded ways to share his time and thought with those who were inconspicuous as with those who sat in high places; to have been no less universally respected for his great learning than beloved for his personal charm and companionability; to have stood knee-deep in honours unsought and to have remained seemingly unaware of them; to have rounded out with distinction two successive university positions and, with enthusiasm undimmed, to be now well launched on a third which he is no less certain to adorn—
>
> To have done so much, in so many ways, for so many years, and to have aroused no shadow of envy or enmity on the way, betokens not only unselfishness of purpose but that fineness of character which always has been and always will be an inspiration to mankind.

The celebration had world-wide repercussions. President Hoover's address at the luncheon was broadcast around the world and forty-five similar celebrations were held simultaneously in several countries—England, France, Italy, Switzerland, and China, to name but a few. To one of his pupils abroad H.C. sent a vivid account of Popsy and this famous birthday party:

Popsy came down for a late breakfast [at his nephew, Senator F. C. Walcott's house], set for him at a table in the living room, and we had a most entertaining time as he opened one after another of the many cables and telegrams of felicitation and boxes of flowers, notes and packages of books. From Mildred Bliss, eighty out-of-season cornflowers, appropriate both to Popsy's singleness of life and to his college. There was one special one with a tricolour ribbon marked "To be worn." This he promptly did, but an Army officer removed it, I may add, just before the formal gathering, saying that it was against regulations to cover a D.S.M. emblem with a boutonnière. Fred had given him a first edition of "Dr. Syntax in Search of a Wife" in three volumes with the Rowlandson coloured prints. . . .

As usual, Popsy was most apologetic about his coming address (which a stenographer in the next room was busily manifolding for the press), never realising what an important function it was to be—he thought he was merely to meet a few friends, had written the address on the train coming over, etc., etc. Finally about eleven, Fred and I insisted that he should retire somewhere, get his mind on what was coming, and Fred suggested that he might read the address over to me. So we were pushed into an upstairs room and the door closed while he read it over, meanwhile interrupting himself frequently to explain what was hidden behind his brief allusions: such, for example, as regards preventive *versus* curative medicine. He said it was the first time in years he had written out a speech and he found he had quite forgotten how. He had become accustomed to taking his cue from what had gone before and was sure he could do much better this way. . . .

The celebration was held in the Memorial Continental Hall in which the Naval Conference was held in Harding's administration. Fred, Popsy and I motored down. . . . All of the people filing in late wanted to shake hands with Popsy and we had difficulty dragging him away and around devious passages and back rooms where people with transmitters were preparing to relay the addresses around the world, until finally we came to a room where the inner circle was gathering. They were all dressed as for a funeral or a wedding except myself.

Word soon came that the President was in the building and so the Chief Justice *et ux.* and Fred and I made our way back to the front of the hall where four front seats were reserved—an embarrassing process. We had no sooner gotten seated than the performers came on the platform, the President with his two aides whose uniforms afforded the only bit of colour, so far as concerned the audience. Farrand gave what might be called a felicitous address and which I think was admirably suited to the occasion. He introduced Flexner who did exceedingly well. Then the secretary of the committee, John A. Kingsbury, of the Milbank Memorial Fund, took two or three minutes to wave a bundle of messages from scientific institutions and prominent people scattered over the world. He read a few extracts from some of them, pointing hopelessly to a chair full of others which had been pouring in. Mr. Hoover then spoke and though his voice was low and husky because he evidently had a bad cold, what he had to say was in the best of taste. Unquestionably with the weight of his position behind it, it was the most important utterance of the hour—Popsy, "the statesman of science."

We had been getting up and down on various occasions but when Farrand called on the octogenarian himself, we all got up again and applauded warmly. Popsy was the most composed person in the Hall. He was, to be sure, pretty well concealed by radio transmitters, and the reading desk was too high for him. He was so unaccustomed to reading what he had to say that he began with the first sentence as he remembered it and then found he couldn't see to read. So he began systematically going through his clothes, just as though he were looking for a lost railroad ticket, and finally after a prolonged search about his capacious person, extracted his specs, to the relief of everyone, from his right starboard pants' pocket. From then on, all went off smoothly and well. He of course said just the right thing about everybody (himself included) and explained that the tribute was of course being paid to the many other workers in medical science through him as an accident.

After it was all over, we made our way back to S Street where some eighty people (a mixture of pundits, relatives and friends) turned up for a buffet luncheon—a most delightful gathering. There was a huge birthday cake with eighty candles which Popsy, whale-like, blew out in three blows; and as he inserted his knife in it he said this was the last birthday cake he was going to cut (loud applause!) and that henceforth it would be my duty to cut the birthday cakes on April 8th as I was going to succeed him (feeble applause). I wanted to stay and "sit in" after the guests had drifted away, the best hour of any party, to hear the gossip of the morning and to see more packages opened up, but Garrison insisted that I should go with him to see Colonel Ashburn about the problems of the Surgeon General's Library, of which I know nothing; but I could not well refuse. He had his flivver full of people to whom he was going to show the cherry blossoms and so he dropped me at the Library. . . .

I found Fred and the Adamses just getting ready to accompany Popsy while he paid a call on a contemporary of his, an old lady who had come all the way from Norfolk with a trained nurse on purpose to hear the morning exercises and who, according to Fred, had been in love with Willie Welch ever since she was three years of age. Popsy was very frisky about it and began to quote Tom Moore at considerable length—"The light that lies in woman's eyes has been my soul's undoing, etc." And though Fred told him that flowers had already been sent to her that morning in Popsy's name, he snitched three large red roses from the many that had been sent to the house and off we went to the Bellevue-Stratford into which Popsy waddled with three rather limp and naked roses clutched in one hand and a dead three-quarters-smoked cigar ditto in the other. . . . We got back in time for a hurried supper in the midst of which I had to leave to catch the eight o'clock train back home. It was a great day.

During May H.C. avoided his usual run of spring meetings partly in anticipation of Charles Singer's visit to Boston (which was eventually called off) and partly to enable him to keep time free for his Swedish colleague, Gunnar Nyström, who came during the third week in May to act as Surgeon-in-Chief *pro tempore*. H.C. had been profoundly impressed the preceding September by the surgical clinics of Sweden, as is evident from the note concerning Nyström in his Annual Report for 1930:

> The desire to have a representative of one of the three great Swedish clinics live in for a time with our junior house-staff was born of a visit which I had the great pleasure to pay in 1929 to Lund and Stockholm and Upsala; and the opportunity was taken of Professor Nyström's presence in the country last May to invite him to the clinic. Anyone who has seen the almost ideal conditions under which the medical faculty at Upsala conduct their work within a superb modern hospital placed in the sylvan surroundings of a charming university town can appreciate how crude and unattractive must seem our institutional life, crowded as it is into a small space, beaten in upon from all sides by the increasing clamor of a noisy American city. But we at least can emulate the Upsala spirit of enthusiasm for teaching and research; and the effect of Professor Nyström's visit has already become apparent in the activation of interest in some of those special fields of work such as emergency operations for the removal of vascular emboli to which he has been a notable contributor. . . .

During May the Cushing family were making preparations for Betsey's wedding early in June. On 21 May H.C. apologized to Klebs for an oversight, "This [failure to consult Klebs' 'Pestbook' for desired information] may be due to an approaching wedding which has given me prematrimonial neurasthenia, which is nowadays purely a parental disease, whereas once it was supposed to affect the major participants." The ceremony was held at St. Paul's Episcopal Church in Brookline with a reception on the Cushing grounds at 305 Walnut Street. Birthday festivities were one thing, but if one may judge from his letter written on 4 June to the somewhat cynical Klebs, weddings were something that had to be put up with. "Betsey's wedding day. Temp. 90°± but better than the Nor'easter we have been having for a week. The town is full of Delanos and Roosevelts and motorcycle policemen and detectives. Our front yard looks like a circus and I feel like Mr. Ringling—the wedding ringling. I have reserved a special tent for myself in which I shall sulk, Achilles-like; 10 cts. extra—peanuts and lemonade and camels (cigarettes)." Although he usually avoided formal dress, H.C., despite the heat, appeared in most correct attire with topper, morning coat, spats, a lively pair of grey trousers, and a huge dress cravat. One who attended wrote: "Betsey's wedding went off very nicely, as you no doubt have heard—Dr. Cushing arrived with her at the church only a few minutes late, which was good considering his operating room record. It was something to have him there at all for he had threatened to be too busy to be on hand and had told Betsey that probably Gus would have to give her away."

After the wedding H.C. began working in earnest on his Lister Memorial Lecture, a triennial award made by the Royal College of Surgeons of England; he also had the responsibility of unveiling a plaque to Sir Anthony Bowlby, which was being presented to the College BY THE MEDICAL OFFICERS OF THE AMERICAN EXPEDITIONARY FORCE WHO SERVED UNDER HIM IN FRANCE, 1917-1918, IN GRATITUDE AND AFFECTION. The idea had originated with Crile and Cushing, and H.C. had raised the necessary funds and conducted with Lord Moynihan the negotiations concerning this appropriate gesture.

Neurohypophysial Mechanisms

The backgrounds of Cushing's Lister Lecture are of some interest; in this carefully considered statement he largely abandoned a view to which he had held tenaciously for twenty years, namely, that disturbances resulting from encroachment upon the pituitary gland are due entirely to glandular dysfunction and not to impairment of adjacent nerve centers of the brain. Even in his Cameron Lectures in 1926 and the Medical Society of London Lecture of 1928 he had continued to be "pituitary minded." Prior to his Lister Lecture he had largely ignored the work of Bailey and Bremer in his own laboratory; the person chiefly responsible for convincing him that nervous factors must be considered was John Beattie, then of Montreal, who spoke at the Harvard Medical Society in January 1930 on his recent work on the excitability of the hypothalamus, that part of the brain which we now know to play an important rôle in the regulation of pituitary function. Beattie, with his associates, G. R. Brow and C. N. H. Long, had also obtained evidence (in animals) that the hypothalamus harbors centers that control visceral processes, such as activity of the stomach, sweat glands, and blood vessels. It was not long before H.C. reached a similar conclusion concerning the human hypothalamus: namely, that a parasympathetic center as well as a sympathetic region of control had functional localization within the hypothalamus.[8] This he deduced from observing the effects of injecting posterior pituitary and pilocarpine solutions into the cerebral ventricles of conscious human subjects. These studies were begun in 1930, and Beattie had found that electrical stimulation of the hypothalamus of animals also gave rise to "parasympathetic" effects—blushing, sweating, pupillary constriction, and increased activity of the stomach and intestines—reactions precisely similar to those which Cushing had observed with his intraventricular injections in man. Since reactions of this kind are seen in human beings under conditions of great emotion, Bard and others had concluded that emo-

[8] "I. The reaction to posterior pituitary extract (pituitrin) when introduced into the cerebral ventricles. . . . VI. Concerning a possible 'parasympathetic center' in the diencephalon." *Proceedings of the National Academy of Sciences,* April, May 1931, *17,* 163-180; 239-264.

tional reactions are integrated at the hypothalamic level. In all this Cushing was profoundly interested, because he had frequently encountered emotional disturbances after operations involving this region of the brain, and his colleague, Bailey, had studied the incidence of emotional disturbances in cases of tumor of the third ventricle which impinged on the hypothalamic area. This then formed the immediate background of his lecture.

By the end of June Cushing was again on the Atlantic and arrived in England on 7 July for his Lister Address at the Royal College of Surgeons. For the first few days in London he joined Betsey and James Roosevelt at Garland's Hotel. A friend who took lunch there with H.C. on the day of the lecture recalls that he was revising his MS. up to the last minute. During the meal he had one new idea after another and wandered back and forth in Betsey's suite without eating a mouthful; the bewildered waiter had apparently never seen anyone quite like him and appeared to doubt his sanity. So wrought up was H.C. by thought of the address that he temporarily forgot he would be called upon just before the lecture to unveil the Bowlby plaque; he drafted his remarks for this about fifteen minutes before leaving the hotel, and continued writing while in the taxi. On arrival at the Royal College of Surgeons punctually at four o'clock he was met on the doorstep by Sir Arthur Keith, who hurried him inside so that he might have a chance to collect his thoughts. Arnold Klebs had come from Geneva, Morelle from Louvain, and Oljenick from Amsterdam to hear the lecture. The College was thronged and just before the address the crowd assembled on the steps and in the Hall in front of Bowlby's portrait; Cushing stepped forward in his College robes and drew back the Union Jack covering a silver plaque which had been mounted beneath Bowlby's portrait and read a brief appreciation of Bowlby and his relation to the American Expeditionary Forces in 1917-1918:

> Sir Anthony Bowlby carved for himself a notable career. His father had died in tragic circumstances in China, leaving him a mere child; but by dint of perseverance, native ability and character he made his way into the profession he came to adorn. As a young surgeon at St. Bartholomew's, by arduous study he acquired that clinico-pathological acumen and judgment that made him rank high among his professional fellows. His service in the South African War gave him the experience which led to the high position he held from the first with your Expeditionary Force in the late war. His knowledge of every detail of the army medical organization, unusual for a civilian, was distributed lavishly upon those of us who came unduly late into the struggle.
>
> But it is not of his capacity for work, his ability as an organizer, his instinctive good judgment of men and affairs that I would speak. Nor of his record as soldier, as citizen, or as surgeon—a one-time most worthy President of this College. It is not to recall these facts that we have asked the privilege of placing this modest tablet here. It is to recall something far more personal. It is to

recall those rare qualities of unfailing cheerfulness, unfailing consideration of others, unfailing sympathy for the ill and the wounded, that made so great an impression on the American medical officers whose good fortune in being apportioned to the British forces in Flanders brought them in contact with him.

The President of the College, Lord Moynihan, also in his robes stepped forward and accepted the plaque in the name of the Royal College of Surgeons. The gathering then proceeded into the lecture theater, and presently the mace-bearer appeared, followed by Lord Moynihan and the members of the Council. When Cushing entered, there was prolonged applause. He read from his manuscript during the first ten or fifteen minutes but then continued extemporaneously describing his conception of hyperthalamic mechanisms:[8a]

The pituitary body is a combined neuro-epithelial organ present in all craniates. Its purely epithelial lobe is the first of the endocrine organs to be differentiated in the embryo; its neural portion is an outgrowth of the oldest part of the brain to be laid down. If the rudimentary organ is removed from the amphibian embryo its further growth and metamorphosis are promptly checked; if reimplanted, these effects do not occur, but the rudiment will not long remain functionally active unless neural tissue is included in the transplant. The infundibular lobe is an expansion of that ancient portion of the cerebrum, the diencephalon, which retains its simple structure in all creatures that can boast of a brain at all. Herein lie ancestrally important mechanisms common to all species which have to do not only with their vegetative functions, but with their primitive instincts—in mating, in satisfying hunger and thirst, in restoration from fatigue by sleep, in regulation of body temperature, in self-protection by combat or escape. From the diencephalon non-medullated nerve-fibres pass direct by way of the infundibulum to be distributed in the posterior lobe and its epithelial envelope. Extracts of this lobe contain a peculiarly active substance or substances, the injection of which serves to counteract one, at least, and probably more than one of the symptomatic effects of irritative or paralytic injuries to the suprajacent interbrain. Non-medullated nerve-fibres also connect this ancient station by way of the spinal cord and the sympathetic nervous system not only with the thoracic and abdominal viscera but some of them even turn back to act upon the anterior hypophysis itself. Hence diencephalic messages may be relayed to this somewhat insulated part of the gland on whose hormones depend not only normal body growth and the normal function of certain subsidiary endocrine organs but, indeed, the very perpetuation of the species. For without the presumably emotional discharge from this source of the hormone of sex, the chain of events leading to the escape, fertilisation, and implantation of the ovum cannot take place.

Though information may be gained by the independent study of its separate parts, physiologically the diencephalo-hypophysial mechanism can only be properly interpreted when looked upon as a whole and even then only when its influence on the entire organism is taken into account. So, at the end, I may appropriately quote what Thomas Willis said of that "divine artifice," the *rete mirabile* and its function: "There is nothing in the whole fabric of an animal body more worthy of admiration . . . nothing can be conceived as more skilful, and nothing which argues more forcefully the providence of a divine Author."

[8a] "Neurohypophysial mechanisms from a clinical standpoint." *Lancet,* 1930, **2**, 119-127; 175-184.

At the end Lord Moynihan arose and moved a vote of thanks in which he referred to Cushing as "an old and valued friend." He then presented him with the Lister Medal "for distinguished contributions to surgical science." H.C., Betsey, and James Roosevelt dined that evening at the House of Lords with the Council of the College, as guests of Lord Moynihan.

The next day Klebs and Cushing were discovered listening to E. P. Goldschmidt's beguiling siren songs about incunabula, Vesaliana, XIVth century MSS., etc., many of which were spread about on tables, with Goldschmidt darting hither and yon in a room so thick with cigarette smoke that one could scarcely see across it. As they departed Cushing was heard to mumble something about having "sanctified" another honorarium—probably several times over.

In the evening a dinner had been arranged for former members of Cushing's staff of the Brigham Hospital. It turned out that there would be thirteen at table, so Klebs was induced to join the group. Geoffrey Jefferson, in proposing the health of "the Chief," began by saying that there were many surgeons who had achieved great honor in public life, but there was none who had so devoted a body of pupils—this and much else in similar vein. Cushing in responding said that at his age the only thing that mattered was his pupils, and he hoped they would continue to show that *esprit de corps* which was so essential for the advancement of the work they were doing, and that their success would continue to give him great joy.

The next few days were spent with Klebs resting up with friends at Oxford. He visited the Bodleian—as usual in quest of Vesalius. Someone at Bodley overheard Mr. Falconer Madan, the eminent Oxford bibliographer, say to Klebs and Cushing, "What on earth have you two in common—one a surgeon and the other a bibliographer?" H.C., quick as a flash, replied, "Ah, we have you, my dear Madan!"

On Saturday the 12th (Osler's birthday) they returned to London for a meeting of the Osler Club—a group of historically minded students including Alfred Franklin (*aet.* 23) and D'Arcy Power (*aet.* 75)—where H.C. gave the third Oslerian Oration. There was a dinner beforehand at the Langham Court Hotel at 6:30, a very pleasant gathering with much amusing chatter, H.C. planning his speech between sentences. The meeting was held at Franklin's house, where nearly fifty people had gathered.

Having made it quite clear that his oration was going to be of true Oslerian informality, he went on to describe incidents in the early life and education of W.O. Warming to the subject very rapidly and carrying everyone in the room with him quite spellbound, he told of Father Johnson and James Bovell and of the vigorous life they led;

he showed Johnson's notebook, which in righteous dishonesty he had acquired from a Johnson descendant, and then proceeded to present it to the Club, whose members would hold it as trustees for any other descendants of Johnson who might wish to reclaim it!

Throughout his discussion Cushing referred to the biography as though he had had very little to do with it and had written it at least fifty years before; his quick-wittedness and quiet modesty combined with an undercurrent of scintillating humor gave insight into his character. Afterwards H.C. singled out each member of the Club in turn and talked with him. Before the evening was over he came to appreciate more fully what influence his labor of love had exerted, and how the hope expressed in his dedication ("that something of Osler's spirit may be conveyed to those of a generation that have not known him") had indeed been realized. H.C. stayed the night with his bibliophilic friend, Geoffrey Keynes, who motored him down to Oxford the next morning with Sir Walter Morley Fletcher. After lunch they proceeded to the Almshouse at Ewelme, where a tablet to Sir William, Lady Osler, and Revere was dedicated by the Bishop of Oxford. For this ceremony the Osler Club turned out in force.

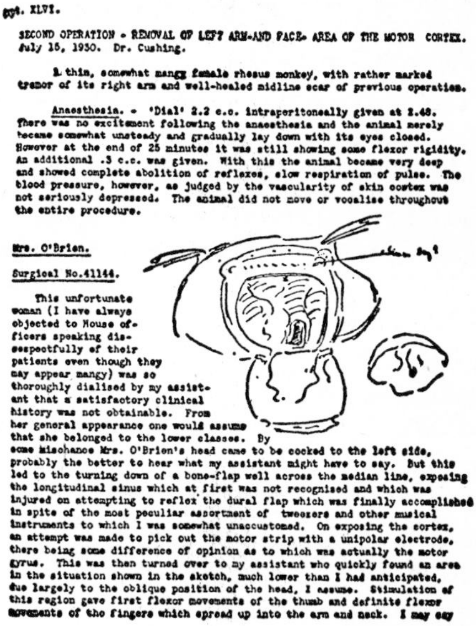

Ept. XLVI.

SECOND OPERATION - REMOVAL OF LEFT ARM-AND FACE- AREA OF THE MOTOR CORTEX.
July 15, 1930. Dr. Cushing.

A thin, somewhat mangy female rhesus monkey, with rather marked tremor of its right arm and well-healed midline scar of previous operation.

Anaesthesia. - 'Dial' 2.2 c.c. intraperitoneally given at 2.48. There was no excitement following the anaesthesia and the animal merely became somewhat unsteady and gradually lay down with its eyes closed. However at the end of 25 minutes it was still showing some flexor rigidity. An additional .3 c.c. was given. With this the animal became very deep and showed complete abolition of reflexes, slow respiration of pulse. The blood pressure, however, as judged by the vascularity of skin cortex was not seriously depressed. The animal did not move or vocalise throughout the entire procedure.

Mrs. O'Brien.

Surgical No.41144.

This unfortunate woman (I have always objected to House officers speaking disrespectfully of their patients even though they may appear mangy) was so thoroughly dialised by my assistant that a satisfactory clinical history was not obtainable. From her general appearance one would assume that she belonged to the lower classes. By some mischance Mrs. O'Brien's head came to be cocked to the left side, probably the better to hear what my assistant might have to say. But this led to the turning down of a bone-flap well across the median line, exposing the longitudinal sinus which at first was not recognised and which was injured on attempting to reflex the dural flap which was finally accomplished in spite of the most peculiar assortment of tweezers and other musical instruments to which I was somewhat unaccustomed. On exposing the cortex, an attempt was made to pick out the motor strip with a unipolar electrode, there being some difference of opinion as to which was actually the motor gyrus. This was then turned over to my assistant who quickly found an area in the situation shown in the sketch, much lower than I had anticipated, due largely to the oblique position of the head, I assume. Stimulation of this region gave first flexor movements of the thumb and definite flexor movements of the fingers which spread up into the arm and neck. I may say

A SIMIAN CRANIOTOMY

H.C.'s sketch and note of operation carried out on a monkey at Oxford in July 1930

On 15 July Cushing lunched at New College with R. S. Creed and his wife, both members of Sherrington's staff; and in the afternoon he was induced to operate on one of Sherrington's monkeys. He turned back a left-sided bone flap, employing almost the same technique that he would use on a human being, fussed and fumed over the instruments much as he did in his own operating room, and made one of his former assistants who was present at the operation feel quite at home. After identifying the arm area of the motor cortex electrically and extirpating it, he dictated a long and amusing note, and drew one of his skilful diagrams to show what had been done.

The next day his old friends, Sir Henry and Lady Head, invited him to Hartley Court, a beautiful estate near Reading where Sir Henry had retired on account of his advancing paralysis agitans.

H.C.'s description of the visit illustrates his powers of observation—and much else.

. . . I had not the slightest conception what Hartley Court would be like but merely knew that it would be somewhere on the outskirts of Reading, imagining a street of houses with possibly a garden. Not knowing the number, I was surprised when the taxi man seemed to know without question just where to go. And then when we drew up into a lovely park-like place and I found I was there, with Lady Head at the door, my delight knew no bounds. An old house set in a lovely grove of trees with a pasture newly mown extending before it—water wag-tails flitting about on the lawn, some magnificent oaks, old as the history of England—a clump of ancient Scotch firs, a huge linden or two. The house has some magnificent old Jacobean paneling and was made over, as the arch in the hallway and the windows of the bay make evident, either by Soane himself or one of his pupils.

Lady Head hurriedly showed me around through the rooms—the library where Henry sits in a huge chair after tea and is read to, another room to which he goes after lunch for an hour of quiet, the charming parlor where she receives her own guests, and into which I was secluded for a few minutes while Henry was being brought downstairs for his breakfast. Supposing that I would have to wait until he had finished, I was surprised to have her call me, saying, "Harry wants to see you now." He was sitting at the end of the table—a typical advanced Parkinsonian, practically rigid except for the movements of which I shall tell. He spoke in his customary cheery voice and when I sat down beside him said: "Don't sit there, I can't turn my head, sit over there opposite me." This I did and we had an interesting conversation while he was being fed. He is still on a moderately restricted diet owing to his diabetes (diencephalic?) which was discovered about the time his malady first began to be apparent. Occasionally the attendant would put food into his mouth, or wipe his moustache and finally when he came to finish off with an apple, which had been peeled and cut into mouthfuls, a fork was wedged into his tremulously rigid right hand with which he managed to spear a fragment, and then the attendant would merely push his elbow in such a way that the hand and arm would rotate round so precisely that the fragment would go into his mouth and be captured. It looked much as though he were feeding himself. Breakfast over, his chair was pushed back, the attendant drew him out of it on to his feet and in a crouching attitude he was led out, and the attendant, holding both hands backed up the winding stairs, H.H. in festinating fashion following him.

I judge that people are usually taken into Lady Head's parlor before he is moved and even I, the next time I saw him, found him packed and wedged into his motor ready for the morning drive which he takes daily with great enjoyment as the motion of the car appears to relieve him somewhat from his stiffness. Meanwhile, Lady Head told me the whole story: of the fact that Henry had always been economical, had invested his savings well so that it was possible for them with care to live the life they were leading which necessitated three attendants, a chauffeur, motor car, etc. How in 1919 he had just bought the house across from 4, Montagu Square into which they were going to move, how she first noticed the way he dragged his cane so that the ferule kept getting worn off, how the malady progressed so that they never went out to any social events, how awkward it became when people began to ask her what was wrong with him when they saw him festinating down the street, how hard he worked to get the aphasia work completed; and when this was done, and not till then, did he ever speak to her of what he knew was in store for him. . . .

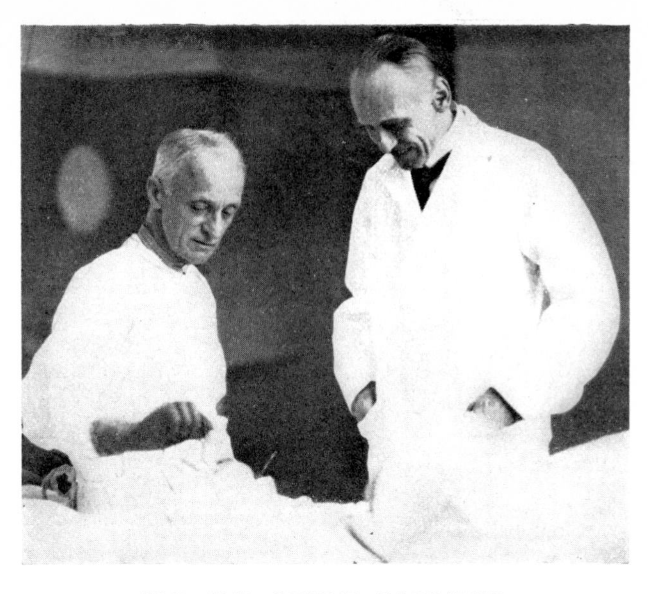

H.C. AND OTFRID FOERSTER

A young cerebellar patient being demonstrated to the Surgeon-in-Chief *pro tempore* in October 1930. From a photograph by Walter Boyd

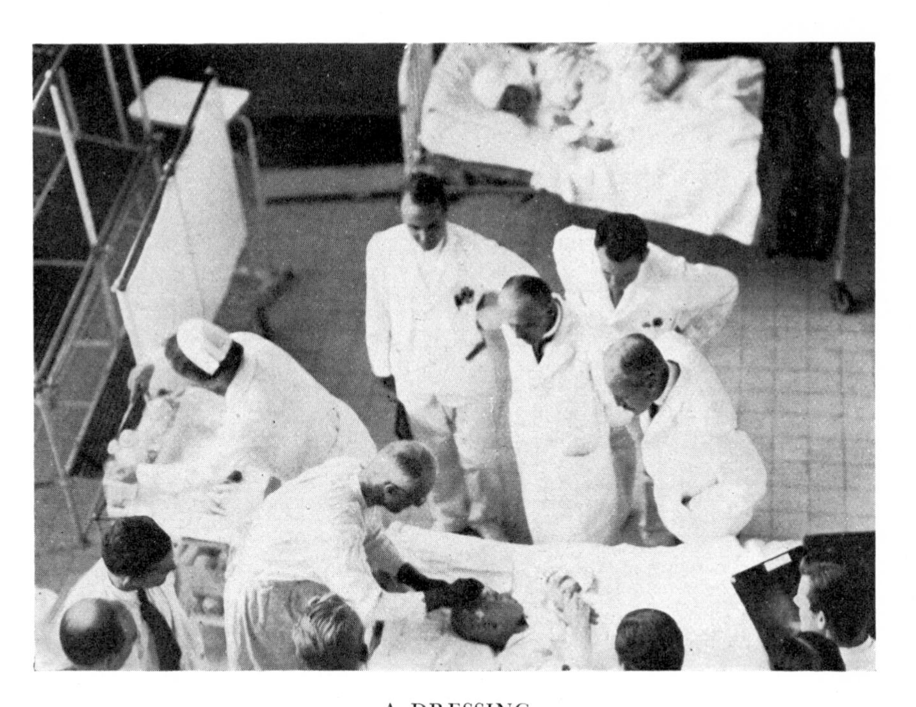

A DRESSING

William Henderson, Otfrid Foerster and David Cheever looking on, October 1930. From a photograph by Walter Boyd

WELCH AND H.C., FEBRUARY 1931
From a photograph by Walter Boyd

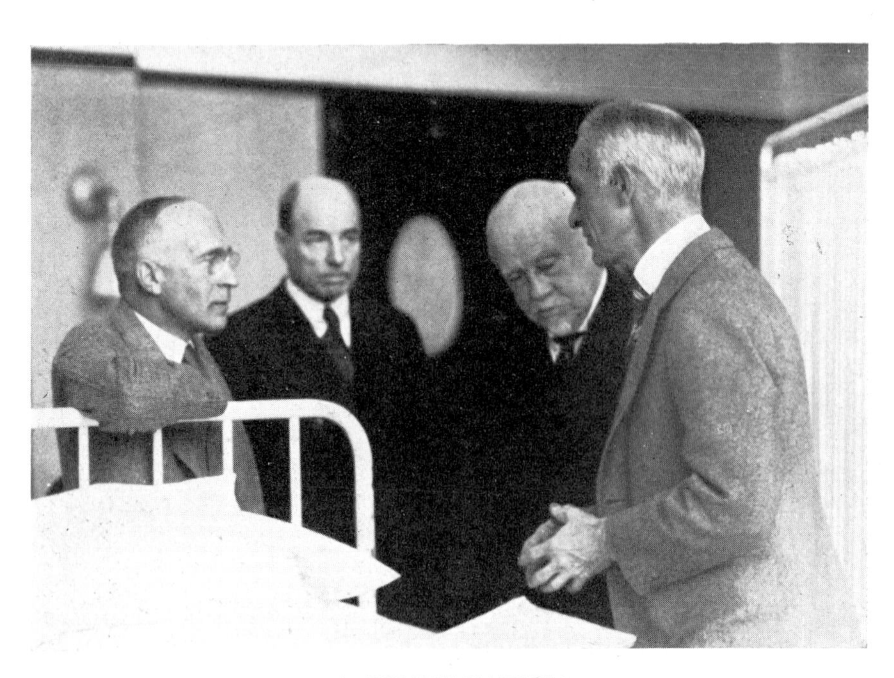

A CONSULTATION
S. Burt Wolbach, Richard P. Strong, William H. Welch and H.C. in consultation, February 1931. From a photograph by Walter Boyd

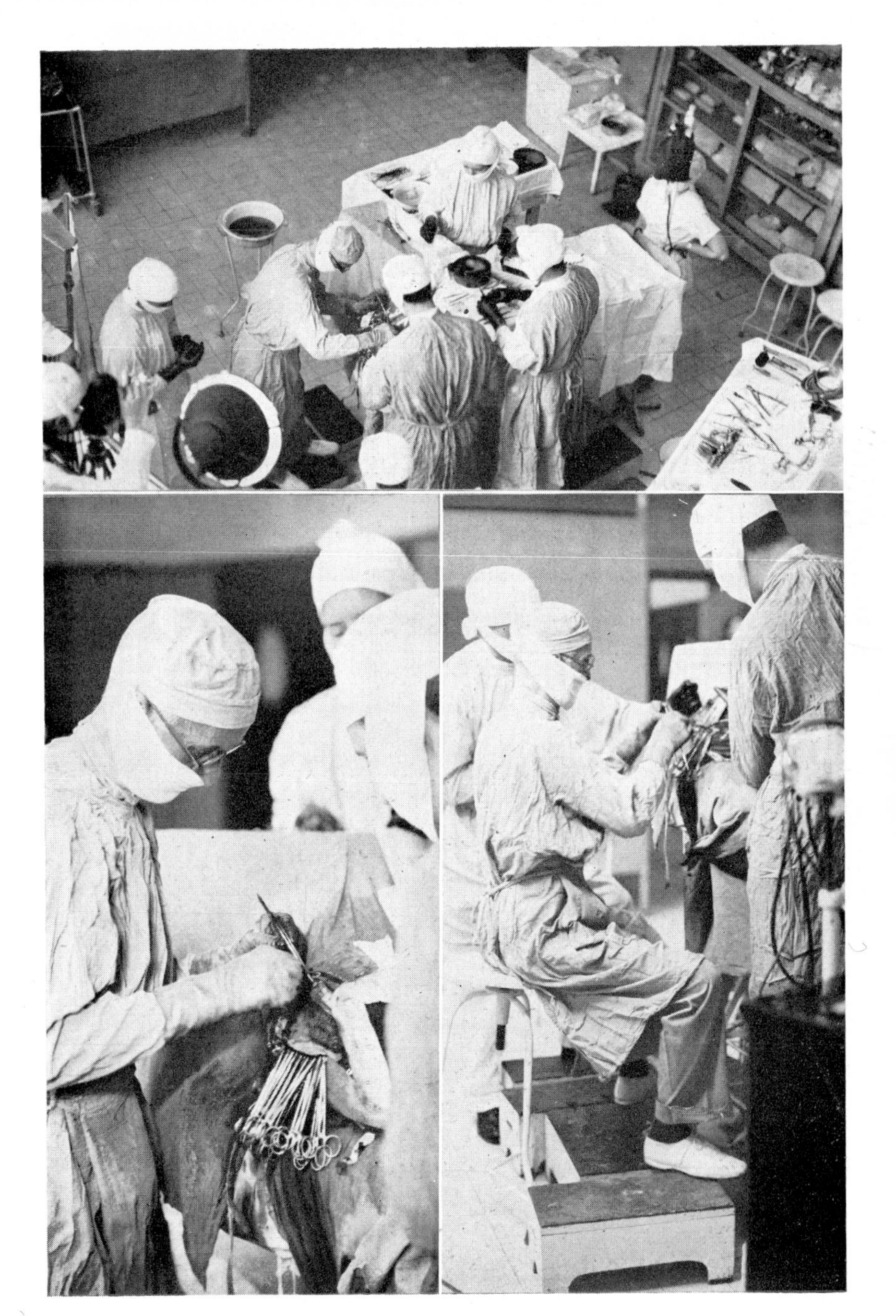

THE 2000th VERIFIED BRAIN TUMOR

Three views of the operation on 15 April 1931 in which a pituitary tumor was removed. From photographs by Walter Boyd

JOHN HOMANS AND THE 2000th TUMOR

Presenting H.C. with a token from the staff to mark the event. From a photograph by Walter Boyd

Such a lovely drive as we had for an hour and a half along the Thames valley—great sweeps of newly harvested country—long winding roads through magnificent beech forests—along country roads—beside the river now and then—all England at its very best. Meanwhile, he talked incessantly and brilliantly—about his pupils, George Riddoch in particular—about recent trends in neurology—about our accidental and happy friendship. He recalled incidents that I had long forgotten—each of the visits K.C. and I had paid them and the things we talked about. . . .

Well, we got back again to pleasant Hartley Court and I was once more shown into Lady Head's reception room where were some nice books and I soon got lost in the delightful essay of Walter Raleigh's on *Style*. When I was summoned again, here was H.H. already at his seat at the table where we went on with more things, Professor Whitehead who was a contemporary of H.H. at Cambridge, and the Trinity Apostles; also Bridges' *The Testament of Beauty* and Lowes' *Road to Xanadu* (they seem to have read everything). But to go back to Bridges. Head had known him and, if I understood him correctly, they had taken their membership examination for the College of Physicians at the same time. . . . Head went on to explain the formalities of the examination to become consultants. One part of the examination in those days (and perhaps it continues to this day) was to translate a Greek and a Latin passage. As the paper did not say into what language they were to be translated, Bridges put the Greek passage into Latin and the Latin passage into Greek.

After lunch he was again led out and up the stairs by his faithful attendant. Lady Head stood holding the door open and as he tottered by kissed him on the cheek, and he said, "Thank you, my darling."

H.C. had an active week in London. In addition to seeing the Heads, he had been at Queen Square keeping an eye on Walter Cannon who was ill, and had gone out to Down with Sir Arthur Keith and Mr. Buckston Browne to see the Darwin relics. In 1928 Buckston Browne, on retiring from surgical practice at the age of seventy-eight, had purchased Darwin's house and presented it to the nation. Sir Arthur Keith had established himself there in a near-by cottage and was in process of setting up an experimental laboratory for the Royal College of Surgeons. Learning that the cottage needed a timepiece, Cushing again "sanctified" his Lister Lecture fee by presenting Lady Keith with an attractive mahogany clock. Later Sir Arthur wrote that H.C. had commissioned Buckston Browne to get the clock, "all unbeknownst to my wife and me, and it still [1940] keeps time in the cottage."

Cushing returned to Oxford for a second week-end as the guest of the Sherringtons. Sir Charles took him to dine at Magdalen College on Sunday, the 20th; his conversation and also his profile seemed to fascinate members of the Common Room, both young and old, and many asked who Sherrington's guest was. Leaving Oxford on Monday, he spent another week browsing in the London bookshops and libraries and calling on old friends; and even as he complained in 1900 that it had been difficult to follow Osler's trail in London, several of his younger associates during the summer of 1930 admitted being similarly breathless in attempting to keep up with H.C.'s multifarious interests. One sidelight has come from Sir Henry Bashford, eminent writer and physician:

> I had a further delightfully overwhelming surprise when, on Saturday, July 26, 1930, Dr. Cushing turned up at my house in Hampstead for tea. I tried, I remember, to say something about his work on the pituitary gland. But he brushed this aside very tactfully, probably realizing that I was wholly incompetent to talk about it, because, I think, he really wanted to talk about books, which we did. One anecdote he told me then I remember. It concerned Walter de la Mare, the English poet, who was in America and who apparently was very anxious to see a living human brain. Cushing allowed him to watch a four-hour operation—the only layman, Cushing told me, whom he had ever admitted to his theatre for such a purpose.
>
> When he came to see us a second time—and this was the last time I saw him—it was on Sunday, September 20, 1931, when he brought Hugh Cairns, now at Oxford, who had studied under him in America. Our other guest was Miss Llewellyn Davies, a friend of J. M. Barrie's, and one of whose nephews was, I believe, the original of Peter Pan; and once again it was about books and plays that he wanted to talk. He had become very lame then and after tea I took him in a car to see Keats' house in Hampstead, every detail of the house and its garden enthralling him. We then drove for awhile about old Hampstead looking at Romney's old house, the house where Robert Louis Stevenson was said to have once lodged, the houses of George du Maurier, who wrote *Trilby,* and his son Gerald, the actor. He was a wholly delightful companion and apparently quite unconscious of his own greatness and the honour he was conferring on us, his hosts of the moment.

Cushing returned to Boston on or about 8 August, a little sooner than he was expected. The trip had refreshed him much more than that in 1929, and the tempo with which he caught up with his work left both his secretarial and surgical staffs in a state of suspended animation.

A neurologist whom he had come greatly to admire and who, like Clovis Vincent, was now surgeon as well as neurologist, arrived from Breslau on 1 October to act as Surgeon-in-Chief *pro tem.* Otfrid Foerster, who had first come to the United States in 1900 on a special consultation for a member of the Rockefeller family, had risen to a commanding position among European neurologists. Like Cushing, he was a man of omnivorous curiosity, giving meticulous attention to detail, and also like Cushing he preferred to do his "scribbling" standing up at lectern or mantel. He had a theory that his brain worked better when sensory impulses were arriving from the muscles of stance than when they came from those of the seat. He and the house staff had many late evenings discussing this and other cosmic problems; but Foerster was the despair of Cushing's staff (as he had been to a succession of men who went to Breslau to work with him), for he could regularly keep them up in an animated discussion until three in the morning and be down in the operating room at seven, refreshed and ready to operate all day. When he departed, Cushing and his team all disappeared for a long week-end. Later Cushing wrote of Foerster: "Apart from the fact that his presence in the clinic was a constant stimulus to every member of the staff, I do not believe that any visitor has ever endeared himself more to our hospital family, nor have we been obliged to make our farewells to anyone with more profound regrets than to him."

Several days after Foerster's arrival Cushing went to Chicago to give the Arthur Dean Bevan Lecture before the Chicago Surgical Society and affiliated medical societies in the Chicago area. It was a technical paper on the cystic tumors of the cerebellum.[9] When published, it proved to be one of the most elaborate of his separate reports on a particular group of tumors, and to neurosurgeons one of the most gratifying, for such tumors are common and slow-growing, and the majority, when once removed completely, tend not to return.

While in Chicago he discovered that Welch was there, having just returned from several months in the Huntington Library in California. They went to bookshops together and Welch regaled H.C. with tales about early Spanish medical publications. He also stressed the importance of obtaining photostats of the more outstanding items for the new library. Together they called on Robert Hutchins, President of the University of Chicago, and also upon Breasted to congratulate him on his translation of the *Edwin Smith surgical papyrus*. Cushing added that "it was one of the most enjoyable and satisfactory visits I ever had with Popsy, though I was embarrassed by his constant public allusion to my being his successor, and that he was only buying all these books for me some day to use. I had no possible comeback to all this, except to make a silly face."

An unusual and somewhat peculiar honor for a surgeon came in December when the Montclair Yale Club of New Jersey in a boisterous Yale alumni ceremony, held in a New Jersey barn, presented to Cushing their revered athletic token—a silver Yale Bowl—in recognition of the fact that even as H.C. had won his "Y" on the baseball team in college, so now he had achieved his "Y" in life!

The last part of the year was largely spent in his operating theater. His verified tumors were mounting steadily and some time in December Dr. Eisenhardt informed him that within a few months his 2000th tumor would have been verified. This came at an opportune moment for he had already begun to cast about for a theme to present the following summer when the first International Neurological Congress was to be held at Berne. With keen histrionic sense he attached particular importance to the Berne meeting since it

[9] "Experiences with the cerebellar astrocytomas. A critical review of seventy-six cases." *Surgery, Gynecology and Obstetrics,* February 1931, *52,* 129-204.

meant that after thirty years he was to have the opportunity of reporting once again upon the progress of work originally begun in those stimulating surroundings.

Cushing wound up the year's meetings by attending with Welch and Klebs a meeting of the A.A.A.S. in Cleveland where they had two "rollicking" days attending sessions of the History of Science Society. His recollections were found among his Welch memorabilia:

Days in Cleveland were theirs at the History of Science Society — a wonderful 2 days — rollicking days. They were simply marvellous. If you had only been along it would have been still better. I'm no artist as you know but here is what we would have looked like somewhat. No chance for seeing me. My weight and measure shrink daily for want of a sight of you. Affly H.C.

H.C. E.S. A.C.K. W.W.

ROLLICKING IN CLEVELAND

We found on the morning of the first day a very small scattering of people and some papers were to be read—one on Chinese medicine, I believe. The speaker had not appeared and the presiding officer was about to call the next when Dr. Welch arose saying it was too bad to pass over so important a topic without at least a word, so he launched out into a delightful ten-minute discourse on the subject. This led to a discussion in which many took part.

We motored back to Bratenahl for lunch [at Mrs. Edward Cushing's house] and hurried through to be on hand for the 2 p.m. session. The presiding officer was late, so Dr. Welch took the chair—and continued in it for the remainder of the afternoon. It was on Kepler, if I remember correctly, and people kept dropping in and remaining. The upshot was that he was elected president for the next year.

We saw the Pol books[9a] late in the afternoon at the library and in all respects had a delightful time. I had to go back to Boston that evening, as did also Klebs,

[9a] Part of the library of Nicolaus Pol (*b.ca.* 1470; court physician to Emperor Maximilian I) with its many celebrated medical incunabula passed from the Collegiate Library at Innichen into private hands in 1907; it was later sold to Maggs Brothers of London who in turn offered it for £2500 in 1929. Dr. E. H. Cushing obtained it for the Cleveland Medical Library before his uncle had had a chance to bid. Later, however, H.C. acquired eleven other Pol items for his own library. A detailed catalogue of all known Pol books is being compiled by Dr. Max H. Fisch to commemorate the 50th anniversary of the Cleveland Medical Library Association.

but Dr. Welch stayed for a party of young people who were gathering to see the New Year in and joined in the festivities like a youngster.

Writing to Simon Flexner a few days later, Cushing added: "I have just been spending two days with Popsy and Klebs at the Cleveland meeting. I don't know when I have enjoyed myself more. I have never seen Popsy in better form or more full of spirit. As Garrison says, he has got his second wind and it's difficult to keep up with him."

1931

In the early weeks of 1931 Cushing began to show signs of fatigue. His family and staff became aware that he was more irritable than usual and less able to stand the strain of long hours in his operating theater. When not operating he smoked excessively, and the poor circulation in his feet finally came to such a pass that gangrene threatened in both lower extremities. He presided at a meeting of the Harvard Medical Society on 27 January at which Esmond Long spoke. Long recalls that he was evidently in some difficulty from his feet on that occasion,[10] but he persevered until 15 February, on which day he attended General Edwards' funeral. Cushing had held Clarence Edwards in high esteem and at the funeral he spoke from his heart:

> . . . Naturally enough a personal grief is felt today in thousands of New England households. To have been "The Daddy" of the Division means more just now than even battles won a decade ago; and there *were* battles won, not only in the field, but battles to overcome a grievous disappointment as well as a personal and crushing sorrow.
>
> And so, Great Heart, you are now at last in peace. And somewhere beyond the limits of this expanding universe, light-years away, whatever may be our individual *Confessio fidei,* we may all hope and believe that from this New England whence your forebears sprang and to which from affection for its people you chose to return to live, your spirit went yesterday, to see again that soldier daughter from whom you were so cruelly parted, and to rejoin her mother, who understood you so well and who, like you, found her way deeply into the hearts of the people.

The ceremony over, he betook himself to the Brigham as a patient for the next six weeks. When he entered the hospital he believed

[10] Dr. Long recalled further: "What I remember best about that visit is his enthusiasm over his books. He came down to breakfast somewhat late after a previous long and hard day. I was already there, talking with his daughter. Although he had a difficult operation to perform at 9:00 o'clock, he spoke up suddenly after breakfast and said, "I think we can take ten minutes in the library before we go to the hospital." Those ten minutes were priceless, and I shall never forget his enthusiasm. He forgot all about the operation for a few minutes and pulled down book after book which had something of immediate interest for him. After that we went to the hospital, where he went to work with all his skill, and with his usual insatiable curiosity. The patient was under local anesthesia and talked to us throughout the operation."

that amputation was inevitable, and in a moment of depression he scribbled a note on the manuscript of his remarks at General Edwards' funeral, stating that he expected this paper to be his last. He was not the easiest of patients. His contemporaries could do nothing with him, but Richard Meagher, one of his junior house officers who understood him and was deeply devoted to him, for a time made him toe the line. A tobaccoless régime together with a course of physical therapy for his extremities soon reduced the pain and largely healed the several gangrenous areas on his feet. In Meagher, Cushing found a fearless Irish wit quicker than his own, and in their frequent verbal encounters it was always Meagher who got in the first, and often also the last word, and Cushing had no alternative but to follow the emphatic injunctions of his young, and all-too-soon-to-be-lamented, house officer, for Meagher himself succumbed a few years later to malignant hypertension at the early age of thirty-four.

While in hospital, as his pain and depression lifted, Cushing began to write, first an excellent review of John Homans' 'Surgery,' which had just appeared, and then an amusing letter to the Editor of the *Journal of the American Medical Association* on acknowledging reprints. The review of Homans' 'Surgery' ran:

> Fresh from the press, an entirely new order of surgical textbook has appeared. Textbooks of surgery, like other textbooks, have, for the most part, been written at the behest of some publisher who has seduced by flattery his unsuspecting victim to undertake a task the magnitude of which was beyond the scope of his imagination. Here, on the other hand, is a book written for a purpose, long planned and for which a publisher finally had to be sought. The generality of works of this kind had been from the outset, or has subsequently grown into, copious tomes in which one might conveniently and profitably search for new information or refresh one's memory on a topic hazily recalled. They have been, in other words, most of them, carefully prepared and all-inclusive compilations of facts and in this respect have been highly useful. . . . The brief historical introduction to several of the chapters will be particularly appealing to many and will serve as a lure to pull by the nose even the reluctant undergraduate through the more detailed subject matter which follows. These preliminary notes were apparently an after-thought on the author's part during the progress of the work and he may at another time come to fill in the gaps for some of the sections not so introduced.
>
> The publisher has done his part of the work admirably. The book is small, compact, businesslike in appearance, and its pages turn well. Both the publisher and the author have resisted the temptation to make a picture book by employing color plates and photographic reproductions, and in restricting themselves to the use of line drawings they have been able greatly to reduce the price of the volume, for which medical students will be duly appreciative.

During the first months of 1931 Cushing, despite his illness, occupied himself with two principal themes on which he worked more or less simultaneously. The first was the relation between hypothalamic disturbances and the activity of the gastro-intestinal tract.

His Lister Lecture the year before had focused his attention upon this part of the nervous system and its relation to visceral function. Over the years he had had cases of acute gastric complications following pituitary operations and operations on the cerebellum. Patients who prior to such an operation had not had gastric difficulty might have a severe gastric hemorrhage or an actual perforation of the stomach a day or two after the surgical procedure. He had also seen similar complications following localized infection of the base of the brain. Therefore, in preparing for his Balfour Lecture[11] to be given in Toronto in April he searched his records and analyzed all the cases in which gastro-intestinal disturbances had complicated post-operative recovery from a cerebral operation. He found clear-cut evidence that only the operations which encroached upon the nerve centers near the base of the brain were followed by gastric complications—centers which on stimulation give rise to gastro-intestinal reactions in animals (Beattie). Although Cushing's conclusions were received at the time with somewhat greater skepticism than usual, his general position has been subsequently vindicated both experimentally and clinically, and the lively discussions which followed the presentation of his paper have stimulated many fruitful experimental studies. To give the Lecture he emerged from his hospital bed; and although he was still weak, the trip to Toronto on 6 April and the responsibility of a lecture had an exhilarating effect and he behaved much like a race-horse going once again to the track.

The second theme to which Cushing devoted attention in the early months of 1931 had already been touched upon in the Lister Lecture, but since the summer of 1930 he had obtained further evidence of the existence at the base of the brain of centers controlling visceral functions. Normal individuals exhibit profound sweating, flushing, fall of body temperature, and signs of gastric peristalsis when pituitrin or pilocarpine is injected into the ventricles. He now disclosed two other important facts. First, that the flushing and sweating failed to occur in areas of the skin which had been denervated, for example, on the skin of the forehead after a craniotomy; this provided clear proof that the drugs in question must exert their effect through central action (directly on the brain centers). The second disclosure was that if the third ventricle is occluded by the presence of a tumor, pituitrin and pilocarpine no longer act when introduced into the cerebral ventricles; this, he believed, indicated that the centers in

[11] "Peptic ulcers and the interbrain." *Surgery, Gynecology and Obstetrics,* July 1932, 55, 1-34. These studies formed the basis of his William H. Welch Lecture given at the Mount Sinai Hospital in New York on 30 April (see p. 591). They were reprinted in 1932 with the Balfour and Lister Lectures in a monograph entitled *Papers relating to the pituitary body, hypothalamus and parasympathetic nervous system* (C. C Thomas).

question must lie in the walls of the third ventricle. The intraventricular studies may well be regarded as one of H.C.'s basic contributions to physiology.

Beating His Own Score

During the interval between the Balfour and the William Welch Lectures, Cushing's physical condition improved sufficiently to permit his undertaking the operation which served to verify the 2000th brain tumor in his series. Without his knowledge the staff had made elaborate preparations for photographs, movies, and a gala tea party reminiscent of that held on his sixtieth birthday. Richard Upjohn Light, pilot, house officer, and a photographer as accomplished on the ground as in the air, had moved his aerial cameras and other necessary equipment to the hospital for the occasion, and Walter Willard Boyd, another photographer of distinction, vied with Light for the pictorial laurels of the day. Buoyed up by the Balfour Lecture, Cushing was in fine fettle and operated with his old fire.

> This woman [his operative note read] has a mild grade of acromegaly associated with bad headaches and a moderately enlarged sella. The fields of vision have not been particularly definite and I consequently was somewhat uneasy in regard to what we would find, fearing that there might be a prefixed chiasm between the legs of which I would be unable to accomplish very much in the way of removing the adenoma. As a matter of fact the chiasm was found widely expanded and I am sure that the bitemporal hemianopsia must have been much more definite than was presupposed. The operation was relayed with Dr. Horrax. It happened to be our 2000th verified tumor which led to a display of cameras and searchlights somewhat inhibiting one's customary surgical reflexes which are at their best when a surgeon is unconscious of his surroundings and the fact that anyone is looking on.[12]

Louise Eisenhardt, fully prepared for the occasion, had all the tumor statistics available and was able to point to a steady lowering of Cushing's mortality rate during the previous ten years, save for a brief increase, for reasons already mentioned, immediately after the introduction of electrosurgical methods. Since there was no other comparable tumor series with which to compete, Cushing had become consumed with a desire to improve his own figures from year to year. He accordingly began in earnest to prepare on these lines for the "paper" to be read at the International Neurological Congress in Berne—a paper which grew into a monograph and was later published by his friend, Charles Thomas.[13] The book stands as a highly signifi-

[12] The patient had a subsequent operation in December 1931; she was still doing well in 1945.

[13] *Intracranial tumours. Notes upon a series of two thousand verified cases with surgical-mortality percentages pertaining thereto.* Springfield, Illinois, Charles C Thomas, 1932, 150 pp. A German translation was issued at Berlin in 1935, and a French translation, with additions, in Paris in 1937.

cant landmark, since it represents an over-all report on Cushing's life work. And it represents also the final report of the series which he had started in January 1905 on the "special field of neurological surgery." After its publication he had many appreciative letters but none pleased him more than that from Lady Head (4 April 1932):

"Henry" asks me to write for him, because as you know he cannot now write at all himself and finds even dictation of letters a burden. You may be sure I undertake this pleasant task very willingly, especially as H. has told me he wishes me to congratulate you warmly on the fine volume, representing your life's work, which you have so kindly sent him. He says the book bears witness magnificently to your fine technique and unrivalled mastery of your art. He did not put it quite like that, but that is how it sounded to me, and his pride in your achievement was evident in his voice.

Shall we see you here this summer? What a gala day it would be for us if you came. I never look at my old glasses on the Welsh dresser without patting myself on the back and remembering your approbation of the way they got and held the light. If you come, you will find H. much the same, just a little feebler in movement and a little slower in speech, just a little less able for any form of exertion, otherwise the same "Good Companion" I have always found him! We join in affectionate greetings to you both.

His two lectures behind him Cushing cancelled all other speaking engagements until the Berne Congress save two: an address to the Massachusetts Medical Society (one of his less impressive discourses[14]), and an address at the meeting of the American Neurological Association held at the Brigham on 24 May. He used this latter as a "trial balloon" for his Berne paper. Statistics concerning his 2000 brain tumors were well received, and after the meeting he had a certain amount of constructive criticism concerning the organization of the paper. During June he received two honorary degrees, both D.Sc.'s, one from the University of Rochester, where John Morton said of him, "His greatest achievement has been as a teacher. By his inspiring example he has attracted men from all parts of the world, and he has sent out an ever-widening circle of pupils who have learned from him to spend their lives in the service of humanity, to forward their art by constantly striving to improve it; and to pass on the ideals of their profession to those who follow." The second degree came from Harvard. He lightheartedly referred to it in a letter to Klebs as his "honorary P.D.Q." Mr. Lowell's brief citation ran: "Adroit with both scalpel and pen, a charming writer and the most renowned cerebral surgeon in the world." A day or two later he was in New Haven relaxing at his fortieth reunion, and on the 22d he wrote to a friend in Cleveland, "Perry Harvey and I are renewing our youth by rooming together once more."

[14] "One hundred and fifty years. From tallow-dip to television." *New England Journal of Medicine,* 11 June 1931, *204,* 1235-1244.

Cushing's Return to Berne

Eager to promote international cooperation in medicine, Cushing had strongly endorsed a proposal made in 1928 to the Council of the American Neurological Association that plans be set in motion for an International Neurological Congress. Neurologists in Europe insisted that because of wartime jealousies and rivalries among Continental neurologists the United States was the only country that could successfully arrange an international congress. Bernard Sachs, one of the senior members of the American Neurological Association, was elected president of the Congress by the International Committee, and he and Henry Alsop Riley, the American secretary of the Congress, settled on Berne as the place for the meeting and managed to arrange the program and to run it off successfully, almost without international incident.[15]

The Congress was important for three reasons: for its revelation of the newer trends in neurology, especially the growing preëminence of the neurosurgeon; for the international recognition of a new "school" in the ranks of medicine; and for the outstanding personalities among the some 700 delegates from all over the world. A contemporary account brings a few men into vivid perspective:

> The more outstanding personalities of the meeting were: Cushing, Foerster, Pavlov, and Sherrington, with Welch the *doyen* of them all. Dr. Welch floated about like an apparition of a generation past, and in his shadow walked Ludwig, Virchow, Koch, Lister, Cohnheim, and Rokitansky. Could they have come back to observe the newest offspring of Medicine, they could not have evinced more interest than he, and they would probably have looked on with the same charitable enthusiasm, for Dr. Welch was never critical and seemed to think as often of the future as of the past.
>
> Much of the life of the Congress centered about Dr. Cushing. He was returning after thirty years to the town where he grew up, as it were, and where he received the greatest inspiration for his life's work—and he was returning now to give an account of himself in the interval. His paper was brilliant but there was a tragic air of finality about it, which everyone felt even though unexpressed. Old animosities were put aside and he was hailed by everyone as the supreme master of a great specialty. No one begrudged him the applause, and many observed with some astonishment his twenty-five pupils, most of whom had crossed the ocean primarily to hear him read his paper. Dr. Welch remarked that it was more to H.C.'s credit that he founded a "school" than that he had created the special field of neurological surgery.
>
> Sherrington's presence also created a great stir. It was the first international gathering that he had attended since the War and many of the German neurologists fancied him dead. Asher's characterization of him as "the great

[15] Two months before the Congress was scheduled Sachs received a strongly worded protest from the French contingent, saying that they would withdraw in a body unless eight conditions were met. Sachs took the next boat to France and invited all who had signed the French protest to an epicurean dinner and by the end of the evening had talked them in turn out of each one of their eight conditions.

philosopher of the nervous system" brought thundering applause and was probably the best thing said at the Congress. It reminded them that the man who had first formulated the modern interpretation of the nervous system was yet alive and walking amongst them.

Foerster seemed more ghost than man—thin, gaunt, pale, and slightly stooped, with sunken eyes which nevertheless radiated fire. He looked at first sight worn and broken, but when he spoke everyone was silent; his diction was perfect and what he said was at once authoritative and beautiful. His speech at dinner marked the high point of the Congress.

Pavlov also looked worn and much older than in 1929 when he attended the Physiological Congress in Boston. He and "Popsy" were both centres of attention. When Pavlov was called upon for his paper, the whole room was thronged. As soon as he mounted the platform, they all stood and cheered for several minutes. As usual he looked pleased, but not in the least surprised!

More significant than the papers read was the social interchange at the Congress. Arnold Klebs, a native Berner, saw to it that Cushing and his pupils were entertained in the best traditions of Swiss hospitality. Cushing had left for the Congress with one of his pupils on the *SS. Deutschland.* On 27 August they were joined by Hugh Cairns at Cherbourg whence they proceeded to Hamburg where they were met by Georges Schaltenbrand. H.C. then went immediately to Munich where, after a good lunch given by his scholarly bookseller friends, Drs. Taeuber and Weil, he bought out most of the shop and was obliged to send home for another letter of credit. He reached Berne on Sunday, the 30th, where Arnold Klebs was awaiting him with a large corner suite in the Hotel Bellevue overlooking the gorgeous Bernese Oberland. Welch was already settled in an adjacent room. Presently Foerster appeared, then Sherrington, and, as a surprise, a group of Brigham house officers—Richard Meagher, Franc Ingraham, and Richard Light. Cushing had been in his room but a few minutes when the telephone began to ring; the news of his return to Berne had spread through the town like a prairie fire, and his old friends of both sexes sought at once to entertain him. So embarrassingly insistent were some of the messages, that in self-defence he presently appointed one of his former house officers social secretary. What he really needed was a career diplomat who could make polite excuses in ten languages!

The Congress opened on Monday, 31 August, in the Municipal Casino. The high point of this session was the awarding (by the University of Berne) of honorary degrees to Cushing and Sir Charles Sherrington. That the degrees were to be given had been kept in the utmost secrecy and was to be a surprise to both of the recipients. Considerable difficulty was encountered in persuading Cushing that his presence at the session was imperative, for as usual he was belatedly putting the finishing touches on his paper for the afternoon session. However, he and Sir Charles were finally seated near the platform, and the degrees were presented in due course by Professor Asher, now Rector of the University of Berne, in words of extravagant praise. The addresses of welcome were cordial and timely, as was Bernard Sachs' presidential address with its references to Switzerland as the home of human liberty.

In the introduction to his paper, fourth on the program of the afternoon session, Cushing described his experiences in Berne in 1900-1901. At the beginning he spoke somewhat haltingly, but within a few minutes the hall was silent as he described the various factors which had led to the dramatic fall in his mortality rate in cerebral operations. "Younger men," he went on to say, "picking up where I leave off, can reduce the mortality still further." Then came the devastating and unexpected climax: "Gentlemen, this will be the last report on the statistical results of brain tumors as a whole that I shall ever publish." After a moment of complete silence there was a burst of prolonged applause. The Chairman, Ariëns Kappers of Amsterdam, broke the precedent of no votes of thanks for individual papers by expressing heartfelt gratitude to Cushing in the name of the Congress for placing before them in such an inspiring way the brilliant results of his life's work.

That evening Arnold Klebs had arranged a dinner in honor of Welch and Cushing. Every detail had been planned with the utmost care, and the forty international guests found it a most brilliant and happy affair. To Klebs' warmhearted speech of welcome, Welch replied in his most charming vein, characterizing their host as "one who had the rare gift of friendship." The next morning Cushing was inspired to give a dinner himself to which he would invite all of his former pupils to meet his 'masters'—Welch, Sherrington, de Martel, and Klebs. Arrangements were quickly made, and the dinner proved a most memorable occasion. H.C. spent an hour or more over the seating, arranging his handwritten place cards thus:

H.C.

Thierry de Martel (Paris)	Dimitri Bagdazar (Bucharest)
Paul Martin (Brussels)	Percival Bailey (Chicago)
Daniel Petit-Dutaillis (Paris)	Georges Schaltenbrand (Hamburg)
Tracy Putnam (Boston)	Frederic Schreiber (Detroit)
Jean Morelle (Louvain)	Richard Light (Boston)
John Fulton (New Haven)	Herbert Olivecrona (Stockholm)
Dr. Welch (Baltimore)	Dr. Klebs (Nyon)
Richard Meagher (Boston)	Hugh Cairns (London)
Francis Grant (Philadelphia)	Ignaz Oljenick (Amsterdam)
Norman Dott (Edinburgh)	George Armitage (Leeds)
Frank Fremont-Smith (Boston)	Gaston DeCoppet (Berne)
Frédéric Bremer (Brussels)	Franc Ingraham (Boston)
Sir Charles Sherrington (Oxford)	Geoffrey Jefferson (Manchester)
	Otfrid Foerster (Breslau)

Wilder Penfield (Montreal)

There were only two speeches. When his health was proposed, H.C. responded with one of his amusing stories, but he ended in a more serious vein:

> Hold together. Keep up your friendships—form societies where you can meet together frequently to exchange ideas, and to criticize one another's technique. Keep your finger on neurology, but don't get lost in scientific minutiae—a medulloblastoma or a perineural fibroblastoma by any other name is just as sweet! Don't let neurological surgery get too far away from general surgery. It is the greatest possible compliment that we have been adopted by the neurologists and accepted as one of them. Be this as it may, we did not grow wholly out of neurology, for our roots are in the fertile soil of general surgery. I like to think that our specialty is perhaps the richest in the field of Medicine, and it will be if you make it so.

Two days later H.C. had another inspiration and one that deeply touched the citizens of Berne. Kronecker, Kocher, and Edwin Klebs, father of Arnold Klebs, were all buried in the same cemetery at Berne, and Cushing decided to have an informal ceremony during which wreaths would be laid on each of the tombs and a few words said by someone who had known the men personally. Accordingly, on the morning of 3 September, the group which had attended Cushing's dinner, together with a few others from Berne, including de Quervain, the Professor of Surgery, proceeded in the rain to the cemetery for an unforgettable ceremony. Sherrington spoke at Kronecker's grave—"His silvered head will be remembered with affection, not only by those who recognize him as an honoured man of our science but by many who, apart from all that, knew and loved him for his nature as a man." Welch, standing bareheaded with the drenching rain spattering on his bald head, then spoke extemporaneously for nearly fifteen minutes of Theodor Albrecht Edwin Klebs, characterizing him as "a wandering scholar"—one who had first described acromegaly, as well as the diphtheria bacillus (with Loeffler), and much else. Cushing, after placing a large wreath at the foot of Kocher's tablet, walked forward to the edge of the plot, and after referring briefly to his work with Kocher, went on:

> . . . So in placing this wreath, in loving tribute, on the grave of one of these masters, I feel that I am merely the agent of the other, his admiring friend, whose memory I hold in equal affection and gratitude. The most precious heritage of our profession lies in its noble traditions. What has been accomplished does not die, but too often, alas, the personality of those who have handed the torch from one generation to another soon fades into oblivion. So for those of you—his spiritual grandchildren—who have gathered here and to whom Theodor Kocher is little more than the name of a street which you have frequently traversed the past few days, I would like to give at least an impression of what he was in life—a slight, spare man of personal neatness, of quick step and alert bearing, of unfailing courtesy and dignity, precise and scrupulous in all his dealings, professional, public and personal—a man to trust.

His clinic at the Inselspital had long been a surgical Mecca and when in 1900 I came here hoping to find an opportunity to work under his guidance, he finally gave me a problem which took me away from the clinic to the physiological laboratory. . . . I last saw him on his seventieth birthday when in 1912, shortly after he had been made a Nobel laureate for his contributions to our knowledge of the thyroid gland, a *Jubiläum* was held here in his honour and at this great festival tributes from every part of the world poured in upon him. From hard work and responsibility surgeons are prone to burn themselves out comparatively young, but Kocher had been blessed with an imperturbability of spirit which enabled him to bear his professional labours, his years, and his honours with equal composure to the very end. The current of his long and active life was as steady, cool and uninterrupted as that of the Aare encircling his beloved Berne.

Otfrid Foerster, much moved, remarked afterwards, "Harvey Cushing was inspired to think of this, and to have been present was the greatest privilege I ever had."

Immediately after the ceremony they were expected at a luncheon given by the Ashers but they were all soaked from the rain and H.C. commented in his diary, "Klebs and I hustled back to the hotel and changed completely. Popsy disdained any such evidence of softness and went as he was, leaving a puddle wherever he sat down. Anyone else would have died of pneumonia." The official banquet followed on the evening of the 3d. H.C. and Welch both spoke extemporaneously, but the high point of the evening was Foerster's eloquent plea for the recognition of neurology as a separate discipline.

And so the Neurological Congress of Berne drew to a close. Arnold Klebs, through his warm affection for Harvey Cushing and his unusual capacity for bringing people together, had made it an event with few parallels in the history of such gatherings. A new "school" in the ranks of medicine had come suddenly to have international recognition; and the *esprit de corps* which this recognition has fostered in the group itself has found substantial expression in countless ways—but in none more significantly than in the elaborate organization for dealing with head injuries in all European countries lately at war. In each country those responsible for these services have been trained by Cushing or by the pupils whom they in turn have inspired.

The next day Klebs gathered up Welch and Cushing and started over the mountain passes for Nyon, stopping on the way in Fribourg at one of Welch's favorite restaurants under the shadow of an old Benedictine monastery, where they spent three hours consuming an enormous fondu. At Nyon, in the Klebs' picturesque villa on the shore of Lake Geneva, H.C., Klebs, and Welch had a happy week browsing and exchanging scholarly anecdote until all hours.

The end of the week found H.C. in Paris with Welch who induced Cushing to take his place as American delegate the following week at the Centenary Celebration for Michael Faraday which was being held in London at the Royal Institution. It was an elaborate two-day affair and Cushing characteristically collected all of the voluminous printed proceedings, diaries, photographs, etc., and brought them home to his library. Unfortunately the account of the meeting, which he had written out on the boat coming home, was left in a book in the ship's library and was not recovered. On arriving in Boston on 30 September he wrote Klebs:

> . . . I got a few books in London but nothing much. The Faraday celebration was interesting but I scarcely knew any of the five thousand or more electrically minded people who were in attendance, so that I did not get very much out of it except an increasing admiration for Faraday himself. You will probably have received a copy of the special edition of *The Times* of Monday, the 21st, which has some good papers about him from various sources. . . . I left Popsy in Paris, we both pulling out of the Gare du Nord at 8.30 a.m. on parallel trains . . . you can imagine my surprise, therefore, when I landed yesterday morning to find Leonard Mackall at the dock saying that Popsy had landed only half an hour before and I was to lunch with him at the Century Club to meet Sigerist and some others. I so did, and Popsy had a six-course lunch from which I had to escape to get my 3.30 train to Boston, having a date to meet Mary Cushing on it.
>
> I reached home to find everyone fit and well. But during my absence, in a burst of enthusiasm, the family had decided to shift me from my long occupied side of the house to the other, and as Gus moved the books you can imagine what state they are in; I feel like a cat in a strange garret. However, I shall try to summon what equanimity I can and adjust myself to my new quarters.

The academic year 1931-1932 was particularly trying, for although Cushing had announced in his paper at Berne that it was to be his swan song as far as brain tumor statistics were concerned, he worked under great pressure through the whole year, since so many things that he had hoped to wind up before his retirement in June were still unfinished. Yale and Hopkins continued to importune him for a decision, but he had mounting misgivings about his health, and he had also begun to have periodic episodes of gastric pain and distress which, in retrospect some years later, he laid to fatigue, indecision, and a disturbed hypothalamus. He knew that he had all the classical symptomatology of a gastric ulcer but until just before he came to New Haven in 1933 he refused to admit it.

After his arrival in Boston at the end of September, he had the usual accumulation of patients and correspondence, as well as an eager group of young assistants. William deG. Mahoney had the principal Assistant Residency, beginning in March 1931, and was joined in October 1931 by Bronson S. Ray who also became an Assistant Resident. When Mahoney left in April 1932, Ray took his place and Richard Light came on service from April to August. In the course of the year there were also six voluntary assistants.

On 15 October Cushing spoke at a dinner for Walter Cannon in recognition of his twenty-fifth year as Professor of Physiology at Harvard. A few days later he motored to New Haven to attend the meetings of the Society of Neurological Surgeons, which gathered in Samuel C. Harvey's clinic in the New Haven Hospital. He stayed with friends and occupied the first evening attempting to teach his host how to apply "leather vita," a newly introduced preparation for the preservation of old bindings. When the president of the society and Dr. Ernest Sachs arrived for a formal call, he received them on the floor in his shirt sleeves and promptly put them to work rubbing bindings. He spoke at the dinner the next evening and made the gracious gesture of calling upon J. G. Dusser de Barenne, Yale's newly appointed physiologist from Holland, to tell the group about the history of Dutch physiology.

During November he received a series of distinguished visitors: E. D. Adrian, the Cambridge physiologist, on the 2nd, Sir Thomas Lewis, the British cardiologist, on the 3rd, and Sir Wilfred Grenfell on the 10th. On 16 November he was in New Haven again, this time to attend a meeting of the National Academy of Sciences. On this occasion Dr. John C. Merriam gave an account of his celebrated excavation of the sabre-toothed tigers found in the asphalt pits of Rancho La Brea, and H.C. could speak of little else for several days. During this visit at Yale there was further discussion of the possibility of his coming to New Haven permanently, but again he did not commit himself. On the 24th he appeared at the Richard Wheatlands' house in Topsfield, Massachusetts, at the reception following Franc Ingraham's marriage to Martha Wheatland, and as usual on such occasions he proved the life of the party.

Earlier in the year Dr. Welch had invited Henry Sigerist, Director of the Institute of Medical History at Leipzig, to give a series of lectures in Baltimore on the history of medicine. Other lectures by Sigerist were arranged elsewhere in the country, including Boston, Cushing having invited him to speak at the Brigham on Monday, 30 November. The lecture was received with the greatest enthusiasm, and on the basis of it Cushing formally declined the invitation from Hopkins to succeed Welch as Professor of the History of Medicine and emphatically recommended that a formal offer be made to Sigerist:

H.C. to William H. Welch *23 November 1931.*

Dear Dr. Welch: I have been hearing from all sides of the brilliant success that Sigerist has been making of his lectures in Baltimore and at the same time of the delightful impression he has made upon everyone. I hope you will not feel that the renewed overtures you have made to me will prevent your sounding him out as to the possibility of his looking favorably upon coming here to live.

ARNOLD C. KLEBS

At Hotel Bellevue, Berne, 2 September 1931. From a photograph by R. U. Light

H.C. AND VITTORIO PUTTI
During Professor Putti's sojourn as Surgeon-in-Chief *pro tempore* in June 1932. From a photograph by R. U. Light

LEADERS IN SCIENTIFIC MEDICINE
Sir Charles S. Sherrington, H.C., William H. Welch. From a photograph by A. C. Klebs taken at Nyon, Switzerland on 5 September 1931

THE HARVEY CUSHING SOCIETY

Original members at first meeting held at the Peter Bent Brigham Hospital 6 May 1932. *Back row* (left to right): R. Glen Spurling, R. Eustace Semmes, Temple Fay, Eric Oldberg, Stafford Warren, William J. German, W. Edward Chamberlain, J. G. Lyerly, Merrill C. Sosman, William P. Van Wagenen, Frank Fremont-Smith, Leo M. Davidoff, Roland M. Klemme, Frank R. Teachenor. *Front row:* Edgar A. Kahn, Paul C. Bucy, Franc D. Ingraham, Louise Eisenhardt, John F. Fulton, Tracy J. Putnam, Franklin Jelsma

LE DOCTEUR, *honoris causa,* PARIS, 1933

Left to right: L. Civita, University of Rome; C. Vivante, Faculty of Laws, Rome; J. Puig y Cadafalch, architect and historian of art, Barcelona; S. Charléty, Rector, University of Paris; H.C.; G. Roussy, Dean of the Faculty of Medicine, Paris; F. Volhard, University of Frankfort; L. van Itallie, University of Leyden

When I met him that day in New York, I felt instinctively that he was the man. I hoped to come down to hear his last lecture but caught a bad cold that week and thought that I had better not inflict myself upon others. . . . He is young and able and vigorous and historically trained, and in none of these real essentials for the post do I in comparison count for anything at all.

They have not yet definitely chosen my successor here and until that is done I can't seriously put my mind on my own future plans. I have been very uncomfortable over this indecision and my procrastination must have been embarrassing to you and also to President Ames, though neither of you has even hinted as much. . . . To be Professor of the History of Medicine at Johns Hopkins is undoubtedly the blue ribbon position in American medicine. I would have been proud and happy to occupy it. . . . If you have not sounded him [Sigerist] out in Baltimore, will you permit me to broach the subject to him while he is here with me this coming week-end?

To this Welch replied:

. . . Sigerist has made a fine impression, but unless he is utterly discouraged about the future of his Institute at Leipzig, I hardly suppose that he would give it up for a position in this country. He has not been approached (so far as I know) about coming here, and I should be interested in learning how he may feel on the subject, if you sound him out, which I hope you will do. I am very glad that he is to stay with you so that you can get a line on his intentions and personality. I am sure that you will like Sigerist more and more as you get acquainted with him. He is simple and unaffected and modest, really charming. . . .

After Sigerist had given his lecture in Boston, H.C. dispatched an enthusiastic telegram to Welch: "SIGERIST HAS CAPTIVATED EVERYONE HERE BY HIS MODESTY, LEARNING, LIVELY INTEREST IN EVERYTHING, AND PERSONAL CHARM. I CANNOT IMAGINE A MORE SUITABLE PERSON FOR THE POST OR ONE MORE CERTAIN TO DEVELOP IT IN THE WAY YOU WOULD DESIRE. HE IS CERTAIN TO HAVE A GREAT FOLLOWING. AMERICA FASCINATES HIM AND I BELIEVE HE WOULD FIND AN OFFER DIFFICULT TO REFUSE." Some weeks later, as all know who follow medical history, Sigerist was invited to succeed Welch at Johns Hopkins; he accepted and has already completed fifteen years of brilliant and productive leadership in the new Institute of the History of Medicine.

1932

For Cushing the year began auspiciously since Harvard had elected as his successor in the Moseley Chair of Surgery a man of his own choosing; and also, early in January, he was able to describe a new clinical syndrome which has since then been known as Cushing's disease—"pituitary basophilism." The notification of Elliott Cutler's appointment came in a letter of 12 January from A. Lawrence Lowell: "In accordance with your own preferences," he wrote, "Dr. Cutler, who was elected your successor by the Corporation, was confirmed by the Overseers this afternoon. Now there comes a little awkwardness because we cannot very well announce his election so long as you have not formally resigned. You see our embarrassment." To this Cushing replied somewhat acidulously, "I am glad to know that Dr. Cutler has finally passed his last hurdle. It has been like getting a camel through the eye of a needle—successive needles. . . . Since my term of service at the Brigham Hospital automatically ends this year, it did not occur to me that it was a matter requiring resignation, a term which implies relinquishing something you are entitled to hold. I nevertheless . . . hasten to submit the resignation at once." President Lowell then sounded out H.C. about a Professorship of the History of Medicine, saying that Lawrence Henderson, among others, would be solidly behind it. But again H.C. declined to commit himself.

Office of the
President and Fellows
of Harvard College
5 University Hall, Cambridge

Sir

I beg to inform you that on the twenty-fifth day of January, 1932 your resignation as Moseley Professor of Surgery was accepted by the President and Fellows to take effect on the first day of September 1932 and that in accordance with their vote of November 28 1924 duly confirmed by the Board of Overseers you were appointed Moseley Professor of Surgery, Emeritus from that date.

Your obedient servant
F. W. Hunnewell
Secretary

Dr Harvey Cushing

RESIGNATION FROM MOSELEY CHAIR

Pituitary Basophilism

For those who believe that the originality of most men reaches its peak before the age of forty and that it would be a good thing if most of us were chloroformed at sixty, it is a fact of some significance that one of Cushing's most original single contributions to clinical medicine was made in his sixty-third year as he was about to retire. He had done many other things that exhibited originality and scientific imagination, but his primary achievements had come by dint of hard work. However, the recognition of an entirely new disease entity and the establishment of its pathogenesis must be regarded in the same category as the recognition of other eponymic syndromes, such as Addison's disease (tuberculosis of the adrenal glands), Graves' disease (hyperthyroidism), and Bright's disease.

Among his pituitary patients Cushing over the years had observed a special group with a condition which had been somewhat vaguely labelled "polyglandular syndrome." They were seldom subjected to operation because, unlike his other pituitary cases, they did not exhibit visual difficulty or signs of increased intracranial pressure; and since none had come to autopsy he had had no opportunity of definitely establishing the fact that their difficulties were of pituitary origin. In the anterior lobe of the pituitary there are at least three types of cells: (i) neutrophil or "chromophobe" cells that stain with difficulty and commonly give rise to tumors that tend to destroy the other cells; (ii) acidophil cells, having an affinity for acid dyes (when in excess these cells cause gigantism and acromegaly); and (iii) basophil cells which attract the basic dyes. Until 1930 Cushing had never seen a basophilic tumor of the pituitary but he had often suspected that such might occur. He tells how his interest was aroused anew:

> . . . The next case, also with autopsy, figures in a report made from Professor Biedl's clinic in Prague in 1924 by Dr. William Raab on the general topic of hypophysial and cerebral adiposity, or what is commonly called adiposo-genital dystrophy. The subject was approached largely from its roentgenological aspects, and it was a mere chance that in 1930 when preparing for my Lister Lecture I happened to hit upon the fact in reading this paper that in one of the patients (Case 2) a basophil adenoma had been disclosed at autopsy. The photographs of the patient were so striking and bore such a close resemblance to the appearance of a patient at the time under observation in my own wards that I felt little doubt but that they had been afflicted in all certainty with the same disorder.

Cushing then described his case in detail, and since the patient had responded favorably to X-ray, he was permitted to return home without operation. He reported frequently and died in 1935, several years after Cushing's paper on the new disease was published. Cushing did not hear of his death until three days after the funeral but his relations with the family had been so cordial that he had little difficulty in persuading them, in the interests of science, to have the body exhumed, and it can now be recorded that a well-circumscribed basophilic adenoma was disclosed.

Following the lead which the Raab-Kraus case had given, Cushing's interest in the condition was further stimulated by H. M. Teel's report of a basophilic tumor in 1931,[16] and his enthusiasm then became almost without restraint. It had always been characteristic of Cushing "to leave no stone unturned" to obtain autopsy examination on all his cases, and after Teel's basophilic tumor had been disclosed, his determination to obtain postmortems on all patients who might succumb was tenfold intensified. Cushing first described his deductions concerning the basophil tumors before the New York Neurological Society on 5 January 1932. He presented the same material again at the Harvard Medical Society on the 20th, and on

[16] Teel, H. M. "Basophilic adenoma of the hypophysis with associated pluriglandular syndrome." *Archives of Neurology and Psychiatry,* 1931, *26,* 593-599. It is a matter of some interest that at the time of Cushing's original paper on basophilism no one of his own cases had yet come to autopsy. Three patients, however, who died after the paper was published all proved at autopsy to have basophilic adenomas.

24 February he made it the subject of an Alpha Omega Alpha Lecture in New Haven. The Yale audience was so much larger than anyone had anticipated that the meeting was transferred from the small medical school amphitheater to that in the Yale Law School where, as Myron Wegman, then secretary of the society, recalled, there was unhappily no lantern or projection equipment. There was much embarrassment but, as Dr. Harvey pointed out the next day, the audience was really fortunate, since otherwise it would not have heard Cushing's masterful verbal descriptions of his slides. These first three accounts of basophilism were merely curtain raisers, for his official presentation was given before the Johns Hopkins Medical Society on 29 February, and the full text appeared in the March number of the *Johns Hopkins Hospital Bulletin*.[17]

In one of the intervals between his lectures on basophilism, Cushing attended the dedication of the Henry Barton Jacobs Room at the Welch Library, and on this occasion he gave his whimsical recollections, cited earlier, of latch-keyer days at 3 West Franklin Street.

John Beattie, invited again by the Harvard Medical Society, gave a progress report on 9 February of his work on hypothalamic functions. Cushing discussed the paper and spoke with even greater assurance about the existence of specific centers for the control of individual visceral functions, Beattie having argued that the hypothalamus was the motor area of the visceral nervous system.

March and April were crowded with clinical work. Many of his former patients with symptoms of tumor recurrence, on learning that Cushing was about to retire, flocked into the hospital because, if they were to require another operation, they wanted him to do it.

The Harvey Cushing Society

A scant two months before his retirement a group of young neurosurgeons and neurologists, for the most part too young for membership in the Society of Neurological Surgeons, banded together to form a new society which, with H.C.'s permission, took his name. The first meeting of the Harvey Cushing Society was held at the

[17] "The basophil adenomas of the pituitary body and their clinical manifestations (pituitary basophilism)." March 1932, *50*, 137-195. Cushing's deductions concerning his polyglandular syndrome came in at first for sharp criticism from a number of sources. It was known, for example, that tumors of the adrenal cortex may be associated with a clinical picture closely similar to that of pituitary basophilism in patients in whom no trace of basophilic tumor was found at autopsy. This might have been regarded as disturbing had it not been for the fact that, in causing their symptomatology, the basophilic cells of the pituitary exert their effects partly, if not wholly, by activating the adrenals. Indeed, it seems highly probable that the basophilic cells are responsible for elaborating the adrenotropic hormone which normally activates cells in the adrenal cortex (see *British Medical Journal*, 9 March 1946, 358-359).

Brigham Hospital on 6 May with William Van Wagenen acting as president and Glen Spurling as vice president. A diary note of one of the members gives a few details of the meeting:

. . . Van Wagenen of Rochester and Spurling of Louisville have been largely responsible for organizing the group, and it contains about thirty-five members

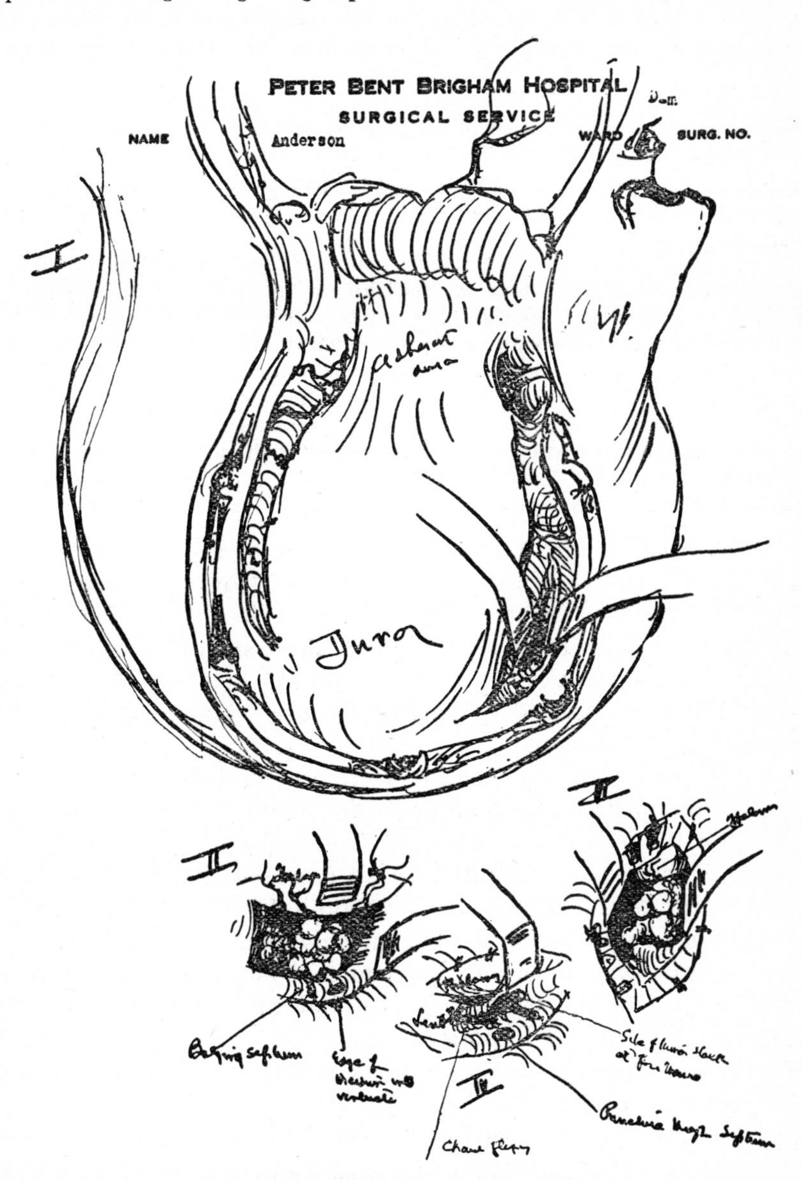

OPERATIVE SKETCH ON 6 MAY 1932
Drawing made following operation carried out for Harvey Cushing Society at its first meeting

from all parts of the country. There were two from Chicago, one from Kansas City, one from the Pacific Coast, and a scattering from the eastern seaboard. Dr. Cushing received them this morning at ten o'clock, and he said that he felt like an obstetrician bringing a new and protesting offspring into existence. He welcomed them warmly, nevertheless, asking them only to remember that in ten years' time another group would be coming along which would look upon the present one as senile and antiquated. His remarks were in the happiest vein, and I wish that they could have been recorded in full. He then operated in the large amphitheater before the entire group, exposing a third-ventricle tumor through a transcortical incision and removing a large part of it.[18] I have never seen him operate with greater ease and sureness. It seems to me that his technique has progressed even during the last year, and Dick Meagher insists that he has been doing things in the last few months that he would never have dreamed of doing a year ago. His physical health seems excellent and his spirits were never better.

In the afternoon we had a session of papers at the Children's Hospital, much the best of which were those of Blackfan on cerebral oedema and Bronson Crothers on obstetrical injuries to the spinal cord. Dr. Cushing gave a clinic at the Brigham in the evening, and had invited the Boston Society of Psychiatry and Neurology. Once more he was at the very top of his form. There was a succession of remarkable patients, including the one who had been operated upon the same morning. A case of the day before was sitting up, and the case of two days previous was knitting in a wheel chair, forty-eight hours after a pituitary adenoma had been removed by the transfrontal route. Five years ago such a thing would have been undreamed of.

After the meeting Putnam, the secretary of the Society, received a gracious acknowledgment, "Thanks much for your note and for the photograph of the newborn club. They look like a very serious and hard-working group, all except the three squatting figures in the center of the picture. . . . I am very proud of you all and that I should have been immortalized by having you use my name is a source of pride and gratification."

A few weeks after the meeting there was published a neurological monograph entitled *The Sign of Babinski* and dedicated to H.C. Immediately upon receipt of his copy, Cushing sent off an entertaining acknowledgment accompanied by an amusing sketch.

The visit of Vittorio Putti, Surgeon-in-Chief *pro tem.* in June, brought great satisfaction to H.C. and his staff. After speaking of the close association which the Brigham had enjoyed with the orthopedic service of the Children's Hospital in Boston, Cushing continues in his Annual Report:

. . . In recognition of this long enduring inter-hospital alliance, it appeared to be a particularly appropriate gesture should an orthopaedist be invited to act as my *locum tenens*. There could be only one choice, namely, Professor Vittorio

[18] The patient, who was shown at the evening clinic the day of her operation, turned out to have had a most favorable tumor (an astroblastoma). She was married a short time later and is still living and well, with a family of two children (Nov. 1945).

Putti, and he was given an official leave of absence by the University of Bologna for the express purpose. As all orthopaedists know, Professor Putti is a bachelor who lives and conducts his celebrated clinic in a most picturesque XVIth century Benedictine Monastery known as S. Michele in Bosco situated on an isolated hill overlooking the ancient city of Bologna where the university idea had its birth. That he was willing to drop his important work and after a long voyage exchange his comfortable abode in its quiet sylvan retreat for a cot in the Resident's quarters facing the noisiest street corner in Boston was a tribute not only to the Brigham but to the Children's Hospital as well. For his skill as a surgeon and contributions to his special subject, Professor Putti has a world-wide reputation. Besides this, he is a student of medical history, a bibliophile, and a scholar whose charming personality will not easily be forgotten by the young men who were privileged to come in contact with him as a co-worker.

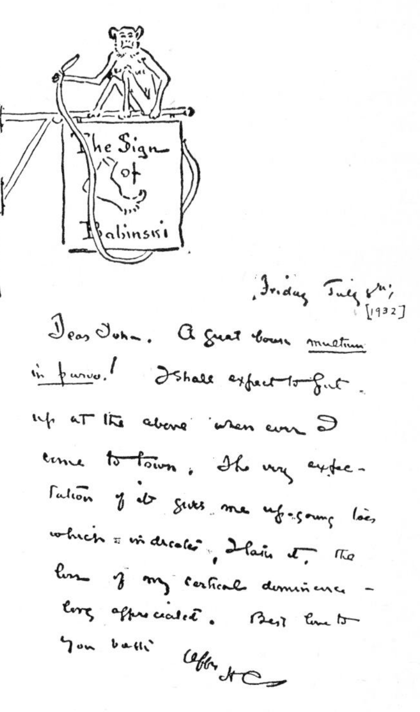
PETER BENT BRIGHAM HOSPITAL
BOSTON, MASSACHUSETTS

Friday July 8th, [1932]

Dear John. A great boon *multum in parvo*! I shall expect to put up at the above whenever I come to town. The very expectation of it gives me up-going toes which = indicates, I claim it, the loss of my cortical dominance — long appreciated. Best love to you both.

Affly H.C.

THE SIGN OF BABINSKI

Cushing's physical condition had improved somewhat in the course of the winter and his letters during the spring indicated a strong urge to continue his surgical endeavors after his retirement in September. Toward the end of May President Robert E. Vinson of Western Reserve paid him a visit, urging him to become Cutler's successor at the Lakeside Hospital. The idea of exchanging places with one of his favorite pupils intrigued him greatly. "For a time," he wrote later, "I was strongly tempted to take the group of Brighamites that finally went to Cornell to be under Heuer out there with me to start afresh. They were a fine group—Meagher, Glenn, Ray, Bishop, Mahoney, and Kendall—and would have made things easy for me." President Vinson wrote that the department budget for surgery was $87,300 which was vastly more than he had ever had from University sources at the Brigham. After turning it over in his mind for a week or so, he finally wrote Vinson on 31 May: "I have gone over the proposal fully with Mrs. Cushing and she feels, as I do, that at my time of life and with my physical activity handicapped . . . it would be foolish of me to think that I could take over this important position. . . . I say this with the greatest possible regret, for nothing would have given me greater happiness than to spend the next five or six years in some official contact with the University with which my father and brothers had such close association."

This decision gave George Heuer, who was reorganizing the Department of Surgery at Cornell, opportunity to secure the group of highly trained men in whom Cushing placed so much confidence. H.C. promptly invited Heuer, during July, to act for a week as the second Surgeon-in-Chief *pro tem* for the year, during which time Heuer was able to see at first hand the men who were going to be with him in New York. Of Heuer's appointment, Cushing wrote:

After Dr. Heuer's graduation from the Johns Hopkins Medical School in 1908, he served as my personal clinical assistant for the ensuing year, this being the first appointment of the kind I was permitted to make. His subsequent career at the Johns Hopkins and at the University of Cincinnati, now capped by his appointment to Cornell, has been followed with the greatest pride, and my suggestion that he do me the honor of acting as my last official substitute here at the Brigham he generously and promptly accepted. From the students' standpoint, it is regrettable that his all-too-brief term of service should have come in mid-summer for he not only is an inspiring teacher and a clinician who instills the utmost confidence in his patients, but his skill, resourcefulness and composure at the operating table put him in a class by himself as an ace of operating surgeons. What his stay among them meant to the house staff, some of whom are soon to join him in his new hospital in New York, can be readily appreciated.

During June H.C. had received an honorary D.Sc. at Northwestern University, at the instance, no doubt, of Irving S. Cutter, surgeon and fellow bibliophile, who felt keenly about H.C.'s retirement.

Chicago,
Irving S. Cutter to H.C. *18 February 1932.*

. . . What a wonderful opportunity Cutler will have as compared with the situation that you faced some years ago. He is no doubt the most promising man of his age in surgical America. I cannot view your retirement at Harvard with complacency. It will never be quite the same. Your influence on world medicine and particularly your stimulation of scientific ideals and accomplishment must continue with increasing power for many many years. It would be wonderful if you could see your way clear to go to Baltimore and there create a veritable Mecca for historically-minded pilgrims. Somehow or other I cannot see you retiring from surgery and any plan that you contemplate should incorporate in it two or three days of each week which you will devote to your chosen surgical field. Heaps of us depend upon you for that rare encouragement which only you can give.

H.C.'s reply was characteristic:

20 February 1932.

Dear Cutter: . . . It is pleasant of you to say such nice things about my small accomplishments and to lament my retirement. But it's about time I gave someone else the chance that I have had here, and I am sure that Cutler will make as much of my job as anyone could. Perhaps my retirement from active surgery, if that is what it is going to be, will enable me to see a little more of my friends and play about with some historical matters with you and others.

Cushing's resignation from Harvard University might have been effective on 1 July, but since his hospital appointment carried over until September his Moseley Professorship was terminated on 1 September, and thus he completed twenty years to a day in the chair. During the summer he carried on a heavy operating schedule, and when he operated on 17 August, few could realize that this was the last surgical procedure of his own that he would undertake.[19] The next day he was on the *Majestic* on his way to the International Physiological Congress in Rome.

H.C. had a disconcerting habit of waiting until the last minute to catch trains and boats. The resourceful Gus on one occasion made the two miles from the Brigham Hospital to Back Bay Station in three and a half minutes. On the night that Cushing boarded the *Majestic,* he had been dining with Richard Meagher and had allowed but fifteen minutes to get from the east side of New York to the Cunard Line pier across town. "I was finally bundled in," Cushing wrote in his diary, "through an aft opening in the stern after she had swung away from the pier—not a good experience for a gastric ulcer. A crate of boiled milk for infants saved me on the voyage." He landed on the 26th and caught a 4.30 plane to Geneva, where Klebs was impatiently awaiting him. Henry Viets of Boston was already at Nyon, and on the morning of the 27th they started off over the Simplon Pass to Italy, spending the night in Bologna. Klebs, hearing in the distance the strains of "Funiculì, funiculà," grew lyrical about the happy Italian people, who were always singing. As they came near H.C. was consumed with mirth, for they discovered that the music was emanating, not from the throats of happy towns-folk, but from a gargantuan loudspeaker in the middle of a square.

On Sunday the 29th they drove over the Apennines to Florence via the Futa Pass. Cushing had been in Italy only once since 1901 when he had worked with Mosso, and he had never previously been in Rome. With his intimate knowledge of Italian history, art, and

[19] On 5 November 1932 a physician's daughter who proved to have a large and highly vascular meningioma was operated on by Dr. Horrax. Horrax had attempted to persuade Cushing to do the operation in the first instance, but having made his decision to stay out of the operating room H.C. had consistently refused. Horrax accordingly started the operation and in order to have the benefit of H.C.'s large experience with these difficult lesions, he sent word to his chief that he was having difficulty. Without saying a word Cushing scrubbed and finished the operation as Horrax had hoped he might. Thereafter H.C. steadfastly refused all requests to operate.

literature, particularly the period of the Renaissance, Klebs was able to make the trip, hurried though it was, intensely interesting. They stopped for lunch at Siena and went into ecstasies over the Duomo (and the local chianti). Proceeding toward Rome after lunch, they passed through Aquapendente where H.C. dutifully photographed the monument to the great anatomist Fabricius who, while holding the chair at Padua, had demonstrated the valves in the veins to William Harvey. Going on through Montefiascone and Viterbo they followed the Via Cassia, coursing beside the Etruscan hills, and entered Rome by the Porta del Popolo.

From their headquarters at the Hotel Majestic they made their bow to the Congress and spent the first two days sightseeing. H.C. was present, however, at the plenary session in the Campidoglio on the Capitoline when Mussolini, surrounded by the effigies of the Caesars, gave a pompous address of welcome. Afterwards H.C., who was beside Pavlov, was fond of telling of the old gentleman's remark when watching Il Duce throw his head back imperiously in the Fascist salute. On witnessing the comic gesture, Pavlov exclaimed audibly, "A conditioned reflex." On the platform with Mussolini were Bottazzi, Herlitzka, Marconi, A. V. Hill, and several state officials. They all spoke briefly, and Hill then gave his inaugural address, which lasted about twenty minutes. During the address Mussolini watched him closely and appeared to understand him readily. After Hill had finished, Mussolini spoke briefly in Italian, offering the members once more a hearty welcome to Rome and to Italy, and wishing them success in their deliberations. He then gave the salute dismissing the audience, and walked over to Hill, shook his hand and said a few words to him, smiling easily and graciously.

During this trip H.C. kept the last of his travel diaries. It is not a very complete document and has few illustrations compared to the diaries of thirty years earlier, but it gives a good idea of his interests and pursuits. A visit to St. Peter's stimulated him to read a history of the Popes. He was also much stirred by the Keats memorial on the Spanish Steps—but of course the Steps led to Rappaport's bookshop where he again "sanctified" his surgical fees for the summer. Meanwhile he renewed his association with the Bastianellis. With Raffaele, the surgeon, he had much in common, but he was also fond of Giuseppe, the physician brother, who entertained him at a dinner given in honor of 'Drs. Van Slyke and Peters.' Bastianelli had intended to entertain the distinguished authors of the book which he so much admired *(Quantitative clinical chemistry)*, published a short time before in Baltimore. The guests soon discovered, however, that while Van Slyke was present, Rudolf Peters of Oxford, instead of John P. Peters of New Haven, had received the other invitation.

Cushing's paper at the Congress was scheduled for the last day (2 September). He followed Pavlov in an afternoon session with an account of his intraventricular injections of pituitrin and pilocarpine, in which he summarized the evidence for the existence in the human hypothalamus of special centers regulating visceral processes. The paper was well received and was followed by prolonged applause. Immediately after the paper, Klebs started off by the Via Flaminia and carried the party 186 kilometres to Perugia in time for late dinner. H.C.'s diary notes of this trip indicate his vivid impressions of the journey:

On Bastianelli's advice, on reaching Terni, we turned to the left via Orvieto and Todi rather than via Spoleto, Foligno and Assisi. There are countless other hill towns in this Umbrian basin that would have been equally interesting and individual even seen casually in transit. They are all walled and once strongly fortified places from the earliest times—the walls of Assisi, for example, dating from 400 B.C.—and they all have tempestuous histories. How the people have had the tenacity to live in them, much less to get a simple necessity as water in amounts enough to supply their fountains, much less the needs of life, is beyond me.

Otricoli I don't even find on my small map, nor Narni with its spectacular gorges—nor indeed Todi. We must have gone through Orvieto and perhaps seen its marvelous Duomo which Margaret Symonds says "stands like a peacock in a hen coop—a dream in stone to commemorate a dubious miracle." It was here the Popes used to beat a retreat in troublous times. And it's difficult to realize that Clement VII when he took refuge here in 1527 built the colossal wall for which he employed the same architect who built Paul III's fortress at Perugia.

Spoleto and Foligno as I take it were on the old Flaminian way and were exposed to constant attacks by passing armies and hordes in addition to their local Umbrian strifes—Guelph & Ghibelline. Spoleto, for example, was Ghibelline in spirit and in constant quarrels with the Pope and the towns that supported him.

At Perugia they had opportunity of becoming reacquainted with the Peruginos, and H.C. was also much struck by the portrait of the young Raphael. Portraits always fascinated him and, being himself an artist, he doubtless saw more in them than those less talented. He writes:

The heart of Perugia throbs in the Piazza di San Lorenzo with the Duomo to the north, the Palazzo dei Priori (Palazzo Pubblico) to the south, and the Fontana Maggiore with its picket fence on which warring factions used to stick one another's heads—Baglioni and Oddi. The cathedral suffered more in these factional fights of the early 16th Cent. than did the palace of the people, parts of which were given over to the several guilds that vied with one another in the richness of the decoration of their chambers. From the Piazza massive open air steps lead up to the north door of the Palazzo which is guarded by a bronze griffin on one side, emblem of the city, and a bronze lion on the other, emblem of the Guelphs. This north door leads to the huge Sala dei Notari—a great vaulted hall, surrounded by stalls with a frescoed ceiling. Above this room is the library of 50,000 vols. and many painted missals.

From Perugia Klebs, still bursting with the erudite gossip of the ages, took them over a steep Apennine pass to Gubbio, another of the hill towns, where H.C. became fascinated with the Eugubine tablets bearing the ancient Etruscan inscriptions that gave the clue for deciphering all later Etruscan inscriptions. From Gubbio they went on to Urbino in quest of Polydore Vergil; and from there to Rimini, where they passed the night. The next day they motored to Ravenna, where Klebs and H.C. were deeply moved by the 5th century mosaics in the glorious Basilica Sant' Apollinare in Classe. The trip was hurried, but Cushing found these glimpses into the early centuries of Italian art and architecture fascinating to a degree, and in the letters which followed during the next year between the two men there are innumerable references to the details of this flying trip. At Ferrari they were particularly struck by the 14th century castle of the d'Este family; their brief stay in Padua later in the day was of even greater interest because of its medical traditions.

They reached Venice and the Hotel Danieli the evening of the 5th. The next morning, while Viets made an early morning tour of the churches of Venice, H.C. and Klebs were measuring the plates of the unique copy of Vesalius' *Tabulae sex* in the library of San Marco. In his brief notes, "Leaves measure 50.5 cm. by 37.7 both of Vesalius' *Epitome* and *Tab. sex*. Evidently the sheets of the *Epitome* were folded two ways originally. The *Tab. sex* has water mark [which he sketched in his notes]. Putti's copy measures 51 by 34 cm." This information eventually found its way into H.C.'s detailed *Bio-bibliography of Vesalius* on which he was working at the time of his death.

The remainder of this memorable trip carried H.C. from Venice to Cortina, where Vittorio Putti had his orthopedic hospital (Istituto Codivilla). After a night at Cortina, they took leave of Putti and by way of the Brenner Pass, over which Vesalius had sent the wood blocks of the *Fabrica* from Venice to Basel, they reached Innsbruck in time for lunch. They arrived at Munich and the old Hotel Continental to find Winston Churchill at the next table to theirs at dinner (the year before their dining companion at the same hotel had been the former Crown Prince Wilhelm). But Mr. Churchill did not hold them for long and they were presently off for a late evening at Taeuber and Weil's bookshop, where many purchases were made, including the Ellenbog collection of incunabula.

At the Munich Library the next morning H.C. listed all its Vesalian holdings and examined the original wood blocks used for the *Fabrica*. On Thursday they were off again to Switzerland via Zurich. On Sunday at Nyon Klebs and Cushing spent most of the day in conference with Dr. Willy Wiegand, the head of the Bremer Press at Munich, concerning the plan of the New York Academy of Medicine to reissue an edition of the Vesalian plates from the original wood blocks. H.C. and Klebs were strongly of the opinion that there would be no real point in issuing the wood blocks unless accompanied by either a translation or some attempt at scholarly bibliographical analysis. Cushing noted: "Wiegand says Vesal was about nine months in Basel for the printing of the 1543 edition and he ascribes its beauty and success to him rather than Oporinus." Cushing, as it turned out, was to have little hand in the elaborate Vesalian publication, which was finally issued in 1935 at $105 a copy as a collection of plates *(Icones anatomicae)* superbly reproduced but without annotation save for the Latin explanations and Wiegand's useful index.

On 12 September H.C. flew from Berne to Paris in a plane with a 12-cylinder engine, "three of which were held together with safety pins." He stopped at Hôtel Metropolitain, where he encountered President and Mrs. Angell of Yale, who evidently had chosen that somewhat dreary retreat in the rue Cambon for the same reason as H.C., namely, to be quite certain that they would encounter no one they had ever seen before. Mr. Angell recalls that they went together the next day to see Chartres and H.C. recorded: "the windows, alas, without sun but still very beautiful. Like the human soul, very plain without—one must be inside to see their beauty."

By this time H.C. had become an intrepid flier, despite the hazardous 'crates' then in passenger use, and on the 15th he and Viets took off for England in a French plane which made an emergency landing in Brex before limping across the Channel to Croydon. He made his headquarters at Welch's noisy Hotel Victoria, where he found Donald Armour, and the next day he visited the London Hospital to see Hugh Cairns, H. M. Turnbull, and William Wright, the Vesalian scholar. During the next few days he paid a visit to the Sherringtons who were then vacationing at Bexhill-on-Sea; later he had tea with the Geoffrey Keynes and their offspring, Richard, Quentin, Milo, and a baby then unnamed. He sailed on the 17th on the *Berengaria* and found himself once again with the Angells. "The only entertaining thing [during the trip] was Mr. Angell's presiding at the concert and his introduction of the whistling lady . . . and the Chez Florence (black) quartette."

Mrs. Cushing had made a point of coming to New York, unannounced, to meet the boat, but H.C., with his usual impatience had arranged to be first off the boat and, being first through the customs, was (he records) "off like a jack rabbit, missing K.C." He lunched with Meagher at the Century Club, went out to the New York Hospital to see Heuer and his old house officers, and then caught the five o'clock train to Boston.

For the first time Cushing returned from Europe without having to face clinical responsibilities. Cutler, knowing that he wished to be relieved completely of patients, had arranged a place for him in the surgical laboratory, where he would be at liberty to consult his case records, but where he would no longer assume any part in the direction of the clinic. Cutler had begun at once to rearrange the offices which he had inherited from Cushing and to alter the routine of the operating room. Psychologically, the return to the clinic which he had once directed was naturally upsetting, and while he kept his peace with Cutler, he seemed unconsciously disappointed that he had been so completely superseded. Since Cutler knew Cushing's temperament, he acted in the belief that complete abrogation of Cushing's responsibilities was essential—not only in theory but in fact. Without question this wounded H.C. immeasurably for he had no doubt hoped that even in retirement he would be consulted not only by Cutler, but by his junior staff. The hurt was perhaps somewhat ameliorated by an appreciative vote of the Brigham Trustees appointing him Surgeon-in-Chief Emeritus:

> VOTED, to appoint Dr. Harvey Cushing as Surgeon-in-Chief Emeritus as nominated by Dr. Christian and recommended by the Executive Committee of the Staff. The members of the corporation of the Peter Bent Brigham Hospital take this action as a token of their high esteem and personal regard for Dr. Cushing, their admiration of his marvelous professional work and attainments, and their deep appreciation of all that he has done for their Institution in his constant and generous attention to its needs, in the lustre and world-wide reputation he has brought to its name, and for the inspiration and sending out of a host of young men to maintain and carry on in widely distant places its high medical standards.

He also learned that he was to receive an annual pension of $1750 from Harvard's coffers.

Cushing slowly grew accustomed to his changed status. He went in and out of the hospital through the students' entrance and set up his office in a small room previously used for photography. Toward the end of June he had decided tentatively to go to Yale, and now his intention became definite. Accordingly, on 12 October, he and Mrs. Cushing went to New Haven for a four-day visit, and he seemed glad to be in the friendly surroundings of his youth. During this trip he reaffirmed his decision to the University authorities, but again requested that it be kept in confidence until he had made a little more progress in winding up his affairs in Boston. Mrs. Cushing, meanwhile, occupied herself with the somewhat discouraging problem of finding an appropriate house in New Haven.

On the 14th Cushing had conferences with Harvey and Winternitz about hospital facilities, and later attended a meeting of the Beaumont Medical Club, where he received an enthusiastic welcome. His old friend, Walter Steiner of Hartford, read an interesting paper on Elisha North, which Cushing discussed at length. The next day H.C. met a number of the medical students and reviewed some of the research projects under way in the departments of surgery and physiology. The Yale students and staff in almost every department of the School were eager to seek his counsel. Inevitably certain contrasts must have occurred to him. Shortly after his visit he was elected an Associate Fellow of Trumbull College.

A pleasant interlude occurred later in October when he went off to a houseparty at Senator Walcott's in Norfolk, Connecticut, with Dr. Welch.

> . . . The countryside was in its autumnal glory. Fred Dennis took me off one day to his bungalow on a hilltop filled with the memorabilia of his professional life. Among other things he had framed the documents relating to his effort to keep Dr. Welch in New York—even to the signed check of Andrew Carnegie to pay for the laboratory which was to keep him there rather than allow him to go to Baltimore. Dennis never quite forgave him.
>
> Knowing that we were having a houseparty in Norfolk A. C. Klebs, who had sailed a few days before for Europe, called us up from mid-ocean. There was a perfect connection and we all had a few words with him—even Pupin [inventor of the wireless telephone] who was lunching with us. Klebs did not quite understand who it was, so Pupin repeated his name several times and finally said, "I am Pupin, the man who made it possible for you to hold this conversation."

Cushing's letters during October and November indicate that he was following the Roosevelt-Hoover campaign with lively interest. Except in matters international, Cushing still remained an Ohio Republican, and Mr. Hoover, despite his political ineptitude, appealed to H.C. because, among other things, he and his wife were good classical scholars and had translated Agricola's *De re metallica*. Mr. Roosevelt also interested Cushing for many reasons, but it was some time before he could speak unemotionally about the so-called "New Deal," which he felt put a premium upon idleness and destroyed the incentive to work. When the news came of F.D.R.'s overwhelming landslide, H.C. nevertheless sent his warm congratulations. Mrs. Roosevelt replied on 14 November:

> I want to send you just a line though I am sure Franklin also is going to write you his thanks for your nice letter. I wish you had been able to be here, but I realize that "someone must stay at home," and of course, a grandfather is very necessary to the welfare of his grandchild! Franklin has come through in splendid condition and I think is going forward to what, to me, seems extremely difficult work. I confess to a certain amount of trepidation. However, as the responsibility is not mine, I suppose this is an unnecessary fear on my part. I hope we will see you before very long. It is always a joy and we were indeed glad to have Mrs. Cushing with us.

Off and on for several years Cushing had been seeking information on an obscure Italian anatomist, Ercole Lelli, whose famous anatomical figures, the so-called écorchés, he had first seen when he visited Bologna in 1901 and had examined again more in detail when he visited Vittorio Putti in 1931. In December he was committed to reading a paper before the historical section of the A.A.A.S. at Atlantic City, and he accordingly made Lelli the subject of the address.[20] He refers to the meeting in his Welch memorabilia:

> During the afternoon we went again to the History of Science Society meeting at which Sigerist was presiding. We parted about 5 p.m., Popsy saying that he wished to make a few notes. At the evening meeting the small room was packed. Karsner spoke, Sigerist on the Edwin Smith Papyrus, and I on Ercole Lelli. At about 10.30 Popsy arose to say that it was the Tercentenary of Leeuwenhoek's birth which was being celebrated throughout the scientific world—that so far as he knew no one had made mention of the fact—certainly not at any meeting of the association—and he proposed therefore to make some rambling remarks about the man. He produced Dobell's book and for thirty minutes or more held the audience—packed and standing—absolutely spellbound. It was one of the best things I ever heard him give—a feat for a man 82 years old after a long day.

1933

During the first months of 1933 H.C. devoted the greater part of his time to working with Louise Eisenhardt on the meningioma monograph which he had started in 1913 and had repeatedly put aside to make way for other things. The source material lay in the voluminous Brigham Hospital records, and without this material at his elbow it would be impossible to proceed with the text. Before many months had passed it became apparent that he could not possibly finish within a reasonable time; and since the new regime in the department of surgery had made him uncomfortable, he later decided to have the clinical records of each one of his 2201 cases of verified tumor (along with a few hundred others) reproduced photographically and brought to New Haven with the Brain Tumor Registry. The Registry was later set up under a fund generously donated to Yale University in 1939 by Mr. Howard M. Hanna of Cleveland in memory of his son of the same name who had succumbed to a malignant brain tumor. The services of Frederic Ludwig of Yale (who has been responsible for preparing the illustrations in this biography) were enlisted and during 1935 and 1936, 50,000 sheets of Brigham histories were photographed for Cushing's New Haven files.

Before coming to New Haven Cushing gave five addresses and attended the 20th Brigham reunion. On 19 January he delivered a Harvey Lecture in New York which, as it happened, was an unusual honor for it was the second occasion on which he had been asked to contribute to this important series. His first Harvey Lecture had

[20] "Ercole Lelli and his écorché." *Yale Journal of Biology and Medicine*, Jan. 1937, *9*, 199-213.

resulted in his pituitary monograph in 1912. He accordingly chose as his title for the second lecture, "Dyspituitarism twenty years later,"[21] making it the occasion for a summary of twenty years' progress in the study of pituitary function, and devoting particular attention to the latest development, namely, pituitary basophilism.

While in New York in January H.C. attended a ceremony at which Dr. Welch gave a recording on a sound film; he set down a lucid description of the occasion in his Welch memorabilia:

> This ceremony was made highly entertaining by Dr. Welch's preliminary remarks. He must have sensed the probability that Flexner's and John D. Jr.'s speeches would be embarrassingly laudatory and to offset this, he told the story of the film in his own inimitable way before it was shown. It's a great pity no one was there to take down his remarks, for if they only could have been preserved to be given as a curtain-raiser for the film in days to come a true picture of Popsy would have been given. Otherwise the film was a good deal like listening to a full moon addressing an imaginary audience across space. He told how he had been led into it by W. G. MacCallum who told him they had only raised enough money for a ten-minute film, in which time he would be supposed to give an account of his life as though speaking informally to a group of his pupils. Flexner was elected to represent said pupils and to inspire him by his presence.

In December Dr. Welch, after a speaking engagement in Hartford, had been scheduled for a Beaumont Lecture in New Haven, but on the morning of the day the address was to have been given his New Haven friends were distressed to learn that he had had an attack of acute retention and on Walter R. Steiner's advice had returned immediately to Baltimore. He was not seriously discommoded again until February. Then, Cushing writes:

> He entered the hospital at that time not again to leave it. . . . In spite of good intentions I saw him only twice during this long interval, during a good deal of which I was more or less laid up myself. There was a meeting of the National Academy of Sciences on April 24-26 [1933] and I stopped over in Baltimore on my way down to Washington and found that I might see him. This was only a week after the third operation and he was of course in bed. He looked white and had evidently lost much weight, but one would never have known that anything was amiss, for he was cheerful and interested in everything and insisted on doing most of the talking during the short time I stayed. It hardly seemed possible that a week or two before he had been uraemic.

When H.C. saw him again (for the last time) he wrote:

> . . . The Congress of Physicians and Surgeons met in Washington [9 May 1933] and [I] having seen F. C. Walcott there on two or three occasions he proposed that K.C. and I motor with him to Baltimore to see his uncle, for he was in the habit of paying him a weekly visit. On the way over he had much to say of his [Welch's] mental activity in spite of all he had been through, and it was just

[21] " 'Dyspituitarism': twenty years later. With special consideration of the pituitary adenomas." *Archives of Internal Medicine,* April 1933, *51,* 487-557.

at that time when there was some discussion as to whether the pathological tissues had actually shown carcinoma. However, Dr. Welch had never asked any questions about it whatsoever.

We found him sitting up on an upper balcony, wrapped in blankets and reading and holding quite a heavy book which had just been issued, and which I think had something to do with the early history of the Carolinas and the migration westward. He insisted that I must get the book and read it, for it was full of interesting doctor people and he thought it was one of the best things he had read for a long time. He was full of talk, asked me if I had met the new President of Harvard. . . .

The occasion for H.C.'s call on Dr. Welch in April was, as he said, the annual meeting of the National Academy of Sciences, at which he presented one of his less important papers entitled "Hyperactivation of the neurohypophysis."

Cushing had many staunch friends among his medical colleagues in Boston—Hans Zinsser, Robert B. Greenough, Robert B. Osgood, to mention only a few—but there was no one over the years more loyal and devoted than William T. Councilman who had admired Cushing in his Hopkins days and had been largely responsible for bringing him to Harvard. It was natural therefore that H.C., following Councilman's death on 26 May, should try to express in writing some of his respect and affection for this colorful personality.

Throughout his long life Councilman was a man of ardent and generous enthusiasms. It was this quality, combined with his utter informality, which made him such an inspiring teacher for the young and such a delightful companion both for young and old. There was a picturesque ruggedness in his personal appearance, an unexpectedness in his turn of thought, a shrewdness and independence in his observations concerning people, things and events that set him apart from the common mould. He had escaped from early educational and environmental inhibitions by which many persons come to be afflicted and subdued. Combined with an utter unconsciousness of self, there was about him a certain sturdiness of mind, frankness of opinion and honesty of purpose which were no less disconcerting to the self-complacent than refreshing to those who appreciated his outspoken sincerity. . . .

On the opening in 1913 of the Brigham Hospital to which he was appointed pathologist, the scope of his work was greatly enlarged though at the same time his responsibilities were doubled. . . . The lengthened number of hours he was obliged to spend in the microscopical study of dead tissues may possibly have served to accentuate—if anything could—his love of the outdoors and his interest in growing things. . . . On relinquishing his chair and with it his hospital position, Councilman merely shifted his attention from the diseases of man to those of plants. . . .

One object of his attention was the root fungae essential to the growth of his favorite wild flower, and "it was characteristic of him that he could not leave the trailing arbutus without unburdening himself about 'its fatal gift of conspicuous beauty'." After mentioning its slow growth and the unthinking way in which it had been pulled up, Councilman added that "apparently like all wild beautiful things which man covets, it must go, but the loss of such things is a serious loss for man." And so H.C. concluded:

Thus Councilman went through life observing, studying, recording and speculating on things small and on things large, but always with consuming interest in the quest that engaged him and living up to his maxim that the chief happiness lies in work. When uprooted from his warm and fertile Maryland soil and transplanted to the rugged shores of Puritan New England, there must have clung to him some of the "essential native humus" which guaranteed more than a precarious foothold. Though "deeply engraved on his memory" was the bursting springtime of his boyhood home, he came to appreciate no less the beauties of a slower year's awakening. So it is suitable to leave him—engrossed in the study of the tiny Mayflower and vigorously championing its right to survive.

Meanwhile the Brigham Hospital was celebrating its twentieth reunion and the Boston Surgical Society took occasion the night before to present Cushing with the Bigelow Medal. It was the most pleasant gesture that had been made in connection with his departure from Boston. Prior to the presentation Cushing read an amusing address entitled "Homo chirurgicus," which began with a diverting definition, "Biologically speaking the chirurgeon is a peculiar animal of a comparatively recent era with a pair of hands terminating in ten more or less highly specialized digits." The address was a warm-hearted satire on his surgeon colleagues, entirely without bitterness, in which he signed himself "M. Ch. (Dublin)." He took leave of his friends in Boston in these words: "And finally while adjusting the dressing and pinning the binder as comfortably as I may, it is unnecessary to remind you that as a class we chirurgeons often do things better with our hands, when our heads and hearts are not allowed wholly to govern our actions. For if I had permitted you to know, during the course of this operation, what was really in the back of my head and what lay deep in my heart to say to you, you would have judged me to be a sentimentalist rather than the eminently practical person which every *Homo chirurgicus* outwardly feigns to be." David Cheever, in presenting the Bigelow Medal, made gracious reference to Cushing's achievements in a moving speech too long for full quotation. The following paragraphs doubtless touched Cushing deeply:

. . . Somehow in your busy life you have found time to indulge your love of the humanities. You are a bibliophile and have assembled a notable library, whence the stimulating traditions of medical history have seeped by way of your talk and writings into the minds of those about you. Two hundred and fifty titles scarcely comprehend the total of your contributions to medical and lay literature—papers whose scientific importance is equalled by a fertility of imagination and a charm of literary style which make their reading a double pleasure. And then your admiration for one of the greatest figures in contemporary medicine led you, in recording imperishably the life of Sir William Osler, to write one of the greatest of medical biographies. . . .

How now may this modest group in Boston presume to add to these tributes? At least we might have taken pride in offering you your first gold medal, but a relentless Fate, in reconstructing a shattered world, has ordained that this precious element must—in trade at least—lose its pristine value. But this medal is a symbol—not of a trade, but of a splendid profession; its exquisite workmanship typifies the consummate perfection of your handicraft, and the metal of which it is composed, which does not tarnish or corrode with age, symbolizes the changelessness of scientific truth, for which you have striven. And we dare to believe that among your honors it will not rank least, because it will always remind you of our admiration and affection.

There were other tributes during the next two days of the Brigham reunion. On Friday evening at a formal dinner in Vanderbilt Hall at which Elliott Cutler presided, oil paintings of Cushing and Christian were presented respectively to the Hospital and the University, Francis Blake making the presentation on behalf of Christian's former students, Gilbert Horrax on behalf of Cushing's. H.C.'s portrait, showing him in his operating gown examining an X-ray film, had been executed by Mrs. Calvin G. Page of Boston. He had been no less restless a subject than in 1910, which possibly accounts for the somewhat stern expression that the portrait depicts.

Immediately after the reunion H.C. was in Washington giving his presidential address at the XVth Congress of Physicians and Surgeons on the theme, "Medicine at the crossroads," before an audience of 1,500 people (and as many were turned away). One who attended referred to Cushing that night as "a man who, through the guise of allegory always light and never severe, attempted conscientiously to convey something of the richness of his own life's experience. His comments on the ethics of the medical profession assumed the form of gentle advice but it was impelling and authoritative."

Early June brought the pleasant announcement of his election on 25 May as a Foreign member of the Royal Society of London. Recognition of American scientists by this august body has been infrequent, only thirty-four having received membership in the course of one hundred and fifty years, and Cushing was the first American surgeon to be so honored.

The summer of 1933 slipped away. In September, after several months of repeated attacks of gastric pain, which he had confessed to no one, he had X-rays taken which disclosed a deeply penetrating ulcer on the lesser curvature of the stomach. He modified his dietary habits and managed to keep his difficulties under control for nearly four months.

In October there were two ceremonies in which he was most interested. The first was an exercise on the 6th and 7th in commemoration of the 150th anniversary of the Harvard Medical School. On the first day papers were read describing some of Harvard's recent important contributions to medical research: the work of Cecil Drinker on lymph, William Castle on pernicious anemia, Alexander Forbes and Hallowell Davis on electrophysiology. Reginald Fitz, who had planned the observance with excellent histrionic sense, arranged that James B. Conant, the new president of the University, should have an opportunity to meet and to speak to the medical faculty, many of whom had never seen or heard him. When they gathered in Sanders Theater in Cambridge, there was an air of expectancy in the audience—they sensed that something highly significant in the life of the University was about to occur. Presently their expectations were fully justified, for the young and energetic figure, so thoroughly identified with science and the modern world, arose quickly to his feet and in a beautifully turned fifteen-minute oration outlined the history of the Medical School's relations with the University and indicated in no uncertain terms that he as president intended to take an active part in the affairs of the school. The ceremony gave the Harvard Medical School a new sense of confidence, vigor, and hope.

On the 9th a tablet was unveiled in the Harvard Memorial Chapel to that gallant soldier, Major General Leonard Wood, who as a patient had figured so prominently in Cushing's surgical career and whose death had been such a disturbing loss.

On 12 October the family left for New Haven, Mrs. Cushing having finally found a house at 691 Whitney Avenue. That morning Cushing called on President Conant to take formal leave from the University, for he was ever punctilious in such observances and, incidentally, it precluded a call on his Dean. Mr. Conant asked H.C. whether there was anything about the Medical School he would like to discuss. The conversation was unrecorded, but Cushing said the next day with a twinkle that he had told Mr. Conant what the Harvard Medical School really needed! After seeing Mr. Conant, he and Mrs. Cushing made a final stop at the Hospital to pick up Miss Stanton. His departure from the institution which he had served for twenty years passed unnoticed.

Harvard University, now separated from this vigorous pioneering spirit, could settle back into a more peaceful way of life without his periodic agitation about medical education, the full-time plan, internationalism, and the sanctity of the Common. Yale in its turn regained her most eminent son in medicine, and she also acquired a unique pathological collection and one of the great libraries of our time.

CHAPTER XVIII

Return to Yale: The Professor of Neurology

1933–1937

THE full significance of Cushing's return to Yale was not widely appreciated, for there were few among his professional colleagues who were aware of his passionate devotion to his college, and few knew of his lifelong interest in the School of Medicine. Several of his Yale classmates understood, men like Lafayette Mendel and Elliott Joslin; others, such as F. C. Walcott, Starling Childs, and Grosvenor Atterbury, likewise understood, as did Russell Chittenden. New Haven was one place in the world outside the Western Reserve where Cushing had known real happiness, and throughout the years he had always been much refreshed by his trips to Yale, however brief his stay. It is scarcely surprising therefore that he decided to enjoy his declining years amidst surroundings that had appealed so strongly in his youth. He found a rapidly growing university library, a young and vigorous medical school which at long last had a university hospital, and an eager undergraduate body, both in the College and in the Medical School. There were, besides, friendly groups such as the Elizabethan Club, of which he soon became president, the Beaumont Medical Club, and a dining club or two. Finally, many of his old Yale associations, including his senior society, still remained. Had he followed advice and rested tranquilly in these congenial surroundings, a large gastric ulcer would no doubt have healed promptly, but he was scheduled for a lecture in London in November and to receive an honorary degree a few days later from the University of Paris—responsibilities he was ill-equipped to meet. On his return from Europe he went into the hospital where he passed the next three months, bored almost to death by a Sippy diet; but he recovered despite the diet, no doubt because he was again at Yale.

As indicated earlier, the negotiations which led to Cushing's return to New Haven began in 1930, and the exchanges between President Angell, Dean Winternitz, and other friends on the Medical School faculty continued through 1930 and 1931. Thus on 17 October 1931 Angell sent off a handwritten note: "I am not unmindful of our promise not to annoy you . . . and my flexible conscience allows me to say that at the beginning of another year we often think of you. . . ." A short time later Angell had an entertaining rejoinder (also by hand and with his usual misspellings):

H.C. to President Angell *18 November 1931.*

Dear Mr. Angell: We had a delightful time in New Haven and enjoyed particularly the privaledge [*sic*] of staying with you. That you are making one of the greatest of Yale Presidents is common knowledge but that you are an equally good chauffeur is a secret known to few. Had I been the typical absent-minded Professor *et ux.,* I would have offered you a *pourboire* at the station. As a matter of fact I did not even give you a tip in regard to my feelings about the proffered chair. This is largely a matter of legs—mine and the chair's. I'm much better than I was a year ago but I still tire with disconcerting ease and I consequently hesitate to inflict myself on anyone who may expect more of me than I can give.

My grandfather when he was approaching 90 betook himself to an upstairs room in the house where my father had his office and there busied himself for his last two years cataloguing his library. He requested the family to keep away for the simple reason, as was learned, that he could not escort them on their departure—as a gentleman should—to the front door. Though I don't compliment myself on having such good manners, something of the same feeling is in my own blood. Were I wholly fit I would say 'Yes' without hesitation *now.* If you can properly wait, I can give you a definate [*sic*] answer by the Spring. It gave me—and I hope you too—cheer to see how greatly Mrs. Cushing enjoyed her visit.

Mr. Angell was always at his best when dealing with this kind of wit:

President Angell to H.C. *20 November 1931.*

Dear Dr. Cushing: . . . With every respect for your excellent grandfather, I trust you will not feel that you must adopt at sixty—or thereabouts—the regimen he found appropriate at ninety. Also I hope you will accept at its real import our assurance that we are all eager that you come down here under any conditions that may seem to you attractive and practicable. It is our belief that we can make literally any arrangements which your recalcitrant underpinning may render expedient as to your physical quarters, and equally as to your scientific and professional occupation. All we want is a hint as to what would make you happy and content.

If you cherish them—and I suspect you do—for heaven's sake wipe out of your critical and over-conscientious mind any scruples about "special treatment" and soft adjustments and the like. You have made the most brilliant contributions to your profession and to mankind. You have reached a point where institutional regulations necessitate some change in your procedure. You have many years of fine work before you and all we ask is a chance to furnish the conditions in which you can carry on to your own satisfaction.

Nor did Mr. Angell forget the distaff side of the household, who always played a large part in most important decisions:[1]

[1] At the end of a long (14-page) handwritten preface to his volume of correspondence on 'University and Hospital Appointments,' H.C. wrote: "I have always felt that what precipitated the slow-moving Harvard people to action was the operation on Leonard Wood. He was a great friend of A. T. Cabot's (who indeed had done the first operation) and at the second-stage procedure A.T.C. with his wife went down to Baltimore and that afternoon had tea with us at 107 East Chase Street where they for the first time

Dear Mrs. Cushing: I am glad to recognize and welcome another low-brow, who finds satisfaction in the ceremonies of Saturday in the Stadium. So many of my own contemporaries are superior to such enthusiasms! There *is* a decent amount of salt in New Haven, no doubt. But we sadly need more—and especially a variety now found only in Brookline. We hope you will look with a sympathetic eye upon our need and help us to secure our heart's desire.

The next exchange occurred in May, when Mr. Angell no doubt hoped that a decision would be made in time for an announcement at the June Commencement. Samuel C. Harvey, the Professor of Surgery, had been called to Lakeside Hospital in Cleveland but had decided to remain in New Haven:

Mr. Angell to H.C. *30 May 1932.*

Dear Dr. Cushing: I want you to know—as you probably do—that Harvey is staying here and that the department and medical situation has been appreciably stabilized as a result of the give and take incident to the episode. I hope you can let us knit you into the picture before we start the new year and that we can work out something which would be agreeable to you.

Cushing replied:

Thanks for your note. I rejoice that Harvey has been prevailed upon to stay. He is too good a man for you to lose. I told you that I would let you know this spring what my final decision would be, and as the spring draws to a close, it's high time that I came to a decision. I am glad to say that the Baltimore matter has been satisfactorily settled by the appointment of Professor Sigerist of Leipzig to the place that had so long been kept open for me. This at least eliminates one of the elements that held up my decision. Just at the moment, what delays me is the condition of my financial affairs, for I had supposed that the trust fund that I had established for my family was as secure as anything could legally be. I now learn that the people who had my affairs in hand have so manhandled them that I may have to start in afresh as a wage earner, which is not so easy at my time of life. . . .

Cushing's financial worries had been precipitated by the collapse of the Boston banking firm which for many years handled all his local business affairs. Finally, on 17 June, he reached his decision and sent the following carefully worded letter to Mr. Angell, again written by hand, and his files indicate that it had gone through many drafts:

I am obliged for your letter of June 12th which I would have answered more promptly had I not been out of town. I appreciate highly all that you say, though I have misgivings as to whether I can live up to all that is expected of me. I have seen Mr. Ripley and have explained to him the reasons for my present hesitation and reservations, hoping that he might personally lay them before the Corporation. Unfortunately he will not be at the meeting; but he has frankly told me that the University has even more reason to hesitate about making a new appointment, just at this time, than I have to accept it.

---

met K.C. This must have settled the matter for them; and A.T.C. being on the Corporation, I can imagine his announcing to that august body that the female of the species was better than the male."

If I remember correctly you hinted that the Sterling professorship carried a $10,000 salary and a *circa* $5,000 budget. This, at the time, did not particularly interest me as I assumed—erroneously as it turns out—that I and my family were well provided for and that I needed no future salary.

I have no preference regarding a title, and this, I suppose, need not be definitely acted upon now. I merely wish that my coming in no way be interpreted by outsiders as changing Dr. Harvey's status as head of the department. This interpretation might be made should I also simply be called Professor of Surgery. In short, if the University's finances—and mine—prove to be in a state justifying my transfer to New Haven by the first of the coming year, if not earlier, I shall be happy to come and will do my best to live up to your expectations.

The Yale Corporation files disclose two votes passed within forty-eight hours of the receipt of Cushing's letter authorizing the President to invite him to occupy a chair in the Medical School and setting aside $15,000 per annum for salary and office expenses. In acknowledging the Corporation vote, Cushing added: "I have heard glowing accounts of the Commencement exercises. Garrison was, of course, much elated by his degree. There is no place in the world where graduation ceremonies are carried off with such colour combined with dignity."

Although Cushing had confidently expected to go to New Haven by the first of the year, he had further doubts about taking up surgery again and many more letters were exchanged with the result that the title "Professor of Neurology" was settled upon rather than "Professor of Neurosurgery," and he asked for a six-month deferment in his appointment. After a long letter filled with doubts and reservations, which Mr. Angell had happily ignored, H.C. wrote on 17 June 1933: "I don't see how you could have failed to understand my letter! Perhaps you couldn't read it. Anyhow it's too late now to try and *make* you understand, and all I request is that when you make the announcement at Commencement you don't mention the Fitches [the Fitches being the offspring of a remote Cushing forebear who had Mormon tendencies]." The announcement was eventually made at the June Commencement, after which Mr. Angell, on 23 June, sent one of his more characteristic notes to H.C.: "Even your modesty would have been flattered by the tempestuous applause when I announced to the great gathering of our alumni Wednesday the fact that you were coming back to your first love and that the new Sterling Chair was at your disposal. I am sorry you could not have been on hand to sense for yourself the enthusiasm of the gathering. With warm regards to the Fitches and their illicit descendants."

The house on Whitney Avenue, which the Cushings had rented from the McLanahans, old friends of the family, was a large frame affair, well set back from the street. It was similar, both in appearance and atmosphere, to 305 Walnut Street in Brookline and the furniture, once it had been arranged, looked as though it had always been there. New bookshelves soon appeared beside the three churchwarden bookcases that had followed H.C. since 1901, when he had first become bitten with book collecting in his 3 West Franklin Street days. His directions to the local carpenter who was making the shelves were so specific that at one juncture the Irish craftsman threw up his hands and invited H.C. to finish the work himself.

But this is getting a little ahead of the story for in October H.C. went promptly to Europe while the house was being settled, sailing on the 19th on the *SS. Olympic.* He had been invited by the Medical Research Society of University College, London, to inaugurate a new lectureship. The paper had to do with a highly controversial subject, namely, the relation of the posterior pituitary to the toxicities of pregnancy and to other hypertensive states. In postmortem examinations on several patients who had died of eclampsia, Cushing had found evidence of great increase in activity of the secretory cells of the posterior lobe, and since similar activation of those cells had been observed in pituitary basophilism, he believed that the elevated blood pressure in the two conditions must have a common cause. To his considerable annoyance, Sir Thomas Lewis, who was editor of the journal in which the paper was to have appeared, refused to publish it.[2] H.C., disgruntled by Lewis's reaction, left London the next day with Klebs for Paris where they found Mary Cushing and her friend Katherine Halle of Cleveland, with whom she was travelling in Europe, as well as H.C.'s warm friend from Boston, Mrs. William Hooper, whom Klebs irreverently referred to as "the benevolent battleship."

On the 4th, with appropriate ceremony, the University of Paris conferred on H.C. the degree of *Docteur, honoris causa.* In pronouncing the encomium Professor Roussy, Dean of the Faculty of Medicine, said the University wished to pay homage not only to one of the greatest surgeons of the United States, but also to the man whose work as anatomist, physiologist, and clinician had greatly advanced neurology, to the genial inventor whose new techniques, during almost thirty years, had made it possible to save thousands of human lives. Following the degree-giving ceremonies there was a round of festivities, formal and otherwise. On the 6th he attended Professor Guillain's official dinner. The next day, at the General Assembly of the Academy of Medicine, Professor Hartmann greeted him affectionately and Cushing recalled that Hartmann was "the only man [in France] who took an interest in me in the early days [1900]."

[2] The paper was eventually published in the United States. "Hyperactivation of the neurohypophysis as the pathological basis of eclampsia and other hypertensive states." *American Journal of Pathology,* March 1934, *10,* 145-175.

Hartmann escorted H.C. into the Assembly where he was to have spoken but, owing to his internal discomforts, he had asked that he be not called upon. Even Klebs, who had phenomenal endurance, confessed to having been fatigued by the week's activities, and H.C. was almost in a state of collapse. However, he pulled himself together the next day to attend the state funeral at Notre Dame of the great French bacteriologist, Émile Roux. He described the ceremony in a letter to Klebs (who had returned to Nyon): "Thursday morning [9 November] fortunately was clear for Roux's funeral. I do wish you had been there. Such a tribute! The cathedral packed—a magnificent service—such music as I've scarcely ever heard at a church service—all the nation's dignitaries from the President of the Republic down through the Supreme Court, the Chamber of Deputies, ambassadors, military, naval, academicians, etc. etc. down to me wearing my rabbit skin on my left shoulder." Continuing to Klebs: "On Friday morning [10 November] at the Salpêtrière I found a large gathering of neurologists and students in Charcot's old lecture room and pulled off my little speech better, I think, than I did in London. They at least seemed to take in what I was driving at."

Returning from Europe on the *SS. George Washington,* he arrived in New York on the 18th, and was at home in time to greet Arturo Castiglioni of Padua who had come to New Haven for a lecture before the Yale Medical Society. Cushing joined him for lunch on the 22d and later entered into a lively discussion at a seminar on Andreas Vesalius which had been arranged for Castiglioni. In the evening the distinguished Italian historian outlined major developments in the history of ideas concerning infection before a crowded session of the Yale Medical Society.

On the 24th Henry Sigerist, who was now in Baltimore as Director of the new Institute of the History of Medicine, came to New Haven to give the annual Beaumont Lecture; 1933 was the anniversary year of the publication of Beaumont's book on the gastric juice, and Sigerist, in a brilliant analysis of the significance of Beaumont's work, held a large audience spellbound for an hour and a quarter. He was already speaking idiomatic English with scarcely a trace of accent, and H.C. remarked after the lecture that his judgment in recommending Sigerist to Welch had been richly vindicated.

The crossing from Europe had been rough and on arrival H.C. had looked drawn and weary. He took things easily for a few days, but friends in New Haven began to rush the Cushings unmercifully with luncheons and dinners and H.C. was forced to escape on 28 November into the hospital, where his diet could be more carefully supervised. A telegram mentioning his illness was overheard in James Roosevelt's office in Boston, and on the morning of the 29th the

Boston papers announced his illness in prominent headlines—indeed they all but published his obituary. His improvement in hospital was slow and tedious, for he not only was combatting his ulcus, but his feet had begun once more to cause him great pain. His attendants were therefore in a constant state of indecision; no sooner did one disease yield to medication than the other became exaggerated. He lost his appetite, slept poorly, and was given barbiturates for sedation, which precipitated an acute depression persisting for several weeks. Meanwhile, everyone tried in some small way to bring him cheer. Klebs' arrival at Christmas time helped; and there was one incident which kept him chuckling for days on end. Barbara appeared one afternoon in his room attired according to all the suggestions she had ever had from her father—flat-heeled shoes, long skirt, high-necked blouse, ultra-conservative hat, no lipstick, no rouge, no nail polish, unsmiling and with an air of prim propriety. From this attitude her father could not shake her—not a smile (except a very proper, saccharine one), not one lighthearted remark. Finally, unable to stand the spectacle of such a metamorphosis, he shooed her out of his room to entertain one of her friends across the hall—and it is to be doubted whether he ever again made any suggestions about apparel to his youngest daughter.

1934

During January and February Cushing worked by fits and starts in his hospital bed. He had been scheduled to give an address at the celebration of the 150th anniversary of the New Haven Medical Society, but this of course he was unable to do. He wrote many letters, those in December and January nearly all indicating that he was low in his mind; but in February when his spirits had lifted, the tone of his letters changed, as is apparent in a note to Mrs. H. F. Reid:

> . . . I have been laid up here in bed almost ever since we reached New Haven, while Kate has been having a wild fling, accepting with a smile and apparent delight all the entertaining and dining out that I happily have been spared. We can say that in spite of my hospitalization we both like our change of base very much indeed, and have been very happy here. But it's very amusing that we should have thought of coming down here to pass our declining years in quiet and give the children a chance to strike out on their own, to find that we can't by any possibility shake them off, for they insist on making this their headquarters with but few and short intermissions.

Early in March he remarked to Klebs that he was back in his office for the first time in three months. Almost immediately he turned his attention to the meningioma monograph, at which he continued to work off and on for the next four years.

In April word came that Dr. Welch was gradually failing; and his death was announced on the 30th. Cushing, unable to go to the Baltimore service on 2 May, attended his funeral at Norfolk, Connecticut on the 4th, and his fine appreciation, which appeared under the title, "The Doctors Welch of Norfolk," is one of his warmest and most happy pieces. It runs (in part):

Over the northerly part of Litchfield County in Connecticut sprawl the rugged and heavily wooded foothills of the Berkshires, and in early May they are possibly even more lovely than when the first frosts of late September have suddenly turned to crimson the swamp maples of their lower valleys. But whatever the time of year, no part of Litchfield County is more quietly satisfying than the township of Norfolk which must have changed scarcely at all since Hopestill Welch decided to settle there one hundred and sixty-two years ago.

If the beauty of the countryside is thus felt by the casual visitor, how much more deeply must those feel who, born and bred in Norfolk village, have roamed the neighboring hills, fished the streams, and swum the ponds in boyhood days. And so the great-grandson of this Hopestill Welch, though in the course of his eighty-four years he had wandered far and attained world renown, never lost his affection for the place of his birth and requested that it also be his place of burial just as it had been of his medical forbears. . . .

There is a touch of sadness and melancholy about Autumn which would seem the more natural time of year for an old man to die. But so far as anyone could ever tell, sadness and melancholy were moods of which he was incapable and it was as though he whose youthful spirit and reactions so belied his years had deliberately waited for Spring—waited at least as long as he could, for the season had been delayed by the hard winter and the venerable elms have not as yet burst their winter buds. . . . A few people had gathered at the knoll—his relatives and three or four others. Appropriate verses from *Ecclesiasticus* were read by the local clergyman and followed by a simple prayer. Then two of his great-nephews who were at the same time his namesakes lowered the casket into its place. That was all—except for one incident.

In the small gathering was a frail little old lady whose many wrinkles could not conceal that she must once have been beautiful. She arose with some difficulty from the camp chair that had been provided for her and, refusing aid, walked over to where lay a spray of red roses she had brought and lifting them she placed them with her own hands beside the grave. Then turning away she said as to herself, "I shall now go." Only six months younger she was than this friend of her childhood; they had long ago been playmates—perhaps, on her part, something more than that.

It was the same little old lady who four years before had been taken in a wheel chair all the way to Washington so that she might hear in Continental Hall what the President of the United States and other notables would have to say about her lifelong friend; and also what in return he would have to say for himself on that day when speeches in honor of his eightieth birthday were broadcast to all quarters of this country and abroad. . . .

It had been urged that the National Cemetery at Arlington was the proper place for him to lie in view of his distinguished service during the War. He had merely volunteered on an April day in 1917 to help his friend, the Surgeon-General, open his rapidly overwhelming mail; and the close of the War found him still there—much to his surprise and somewhat to his amusement—a Brigadier-General. But a military funeral, with gun carriage, firing squad, the Last Post and all that, just because he had done his duty as he saw it, would have been incongruous and unsuited to his real character and life, public though much of it had come unsought to be. It was wholly consistent and typical of him that he should choose to rest where to the future passer-by he would be just another of the many Doctors Welch of Norfolk. Even now, should you happen to ask the aged apothecary in the village which of the Doctors Welch was the more celebrated, he would certainly say William Wickham, the father of this William Henry. . . .

So it would seem there must have been at least ten doctors in these three generations, all apparently men of very similar type, good judges of people and good public servants, men able to instill confidence and win regard, all of them blessed with a rare capacity to gain and retain friendships with young and old, all of them apparently men who were respected, admired and beloved. And then, to follow the old apothecary's advice, you go down the road and find cut on the rim of the fountain erected in memory of your friend's father—the last of the Doctors Welch to pass his life wholly in Norfolk—what might be no less appropriate to William Henry his son:

FONS SUM SOLATI TALIS ET IPSE FUIT

This prose-poem about Welch evoked a flood of appreciative comment, including an editorial in the *New York Times* (24 June), but a brief letter from an 87-year-old ecclesiastical friend at Harvard must have given Cushing particular gratification:

Northeast Harbor, Maine,
Rev. Francis G. Peabody to H.C. *4 September 1934.*

My dear Dr. Cushing: . . . Let me only add that I have heard scores of obituary eulogies and have indeed perpetrated a great many, but you have done what no eulogist ever even attempted and the result is overwhelmingly searching and touching. To give a great figure a background of heredity, and lift an address into a searching sermon, was a triumph both of insight and eloquence.

Every one misses you terribly at Harvard. A grievous administrative blunder must now be interpreted as a fraternal gesture of generosity to Yale.

On 17 May, at the instigation of Stanhope Bayne-Jones, a memorial service was held at Trumbull College in memory of Dr. Welch at which Cushing and Winternitz were the chief speakers—even undergraduate students had felt the death of William Welch.

The Brain Tumor Registry

From the time the Pathology Department at the Hopkins lost Mary Donnelly's pituitary cyst in 1902, H.C. had insisted on being responsible for all of his own pathological specimens, whether obtained at operation or at autopsy. Welch and MacCallum had taken his insistence indulgently, but at Harvard his acquisitive propensities for brains and their tumors had brought on some difficulty, first with his warm friend Councilman, and later with S. Burt Wolbach, Councilman's successor. The development, furthermore, of his own neuropathological laboratory under Percival Bailey's direction and the publication of the glioma monograph from the department of surgery, with scant reference to the department of pathology, did not serve to foster as friendly relations as perhaps should have existed between him and his colleagues in pathology. Although the pathology department had conducted many of the autopsies on Cushing's cases and wrote full reports on all the general pathology from his surgical service, Cushing stored and cared for all his own brain specimens. He likewise insisted on retaining under his immediate custody the entire collection of his 2000-odd verified tumors.[3]

It is not surprising that when H.C. came to leave Boston he found himself in something of a dilemma, for the pathological specimens would not be of much use in the absence of the clinical histories, and it was obviously inappropriate for him to attempt to purloin his histories from the Brigham Record Room, as he had attempted to do with his Hopkins histories when leaving Baltimore. On 8 April 1932, Wolbach wrote: "A chance remark dropped by Elliott Cutler yesterday that you contemplated destroying your collection of brains quite horrified me." To this came the prompt rejoinder: "Nothing under the sun would induce me to destroy the brain collection. After all, they don't belong to me but to you and they are merely in my hands owing to your everlasting goodwill and courtesy. The whole series is so carefully recorded that it ought to be of permanent value as a library. Indeed, there has been a movement on foot on the part of the young neurosurgeons of the country to establish a brain tumor center to which obscure specimens might be sent." The Harvey Cushing Society was in process of being formed at this time and William Van Wagenen, one of the prime movers, had been responsible for suggesting the formation of a brain tumor registry, using the Cushing collection as the primary focus.

In June 1933 the idea came to a head and on 16 June President Lowell, after conference with Wolbach and Edsall, suggested that the brain tumor collection be housed permanently in the Warren Museum of the Harvard Medical School across the street from the Brigham Hospital. For a year H.C. attempted to foster the plan and appointed a board of directors for the proposed registry, but financial difficulties loomed large. Salaries for a director and technical assistant

[3] Dr. Eisenhardt writes: "Dr. Cushing faithfully sent to Pathology a specimen in every case in which tissue was removed at operation or autopsy. If a surgical specimen happened to be too small for each laboratory to have a piece, all of it would go to Pathology. The pathology department wrote up their own microscopical descriptions. The Chief cut all the brains in his own cases, and dictated his descriptions of gross findings for the pathology department records and for our records and supplied them with copies of all the numerous photographs taken. When microscopical descriptions from the pathology department came through, we checked diagnoses to see if we agreed. If not, in our own records we appended our own description and diagnosis. We used to confer with one another in the most unusual cases. We gave the pathology department many sections stained in our laboratory by special techniques."

would be required, and structural changes in the Warren Museum essential to house the collection would amount to $4,000. Mr. Conant, who had meanwhile become president of Harvard and with whom H.C. had discussed the project on Columbus Day in 1933, attempted to secure the necessary funds and exchanged several letters with H.C. on the plan. However, it developed in June 1934 that there was little real enthusiasm for the project on the part of either Wolbach or Cutler, and once this became clear, H.C., after obtaining authorization from Mr. Conant, rapidly took steps to have the entire collection moved to New Haven. Louise Eisenhardt was appointed Director of the Registry, and Milton Winternitz, as head of the department of pathology at Yale, allocated suitable space to receive the collection, including office and laboratory space for Dr. Eisenhardt. She arrived with the specimens in September 1934.

A second problem, alluded to earlier, had now to be faced, namely, what, if anything, could be done about making the records available. Early in 1935 H.C. began to explore the feasibility of having a large proportion of them photographed and presently was able to make arrangements to have a complete photographic copy of every history for which he had a pathological specimen, and several hundred others which were needed for special reasons. The Registry, financed at first from the Bolton Fund, and for four years generously aided by a grant from the Childs Fund, was handsomely endowed at the time of Cushing's death by Mr. Howard M. Hanna of Cleveland; it has now been transferred to the department of physiology and continues to flourish under Dr. Eisenhardt's loyal direction.

* * * * *

During April and May, Cushing worked industriously preparing for the centenary celebration of the College of Medicine at Syracuse which had been founded at Geneva, New York, in 1834. He chose as a title, "The pioneer medical schools of central New York," a theme that was most congenial for his father had attended Union College in nearby Schenectady. He took occasion again to describe the migrations of the Williams family and of Erastus Cushing and to pay tribute to the peripatetic professors of the early days with whom, he had moments of believing, he had much in common. At the close of the celebrations he was awarded an honorary LL.D.

On 20 June the yacht *Sequoia* cast anchor in New Haven harbor, and that morning, in one of Yale's most picturesque ceremonies, an honorary LL.D. was conferred on Franklin Delano Roosevelt. The next day H.C. sent off a vivid description to Senator Walcott:

> . . . I do wish you had been here yesterday. It was certainly the best Commencement they have ever had, a gorgeous day and great enthusiasm. Perhaps the

climax of the day was the surprise LL.D. given to Billy Phelps by Governor Cross. Everybody, particularly Billy, thought the Governor had gone out of his head when he got up in the middle of the exercises and said he wished to interrupt the ceremonies to propose, and so on. Of course this had all been prearranged, but it was done with such grace and Billy's embarrassment and surprise were such that the entire audience responded with enthusiasm, as you can imagine. The Alumni luncheon too was excellent, and Conant and Mr. Roosevelt both made a great hit. They certainly do stage these things well here, in the tradition of Anson Stokes well carried on by the present Secretary, Carl Lohmann.

During the summer while the family were away H.C. worked on the meningioma monograph, avoiding social entanglements as far as possible. His principal relaxation lay in his excellent game of croquet on which he prided himself, and which he managed to enjoy despite his handicapped 'underpinning.' Having discovered that Cushing was settled in New Haven, friends began to stop off for brief visits. On 29 July he was especially pleased by a visit from Lucien Price—he of "Hardscrabble Hellas." They reminisced well into the night about the early days in Ohio, and discussed the latest novels, Hitler, Hindenburg's death, and other current affairs.

Cushing was also much interested in the round-the-world flight of Richard U. Light. Light was flying the Atlantic by the northern route via Labrador, Greenland, Iceland, and the Faroe Islands to Edinburgh. From there he went to visit H.C.'s friends in Sweden (who had recently honored H.C. with election to foreign membership in the Swedish Royal Academy of Sciences); also Holland and Switzerland, going to Nyon to see A. C. Klebs.

The end of September found H.C. in Montreal where he gave an address at the opening of Wilder Penfield's Neurological Institute. On entering the new building he was somewhat taken aback to find, among the illustrious dead, his own name on the foyer wall along with those of three other living neurologists, Cajal, Sherrington, and Pavlov, but he was greatly pleased by the Greek inscription (which had been found in Galen by W. W. Francis, the Osler Librarian) on the roof of the foyer, "I have seen a badly wounded brain heal." In his address, after describing the National Institute of Neurology that had been proposed in 1919, he launched into an impressive discourse which ended:

. . . But in the last analysis this [neurological training] will depend not upon the well-equipped edifice we are here to dedicate, but on those who are to control its activities. There has recently been erected at Yale a massive neo-Gothic structure with a cathedral-like entrance—the new Sterling Library which people come from a distance to admire. It is told that the librarian, apprehensive of the impression visitors might carry away, requested that an inscription be carved over the portal something to this effect: "What you see before you is not the Yale library—the Yale library is inside."

So the measure of this fine institute will not be what one can outwardly grasp of its carefully planned body, for that is a mere matter of morphology—of its soma. The real measure will lie in its psyche, the intangible spirit of the laborers within; and for this, as we have seen, there is no standard yard-stick. History has repeatedly shown that an institutional esprit, however widely spread throughout a group, is primarily distilled from the ventricles of one of them. So we may well expect that under the widely-trained and many-sided director of this new institute neurology will receive a new impetus, making of this place still another mecca for workers in the great subject in which we all feel so vitally interested. We may rest assured that here not only will the story of neurology's great past be cherished but that a new and significant chapter will be added to it.

Penfield had not worked directly under Cushing, but he writes: "I was very greatly influenced in the development of my own particular technique by the Cushing ritual. . . . I made drawings of every instrument and listed the routine steps of every operation." He continued:

Dr. Cone joined me in New York, and we came to Montreal together, and we have steadily altered our technique in one way or another, but frequently when debating any change in routine operative surgery we have referred back to the complete notes which I have of Cushing's every move. I make a point even now of demonstrating to each resident Cushing's method of suturing the aponeurosis and point out the differences in his routine procedure from our own. I try to point out at the same time that no one has ever excelled Cushing in fastidious care and devotion to detail. It seems fair to say, therefore, that throughout my surgical career I have used Cushing's method as a sort of classic and have constantly referred to the general principles which he laid down in neurosurgical operating. We have departed from his procedures in a manner that I believe he would have approved. In my opinion he would never have adhered to his own ritual as slavishly as some pupils might.

Plans for his Library

The trip to Montreal in September of 1934 offered Cushing opportunity once again to see Osler's books—they had been in place now for five years and had come to play an important part in the life of the School—and it was on his trip back on the night of the 28th that he decided to leave his own Library to Yale; and at that time he also conceived the idea of persuading several of his friends, especially Arnold Klebs, to do likewise. After turning the plan over in his mind for a few days and discussing it with Mrs. Cushing he sent a handwritten proposal to Klebs (4 Oct.):

As I may have intimated to you in times past I have always intended to have a check list of my books made and then to have them sold by my Executors so that others might have the pleasure of collecting them as I have done. This idea has begun to wane in favor of leaving them to Yale to be kept together (Keogh tells me this is quite possible) as the basis of a medico-historical collection. I have talked the matter over with John and though I did not press the matter I gather that he would like to leave his books also when the time comes. . . . I wake up in the middle of the night with the thought—why not a Klebs-Fulton-Cushing Collection so that the three could go down to bibliographic posterity hand in hand. Just imagine some young fellow long hence stumbling on our diaries and papers and correspondence about books. I envy him to think what fun he would have for I think in a certain way our three collections have a more personal and intimate provenance than has W.O.'s library.

All this has come up to me for I am redrawing my will and I plan to leave enough to start a professorship of the history of medicine. It's just possible the University might switch my Professorship to that purpose and then the income of my bequest would be used for book purchases. I don't know what your own plans may be if you have any. I know that you once thought of establishing at Les Terrasses a foundation for medico-historical studies. This you may still intend to do but if not and if this other idea has any interest for you do let me know. Anyhow let me play with the idea and see what comes of it. Meanwhile John and I will not duplicate our purchases but will try to point toward a common goal.

Klebs was a little taken aback by this cool suggestion concerning the disposition of his library, but after discussing a good many angles of the proposal he responded favorably:

A.C.K. to H.C. *Nyon en Suisse, 14 October 1934.*

Dear Harvey, . . . Now comes your holograph about the destiny of yours and John's and my books. Not long ago you made me see that it was not so bad an idea to turn one's books back into the commercial stream that brought them to you. Why shouldn't the other fellows have the fun of collecting again as you had? I have here a few books with interesting provenances of my father's, of Choulant's, of Davidson's, of yours, of Osler's, etc. They have a peculiar interest because of the marks of their former owners. Some of them I could not have unless they had been turned back into the stream. When once institutionalized they are withdrawn, but perhaps from the alluvial soil they form more fruitful crops next spring. . . .

The fun of mere acquisition may be great, and indeed it is a necessary phase, but the working with the books, the discussion about them and the comparison is after all what really is most worth while, don't you think so? When I saw what work I had put you to with this Galen and which I had not fully forseen, I thought I ought to have got the information in some other way from the copy in Leipzig, for instance, dug out by one of Sudhoff's students. But after all I concluded I had done right for it forced you to what, after all, was not without fun. And probably you with your habit of exact observation saw some things that another would not have seen. So I have come to the conclusion that it does not really matter much what becomes of our books—whether we sell them or keep them together under the aegis of an institution. What I think does matter is to keep, if we can, the particular, the peculiar spirit of curiosity and search that somehow is exuded from collections such as we have brought together. . . . I am heart and soul with your plan if you can insure to it, as well as in one's power, the continuity of personal interest and influence. If you can give ten more years to it, perhaps with a little help from me and a great deal from John, something lasting might be started. At any rate we will continue to play with your idea.

Thereafter Klebs and Cushing and others who were interested began to collect systematically, each one in a few specific fields so that the collections, when brought together, might have unity, and overlapping and duplication might be avoided.

During the winter of 1934-1935 H.C. took up the problem of a library building with Mr. Andrew Keogh, who had indicated that space for the collection might be found in the University Library; this suggestion, however, did not wholly satisfy Cushing, since he was 'set' on having his books made freely available to medical students, and the University Library at Yale is nearly a mile away from the School of Medicine. With encouragement from President Angell and Dean Winternitz and a special appropriation from the Corporation for architectural plans, Grosvenor Atterbury, Cushing's warm friend and classmate, was engaged to draw up plans for "A special library," to use the Corporation's designation. Atterbury came to New Haven early in June 1935 for a conference and on the 25th submitted preliminary sketches.

For the next four years plans were drawn and redrawn. One set called for a large independent building on a plot of land near the Medical School that would have cost several million dollars. More reasonable was a secondary plan which placed the proposed new library in the center of gravity of the School where it could be readily entered from any point in the Medical School. This Y-shaped building, although it called for the sacrifice of some tennis courts, was vigorously sponsored by Stanhope Bayne-Jones (who had become dean in July 1935), but funds for the erection of the building did not become available until the summer of 1939, even though the plans had been in readiness for nearly two years. Finally, through the energetic support of Wilmarth S. Lewis, the youngest member of the Yale Corporation, $600,000 was appropriated by the Sterling Trustees and, although the war had broken out on 1 September, the Corporation accepted the revised plans on 3 October and, four days before Cushing's death, authorized Mr. Atterbury to proceed with the building.

President Charles Seymour to H.C. *3 October 1939.*

Dear Harvey: I am sending you this note simply to confirm our talk on the telephone last Saturday evening. I decided that it was important that the plans for the Medical Library should not be postponed. They are going forward accordingly and I presume that we shall soon make a public announcement. I look forward with interest to discussing with you the possibility of securing endowment for the operation of the Library. With constant appreciation, Always yours, CHARLES SEYMOUR.

* * * * *

During October and November of 1934 H.C. came more into the swing of life at Yale. He had been elected to The Club—a group of senior New Haven citizens who, like those of The Club in Boston, enjoyed good conversation (see Ch. XIX, p. 690). He began to attend meetings of the Board of Permanent Officers of the School of Medicine, which he seemed to enjoy, and he was likely to brighten up those stately occasions by asking awkward questions of his deans. He was always a dean-baiter; his best friend, if made dean, would automatically become someone to stick pins into.

With his plan for the Library crystallized Cushing began to devote more and more time to perusing book catalogues and to the study of the books themselves. Long letters were exchanged with Klebs, sometimes two or three a week, discussing books he proposed to buy, or some unusual item, long forgotten, which had turned up on one of his shelves. These annotations and memoranda were laboriously typed out on a size of paper that would exactly fit the book in question and would be inserted along with letters, photographs, cuttings from catalogues—anything that would lend interest to the book in question. He took special interest in the previous history of his rare items and prepared himself a catalogue of the books in his own library having an interesting provenance.

He was also most observant of the condition of his older books and generally felt that no one could be entrusted to repair them—no one other than himself. And he gave the same fastidious attention to patching up a torn back or corner of an old leather binding that he would have given to matching wrinkles and pores in order to obtain an invisible scar on a woman's face. During these years he began putting together bound volumes of interesting correspondence—family papers, the Welch memorabilia in four volumes (this he began immediately after Welch's death). He personally mounted and individually annotated the letters, photographs, dinner menus, and other memorabilia that have proved so useful in tracing the growth of Welch's influence on Cushing. Similarly, he had the Klebs correspondence bound up, also in four volumes, but in this instance long before Klebs died.

Compulsory Health Insurance

In 1932 a Committee on the Costs of Medical Care (C.C.M.C.), sponsored by the Milbank Fund and other foundations in New York, published a report in which the need for a national program of health insurance was urged as a means of improving the quality of medical care in underprivileged areas. The report was highly publicized, and while its chief sponsors came from outside the medical profession, it was clear that public opinion had been influenced by the committee's findings, and the Federal government presently felt the repercussions. This, however, was merely a phase of a liberal movement that was sweeping not only the United States, but the world at large. On 29 June 1934 President Roosevelt issued an executive order establishing a Committee on Economic Security (C.E.S.)

with instructions to report back to the President not later than 1 December 1934. The committee consisted of Frances Perkins, Secretary of Labor, Henry Morgenthau, Jr., Secretary of the Treasury, Homer S. Cummings, Attorney General, Henry Wallace, Secretary of Agriculture, and Harry L. Hopkins, Federal Relief Administrator, with Edwin E. Witte acting as Administrative Director. In October Miss Perkins formed a Medical Advisory Committee to the C.E.S. which was asked "to study practicable measures for bringing about the better distribution of medical care in the lower income groups of the population and more satisfactory compensation of physicians and others who render medical services to individuals in these groups." Cushing was asked to serve and, although he had little taste for Washington politics, he looked upon it as his duty since his selection had undoubtedly come at the request of the White House. His reply to Miss Perkins was pointed:

H.C. to Miss Frances Perkins *8 October 1934.*

Dear Miss Perkins: I have your letter of October 6th suggesting that I act as one of the group of physicians and surgeons to give advice to the Committee on Economic Security which the President has recently established. I am glad the Committee has thought of establishing such an advisory group, particularly since most of the agitation regarding the high cost of medical care has been voiced by public health officials and members of foundations most of whom do not have a medical degree, much less any actual first-hand experience with what the practice of medicine and the relation of doctor to patient means.

I should be most happy to serve as a member of this group if you think it is wise. But I hasten to say that I have not been well for this past year and have only once or twice been out of New Haven, so that I am not likely to be at all useful as an adviser, particularly should it necessitate frequent visits to Washington as I assume it will. . . .

Cushing had given some thought in the past to problems of medical economics but he knew little of the history of economic theory and, as his letter to Miss Perkins indicated, he was inclined to be impatient with social reformers outside the medical profession who were injecting themselves into problems of medical practice. He was convinced, however, that health insurance and health legislation on a national scale were inevitable, but he was also equally strong in his conviction that any social legislation affecting the physician should be brought about in the first instance with the full cooperation and, if possible, through the initiative of the medical profession itself. He was fearful at first that the Medical Advisory Committee would be made up largely of theorists who had never practised the art, but he was considerably relieved to discover that, apart from the Chairman, Mr. Edgar Sydenstricker, every member of the committee had an M.D. degree and had at one time or another been in practice. The American Medical Association was represented by Walter L.

Bierring, its President; prominent also on the committee was Thomas Parran, then New York State Commissioner of Health. Perusal of the voluminous correspondence which rapidly accumulated in connection with the committee's activities indicates that Cushing acted as an effective balance-wheel. On the one hand, he repeatedly urged Drs. Morris Fishbein and Olin West of the A.M.A. to cease their active publicity against health insurance, pointing out that it was coming inevitably and that the A.M.A. would be in a far stronger position if it cooperated in bringing about the reform than if it continued in its reactionary opposition. Thus on 14 December to Fishbein: "You have it in your hands more than anyone else to make things run smoothly and to get the profession adjusted to the possibility of some sort of sickness legislation. I am sure that if we bury the hatchet about the C.C.M.C. report and take a fresh start we may be able to get somewhere and preserve the things which most of us regard as precious in our age-long profession. Reassurances from you on this matter from time to time will do more good than anything else." On the other hand, to Sydenstricker, who was leading the campaign for a sweeping health insurance act, he wrote on 17 November 1934, a few days after their first meeting:

> I thought the meeting went off extraordinarily well. If any of the separate and conflicting groups had anything secret up their sleeves, it at least was not apparent. In any event, you have succeeded by your masterly presiding in encouraging frankness, goodwill and a friendly feeling of give-and-take which just at this juncture it seems to me is half the battle. I do hope that so far as you can, you will persuade those who are putting out propaganda favouring insurance to keep off the grass for the time being. I have written Olin West to quit putting out any counter propaganda, which I suppose they felt obliged to do in defence of their position. The less these differences of opinions come to be ventilated in the public press just now, the more likely we are, it seems to me, to get together and accomplish something with a united front.
>
> And if our sub-committee can engender as good feeling as we have somehow by good luck managed to start out with in our own group, and if we can get some mutual way of controlling what sort of propaganda is fairly to be let out for public consumption, we can get the people in general and the doctors in particular pulling our way even before we make our final recommendations. That at least is the way it looks to me. Much power to your elbow.

Immediately Cushing had had news of his appointment to the Medical Advisory Committee, he had sought advice from every well-informed source that came to mind, including the New York Academy of Medicine, the Rockefeller Foundation, and the League of Nations; he also corresponded with prominent individuals, liberal and conservative alike. In the Yale medical faculty he had the benefit of advice from C.-E. A. Winslow, who had long agitated for reform, John P. Peters, another zealous liberal; also from Stanhope Bayne-Jones, Francis G. Blake, Samuel C. Harvey, and others who were more conservative. In short, he took the duties of his new assignment most seriously, and from the correspondence and the ultimate recommendations of the committee, it is clear that Cushing did much to bring together the opposing factions. There can be no question that he succeeded to some extent in liberalizing the counter propaganda of the A.M.A. Mr. Sydenstricker was able in consequence to present a unanimous report to Secretary Perkins on 19 November, the text of which ran as follows:

I am requested by the Medical Advisory Board to transmit to you the following statement approved by all its members, namely, Doctors Walter L. Bierring, Rexwald Brown, James Deacon Bruce, George W. Crile, Harvey Cushing, Robert B. Greenough, J. Shelton Horsley, James Alexander Miller, Thomas Parran, Jr., George M. Piersol, and Stewart R. Roberts:

"The Medical Advisory Board, at its meetings on November 14th and 15th, took up for consideration the subject of medical care for persons of average or small means, which was referred to us by the President and the Committee on Economic Security. We recognize that heavy risks and losses are occasioned by sickness; that the expenses of sickness create a problem for many persons and the uncertainty and insufficiency of payment create insecurity for many physicians.

"In discussing these matters we have taken up three topics:

"First, *preventive measures:* A logical step in dealing with the risks and losses of sickness is to begin by preventing sickness so far as is possible by methods of demonstrated effectiveness. At the present time we believe that appropriations for public health work are insufficient in many communities, whereas a fuller application of modern preventive medicine, made possible by larger public appropriations, would not only relieve much suffering but would also prove an actual financial economy. Federal funds, expended through the several states in association with their own state and local public health expenditures, are, in our opinion, necessary to accomplish these purposes and we recommend that substantial grants be made.

"Second, *public medical care:* In addition to preventive services of health departments, a considerable amount of medical care now is furnished through taxation, particularly in the care of the insane and tuberculous, and in the medical services being furnished to the large proportion of the population on relief. Such tax support is, however, inadequate to meet even the minimum needs. We recommend federal action to assist and supplement local efforts to build rural hospitals in about 500 areas and mental and tuberculosis hospitals where needed as a part of the federal public works program. We recommend also the use of federal relief funds to supplement local funds to pay physicians for treatment of indigent patients in their homes and in clinics, to pay for hospitalization of such patients, to pay for health protection of relief clients, and in general to give assistance to states and localities in minimizing the hazard to economic security occasioned by illness among persons of small means and persons on relief.

"Third, *health insurance:* The insurance principle as a means of distributing the costs of sickness has been extensively utilized abroad and in a number of voluntary health insurance plans now in operation, though on a small or experimental scale, in this country. The subject is a complex one and requires the study of a considerable body of facts, some of which are now available and others which will shortly be secured. We would like, therefore, to avail ourselves of the suggestion which you made, that we might have more time for this survey than has been available during these few days; and will, if you desire, undertake the responsibility of pursuing the study and of giving you, as soon as we can, our findings and recommendations."

Having collected opinions from as many quarters as possible, Cushing decided also to offer a personal suggestion, which in retrospect seems highly constructive and which may sometime engage the attention of the nation, namely, that all the Federal health agencies be consolidated into a single department which would have a seat in the Cabinet. The letter conveying the recommendation (which went through many drafts) was sent directly to Mr. Roosevelt.

H.C. to President Roosevelt *10 November 1934.*

Dear Mr. President: May I venture to hand on to you a suggestion for what it may be worth? You are probably aware that there is a sharp difference of opinion between the American Medical Association representing the medical practitioners and the representatives of the Milbank Fund who are agitating and financing a movement for national sickness insurance. This being so, before Mr. Witte's Medical Advisory Committee gets deep in this tangled subject, would it not be a good move just at this time to take into consideration the establishment—if not of a governmental department—at least of a super-bureau of public health to coordinate a number of welfare agencies?

Such a department would naturally include such scattered interests as infant welfare and the Children's Bureau, old age insurance, possibly the matter of the veterans' hospitals and health compensation, vital statistics, the administration of the Food and Drugs Act, and the existent public health and marine hospital service.

I know that such a fusion would be difficult owing partly to inter-departmental jealousies, and particularly because of the fear lest the military officialdom of the Marine Hospital service group come to be generally introduced. But I am sure that opposition could be overcome and it certainly would mean a great saving of energy, prevent much duplication of work, and lead to a proper concentration of authority on subjects that have to do with public health. This is not infrequently an interstate matter as, for example, when Chicago dumped her sewage into the upper waters of the Mississippi River.

There will be difficulties about such a concentration, but you are accustomed to overcoming difficulties, and such a favourable opportunity as the present may not occur again. When the "Committee of One Hundred" some years ago broached such a proposal to Theodore Roosevelt, he admitted the importance of the project but said the time was not ripe for it. The time may be ripe for it now—or you may be able to ripen it, which amounts to the same thing. One difficulty is the proper man to head such a department. Welch could have done this admirably, to the satisfaction of all contending interests. Whether another such man could just now be found I am not sure, but the opportunity usually brings the necessary man to the surface.

There is an old adage of the operating room that suggestions spoil good surgery—that is, that the assistant is not supposed to draw a red herring across the operator's path while he is at work. Nevertheless I hand this suggestion on to you for what it is worth, thinking that you perhaps might mull it over when you are on your vacation. Could the organization of such a department or bureau be taken under consideration at this time, the discussion of this difficult project regarding sickness insurance might well be postponed until a department was in existence which could properly and permanently administer it.

Our common, not to say uncommon, grandchild arrived here last night for a brief sojourn and she is a fascinating child. Which of us is most responsible for this I will leave to others to decide.

In acknowledging this letter, Mr. Roosevelt indicated that he thought the time was still not ripe for a move so drastic.

The White House,
Franklin D. Roosevelt to H.C. *13 November 1934.*

Dear Harvey: I am glad that again your mind runs along with mine. I am giving much thought to the general consolidation of health and allied welfare organizations. Perhaps some day it will be a department, but I doubt if the time is wholly ripe. The difficulty is that, in the meantime, shuffling bureaus between existing departments raises much ruction.

All goes well here. I wish I had the same opportunity that you have to see our very uncommon grandchild. Love to you all, As ever yours, FRANKLIN D. ROOSEVELT.

The Medical Advisory Committee continued its deliberations well into 1935 and on 15 January Mr. Witte was able to forward to the President a final report which incorporated a few of the above-mentioned recommendations.[4] The publication of the report again caused a storm of protest from the A.M.A. and from individual physicians. A particularly interesting reaction came from a young British practitioner who had had first-hand experience with the operation of the British health insurance act:

Donal Sheehan to H.C. *16 January 1935.*

Dear Dr. Cushing, My father was a graduate of Edinburgh, and had a very busy general practice, largely among the poor, in Carlisle (60,000 population). He was a typical family doctor of the old type that is now rapidly disappearing in England since the introduction of the panel system. The practice is now conducted by my elder brother, and I understand they have about 3500 patients on their list. On account of the state insurance scheme, there is a much greater financial security than in my father's time. The work is, however, no longer one of medical attendance, but is chiefly clerical, filling out certificates and keeping records.

This I believe to be typical of most of the general practices in England today, *i.e.*, financial improvement and security but an intellectual demoralisation for the doctor, and a much greater but very questionably more efficient service for the patient. It is for this reason that most of the general practitioners are in favour of holding on to the state insurance scheme, a viewpoint that you will see often in the *British Medical Journal*.

I have done G.P. in England as a locum on many occasions, and it served to smash most of my illusions about the family physician as existent today. There is an enormous increase in semi-malingering, owing to the scheme, which is of

[4] *Report to the President of the Committee on Economic Security*. Washington, Government Printing Office, 1935, 53 pp.

course pandered to by the doctor. There is in addition a fabulous expenditure and waste on medicines, as every patient demands and gets a bottle of 'something' for the most trivial of ailments, and they come up for 'refills' week after week *ad nauseum.* All the druggists are therefore wholeheartedly behind the scheme. There is unquestionably a grave need for some sort of insurance of medical attendance for the poor, but under the present system there is a gross mismanagement of the funds available. Having made the assumption that all doctors must be thieves, the state has had to pay for hosts of other thieves to watch 'em!

The committee continued in active correspondence for five months and, on receiving a general communication from Cushing recommending further study, all but one signed the following letter to Witte (22 May 1935):

Dear Sir: We, the undersigned members of the Medical Advisory Board, have individually received under the date of April 5, 1935, the Preliminary Draft, drawn up and signed by Mr. Edgar Sydenstricker and Dr. I. S. Falk, of a "Report to the Committee on Economic Security on the Extension of Public Health and Public Medical Services and on Health Insurance."

At the first meeting of our Board in November 1934, Secretary Perkins expressed the hope that we might find ourselves in agreement in regard to a provision for medical services in the general program for social security. At that time, following a "Discussion of General Principles" by your Technical Staff, "abstracts" of the following subjects were presented for discussion: (1) a *Program for more Adequate Public Health Service;* (2) a *Program for the Extension of Public Medical Services;* (3) a *Program for Social Insurance against Illness.*

Over the desirability of the first two items we expressed agreement and found ourselves in accord with the proposals outlined. Accordingly, on the recommendation of the Technical Staff they were promptly included by the Committee on Economic Security in their Report to the President and are now incorporated in the Social Security Bill, H.R. 4120 as presented to Congress.

Before discussing the question of Health Insurance, the Committee asked for delay in order that representatives of the Technical Staff might meet with the Bureau of Medical Economics of the American Medical Association and be given an opportunity so far as possible to harmonize certain differences of opinion likely to arise in regard to some of the more debatable issues involved in the Program.

At our second meeting in January 1935, the details of a carefully prepared plan for health insurance were presented for discussion and the present "Preliminary Draft" now before us represents the interpretation of your Technical Staff of the general outcome of our deliberations. We fully realize with what painstaking industry these gentlemen not only drew up the original documents laid before us, but what a task was put upon them to prepare the present abbreviated draft of a report to be submitted on a stipulated date to the Committee of which you are the Executive Director. We however feel that the data on which the original Program was based were largely derived from the experience in foreign countries with plans for health and sickness insurance which, even after the elimination of many of their objectionable features, are not necessarily applicable to conditions in this country. Unquestionably, however, public interest in the subject has been awakened and, partly through our meetings, the medical profession has been aroused fully to sense their responsibilities in the matter.

At the present time, experience is being rapidly gained with various forms of health insurance not only in the United States but in Canada where the conditions are very similar, through the operation of various relief programs and voluntary plans for the better delivery of medical services to the different income groups. It is our opinion that the study and analysis of these experiments will soon provide information of the greatest value in solving the peculiar problems with which a workable plan for health insurance in this country finds itself involved. We therefore recommend that any Federal or State legislative action be deferred until these various experiences under different conditions in diverse localities can be suitably analysed and made available for the ultimate drawing up of a satisfactory plan adaptable to the needs of our people and acceptable both to them and to the medical profession.

We are fully sensible of the honor accorded us by an invitation to serve on the Medical Advisory Board and are appreciative of the consideration given to us at our meetings in Washington by you, Sir, as well as by the members of your Technical Staff, and we shall be glad at any future time to be of what assistance we may in the further consideration of plans to diminish through legislation the risks to the economic security of the people arising out of ill health.

The controversy continued both in the medical and the public press and pressure was such that Congress also tabled the bill. In 1946 through the Murray-Wagner-Dingell Bill compulsory health insurance is once more pending.

While agitating about compulsory health insurance Cushing was also occupying himself with correspondence on another, and to him a much more absorbing subject. During the spring and summer Edward Weeks of the Atlantic Monthly Press had induced Cushing to prepare a series of four articles based on his war journal. The first on "The Harvard Unit" appeared in the October *Atlantic,* the second on "The Battle of Boston Common," which caused lively comment, appeared in November. His folder of correspondence on these articles became almost as thick as that with Miss Perkins and the Medical Advisory Committee. Most Bostonians took it good-naturedly, some were highly entertained, but his more serious-minded friends on Beacon Hill felt that he was a renegade who had broken faith. The response to the *Atlantic* articles, however, encouraged him to expand them into his book (*From a surgeon's journal,* 1936) mentioned earlier.

On 28 December he delivered his presidential address before the History of Science Society on "The humanizing of science,"[5] in which his recent "social" thinking comes to the fore. Thus he says of Henry Wallace:

... People in general are unquestionably becoming more socially minded—that is, more "humanistic" in its broader sense—and this is everywhere reflected in

[5] *Science,* 8 February 1935, *81,* 137-143.

the governments that undertake, however feebly, to represent them. In a brilliant and courageous address just a year ago [*Science,* 5 January 1934] before the American Association for the Advancement of Science, that modern Cato, the present Secretary of Agriculture, challenged the assembled scientists and engineers to tell where they were heading; and lest Spengler prove to be right in his pessimistic prophecies, he appealed to them to bend their talents to higher human aims than the mere increase of productive power.

1935

During the first months of 1935 H.C. occupied himself with his war journal. It had been bound up in nine fat volumes of approximately a thousand pages each and while he extracted a good many entries bodily for the published volume, it is of some interest that he "edited" nearly every passage, now and again adding and subtracting—additions being made on the basis of other contemporary records. He was inclined to hold his own memory in contempt, and as a rule was over-conscientious about avoiding additions which could not be fully documented. The other changes were purely verbal, for H.C. continued till the end of his life dissatisfied with his own prose.

On 25 January the Cushing family were much relieved to learn of Richard Light's safe return to New York after his flight around the world. That same night H.C. entertained the Nathan Smith Club, an undergraduate society of medical historians, at his house. Herbert Thoms gave an entertaining account of the five physicians who signed the Declaration of Independence, and Cushing followed with a diverting paper on his seventeenth-century friend, Nicholas Culpeper, herb doctor and charlatan, who had interested H.C. because of the wide influence exerted by his nostrums. H.C. had always been intrigued by fantastic personalities, and Culpeper, as a self-confessed impostor, engaged his attention to such an extent that he brought together over the years 119 different editions of his various writings.

In February he again entertained Lucien Price who was most enthusiastically received at the Elizabethan Club where he had been invited to speak. The next day H.C. presented his Ercole Lelli paper once again, this time before a meeting of the Charaka Club, a group of physicians in New York who concern themselves with literature and history. During February and March he began to be more fit physically and he accordingly started to see patients again and to accede to requests for consultations. He also tried to do more in the way of teaching and meeting students, and on 5 March he addressed a crowded amphitheater of first- and second-year students on the history of the pituitary body from ancient to modern times. The meeting was so successful that he was later prevailed upon to present some of the same material before one of the advanced seminars in the department of physiology. On the 13th there was a meeting of the Yale Medical Society at which Harry Zimmerman (a colleague in Pathology), Louise Eisenhardt, and H.C. described their latest work on pituitary basophilism, H.C. giving a spirited presentation of his ideas concerning the relation of the pituitary body to hypertension. A contemporary letter sent to England gives further details:

> Zimmerman has cut serial sections of pituitaries in twenty-two cases of hypertension that have come to autopsy within the last year. He has cut similar sections of twenty-two miscellaneous cases with normal blood pressure. In all but four of the hypertensive group there was very marked basophilic infiltration of the posterior lobe and in each of the four, acute nephritis had been the cause of death (and evidently also of the hypertension). In the twenty-two miscellaneous cases there was not one of basophilic infiltration. I had no idea that Zimmerman had carried the work so far; in view of the striking fall in blood pressure which follows radiation of the pituitary, I am forced to believe that there is much more to the story than I had imagined a year ago, and H.C. may be vindicated in his belief that pituitary basophilism of this character is the essential pathology of the non-renal hypertension. There are still many gaps and inconsistencies but with all the cases recently reported in England (see the *Lancet* for 23 Feb.) I am inclined to agree, Thomas Lewis to the contrary notwithstanding.

One night in April H.C. had opportunity to reciprocate for some of the hospitality which he had enjoyed in Sweden. Professor and Mrs. Gunnar Nyström were travelling in America and the Cushings gave a dinner prior to Nyström's lecture before the Yale Medical Society. Following Swedish custom H.C. made an amusing speech about his guest, and Nyström, with characteristic Swedish grace, responded that H.C. emanated waves of positive and negative pressure—his positive pressure had sent students far and wide to carry his teaching to other lands on a plane higher than any ever before achieved by a surgeon, while his negative pressure had attracted students who came seeking the inspiration of his great example.

The National Academy of Sciences

Cushing's lively interest in the National Academy of Sciences and in its closely related organization, the National Research Council, has already been indicated. The Academy, like the Royal Society in England, is the nation's foremost scientific body, and Cushing nearly always made a point of attending its meetings. He went out of his way after Mr. Roosevelt went to the White House to point out to the President that the Academy, by virtue of Mr. Lincoln's executive order, is the official advisory body to the Federal government in all matters pertaining to science. Each year when the Academy held its annual meeting Cushing, through Miss LeHand, the President's personal secretary, or through James Roosevelt, saw to it that the President sent official greetings for the opening.

In 1934 the President, without seeking advice from the Academy, had appointed from the ranks of the National Research Council a Scientific Advisory Board to report on certain special problems then of interest to the Federal government, the Board to report directly back to the President without reference to the Academy. Certain members looked upon a board so authorized as an affront to the Academy itself and Cushing, having the ear of the White House, on two occasions was called on to intercede in its behalf. The President listened politely and sent his appreciative annual message to the Academy, but he seems to have been well satisfied with the report submitted through the National Research Council.

In April Cushing suddenly made up his mind to go to Washington. His loyalty to the Academy was probably in part responsible for this impulsive decision, but more particularly his desire to see his old friend, Thomas McCrae, who was seriously ill in Philadelphia. Since he felt unable to make the trip except by air, he requested Richard Light, then working as a research fellow in the department of surgery at Yale, to fly him there and back. The hazards of the flight seem to have caused him not the slightest concern.

Flying log of Richard Upjohn Light

April 21, 1935. Waco cabin, Continental engine. From New Haven to Camden, N.J. with Harvey Cushing, en route to the National Academy meetings. 1 hr. 30 min.

April 21, 1935. Camden to Washington. Harvey Cushing. Rain and light fog. 1 hr. 15 min.

April 22, 1935. Washington to New Haven. Harvey Cushing. Dark, New York to New Haven. 2 hr. 45 min.

Briefly, this was a week-end trip arranged at Dr. Cushing's insistence and against my better but unconvincing judgment. He called me about 10:00 o'clock on Sunday morning saying that he wanted to go to Washington right away, and could not manage on the trains with his lame leg. I replied that my airplane was at the factory being overhauled, and I would be unable to accommodate him. He suggested pointedly that another plane be chartered but I knew that the only available plane in New Haven was an ancient Waco which had seen too many hours of instruction. I once was an unhappy passenger in that aircraft when a professional airlines pilot was showing us some tricks of blind flying, in the midst of which the roof caved in, and I therefore bore no love for the ship, especially if it were to carry so precious a cargo as Dr. Cushing. Nothing I said made any difference, however, and the ship was chartered. I flew from the left-hand seat and H.C. sat beside me on the right. We reached Philadelphia without incident and he there called a halt so he might visit Dr. McCrae. While he went up to the hospital I journeyed down to New Castle (Delaware) for a visit to the Bellanca factory, but returned in time to take him on to Washington. On this leg of the flight the weather changed to rain and low clouds, and we flew in from Baltimore by following closely the railroad track, Dr. Cushing's head out the right window and mine out the left, because the windshield was opaque with streaming water. We finally found the little triangular strip that was then known as an airport [Washington], and I cut the engine back to land, but, instead of idling, the engine died and we were left with a deadstick landing.

We went to a hotel and H.C. picked up the phone to call the White House and said that we were coming up for tea. It proved to be one of the few occasions on which I had ever seen Dr. Cushing not wholly welcome. Apparently on this Easter Sunday plans had been made with some care and the impromptu arrangement did not please his hostess. It was otherwise an interesting time, however. Mr. Roosevelt came in and turned the talk to aviation, explaining that Pan American Airways were forced to open their overseas service in the Pacific because the British would not grant an American company operational bases in the Atlantic (Bermuda and the British-controlled Portuguese Azores, etc.). That subject interested me, but the Chief moped then, and more later on at the hotel, over what he thought was a pretty chilly reception by an 'in-law.'

The National Academy meetings began the next day and we attended. There was a paper by a Cornell geneticist [Stockard], illustrated with movies, showing his dog crossbreeds, all of them freaks. The Chief remarked that this was a magnificent exhibition of the power of the pituitary. Lunch with MacCallum and Isaiah Bowman. Then, fully aware of the character of my passenger, I made it plain that if he wanted to return to New Haven that afternoon we must depart for the airport not later than 2:00 o'clock. It was agreed. At 2:00 we left the lecture room, hailed a cab and set forth to pick up the luggage on the way. As we drove, the Chief quizzed me on my knowledge of the city and asked if I had ever visited the Folger Library. I was watching the sky, thinking of the weather and the hours of daylight left for the flight to New Haven and, without thinking, said no, I had never seen the Folger. Promptly he instructed the driver to turn around and go to the library, and for two hours I was shown through the great Shakespeare collection with all the care and charm of which Dr. Cushing was capable, all the while watching with heavy heart and deep foreboding the darkening of the sky and disappearance of the afternoon. It was nearly dusk when we finally took off. The battery and the lighting system were dead, we were caught again by rain, darkness was total from New York on, and the engine quit in the air over the New Haven airport. I doubt, however, if the Chief was even remotely concerned about the pilot's troubles, and he seemed amused, if anything, to have got us in such a spot.

In April Cushing was much distressed to learn almost simultaneously of the deaths of Fielding Garrison and Sir Edward Sharpey-Schafer. Of the former he wrote to Klebs:

. . . I hope you will write something about Garrison, for no one could do it better. I happened to be reading his obituary note in the April number of Archie's *Bulletin* [of the New York Academy of Medicine] about poor Ruhräh, an excellently written note in Fielding's best style. It's sad that he should have come so soon to follow on himself into a better and less troubled world. A unique personality he was and, as you say, he leaves a gap that cannot be filled. I have had Miss Stanton get together what letters she could, for they certainly ought to be kept for our historical collection. Somewhere I have a photograph he gave me of a scene in the old library with Fletcher at the desk and Fielding sitting up on a stool in a distant corner looking like a little errand boy waiting for orders.

YALE MEMBERS OF THE NATIONAL ACADEMY OF SCIENCES

Standing: W. R. Miles, Y. Henderson, C. L. Hull, C. R. Longwell, L. L. Woodruff, F. Schlesinger. *Seated:* H. Cushing, R. Dodge, C. Schuchert, R. H. Chittenden, J. R. Angell, E. W. Brown. From a photograph taken 1 June 1936; courtesy of Dr. Walter R. Miles

LISTENING TO A PAPER AT THE BEAUMONT CLUB
H.C. is seated at front center

"LULU" AND H.C.
At the Yale School of Medicine in May 1935

H.C. AFTER HIS OXFORD DEGREE
What next? An intimate study by Hugh Sinclair of Magdalen College

H.C. AND SIR CHARLES SHERRINGTON
Caught by Arnold Klebs' camera at the Royal College of Surgeons on 12 July 1938

DOCTOR OF SCIENCE, OXFORD 1938

A photograph of the distinguished group which gathered at Balliol College on 16 July to do Cushing honor. H.C. is seated third from right. The lettering is by H.C.

The first week in May was taken up with the fourth annual meeting of the Harvey Cushing Society, which met on the 1st in New Haven where they were entertained by Dr. and Mrs. Cushing at a buffet supper. The next day H.C. presented an account of pituitary basophilism and Louise Eisenhardt introduced the Society to the Brain Tumor Registry. At a dinner on the 2nd Richard Light gave an illustrated account of his flight around the world during the preceding summer. Throughout the two days of the meeting H.C. took an active part in all the sessions and appeared much gratified by the enthusiasm evident in the group.

On 9 May a large dinner was given in his honor by the National Institute of Social Sciences in the course of which, along with Senator Carter Glass, he was awarded the Institute's gold medal. The presentation was made by Willard C. Rappleye who spoke of Cushing as one of a long line of physicians—"a true son of Aesculapius," who had been awarded the gold medal "in recognition of your distinguished contributions to modern medicine and your contributions to science and literature." In accepting the medal Cushing had a good opportunity to say what he felt about the pending social legislation. After expressing his thanks he proceeded first in a light vein, but then continued:

> It has been said by an experienced student of the subject, in a country where comprehensive social programs have long been in operation, that unemployment insurance destroys the incentive to find work; that accident insurance weakens the natural desire for recovery; that old age insurance removes one of the prime motives for thrift. One need not be a psychologist to understand how these essentially normal human reactions may serve disappointingly to offset the expected benefit of the legislative acts.
>
> Compulsory sickness insurance is just now being strongly urged by an influential group of people who look upon such a program on a national scale as one of the most urgent of present-day needs. Health officials and social workers, generally speaking, show enthusiasm for the proposal, but most medical practitioners apprehend that the degree of socialization of the profession necessary to carry out any such legislation will defeat its very purpose, for a less desirable body of candidates will be tempted to study medicine with the consequence that the quality of medical service will certainly deteriorate. You will see how difficult these problems are and how they engender honest differences of opinion.

Connecticut was first settled in 1635 and the tercentenary year likewise marked the 150th anniversary of the birth of William Beaumont, the centenary of whose book on the gastric juice had been observed two years previously. Beaumont had been born in the village of Lebanon, Connecticut and, since a large state highway through the town was nearing completion, a part of the state's observance of its anniversary consisted of the dedication by Governor Cross of the new road as "The Beaumont Memorial Highway." This was followed by exercises in the church on Lebanon Green, at which Cushing delivered the principal address. Russell Chittenden (then in his eightieth year) presided at the ceremony. Cushing's address on Beaumont,[6] given from the pulpit, was both moving and illuminating, and the introduction was well attuned to the ecclesiastical surroundings:

> There migrated from England in 1635, to settle five years later at Saybrook, in John Winthrop's new colony, a certain William Beaumont of Huguenot descent. His grandson of the same name left Saybrook a century later and moved to what was known as "The Purchase," a parcel of land bought by four proprietors from Owaneco, son of Uncas, first Sachem of the Mohicans.
>
> Included in this purchase was the present town of Lebanon at whose historic village center—known as "Town-street" and scarcely altered by the passage of time—we are now assembled. And near here, just one hundred and fifty years ago, this second William's grandson, yet another William Beaumont, was born in the farmhouse still standing on Village-hill, a short distance off the road that runs in the direction of Willimantic from the northern point of the generous "Commons," which "Town-street" splits to enclose.
>
> Thus five generations of Beaumonts appear in minor parts on the Connecticut scene, marry, beget children, and are gone, leaving little behind them other than the bare record of their separate entrances and exits. They were doubtless rugged, devout, and law-abiding people who differed no whit from many others who managed in Colonial days to harvest a precarious sustenance from the hillsides and from between the boulders that stud Connecticut's glacial soil. The peculiar disposition of the heavens as seen from Village-hill on the twenty-first of November 1785, when (as the third child in a family of nine) the last of these William Beaumonts came into the world is unrecorded. . . .

He then told how Beaumont had gone forth from the village as a mere lad and how through the development of his native talents, particularly his powers of observation, he had become the most widely known physiologist of his day.

Following the exercises Cushing, Chittenden, and others paid a visit to the farmhouse, three miles away from the village, where Beaumont was born. Then George Dudley Seymour, the distinguished Connecticut historian, took the group to his house at South Coventry, the birthplace of Nathan Hale where, with Ross G. Harrison and other members of the Beaumont Club, they paid their homage to the great American patriot by sipping tea from a service that had once been his. Pilgrimages such as these to places filled with the spirit of men whom history has called great testified to Cushing's reverence for the past, whence came much of his inspiration. Although he devoted his life to relieving suffering, he was never, in the common interpretation, a religious man. He almost always spent Sunday at his desk and rarely attended religious services save for weddings and funerals. But he was profoundly stirred and influenced by the lives of men who had dedicated themselves to serving their

[6] "William Beaumont's rendezvous with fame." *Yale Journal of Biology and Medicine*, December 1935, *8*, 113-126.

fellows—wherever and in whatever field they had cast their lot. His religious philosophy, if it can be so characterized, is well delineated in George Eliot's inspired lines:

> O may I join the choir invisible
> Of those immortal dead who live again
> In minds made better by their presence: live
> In pulses stirred to generosity,
> In deeds of daring rectitude, in scorn
> For miserable aims that end with self,
> In thoughts sublime that pierce the night like stars,
> And with their mild persistence urge man's search
> To vaster issues—

* * * * *

During June there was a series of conferences about plans for the new Medical Library held jointly with Mr. Atterbury, Dean Winternitz, and Mr. Thomas W. Farnam, Treasurer of the University and Chairman of the University's building committee. These sessions were promptly followed by letters to Klebs reporting on latest book purchases and the progress of building plans (28 June):

> You will remember in that last Goldschmidt catalogue you marked a Luca Paccioli, *Divina Proportione,* Venice 1509, as an important book. I have just had a catalogue from Rappaport in which he quotes a 1494 edition which I assume is the same book, or at least contains the *Divina proportione.* Please let me know which you think is the more important, or whether you thought only the 1509 Italian edition was important. Goldschmidt wanted £85 for it, and the Rappaport volume is earlier and cheaper. Smith gives it as the first edition, quoting another, Toscolano 1523, but he does not mention this 1509 Italian edition.
>
> I am sending you a copy of a screed just received from Grosvenor Atterbury showing that his mind is at work on our problem. I wrote to say that I could tell better when I saw where the building [or buildings] was to go on the lot. He evidently is mulling over the idea of having some of our personal memorabilia hanging around, which I of course would like; but whether he can work any such thing out, I can't foresee.

The Army Medical Library

When writing papers in his Baltimore days Cushing frequently went to Washington to spend a day in the Army Medical Library. Through these visits he had come to know Robert Fletcher and his assistant, Fielding Garrison. He was fascinated by seeing the *Index-Catalogue* in the course of preparation, and in time he began to take a keen personal interest in the future of the Library. Realizing that its facilities were badly outmoded, that the books were deteriorating since they were frequently soaked whenever the roof leaked, he began, as early as 1933 (probably even before), to back the Surgeon General in agitating for a new building. The War Department in those days had had its appropriations cut to the vanishing point, and there seemed little hope of increasing the appropriation for the library or of obtaining government funds for the erection of a new building. Soon after Mr. Roosevelt went into the White House Cushing brought the question of the new building to the President's attention. Thus he wrote to F.D.R. on 21 August 1933:

Dear "Governor": . . . You of course know all about the Surgeon-General's Library, for which John S. Billings was originally responsible. It is the only great medical Library in the world, and the *Index Medicus* and the *Index-Catalogue* are probably more widely used throughout the world than any other medical books which have ever been published since the book of Isaiah. . . . The question of what to do with the Library in the future, for it will have to be moved away from the present site soon, has been a problem long agitated. . . .

Mr. Roosevelt was obviously interested, but the next spring he was forced to reply in the negative to Cushing's first appeal:

F.D.R. to H.C. *9 May 1934.*

My dear Dr. Cushing: I have your letter of April 25 reminding me, as you did a year ago, that the Government can be of service to the united medical profession by properly housing the Surgeon General's Library and Museum. I agree that the facts as they are subdivided in your letter undoubtedly are well taken and that this Library and Museum could be considered as strictly utilitarian. The question naturally arises, however, as to the wisdom of asking for $2,000,000 for an expenditure of this kind at this time. If surplus monies were available, I would have no hesitancy in endorsing the request. Insofar as plans and specifications are concerned, I find none has been prepared. The estimated cost of $2,000,000 is more or less tentative and the plans have never exceeded the sketch stage. The project could be placed on a preferred list should surplus monies become available for work of this kind. However, as matters stand today relative to the building program for the District of Columbia, it does not appear that we could include it in the present-day comprehensive plan. Sincerely yours, FRANKLIN D. ROOSEVELT.

Inserted in this letter was a handwritten note which read: "H.C. The above is the 'official' answer—all the same I am going to try to get that building started next year! F.D.R." Later in the year there was further discouraging news:

F.D.R. to H.C. *25 August 1934.*

Dear Harvey: The situation in regard to the building for the Surgeon General's Library is this. We are all tremendously keen about a new building for it. However, out of Public Works funds we must keep the District of Columbia somewhere within a reasonable ratio of expenditures compared with population, remembering that these Public Works appropriations are primarily to relieve unemployment. We have to consider the most pressing needs first and, therefore, have allocated this year enough money for a) One new building to take care of actual Government workers; b) A new sewage disposal plant, very much needed, as my nose on River trips testifies; c) A T.B. sanitarium to meet a serious T.B. situation; d) A stack room to take care of important current documents.

These projects all put together exceed what should be the District's quota by about 100%. Therefore, with much reluctance, I have to put the Surgeon General's Library building over to another year. . . . As ever yours, F.D.R.

The original plan had been to erect a new building in the vicinity of the Walter Reed Hospital, where the Army had developed a medical center some five or six miles away from central Washington. In 1935, however, it became clear to the Surgeon General's Office that the Library would be at a disadvantage if away from the center of town, and a plan was evolved to erect the new Army Medical Library building on Capitol Hill in close proximity to the Library of Congress. Since the Army Medical Library is the greatest collection ever brought together in the field of medicine in any country, it was felt that the collection should be regarded as something of a national monument, which would be strengthened so as to become in fact *the* national medical library. The Library of Congress was rapidly outgrowing its available shelf space and if the Army Medical Library could be placed in physical proximity, the medical holdings of the two collections could be consolidated. All this appealed strongly to Cushing and once again he turned to F.D.R. This time Mr. Roosevelt replied: "I am delighted to know of that new suggestion in regard to the Army Medical Library [placing of building on Capitol Hill]. We might even add another story to the new [L.C.] Annex and architect [*sic*] it to look like a pillbox."

Cushing's gentle persistence continued. Thus the following year he wrote:

H.C. to F.D.R. *21 August 1936.*

Dear Franklin: Knowing that you have much to do, I will be brief. I am informed by the Surgeon-General that preparations are on foot to celebrate the centenary of the founding of the Surgeon-General's Library sometime in November. He has asked me to deliver an address on the occasion; but my brain being not much better than my legs these days, I felt obliged to decline, and suggested that some distinguished foreign medicos be invited to come and take part in the ceremonies.

This recalls to me that two years ago the present urgent needs of the Library were brought to your attention and the desirability of moving it from its present site to that long allocated for the purpose near the Walter Reed Hospital. You kindly replied, explaining why it was impossible to allocate funds at the time, but enclosed a pencilled note to the effect that you would bear it in mind and strike when the circumstances were more favourable.

Could you possibly find the ways and means now, there would be abundant reason to celebrate this 100th anniversary of the Library's foundation, either by starting the evacuation for the new building or even possibly actually laying its cornerstone. The occasion would be doubly worth celebrating should it more or less coincide with the beginning of your second term of office, about which I haven't the slightest manner of doubt. Always affectionately yours, H.C.

To this F.D.R. sent a goodnatured reply:

F.D.R. to H.C. *25 August 1936.*

Dear Harvey: I wish I were the dictator you assume me to be! I most assuredly do want to get the proper housing for the Surgeon General's Library started but it must be a monumental building and cannot be done out of Work Relief funds: therefore, it will require an Act of Congress. We have had such demands for office space these two years that all special buildings of this type have been deferred. I hope much, however, that the next Congress, either at the first or second session, will authorize it.

Perhaps I could say as much as this at least when the Centenary takes place in November. As ever, F.D.R.

Meanwhile Cushing had been corresponding, first with Surgeon General R. U. Patterson, and later with Major General C. R. Reynolds, but prior to 7 December 1941 Congress was in no mood to do anything for the War Department, be it a library that was wanted or a military installation.

* * * * *

During the summer of 1935 Cushing's correspondence with Arnold Klebs reached a high point, both in interest and in volume, and one can reconstruct the interval from July, when Klebs returned to Switzerland, until December through excerpts from the letters that went at frequent intervals from New Haven to Les Terrasses. These letters, incidentally, indicate something of the wealth of bibliographical information which was passing back and forth between the two collectors. Klebs at this time was attempting to complete his annotated catalogue of medical and scientific incunabula, but unfortunately did not live to see its publication. As with the Vesalius Bio-bibliography, a heavy responsibility falls on his literary executors.

25 July 1935. It's been a sad place since your departure. . . . I suppose you are back at work with your nose to the grindstone, but nevertheless I shall interrupt you long enough to ask something about the *Opera* of Flavius Josephus, edited by Hieronymus Squarzaficus (Venice, Joannes Rubeus Vercellensis, 1486) which Mr. Chittenden [son of Dr. Arthur S. Chittenden] proposes to send on to me for inspection and for which he asks $75. I don't know the book, but it's all right with me if you say the word.

12 August. I have neglected you of late—the chief reason being that I am just now pressed by Mr. Weeks to give him MS. of that journal [*From a surgeon's journal*] which he proposes to get out sometime this autumn. It's been quite a chore—chiefly on Miss Stanton's part. I hope it will prove as readable as friend Weeks seems to think it is going to be.

But my reason for inflicting you at the moment is that there has just arrived from Rappaport the *Summa de arithmetica* of Paccioli which you recommended to me and concerning which you wrote me a delightful letter on July 1st which settled the matter so far as I was concerned. Rappaport has come down ten per cent on his price at my solicitation and the book is a perfect beauty, in grand condition and with a most marvelous frontispiece following eight preliminary leaves of dedication, epistle, summary and index, the colophon being on the verso of the first of these leaves. It is unquestionably a great book.

Goldschmidt is also sending the *Divina proportione* so that they can be together, for you say they are key books.

Much has been going on here during this month. We have had a new bookcase built in my office and it is already nearly filled up with books from Chittenden and other sources. I have brought all the Harveys down to give me more room at home, and have never had a chance to show them together before or, indeed, to find individual ones when I wanted them. . . . Atterbury turned up a few days after you sailed so as to catch Keogh before he went on his vacation. They had a long pow-wow together. They seem to be in unanimity and I must say that G.A.'s plans for the rare book room are simply ripping. . . .

31 August. . . . John brought me the plan for your shelves—admirable! You should have been an architect. I shall send it on instanter to Atterbury for it will give him exactly the sort of information he wants. You have enough to fill the entire rare book room building, and I hope I may see you there some day in it and surrounded by your books in the way you want to have them. But all this must wait for your *magnum opus* in which I suppose by now you are beginning to resaturate yourself—all the better for having had a change of scene.

The reprint of your prophetic essay read on December 8, 1913 at the J.H.H. has come safely and I read it, as I must have done once before without fully appreciating its significance and worth—read it, I say with a great thrill. It couldn't possibly be better, and I shall be passing it around among some of your new-found friends here to let them see what sort of person you are and what your interest in Yale and in our present project will mean to the institution. . . .

That man Erik Waller is always getting ahead of us. Still, two years ago before our tripartite program developed, I wasn't so keen on incunabula as I am now through the hope of getting a sufficient number of good things to illustrate your bibliography. If you think Spaeth still has that Algorithmus collection, we might touch him up for it. . . .

4 October. So much to say to you, and so little time in which to say it. We are having a very hectic time here with the opening of the autumn term and many visitors. Cairns, for instance, is here for a two weeks' period working in the Tumor Registry to get out an eight-year end-result on his series of cases. Meanwhile, he is enjoying the place, I think, and doing much the sort of thing you did, meeting people and going to the colleges and getting generally acquainted.

From all I can make out, he holds a very strong position in London, and whether or not he will go to the National Hospital where the neurologists still look scornfully on the neurosurgeons, I am not quite sure. The Rockefeller people have made them a large gift which they are to duplicate, which means a renovation of the whole place and operating rooms and for the first time in their history some private beds. . . .

Isn't this Italian-Ethiopian mess a beastly business! Everyone here very much excited about it and about the question of sanctions. Whether they will ever be able to pull this off and make something of the League at this late date Heaven only knows but you are right in the midst of it yourself and you probably hear more first-hand talk regarding it than we do. . . .

26 October. . . . And then I have bought from Davis & Orioli a Sacrobosco MS. signed and dated a year or two before the first printed edition. It also has some material in it that does not appear in the printed edition and a number of diagrams which I at least don't find in my copy. So that will strengthen our astronomical books and give me something to show to Hubble who is here giving the Silliman Lectures and who is coming in this afternoon to see my astronomical books. I wish you were here to tell him about them; but I shall begin with the Euclid and then the Serlinger copy of *Regiomontanus* and my few Galileos, Tychos, the Copernicus, one or two Keplers and so on, which will, I hope, interest him.

You mentioned having a visit from Erik Waller who is an ardent collector. I think I must have written you already about the Canano, for my copy had the same watermarks that you had so carefully drawn out from his copy; so there is no question of these being facsimiled copies. But I think our counts of the number of existent copies do not agree. Anyhow, I can't tell you about this at the moment for I must have left them at home in my own book.

7 November. . . . Forgive this long, and I fear somewhat confused letter. Miss Stanton and I are busy checking up on the proof of the war journal which we have persuaded the Press to set up again throughout. Their first lot of galleys was so poor we registered a strong protest. There turns up a letter from Rappaport with some incunabula quotations. Do look them over and check them as important or unimportant. I take it for granted that you know pretty well what I have. I hate to bother you about this and don't like to run any risk of dragging your nose away from your own grindstone. . . .

21 November. . . . I am sorry to have bought Kircher's *Peste,* Rome 1658, but I suppose it is inevitable that we will have more or less overlaps; and some day in the distant future we can have a sale of our duplicates, of which I fear I may have a good many in my own shelves. Possibly next summer I can get Keogh to loan someone to me to make a check-list of what books I may have, for the only lot which I have properly catalogued so that I can tell where I stand are the Vesalian things, and now the list of incunabula, thanks to you, and another list of "near incunabula" which I am gradually building up. . . .

7 December. . . . I glanced over Carrel's book when it was first sent to me by the publishers asking me if I would review it. Indeed, I think they telephoned me and asked me if I would review it before I had even seen it. I said *no.* . . . In a long account in *Time,* it was rather damned with faint praise and the statement made that if he had not made an alliance with Lindbergh, no one would ever have known who he was. What I made out of it from my casual turning of the pages was that it was the sort of book a man might be tempted to write when he reaches our age of maturity, but he had much better resist the temptation.

16 December. Your letters both inside and out are always interesting. If only a corner of an envelope protrudes from the morning mail, I can promptly identify it as from you, and the rest of the mail goes pronto by the board. Here is yours of December 6th with a long row of Swiss stamps ending up with a sturdy-looking burgher named Stefano Franscini and your directions, "Voie de Cherbourg par *SS. Europa.*"

I knew nothing of Collenuccio and of the importance of his book; and in view of what you say about it I would have no hesitation in giving him the *ca.* $300 which I believe 1600 Austrian shillings represents. So I hope by this time you will have closed with him and have asked him to send the book on to you to use as long as you want. Still, you evidently know all about it and may not care to be bothered with receiving and trans-shipping it. I suppose I might have known enough to look him up in Thorndike, and I shall promptly do so. . . .

23 December. . . . You speak about the sale of the Bonnet books which some day you will tell me about. And you also speak about your first herbal bibliography which I am sure I have never seen and knew nothing about. . . .

So now that I am going in for herbals so suddenly, perhaps you had better send me a copy for my guidance, that is if you have one to spare. If you haven't one to spare, don't bother and I will send Stanton over to steal John's copy without his knowledge.

In November Cushing's health took a sudden turn for the worse. The family had a new cook with a weakness for pepper and other condiments which again precipitated H.C.'s ulcer symptoms; it is of some interest physiologically that when his gastric pain returned he began at the same time to have trouble with the circulation in his feet, for pain, whatever the source, causes small vessels in many parts of the body to contract. During November and December the pain in his left foot became steadily worse. On 28 November James White of Boston was called in consultation about interrupting the sympathetic nerve supply to his legs, and a few days later Gilbert Horrax and John Homans consulted with Ashley Oughterson, who was in charge of H.C., about amputating the foot or the toes. On 8 December they temporized, and Oughterson and Samuel Harvey severed the nerve supply of his gangrenous left middle toe under local anesthesia: H.C., supporting himself on his elbows, looked on over the drapes while the surgeons uneasily attempted to find the tiny nerve twigs. He thoroughly enjoyed the operation; it gave him satisfaction to watch his colleagues in their capacity of worried surgeons and also it was the first time in some weeks that his toe had not been a source of excruciating pain. Although the nerve section improved things considerably, it did not save the toe, and by the first of January 1936 the main part of the ulceration was coagulated with the Bovie unit. By the 8th it was clear that the toe must come off, and this time Oughterson saw to it that H.C. had a general anesthetic. Considering the fact that circulation was very poor in the entire extremity, it was a tribute to Oughterson's surgical skill that not only did the wound heal almost invisibly by primary intention, but the other toes, which were near ulceration, promptly healed.

1936

Cushing was much heartened on New Year's Day by a ten-minute telephone call from President Roosevelt who, on learning of his hospitalization, thus sought to send him a word of cheer. He remained in hospital throughout the month, but was in far better spirits than he had been during his previous illness. Since he had now learned at first hand something of the hazards of a Sippy diet, he was soon able, by cutting down his smoking and avoiding condiments, to continue on a well-balanced diet without adding Sippy avitaminosis to his difficulties.

His cheerful missives to Klebs began again on 11 January. "I have suddenly come out of my chrysalis this morning, doubly conscious that I am in arrears with you because in the morning's mail there are several Swiss letters, together with a large envelope from the White House, unmistakably not from you, and looking like the sort of invitation handed out in Alice's adventures in Wonderland." The communication in question from the White House was not an invitation, but rather one of F.D.R.'s more amusing references to his encrusted friends in Wall Street:

F.D.R. to H.C. *The White House,*
[Marked "Private!" in F.D.R.'s hand at the top] *8 January 1936.*

Dear Harvey: I am glad that you both chortled over the speech. I wish you could read some of the comments from my friends in New York City, whom I call "fat cats." Did you ever see a "fat cat" having a fit? Not even a good veterinarian [underlined with pen] like you could cure one. The highest type of brain surgery has been tried on "fat cats" but it only makes them "fittier." Nevertheless, I think the country will survive. Very sincerely yours, FRANKLIN D. ROOSEVELT.

By the 17th H.C. had recovered sufficiently to receive friends in the hospital, and Dr. E. P. Goldschmidt, the scholarly London bookseller, descended with his usual array of early manuscripts and incunabula. On the next day came Professor Bernard Houssay, the physiologist of the Argentine, who for many years had followed Cushing's work on the pituitary with profound interest. H.C. at this time was distressed by the news of Rudyard Kipling's death, for he had always admired him and had exchanged letters with him on several occasions. And H.C. frequently told the story of having heard him address a student audience in London extemporaneously, so it appeared, and seemingly with no effort. When he asked Mr. Kipling afterwards how he managed to speak in such a finished manner so easily, Kipling replied that he had worked on the address for a month, and had delivered it at least fifteen times from memory; he then withdrew from his pocket the manuscript which he forthwith turned over to a reporter from the *British Medical Journal.*

By 6 February H.C. was home again after eight weeks in hospital. He spent the first month at home annotating his books and dispatching an occasional bibliographical enquiry to Klebs. In one of them he made an interesting comment on Santayana:

. . . You want to know what I thought about *The last Puritan.* It is so long since I have read it I have almost forgotten. What is more, I read it rapidly in large blocks, whereas Santayana told Elsie that it should be read only a paragraph or two a day to get what he really meant out of it.

It seemed to me that the book was more revealing about Santayana than it was about the last Puritan. And I wondered whether if he had written it before he was appointed Professor of Philosophy at Harvard, he would ever have been appointed; or to put it another way, if the Harvard Corporation could have foreseen that he would write this novel twenty-five years after leaving Harvard, would they have hesitated to take him on the Faculty? . . .

News of Pavlov's death came in March and H.C. promptly set down a series of interesting anecdotes:[7]

Having saved enough of his Nobel Prize to pay for a trip to America, Pavlov, accompanied by one of his sons, made his first visit here not long after the war. Landing in New York, they found their way to the Grand Central Station, purchased tickets to Boston and boarded a train on which Pavlov was promptly and deftly separated, at the point of a revolver, from his pocketbook containing what was left of his prize money. On reaching Boston quite penniless, he remarked that the U.S.A. was apparently a more dangerous place in which to travel than the U.S.S.R.; he at least had never been robbed there.

During that visit he made warm friends, all of whom rejoiced when in 1929 he again came to America to attend the International Physiological Congress On that occasion other aged congressists of great distinction gathered in Boston—Hans Horst Meyer of Vienna, for example—but the octogenarian Pavlov appeared unaware of his years. He was not only acclaimed the most notable figure of that great assemblage but he proved in fact to be the most eager and untiring participant in the long-drawn-out program that had been arranged for it. . . .

Cushing's first public appearance after his illness was on 22 March, when he attended a farewell dinner for Charles Best, the Toronto physiologist who had participated in the discovery of insulin. Best had been spending a month in New Haven as a visiting lecturer, and H.C. had always been particularly drawn to him because of his simplicity, directness, and scientific acumen.

Literary interests during the spring of 1936 came to be centered upon his bibliography of Galvani on animal electricity, and as a preface to it he wrote a particularly attractive appreciation of the great Italian physiologist, and of his wife Lucia, which was published in July 1936.[8] He also occupied himself during these months of limited activity by putting out an eight-page list of *corrigenda* to the Osler biography.

In the previous December H.C. had been saddened by the death of his classmate and colleague, Lafayette Mendel. A memorial service was held in the University on 16 April 1936 and Cushing, feeling unable to attend, sent a letter which was read by Frederic Walcott, another member of the Class of '91. The dignified service was relieved by their intimate reminiscences—Walcott recalled Mendel's remark that Moses, an ancestor of his, was the greatest public health officer in history for he had taken ten thousand people through tempest and flood without an epidemic; H.C. described Mendel's early career at Yale:

[7] "Ivan Pavlov." *Soviet Russia Today* (New York), April 1936, p. 9.

[8] "A bibliographical study of the Galvani and the Aldini writings on animal electricity." *Annals of Science*, July 1936, *1*, 239-268.

I first came into close contact with "Laffy," as he was familiarly known to us, in junior year when those few of us who were thinking of going into medicine took the course in physiological chemistry that was offered in Sheff by Professor Chittenden. A famous little textbook on elementary physiology written by Thomas H. Huxley and his pupil, Newell Martin, was first put before us; and the next year, those who survived this test progressed into a practical course held in a chemical laboratory set up in what was once the parlor, I believe, of the old Sheffield residence on Hillhouse Avenue. Physiological chemistry—something quite new in this country—was taught with great enthusiasm by a man who a few years before had returned from Heidelberg where he had so distinguished himself that when I visited there in 1900 just twenty years later, I was solemnly shown as a holy place the corner in Kühne's laboratory where he had worked. This course in the Sheffield Scientific School was already coming to be looked upon by Yale undergraduates as the only possible highroad to medicine. In our senior year we found Joslin of the class ahead of ours acting as a graduate instructor; and so in turn from our little group Professor Chittenden with his unerring flair for worthwhile pupils singled out Laffy to remain for postgraduate study. Ere long he won his Ph.D. and this was followed by two years more as an Instructor and then by two years abroad, chiefly with Heidenhain in Breslau, after which he returned to be made an Assistant Professor and to start out upon his thirty-eight years as a productive scientist and faithful servant of his Alma Mater. . . .

The man who blazes the way for others should theoretically share the credit of a great discovery, but scientists aware that each one merely stands on the shoulders of some predecessor do not so look upon the matter and full credit is accorded to the single individual who first arrives. Had this not been so, Mendel might well enough have been a Nobel laureate, or at least have shared in the Prize. But he had ample reward as it was in the knowledge that he had continued to add lustre to a department in the University which was one of the first in the country to be established and which was for half a century the principal contributor to those carefully controlled studies of nutrition that are the basis of our national dietary and more than any other factor serve to explain why the present college undergraduate on the average is considerably healthier, taller and heavier than he was in our day.

Two days later *From a surgeon's journal* was published, and for the next month he was largely occupied with the correspondence which followed. He enjoyed seeing the reviews (all of which were more laudatory than could have been anticipated) particularly that of Lucien Price which had appeared on 26 April in the *Boston Sunday Globe:*

An eminent surgeon who is also a distinguished man of letters, writing on scraps of paper often at 2.30 a.m. after days of operating on war wounded at the Western Front, has produced a work of literature unique of its kind. As a panorama of war it is Homeric; every sort of human being is seen vividly, from common soldier to high command, from peasant to pundit, from prisoner to royalty. Its scenes range from great battles watched from strategic heights to college halls in Oxford and Dublin, from dugouts to London town houses and French châteaux. Everything interests this man of science, from the comically pathetic flower garden planted round his tent by his predecessor to the unselfconscious narratives of modest heroes who told him their stories while he extracted shrapnel from their brains under local anaesthesia.

By the end of May, however, he had begun to forget about the book. He urged Klebs not to review it, fearing that the outspoken comments about the Germans might arouse in Klebs some of the old unrest that his German origin had caused him to experience while the war was going on. H.C. added, "I have almost forgotten about the book already and when young medicos appear with copies in which I am to inscribe my name, I sometimes wonder how it ever came to be printed—much less written during those days which I hope we may never see again." In this interesting letter to Klebs there is also a modest confession about his own educational shortcomings:

> . . . I wonder how Putti really feels about the new Roman Empire. I screwed up my courage to write him a few days ago, but it was about Ercole Lelli and whether he would kindly look over my paper written several years ago after my return from Cortina with that large roll in hand. Archie wants it for the Charaka Club volume, but my knowledge of Italian is so limited I don't know how even to spell proper names—whether Aldrovandi, Aldrovando or Aldrovandus-a-um is correct. . . . I become more and more conscious of the awful gaps in my education as the days go by and wonder how I've ever dared to write books. But then of course they go through the hands of a conscientious secretary and through hands of proofreaders galore. Councilman once said he wouldn't give a tinker's damn for a man who couldn't s-spell a w-word more than o-one way. But Counce didn't care a hang for the opinion of others, and I'm afraid I do, even as you make every effort to be sure no errors, even typographical, will slip into your magnum opus, lest some Mackallian bibliographer with fiendish glee call attention to them—as though it mattered.

The 1st of June found him lunching with the Yale members of the National Academy at Jonathan Edwards College, the group at that time consisting of the largest representation of any university save Harvard. The principal topic of conversation at this learned gathering seems to have been the *Queen Mary* which had steamed into New York harbor that morning on her maiden voyage. The American public were keenly interested in the ship and radio messages of her remarkable progress had been broadcast several times a day for several days before her arrival. H.C. felt impelled to write Klebs a letter timed to go back on the *Queen Mary's* return trip. The letter carried news of his son Henry's wedding to Marjorie Estabrook, "a nice young girl whom we all like very much." H.C. did not feel up to motoring to Marion, Massachusetts, where the wedding occurred and was much disappointed to miss the ceremony.

His letter of 2 June also carried the unhappy news of Richard Meagher's premature death from a coronary occlusion. Klebs, knowing how much this would distress H.C., wrote: "It saddens me deeply the thought of Dick Meagher coming home sick and tired from unhappy experiences in Chicago [his sister had been similarly stricken], going over to the hospital to have a minute with his beloved Chief's daughter [Mary was ill with jaundice] and then turning in at his flat never to wake again. He struck me as a loveable but tragic figure. I wonder whether Mary anticipated the tragedy? I know it is a grievous loss to you and I press your hand." A day or two later (6 June) H.C. was obliged to report the death of another friend and colleague, Campbell Howard. "It removes another of the old Osler guard [Dr. McCrae had died on 30 June 1935] which will perhaps serve to draw the rest of us a little closer together as we close up the ranks."

On the 8th the expansive Leon Asher descended upon New Haven in the course of a whirlwind lecture tour of the States. He addressed a large gathering of students in the afternoon, and Cushing arranged a formal dinner for him in the evening at which Asher's speech carried them well into the night. He reminisced most entertainingly about H.C.'s days at Berne and managed to embarrass Cushing not a little by recalling his lighter moments there, all with a full measure of continental innuendo. The next day when Cushing made the gesture of seeing him off on the train, he was further embarrassed when Asher kissed him explosively on both cheeks, to the vast amusement of a group of irreverent undergraduates.

During the summer Mrs. Cushing and Barbara were abroad, and H.C. settled down with his books and he returned again to the manuscript of the meningioma monograph which had lain dormant for two years. By now the Brigham records had all been photographed and Louise Eisenhardt had had them arranged in the Brain Tumor Registry. During the next two years the greater part of his free time was devoted to the drafting of this remarkable clinical report.

Cushing had taken great interest in plans for the Harvard Tercentenary and, although he was unable to attend the three days of ceremonies, he promptly passed on a second-hand account to Klebs (21 September 1936):

> Your, as usual, altogether delightful letter of September 17th via the *Queen Mary* has just reached me and I shall take a few minutes in this rather hectic day to get an answer off to you on the same boat. I have just been lunching with the Master of Emmanuel, John Harvard's college, who has come down here after participating in the Harvard Tercentenary as one of the many representatives from Cambridge, nine of whom, I believe, mostly Nobel laureates, were given degrees.
>
> It was evidently a great function, magnificently pulled off in the grand manner, all but the last day when Jupiter Pluvius got the best of them, and in their gorgeous robes they were obliged to sit in the rain on the edge of a tornado that swept up the Coast, until umbrellas began to be put up and people began to fly into the Widener Library from which they had emerged shortly before in bright sunshine. This was altogether too bad, but it gave Mr. Angell the chance to get off one of his characteristic jests, for in his speech he

alluded to the weather and said he judged it to be a demonstration on Harvard's part of her method of soaking the rich. . . .

During October when the Professor of Surgery fell ill, H.C. took a hand at teaching. He wrote to Klebs: "I have given the first two Wednesday clinics and find myself much embarrassed at appearing in public after four years of retirement. A week ago over a borderline appendix I ventilated myself on the bacteriological era which made surgery possible. This took me back to Fitz, 1886; and so today going back to Marie (not to mention your father, of whom I of course spoke), I tried to induct them over a borderline case of pituitary adrenal disease." He continues to Klebs:

. . . We've been having a hectic time with visitors—an aftermath of the Tercentenary. Hele from Emmanuel College, Cambridge; then Janet, very amusing, as I must have written you—he's an amateur botanist and collector of herbals, of which I learned too late to profit by; then Barcroft, who is giving a course of well-attended lectures on the Terry Foundation—a Divinity School affair. He is talking about the religion of the foetus, so far as I can make out—goats and sheep—and yesterday showed moving pictures of them at successive weeks. The interesting thing seems to be, if you hit a foetus on the nose anywhere between the 43d and 67th day, he jumps, and after that he doesn't which of course is highly peculiar and a reaction not at all to be surprised at. I'm never sure of my figures and it may be between the 28th and 35th days he jumps.

After President Roosevelt received a copy of the 'Surgeon's Journal' he had written, "Your book is here and I am reading it a little bit at a time—this is the greatest compliment I can pay it. When this blankety-blank campaign is over, come down and have supper with me all alone." The 'blankety-blank' campaign was reaching a climax at the end of October when the Roosevelt retinue arrived in New Haven on the 22d for a campaign speech. Klebs shortly received the following account of the episode:

As I am sure H.C. will not tell you of the goings on today I should like to give you a brief second-hand account of the proceedings. Instead of going home to lunch about 2.15, as is his usual habit, he pranced out of his office shortly after 12 with the help of John [the chauffeur], Miss Stanton, and a wheel chair, saying that he had important business at home. It seemed that Mr. Roosevelt was making a somewhat unexpected visit to New Haven and without much notice had announced himself and his retinue for lunch at 691 Whitney Avenue. He had been speaking, Mr. Roosevelt that is, this morning at Hartford and the crowds were such that the car and retinue had great difficulty in getting out of the city. The Cushings had invited no one for lunch except a few officials, Mrs. Homans who is staying in the house and who wore a Landon button, and a few other intimate friends.

About 2.20 they finally arrived for lunch which had been scheduled at 1.15, and to fool the crowd Mr. Roosevelt's car drove up across the back lawn directly to the veranda steps leading from the house to the garden. A ramp had been erected there which he mounted without much difficulty. The other cars, including those of the Governors of the State, the Mayor of the City, the Attorney General, the secret service, the press and Mrs. Roosevelt (not to mention Betsey and a number of her friends) all arrived in due course and a quiet little luncheon was served for about thirty-five. The President sat in the Chief's library with his head against the Vesaliana and Betsey served him his lunch. Mrs. Cushing had played solitaire from 1.15 to 2.20 in the drawing room but I am afraid H.C. was just a dash restless. The President was in no mood to leave in a hurry. He kept a crowd of 30,000 waiting on the Green for an hour and a half. When his car appeared the police lost control and he could not reach the speaker's platform and his brief address was therefore cancelled and he went on to Washington. And so the campaign goes.

In inviting his guests H.C. had had the delicate problem of being careful lest he inadvertently include any of Yale's more rabid Republicans. However, there were no untoward incidents and August Heckscher, one of H.C.'s young Elizabethan Club friends, wrote the same day:

. . . Not for a long time, if at all, will any of the details of this day pass from my mind. That picture of Mr. Roosevelt, warm in his affections, gay, untroubled—in the very midst of his power and achievement—is one that I shall always keep. Among the crowds where we motored afterwards there were faces I shall not forget because they looked to the President with so much faith. I believe we can look confidently toward the victory of November 3!

H.C. was so pleased with Heckscher's note that he sent it on to F.D.R. who responded:

The White House,
F.D.R. to H.C. *10 November 1936.*

Dear Harvey: That's a nice letter from young Heckscher and my luncheon with you and yours was even nicer. Hereafter if the only way I can lunch with you is to run for the Presidency, I shall violate all rules and do it again in 1940, 1944 and 1948.

The Yale booing was not nearly as hearty as the Harvard booing. Perhaps this is because I am a more recent graduate of Yale—they have not yet learned to know me for what I truly am. Faithfully yours, FRANKLIN D. ROOSEVELT.

Two days after the election landslide the Cushings motored to Hyde Park to attend the christening of their second grandchild, Kate. Writing a few days later to A. V. Hill, H.C. said that the ceremony was interesting and continued: "I have no doubt that the President will keep his head and will stay in the middle of the road whatever the efforts to pull him to right or left."

The Army Medical Library was to hold its centenary celebration on 16 November and H.C. had taken a lively interest in the occasion since, feeling unable to accept the invitation himself, he had suggested that Sir Humphry Rolleston be invited from England to give the principal address. H.C., still in a wheelchair on account of his feet, did not feel strong enough to make the trip to Washington, but he entertained Rolleston in New Haven beforehand.

For many years H.C. had been interested in Osler's hero, Dr. Elisha Bartlett. On learning that Bartlett's two nieces, who live in Brooklyn, were in possession of many of their uncle's papers, he invited them to come to New Haven. On the 14th two most gracious maiden ladies arrived for tea bearing letters, miniatures, and other fascinating material concerning their uncle, the great authority on fevers, and immediately requested that H.C. one day write an account of his life. Many of these important source materials are still on deposit in his library, for he had promised to write the account of Bartlett after he had finished his bio-bibliography of Vesalius.

When Arnold Klebs reached New York on 20 December he found a characteristic note from H.C.: "Welcome to you! I hope you will have had a better crossing than others seem to have been having of late. I wish I could meet you at the boat, but when you arrive you will find out the reason why I can't. . . . I have thousands of things to talk over with you. Your note from London arrived this morning telling me that you had sent your screed to Chapman. Your recent missives sound as though you had been going at a great pace and I hope you will have had a good rest on the boat." Klebs spent nearly a week in New Haven, annotating Cushing's latest book purchases and laying further plans for the ultimate union of their libraries.

During these weeks H.C. was making preparations for an address about his cousin Perry Harvey. Two years previously he had promised Mrs. Harvey that he would write an appreciation of his cousin, but the proper inspiration had been slow to come, doubtless because of his own ill health. He had meanwhile enquired about the disposition of his cousin's Baskerville collection: "I wonder what you are planning to do with the Baskerville collection. The Sterling Library of course would treasure them, and I have an idea that Perry would be pleased to know that they were featured here in the Rare Book Room with his bookplate. I am planning to leave my library to Yale, and a young friend of mine and also Dr. Klebs have agreed to combine their libraries with my own so that they may perhaps some day be a nucleus for a collection that would justify our establishing a professorship of the history of medicine such as exists at the Johns Hopkins in Dr. Welch's name." The seed having fallen on fertile ground, the books were presented to Yale by Mr. Harvey's heirs, and at H.C.'s suggestion a small celebration was staged at the time of presentation. "Large numbers of my relatives are coming on from Cleveland," H.C. wrote Klebs on 4 January, "and will be scattered about the house for the night in cots and shake-down emergency beds. You meanwhile are comfortably fixed at the Ritz."

The address on Perry Harvey reveals Cushing in one of his happiest veins. He had been devoted to "Tot" Harvey since the days of his youth; they had shared lodgings at 166 York Street when they first came to Yale and during their declining years their common interest in books had brought them once again together. The address, deep in its feeling, is as much a tribute to Yale as to Perry Harvey:

It is gratifying that the set of Baskerville editions on display should be deposited here as a permanent memorial to one of the most popular and lovable Yale men of his time. Had "Tot" Harvey, as he was affectionately known to everyone, lived to attend last June's reunion of the Class of '91, he would have been no less surprised than were other graduates, who from force of circumstance had more or less lost touch with present-day Yale, to find that a great library had come to be recognized as the very *cor et anima* of the University. . . .

The Chittenden annex which bore scant architectural resemblance to anything else on the campus, much less to the parental repository for books, was erected in our Senior year just in time for us to get a photograph of its greatly admired Tiffany window to insert in the annual *Pot Pourri*. Just in time also for the story to be circulated that, at closing hour on a certain overcast afternoon, someone dropped in to consult the librarian and found him looking for his umbrella under "U" in the newly made card catalogue, the pride of his heart. . . .

First cousins, near neighbors, and almost precisely of the same age Perry and I would have found—had we been at all interested in the subject—that among our common forbears were Williamses and Fitches, Mygatts and Knapps, Days and Starrs, from this section of New England, who with their Bibles, shotguns, spinning wheels, and other belongings, including a black boy or two, had joined the great migration in ox-drawn carts to the promised land of the Western Reserve. There, in due course, we were inconspicuously born, along with other siblings galore, and came to be baptized at a Presbyterian font with a partially inverted combination of names—his mother's name, indeed, having been Mary Cushing Williams Harvey.

With an equal start in life, with the same astrological influence to affect our houses, and with similar opportunities, one might have expected us to be more alike. But whether because he was the oldest of his three brothers and I the youngest of my six, or for some other reason, he matured more rapidly and during the long years of our constant companionship invariably proved in all our competitions, in or out of school, the better of the two. Blessed with a quick perception and a retentive memory, he could race through his lessons, even in college days with a room full of noisy companions; while I, always a plodding learner, with cotton in my ears, would be sporting my oak and tearing my hair somewhere in seclusion. . . .

So it came about that while the whirling spindle of our lives spread widely apart as we became of middle age, we always found an unending source of reminiscent interest in the years of which I have endeavored to give a brief picture, when the threads were closely intertwined. And I am happy to say they began again to draw together in later years, through a common interest in the perusal of sales catalogues and in the collecting of books.

His was truly a happy and useful life; and when it so abruptly came to a close on that sunny May morning four years ago amid surroundings he so greatly loved, with magnolias, Cherokee roses, camellias, and sweet-scented tea olives still in bloom while the pink blossoms of his favored thunderbush were just coming into flower, he left behind him not only a fine record of public service but a host of sorrowing friends, both young and old.

A man's individuality is something too elusive to put into words, particularly if he was the sort of person who was never seen out in front but who always chose to stand inconspicuously at the back of the house where, with humor and tolerance, he could get a better view of the world's stage. So I shall make no attempt to depict him beyond letting you see his profile in a chance silhouette. It must suffice to recall what someone once remarked of Dr. Johnson, that "No man can be said to put you in mind of him"—even of his shadow.

* * * * *

Cushing's uneasiness about teaching had led to the happy idea of suggesting that John Homans, his warm friend and one-time associate, be invited to serve for a year in Dr. Harvey's place as acting Professor of Surgery. The authorities approved, Homans accepted, and came to New Haven late in October. He conducted clinics and ward rounds in the Brigham tradition, his humor delighting students and staff alike. His presence meant a great deal to H.C., and Homans frequently consulted him about clinical problems. Cushing took him to meetings of The Club and also of the Beaumont Club where, on 11 December, Walter Steiner of Hartford read a particularly interesting paper on the activities of the U.S. Sanitary Commission during the Civil War and the part it had played in fostering both the International Red Cross and the U.S. Public Health Service. Cushing entered freely into the discussion, indicating that he, like his father, had been an eager student of Civil War military history.

At this time Cushing had had a visit from Willy Wiegand of the Bremer Press in Munich which had recently issued the elaborate edition of the Vesalian plates from the original wood blocks. "He certainly got ahead of Putti and me in our projected tour to identify the Calcar landscape," he wrote to a friend. "I talked to him about an English *Epitome* [of Vesalius] which he seems to think might be done." For many years H.C. had been attempting to identify the Italian landscape which formed the background of the elaborate anatomical plates in Vesalius' *Fabrica*. Wiegand, by piecing together photographs of the muscle and skeletal plates and by study of contemporary prints, had established that the landscape was the picturesque region of the Euganean Hills a few miles from Padua. This encounter with Wiegand set Cushing once more to work on Vesalius and the definitive bibliography which he had been contemplating for several years.

His historical ruminations, which had been precipitated by the visits of Klebs and Wiegand, were interrupted shortly before Christmas by the political agitation concerning the Pure Food and Drug legislation in which he became involved. He addressed a long letter on the subject to the President and as usual sent it through Miss LeHand, the President's personal secretary, with whom the Cushings had come to be on intimate terms.

H.C. to Miss LeHand *22 December 1936.*

Dear Missy: I am enclosing a letter that I want you to give the President when you think he has a moment of freedom to read it. It is about this Pure Food and Drug legislation which agitates me more than is good for my game foot. I want him to get it straight as I see it. You can read the letter if you choose, and I hope I haven't made it too long.

Now for something more pleasant. Betsey has just been spending the night with us and she had much to say about her delightful trip with you in the South. She thinks you are a grand fellow, and so do I. Merry Christmas to you all.

Mr. Roosevelt returned a prompt acknowledgment:

The White House,
F.D.R. to H.C. *28 December 1936.*

Dear Harvey: It is good to get your note and good to hear your voice. You are right about the Pure Food and Drug Act. My difficulty has been a political one. I hope to have someone other than your medical colleague, Dr. ———, handle it at the coming session. Enough said! Love to you all, As ever yours, FRANKLIN D. ROOSEVELT.

H.C. was scheduled to attend a number of meetings of various associations and societies at the end of the month, one of which, the Association for Research in Nervous and Mental Disease, had dedicated its program (which was devoted to the pituitary), to him. The day after the meeting H.C. received the following telegram: "THE MEETING OF THE ASSOCIATION FOR RESEARCH DEDICATED TO YOUR HONOR HAS PROVED TO BE A MAGNIFICENT TRIBUTE TO YOUR GENIUS AND ACCOMPLISHMENTS IN CONNECTION WITH THE PITUITARY GLAND YOUR UNAVOIDABLY ENFORCED ABSENCE HAS DETRACTED FROM OUR PLEASURE AND THE LUSTRE OF THE OCCASION WE WISH TO EXTEND TO YOU OUR HOMAGE AND AFFECTIONATE REGARDS AND OUR HOPE THAT YOU WILL SOON BE ENTIRELY WELL. ASSOCIATION FOR RESEARCH IN NERVOUS AND MENTAL DISEASE."

1937

Cushing was now approaching the time for his second retirement. At the Brigham the stated age had been sixty-three, while at Yale it had been set at sixty-seven, and Cushing was to have his sixty-eighth birthday in April. When inadvertently reminded of the fact in December he had taken it rather distractedly, and there had been a number of unsatisfactory discussions concerning the title which he was to assume as "Emeritus." Various appropriate designations had long been in use at Yale, but when "Research Associate," the most common one, was suggested, Cushing retorted that it sounded as though he were being made a "glorified lab boy." "Lecturer in the History of Medicine" didn't suit him because he did not propose to lecture, and he didn't like "Reader" because he intended to do more writing than reading. Mr. Angell, who on more than one occasion had drawn upon his broad experience as a psychologist, finally hit upon an acceptable formula, namely, "Director of Studies in the History of Medicine."

Cushing, having now withdrawn almost entirely from attendance at meetings, occupied himself more and more with his writing and entertaining the friends who sought him out. In March Chauncey Tinker brought Sinclair Lewis to tea. H.C. admired Lewis' prose but detested in *Arrowsmith* the shallow characterization of doctors as weak, disillusioned scientists. In attempting to convey to Mr. Lewis a little more of the true spirit and traditions of medicine, he by chance mentioned Dr. Howard Kelly, the eminent Johns Hopkins obstetrician, citing Kelly, who was profoundly religious, as proof that all physicians were not atheists. Lewis, after listening for a while in silence, completely deflated his host—"My dear Harvey, what does an obstetrician know about the Virgin Birth?"

In May there was a visit from the Geoffrey Jeffersons of Manchester, old friends whom Cushing had visited in 1927. They had arrived in the United States to attend the sixth annual meeting of the Harvey Cushing Society being held in Philadelphia and came to New Haven to pay their respects beforehand. It was a particularly happy time, for Cushing enjoyed nothing more than showing guests about the University, and in this instance the pleasure was enhanced by the stimulating exchange of ideas since H.C. looked upon Jefferson as having one of the most searching and original minds in British medicine.

Although he had resolved to avoid future meetings, a Yale Library Associates dinner at Frank Altschul's on 27 April gave him a sense of fresh confidence; and the next thing he knew he was in Washington, discussing "astrophysics" at the National Academy of Sciences, all of which is entertainingly related in a letter to Klebs:

29 April 1937.

. . . You will be interested to know that I actually have broken my sit-down strike which has lasted nearly three years, first to go to a meeting of the Yale Library Associates at the home of one Frank Altschul in New York. This was only for a night, but suddenly on Sunday, finding I was none the worse for wear, I went to Washington for two days of the meetings of the National Academy where everybody looked surprised, thinking I was long since dead and buried.

I saw a lot of old Hopkins friends—MacCallum, Howell, Whipple, Robert

Wood, Mr. Edith [Harry Fielding] Reid, Isaiah Bowman, and many others. But it poured rain for two days and the Potomac had so far flooded everything that when I suggested over the telephone to the flying field that I would like to take a plane back to New Haven, they laughed as the flying field had been under two feet of water for two days and couldn't be distinguished from the air from any other part of the Potomac. I spent two nights with Betsey and Jimmy and their bairns who seemed none the worse for chickenpox which they may possibly have given me, for I didn't recall until afterward that chickenpox is one of the few things I have never as yet had.

All this I accomplished without assistance other than for a porter and a wheel chair at both ends of the line. What's more, wearing my own boots. So you see I am very much on the mend.

Meanwhile, I have been pegging along with the meningioma monograph and we have made some progress; but it's slow business, for I find composition increasingly difficult, my sexagenarian loss of orientation, which grows worse rather than better, proving a great handicap, for I can never find my place in the MS. and can't remember over night what I have written.

We have been having a cold, wet Spring which I believe has something to do with sun spots. And the radio goes on the blink every now and then which arouses the great interest of the astrophysicists. I find, by the way, that all these "birds" call themselves astrophysicists now, for I gathered from listening to two days of meetings and getting brainstorms by trying to understand formulae being written rapidly on the blackboard that everything which has to do with the sun or moon or bowels of the earth or the Holy Ghost is astrophysics. So I shall have to reshift my cards and put everything under that heading instead of mixing myself up over light and heat and genetics. Everything is astrophysics, even shining a bright light in a goose's eye which makes him (or her) lay an egg. There's a Frenchman here, or was, working in Allen's department who has discovered this very useful fact. All of which is the principal reason for *pâté de foie gras*. I think you must have had a little too much bright light shining in your eyes which travels down your optic nerves to your pituitary body and accounts for your present maladjustments and being sorry for yourself.

On 22 May the Beaumont Club met to see an exhibit of the works of Sir Kenelm Digby which had been on display earlier in the year at the Grolier Club in New York. Cushing seemed particularly to enjoy these gatherings since they brought him in touch with men such as George L. Hendrickson, Professor Emeritus of Latin and Greek Literature, Allardyce Nicoll, Director of the Yale Drama School (who is engaged in writing a biography of Digby), Ross G. Harrison, Chairman of the National Research Council, and medical colleagues such as Walter R. Steiner and Ernest Caulfield from Hartford, and Herbert Thoms, C.-E. A. Winslow, Creighton Barker and others from the School of Medicine.

The event which was a fitting climax to his professorship at Yale came on Wednesday, 23 June, when he addressed the Yale alumni at the Commencement luncheon. Mr. Angell was also retiring and it was Cushing's responsibility and opportunity to speak on behalf of the alumni of the President's services to Yale. He began in lighthearted fashion with some amusing references to what he termed "the peculiar esoteric influence I have on the outgoingness of college presidents" by reminding his audience that "Daniel C. Gilman and I made our exit from the Johns Hopkins at about the same year. . . . Lawrence Lowell managed to hold on for another year after I was officially separated from Harvard, [so that] it obliged me surreptitiously to linger about until he too could extricate himself, thereby permitting us to join the emeriti together." And now he was to have the "unusual distinction of retiring—with the Angells." He continued in a more serious vein:

Those of you who yearn for "the good old days," and, in a changing world, regret that you can't send your sons to an unchanged Yale, would feel quite otherwise could you have shared with me in the great privilege of coming back to enjoy this extraordinary new Yale that has emerged during the wise and courageous administration now drawing to a close.

Mark my words, Fellow Alumni, Yale is an incredibly better place than in the pre-war decades of which many of us are prone to boast. After our four years here we were callow and sophomoric in our horizons compared to those young men who received their diplomas yesterday and who will be the graduate students of tomorrow. Our education we thought completed; theirs they feel has just begun. If you incline to doubt it, take up your residence for a semester or two in this beautiful city with its incomparable countryside; enter into the life of the new colleges; do some work in library or graduate schools, and find out for yourselves. Your nostalgia for the *Old* Yale will soon be replaced by pride and by amazement at the *New*. . . .

So great becomes one's respect for the position of leadership in a university like the Yale of today, the man who happens to occupy it leads by force of circumstances what is necessarily a lonely life beset with cares, responsibilities and difficult decisions. However much he may long for friendly intimacies and commendatory pats on the back, deference to his high station makes them scarcely possible; and here, about to leave us, is a man who for twenty-five years—as dean, acting president, and much else at the University of Chicago—was commonly known as "Sunny Jim" Angell.

He was of course aware before accepting the post he is about to relinquish that more brickbats than bouquets are shied at Presidents—particularly those who venture to advocate changes to meet new conditions. One may put his arm around the shoulder of a Dean or the Master of a college and say "Well done, old man"—but scarcely the President. Few even among his contemporaries have had the presumption to address by his nickname the man we have gathered here to honour. I know of only one—that privileged character, Billy Phelps, who when they were graduate students together at Harvard organized and played second base on a ball team whose imperturbable pitcher—a promising young psychologist called Jim—had command even then of most bewildering curves and changes of pace.

What gives moral support from day to day to a hard-pressed College President —or any other, for that matter—and enables him to come up smiling in the face of inevitable criticisms are not the laudatory terms ending in *issimi* spread on the honorary degrees that are dealt out to him. It comes rather from something largely denied him—the evidence of sympathy, confidence and affection implied by the friendly linking of arms and use of a boyhood name by those who are his contemporaries.

For my own part, having found to my surprise that I am 30 days his senior, I shall begin to make amends and hope that all of you—at least those who are sexagenarians, for we need not overdo it—will follow suit before the week is over. And when future generations of Elis come to speak of those trying post-bellum decades when chiefly through the benefactions of John Sterling and Edward Harkness the homely old College of the past not only became outwardly beautified but metamorphosed into a vigorous university with that necessary tool of scholarship, one of the world's great libraries, at its very core, it will be gratefully recalled that all this took place under the hegemony of "Sunny Jim" Angell. . . .

It was once said, by Horace Greeley I believe, that: "Fame is a vapor, popularity an accident, riches take wings, those who cheer today will curse tomorrow, only one thing endures—*Character*." In that supreme "quality of Divinity that stirs within us" has lain the strength, the patience, the tolerance and the kindness of heart of Yale's adopted son and devoted servant, James Rowland Angell.

CHAPTER XIX

The Closing Years

1937–1939

WITH his physical activities much restricted, Cushing began to spend more time at home enjoying his family and friends. His influence, however, during these years continued far-reaching, for students and former colleagues came from great distances to discuss their special problems. There is no doubt that these final years of relaxation brought great satisfaction, for he appreciated having his advice sought and he gave it freely. Much was exchanged by word of mouth and there were fewer letters; those to Klebs continued to be the most reliable source of information since H.C. nearly always passed on to him the more important news.

One of his summer visitors was Gustav Eckstein—"a fascinating person," he wrote A.C.K. "When he came in I thought it was Noguchi himself, for he is small of stature with piercing black eyes and looks as if he might be Oriental. In addition to his 'Noguchi,' he has written an astonishing book called 'Canaries' based on his experience with several generations that inhabit his laboratory in Cincinnati. . . . So excited have people become about this that Katharine Cornell has persuaded him to write a play for her. . . . Meanwhile Eckstein seems to know more about Pavlov than anyone else and has made a long sojourn in Russia to get the local color. Pavlov, needless to say, is no canary, nor is he Japanese, but I am sure young Eckstein will do something worthwhile."

Current events were followed at this time with close scrutiny and interest. In the letter just quoted about Eckstein (4 Aug.) he continued: "Where this past month has gone I can't say. The family have been off at Little Boar's Head. The country is bursting into strikes, and F.D.R. seems to have come a cropper on the Supreme Court business. Rather too bad he got into it. Just now the main feature of the news is the Newport races. Harold Vanderbilt is known as the world's best, or the next best, bridge player, and he also seems to be a hard man to beat at the helm of a racing yacht. Anyhow, he has left Sopwith so far behind in the first two races there is no longer much interest." Two weeks later he wrote prophetically: "We are still pegging along with meningiomas and it all seems rather silly to be spending so much time with something which will interest and perhaps be of some value to only a few people. Still, one must keep at something to prevent getting sour in these fallen times. What a mess they seem to be in just now in the East with the military party in Japan running loose. It would probably save a lot of trouble in the future if someone could tow the Japanese Archipelago out to sea and sink it. . . ."

During the summer he came to know George Milton Smith, a fellow collector with whom he had much in common, for Smith had taken a mobile hospital to Europe during the first World War and after the war had continued to be one of the most active protagonists of a broadly implemented program of national preparedness. On 16 August H.C. writes of him to Klebs: "I think I told you about a man here after your own heart, named George Smith, who goes in for fish and has an amazing collection of books on ichthyology. Next time you come over I want you to meet him and we will go down together and see his books which he keeps at his summer place in Pine Orchard [Connecticut]." On several occasions H.C. told Smith with a twinkle what he had decided to do with his books—another studied attempt to gather in other libraries to join his own. His suggestion was not taken amiss, and the great ichthyological collection is now destined for the Yale Historical Library.

Cushing continued to cast covetous eyes on other men's collections. In this same month he paid a visit to his old friend Edward Streeter, a Yale man of generous enthusiasms, and expressed tremendous admiration for his early pharmacy jars and weights and measures.

> . . . He showed us his collection of weights and measures and books pertaining thereto, and I simply gasped. So far as I know, no one else has taken an interest in collecting these things, and he has been picking them up here and there for the past twenty years, old Greek and Roman and Egyptian and Assyrian weights and pots and scales. No doubt therein lay the beginnings of exact measurement which not only was important for commerce but must hold also in some way the kernel of early science. But you probably know as much and more about this than Streeter himself in view of your researches in the history of science. There were about eight hundred volumes on his shelves which I think he is perfectly willing to turn over to us. . . .

Streeter likewise succumbed to H.C.'s subtle persuasion and shortly thereafter several hundred volumes on the history of medicine, many of them rare and unobtainable, were presented to the Library and later his other unusual collections, including an old pharmacy.

The meningioma monograph is mentioned in nearly every letter during the summer; thus on 2 October:

> Dr. Eisenhardt and I have been expecting Charles Thomas, the publisher, to come today and we have been scuffling during the week, in spite of my mental torpidity, to get together some of the more complicated tables and as many

illustrations as possible so that he can take them off and start in on them. I find it is going to be a much larger book than I had anticipated, like everything else I attempt to write. I am always afraid of leaving something out that is important and then at the end am obliged to curtail and expunge, which is a painful process because, as with a stack of cards, if you take anything out, the whole stack falls down, and you have to read pages behind and pages to come to see if they all continue to make sense.

In October he received the first copy of the important short-title list of the medical and scientific incunabula upon which Klebs had been working for nearly twenty-five years. This was to be the basis of a full-scale *catalogue raisonné* which Klebs was to publish under the auspices of the New York Academy of Medicine, but which he did not live to complete. H.C.'s acknowledgment was added by hand to a typed letter of 16 October: "Your inscribed copy of *Incunabula scientifica et medica* I find here on my desk this a.m. It is paralyzing in the amount of labor it represents. It will be a 'float to posterity' if there ever was one. We will make great use of it and begin checking our items and giving them the proper *Klebs* numbers." Klebs' reply is interesting:

The PS of the 18th to your letter of the 16th brings me the first acknowledgement of receipt of my List from U.S. and of course I am happy that it is from you and that on the whole you like the book, or rather its get-up. Thanks for the kind words you have said about it. You are one of the few who know what I have gone through with it all these years and that, when I finally decided to get it out in this form, it was a case of *force majeure*. I should have liked to do better, but since I couldn't, I do hope that it will be of some use.

Now that Lord Rutherford has gone, I rejoice that he should have sent you lately a collection of his reprints. May I add to it some clippings I cut for you from *The Times*. That a man like this, in contact with all the highest scientific aspirations and attainments, should have to die of a strangulated hernia, an accident that even mediaeval barbers knew how to counter, seems to me again one of those many indications that medicine in trying to be scientific has not chosen the best road to work for the best of its patients, in *esse* or in *posse*.

In a later letter Klebs explains the bookish philosophy which doubtless kept him at his long and unremitting labors on the catalogues:

. . . Old books must do something more than merely incite our aesthetical and antiquarian inclinations. They are not only historical documents also, but tracings of human mentality of which we know next to nothing. Why for instance have you just written a 750-page book on certain very limited conditions in the skull capsule, why did Vesalius get together nearly 1,000 on what he thought was the total anatomy, and why did Aristotle put onto I don't know how many pages the fundamentals of human thought in regard to total nature? Those are some of the questions that merit looking into and can be looked into only if we have well-arranged, classified material at hand that puts human thought out of the confining limits of time and space. And how many things besides thought, but distinctly influencing thought, enter such humanistic striving? . . .

When Andrew Keogh, the University Librarian, retired, it was natural that Cushing should have been one of those appointed to select his successor; and as usual, when he accepted such a responsibility, he went to great trouble to inform himself. Some of the details were promptly sent on to Klebs who happened also to be greatly interested in the question whether a scholar or a trained librarian was preferable as director of a large university library.

> . . . And then I have been put on a committee here to try and select a librarian to succeed Keogh who goes out by statutory rulings this next year. I went down with Lefty [Wilmarth] Lewis to see what Herbert Putnam [Librarian of Congress] had to say about our decision that we wanted a scholar for the head position rather than a trained librarian. Putnam said immediately that there was no question in the matter, that in the first place we ought to have a Yale graduate who knew the alumni and had made a mark for himself in world affairs, not necessarily having to do with libraries, though he must of course have sympathy with the significance and function of a library. Under him there ought to be a trained librarian as an administrator of the library. Just what will come out of it and whether we can find the sort of man we want, I do not presume to say, but it takes much time and long weekly meetings. . . .

The committee deliberated for several months and in March 1938 settled upon Bernhard Knollenberg, a dynamic New York lawyer, whose energetic administration of the Library was terminated when he was called to Washington as Assistant Lend-Lease Administrator under Mr. Edward R. Stettinius.

In the course of his deliberations with the Library Committee Cushing became convinced that the members of the Corporation, Yale's governing body, should know more than they seemed to know about the Library. Following an old custom of the Bodleian at Oxford (one in which Osler had been greatly interested), he planned a "perlustration" of the library by the members of the Corporation. Accordingly a luncheon was arranged on 6 November, after which the various departments of the University Library were to be visited. But H.C. had, by some mischance, forgotten about the football game that afternoon and was considerably chagrined to find that most of the august members had vanished when the perlustration had scarcely begun.

In December he attended a meeting of the Association for Research in Nervous and Mental Disease, the program this time being devoted to the cerebral circulation in which he had been keenly interested since his days at Berne. He went rather against his better judgment, for he still found speaking in public very tiring, but he probably had a guilty conscience for having failed them the year before when the program had been dedicated to him. He was asked to propose the health of the Association at the luncheon, and he chose a subject which may have been somewhat unpalatable for a group of specialists. "My theme [he said] is not exactly 'Back to Hippocrates'—for that's a long way to go, so soon after lunch. And yet in a sense that is just what it is. For could the Father of Medicine have foreseen that one of its branches was some day to concern itself solely with the nervous system and its disorders, he would have added this further aphorism: Should you incline to pursue that obscure but important subject called neurology, and wish to succeed therein: *Cultivate your powers of bedside observation.*" As was often the case, he felt that the speech had been a failure and he lamented the next day to Klebs that his remarks had been followed by profound silence. He had spoken in a serious vein, to be sure, so that one might infer that the silence had not indicated disapproval but rather that his hearers were reflecting upon the challenge of his message.

During his time at Yale H.C. maintained a lively interest in experimental work and directed several investigations which had grown out of his studies on pituitary basophilism. Associated with him during these years was Kenneth W. Thompson, who had gone through all the grades at the Brigham and after a year abroad had been brought to Yale by H.C. as his research assistant. Thompson shared his interest in problems of pituitary physiology and collaborated with him in the experimental work on pituitary basophilism,[1] and with Dr. Eisenhardt on its relations to abnormalities of blood pressure.[2] Cushing likewise influenced the research activities of many men who had come to the School of Medicine for postgraduate study in experimental neurology, and they too frequently sought his counsel.

1938

The last two years of Cushing's life were destined to be richer and happier than any since leaving Boston, for his general health had improved and he was able to take an active part in the life of the college and the school. In the autumn of 1937 he began to serve as president of the Elizabethan Club, an endowed undergraduate literary body possessing an unusual collection of Shakespeare quartos and other valuable landmarks in English literature. The founder of the Club, Mr. Alexander Smith Cochran, a retiring Yale College graduate of the Class of 1896, had felt the lack, as an undergraduate, of the stimulus of firsthand contact with the classics of English

[1] "Experimental pituitary basophilism." (With K. W. Thompson). *Proceedings of the Royal Society,* May 1934, *115B,* 88-100. Also: "Inhibition of action of pituitary hormones by animal sera." (With K. W. Thompson). *Ibid.,* January 1937, *121B,* 501-517.

[2] "A brief consideration of the present status of so-called pituitary basophilism with a tabulation of verified cases." *Yale Journal of Biology and Medicine,* May 1939, *11,* 507-522.

literature, and decided in 1911 to give his library of Elizabethan dramatic literature to the trusteeship of Yale University with a fund to establish and maintain an Elizabethan Club "where professors and undergraduates can meet informally," and where "with a great collection of books as a nucleus, talk would follow spontaneously." A suitable house (with a green for "bowls" in the rear) was found on College Street in which a large fireproof vault was installed to house the collection, and the Club soon came to play a prominent part in the life of the College. Cushing, who had been active in the Club since 1934, had always been warmly disposed toward the group, and few things gave him greater satisfaction than his election to its presidency. He made a point during 1938 and 1939 of dropping in almost every week-day between four and six and was soon addressing the members by their first names. His knowledge of the Elizabethan quartos was even more intimate, for he had studied their provenance closely and before long he had stories to tell about many of the individual volumes. As with his sponsorship of the various medical societies of Johns Hopkins and Harvard, he was tireless in arranging for meetings; on 12 January he had planned a dinner at his house for J. T. Sheppard, Provost of King's College, Cambridge, who spoke later on "Lady Macbeth and the Greek tragedy." A week later Lawrence C. Wroth, the eminent bibliographer from the John Carter Brown Library at Providence, gave an informal afternoon address at the Club. The next month, Curt Bühler of The Pierpont Morgan Library, after another carefully arranged dinner, addressed the Club on "Incunabula collecting and research in U.S.A." And so it went throughout the year; in some months he might arrange as many as two or three formal meetings. In March, for example, Dumas Malone, of the Harvard University Press and one-time editor of the *Dictionary of American biography,* addressed the Club on the 2nd, and two weeks later Malone's opposite number of the Cambridge University Press, S. C. Roberts, gave an account of Johnson's *Rambler.* The undergraduates and faculty members of the Club responded enthusiastically to Cushing's energetic leadership and the *esprit de corps* which H.C. seemed to infuse into anything with which he became closely associated carried the Elizabethan Club through the lean war years without the lapse which occurred in so many kindred organizations.[3]

Shortly after his arrival in New Haven H.C. had also been elected to two dining clubs; to one, 'The Club,' founded in 1838 and known

[3] One of the innovations which Cushing fostered during his presidency was the erection of a handsome tablet to Cochran, the founder. It had been sponsored by Mr. Maitland F. Griggs, a classmate of Cochran's, and was executed by Mr. Theodore Sizer of the School of Fine Arts.

among its members as "the old men's club," he was particularly loyal. On being notified of his election he had replied:

H.C. to Professor C. J. Tilden *7 December 1933.*

Dear Professor Tilden: This afternoon Professor Chittenden brought me your note announcing my election to membership in "The Club." Nothing could possibly have given me greater pleasure, for I understand that this is one of the oldest, most famous and best dinner clubs in the country and one of the few clubs of this age in which in course of time gastronomy has not come to be the principle [*sic*] object of its meetings.

I shall look forward with interest to seeing the booklet which you say gives a history of The Club and will hope that my present hospitalization will not oblige me to miss any of your meetings.

The membership of The Club was quite diverse and from time to time each member was called upon to explain his particular speciality, or some branch of it, to the other members. H.C. entertained the group on several occasions;[4] the one which the members seem to recall most vividly was when he spoke on the disease acromegaly, telling how his interest had been originally aroused in this condition, how it had taken him to circuses and sideshows, to graveyards and even to funeral parlors, but how over the years his patients, no matter how little he had been able to do for them, had followed him with a loyalty and devotion seldom encountered in patients suffering from other maladies.

H.C. in addition took pleasure in his association with Trumbull College, of which he was an Associate Fellow. Trumbull was then presided over by his warm friend Stanhope Bayne-Jones, who held a chair of bacteriology in the Medical School, and Mrs. "B.-J." who had found her way into the hearts of the undergraduates as surely as had the Master of the College. The Fellows dined each week on Thursday night, and there was also a succession of lunches and teas for parents and undergraduates. Whenever it was feasible to do so, Cushing attended these functions and came to be on terms of intimacy with many of the Fellows, as well as with numerous undergraduates. In this way he managed to arouse an interest in medicine in many a young student who had not yet decided upon a career. A number of the more incredulous, who had heard of Cushing's reputation, seemed unable to believe that this apparently carefree man, who was never without a good story (or a bad pun), was the

[4] Dr. Cushing was host to The Club at two "open meetings" on 19 December 1934 and on 11 November 1936. He was also host when Professor Chittenden read a paper on "Centennial I—The Club," 12 October 1938. The pamphlet referred to in the letter to Professor Tilden is an anonymous brochure of 76 pages, without title page, but entitled on the cover *The Club 1838-1913;* it was evidently printed sometime during 1914 and is made up of an "Historical Sketch Read on December 17, 1913, at the House of Professor Henry W. Farnam, No. 43 Hillhouse Avenue," followed by a list of members and the subjects discussed since the beginning.

great brain surgeon and literary light about whom they had heard. It is perhaps significant that during these final years Cushing gravitated more to the undergraduates than he did to the medical students, for he seemed to be living over again the days of his youth at Yale College. The students themselves were unconsciously drawn to him and he responded with ease and grace, for he understood them.

He also had many special enthusiasms. His interest in Donald G. Wing's project for compiling a short-title catalogue of English books covering the period from 1641 to 1700 led him to sponsor Wing's Guggenheim Fellowship for study of the holdings in English libraries and to write letters of introduction for the "Wings over Europe." He contributed financially—and urged others to do so—to Miss Henrietta Bartlett's new edition of *A census of Shakespeare's plays in quarto,* which was being issued by the Yale University Press (1939). James Babb, now Librarian of the Yale University Library as successor to Bernhard Knollenberg, recalls that Cushing's visits always fired him with an indefinable zeal for building up the Library; and during the summers when H.C. was alone Babb could seldom resist dropping in for a chat at 691 Whitney Avenue on his way home. Others were similarly drawn in at tea time. Clements C. Fry, another friend and collector, who for many years had been concentrating on Weir Mitchell, had on various visits ingenuously made off with several of H.C.'s rarer Mitchell items. One day he arrived full of enthusiasm over a rare sixteenth century fugitive anatomical sheet on which he sought H.C.'s opinion, and H.C., by ignoring Fry's opening sentence, turned the tables and thanked him most heartily for his generous gift! The experience might have proved disturbing were it not for the fact that H.C. in due time handsomely repaid the victims of his acquisitive tendencies.

Cushing had always been deeply interested in the art of printing, and it was inevitable that on coming to New Haven he would be drawn to Carl Purington Rollins, Printer to Yale University, widely known for the beautiful books he had designed and printed. Rollins concerns himself with all phases of bookmaking, even to producing his own paper. At a Sunday session arranged in the spring of 1936 for H.C. and his bibliographer friend Leonard L. Mackall, Rollins spent the day papermaking, and H.C. was fascinated by his demonstration of how watermarks and chain lines are incorporated in paper and how sheets are later folded into folios, quartos, etc. This demonstration proved the beginning of a close friendship, for Cushing had ever a deep respect for anyone who thus brought art to his craft. Rollins designed the bibliography of H.C.'s writings presented on his 70th birthday. "This superb example of your special art," H.C. wrote, "brings me the greatest pride and happiness."

THE HARVEY CUSHING SOCIETY AND GUESTS ON H.C.'S 70th BIRTHDAY

Back row: Furlow, Crawford, Thompson, White, Shield, Buckley, Lyerly, Groff, Pool, Grant, Horrax, Ray, Craig, Echols. *Fourth row:* Braden, Reynolds, Morrissey, Haven, Crutchfield, Freeman, Schwartz, Campbell, Ingraham, Buchstein, Sjöqvist, Beswick, Gustafson. *Third row:* Dyke, Klemme, Schreiber, Brickner, Poppen, D'Errico, Muirhead, Wilkins, Watts, Olsen. *Second row:* Chamberlain, Kahn, Lillie, Fay, Francis, Pilcher, Van Wagenen, Davidoff, Kubie, Turnbull. *First row:* Light, Spurling, McKenzie, Sosman, Teachenor, Cushing, Eisenhardt, Fulton, German, Semmes, Putnam

THE 70th BIRTHDAY DINNER

Scenes at the speakers' table. The speakers are: *top,* Dean Bayne-Jones and Mr. Muirhead; *center,* Dr. Francis and Dr. Klebs; *bottom,* Dr. Cushing, who begins his address, and stops to call upon Adolph to wipe the brow of Dr. Klebs, to the amusement of Dr. Sjöqvist

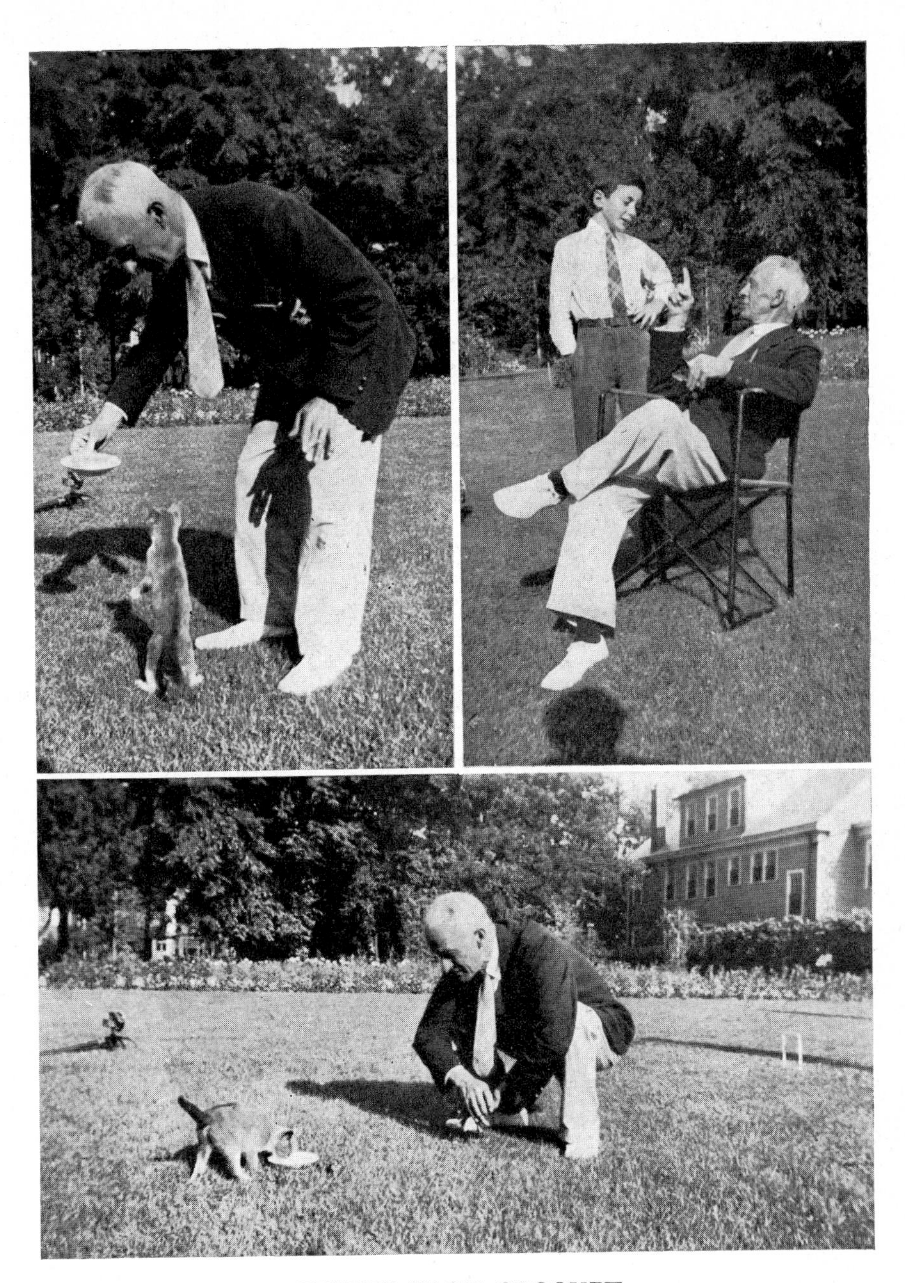

RESPITE FROM CROQUET

691 Whitney Avenue, New Haven, July 1939. From photographs by Miss Barbara Judson

WATCHING THE CROQUET AT TEA TIME
New Haven, June 1939. From a photograph by Robert H. Crowell, Jr.

Deane Keller, the talented artist of the Yale School of Fine Arts, found irresistible fascination in Cushing's face and all that lay behind it, and on three occasions he had executed charcoal portraits. Cushing's artistic gift (and their common love of baseball) offered an immediate basis for sympathetic understanding of his younger artist associate and they found great enjoyment in one another's company. In 1940 Keller executed a posthumous oil at the instance of the State Department as an official gift to the government of Chile for the Cushing Pavilion at the Hospital del Salvador in Santiago.

From his letters to Klebs, which were particularly illuminating throughout 1938, one gains glimpses of his more serious activities. Books were still uppermost in his mind. On 22 January: "I have been having visits from two Goldschmidts; one of them you will recall as our good friend from Old Bond Street. The other, who curiously came at the same hour we had given to the first one for an appointment, turns out to be a new Goldschmidt who is in the same business. . . . Whenever I see E. P. Goldschmidt, I know it is going to be expensive. And so it proved yesterday with the purchase of an Articella MS. from the monastery at Melk." In the same letter he told Klebs that he had been getting his Fielding Garrison correspondence in order for binding and congratulated A.C.K. on having at long last arranged his five hundred or more letters from Sudhoff, the eminent German medical historian.

He was much more preoccupied, however, with the preparation for press of the meningioma monograph on which he and Louise Eisenhardt had been working feverishly throughout the winter of 1937 and 1938. He complains (22 Jan.), "I am getting on all too slowly with the meningioma task and find, owing to my hardening cerebral arteries or to some other cause, increasing difficulty in putting my mind on it." Scarcely a month later however, he reported (28 Feb.): "We have at last sent off the MS. of the meningioma book on Saturday afternoon to Menasha, Wisconsin, and now we all feel completely deflated and turn to our ordinary and long-neglected affairs." In the same letter he laments Thomas B. Futcher's sudden death the previous Friday while conducting ward rounds: "Could anything possibly have been more to his liking? It was with him, as you will recall, that Kate and I shared 3 West Franklin Street after we were married, and he and Tom McCrae were my two most intimate friends of those early days."

Early in March he attended a dinner for another old friend of Hopkins days, Max Brödel. Though their intimate association at the turn of the century had been interrupted when H.C. had gone to Boston and the two men had seen little of one another in the intervening years, they had continued warm friends and H.C. never missed an opportunity to see him and was always interested in the pupils Brödel had trained. He described the dinner at some length:

H.C. to A.C.K. *12 March 1938.*

Dear Arnold: I went down a week ago on a jaunt to Philadelphia to attend a dinner being given for Max Brödel by the present head of the W. B. Saunders Company, young Lawrence Saunders. It was a delightful affair with a great turn-out of some two hundred people to pay a tribute to the man whose name, I suppose, will outlive most of his Hopkins contemporaries owing to the uniqueness of his contribution to medicine. This is of course debatable and something which time alone will determine; but it was unquestionably a tribute well deserved. Lawrence Saunders, I may add, is a delightful and public-spirited young fellow. He was the person who unwittingly purchased Erik Waller's stolen copy of Harvey's 1628 *ed. princeps,* a book which he without questioning returned to its proper owner.

Tom Cullen presided and told the whole story of his securing from Henry Walters the fund to ensure Brödel's continuance at the Hopkins when the Mayos were making advances to him to go to Rochester at his own price, suggesting $25,000, I believe, as a bid. Max decided to stay at Baltimore for a more or less uncertain $5,000, and he has been very happy there and from his appearance will go on turning out pupils for a decade or two to come. Lawrence Saunders had had a portrait made by Corner, the best in my opinion of the many he has made of Hopkins worthies in years gone by. Howard Kelly, showing his years for the first time, was one of the speakers; also Morris Fishbein, and H. L. Mencken on Brödel as a pianist, very amusing. And then the portrait was presented and Max very modestly and somewhat humorously replied in his own behalf. It was the first time I have seen so many Hopkins people together in many years. I happened to sit by John Finney who must be going on 75 and is still actively engaged in surgery, helped out by two sons, and possibly for all I know as many more grandsons. He ate an enormous dinner while I pecked at my somewhat dubious food, including scrapple, if I am not mistaken, though some of it I did not recognize. John Finney also did well by the champagne, much to my surprise, which made me cast a suspicious eye in the direction of Howard Kelly, but he sat where I could not easily spy upon him.

The next day I paid a visit to Tait McKenzie who is still modelling athletes in action and making medallions of people. He took me to lunch at the celebrated Franklin Inn which is a sort of Philadelphia Tavern Club and very enjoyable; and then I went to see W. B. McDaniel who is the librarian of the College of Physicians and a very personable and capable man, I judged. I wish I had had more time to see some of his treasures. . . .

In the same letter he makes further reference to E. P. Goldschmidt who "was here recently separating me from some of my residual cash." These friendly jibes at his discerning bookseller friends crop up from time to time but were completely without malice. He enjoyed mental agility wherever he found it, and once having come to know men "in the trade" as intelligent and energetic, he did not look upon them as scheming fellows to be treated with brusque indifference but as friends sincerely interested in helping him build up his collections. That this all came at a price—often high—was part of the game, and one in which H.C. was by no means always worsted. A recent symposium at the Royal Society of Medicine at which Dr. Goldschmidt and Dr. Weil described some of their recollections of H.C. proved that the association was one of mutual pleasure and satisfaction. Thus Dr. Goldschmidt recalled:[5]

One of the first times Dr. Cushing turned up in my Bond Street office, together, I think, with his friend, Dr. E. C. Streeter, I sold him the Magnus Hundt *Anthropologia* of 1501 with its astonishing skeleton broadside of which only two other copies are known. I was thoroughly convinced of the extraordinary interest and rarity of this early curiosity and my enthusiasm expressed itself in a very stiff price. Dr. Cushing paid that price without wincing. From this fact I felt entitled to draw the conclusion that here was a collector keen on bones. His further instructions to me on the authors and titles he was interested in: Vesalius, Paré, Ryff and others like that confirmed the impression, which was correct in those early days, that Dr. Cushing was primarily interested in the history of anatomical illustration, and that any early book with bones in it was likely to appeal to him unless he possessed it already.

In the following year, 1929, I set out for the first time on a trip across the Atlantic to visit my American customers in their homes. I tried to bring together a collection of books to take with me to show, and my aim was to have one really important item in the special line of each one of my chief customers. I had found a good and complete copy of Paré's *Dix livres de chirurgie,* 1564, a much rarer book than the *Cinq livres* of 1572, so I thought this would be the thing to bring along to Dr. Cushing. . . . When I reported myself as having arrived in Boston, he invited me to his house and we had a grand talk about books. After a time he said: "Well, did you bring anything with you to show me?" "Oh yes," I said, "I brought a very rare Paré octavo, the *Dix livres.* "Oh, the *Dix livres?* That is indeed a scarce and interesting book," he said, "do you know that there are two different variants of the 1564 edition of the *Dix livres?"* And he got up and took me to his bookshelves, and there was a whole row of octavo Parés, about twelve or fifteen of them, including two slightly differing copies of the book I had meant to tempt him with. Obviously the task of supplying Dr. Cushing with important books on anatomy which he did not yet possess was by no means simple.

My talks with Dr. Cushing on this and on following occasions, both here and in America, led to a better acquaintance with his wider field of interest which was by no means confined to "bones." Beyond the history of anatomy, he turned out to be interested in the history of surgery, then in the history of medicine generally. In the course of time the range of our talks spread out and it was soon apparent that Dr. Cushing, who had started with his Vesalian hobby, had conceived a plan of bringing together a library to comprise all the most important books marking the chief advances in all the exact sciences.

Inasmuch as I learned a great deal in these conversations, I might claim to call myself one of Dr. Harvey Cushing's pupils. . . . Here was one of the greatest surgeons of our epoch, the acknowledged master of all the intricacies of the convolutions of the human brain, who would question me on a problem of early printing with the modesty and eagerness of a fourth form schoolboy. But when he spoke about Vesalius, about the relationship of the *Tabulae sex*

[5] *Journal of History of Medicine and Allied Sciences,* New York, 1946, *1,* No. 2, 229-234.

to the *Fabrica,* when he discussed with me the mysterious appearance of the rudiments of the *China-Root Epistle* in a French Galen printed at Tours in 1545, then his tone was that of authority, he knew that he knew, he knew that he himself had examined all the evidence available, and that, whether his opinion was right or wrong, there was nothing to be said in our present state of knowledge that he was not familiar with. A great teacher! . . .

In his discussion of the discourses of Goldschmidt and Weil, Geoffrey Jefferson displayed a keen understanding of Cushing as a book lover and concluded his paper with a telling paragraph:

. . . It calls for no great insight for anyone to understand how great a delight Harvey Cushing had in his books. That it prevented him from going on the ordinary man's holiday to the New England Coast, except under the impossible condition that he take his library with him, was to the family a defect, almost a default. But "hyperbiblism" has its compensations. It added a zest to his visits abroad when a duty-call at a Clinic could be offset by a browse in the city's bookshops, a possibly envious view of the treasures of a famous library that put ideas into his head. Above all he enjoyed throughout his life, but increasingly as he grew older, the privileges of that substitute for bridge as a social ice-breaker, the freemasonry of the true bibliophile. He had thence a passport to happiness and, as it turned out, to immortality for it has been given to few to have a Library rotunda named for them. This would not be his only claim to the respect of future ages; though the details of his scientific achievements will in time be forgotten, for this is the fate of all of us, yet his name will abide. It abides more surely in stone.

During the two years that preceded the outbreak of the Second World War Cushing followed political developments with an apprehensive eye:

. . . I dined last night with Fred Walcott and Starling Childs who has just given a fund here for the study of cancer, and heard from Fred's own lips the story of his final decision not to go with Ellery Sedgwick and Cameron Forbes to interview Franco on the pretext of doing welfare work for the Spanish children of both factions. Ellery and Cam have already gone; but Fred, after a talk with Pershing and Secretary Hull and a few others, very wisely sidestepped the whole business. What is evidently in the air is that Franco will be encouraged to win out with German and Italian help and then they will plant themselves on the Northern side of Gibraltar and flood all the chambers with gas and say: Now how about returning the German Colonies and giving Italy a larger share of Africa? I am glad that I have work to do, and also that you have, to keep one's mind off from long-time militaristic planning of this sort. And as for the Japs and the gallant Chinese, the general opinion seems to be that the Japs will be lured into Central China and there pestered by banditry and raids until they go economically to the wall. . . .

And again on 17 March: "And what astonishing things have been taking place in Mittel Europa these past few days! It's evident how they feel about it in Czechoslovakia; but I wonder how Mussolini really feels, and the non-Aryans who dwell in the German end of Switzerland." He was also much concerned over the refugee problem and his files from 1937 and 1938 are bulging with correspondence about individual cases, many of whom he assisted in finding posts. Klebs had suggested that they should be received freely because North America had been founded by a similar group of political expatriates but H.C. protested, "I don't agree with you that North America was so founded; they were people who left home of their own volition, were allowed to do so and took with them what funds and possessions they owned." He adds: "The stories in the press of this meeting between Hitler and Mussolini are most extraordinary. I wonder what Hitler really thought of it all; for I suppose he is a psychopathic dreamer and not the sort of exhibitionist that Mussolini is. Meanwhile, the world sits with a wet towel around its head wondering what sort of pact they have made."

Although preoccupied with his books and undergraduate affairs, Cushing did not wholly withdraw from affairs of the Medical School. He generally attended the weekly sessions of the Neurological Study Unit, a clinical group made up of students and staff interested in neuropsychiatric and neuropathological problems. Cases were usually presented and if a case happened to be of special interest to H.C., he generally took over the discussion. He was also regular in his attendance at meetings of the Medical Library Committee, and before his retirement from the governing Board of Permanent Officers of the School of Medicine he seldom missed a meeting.

Proofs of the meningioma monograph arrived continuously during April and May and H.C. worked industriously over them with the printer, arranging for all the innumerable "workarounds" and, in general, supervising to as great an extent as possible the actual printing of the book. By July everything was in readiness except the indexes which he left for his collaborator to complete when on 6 July he sailed for England.

This trip to Europe was most gratifying for it was somewhat in the nature of a triumphal celebration. He was in reasonably good health again, he was committed to no speeches, and at Oxford he received the degree of Doctor of Science, *honoris causa,* surrounded by friends and pupils who had come from far and near to pay him homage. Klebs' diary tells much of the story:

11 July. Harvey Cushing and Pat, his nephew, blew in from the boat train of the *Queen Mary.* He looked splendidly, I thought, and he acted as if he never had had a day of illness. We had a spacious drawing-room of the old fashioned kind such as only Brown's provides. Soon H. was in contact with all his friends of London and Oxford. Hugh Cairns, one of his favourite pupils, now Professor of Surgery (Nuffield) at the Radcliffe Infirmary, came in and we had a good chat and dinner.

12 July. Nice time at the Royal College of Surgeons where Beattie, who has succeeded Sir Arthur Keith in the curatorship, showed us the new laboratories, and in the library we found Sir D'Arcy Power and soon were joined also by Sir Charles Sherrington. The latter who is well over eighty (he hates to consider age numerically) seemed younger than ever, sunburned and lively and as elegant in his book tastes as he had been in his experiments. D'Arcy the same dear man, but alas a little more crippled though always gay and smiling. Beattie is a live wire who makes things anthropological hum at the College. He is young and Irish and we will yet hear of him. Sherrington saying that he had lately much admired some of [Lynn] Thorndike's work, made me take a cab to the British Museum where I picked up Thorndike and brought him over, much to the surprise of Sherrington. We had a very good time discussing all sorts of world-moving questions; then to lunch at Sir D'Arcy's hospitable house.

In the evening of this, Sir William Osler's birthday, we attended the annual meeting of the Osler Club where Archie Malloch was to give the annual oration. A big table full of nice people ate dinner together at the Langham Hotel and afterwards Malloch gave an address on old Oslerian platitudes, but it was nice and friendly and in that it represented the Osler spirit. . . .

13 July. We had a delightful evening at Keynes' who showed us interesting pieces of his remarkable collection which makes me wonder always how he in active surgical practice could manage to bring it together and also write those excellent bibliographies of Browne, Harvey, and others. We call him St. Damian, and his wife was a Darwin. Another night Sir Almroth Wright came to dine with us. He is quite old and hard to understand, but still full of fun about his "megistology." He is indeed the G.B.S. of medicine and I regret that this time I could not go to see him at his operating corner in St. Mary's Hospital where years and years ago I had already heard him discoursing with Metchnikov the pros and cons of senile love. Then on Friday the 15th we went down to Oxford, met by Cairns who took us to dinner at his house. Here we found Morelle of Louvain, one of Harvey's boys, also Martin of Bruxelles another one, and the Raffaele Bastianellis who had come all the way from Rome to honour H.C.

15 July. We had very nice rooms at Bardwell Court. The Vice-Chancellor gave H.C. a luncheon at Balliol. About thirty of H.'s friends or pupils had assembled in his honour. I felt highly honoured to be sitting beside the V.-C., Dr. Lindsay, with Sir Cuthbert Wallace on the other side, Sir Farquhar Buzzard (the Regius of Medicine, Osler's successor) and Almroth Wright, while H.C. had on his right the President of Corpus, that delightful Greek scholar Sir Richard Livingstone, R.W.T. Gunther, etc. Among those closest to H.C. were Clovis Vincent, the brain surgeon of Paris who has now received a great institution, also Thierry de Martel of Paris, Oljenick of Amsterdam, Schaltenbrand of Würzburg, Paul Martin and Morelle of Belgium, then his English and Scotch pupils, Jefferson, Cairns, del Río Hortega (Ramón y Cajal's pupil from Valençia now with Cairns), Norman Dott, H. F. Alexander, Prof. Gunn, Pattison, Gibson, Riddoch, Girdlestone, R. B. Johnson, Paterson Ross; John Johnson the printer was due but had to be excused. It was a great gathering around a beloved master such as the world has rarely produced. No speeches, thank the Lord, only pleasant chat such as you get nowhere else. Then we went over to the Sheldonian for the ceremony which no doubt you have seen described, with what Cairns called "the Chief's police record in Latin" read by the Public Orator, Cyril Bailey.

The memorable Latin presentation has been englished by W. W. Francis:

Here we have a chief surgeon who has removed more than two thousand cerebral tumors. The son, grandson, and great-grandson of physicians, he acquired both a doctor's degree and his letter for base ball at Yale University and after his return from pursuing his studies in Europe, he taught and by his deeds proved that the difficult art of operating on the brain—the surgical Northwest Passage [*Symplegadas*] he once called it—could be of the greatest benefit to sufferers. Moreover, the further he progressed in this art, the more he showed that he who works slowest works best. He believed that electricity is of great advantage in these remedial measures; perhaps he mistrusted the healing force of Nature, but certainly he left nothing to chance. His service in the Great War—what he himself went through and how his skill must have eased the sufferings of the wounded—is well known. For twenty years he taught as professor at Yale and Harvard what he of himself had learned, and many of his pupils have to-day achieved great fame. Nor was it only his scalpel but he also made good use of his pen. Witness his many professional writings on the nerves, on the structure of the brain and on the pituitary gland; and for us laymen, has he not written the most famous memorial of his friend, William Osler? Now that this gifted guest comes here for us to offer our tribute to one already loaded with honors, I present to you that most eminent surgeon, Harvey Cushing, Companion of the Most Illustrious Order of the Bath, to be admitted to the honorary degree of Doctor of Science.

Klebs continued:

It was a delightful occasion, doubly delightful for its graceful simplicity and the charm of the hosts; then a Garden party at Cairns', followed by a buffet supper. We all had a great time and no headache from too many cocktails, in fact there weren't any. . . .

17 July. H.C. held a clinic at the Radcliffe. It was fine to see him by a sickbed and listening to the reports, then approaching the subject as a layman would do without any of the mannerism of the maistre—*"docta ignorantia"!* We dined with the President of Corpus Christi at the College and there was some good talk over the port and cigars in the upper room. Of course Sir Richard Livingstone made us take the napkin along and H.C. celebrated the ritual by putting it into his pocket for exportation to the USA. They all thought that this was very funny.

18 July. Next day back to our Brown's Hotel in London where soon W. W. Francis turned up straight from his steamer. There was a sale at Sotheby's with a great collection of Boyles and we decided to see what it looked like. All the best known booksellers, Quaritch, Maggs, Davis & Orioli, Goldschmidt, etc. were there and it was interesting to watch their physiognomies and actions though I must confess it puzzled me greatly in its details.

19 July. We did many other things the next days, all delightful and evidently borne very well by H.C. Of course we were very comfortable, did not rise early, and did nothing strenuous. The nearest to strenuosity was the opening by Queen Mary of the new wing at the Queen Square National Hospital for Nervous Diseases. Sitting right in front of the gracious lady we listened to a good speech by the Earl of Athlone, K.G. and another one by Captain Styles, Chairman of the Board. H.C. was asked to join the Queen in her tour of inspection, but he had to regret on account of his unsteady underpinnings.

On the 21st we three went to Croydon for the plane for Paris and Geneva. H.C. stayed with us till the 26th when he left us for Cannes to join his steamer *Conte di Savoia* while Pat had gone to Rome from where he made a motor trip with friends through the hill towns. Here you have the chronicle of these memorable days. . . .

The trip to England and the days afterwards with Klebs in Nyon had given H.C. a good rest and change as one may infer from the lighthearted letter he wrote his host from the *SS. Conte di Savoia:*

Wednesday, 3 August [1938].
I believe but am not quite sure.

Dear Arnold, I have been talking with the ship's doctor, de Martino by name—a somewhat dry Martino. He tells me that everyone is happier going West than going East because of the longer days. I at all events have profited by the additional hour gained and have slept profoundly. Even Pat, who claims never to snore—most people do—has so tuned up in the small hours I've been obliged to switch on all of the cabin lights and holler "All out for New York, for heaven's sake turn over."

Incidentally we are brown as Indians from sitting in the sun—such parts of us as we permitted to be exposed. Most of the other people on the ship have not been so squeamish. There are votaries even of the knee-chest position who for hours take the sun in that attitude. Just why I have not yet learned. Most everyone wears less than at Cannes, which is remarkable though possible, if you can believe it. There is a certain limit, however, and guards are stationed at the dining room portals to weed out those with fig leaves from the truly nude who are turned back, not from any sense of modesty but for hygienic reasons. The dining room is air-conditioned and they might catch cold. Some nice Spanish people got on at Gibraltar—descendants of Ferdinand de Soto. Really! I've consequently gone quite Franco even though I don't quite know which side Franco is on. Is he for Mussolini or Hitler? I asked the Room Steward and he said "Shish!" The Table Steward looked scared and also said "Shish!" So I don't expect to find out before we dock, which will be tomorrow a.m. about dawn. They say the temp. F.° in N.Y. is in the 90s. I telephoned Kate not long ago and she asked who it was talking I said "Pupeen! Pupeeeen!" This delay cost me nearly a million lira for by the time I was identified, there was only time left for her to say it was hot. . . .

On reaching New Haven he settled down among his books. On Tuesday, 6 September, Mr. Reinhold F. Gehner of the Banta Publishing Company arrived in New Haven bearing the first copy of the meningioma monograph. H.C. could not have been more pleased had it been the first book that had ever come from his pen. He promptly arranged a tea party to celebrate, inviting his collaborator, Louise Eisenhardt, her mother, and several other friends who had watched the book in the process of its development. One of his friends wrote later: "It is not only a beautiful book in itself—a great credit to Thomas and Banta—but it means so much more. It really marks the culmination of Dr. Cushing's professional career and is the embodiment of all the things he has stood for during his life. Without his painstaking case records, the book could never have been compiled. His artistic ability is indicated in his operative sketches, which occur every few pages. His extraordinary knowledge of the day-to-day life of his patients, the fact that he gave as much, if not more, time and attention to the impecunious Tim Donovan as he did to Leonard Wood can be read between the lines and it makes the book irresistibly fascinating."

Letters to Klebs, filled with bookish questions, continued at weekly intervals, and if one may judge from their context, many bibliographical points discussed at Nyon had been left unsettled. Two things, however, distracted him. The first was the September hurricane of 1938, the second, another storm center which developed at the same time at Munich.

28 September 1938.

. . . In a letter sent you a few days ago I must have acknowledged your very welcome cable which gave me as great a kick as did Putti's message to you on receiving your float to posterity. I scarcely remember what may have happened since then, for we have had a hectic ten days what with the hurricane which has played havoc with our corner of the world, as you may have gathered from the chance reports you have seen in the papers. We got off luckily at 691, but thousands of trees were blown down in New England, and the top of Mill Rock was almost swept clean. When the storm struck the Coast at the eastern end of Long Island, it played havoc with all the shore places of Narragansett Bay and the Cape, sweeping out of existence the famous Bailey's Beach of which H. B. Jacobs has been the supervising censor so far as costumes are concerned. It is calculated that some thousand lives were lost and we haven't yet heard much from Vermont or New Hampshire where it ended up. So far as I can make out, this is the first hurricane that failed to sweep out to sea at the end of its course but was caught in the trough between two areas of high pressure and swept inland.

But all this which affected us so seriously in this small corner of the world has been relegated to the back pages of the paper in view of what is going on between the nations of Europe over this Czechoslovakian matter. It looks at this moment as though Hitler had overstepped himself in his second demands propounded at Chamberlain's second visit, for now the opinion of the world seems to have turned against him. His sabre-rattling speech of Monday with its abuse of Benes was so in contrast to Chamberlain's mild reply to Roosevelt's two appeals that the sympathy of most of the world seems to be concentrated on Benes and Chamberlain. Meanwhile, Mussolini seems to have been jockeyed out of his bumptious position.

The extraordinary part of it all to me is the important place the radio and aeroplane have come to play in international affairs. It's not impossible that had Grey been able to fly to Berlin and have a personal consultation with the Kaiser, the last war might have been delayed and possibly somehow adjudicated. If I remember correctly, you don't have a radio at Les Terrasses, which is a good thing for you would probably become as much of an addict as we have become. Fortunately, or unfortunately, owing to the storm we have been without light or electricity and have learned to get along without the hourly turning of the dial to get the last news from Europe. . . .

And again on 5 October:

I am enclosing a page from *Time* which will give you a good idea of the track of the hurricane. We are only just beginning to get returns from New Hampshire and Vermont which have been completely cut off from the rest of the country. . . . We have only just begun to get mail from Boston, and Viets writes me that he is working by candlelight and can quite appreciate the difficulties of the tallow-dip age and wonders how they accomplished as much as they did. The enclosed [account of the hurricane], undated, has just come from Streeter, the centre of the storm having passed about over them. The Blue Hill Observatory seems to have been one of the few places whose meteorological apparatus withstood the gale and was able to record the velocity of the wind which they report to have reached 186 miles an hour—almost unbelievable. . . .

Palmer Futcher, who called on the Cushings about this time, gives some idea of Cushing's concern about Munich:

On September 29, 1938, I spent the night with Dr. Cushing in New Haven; Mrs. Cushing and Barbara had gone to New York and we were alone. It was during the days of Munich and Berchtesgaden, and the radio news was very exciting. Dr. Cushing was tremendously interested in it all. He refused to have dinner in the dining room, but had it brought into the library on a low table; we dined sitting on the sofa so that we would miss none of the news emanating from the radio near at hand. That was the last time I saw him.

Cushing was naturally much interested in his old friend's son, and especially because the young Palmer Futcher when a premedical undergraduate at Harvard had come to him for help and criticism while writing an essay in which the physiology of growth was ably analyzed.[6]

For many years Cushing had looked forward to the time when he would have sufficient leisure to catalogue his library and to annotate the books which had been accumulating so rapidly during the previous ten years. He was particularly interested in the provenance of individual copies, and although he had made a substantial beginning in 1935 and 1936, he set about once again in the autumn of 1938 not only to catalogue his entire library, but to make an index of the more interesting sources from which individual volumes had come. He had had no training in cataloguing, but he soon learned the techniques of book description, and some of his detailed collations are masterpieces of minute bibliographical dissection. Unfortunately for those who had later to revise his cards, he had a gay disregard for consistency, but since the problem of putting his catalogue cards into standard form was not too difficult, his original entries, all written in his own hand (and the majority of them copiously annotated), are proving invaluable to those who are gradually cataloguing his library.[7] While engaged in listing his books he had the usual

[6] *Giants and dwarfs. A study of the anterior lobe of the hypophysis.* Cambridge, Harvard University Press, 1933, 80 pp.

[7] *The Harvey Cushing collection of books and manuscripts,* New York, Schuman's 1943, xvi, 207 pp. This short-title list of the Cushing library was undertaken immediately after his death, the task having first been entrusted to Mr. H. H. Schaltenbrand, who died a year later. Miss Margaret Brinton and Mrs. Henrietta T. Perkins, who had commenced work in the Yale Medical Library in January 1940, are chiefly responsible for compiling the catalogue and seeing it through the press. It is the intention of the Historical Library to publish from time to time detailed and annotated catalogues of its various special collections. One such compilation has already been issued (*A bio-bibliography of Andreas Vesalius.* New York, Schuman's, 1943, xxxviii, 229 pp.).

succession of visitors and academic functions. After a reception he gave for the Society of Clinical Surgery at the end of October, he asked several of his friends whether he looked as much a wreck as other members of the Society, for he seemed to think that *anno Domini* was catching up with them more rapidly than with him.

In November Henry Sigerist appeared in New Haven for a week to give the Terry Lectures—a Yale foundation designed to integrate science and religion. After a few appropriate references to the Almighty, he proceeded to discuss the history of socialized medicine and to predict its future. His position was sufficiently challenging to attract an unusually large audience, but his deductions[8] were too much for one of Cushing's conservative convictions. In a revealing note to Klebs he once more alludes to his distrust of those who attempt to reform the medical profession:

> . . . Henry Sigerist has come and gone, having accomplished his Terry Lectures before full houses of enthusiastic people. He is a most engaging person, but I wish I could see eye-to-eye with him in regard to his expressed views about health. Perhaps it's true that if doctors knew enough to keep people in good health by repeated physical examinations there would be fewer old crocks like ourselves to care for; but then, I rather doubt it. And when the reformers and public health officials reach our age and begin to find their machinery is wearing out, I sometimes wonder what kind of panel doctors they will find to take an interest in them.

In December he wrote Klebs again: "Imagine my excitement to find on my desk this morning, with a Christmas dedication from George Sarton, his special No. of *Osiris* completely given over to you and your great project. Such a tribute to any one is rarely paid and you must have a warm glow in the cockles of your heart"—this without knowing that Klebs had taken quite a different view of the Sarton monograph. Sarton, who had previously published the Klebs short-title list of medical and scientific incunabula (alluded to earlier) had become so impressed with the monumental character of Klebs' labor that he set out to prepare a detailed review. The review grew longer and longer and eventually developed into a monograph of two hundred pages which he issued in November 1938 as a special

[8] A contemporary summary of Sigerist's Terry Lectures ran: "The three lectures on the general theme of 'Medicine and Society' were divided as follows: 2 November, 'The Significance of Disease'; 3 November, 'The Significance of Health'; 4 November, 'The Mission of the Physician'. The themes, dealt with historically, were handled with consummate skill, and by the irresistible force of his logic one was led to conclude that it would be in the best interest of medicine as well as society if the profession became organized through a vast scheme of social insurance so that the wage earner who fell ill could be assured of free medical care, and the physician assured of sound training, regular holidays, and a regular income. The mission of the physician, he said, is to abolish disease so that men will die a physiological death from old age rather than from disease as we now know it. Sigerist is a complete materialist who has erected a superstructure of idealism upon the firm foundation of disillusionment."

fasciculus of the 5th volume of *Osiris*[9] in which the short-title list had been issued. He had immediately dispatched a copy of the review to Klebs expecting that he would be much pleased by the attention. Unhappily this was not the way Klebs reacted, as Sarton related a year later after Cushing's death:

> . . . Since you are even better acquainted with Klebs than I am, you know that his fundamental generosity is sometimes eclipsed by fits of anger and jealousy. This is well illustrated by the "Incunabula" episode. My long memoir on scientific incunabula was written by me—just as H.C. guessed it—as a tribute to Klebs and when the book was mailed to him I naïvely expected a warm letter of thanks from him. Instead of which I received a volley of abuse!! Klebs taking the attitude that I was poaching on his own territory, stealing his thunder, that the incunabula were *his* to deal with, not mine, etc. . . . As I know him well and love him, I answered very gently, and simply waited for a change of weather. It is characteristic of Klebs' generosity and sincerity that he now sends me H.C.'s letter—which is, as it were, the judgment of an impartial observer—now sacred by death. It is very probable that when that letter reached Klebs the latter was still so angry with me that he did not read it well—and that he only understood it now. . . .

A. C. Klebs to George Sarton *18 November 1939.*

> Dear George Sarton . . . Here is also H.C.'s letter to me on receipt of your Incunabula work. I now wish I had taken his simple view of it. He was built on larger lines and I wasn't. That's about all that can be said about it. . . .

Thus Klebs came to accept Sarton's motives for their true worth and harmony was restored so that despite the difficulties of communication during the early years of the war they were able once more to resume their warm friendship.

1939

While attempting to catalogue his library, Cushing became more and more interested in the details of technical bibliography. In 1936 he had collaborated in a paper on the bibliography of Galvani and he had periodically worked at the compilation of a definitive bibliography of Vesalius whose trail he had followed so assiduously through the years. In Vesalius he had found an artistic temperament and an impetuous nature not unlike his own and he felt that he must now, in the time that still remained, gather together everything that his long search had brought to light. Since his trip abroad in 1900 he had been collecting books, photographs, medals, indeed everything that might have even a remote bearing upon the life and work of the great anatomist. He had on several occasions read papers on various aspects of the Vesalian achievement, and his notes concerning the man and his books had become surprisingly voluminous, as had his files of correspondence with the Vesalian scholars he had

[9] "The scientific literature transmitted through the incunabula." *Osiris*, 1938, *5*, 41-245.

consulted throughout the world. But until the beginning of 1939 he had made little attempt to bring the material together into publishable form. During the winter of 1938-1939 and the following spring the plan for a bio-bibliography of Vesalius gradually took shape and in February he sent a provisional outline to Klebs.

When spring came the family was obliged to move out of the dining room since he had confiscated the large table, as well as all the sideboards and window ledges for bibliographic ends. By June several of the early chapters had been drafted and during the summer he worked on the sixth chapter dealing with the *Fabrica*. This delayed him much more than he had anticipated, and when the war broke out in September he was so distracted by the news that he found it almost impossible to concentrate on his task. The *Athenia* went down on the 3rd, with one of his former house officers, John Lawrence, aboard. Fortunately Lawrence was rescued and toward the end of the month he visited Cushing and gave him a vivid account of the episode. Lawrence wrote of this visit to his friend Chauncey Leake:

> . . . During the past five years I had seen Dr. Cushing at least twice a year; and never during this period had he appeared so well and in such good spirits. As usual he showed intense interest in everything that was going on in science, medicine and politics. During the past few years he has been working on a library of the history of science, and in full view of his desk hung a large table of atomic elements; and he showed us carefully arranged complete reprints of all the original articles of men such as Lord Rutherford and C. T. R. Wilson, etc. with personal notes from each of them. He complained that in one or two instances his requests for reprints had not been answered, and he supposed that he had been assumed to be another quack doctor or scientist. When Mr. Walcott asked him why he was interested in the history of pure science and physics, he answered that medicine was the mother and stimulator of all science. It is probable that Dr. Cushing has made the most complete collection of important contributions in the field of physics that exists in this country. Then he got out a volume of papers and letters concerning Popsy Welch and leafed through it and reminisced with Senator Walcott, since both of them knew Dr. Welch so well. . . .
>
> Dr. Cushing and Senator Walcott spoke of their attendance at the funeral of Dr. Welch in Norfolk and of their meeting with Mr. Johnson, who was the owner of the drugstore in that town and who had been a schoolmate of Dr. Welch. He had also been an apprentice to Dr. Welch's father in his medical practice there and finally had been set up in business by the elder Dr. Welch. Mr. Johnson said to Dr. Cushing and Senator Walcott, "Well, boys, they say that Willie did pretty well down south there in Baltimore. Well, you know, he never compared with his father." It was clear that the elder Welch was his hero.
>
> Much of the luncheon time was spent talking about the new addition to the Yale Medical Library, the architect of which is Grosvenor Atterbury. Senator Walcott referred to this as the "Cushing Library", which was denied by Dr. Cushing. . . . We then went to the dining room, which had been completely converted into a research study. The large table and the entire room were covered with books and papers relating to Vesalius, on whom Dr. Cushing was writing

a volume. For an hour we saw volume after volume and plate after plate of Vesalius, with reminiscences on when this and how that rare volume had been obtained, etc. It was an hour of feasting in the history of medicine. We took leave, and Dr. Cushing left the Senator at the Graduates' Club, and we continued on to the hospital. On the way, he talked of the applications of physics to medicine and how important it was to develop this field. I left him in the halls of the New Haven Hospital, and he never seemed more active mentally and physically. Little did I realize that this was my last chance to be with him. . . .

Cushing's Vesalian labors had also been interrupted earlier in the year, but by an event far happier than the outbreak of war. In April the Harvey Cushing Society had come to New Haven to celebrate his seventieth birthday. The Society had laid its plans with care and since there had been a birthday volume at the time of his sixtieth birthday, it was decided for his seventieth to issue a complete bibliography of his writings—a wise choice as it turned out, for since H.C. had meanwhile developed something of a passion for bibliography himself, this detailed record of his own "ink-pot" career seemed especially to please him.[10]

The Society had their usual two-day session of papers, clinics, and demonstrations, followed by a third day of less formal proceedings climaxed by the seventieth-birthday dinner on the evening of Saturday, 8 April. Although Arnold Klebs' health was somewhat precarious, he made a surprise journey from Switzerland, arriving the day before the birthday party, to Cushing's utter astonishment and delight. Many others came from a distance. Olof Sjöqvist of Stockholm, who had been spending a year in New Haven as a Rockefeller Fellow, presented a birthday volume of papers written by Cushing's friends and admirers in Sweden. Cables arrived from friends and colleagues in eleven different countries and twenty-nine states; indeed, the letters and messages were so numerous that the Society decided after the meeting to issue them in a separate volume describing the occasion.[11]

The dinner was memorable for many reasons. The Society had not forgotten Cushing's devoted operating room orderly, Adolph Watzka, who for twenty years had arranged H.C.'s surgical headlight, lifted his patients on and off the operating table, and, even more important, mopped his brow on hot days in the operating room, for Adolph was the only one who knew how to do it without smudging his glasses. Adolph was on hand at the dinner, prepared to serve his Chief once more in any contingency which might befall him in

[10] *A bibliography of the writings of Harvey Cushing*. Springfield, Illinois, Charles C Thomas, 1939, 108 pp.

[11] *Harvey Cushing's Seventieth Birthday Party, April 8, 1939*. Springfield, Illinois, Charles C Thomas, 1939, 146 pp.

the course of the meal. Instead, he mopped beads of perspiration from Arnold Klebs' bald head when he began to speak. Although introduced with this light touch, Klebs' toast came from his heart and epitomized Cushing's career perhaps as aptly as anything that has been written or said of it, for he proposed "Harvey Cushing the artist." "Now the birthday," he said, "is but a temporal locus and the child is weighed by sheer numbers of experienced years. Luckily the tyrannical *ratio* of number, measure and weight one still may escape by that winged mount that possibly a friendly Venus has provided and which guided by loving sensibility, by eyeless vision, by earless hearing and non-tactile feeling he led to Olympian heights—and so to Harvey Cushing the artist I offer my toast!"

Sjöqvist's remarks in presenting the Scandinavian birthday volume were, in best Swedish tradition, most felicitous. Stanhope Bayne-Jones spoke, as dean, "with admiration for his achievements and with deep appreciation of all his presence has meant to the School and the University," and Arnold Muirhead brought warmhearted messages from the Osler Club in London. William W. Francis reminded the gathering of early days at the Hopkins:

> . . . My good years in Baltimore coincided with Dr. Cushing's first neurological gropings, and in the ordinary routine of the fourth-year student's surgical training it fell to my joyful lot one day to "assist" him (in quotation marks!) in one of his early brain tumor operations. After being duly dolled up and even more than duly washed up, I stood around impatient for a close-up glimpse into these new wonders, and trying to persuade myself that "They also serve who only stand and wait." For the ensuing disaster I was not responsible—unless in the capacity of a Jonah. With the scalp incision the patient died! It was one of those tragedies that used to make old Sir J. Y. Simpson turn in his grave when Bigelow in the Elysian Fields would dig him in the ghostly ribs and say, "What else can you expect of chloroform?" Inevitably there were many such discouragements, but, thank God, they could not daunt the pioneering spirit in the fourth generation of the best Western-Reserved, New England medical germ-plasm.
>
> During most of that last year of mine at the medical school, 1901-02, my room at the Hotel Grossler, as Osler called his hospitable house in honor of Mrs. O's first husband, was required for a niece, so I lodged next door with the "latch-keyers." Naturally I developed a lifelong affection for H.C. second only to my feelings toward his kindred spirit, the elder Chief. I wonder if two adjacent houses, with a couple of boards knocked out of the intervening backyard fence (it was a *garden* fence on the Osler side) can ever, before or since, have sheltered such a pair of congenial geniuses, so useful, hard-working, stimulating, informative, Vesaliolatrous, and withal so exuberant, cheery, witty and playful. . . .

The bibliography of Cushing's writings was gracefully presented by Louise Eisenhardt who as president of the Society had been toastmistress at the dinner. In Cushing's reply one finds something of the secret of the *esprit de corps* that he had inspired in his many pupils throughout the world:

My fellow co-workers, guests and friends: neurologists, neurosurgeons, ophthalmologists, printers, publishers, and others unclassified and unexpected including an interloper, Dr. Arnold Klebs, also Dr. William Francis and Adolph:

Some people conceal their age by recognizing no birthdays; some—even women, occasionally confess to a birthday when they happen to feel like it; there are those also who achieve birthdays and those who have birthdays thrust upon them. There was a time when I used to look forward eagerly to the 8th of April because a small coterie of friends customarily dined on that date at the Maryland Club in Baltimore quietly to recognize the natal day of William H. Welch. There was a perennial joke between us that so long as we celebrated *his* birthday, *mine* would pass unnoticed and I would stay forever young. But something went wrong with this. In 1896 when at the age of 27 I first joined the Johns Hopkins staff, he was then about twice my age. Instead of growing appreciably older during the next 34 years, he appeared never to change in any respect save for a noticeably progressive gain in circumference. [After referring to the H.C. Society and urging its members to keep their own operative score, he continued:]

So you see I've spent my neurosurgical life leaning heavily on others: on Percival Bailey and his pupil Louise in histopathology; on Clifford Walker for keeping our perimetry reasonably accurate by periodically coming on from the West Coast to check our procedures; on Larry Reynolds and Merrill Sosman for their unfailing interest in the roentgenological features of the work; . . . and on many more of you for assistance at the operating table, more particularly to Gil Horrax who for so long a time carried the brunt of the load. And the best I can wish for one and all of you is that you may be equally blessed in your future labors with a comparably loyal, capable and hard-working succession of co-workers.

Unhappily some whose faces I miss sorely are not here—doubly dead in that they died so young. Charles Locke, much beloved for his humanity, was a victim of the Cleveland Clinic disaster. Dick Meagher with a brilliant future ahead of him was carried off no less suddenly by a coronary thrombosis. And equally lamentable has been the recent death from accident of that remarkable genius, Arthur McLean, a man of dual personality and his own worst enemy—poet, artist and gifted writer on one side, while on the other he displayed the intolerance of a Scottish Covenanter toward those whose standards seemed to him less high than his own. May he now rest in peace.

I am aware that this is not strictly a society of neurosurgeons and that its membership is open to others in allied lines of work. Of this there might be no end, for practically all disorders, to which mind and body are heir, first or last come to affect the nervous system. Neurology, broadly speaking, is a field for thinkers as well as doers, and it is gratifying that the surgical doers for almost the first time in the history of medicine have come to be recognized as deserving of membership in the societies of those otherwise engaged. This being so, we must look to it that we justify this recognition by the character of our contributions.

While ours is perhaps the most arduous and responsible of the many surgical specialties, we can have the great satisfaction of knowing that only men of a certain type will venture to make it their life work and that, so far at least, both in this country and abroad its devotees have not only shown the kind of sympathetic and encouraging interest in one another's activities that binds men closely together but have at the same time held the respect of the profession as a whole. May this continue for all time to be true.

In closing I may quote a verse from the Talmud which is mindful of the first aphorism of Hippocrates but is none the worse for that:

> "The day is short and work is great. The reward is also great and the Master praises. It is not incumbent on thee to complete the work but thou must not therefore cease from it."

One who particularly wished to attend the birthday party was Clovis Vincent of Paris who, with de Martel, was one of Cushing's most loyal admirers. Vincent had started his distinguished career in French medicine as a neurologist; after his visit to Cushing's clinic in 1927, he returned to Paris and although he had not had even elementary training in surgery, he turned his unusual talents to the problems of the operating room and in the course of time had made himself one of the most accomplished neurosurgeons on the continent of Europe. Cushing had watched his career with the deepest interest and in 1933, when he saw him operate for the first time, he was profoundly impressed by his skill and competence. Vincent's references to Cushing, always generous, were never more forcefully expressed than in the inaugural address referred to by Klebs:

A. C. Klebs to H.C. *Nyon, 6 June 1939.*

Dear Harvey, Here is your most excellent letter of 26 May. Many thanks. It is so full of news and interesting comments that it would take me pages to do it justice not having your happy talent of condensation. So I will for the moment spare you that and confine myself to talking about what is at present closest to my heart: the inaugural lesson by Clovis Vincent which my dear friend and archiater Piotet sent me just before leaving for England, in the No. 40 of the *Presse Médicale* of 20 May, the thoughtful fellow!

Reading it, there came over me again that thrill of a superior beatitude as when you and I that morning at the Pitié for the first time saw Vincent at work. Of course I had no judgment in the matter, but I could not help but feel your silent enthusiasm, your deep satisfaction with what you had not anticipated. That's the way I thought a Perugino must have felt when he peeped over Raphael's shoulder on to the canvas he slowly developed with his brush. And now that same Vincent proves himself a master also with his pen, for it seems to me never has your great theme been so lucidly presented as in this very *leçon*. I just feel that you will be delighted with it.

How terse and how poignant: Cushing s'impose à lui-même une discipline de fer, et l'impose à tous. Il ne connaît pas le respect humain. Il ne connaît que la vie des malades et les progrès de la science. Il a compris que le neuro-chirurgien doit être entrainé physiquement comme un champion olympique, et avoir renoncé à tout, ou presque à tout, comme un trappiste. . . . J'ai voulu montrer que le magnifique monument qu'il a élevé à la gloire neuro-chirurgie américaine, c'est à sa volonté, à son intelligence, à sa conscience, qu'on le doit.

Oh Harvey, I owe you so much, but I must not repay you badly by too many words. Thus VALE.

After the birthday party H.C. settled down again to work at Vesalius. He had become increasingly conscious of his growing physical infirmity and had resolutely declined repeated invitations from his friends in Baltimore to speak at the fiftieth anniversary celebrations of the Johns Hopkins Hospital. Winford H. Smith, Director of the Hospital, on three occasions urged him to reconsider, but H.C. finally replied: "My hesitation to accept the proposal is wholly due to my indifferent health." He continued:

> . . . Concerning this the less said the better; but I have been conscious of a slowly advancing vascular disorder ever since the War, and as long as it chiefly affected my legs I was able to do a little work from time to time. But now that I have begun to claudicate mentally, I think it better to abandon the effort in future to prepare and deliver addresses lest others observe about me what has already become painfully apparent to myself. You will remember Dodgson's old jingle about Father William. An acceptance of this alluring invitation would mean that I had reached a stage more advanced even than his. . . .

Although conscious of his difficulties, he seldom gave the slightest indication of his trouble to any save those with whom he was most intimate. Only rarely did he lose the thread of a story, and his critical faculties, as far as one can judge from the Vesalius manuscript, remained acute until his death.

During the spring and summer he had frequent visits from his many friends, and when alone he nearly always invited guests for tea and dinner. Few felt that they were really interrupting his work on Vesalius, for shortly after the meal their services were generally enlisted in verifying collations or in passing judgment on the newest portion of his manuscript. Another most effective way of occupying his guests lay in his flattering invitations to translate some Vesalian Latin. He had several tough prefaces which could silence even the best classical scholars for hours at a time.

His friend Herbert M. Evans of the University of California paid him a visit in May. On this occasion he summoned his one-time colleague, Frederick T. Lewis from Boston. "We had a Vesalian evening," he wrote, "the outcome of which is the enclosed letter about the tablet in Calcar's portrait which gives me information I had long sought." This was promptly sent to Klebs for his comment. Herbert Evans, who had shared Cushing's enthusiastic interest in the physiology of the pituitary, had finally succeeded in obtaining a pure extract of the growth hormone of the anterior pituitary, which in less pure form H.C. had once tried out on "Edna" and the other dwarfs. When his paper was eventually published in 1936, Cushing wrote: "Catchpole has just shown us your magnificent paper—many congratulations. It is admirably presented and most convincing, and I think it is the best thing you have ever done. It shows how worthwhile is slow maturity of thought on such a complex subject and is worth dozens of papers on isolated facts. . . . One always thinks of William Harvey's waiting twelve years before publishing the *De motu cordis*. . . . We look back on your visit with great delight. You are a kind of walking ferment in trousers."

At this time Cushing had indication, through his election to Honorary Fellowship in the Royal College of Physicians, of the esteem in which he was held by his colleagues in Britain. Although he realized that this was a most unusual recognition for a surgeon, Cushing did not fully appreciate the signal character of his new honor until the Secretary of the College had replied to his letter of acceptance.

Royal College of Physicians, London,
H. M. Barlow to H.C. *20 May 1939.*

I had a fleeting glance at your welcome reply to the President, and saw that you were interested to know whether a Surgeon had ever before enjoyed the honour. No, the distinction is yours alone. King Edward VII, when Prince of Wales, was elected an Honorary Fellow in 1897; and in 1928, to mark the auspicious occasion of the Tercentenary of the publication of Harvey's *De motu cordis,* the College elected four Honorary Fellows, namely, Lord Balfour, Lord Rutherford, Professor Pavlov, and Professor Wenckebach. Of these, Professor Wenckebach is happily with us. You are the only other Honorary Fellow.

It will be an additional interest to you to know that, including yourself, only six individuals have enjoyed the distinction of Honorary Fellowship in the course of two and a half centuries. With kind regards, Yours very sincerely, H. M. BARLOW, Secretary.

Overwhelmed, H.C. wrote Barlow:

Thanks greatly for your illuminating note of May 20th about the honorary fellowship from which I learn that I am the only surgeon to have received this distinguished recognition. I shall have to watch my step carefully lest I do something in my remaining years to cause the College to regret its action.

In June came welcome news that the University had decided to allocate $600,000 for the erection of the new Medical Library, one wing of which was to be set aside for the historical collections that Cushing had brought together and had persuaded others to join in giving. As indicated earlier, there had been some difference of opinion about the site for the new library, but when the President of the University pointed out that the Sterling Trustees, who had authorized the expenditure, could not use their funds for anything but the extension of an existing structure, the plan for erecting a separate building was abandoned. This was all to the good, since it meant that the new library would be an extension of the Sterling Hall of Medicine and would thus lie in the geographic center of the School itself—which, Cushing felt, was exactly where a library should be. In reporting this to Klebs he wrote: "All this may not be very understandable to you, but I am expecting to hear from them any minute to the effect that they have allocated a half million dollars to us, that Atterbury will immediately go ahead to modify his plans for the Y-shaped building in the middle of the present Medical School group and to enlarge it to hold a possible 400,000 books instead of the 200,000 his plans originally called for, and that they propose to start building at once. . . ." There followed a series of conferences with Grosvenor Atterbury, the architect, which continued throughout the summer. By the end of September the plans were in a forward state and in process of being finally approved by the University's Committee on Architectural Plan. Gratified as he was by all this, he was nevertheless greatly depressed by the declaration of war and he spoke frequently of his many European pupils and of the strain and hardship war would bring to them.

He was also disturbed by the deaths, two months apart, of his old friends, Charles H. and William J. Mayo. On hearing of Dr. Will's death he dropped his work on Vesalius to prepare an appreciation which was to be the last piece of writing to appear in his lifetime.[12]

> There was nothing mysterious or supernatural about this twentieth century Lourdes at whose doors incredible numbers of the lame, halt and blind have for years been daily delivered from the ends of the earth. Nothing supernatural—unless possibly the flawless, life-long devotion of two brothers for one another be so regarded. Not since the somewhat mythical attachment of those fifth century physicians, Cosmas and Damian, both of whom in due time came to be sanctified, has there been anything quite like it. . . .
>
> Different as W. J. and C. H. Mayo were from each other, I have always felt that there was something Lincolnesque about them both. It was shown not only by their modesty and self-effacement, but in their shrewd appraisal of other people in whatever walk of life. It was also shown by their quiet dry sense of humor. About this there was nothing boisterous, but I have known them to save, with Lincoln-like readiness, many an awkward situation by an appropriate story more often turned on themselves than otherwise.
>
> Lincoln of course was pitchforked out of his native environment in the old Northwest into a position of responsibility he could not refuse. So the Mayos were ready to serve when called, as they did during the war; but they very much preferred their own countryside with its comparatively simple life, despite the ever-increasing responsibilities and laborious routine of their professional work. They felt only an amused pity for those who thought they were wasting their talents in a small town and who ventured to offer them positions elsewhere of supposedly wider influence.
>
> W. J. once said to me, "When Charlie gets so busy on his farm he forgets to have his shoes cleaned, he takes a night sleeper to Chicago knowing that he will find them well polished under his berth in the morning." Had he been encountered by some traveler on the train who with Mid-West informality asked his occupation, he would have replied, "A Minnesota farmer." Had Dr. Will been similarly asked who he might be by some chance companion, he probably would have replied: "I'm C. H. Mayo's elder brother." . . .
>
> The modern world is all too accustomed to gauge success in terms of net income, and thus measured the returns from the Mayo Clinic exceeded the dreams of avarice; but when in 1915 the Mayo Foundation was established Dr. Will simply stated: "We never regarded the money as ours; it came from the people and we believe, my brother and myself, that it should go back to the people."

On the evening of 3 October, after shifting a heavy Vesalius folio,

[12] "The Mayo brothers and their clinic." *Science*, 8 September 1939, *90*, 225-226.

an attack of substernal pain occurred. There had been several similar warnings earlier in the summer, but they had been dismissed as gastric in origin. By the morning of the 4th the pain had become greatly intensified, and at noon he was admitted to the hospital in acute distress. He improved somewhat during the day but at eleven o'clock that evening another attack occurred and this time he developed signs of heart block. He was placed in an oxygen tent, to which he strenuously objected because he could not see out. The next morning his nephew, Edward H. Cushing, who had been summoned from Cleveland, rearranged the patient's pillow soon after he entered his room. H.C. smiled, and perhaps remembering how Pat at the age of thirteen had so effectively comforted his own father during his last illness, said "Pat, you have the 'touch'—you're a good doctor."

He smiled again the next day when the news was brought that Grosvenor Atterbury had been authorized to proceed with the building of the library. Thereafter, seemingly aware that the things for which he had striven were to come about, he relaxed, and at 2 a.m. the morning of the 7th his heart, which for nearly two days had beat at the rate of 30 per minute, became irregular; forty-five minutes later it stopped.

Roger A. Lewis, the interne who cared for Cushing during his last illness wrote that he had been forcibly impressed by three things concerning his patient:

> First, the accuracy and impersonality with which he described his symptoms, signs and even diagnosis, apparently as he had done many years ago when he wrote the history of his appendicitis and appendectomy. . . . Secondly, the persistent way in which he instructed the nurses and doctors caring for him that they should always warn a patient before giving a hypodermic or any other subcutaneous injection. Finally, I was struck by the man's 'fight;' he wanted to see and know about everything, he objected to the oxygen tent because it limited his vision. He refused sedation, and his last words when he consented to take some luminal were "I will take it if it doesn't knock me out."

Shortly before his death Osler had remarked that he very much regretted he could not attend his own postmortem, for he had watched the case so long that the autopsy findings would have been highly instructive. Cushing felt much the same about his own infirmities and he would have been keenly interested in the disclosures and would have berated his family and friends had they not had a detailed examination in his own case. Drs. Milton Winternitz and Harry Zimmerman reported that the brain showed no sign of atrophy but the arteries were here and there sclerosed; and in line with the superstition that physicians sometimes fall victim to the diseases in which they specialize, a small colloid cyst, one centimeter in diameter, was found in the third ventricle. The coronary arteries were sclerosed and their lumina grossly reduced; a posterior branch which was completely blocked was no doubt responsible for his death. The apices of both lungs showed old scars, probably tuberculous in origin. The most remarkable finding, however, was the complete occlusion of the femorals, the main arteries of his legs, the process being old, and undoubtedly having developed at the time of his illness in 1918.

The funeral services, held on Monday, the 9th, in Center Church on the New Haven Green, brought many from far and near who loved him. The service exemplified the simplicity of his way of life: a pall of tawny autumn leaves and his favorite chrysanthemums, the strains of Sibelius' *Finlandia* which had greatly stirred him, the hymn, 'Oh God, our Help in Ages Past,' a brief Presbyterian service conducted by his friends Sidney Lovett, Chaplain of the University, and George Stewart, son-in-law of Arnold Klebs, who concluded with this prayer:

> Lord, we now give back into Thy keeping, this, Thy son, whom Thou hast entrusted to us these many years. How may we praise Thee as we ought for those qualities Thou didst so richly entrust to him? For fidelity to the tradition from which he sprang, for the eagerness of student days promising the harvest of later years, for his gay and resolute spirit, his rallying courage that helped many to rise and try again, for scientific insight, the gift and the art of healing, for a generous hand which shared the best he had with all who would receive it, for sacrificial labors amid the alarms and thunders of the battle field, and for lonely vigils known only to brave and consecrated servants of their kind, for faithfulness to friends, for gentleness to the untutored and abashed, and stern appraisal of unwilling hand or head, we give Thee praise. For the deposit of diligence and knightly valor he leaves in these ancient halls of learning so dear to him; for the impact of his spirit to arouse, direct and steady a multitude of younger men; the bright impress of his affection given to those of other faiths and tongues; and humility when the heady plaudits of the earth rang in his ears, we give Thee thanks. . . .

His ashes were taken to Cleveland to lie beside his mother and father, his brothers and his son; after many years away from the Western Reserve he had returned to the place that for him had always remained home. "By valor and divine aid" he had more than fulfilled the promise and ambition of his youth: scientist, pathfinder, artist, writer, and bibliophile—yes, but above all "a good doctor."

Here, silent, speak the great of other years,
the story of their steep ascent from the
unknown to the known, erring perchance
in their best endeavor, succeeding often,
where to their fellows they seemed most
to fail;

Here, the distilled wisdom of the years, the
slow deposit of knowledge gained and writ
by weak, yet valorous men, who shirked not
the difficult emprize;

Here is offered you the record of their days
and deeds, their struggle to attain that
light which God sheds on the mind of man,
and which we know as Truth.

Unshared must be their genius; it was their
own; but you, be you but brave and diligent,
may freely take and know the rich compan-
ionship of others' ordered thought.

LINES WRITTEN BY GEORGE STEWART

CARVED OVER THE FIREPLACE IN THE HISTORICAL LIBRARY

AT THE YALE UNIVERSITY SCHOOL OF MEDICINE · MCMXLI

APPENDIX A

Harvey Cushing's Will

CLAUSES PERTAINING TO HIS BIOGRAPHY AND THE DISPOSITION OF HIS LIBRARY

I, Harvey Williams Cushing, generally known as Harvey Cushing, of New Haven, Connecticut, do make, publish and declare my last will and testament as follows, hereby revoking all wills and codicils by me heretofore made. . . .

THIRD: . . . Should he [my literary executor] and my wife, if living, feel that the publication of my biography might be of interest or help to medical students, I request that my executors hereinafter named pay out of the corpus of my estate the expenses of such publication not to exceed the sum of Five Thousand Dollars ($5,000). Any royalties from such biography and all royalties from any of my own writings and publications, I give to and the same shall be paid to Yale University for use by it in connection with the project hereinafter set forth for the Medical Historical Library.

FOURTH: I give and bequeath to said literary executor the sum of Five Thousand Dollars ($5,000) for the purpose of defraying the cost of cataloging my library and having printed and distributed among those interested a check list of the more important historical items, such as the collection of Vesaliana, in said library and for such other similar or kindred purposes as he may think desirable. I expressly provide, however, that he shall not be called upon to make any accounting to any court or person with respect to the use of said Five Thousand Dollars ($5,000), the same being given to him absolutely and not in trust.

FIFTH: I give and bequeath to Yale University my collection of medical-historical books and papers on condition that said University will agree to provide suitable quarters for said collection, preferably in connection with the Yale School of Medicine, subject to the authority hereinafter given to my literary executor regarding the disposition of said medical-historical library. I expressly authorize said Yale University, however, to dispose of such items of my said books and papers as my literary executor, if living, may approve. If my literary executor shall decide that it would be better to have said books and papers, or a substantial portion thereof, sold at public auction in order that others may share in the pleasure which I have had in the temporary possession thereof, he may authorize and direct said University thus to sell the whole or any part of my said books and papers at public auction, or may, himself, arrange for such sale, the proceeds of any such sale or sales to revert to said University for the benefit of the Library of the Yale School of Medicine.

Aware that suitable quarters may not be available either at the Sterling Library or the Yale School of Medicine to equip and properly house a research unit for medical history, I hope, nevertheless, that said collection of books and papers will for the most part be kept together for this purpose and serve as the nucleus for a larger, more diverse and complete working collection. As heretofore stated, however, the decision of the literary executor concerning the disposition of said medical and historical library is to be controlling. . . .

SEVENTH: I direct my executors hereinafter named to divide all of the rest, residue and remainder of my property and estate, both real and personal, of whatsoever the same may consist and wheresoever the same may be situated, including any property over which I may have at the time of my death any power of testamentary disposition into three equal parts in such manner as said executors may deem fair and equitable and in connection therewith I authorize my executors to appraise or reappraise any or all of my said property and estate in such manner as they may deem advisable. . . .

3. One of said three equal parts (to be selected by my executors) I give, devise, bequeath and appoint to said Yale University for the furtherance of the project in connection with the gift to said Yale University of my medical-historical library.

I cannot foresee whether I shall still be holding a Sterling professorship in said University at the time of my death, but should this be the case and should the Corporation of said University deem it proper and should the occasion be suitable, I would be gratified could said Sterling professorship, with its salary, be transferred as was originally suggested into a professorship of the History of Medicine or of Science (as preferred), in which event the income from the gift to Yale University contained in this Article and from the investment of the proceeds of any portions of my collection hereinbefore referred to which are sold might provide a modest budget towards the conduct of such a department.

Should such a professorship be established and should this gift to Yale University be sufficient to justify the Corporation of the University in establishing said department, it might not only influence my literary executor in his decision regarding the ultimate disposition of my collection of books but it might also influence him in the disposition of his own library.

Realizing, as I do, that by reason of a change of circumstances or otherwise the University may find it impracticable to carry out the project which I have outlined above, I do not make the gift to Yale University contained in the Article conditional or contingent in any respect, nor do I impose any inflexible restrictions on the use which the University may make of said gift, having confidence that the University will earnestly endeavor to carry out my hopes and wishes as hereinbefore expressed. . . .

In Witness Whereof I have hereunto set my hand and seal at New Haven, Connecticut, this 8th day of November, 1935.

Harvey Williams Cushing (Seal)

APPENDIX B

Degrees and Honors

Since it has been impossible to mention all of Dr. Cushing's memberships, degrees and other honors, they are here listed in chronological sequence. Those referred to in the text are followed by page numbers in brackets.

Bachelor of Arts, Yale, 1891 [46 *et seq.*]
Doctor of Medicine, Master of Arts, Harvard, 1895 [100]
House Officer, Massachusetts General Hospital, 1895-1896 [100-109]
Johns Hopkins Hospital and Medical School, 1896-1900
  Assistant Resident Surgeon, October 1896-October 1897 [116]
  Resident Surgeon, October 1897-May 1900 [127]
  Instructor in Surgery, 1897-1898 [133]
  Assistant in Surgery, 1898-1899
  Associate in Surgery, 1899-1900 [231]
Student under Theodor Kocher and Hugo Kronecker (Berne) and Charles S. Sherrington (Liverpool), 1900-1901 [176-200]
Johns Hopkins Hospital and Medical School, 1901-1912
  Associate in Surgery, March 1902-September 1912
  Associate Professor of Surgery, 1903-1912
Harvard University Medical School, Moseley Professor of Surgery, 1912-1932; Professor Emeritus, 1932-1939 [338 *et seq.*]
Surgeon-in-Chief, Peter Bent Brigham Hospital, 1912-1932; Surgeon-in-Chief Emeritus, 1932-1939 [338 *et seq.*]
Director, U. S. Army Base Hospital No. 5, 1917-1919 [419 *et seq.*]
Senior Consultant in Neurological Surgery, A.E.F., 1918 [430]
Yale University, Sterling Professor of Neurology, 1933-1937; Professor Emeritus, 1937-1939; Director of Studies in the History of Medicine, School of Medicine, 1937-1939. Associate Fellow, Trumbull College, 1933-1939 [634 *et seq.*]
Consulting Neurologist, New Haven Hospital, 1933-1939

1900 Member, American Association of Pathologists and Bacteriologists
1901 Mütter Lecturer (Philadelphia) [211]
1902 Member, American Association for the Advancement of Science
1903 Member, American Neurological Association (President, 1923) [501]
  Charter member, Society of Clinical Surgery (President, 1921) [232]
1905 Member, American Physiological Society
1906 Fellow, American Surgical Association (President, 1927) [546]
  Wesley M. Carpenter Lecturer (New York)
1909 William Mitchell Banks Memorial Lecturer (University of Liverpool) [291]
  Member, Royal Medical Society of Budapest
1910 Harvey Society Lecturer (New York) [321]
1913 Master of Arts (Hon.) Yale [366]
  Orator in Surgery, XVIIth International Congress of Medicine (London) [327, 368]

Fellow (Hon.), Royal College of Surgeons, England [371]
Fellow (Hon.), Institute of Hygiene (London)
Fellow, American College of Surgeons (President, 1922) [492]
1914 Weir Mitchell Lecturer (Philadelphia) [375]
Foreign corresponding member, Société de Neurologie, Paris
Fellow, American Academy of Arts and Sciences
Member, Washington Academy of Sciences
1915 Doctor of Science, Washington University (St. Louis) [405]
1917 Member, National Academy of Sciences
Fellow, Societas Medicorum Svecana
1918 Fellow, Royal College of Surgeons in Ireland [429]
1919 Honorary Fellow, American Psychiatric Association
Doctor of Laws, Western Reserve University [452]
Doctor of Science, Yale University [452]
Companion of the Bath (Military) [452]
Doctor of Medicine (Hon.), Queen's University, Belfast
Membre associé, Société Royale des Sciences Médicales et Naturelles de Bruxelles
Membre associé étranger, Société Nationale de Chirurgie, Paris
1920 Charter member, Society of Neurological Surgeons (President, 1920 and 1921) [454]
Doctor of Laws, University of Cambridge [475]
Corresponding member, Société de Biologie, Paris
1921 Honorary Fellow, Medical Society of London (Orator, 1927) [546]
Corresponding member, Gesellschaft der Aerzte in Wien (Ehrenmitglied, 1932)
Association for the Study of Internal Secretions (President) [478]
1922 Charles Mickle Fellow, University of Toronto
Cavendish Lecturer (London) [488]
Perpetual Student (Hon.), St. Bartholomew's Hospital, London [488]
Chevalier, Légion d'Honneur [504]
Corresponding member, Medico-Chirurgical Society, Edinburgh
1923 Correspondant étranger 2° Division, Académie de Médecine, Paris
Fellow (Hon.), Association of Surgeons of Great Britain and Ireland
1924 Cameron Prize Lecturer (University of Edinburgh) [522]
Corresponding member, Società Medico-Chirurgica di Bologna
1925 Honorary Fellow, Cleveland Medical Library Association
1926 Member, Society of the New York Hospital
United States Distinguished Service Medal [528]
Doctor of Letters, Jefferson Medical College [533]
Doctor of Medicine (Hon.), John Casimir University, Lwów, Poland
Pulitzer Prize in Letters, Columbia University [462]
Honorary Fellow, New York Academy of Medicine
1927 Honorary Fellow, Royal Society of Medicine, London [551]
Honorary Fellow, Royal Academy of Medicine in Ireland [550]
Master of Chirurgery (Hon.) Trinity College, Dublin [550]
Macewen Memorial Lecturer (University of Glasgow) [548]
Doctor of Laws, University of Glasgow [548]
Doctor of Laws, University of Edinburgh [550]
Fellow (Hon.), Royal College of Surgeons, Edinburgh
Officier, Légion d'Honneur [554]

Honorary member, Society of British Neurological Surgeons [551]
1928 Foreign member, Societas Medica Havniensis (Honorary member, 1932)
1929 Foreign corresponding member, Société de Neurologie de Varsovie
Ehrenmitglied, Verein für Psychiatrie und Neurologie, Vienna
Honorary Fellow, Philadelphia Academy of Surgery
Herman Knapp Prize in Ophthalmology, New York [561]
Doctor of Letters, Dartmouth College [566]
Associé étranger, Académie de Médecine, Paris
Order: El Sol del Perú
Honorary Fellow, Medical Library Association
Corresponding member, Gesellschaft deutscher Nervenärzte (Ehrenmitglied, 1933)
Docteur "honoris causa," University of Strasbourg
Corresponding member, Societas Regia Medicorum, Budapest
1930 Member, American Philosophical Society
Membre étranger (Hon.), Académie Royale de Médecine de Belgique
Honorary member, Royal Medico-Psychological Association, Great Britain
Lister Prize Medalist, Royal College of Surgeons, England [594]
Docteur "honoris causa," University of Brussels
Award: Montclair Yale Bowl [599]
Arthur Dean Bevan Lecturer, Chicago Surgical Society [599]
Honorary member, Société Neurologique Estonienne
Membre associé étranger, Société Nationale de Chirurgie, Paris
1931 Docteur "honoris causa," University of Budapest
Donald Balfour Lecturer, University of Toronto [603]
William H. Welch Lecturer, Mt. Sinai Hospital, New York [591, 603]
Honorary member, Beaumont Medical Club, New Haven
Foreign corresponding member, Società Piemontese di Chirurgia
Professor of History of Medicine, Johns Hopkins University [elect] [599]
Doctor of Science, Harvard University [605]
Doctor of Science, University of Rochester [605]
Docteur "honoris causa," University of Berne [607]
1932 Honorary member, Section of History of Medicine, Royal Society of Medicine, London
Mitglied, Kaiserliche Deutsche Akademie der Naturforscher
Doctor of Science, Northwestern University, Evanston-Chicago [620]
Doctor of Medicine "honoris causa," University of Amsterdam (Tercentenary celebration)
Foreign corresponding member, British Medical Association
Foreign corresponding member, Sociedad Nacional de Cirugia de La Habana
Membro stranièro, Società Radio-Neuro-Chirurgica Italiana
Member, Royal Society of Sciences, Upsala
Honorary member, Società Italiana di Neurologia
Ehrenmitglied, Gesellschaft deutscher Neurologen und Psychiater
1933 Harvey Society Lecturer (New York): second time [628]
Honorary member, Pathological Society of Philadelphia (75th anniversary)
Honorary member, Hungarian Ophthalmological Society
Award: Henry Jacob Bigelow Medal, Boston Surgical Society [631]
Docteur "honoris causa," University of Paris [638]
President, Congress of American Physicians and Surgeons [632]

Foreign member, Royal Society, London [632]
Corresponding member, R. Accademia delle Scienze dell' Istituto di Bologna
Honorary member, North Caucasian Association of Neurologists and Psychiatrists
Honorary member, Norske Medicinske Selskab (100th jubilee)
Foreign corresponding member, Società Lombarda di Chirurgia
Honorary member, American Society of Regional Anaesthesia
Award: "Golden Key," Congress of Physical Therapy
Member, Societas Medica Norvegica

1934 Honorary foreign member, Société de Chirurgie de Lyon
Foreign member, Royal Academy of Sciences, Sweden
Doctor of Laws, Syracuse University (100th anniversary of Medical School) [644]

1935 Honorary Fellow, Indian Academy of Sciences, Bangalore
Award: Gold medal, National Institute of Social Sciences [661]
Foreign member, Royal Academy of Sciences, Amsterdam
Ehrenmitglied, Österreichische Gesellschaft für Erforschung und Bekämpfung der Krebskrankheit (Vienna)
Honorary Fellow, Chicago Surgical Society
Doctor of Science, University of Leeds *(in absentia)*
Académico Honorario, Academia Nacional de Medicina de Buenos Aires
Honorary member, New York Neurological Society

1936 Associate member, Société de Biologie, Paris
Honorary member, Royal Medical Society, Edinburgh
Associé étranger, Académie de Chirurgie (formerly Société Nationale de Chirurgie)
Ehrenmitglied, Gesellschaft der Chirurgen in Wien

1937 Ehrenmitglied, Wiener biologische Gesellschaft

1938 Foreign corresponding member, Harveian Society of London
Foreign active member, Polish Academy of Science
Honorary member, American Ophthalmological Society
Doctor of Science "honoris causa," Oxford University [697]

1939 Corresponding member, Société Suisse de Neurologie
Honorary Fellow, Royal College of Physicians of London [711]
Honorary member, Société d'Endocrinologie, Paris
Honorary Fellow, Royal Society of Edinburgh
Honorary member, American Association of the History of Medicine

INDEX

Abbe, Robert, 262
Abbott, A. C., 228, 467
Abbott, F. F., 36
Abernethy, John, 168, 293, 429
Acland, Sir Henry W., 235
Acoustic tumors, 236, 489-91; monograph on, 410-11
Acromegaly, 288, 299, 301-2; surgery, 301, 546-7
Adami, J. G., 276
Adams, C. A., 28, 31
Adams, C. F., 589
Adams, H. A., reminiscence, 249
Adams, Henry, 359
Addams, Jane, 403-4
Adrian, E. D., 612
Adson, A. W., letter to HC, 455
Agassiz, Alexander, 359
Agnew, D. H., 461
Aikin, John, 252
Alderman, E. A., 225
Aldini, Giovanni, 671
Aldrich, T. B., 359
Aldus, house in Venice, 295-6
Alexander, H. F., 698
Alexander, Samuel, 313
Allbutt, Sir T. Clifford, 220, 235
Allen, D. P., 50, 79, 156, 413; Allen Memorial Medical Library opening, 541-2
Allen, P. S., letter to Lady Osler, 470-1
Allgemeines Krankenhaus, Vienna, *see* Vienna. Allgemeines Krankenhaus
Altschul, Frank, 586, 681
American Academy of Arts and Sciences, 451, 474
American Ambulance, Paris, 387 *et seq.*, 413, 432; organization, 387-8; Harvard unit at, 392 *et seq.*, 418*n;* HC's account of, 404; defense of, 405-7
American Association for the Advancement of Science, 300
American Association of the History of Medicine, 561
American College of Surgeons, 451, 455, 484-6, 492, 496; meeting in Boston, 564
American Defense Society, 404
American Expeditionary Forces, 418*n,* 423, 439-40, 484, 528, 591-2
American Medical Association, 54*n,* 255*n,* 290, 312, 320, 323, 375-6, 379, 382, 386*n,* 474, 478-9, 561, 570, 650-3; dinner to Journal editor, 509-10
American Medico-Psychological Association, 450*n*
American Neurological Association, 287, 290, 312, 365, 407, 501, 503, 509, 560, 605
American Ophthalmological Association, 560
American Philosophical Society, 407
American Physiological Society, 300, 314, 363
American Red Cross, 405, 415
American Surgical Association, 138, 313, 379, 405, 546, 560
Amerman, G. L., 82
Ames, J. S., 613
Anderson, N. M., 18, 26-9, 31; letter to HC, 229
Anemia, splenectomy for, 139, 149
Anesthesia, HC's administration of, 69-72, 74-5, 78-9, 258; cocaine, 120, 141-3, 213; local, 141, 157, 577, 578*n; see also* Ether charts
Angell, J. R., 481, 518, 586, 625, 634, 638, 648, 674, 681-4; letters to HC, 480, 635-7; to KC, 636; letters from HC, 480, 635-7
Animal electricity, 671
Animal experimentation, 167, 219-20, 274, 305, 369, 371, 428
Anrep, G. V., 578-9
Anthrax, student paper on, 73-5
Anthropoid experiments, 197 *et seq.*
Antona, Antonio d', 166
Appendicitis, 7 cases in MGH, 126; HC's attack of, 129-34
Apponyi, Albert, Count, 294
Arderne, John, 581-2
Armitage, George, 584, 608
Armour, Donald, 488, 625
Arnat, Dr., 177
Arnold, Julius, 194
Arnold Arboretum, 65-6
Arthur, Prince, of Connaught, 367
Ashburn, P. M., 589
Asher, Doris, 183
Asher, Leon, 179-81, 183, 191-2, 524, 577, 606, 608, 610, 674; reminiscence, 182
Askew, Anthony, 167, 248

Associated Physicians of Long Island, 287
Association for Research in Nervous and Mental Disease, 680, 688
Association for the Study of Internal Secretions, 478
Astrocytomas, 491; cerebellar, 599
Athlone, Earl of, 699
Atkins, Col., 400-1
Atterbury, Grosvenor, 45, 50-2, 55, 74, 143, 153, 171-2, 634, 648, 663, 667, 712
Austen, Jane, 508
Avicenna, 252, 296
Ayer, J. B., 532
Azan, Maj. Paul, 416-17

Babb, J. T., 692
Babcock, C. H., 64
Babcock, R. H., 247
Babinski, J. F. F., 272*n*, 488
Bacon, Robert, 387, 400, 415
Bacon, Roger, 235
Bacteriology, 121, 149 *et seq.*
Baer, W. S., 121, 204, 265
Baetjer, F. H., 238
Bagdazar, Dimitri, 608
Bagley, Charles Jr., 362*n*, 455*n*, 570
Bailey, Cyril, 698
Bailey, Percival, 366, 410, 454, 487-8, 514, 525, 543, 556, 563, 579, 591-2, 608, 642, 708; work on tumor classification, 508-9, 521-2
Baillie, Matthew, 167, 201, 248
Balch, F. G., 88, 482
Baldwin, Mrs. A. D., 26*n*, 144
Balfour, A. J., 1st Earl of, 711
Balfour Lecture, 603
Ballance, Sir Charles A., 369, 473, 565
Ballard, J. F., 478*n*
Baltimore, dining habits, 118, 123, 138; fire, 218, 233; market, 118-19
Baltzell, W. H., 116
Bancroft, F. W., 220
Banks, W. M., 287, 291
Banks Memorial Lecture, 291-2
Banti's disease, 139
Barbauld, Mrs. L. (A.), 252
Barcroft, Sir Joseph, 428, 675
Bard, Philip, 591
Barger, George, 558
Barker, Creighton, 682
Barker, L. F., 151-2, 228*n*, 262-3, 292, 305, 379*n*, 383, 466, 566
Barlow, H. M., letter to HC, 711
Barlow, Sir Thomas, 90, 368; letter to HC, 327
Barnes, J. S., 45, 55
Barnes Hospital, St. Louis, 521
Barnett, Gen. James, 149
Barney, C. N., 93
Barr, J. S., 526
Barrie, J. M., 598
Barron, D. H., 161*n*
Bartels, M., 272*n*
Bartlett, Elisha, 164, 677
Bartlett, H. C., 692
Bartol, J. W., 478*n*
Barton, L. G. Jr., 391
Base Hospital No. 5, *see* U.S. Army. Base Hospital No. 5
Baseball at Yale, 40 *et seq.*; contrasted with duelling, 195
Bashford, Sir Henry, reminiscence, 598
Baskerville collection at Yale, 677-9
Basophilism, pituitary, 614-6, 658, 661, 689
Bastianelli, Giuseppe, 622
Bastianelli, Raffaele, 294, 435, 622-3, 698
'Battle of Boston Common,' 416-18
Bayliss, Sir William M., 325
Bayne, Col. Hugh, 427
Bayne-Jones, Stanhope, 642, 648, 651, 691, 707
Bazett, Cuthbert, 400-2, 554
Beach, H. H. A., 109
Beall, F. C., 220
Beattie, John, 591, 616, 697-8
Beauchamp, W. L., 7th Earl, 371
Beaumont, William, 205, 560-1, 639; dedication of highway, 661-2
Beaumont Medical Club, 626, 634, 679, 682
Beecher, H. K., 95
Beevor, C. E., 197
Bellevue Hospital, New York, 331
Benedict, F. G., 567
Benes, Eduard, 701
Benet, George, 391
Bensley, R. R., 454
Bergmann, Ernst von, 166-7
Berkshire Medical School, Pittsfield, 8
Bernard, Claude, 54
Berne. University, faculty, 176
Bernhardt, Martin, 263
Bernheim, B. M., 221-2
Bernstorff, J. H., Count von, 403
Best, C. H., 671
Bevan, A. D., 379
Bickerstaff, Isaac, 241-2
Bier, August, 328
Bierens de Haan, 582
Bierring, W. L., 651-2
Bigelow, A. F., 374
Bigelow, Mrs. A. F., reminiscences, of circus, 303; of Cushing family, 373-4
Bigelow, H. J., 54, 109, 360*n*, 495; Bigelow medal, list of recipients, 479; to HC, 631-2; C. Jackson, 564; W. W. Keen,

492-3; R. Matas, 479; W. H. Mayo, 479
Bigelow, Jacob, 54*n*, 207
Bigelow, W. S., 357, 359-61, 416, 418, 479, 495; HC's notes about, 360*n*
Biggs, H. M., 242, 496
Billings, Frank, 292, 313, 376, 447, 473
Billings, J. S., 110, 288, 335, 429, 664
Billroth, Theodor, 142, 182
Bird, C. E., letter to Sir C. Wallace, 487
Birks, G. W., tribute from a patient, 231
Bishop, C. C., 619
Bismarck, Otto, 176
Bixby, W. K., 337
Blackfan, K. D., 618
Blake, F. G., 475, 480-1, 632, 651
Blake, J. A., 390, 393, 395
Blake, J. B., 325, letter to HC, 324
Blake, M. E., letter from HC, 572
Blaschka collection at Harvard, 78
Bliss, R. W., 453
Bliss, Mrs. R. W., 588
Blizzard of '88, 39
Blood-pressure and intracranial pressure, 178-9, 184, 186-7, 190, 211
Blood-pressure determinations, 212 *et seq.;* introduction in U.S., 215; surgical cases, 213-16
Blood-vessel tumors, 563, 579
Bloodgood, J. C., 121-2, 124-5, 127-9, 132, 153, 177, 228*n*, 238, 330, 526
Blumer, George, 116, 228*n*, 333, 517
Boardman, E. G., 64
Boardman, W. J., 82, 143-4, 176
Boardman children, 144
Bock, A. V., 567
Boerhaave, Herman, 5*n*, 168, 293
Boggis, Taylor, 27
Bologna, anatomical theatre, 190, 627-8
Bolton, C. C., 557, (fund) 644
Bone filling experiments, 92
Bonin, Gerhardt von, letter to HC, 323; letter from HC, 322
Boothby, W. M., 362*n*, 390-1, 396, 398, 402-3, 543
Bordley, James Jr., 221, 299*n*, 306
Borgarucci, Prospero, 329
Boston City Hospital, 54, 82, 93, 214, 336, 343, 349, 362, 410, 415, 417
Boston Medical History Club, 484, 494, 565; photograph of 1st announcement, 478
Boston Medical Library, 213, 478, 584-5
Boston Public Library, 93
Boston Surgical Society, 474, 476, 479, 492, 631
'Boston Tins,' 415, 501
Boswell, James, 242, 461
Bottazzi, Filippo, 577, 622
Bovell, James, 594
Bovie, W. T., 537-8
Bowditch, H. I., 73
Bowditch, H. P., 54, 178-9
Bowditch, Harold, 478*n*
Bowditch, Katharine P., *see* Codman, Mrs. E. A.
Bowditch, Nathaniel, 54
Bowen, Eugene, 5-6
Bowlby, Sir Anthony A., 400, 434, 440; plaque in his honour, 591-3
Bowman, Isaiah, 660, 682
Bowman, Sir William, 370
Boyd, W. W., 604
Boylston Medical Society, 60, 71-4, 82
Bradford, E. H., 92-3, 336, 353, 381, 388, 390
Bradford, Sir J. Rose, 428
Bradley, A. E., 427
Brady, A. N., 385, 517
Brain, temperature of, 186
Brain Tumor Registry, 241*n*, 541, 628, 642-5, 661, 667, 674; steps leading to foundation, 273
Brain tumors, *see* Intracranial tumors
Branch, J. R.B., 221
Bratenahl, G. F. C., 74
Brattle, Thomas, 519-20
Breasted, J. H., 599
Bremer, Frédéric, 366, 525, 526*n*, 558, 577, 591, 608
Brenizer, A. G. Jr., 220
Brenner, V. D., 312
Brewer, G. E., 424, 486
Brewster, G. S., 55
Brewster, Robert, 218, 290
Bridgman, W. R., 35-6
Briggs, G. P., 8*n*, 18
Briggs, Mrs. G. P. (Cornelia Cushing), 8*n*
Briggs, J. B., 215*n*, 216
Briggs, LeBaron, 476
Briggs, Mary, 65
Brigham, P. B., 110, 335, 342, 344-5
Brigham Hospital, *see* Peter Bent Brigham Hospital, Boston
Brinkley, Mary, 248
Brinton, J. H., 211
Brinton, Margaret, 702*n*
British Expeditionary Forces, 418*n*, 421, 440
British Medical Association, 234-5
British Museum, 236
Broadbent, Sir William, 164, 166
Brodie, Sir Benjamin C., 429
Brödel, Max, 153, 158, 312, 693; operation on arm, 152
Brödel, Mrs. Max, 133
Brookings, Robert, 306, 337

Brooks, Harry, 72, 75-6, 88
Brooks, Phillips, 57, 70
Brooks, W. K., 263
Brow, G. R., 591
Brown, Freelove, *see* Cushing, Mrs. David Jr.
Brown, John, 566
Brown, Louis, 483
Brown, Rexwald, 652
Brown-Séquard syndrome, 122
Browne, Sir G. Buckston, 597
Bruce, J. D., 652
Bryant, C. H., 220
Bryce, James, 1st Viscount, 255, 284
Buchanan, Florence, 292
Buckler, Mrs. W. H., letter to HC, 253
Bühler, Curt, 690
Bullard, W. N., 261*n*
Bunsen, R. W. E., 181
Burke, Edmund, 485
Burke, H. J., 485
Burrell, H. L., 75, 92*n*, 214, 336
Burton, Robert, 292
Busch, Adolphus, 328, 337
Butler, Samuel, 461, 463-4
Butlin, Sir Henry T., 166
Buzzard, Sir Farquhar, 236, 698

Cabot, A. T., 70-2, 78-9, 109, 221, 285, 312, 635*n*
Cabot, R. C., 213, 566
Cachexia hypophysiopriva, 281
Cairns, Hugh, 423, 535, 537, 541, 558, 565, 598, 607-8, 625, 667, 697-9; work with HC, 539; letter from HC, 539
Cajal, S. Ramon y, *see* Ramon y Cajal, S.
Camac, C. N. B., 130, 135, 228*n*
Cambridge University, 475
Cameron, A. R., 522
Cameron Prize Lectures, 522-5; dedication, 245
Camp, Walter, 476
Campbell, C. Macfie, 482
Camperdown, Earl of (formerly George A. Duncan), 357-9
Cannon, W. B., 106, 223, 315, 377, 419, 428, 561, 578, 597, 612; letter to HC, 340
Canterbury, Archbp. of, *see* Davidson, R. T.
Carey, William, 74
Carlson, A. J., 315
Carmalt, W. H., 479
Carnegie, Andrew, 244, 290, 627
Carnegie Foundation, 306, 346, 379, 383, 451
Carney Hospital, Boston, 343
Carnot, M. F. S., 173
Carpenter, J. G., letter to HC, 240; letter from HC, 241
Carr, J. B., 217-18
Carrel, Alexis, 248, 335, 395-6, 409, 668; letter from HC, 391
Carrel, Mme. Alexis, 396
Carroll, Mme., 207-8, 244
Carroll, Charles, 396
Carroll, James, 150, 154; letter to HC, 155
Carter, E. P., 118, 157
Cartier, Jacques, 113
Case, Eckstein, 13
Case, George, 71
Case, "Squire," 9
Casler, DeW. B., 218
Castiglioni, Arturo, 639
Castle, W. B., 633
Casualty Clearing Station No. 46, 415, 434
Catchpole, H. R., 710
Caulfield, Ernest, 682
Cavendish Lecture, 488
Ceccherelli, Andrea, 294-5
Centre College, Danville, Ky., 476
Cerebellar tumors, 288; astrocytomas, 599; hemangiomas, 579; medulloblastomas, 509, 579; longest survival, 410*n*
Cerebellopontile tumors, 236, 410-11, 489-91
Cerebral circulation, 186
Cerebral compression, blood-pressure in, 184, 187
Cerebral cortex, motor area, 197, 256-7
Cerebral hernia, 267
Cerebrospinal fluid, circulation, 522-3; drugs injected into, 591, 603-4, 623; pituitary secretion in, 313, 315; pressure, 199; studies on, 374
Chamberlain, Neville, 701
Chambers Street Hospital, N.Y., 50
Channing, Walter, 54*n*
Chapin, Mrs. H. B., 250, 356, 425, 577
Chapin, Mrs. Robert, 166
Chapman, R. W., 463, 677
Charaka Club, 285, 657
Charity Hospital, Cleveland, 79
Chatard, J. H., 252
Chauffard, A. M. E., 327, 367*n*
Cheever, D. W., 54, 82, 362
Cheever, David, 54, 362-3, 453, 478*n*, 506-7, 543, 631
Chesney, A. N., 111*n*
Cheyne, Sir Watson, 313
Chiasmal syndrome, 582
Chicago Exposition, *see* Columbian Exposition, Chicago, 1893
Chicago Medical Society, 287, 298
Chicago Surgical Society, 599

Children's Hospital, Boston, 67, 77-9, 88, 214
Children's Hospital, London, 91
Childs, Edward, 31
Childs, S. W., 52, 55, 59, 62, 70-1, 73, 634, 696
Chipault, Antony, 256
Chisholm, A. S., 82, 144
Chittenden, A. S., 666-7
Chittenden, R. H., 37, 47-50, 53, 55, 178, 182, 474, 496, 634, 662, 672, 691*n*
Chittenden Annex, 678
Chittenden Library, 37
Choked disc, 320*n*
Christian, H. A., 341, 344, 347, 350, 354, 363, 365, 377, 379, 381, 383, 472-3, 500, 504, 531, 543, 555, 558, 626, 632; letters to HC, 343, 351; letter from HC, 351
Christiansen, Viggo, 488
Christie, R. C., 542
Churchill, Rt. Hon. Winston, 418, 624
Churchman, J. W., 220
Chute, A. L., 70, 478*n*
Circular suture, 129
Clark, J. G., 228*n*, 313
Clark, W. L., 537
Clayton Greene, W. H., 369-70
Clemenceau, Georges, 453
Cleveland, Grover, 72, 124
Cleveland Academy of Medicine, 239, 266, 471, 600*n*
Cleveland Academy of Natural Sciences, 511
Cleveland Central High School, 27, 33
Cleveland Clinic, explosion, 573-4, 708
Cleveland Manual Training School, 31
Cleveland Medical College, 11, 15
Cleveland Medical Library, 24, 137, 277*n*, 600*n*
Cline, Henry, 168
Clinical teaching, 158, 378, 506
Clopton, M. B., 155
Clowes, G. H. A., 241-2
The Club, Boston, 356-61, 416; membership, 359
The Club, New Haven, 648, 679, 690-1
Club of Odd Volumes, 545
Coats, A. M., 72
Cobb, Farrar, 73
Cobb, S. A. Jr., 362*n*
Cobb, Stanley, 362*n*, 447, 532, 553-4; letter from HC, 559
Cobbe, F. P., 167
Cochran, A. S., 689
Cochrane, Alexander, 338, 344-7, 350-1, 354, 388; letters to HC, 338, 346, 391; to Pres. Lowell, 382; letters from HC, 345, 347-51; from H. A. Christian, 347-50
Codding, M. B., diagram of Wood operation, 311
Codman, E. A., 60, 68-71, 73-6, 82, 87-8, 90, 93-4, 96, 104-6, 122, 143, 212, 259*n*, 268; report on brain tumors at M.G.H., 261; wedding, 155; letter to HC, 340; letters from HC, 95, 317-18
Codman, Mrs. E. A. (Katharine P. Bowditch), 155, 317
Codman, E. D., 345, 376, 556
Codman, Robert, 335
Cody, W. F., 312
Cogswell, G. P., 100
Cohen, S. S., 224
Cohn, Dr. and Mrs. E. J., 577
Cohnheim, Julius, 111, 194
Cohnheim, Otto, 195
Coit, H. H., 9
College of Physicians in Philadelphia, 227-8, 262
Coller, F. A., 391
Collier, Dr., 235
Collins, George, 31
Columbian Exposition, Chicago, 1893, 79-82
Committee on Economic Security. Medical Advisory Committee, 649 *et seq.*
Committee on the Costs of Medical Care, 649, 651
'Comparative surgery', 220, 227
Conant, J. B., 633, 644-5
Conant, W. M., 71-3, 75, 96, 106-7, 109
Cone, W. V., 646
Congress of American Physicians and Surgeons, 11th (1919), 450*n*, 13th (1925), 521, 15th (1933), 629, 632
Congress on Medical Education, 506
Conner, L. A., 500
Constantinus Africanus, 361
Cook, Henry, 215*n*, 216
Cook, John, 290
Cooley, C. P., 45, 63, 75
Coolidge, Calvin, 311
Cooper, Sir Astley P., 168, 207, 429
Cooper, Fenimore, 6
Copeland, C. T., letter to HC, 474
Corey Hill Hospital, Brookline, 362
Coriat, I. H., 478*n*
Corlett, W. T., 26*n*; reminiscence of Erastus Cushing, 9*n*
Cornell, Katharine, 685
Cornell University, 23-4
Corner, G. W., 587
Corner, Thomas, 694
Corning, J. L., 142
Cortical localization, 197

Cortissoz, Royal, 251
Coues, W. P., 478*n*, 544, 567
Councilman, W. T., 68, 74-5, 82, 104, 111, 173, 213, 227, 278, 286, 333, 359-60, 364, 410, 416, 436, 472, 642, 673; HC's obituary of, 630-1; letters to HC, 335, 340, 482
Cox, E. J., 391
Coy, G. J., 326
Crafts, J. M., 358-9
Craniopharyngiomas, *see* Rathke's pouch cyst
Crawford, Miss, nurse at Johns Hopkins, 238
Credé, C. C. B., 128
Creed, R. S., 595
Crehore, A. C., 40, 51, 76
Crehore, M. L., 104
Crehore, W. W., 41, 294
Crichton-Brown, Sir James, 166
Crile, G. W., 26*n*, 180, 213-15, 375, 414, 421, 424, 428, 486, 503, 573-4, 591, 652; war recollections, 440; letter to HC, 340; to W. E. Lower, 389-90; letters from HC, 388-9
Crile, Mrs. G. W., 26*n*, 28
Crockett, E. A., 165, 506-7
Cross, E. S., 220
Cross, W. L., 645, 661
Crothers, Bronson, 532, 618
Crowe, S. J., 220-1, 245, 281-2, 285, 299-300, 303, 323, 325
Crowell, Benedict, 144
Crowell, Katharine Stone, *see* Cushing, Mrs. Harvey
Crowell, W. E., 144
Crowell, Mrs. W. E. (Mary Benedict), 144-5, 273; letter to HKC, 274
Cruikshank, W. C., 201
Cullen, T. S., 158*n*, 694
Cullen, William, 5*n*
Culpeper, Nicholas, 657
Cummer, C. L., 26*n*
Cummin, J. W., 70*n*, 478*n*; reminiscence, 98
Cummings, H. S., 650
Cummins, S. L., 428
Curtis, J. G., 253
Curtis, James, 417
Curtis, T. B., 359
Cushing, Alice (daughter of H. P. Cushing), 23
Cushing, Alice K. (sister of HC), 5, 10, 13, 16, 19, 22-3, 47, 64, 68, 144, 172, 210, 249, 275, 306; letters from HC, 34, 117
Cushing, Alleyne M. (Jinks, brother of HC), 22, 24-5, 29, 244, 251
Cushing, Barbara (daughter of HC), 506, 508, 514, 516, 544, 640, 674, 702; birth, 405; letters from HC, 517
Cushing, Benjamin, 68-9
Cushing, Betsey (daughter of HC), *see* Roosevelt, Mrs. James
Cushing, Charlotte (daughter of Erastus Cushing), 8*n*
Cushing, Charlotte (sister of HC), 22
Cushing, Cornelia (daughter of Erastus Cushing), *see* Briggs, Mrs. G. P.
Cushing, Cornelia (daughter of H. P. Cushing), *see* Peterson, Mrs. V. A.
Cushing, Cornelia (sister of HC), 22
Cushing, Daniel (son of Matthew Cushing, 1589-1660), 4
Cushing, David Sr. (great great-grandfather of HC), 4
Cushing, David Jr. (great grandfather of HC), 3-8, 11, 136; list of books, 5*n*
Cushing, Mrs. David Jr. (Freelove Jenks), 4, 6-7
Cushing, Edward F. (Ned, brother of HC), 19-22, 24, 29, 46-7, 53, 55-60, 63, 65, 68, 73, 76, 79-81, 84-91, 98, 101-2, 106, 112, 114, 116, 123, 125-6, 132, 136-7, 145-6, 170, 247, 249, 275, 284, 293, 319, 321, 324, 340, 503, 574; engagement, 123; death, 318; letter to HC, 67; letter from HC, 116*n*
Cushing, Mrs. Edward F. (Melanie Harvey), 20, 26*n*, 62, 74, 82, 112, 114, 123, 125-6, 144-6, 233, 249, 284, 600
Cushing, Edward Harvey (Pat, son of EFC), 136-7, 145-6, 600*n*, 697, 699-700; 'the touch', 24, 713
Cushing, Erastus (grandfather of HC), 3, 5*n*, 7-10, 19, 23, 25, 29-30, 136, 321, 644; advice to patient, 9; vignette of, 9; last illness, 73; letter to HKC, 11-12
Cushing, Mrs. Erastus (Mary Ann Platt), 8, 10-11, 18
Cushing, George B. (brother of HC), 20-2, 24, 29
Cushing, Harry, *see* Cushing, Henry Platt
Cushing, Harvey

BIOGRAPHY AND CHIEF EVENTS

Early years: ancestry, 3 *et seq.;* Western Reserve, 6-8; reminiscences (of mother) 16-22, (of youth) 17-19; early education, 26-8; camping trips to Maskenoza, 28; earliest letter (to WEC), 29; youth in Cleveland, 144; Yale College, 33 *et seq.;* first medical lectures, 37; Scroll and Key, 45, 274; visit to White House, 43, (recalled) 124; college record, 46; work in physiological chemistry, 47-50, (work recalled) 672
Medical School and subsequent training

(1891-1901): Harvard Medical School, 53 *et seq.;* assistant to Dr. Scudder, 62; second year work, 67; first clinical experience, 68 *et seq.;* as an anesthetist, 69-72, 74-5, 78-9; refusal of scholarship, 82; trip to Cuba, 83-6; possible appointment with Osler, 86; first trip abroad, 88-91; trip to Bermuda, 97-8; H.M.S. marks, 100; M.G.H. appointment, 100; early ether charts, 93-6; first use of X-rays, 104-6; early neurological cases, 259-61; first visit to J.H.H., 101; Canadian trip, 112-15; Assistant resident at J.H.H., 114; 'maiden effort', 123, 261; surgical residency at J.H.H., 124-7; appendix operation, 129-32; Instructor in surgery, 133; family bookplate designed, 135-7; work on local anesthesia, 141-3; trip up Great Lakes, 145-6; engagement (unannounced), 145; bacteriological studies, 149-52; contact with troops in Spanish-American war, 146-8; first call (1899) to Western Reserve, 156; early work (1900) on trigeminal neuralgia, 262 *et seq.;* study abroad, 161 *et seq.;* contacts with Horsley, 163-4; centennial celebration, Royal College of Surgeons, 166-7; International Medical Congress, Paris, 168-9; visit to Le Puy, 172-3; work in Berne, 176 *et seq.;* Haller and his native town (first historical paper, 1901), 168, 456; problem from Kocher, 178; 'grand tour' of Italy and Germany, 184 *et seq.;* portable blood-pressure apparatus encountered, 190, 212; work with Sherrington, 195 *et seq.;* physiology openings at Harvard, 202

Johns Hopkins (1901-1912): 'waiting time', 203-4; move to 3 W. Franklin St., 204, 208; first letterhead, 208, 210; first case of pituitary tumor, 271-2; blood pressure studies, 212-16; Hunterian Laboratory, 217-22; engagement and marriage, 225; call to University of Maryland (1902), 330; birth of first child, 229; death of mother, 230; Associate in surgery, 231; call to Jefferson (1904-06), 233, 330-1; trip abroad (1904), 234-6; 'all-star' performance, 237-9; first report on special field of neurological surgery, 266; birth of Mary, 246; offer from Yale (1906), 248, 331 *et seq.;* first mention of P.B.B.H. (March 1907), 335; contribution to Keen's *Surgery,* 267-70; request for neurological assistant, 272, 278-9; move to 107 E. Chase St., 273; birth of Betsey, 275; Tarbell portrait, 276-7; 1st Lieut. Medical Reserve Corps, 282; Charaka Club member, 285; first case of acromegaly, 288; trip abroad with KC (1909), 291 *et seq.;* lecture in Liverpool, 291; International Medical Congress, Budapest 1909, 291 *et seq.;* call to Washington University (1910), 306, 331, 337; death of HKC, 306-7; operation on Gen. Wood, 308-12; negotiations with Harvard and P.B.B.H., 338-40; birth of Henry, 313; trip to Great Britain with Society of Clinical Surgery (1910), 313-14; death of brother Ned, 318-19; second call to Western Reserve, 318; pituitary monograph published, 320-5; farewell dinner (1912), 328; trip abroad (1912), 328-9

Boston (1912-1933): move to Boston, 329, 353 *et seq.;* membership in 'The Club' & 'Saturday Club', 356 *et seq.;* First Annual Report, 363; International Medical Congress, 366-71; formal opening of Brigham (Nov. 1914), 376; 'full-time' controversy, 379 *et seq.;* offer to resign Harvard post, 380, 384; at the Ambulance Américaine, 392-403; visit to front lines, 400-1; acoustic tumor monograph, 410-11; Director of Base Hospital No. 5, 419-42; with 2d Army (British), 421 *et seq.;* courtmartial threatened, 426-8; first airplane flight, 427-8; Senior consultant in neurosurgery, 430; attack of polyneuritis, 435-6; plea for Institute of Neurology, 443 *et seq.;* citation by Gen. Pershing, 452; work on Osler biography, 458 *et seq.* (to Oxford July 1920), 460, (Pulitzer prize), 462; further report on neurological surgery, 471-2, 30th reunion, speech at Alumni luncheon, 481; trip abroad (1922), 487 *et seq.;* invited to succeed Halsted, 494; third call to Western Reserve, 503; dedication, Sterling Hall of Medicine, 518-19; appearance of 'Osler', 521; trip abroad (Oct. 1925), 524; glioma monograph published, 522; gift to Hunterian Laboratory, 527-8; Bill's death, 534; first use of electrosurgery, 537-8; abroad (1927), 546 *et seq.;* gift to Yale, W. H. Cushing Fellowship, 556; gift to P.B.B.H., Surgeon-in-Chief Fund, 556; *Consecratio Medici* published, 561-2; blood-vessel tumor monograph, 563; 60th birthday celebration, 569-72; International Physiological Congress, Boston, 576-9; trip to Sweden, Holland and Switzerland (1929), 579 *et seq.;* offers of posts after retirement, 584 *et seq.;* Betsey's marriage, 590; trip abroad (1930), 592 *et seq.;* tribute to Sir A. Bowlby, 592-3; Osler Club oration, 594; hospitalization, 601-2; 2000th tumor operation, 604; 40th reunion, 605; trip to Berne (1931), 606-10; declination of Hopkins post, 612; description of new syndrome, 614; Harvey Cushing Society formed, 616; fourth call to Western Reserve, 619-20; retirement from P.B.B.H., 621; last operation, 621; trip abroad (1932), 621-5

New Haven (1933-1939): decision to return to Yale (Oct. 1932), 626; elected Fellow of Trumbull College, 627, 691-2; departure for New Haven (Oct. 1933), 633; trip to London and Paris (1933), 638 *et seq.;* in hospital, 640; Brain Tumor Registry, 642-4; plans for library, 646-8; Medical Advisory Committee, C.E.S., 649-56; further hospitalization, 669; retirement from Sterling professorship, 680-4; President Elizabethan Club, 689-90; 'The Club', New Haven, 690-1; last trip abroad (1938), 697-9; publication of meningioma monograph, 700; 70th birthday party, 706-9, (bibliography) 706, (remarks) 708; last illness and death, 713-14; will, 716-18

CHARACTERISTICS, CONTACTS &C

Book collecting: interest in books, 117; Shakespeare inkstand, 208; book cases, 208; bookplate, 135-8; book repairing, 649; plans for historical library, 646-8, 663, 667; cataloguing of books, 668, 702, 704; soliciting friends for their libraries, 686-7; acquisitions to library, 137-8, 148, 206, 232, 237, 252, 294, 296, 528-9, 581-3, 600*n*, 624, 647-9, 663, 666-8, 693, 695

Early interests (professional): bacteriology, 149 *et seq.;* medicine, 46-7, 50-1; orthopedics, 92, 121, 126; physiological chemistry, 47-9; neurosurgery, 162, 257-9, 261

General interests: art, 60, 67, 71, 73, 293, 296-7, 623-4; astronomy, 519-20, 667-8, 681-2; athletics, 26, 476-7, (baseball) 40-44; (croquet) 520, 645, (tennis) 373-4, 476, 520; botany and natural history, 47, 53, 65-7, 78, 98, 113, 118; circus, 40, 77, 303, 691; music, 63-4; welfare of students, 353-4

Health: Colles fracture, 17; concern over, 75, 83-4, 86-7, 184, 251; polyneuritis, 454, 520; complications from return of polyneuritis, 601-2; state of health (1931-2), 611; (1933), 632, 634; illness in hospital (1933-4), 639-40; (1935), 669-70, 709-10; death and autopsy, 713-14

Personal traits: generous instincts, 476, 516, 527, 556-7; good teacher, 107; humor, 103, 504-5, 675; impatience, 350; patriotism, 418; persistence, 450; pride, 203-4; the reformer, 129, 332, 353; 'Selbstständigkeit', 184, 192-3; taskmaster, 107

Professional relationships: advice to juniors, 202; advice to neurosurgeons, 539-40, 609; attendance at meetings, 313; belief in importance of autopsies, 363-4; belief in telling patients truth, 265; belief in value of meetings, 454, 609; class room characterizations, 499-500; clinical histories, viii; criticism of Dandy, 489-90; dissecting, 58-60, 68, 74-5; feeling about deans, 531, 649; a good physician, 568; keeping in touch with patients, 240-1; operations at Corey Hill, 362; operative routine, 535-6; out-of-town consultations, 231; reactions to HC, 107; refusal to operate outside own hospital, 285, 507; relations with assistants, 569, with Halsted, 120-2, with patients, 498-9; surgical fees, 555-6; surgical training, 125, teaching at Yale, 675

Other characteristics: Ability to refresh himself, 535; alertness, 249-50, 537*n;* animal trainer, 544-5; annoyance with journal editors, 489, 509-10, 546; architect's drawings, 350, 648; backward somersault, 44; *confessio fidei,* 496-7; conversation (art of), 356, 544; cure for indecision, 32; daily routine, 371-4; diary habit, 79, 83; disapproval of smoking, 516; dislike of formality, 64, 356; drawing (for Halsted) 123, (pupil of Brödel) 158, (sketching) 172, (for Sherrington) 199, (for trigeminal neuralgia paper) 262, (artistic ability) 700; educational shortcomings, 673; family likenesses, 34; 'faults and virtues', 314; financial worries, 37-8, 42, 56, 58, 73, 78-9, 88, 106, 124, 225, 636-7 (expense accounts) 38, 80; food and drink, 89, 91, 118, 123; lack of enthusiasm for new places, 34, 55, 115-17, 123; manuscript page, 519; moustache, 183;

playing jokes on colleagues, 506-7; poetical whimsy, 133; prose writing, 431-4, 456-7; relation with printers and publishers, 563-4; religious philosophy, 663; social contacts, 59, 62-3; spelling, 47, 49, 55, 66, 87, 635

ADDRESSES: HISTORICAL

Dr. Garth the Kit-Kat poet (Dec. 1904), 239-41
Holders of the Gold-headed cane as book collectors (Jan. 1906), 247
Notes concerning 'John Locke as physician' (Mar. 1907, not pub.), 252
Realignments in greater medicine (Aug. 1913), 327, 368
A centripetal *versus* a centrifugal hospital service (Nov. 1914), 376
William Osler the man (Jan. 1920), 472
The personality of a hospital (Ether Day address, Oct. 1921), 481-4
Laboratories: then and now (Oct. 1922), 491
The physician and the surgeon (Oct. 1922), 492
Louisa Parsons (Nov. 1922), 493-4
The 'Boston Tins' (May 1923), 501
The Western Reserve and its medical traditions (Oct. 1924), 511-13
Experimentum periculosum (Feb. 1925), 518-19
Consecratio medici (June 1926), 533
Doctor and his books (Nov. 1926), 541-2
Emancipators (July 1927), 457, 551
Who put the fox in foxglove (May 1928, not pub.), 561
The medical career (Nov. 1928), 565-6
Binding influence of a library (Oct. 1929), 583-4
An American tribute to Sir Anthony Bowlby (July 1930), 592-3
Eulogy of Major-General Clarence R. Edwards (Feb. 1931), 601
One hundred and fifty years (June 1931), 605
Ercole Lelli (Dec. 1932), 628
Homo chirurgicus (May 1933), 631
Medicine at the crossroads (1933), 632
Pioneer medical schools of central New York (1934), 644
Psychiatrists, neurologists and the neurosurgeon (Sept. 1934), 645-6
Humanizing of science (Dec. 1934), 656-7
William Beaumont's rendezvous with fame (June 1935), 661-2
Perry Williams Harvey (Dec. 1936), 677 *et seq.*

ADDRESSES: MEDICAL

Method of total extirpation of Gasserian ganglion (Apr. 1900), 262
Some experimental and clinical observations concerning states of increased intracranial tension (The Mütter Lecture, 1901), 211
On routine determinations of arterial tension (Jan. 1903), 213
Special field of neurological surgery (Nov. 1904), 239, 266
Instruction in operative medicine (Feb. 1906), 248
The hypophysis cerebri (June 1909), 290
Recent observations on tumours of the brain and their surgical treatment (Banks Memorial Lecture, 1909), 291-2
Special field of neurological surgery, five years later (Jan. & Oct. 1910), 305
Dyspituitarism (Harvey Lecture, Dec. 1910), 321
Psychic disturbances . . . disorders of the ductless glands (Apr. 1913), 364
Concerning diabetes insipidus (Shattuck Lecture, June 1913), 365
Surgical experiences with pituitary disorders (Weir Mitchell Lecture, Feb. 1914), 375
Concerning . . . a National Institute of Neurology (June 1919), 443-50
The major trigeminal neuralgias (Hatfield Lecture, Dec. 1919), 451
The special field of neurological surgery after another interval (Oct. 1920), 471
Disorders of the pituitary gland: Retrospective and prophetic (June 1921), 478
Les syndromes hypophysaires (Paris, June 1922), 487
The meningiomas (Cavendish Lecture, June 1922), 488
Surgical end results . . . cavernous haemangioma of skull (Oct. 1922), 492
Neurological surgeons: with the report of one case (May 1923), 501-3
Experiences with orbito-ethmoidal osteomata (May 1927), 546
Acromegaly from a surgical standpoint (London, June 1927), 546-7
Meningiomas arising from olfactory groove (Macewen Memorial Lecture, June 1927), 548-9
Experiences with cerebellar medulloblastomas (Lund, Sept. 1929), 579
Neurohypophysial mechanisms from a clinical standpoint (Lister Memorial Lecture, July 1930), 590 *et seq.*

Experiences with the cerebellar astrocytomas (Bevan Lecture, Oct. 1930), 599
The posterior pituitary hormone and the parasympathetic nervous system (Welch Lecture, Apr. 1931), 591, 603
Intracranial tumours . . . 2000 verified cases (Berne, 1931), 604-5
Peptic ulcers and the interbrain (Balfour Lecture, Apr. 1931), 603
The basophil adenomas of the pituitary body and their clinical manifestations (pituitary basophilism (New York, 1932), 614-16
'Dyspituitarism': 20 years later (Harvey Lecture, Jan. 1933), 628-9
Hyperactivation of the neurohypophysis (London, Nov. 1933), 638

BOOKS

The pituitary body (1912), 320 *et seq.;* plans drafted for, 298; dedication, 321; reception of, 324-5
Tumors of the nervus acusticus (1917), 409-11
Story of U.S. Army Base Hospital No. 5 (1919), 451
Life of Sir William Osler (1925), 457-71, 521
Classification of gliomas (1926), 521-2
Studies in intracranial physiology and surgery (Cameron Prize lectures for 1925, pub. 1926), 522-4
Tumors arising from the blood-vessels of the brain (1928), 563
Consecratio medici (1928), 533, 561-2; review of, 562-3
Intracranial tumours (1932), 604-5
Pituitary body and hypothalamus (1932), 603*n*
From a surgeon's journal (1936), 656-7, 666, 668, 672-3
Meningiomas (1938), 260-1, 628, 640, 645, 674, 679, 685-7, 693, 697, 700
The medical career (1940), 565-6
Bio-bibliography of Vesalius (1943), 624, 702*n*
A visit to Le Puy-en-Velay (1944), 172

DIARIES

H.M.S. (1893), 69-82
Columbian Exposition (1893), 80-1
Cuba (1894), 83-6
England (1894), 88-91
Bermuda (1895), 97-8
Gaspé (1896), 112-15
Great Lakes (1898), 145-6
England & Continent (1900-01), 164-201
Le Puy (1900), 172*n*
England (1904), 234-6
England & Continent (Budapest Congress, 1909), 292-7
The German Clinics and Oxford (1912), 328-9
London Congress (1913), 366-71
American Ambulance (1915), 392 *et seq.*
Great War (1917-19), 414 *et seq.*
Italy & Switzerland (1932), 623

DRAWINGS & SKETCHES REPRODUCED

Edward Fitch Cushing, 24
Room at Yale, 35
Crystals for Chittenden, 49
Grecian boxer, 61
Before and after (Anat. exam.), 77
Chicago Exposition, 81
On the streets of Havana, 83
From Havana Travel Diary, 84
Scenes in Cuba, 85
After "Rubens" [?Rembrandt], 89
The Cabby and Jonathan Hutchinson, 90
Sketches from Bermuda, 97
Spilling the coffee beans, 114
Sketches of Canada, 115
Christmas greetings to KC, 119
How Dr. "Cushong" took "Efur," 134
Pat and the Captain, 145
K.C., 146
A boat acquaintance, 163
The Latin Quarter, 170
Ollier, Reverdin & Roux, 174
Gastro-intestinal anastomosis, 175
Theodor and Albert Kocher, 177
Hermann Sahli, 180
Patient of Angelo Mosso, 186
Eck's fistula, 189
Hans Strasser, 192
Bernard Naunyn, 193
Schmiedeberg, Fürstner and Erb, 194
E.F.W. Pflüger, 195
Jonathan Hutchinson, 197
"Ye Sturdy Scot", 201
Diagram of Riva-Rocci's apparatus, 212
Diagram of perfusion experiments, 223
Osler working in his stateroom, 234
Honorary degree at Sheldonian, 235
Harvard Lecture notes, 258
Sensory distribution of trigeminal nerve, 264
Cyst of pituitary gland, 272
General Wood's tumor, 309
Richard Pearson Strong, 392
H.C., magnet, and nail, 398
Tent at Mendinghem, 432
Ypres, Oct. 1917, 433

A simian craniotomy, 595
Rollicking in Cleveland, 600
Operative sketch, 617
The sign of Babinski, 619

ICONOGRAPHY

Tarbell portrait, 276 *et seq.*, 304-5
Sargent sketch, 505-6
Axenstrasse portrait, 583
Mrs. Calvin G. Page's oil painting, 632
Keller charcoals, 693

Cushing, Mrs. Harvey (Katharine S. Crowell), v, 5, 37, 63-4, 75, 82, 119-20, 139-40, 144 *et seq.*, 153, 202, 206, 208, 225, 229, 232, 234, 236, 244, 248*n*, 269, 274, 282, 287-8, 290-1, 293-8, 305, 307, 312, 328-30, 333, 339, 341, 350, 355-7, 359, 368, 371, 373-4, 459, 461, 476, 486-8, 491, 504-5, 508, 512, 516, 527, 544-5, 554, 560, 572, 597, 619, 625-7, 629, 633, 635-6, 640, 646, 661, 674, 676, 693, 702; visit to Baltimore, 145; letters to HKC, 233, 242, 246, 250, 282; to J. F. Ortschild, 251; letters from HC, 138, 146, 170, 185, 188, 228, 460; from H. A. Killick, 424; from Lady Osler, 425; from WO, 425; from L. H. Weed, 528
Cushing, Hayward W., 92*n*
Cushing, Henry Kirke (father of HC), 3, 5*n*, 7*n*, 8-23, 43, 145, 225*n*, 232-3, 308, 321, 515-6; education, 11, 644; Civil War service, 12-13, 143; drawing, 13; scientific interests, 14; advice to HC about money, 15; Franklin-Heberden paper, 15, 233; periods of silence, 16, 22; list of children, 22; conditions imposed on HC, 41; advice to defer judgment on Baltimore, 117; unsolicited funds to HC, 118; dedication of Laboratory of Experimental Medicine, 284; admonitions, 307; death, 306; letters to HC, 25, 36, 41, 55 ('Chesterfield letter'), 65, 102, 117, 125, 135, 157; letters from HC, 34-6, 38, 41-2, 44, 47-50, 56-8, 60-2, 67, 73-4, 76, 79-80, 86-7, 100, 104, 106, 117, 123-4, 126, 132-8, 147-9, 151, 153, 157, 159, 164, 166, 169, 172-3, 176, 179, 185, 189, 194-5, 198-9, 203, 205, 207, 210-11, 228, 243-4, 246-7, 249, 251, 262, 269, 273-7, 287-8, 298, 304
Cushing, Mrs. Henry K. (Betsey Maria Williams), 3, 23, 35, 76, 225*n*, 275; early life, 16 *et seq.;* death, 230; letters to HC, 125, 156, 265; letters from HC, 29-31, 36, 39-40, 43, 47, 49, 55-7, 59, 62-6, 77-8, 99, 102, 116-19, 123-5, 132, 137, 139-40, 143, 148, 155, 159, 162-3, 165, 175, 200
Cushing, Henry K. (son of HC), 317, 340, 514-15; birth of, 313; marriage, 673
Cushing, Mrs. Henry K. (Marjorie Estabrook), 673
Cushing, Henry Platt (brother of HC), 16, 19-24, 29, 39, 136, 451
Cushing, Jeremiah (son of Matthew Cushing, 1589-1660), 4
Cushing, John (son of William Cushing), 3
Cushing, John (son of Matthew Cushing, 1589-1660), 4
Cushing, Mrs. John (Sarah Hawke), 4
Cushing, Mrs. John (Deborah Jacob), 4
Cushing, Josiah, 4
Cushing, Julia (sister of HC), 22
Cushing, Kirke W. (son of H. P. Cushing), 17, 23, 136; death, 451
Cushing, Lydia (sister of Erastus Cushing), 5
Cushing, Major, 58, 72
Cushing, Mary Benedict (Schwester, daughter of HC), 269, 274, 317, 374, 514, 517, 544-5, 611, 638, 674; birth, 246
Cushing, Matthew (1589-1660), 3-4
Cushing, Mrs. Matthew (Nazareth Pitcher), 4
Cushing, Matthew (son of Matthew Cushing, 1589-1660), 4
Cushing, Matthew (1665-1715), 4
Cushing, Peter, 3
Cushing, Thomas, of Hardingham, 3
Cushing, Thomas 2d, of Hardingham, 3
Cushing, William (son of Thomas of Hardingham), 3
Cushing, William D. (son of Erastus Cushing), 8*n*
Cushing, Mrs. William D. (Caroline Shaw), 8*n*
Cushing, William E. (brother of HC), 19-23, 25, 30, 34, 55, 170, 247, 276; notes about Erastus Cushing, 4; memories of HKC, 12-14; letters from HC, 29, 66
Cushing, Mrs. William E. (Carolyn Kellogg), 19, 23, 137, 155, 276
Cushing, William H. (son of HC), 230, 250, 269, 274, 282, 288, 298, 317, 329, 361, 374, 505, 514, 556; birth, 229; death, 534; letter from HC, 515-16
Cushing, William L., 35-6
Cushing Brain Tumor Registry, *see* Brain Tumor Registry
Cushing Laboratory, *see* H. K. Cushing Laboratory of Experimental Medicine at Cleveland
Cushing Library, *see* Yale University. School of Medicine. Historical Library
Cushing motto, 135-6

Cushing Society, *see* Harvey Cushing Society
Cushing's disease, *see* Basophilism, pituitary
'Cushing's men', 316
Cushny, A. R., 522, 525, 558
Cutler, E. C., 121, 224, 362*n*, 376, 391, 419, 504, 510, 559, 569-70, 572, 613, 619-20, 626, 632, 643; letter from HC, 223
Cutter, I. S., 561; letter to HC, 620; letter from HC, 620
Czerny, Vincenz, 194

Dabney, Mr., 345
Dachshunds, 138-9, 254-5
Dakin, H. D., 396, 409, 447
Dalzell, W. S., 82, 116
Dalziel, T. K., 149
Dana, C. L., 262, 445
Dana, J. D., 37
Dandy, W. E., 220-1, 245, 316-17, 320, 476, 489-90
Daniëls, C. E., 293
Darrach, William, 424
Dartmouth Medical School, Hanover, 565
Darwin, C. R., 137
Davidoff, L. M., 525, 537, 539, 556
Davidson, R. T., Archbp. of Canterbury, 250
Davies, Llewellyn, 598
'Davis, Egerton Yorrick', 206, 228*n*
Davis, Hallowell, 577, 633
Davis, J. S., 221
Davis, S. G., 221
Davison, H. P., 507
Davy, Sir Humphry, 167
Day, E. L., 16-17, 30, 513
Day, G. P., 385
Day & Williams Glass Mfg. Co., 16
Decompression for brain tumors, 267; steps in, 471
DeCoppet, Gaston, 584, 608
De Kruif, P. H., 469
De la Mare, W. J., 598
Delamater, John, 511
Delano family, 590
Delavan, Bryson, 50-1, 63, 74
Delta Kappa Epsilon Fraternity, 44
Deniker, Michel, 411*n*
Dennett, J.R., 359
Dennis, F. S., 627
Denny, F. P., 88, 102
Denny, G. P., 432
De Quincey, Thomas, 232
Derby, G. S., 531
Derge, H. F., 220
Dexter, F. B., letter to HC, 33
Diabetes, pancreatic, 82, 325
Diabetes insipidus, 365-6, 525-6
Dibdin, T. F., 248
Diencephalon, *see* Hypothalamus
Dieulafoy, G., 150
Digby, Sir Kenelm, 232, 682
Dillingham, Laura, 517
Dittrick, Howard, 9, 26*n*
Dobell, Clifford, 628
Dochez, A. R., 220
Dock, George, 337, 361; letter to HC, 340
Dodd, W. J., 105*n*, 483
Dodd, Mead & Co., 136, 138; letter to HC, 135
Dolet, Étienne, 542
Dollinger, J., 295
Dolliver, G. C., 72, 88
Donley, J. E., 478*n*
Donnelley, T. E., 563
Donnelly, Mary, 642
Donovan, Tim, 700
Dor, Henri, 173
Dor, Louis, 173, 176
Dorsey, J. S., 252
Dott, N. M., 525, 535, 558, 583, 608, 698
Dougherty, D. J., Card., 485
Dow, Prentiss, 18
Dow, Mrs. Prentiss, 12, 18
Dowman, C. E., 455*n*
Draper, E. S., 345
Drew, John, 82
Drinker, C. K., 472, 633; letter to HC, 533-4
Drinker, Elizabeth, 472
Drinker, K. R., 472
Dryden, John, 236, 239-40
Drysdale, C. R., 293
Dublin zoo, visit to, 430
Dubois, F. T., 51
DuBois-Reymond, E. H., 181
Du Bouchet, G. W., 387, 398; letter from R. B. Greenough, 390
Ductless glands, disturbances of, 364, 371, 478
Dufferin and Ava, F. T., 1st Marquis of, 550
Duggan, John, 675
du Maurier, George, 208, 598
Duncan, George A., *see* Camperdown, Earl
Dunham, E. K., 553*n*
Durante, Francesco, 256
Dusser de Barenne, J. G., 612
Dwarfs, 302-4, 575-6, 702, 710
Dwight, Thomas, 54, 60, 71, 82
Dwight, Timothy, 277
Dyer, J. M., 26*n*
Dyschromatopsia, 320*n*
Dyspituitarism, 321, 323, 628-9

E. K. Dunham Lectureship, 553-4
Eck's fistula, 189
Eckstein, Gustav, 685
Eclampsia, neurohypophysis in, 630, 638
Edes, R. E., 58, 72-3, 82
Edes, R. T., 275
Edison, Thomas, 104
Edsall, D. L., 307, 586, 643
Education, medical, full-time plan for Harvard, 377 *et seq.*
Edward VII, King of England, 371*n*, 711
Edwards, Maj. Gen. C.R., 419, 484, 552; HC's funeral oration, 601
Ehrlich, Paul, 182, 233-4, 327-8, 367
Eiselsberg, Anton, Freiherr von, 271, 275, 294-5, 328
Eisenhardt, Louise, 241*n*, 256*n*, 364, 410, 487, 514, 541, 557*n*, 561*n*, 599, 604, 628, 643*n*, 644, 658, 661, 674, 686, 689, 693, 700, 707-8
Elder, Col., 434
Electrosurgery, 536-8, 548-9, 550; first operation with, 537-8
Eliot, C. W., 37, 54, 249, 337, 357, 359-60, 417, 475, 494; excerpt from 'Pasteur as a democrat', 495; letters to HC, 227, 341, 497; letter from HC, 496
Eliot, Ellsworth Jr., 74
Eliot, G. E., 63
Eliot, George, 663
Elizabethan Club, Yale, 329, 634, 657, 689
Elkin, D. C. Jr., letter from HC, 552
Ellenbog incunabula collection, 624
Elliot, J. W., 88, 104, 107, 109, 129*n*, 259-61
Elliott, Howard, 476
Elliott, T. R., 428-9, 524
Elsberg, C. A., 455*n*
Ely, C. R., 34
'Emancipators', delivered, 551; quotation from, 457
Embree, E. R., 446
Emerson, E. W., 416
Emmons, R. VanB., 401
Enderlen, Eugen, 328
Endocrinology, 478
Endotheliomas, 410; *see* Meningiomas
Erb, W. H., 194
Erie Canal, 6, 11
Erlanger, Joseph, 338
Estabrook, Marjorie, *see* Cushing, Mrs. Henry K.
Ether charts, 93-6, 213
Ether Day address, by W. H. Welch, 277-8; by HC, 483-4
Evans, H. M., 220, 303, 710
Ewart, William, 164
'Experimentum periculosum', 518-19
Fabricius, H. ab Aquapendente, 174, 189-90
Facial neuralgia, *see* Trigeminal neuralgia
Facial paralysis, treatment of, 266
Falk, I. S., 655
Faraday, Michael, 105*n*; centenary celebration, 611
Faradic stimulation, of post-central gyrus, 200, 314
Faris, C. M., 220
Farlow, J. W., 289, 478*n*
Farnam, H. W., 691*n*
Farnam, T. W., 663
Farrand, Max, 588-9
Faust, E. S., 194
Feil, Harold, 26*n*, 27
Feller, R., 176
Ferguson, M. W., 410*n*
Ferrier, Sir David, 200, 231, 256*n*, 522, 547
Fibrin, as hemostatic, 536
Field Ambulance No. 8, 400
Fincher, E. F. Jr., 526
Finney, J. M. T., 101, 125, 127, 140, 147, 159, 203-4, 217, 228*n*, 254, 264, 305, 327, 439, 447, 479, 486, 494, 694; letter to G. M. Smith, 237
Fisch, M. H., 600*n*
Fishbein, Morris, 571, 694; letters from HC, 570, 651
Fisher, J. A., 1st baron of Kilverstone, 412
Fisher, P. E., 74
Fiske, John, 359
Fitch, Haynes, 7
Fitch, Lucy, *see* Williams, Mrs. William
Fitch, Zalmon, 16, 20, 25
Fitz, R. H., 54, 82, 87, 93, 129, 286, 675
Fitz, Reginald, 633; letter from HC, 552
Fleming, H. W., 453
Fletcher, C. R. L., letter to Lady Osler, 470
Fletcher, Col. L. Z., 311
Fletcher, Robert, 288, 660, 663
Fletcher, Sir Walter M., 402, 511, 577, 595; letter to HC, 467; letters from HC, 477, 540
Flexner, Abraham, 222, 306, 337, 369, 377, 379-81, 383, 391, 444; letter from HC, 450
Flexner, Simon, 111, 149-55, 159, 211, 248, 262, 285, 355, 477-8, 479-80, 495-6, 522, 588, 601, 629; letters to HC, 152, 286, 340; letter from HC, 152
Flint, J. M., 384, 476, 479-80
Fock, Gustave, 361
Foerster, Otfrid, 474, 590, 598-9, 606-8, 610
Foley, F. E. B., 471
Follis, R. H., 238

Follow-up system, 96, 450, 541; plea for, 492
Forbes, Alexander, 554, 633
Forbes, W. Cameron, 356, 696
Ford, Henry, 403-4
Foster, Sir Michael, 110, 196
Fothergill, John, 287, 546
Fothergill, Rev. Samuel, 546
Fournier, Denis, 230
Francis, W. W., viii, 208*n*, 239, 463, 574-5, 645, 698-9, 708; remarks at HC's 70th birthday, 707
Franco, Francisco, 696
Frank, E., 366*n*
Frankl-Hochwart, Lothar von, 294
Franklin, Alfred, 594
Franklin, Benjamin, 13, 15, 21, 211, 228, 233, 496
Franklin-Heberden pamphlet, 15, 233
Frazier, C. H., 263*n*, 455*n*
Freeman, Miss, 17
Fremont-Smith, Frank, 608
French, D. C., 73
French, E. D., 136
French, J. R. L., Viscount, 429
French medicine and surgery, 168 *et seq.*
Frick, Alice, *see* Jacobs, Mrs. H. B.
Fried, B. M., 526
Friedenwald, Jonas, 494
Fries, A. A., 428
Fritsche, 301
Frobenius, Wilhelm, 111
Fröhlich, Alfred, 197-200, 275, 281-2, 294-5; syndrome, 271-2, 281, 322-3
Frothingham, Channing, 507
Fry, C. C., 692
Fuchs, Leonhard, 561
Fürstner, Karl, 194
Full-time plan, 377 *et seq.;* historical background, 378; Flexner report, 379; original proposal, 379*n;* and Osler, 464-5
Fuller, Margaret, 119
Futcher, P. H., reminiscence, 702
Futcher, T. B., 204, 208-11, 225, 228*n*, 233-5, 248, 252-4, 273, 693
Futcher, Mrs. T. B. (Gwendolen M. Howard), 211, 273

Gale, Charles, 13
Galen, 190, 292, 296, 645
Galilei, Galileo, 189-90
Galton, Francis, 76
Galvani, Luigi, 453, 704; and Lucia, 671; bibliography of, 671
Gamble, C. B., war recollections, 439
Gamgee, Arthur, 229
Gannett, W. W., 68, 72-3, 75
Gardner, Anna, 126
Garfield, Abram, 82, 87, 144; letter to HC, 98
Garfield, Mrs. Abram, 26*n*
Garfield, I. McD., 82, 144, 337, 345
Garrè, Carl, 328
Garrett, A. S., 103
Garrett, Robert, 210
Garrett, Mrs. Robert, *see* Jacobs, Mrs. H. B.
Garrison, F. H., 327, 466, 530, 560-1, 589, 601, 637, 660, 663, 693
Garth, Sir Samuel, 230, 286; paper on, 239-41
Gas warfare, first casualties from, 397; treatment of casualties, 409; M.R.C. session on, 428-9
Gask, G. E., 473, 477, 486, 488
Gasserian ganglion, first case of resection, 154; paper on, 157; surgical methods, 158, 262, 265; meeting, 494
Gastric lesions, *see* Peptic ulcer
Gastro-intestinal anastomosis, 175
Gatch, W. D., 220
Gehner, R. F., viii, 563, 700
General Education Board, 379-84, 444-5, 464
General Hospitals, No. 11, 421, 423; No. 13, 430; No. 22, 415
George V, King of England, 401, 412, 452
George Gorham Peters Travelling Fellowship, 557*n*
Geraghty, J. T., 220
Gérard, 180
Gerber, W. von, 220
German, W. J., 526
German Surgical Society, 148
Gerrard, G. M., 454
Giacomini Museum, 188
Giants, 299, 302, 702*n;* Irish giant, 303; letter to 'Time', 304
Gibbons, James, Card., 466
Gibbs, J. Willard, 37
Gibson, A. G., 698
Gilbertus Anglicus, quotation from, 492
Gildersleeve, B. L., 110, 207, 242
Gillett, F. H., 551-2
Gilman, D. C., 110-11, 224, 683
Gilman, P. K., 220-2, 245
Giordano, Davide, 189
Girdlestone, G. R., 698
Glass, Carter, 661
Glasser, Otto, 106*n*
Glenn, F. N., 557*n*, 619
Gliomas, 522-3
Godlee, Sir Rickman J., 366
Goethals, G. W., 412
Goetsch, Emil, 220-1, 245, 313-14, 320, 326, 354, 362, 365*n*

Gold-headed cane, 167, 247
Goldschmidt, E. P., 529, 594, 667, 670, 693-4; recollections, 695-6
Goldsmith, Oliver, 485
Goldthwait, J. E., 73, 428
Gomperz, Theodor, 232
Goodell, William, 306
Goodnow, F. J., letter from HC, 527
Goodwillie, Thomas, 117-18, 123-4, 139, 143, 145, 148-9, 153, 156, 204, 233, 275, 298
Goodwillie, Harriet, 144
Goodwillie, M. C., 26*n*, 60, 63-4, 75, 82, 148, 204; reminiscence, 144
Gordon Taylor, Gordon, 428
Gorgas, W. C., 360*n*, 387, 412, 414, 418-19; letter to HC, 413; letter from HC, 413
Gould, G. M., 157
Gouraud, Gen., 504
Gowers, Sir William R., 90, 166, 436
Graham, Capt., 421
Graham, E. A., 473, 521, 526; letter to HC, 524
Grant, F. C., 526, 608
Grant, U. S., 13
Graves, W. P., 45; letter to HC, 107
Gray, J. C., 358-9
Gt. Ormond St. Hospital, London, 90
Greeley, Horace, 14
Green, R. M., 386, 478*n*
Greenough, R. B., 214, 391, 537, 630, 652; letter to HC, 341; to G. W. Du Bouchet, 390
Greenslet, Ferris, 2
Gregg, Alan, reminiscence, 386; letter to HC, 443; letter from HC, 443
Grenfell, Sir Wilfred, 253, 566, 612
Grey, A. H. G., 4th Earl, 250
Grey, Sir Edward, 367
Grey, E. G., 362, 536
Griggs, Gen., 147
Griggs, M. F., 690*n*
Grinnell, C. E., 358-9
Gros, E. L., 387
Gross, S. D., 206, 232
Gross, S. W., 207, 232
Gross, Mrs. S. W., *see* Osler, Lady
Growth hormone, 303, 575-6, 710
Grünbaum, later Leyton, A. S. F., 197-9, 234
Guidarelli, Guidarello, 226
Guillain, Georges, 638
Gunderson, Trygve, 526
Gundrum, F. F., 220
Gunn, J. A., 698
Gunther, R. W. T., 698
Gus, *see* Schneekloth, G.
Gustav V, King of Sweden, 581
Guy's Hospital, London, 164, 167
Gwyn, N. B., 119, 149, 152, 228*n*

H. K. Cushing Laboratory of Experimental Medicine at Cleveland, 284
Haag, Elsa, 183
Haberer, Hans von, 294
Hadley, A. T., 207-8, 331, 336, 480-1; letter from HC, 333
Haeckel, Ernst, 181
Haematomyelia from gunshot wounds, 122-3, 135, 261
Hagedorn, Hermann, 308*n*
Haight, C. L., 526
Haldane, J. S., 409
Hale, Charles, 359
Hale, E. V., 45, 72
Hale, Nathan, 662
Halford, Sir Henry, 577
Hall, Albert, 367
Hall, C. M., 362
Hall, H. J., 100
Hall, J. D., 142
Hall, Richard, 142-3
Halle, Katherine, 638
Halle, Mr. and Mrs. Samuel, 26*n*
Haller, Albrecht von, 168, 174, 180-1, 247, 284, 456
Hallerianum, 76, 180-3
Halpenny, Attracta, 584
Halsted, W. S., 102-4, 110-12, 115-17, 119-30, 132, 138-43, 145, 148, 150, 152-3, 155-6, 158-60, 164, 166, 177-8, 182, 198, 203-5, 207, 217, 221, 237-8, 246-7, 254, 266, 278, 280, 316, 320, 330, 355, 472, 493-4, 504-5, 535, 549, 576; HC's appreciation, 119-21, 125; HC's reminiscence, 160; death of, 493; letters to HC, 101, 103, 114, 127-9, 159, 254, 270, 279, 327-8, 340; to WO, 142; letters from HC, 172, 279
Halsted, Mrs. W. S. (Caroline Hampton), 138, 140, 207, 238, 254; letter to HC, 141
Hampton, Gen. Wade, 138-9
Hanna, H. M. Sr., 218, 284
Hanna, H. M., 244, 628, 644
Hanna, M. A., 233
Hanover Surgical Club, 314
Hansen, Harry, 578*n*
Harding, W. G., 484
Harjes, Herman, 391
Harkness, C. W., 385
Harkness, E. S., 684
Harlan, H. D., 237
Harrington, F. B., 88, 109, 344; letter from J. P. Reynolds, 344

Harris, N. MacLeod, 205, 229
Harrison, Benjamin, 43, 124
Harrison, P. W., 221
Harrison, R. G., 449, 479-80, 662, 682
Hart, Horace, 292, 329, 361
Hart, T. S., 74
Harte, R. H., 375, 486
Hartmann, Henri, 171-2, 638-9
Hartwell, J. A., 74
Harvard Cancer Commission, 286-7
Harvard Law School, 21, 23, 55
Harvard Medical Alumni Association, 74, 353
Harvard Medical School, 53 *et seq.*, 257-9, 283, 380, 384, 390, 414, 497, 569 *et seq.*
  Arthur Tracy Cabot Fellowship, 221
  Boylston Medical Society, 60, 71-5, 82
  clinical training, 342-3
  Dept. of Surgery (blood pressure circular) 214, (Surgical Laboratory) 221, 360*n*, 374
  full-time proposal, 377 *et seq.*
  Library, 353, 552
  new buildings (dedication of) 248-9, (architect's drawing) 344
  1926 class book, 542-3
  150th anniversary, 632-3
  Saturday morning clinics, 378
  student dormitory (plans for) 353-4, (opened) 554
  textbook of surgery, 543-4
  Unit at Neuilly, 387 *et seq.*, (plans for) 390, (roster) 391, (accounts of) 404*n*, 418*n*, 656
  Warren Museum, 643-4
  See also American Ambulance; U.S. Army Base Hospital No. 5
Harvard Medical School and HC
  curriculum and faculty in 90's, 53-4
  quiz, 58, 71-3
  anatomy exam, 60-1
  size of class, 68*n*
  end of 3-year course in medicine, 86
  negotiations (1906-10), 333, 335-6
  first official letter, 338
  relationship of Moseley Professor & Dept. of Surgery, 338-9, 341-2
  appointment, 339
  congratulations, 339-41
  formal notice, 342
  budgetary difficulties, 203, 557*n*
  offer of post, 586, 614
  successor chosen, 613-14
  Moseley professorship ends, 621
  pension, 626
Harvard Medical Society, 376, 386, 404, 407, 472, 475, 494, 500, 506-7, 521, 530, 553, 559, 565, 567, 591, 601, 615-16; account of meeting, 553
Harvard University, vii, 3, 210, 476, 605, 633; Tercentenary, 674
Harvey, A. F. (cousin of HC), 27-8, 30, 63, 72, 144; reminiscences, 26, 32
Harvey, E. H., 29, 31, 56, 79, 112, 114
Harvey, Mrs. E. H., 74, 82, 112, 114
Harvey, Mrs. H. A. (Mary Cushing Williams, sister of BMC), 20, 30, 678
Harvey, M. C. (cousin of HC), 30
Harvey, Melanie, *see* Cushing, Mrs. E. F.
Harvey, P. W. (cousin of HC), 16, 27-8, 30-1, 33-5, 38-40, 45, 51-2, 63, 97, 144-5, 269, 605, 677-9
Harvey, Mrs. P. W., 677
Harvey, S. C., 221, 455*n*, 480-1, 524, 537*n*, 612, 616, 626, 636-7, 651, 669, 679
Harvey, William, 189, 226, 236, 284, 286-7, 370, 518, 622, 667, 698, 710; 300th anniversary of *De motu cordis*, 558-9; *De motu cordis*, copy offered, 255; copy secured, 558; stemma, 190
Harvey Cushing Fellowship, 528
Harvey Cushing Society, 455, 563, 616 *et seq.*, 643, 661, 681, 706; first meeting, 617-18
Harvey Lectures, 321, 628-9
Haskins, C. H., 416
Hatfield Lecture, 451
Hawke, Matthew, 4
Hawke, Sarah, *see* Cushing, Mrs. John
Hay, John, 207
Haydn, H. C., 19
Hayes, R. B., 43
Head, Sir Henry, 293-4, 400, 595, 605; HC's story about, 532-3; visit from HC, 596-7
Head, Ruth, Lady, 595-7; letter to HC, 605
Head injuries of warfare, 440
Health Insurance, 649 *et seq.*, 661
Hearne, Thomas, 240
Heberden, William, 15, 233
Heckscher, August, II, 52*n*; letter to HC, 676
Hedin, Alma, 575, 582; reminiscence of Stockholm visit, 580; letters from HC, 581
Hedin, Sven, 575, 580; letters from HC, 581-2
Heffelfinger, W. W., 45
Heffter, Arthur, 190
Heidenhain, R. P. H., 672
Hele, T. S., 674-5
Helmholtz, H. L. F. von, 181-2, 429
Hemangiomas, of brain, 579, skull, 492*n*, cerebellum, 491
Hemenway, Augustus, 345
Hemorrhage, methods of controlling, 536
Henderson, L. J., 359, 494-6, 614
Henderson, W. R., 583-4

Hendrickson, G. L., 46, 682
Henry, G. W., 220
Henry, Patrick, 72
Henry E. Huntington Library, San Marino, Calif., 599
Herczel, Manó, 294
Herdman, S. B., war recollection, 439
Herlitzka, Amedeo, 622
Hernia, 125*n*, 141*n*
Herpes zoster, 266
Herrick, M. T., 387, 391
Herrick, Robert, 566
Herring, P. T., 323
Herringham, Sir Wilmot P., 367, 428, 477
Hersey, Miss, 60, 82
Herter, Albert, 153
Herter, C. A., 143, 502
Herter Lectures, 234, 276
Heuer, G. J., 220, 245, 254, 278-9, 320*n*, 474, 489, 619-20, 625; reminiscence, 280
Hewes, H. F., 88
Hewlett, A. W., 473
Hibben, J. G., 366
Hibernation, 325-6
Higginson, H. L., 357-9, 361, 377, 417, 459, 505; HC's note about, 356; letter to HC, 391
Hill, A. V., 622, 676
Hill, G. H., 88
Hill, Leonard, 179
Hill, R. H., 462
Hippel, Eugen von, 579
Hippocrates, 190
His, Wilhelm, 182, 369
Historical Library, *see* Yale University School of Medicine
History of Science Society, 600, 628, 656
Hitchcock, G. C., 63, 70-1, 73, 76-8
Hitler, Adolf, 697, 700-1
Hobart, Rev. Peter, 4
Hoch, August, 228*n*
Hochenegg, Julius, 328
Hoeber, Paul, 560
Hofmeister, Franz, 194
Hofmeister, Franz von, 328
Hog cholera bacillus, 151
Hoke, Michael, 117
Holmes, Gordon, 293, 399-401
Holmes, O. W., (1808-94) 54, 63, 215, 475, 555
Holmes, O. W., (1841-1935) 358-9, 469
Homans, John, (1836-1903) 54, 95-6, 109, 259-60
Homans, John, (1877-) 221, 280, 299-300, 323, 325, 362-3, 506, 559, 563, 602, 669, 679; recollections of hypophysial studies, 281-2; *Textbook of surgery*, 543-4
Homans, Mrs. John, 675
'Homo chirurgicus', 631
Hooper, E. S., 359
Hooper, Mrs. William, 544, 638, 670
Hoover, C. F., 473; letters from HC, 503-4
Hoover, H. C., 587-8, 627
Hôpital Complémentaire 21, 396
Hopkins, E. M., 566
Hopkins, H. L., 650
Hopkins, J. G., 220
Hopkins, Johns, 110, 342
Hopkins, Mark, 8
Hoppin, G. B., 45, 55
Hornaday, W. T., 325
Horrax, Gilbert, 221, 262, 362*n*, 415, 447, 453, 455*n*, 491, 525, 534-5, 537, 560, 583, 604, 620*n*, 632, 669, 708
Horrax, Mrs. Gilbert (Geraldine K. Martin), 391, 454
Horsford, E. N., 54*n*
Horsley, J. S., 652
Horsley, Sir Victor, 162-4, 168, 197-8, 200, 236, 256, 257, 259, 261, 267, 278, 288, 314, 328, 478, 522, 524, 536; recollections, 163; letter to HC, 270; to R. A. Ould, 167
Hortega, Pio del Río, 698
Hosack, David, 8
Hospital del Salvador in Santiago. Cushing Pavilion, 693
Hotchkiss, Miss, 38
Hotchkiss, L. W., 143
Houssay, B. A., 325, 670
Houston, D. F., 337
Howard, C. P., 460, 674
Howard, Gwendolen M., *see* Futcher, Mrs. T. B.
Howard, H. B., 345, 347, 354
Howard, Gen. O. O., 124
Howard, R. P., 211, 273, 367
Howe, H. S., 345
Howe, M. A. DeW., 359, 404, 416, 459, 561
Howell, W. H., 74, 226, 355, 385, 522, 531, 561, 681; letter to HC, 225; letter from HC, 320
Howells, W. D., 358-9
Howland, C. P., 62, 75
Howland, John, 338
Howse, Sir Henry G., 167
Hoyt, M. B., reminiscence, 250
Hubble, E. P., 667
Hughson, Walter, 527
Hull, Cordell, 696
Hummel, David, 575, 580-2
Humpton, B. O., 247
Hunnewell, Walter, 345
Hunt, Reid, 478*n*
Hunter, John, 61, 164, 168, 201, 207, 219, 228, 232, 292-3, 369, 378, 429, 518, 548, 577; bicentenary, 567
Hunter, William, 168, 201, 248, 292, 548

Hunterian Laboratory, 204, 212, 274, 276, 280-3, 288, 313, 315-16, 320, 323, 365n; origin, 217 *et seq.;* name, 219; stand on antivivisectionists, 220-1; 'Comparative surgery', 220, 227; diener, Jimmie, 220, 317; list of appointees, 245; anonymous gift to, 527-8
Hunterian Museum, Glasgow, 548; Library, 201
Huntington, R. P., 177
Hurd, H. C., 34
Hurd, H. M., 111, 127-8, 157, 202, 205, 253, 459; letters to HC, 140, 203, 340
Hurwitz, S. H., 362*n*
Hutchins, H. T., 218
Hutchins, Horace, 31
Hutchins, Robert, 599
Hutchinson, Sir Jonathan, 90, 164, 166, 195, 235, 429; drawings of, 90, 197
Huxley, T. H., 110, 128, 368, 429, 672
Hyperpituitarism, *see* Hypophysial disorders
Hypertension, 216; neurohypophysis in, 630, 638
Hypophysectomy, 567-8; experimental, 299
Hypophysial adenomas, 629; anesthesia in cases of, 318; operations for, 322, 375, 487; operative mortality, 376; optic atrophy in, 272; perimetry in, 365*n;* sexual dysfunction in, 271-2
Hypophysial disorders, clinical aspects, 290, 299, 320 *et seq.*, 371, 375, 478, 487, 523; introduction of terms hypo- and hyper-pituitarism, 299, 323; polyuria, 365-6, 525-6. *See also* Acromegaly; Basophilism, pituitary; Dyspituitarism
Hypophysial extracts, *see* Pituitrin
Hypophysis, 267; autonomic control, 363; bibliography of, 523; function of, 327, 523, 591; history of, 657; in carbohydrate metabolism, 314, 363; in hibernation, 325-6; pancreas and, 325; relation to life, 280; secretion of, 313
Hypophysis, anterior, 299, 702; experimental study of, 280-2, 553; feeding experiments, 525; secretion of, 303
Hypophysis, posterior, 313-14; hyperactivation of, 630, 638; injury to, 366; mechanism, 591
Hypopituitarism, *see* Hypophysial disorders
Hypothalamus, 273*n*, 603, 623; early work on, 366; Beattie's experimental work on, 591

Infantilism, sexual, 271-3
Ingraham, F. D., 526, 557, 573, 607-8, 612
Ingvar, Sven, 558
Insulin, 325
Interbrain, *see* Hypothalamus
International Medical Congress, 13th (Paris 1900), 168-9; 16th (Budapest 1909), 291, 294-5, 302, 305; 17th (London 1913), 206, 327, 366, 464, 477
International Neurological Congress, 1st (Berne 1931), 606 *et seq.;* idea for paper, 599-600; report for, 604; degrees to HC & Sherrington, 607
International Ophthalmological Congress, 13th (Amsterdam 1929), 582
International Physiological Congress 13th (Boston 1929), 558, 576 *et seq.;* 671; reprinting Beaumont, 561; 14th (Rome 1932), 621-3
Intestinal perforation, laparotomy for, 146, 148-50
Intestinal sutures, 140
Intracranial hemorrhage, 96-7, 267
Intracranial tension, 184, 187, 215*n;* effect of salt in, 471; cerebrospinal fluid and, 522-5
Intracranial tumors, bibliography, 523; categories, 521-2; classification, 454, 508-9; complete removal, 491; decompression for, 267; early cases, 259, 268; end results, 492, 540-1, 608; epilepsy in, 312; first successful removal, 256; longest survival, 410*n;* oculomotor palsies with, 312; physiology, 287, 298; statistics, 305, 451, 471-2, 487-9; surgery, 291, 314, 318, 371, 523, 538*n;* surgical mortality, 268, 305, 376, 604-8
Intraventricular injections, 591-2, 603-4
Ireland, Maj. Gen. M. W., 427, 447, 452, 482, 484
Ireland, R. L., 244
Ito, Hiroboumi, Marquis, 207

Jaboulay, Mathieu, 173
Jack, F. L., 261*n*
Jackson, Chevalier, 479, 506-7, 564
Jackson, H. C., 179-80
Jackson, J. B. S., 54*n*
Jackson, J. H., 164, 256*n*
Jackson, J. M., 213
Jacksonian seizures, 257
Jacob, Deborah, *see* Cushing, Mrs. John
Jacobaeus, H. C., 580
Jacobi, Abraham, 288-9
Jacobs, H. B., 159, 164, 208 *et seq.*, 228*n*, 232, 242, 290, 318, 376, 701; letter to HC, 229; letter from HC, 289
Jacobs, Mrs. H. B., 210, 290
Jacobson, Conrad, 220-21, 245, 314, 317*n*,

320, 326, 354, 362-3, 365*n*, 453; appraisal of HC, 315; reminiscence, 316
James, Henry, 358-9
James, Walter, 143
James, William, 76, 359
Janet, Pierre, 402, 675
Janeway, E. G., 520
Janssen, Cornelius, 226
Jefferson, Geoffrey, 549, 594, 608, 681, 698; recollections, 696
Jefferson, Mrs. Geoffrey ('Trotula'), 549
Jefferson Medical College, Philadelphia, offer to HC, 233; call from, 330; address and degree at, 533
Jendrássik, Ernö, 294
Jenks, Dr., 4
Jenks, Freelove (Brown), *see* Cushing, Mrs. David Jr.
Jenner, Edward, 168, 207, 407, 518
Jessop, Walter, 294
Jex-Blake, A. J., 293
Jimmie (Hunterian diener), 220, 317
Johns Hopkins Historical Club, 15, 386; Garth paper at, 239-40; Gold-headed cane, 247; message to W.O.'s mother, 250; meetings, 252-3, 282, 289, 305; HC's presidency, 255*n;* reelected president, 275
Johns Hopkins Hospital, 86, 101-4, 105*n*, 110 *et seq.*, 205-6, 210, 216-17, 233, 249-50, 253, 265, 278, 312, 316, 343-4, 346, 365, 383, 410, 466, 667
  early days, 110-1
  in 1896, 121
  Osler's secret history, 207
  new surgical amphitheatre, 237-9
  use of rubber gloves, 238
  HC's assistant residents, 245
  early neurological cases, 261
  25th anniversary celebration, 376
  plans for 50th anniversary, 710
Johns Hopkins Medical School, 103, 110-12, 126*n*, 225-6, 237, 248, 283, 337, 378, 380, 382-3, 517
  opening, 111
  first graduating ceremony, 112
  Committee on Graduate Instruction, 158
  courses in operative surgery, 204, 219-20, 225
  budgetary problems, 218, 225, 326
  Library, 252
  Unit, 415
  See also Hunterian Laboratory; Welch Medical Library
Johns Hopkins Medical Society, 106, 123, 141, 288, 553, 616; blood pressure determinations, 215*n;* paper on acoustic tumors, 410
Johns Hopkins Surgical Society, 527
Johns Hopkins University, 153, 210, 284; faculty, 110-11; Institute of the History of Medicine, 613, 639; 25th anniversary, 224-5; Tudor & Stuart Club dedication, 526
Johnson, Mr., druggist, 705
Johnson, F. B., 516
Johnson, John, 463, 698
Johnson, L. H. H., 345
Johnson, R. B., 698
Johnson, Samuel, 89, 227, 232, 242, 461, 544, 577, 679
Johnson, Rev. W. A., 594-5
Jones, A. P., 139*n*
Jones, H. F., 461, 463-4
Jones, Henry, 250
Jones, Sir Robert, 313, 429
Joslin, E. P., 37, 58, 70, 72, 76, 82, 88, 192, 325, 466, 634, 672

Kappers, Ariëns, 608
Karnosh, Louis, 26*n*
Karsner, H. T., 628
Kean, Col. J. R., 419
Keats, John, 226
Keen, Florence, 330
Keen, W. W., 150, 157, 164, 166-7, 226, 233, 252, 259, 262, 270, 272, 306, 410, 413, 479, 486, 492, 496, 547, 564; *System of surgery*, 267 *et seq.;* beginning preparation, 245; letters to HC, 149, 215, 269, 408; letter from HC, 330 (reproduced, 331), 409
Keith, Sir Arthur, 292-3, 303, 323, 488, 592, 594, 597, 697
Keith, Lady, 597
Keller, Deane, 693
Kellogg, Carolyn, *see* Cushing, Mrs. W. E.
Kellogg, Mrs., 34, 143
Kellogg, W. R. M., 217
Kelly, H. A., 111, 158, 233, 246, 252, 504, 566, 681, 694; letter to HC, 340
Kendall, L. G., 619
Keogh, Gen. Sir Alfred, 402, 420, 429
Keogh, Andrew, 646, 648, 667-8, 688; letter from HC, 586
Kepler, Johann, 600
Ker, C. B., 149
Kerr, H. H., 436
Key, Einar, 580
Keynes, Geoffrey, 595, 625, 698
Keynes children, 625
Killick, H. A., letter to KC, 424
Kingsbury, J. A., 588
Kipling, Rudyard, 129, 175, 670
Kirtland, J. P., 511, 518

Kit-Kat poet, 239-40
Kittredge, G. L., 545
Klebs, A. C., 373, 407, 529, 545, 567, 575, 579, 582-3, 590, 592, 594, 600-1, 605, 607-10, 621-5, 627, 638-40, 645, 649, 673-5, 680, 689, 693, 703-11, 714; first contact with, 247; his 'prophetic essay' read Dec. 8, 1913, 667; herbal bibliography, 668-9; *Incunabula scientifica et medica,* 687; Sarton's review of, 707-8; diary of HC's 1938 trip abroad, 697-9; letters to HC, 193, 318, 647, 687, 709; to G. Sarton, 704; letters from HC, 192, 355, 573-4, 611, 646, 660, 663, 666-70, 677, 681, 685-6, 688, 694, 700, 701-2, 708
Klebs, Edwin, 247, 301, 609-10, 675
Kluck, Gen. A. H. R. von, 395
Knollenberg, Bernhard, 688, 692
Koch, Robert, 51, 111, 182, 465, 518
Kocher, Albert, 177, 294, 399
Kocher, Theodor, 160, 162, 166, 176-8, 180, 182-4, 187, 189-93, 199, 375, 396, 526, 549, 569, 584, 609-10; Jubiläum, 328; letter from HC, 191
Kölliker, Albert von, 181-2
Koenig, Franz, 166
Körte, W., 127-8, 328
Kraus, F., 369
Krause, Fedor, 295
Krehl, L., 369
Krogh, August, 577
Kronecker, Hugo, 176, 178-84, 190-3, 199, 217, 223-4, 294, 375, 526, 609
Kronecker, Lotte, 179, 182
Kühne, Willy, 48, 181-2
Kümmell, Hermann, 328
Kussmaul, A., 194

Ladd, G. T., 34, 40, 42-3, 48, 67, 257
Ladd, Mrs. G. T. (Elizabeth Williams) 34
Laennec Society, 234
Lafayette, Marquis de, 432
Lafleur, H. A., 228*n*
Lahy, J. M., 215*n*
Lakeside Hospital, Cleveland, 79, 504
Lambert, Alexander, 311
Lane, Sir W. Arbuthnot, 91
Lanfranc, quotation from, 492
Langenbeck, Bernhard von, 182
Langley, J. N., 196
Lannelongue, O. M., 167-8
Laplace, Ernest, 496
'Latch-keyers', viii, 206, 208
Lawrence, J. H., recollections, 705
Lawrence, Sir Thomas, 167
Lawrence, Rt. Rev. W., 431, 484
League to Enforce Peace, 403
Leake, C. D., 705
Leary, Timothy, 478*n*
LeBourgeois, Elizabeth, 165
Lecène, Paul, 150
Lee, B. J., 439
Lee, F. C., 528
Lee, R. I., 429*n*
Leeuwenhoek, A., tercentenary, 628
LeHand, M. A., 658; letter from HC, 680
Lehman, E. P., 362*n*
Lehman, Walter, 526
Lelli, Ercole, 188, 190, 627, 657, 673
Leonardo da Vinci, viii, 407
Leriche, René, 473, 575
Lettsom, J. C., 546-7
Levi, Ettore, 294
Levine, S. A., 500; reminiscence, 507-8
Lewis, D. D., 455*n*, 477, 526, 528; letter from HC, 473
Lewis, F. T., 533, 567, 710
Lewis, R. A., 713
Lewis, Sinclair, 469, 681
Lewis, Sir Thomas, 473, 612, 638, 658
Lewis, W. S., 586, 648, 688
Lexer, Erich, 328
Leyton, A. S. F., formerly Grünbaum, 197-9, 234
Liebel, G. H., 538
Liebel Flarsheim Company, 538
Light, R. U., 536*n*, 537*n*, 604, 607-8, 611, 645, 657-8, 661; reminiscence, 659-60
Lincoln, Abraham, 12, 407, 457, 496, 551, 658
Lindau, Arvid, 579, 582
Lindau's disease, 579
Lindsay, A. D., 698
Lindsey, William, 390
Linné, Carl von, 580
Linnehan, F. H., 108
Lisser, Hans, recollection, 285*n*
Lister, Joseph, 1st Baron, 51, 167, 314, 370, 409, 429, 457, 495, 500, 518, 522-4, 548
Lister Centenary, quotation from speech, 457; delivered, 551
Lister Memorial Lecture, 590 *et seq.*
Livingood, L. E., 149, 151, 157
Livingstone, Sir Richard, 698-9
Locke, C. E. Jr., 453, 570, 574, 708
Locke, F. S., 212, 222
Locke, John, 206, 235, 239, 252, 324
Loeb, Jacques, 222
Loeffler, Friedrich, 247, 609
Lohmann, C. A., 645
London University, 167
Long, C. N. H., 591
Long, E. R., recollection, 601*n*
Long Island College Hospital, Brooklyn, N.Y., 362
Longcope, W. T., 473, 494

Longfellow, H. W., 494
Lord, S. M., 75
'Lost Legion', 564-5
Lovett, R. W., 295, 476, 511
Lovett, Sidney, 714
Lowell, A. Lawrence, 341, 347, 359, 377, 413-16, 469, 476, 484, 586, 643, 683; letters to HC, 338-9, 342, 380-1, 613-14; letters from HC, 339, 379, 381, 504-5, 613; from A. Cochrane, 382
Lower, W. E., letter from G. W. Crile, 389-90
Lowman, Dr., 50, 63
Lowman, John, 13
Loyal Legion, 149
Ludwig, Carl, 54, 168, 181, 184
Ludwig, F. G., viii, 628
Lund, F. B., 71, 78, 88, 261*n*, 313
Lusitania, sinking of, 402-3, 415
Lusk, Graham, 37
Lydstron, Frank, 289
Lyman, Hart, 51
Lynam, Frank, 69-70
Lynch, A., 27

Macalister, Alexander, 61, 292
McBride, Herbert, 28, 31, 40, 51, 144
McBride, Thomas, 142
MacCallum, W. G., 130, 139*n*, 143, 170, 204, 218, 221, 273, 449, 494, 527, 562, 629, 642, 660, 681; letter to HC, 324; letter from HC, 325
McCann, W. S., 221
McCarthy, D. J., 443, 445
McCaw, Col., 427-8
McClure, R. D., 220
MacCormac, Sir William, 167
McCouch, Grayson, 554
McCoy, Frank, 308
McCrae, Annabella, 483
McCrae, John, death of, 434-5
McCrae, Thomas, 143, 148, 153, 156, 159, 165, 167, 196, 200-1, 203-4, 228*n*, 229, 234, 236, 247, 288, 327-8, 434, 458, 533, 548, 659, 674, 693
McDaniel, W. B., 694
Macdonald, J. S., 197-9
Macewen, Sir William, 112*n*, 201, 235, 294-5, 523, 548-9
Macewen Memorial Lecture, 548-9
McGee, Hugh, 483
McGill University, dedication of Biological Laboratories, 491; Neurological Institute, *see* Montreal Neurological Institute; Osler Library, 574
Mackall, L. L., 611, 692
Mackenzie, Sir James, 525
McKenzie, K. G., 453, 571
McKenzie, R. Tait, 694
McKernon, J. F., 428
McKinley, William, 126; inaugural, 123-4
McLachlan, H., 252*n*
McLanahan, Mrs. George, 637
McLane, J. W., 74
Maclaren, Ian, 565-6
McLean, A. J., 557*n*, 708
McLean, Jay, letter from HC, 217-22
Macmichael, William, 167
McLean Hospital, *see* Massachusetts General Hospital
Macpherson, Maj. Gen. Sir William G., 424
Macy, J. A., 105*n*
Madan, Falconer, 594
Madelung, Otto, 194
Magnus, Rudolf, 194, 558
Mahoney, W. deG., 557, 611, 619
'Maine' disaster, 137, 146
Mains, James, 67, 483
Major, R. H., 215; letter to HC, 562; letter from HC, 216
Makins, Sir George, 400
Mall, F. P., 111, 158, 204, 218, 361, 447
Mallinkrodt, Edward, 337
Malloch, Archibald, 459, 559, 660, 673, 698; letter to HC, 566-7
Mallory, F. B., 410
Malone, Dumas, 690
Maloney, John, 259-61, 532
Malpighi, Marcello, 190, 567
Mann, Gustav, 236
Manson, Sir Patrick, 166, 235
'Manx Club', 199
Marburg, Otto, 299*n*
Marburg, W. A., 252, 289-90
Marconi, Guglielmo, Marchese, 622
Marie, Pierre, 301, 488, 675
Mark, L. P., 323
Marsh, O. C., 37
Martel, Thierry de, 411, 554, 558, 608, 698, 709
Martin, E., 92*n*
Martin, Edward, 313-14
Martin, F. H., 485; letter to HC, 493
Martin, Geraldine K., *see* Horrax, Mrs. Gilbert
Martin, H. Newell, 110-11, 672
Martin, Paul, 443, 487, 535, 558, 608, 698
Mary, Queen of England, 699
Maryland, University, 330, 493-4
Maryland Club, 275
Mascagni, Paolo, 201
Maskenoza Club, 63
Maskenoza Island (Lake Huron), 28
Massachusetts General Hospital, 46, 50, 62, 67-9, 71-4, 79, 87, 95, 98, 100-2, 104-6, 114, 116*n*, 117, 121-3, 126, 164, 202,

211-2, 214, 308, 336, 339, 342-3, 349, 356, 363, 386, 390, 415, 487, 495
house-officer posts, 54
changes on surgical side, 88, 92-3
Convalescent Home, Waverly, 38
HC's reactions to, 107, 108-9
etherizing at, 258
early cases of brain tumor, 259-60, 261
Ether Day (1909), 277 *et seq.;* (1921), 260, 481-4; centenary celebration, 481-4
McLean Hospital, 98
Massachusetts Medical Society, 365, 451, 605
Matas, Rudolph, 364, 479, 509
Max Müller, F., 246
Mayo, C. H., 245, 288, 302, 375, 486, 694, 712
Mayo, W. J., 169, 245, 360*n*, 375, 455, 486, 510, 694, 712; letter from HC, 479
Mayo Clinic, 369, 375, 712
Mead, Mrs. F. S., 415, 501
Mead, Richard, 167, 248
Meagher, R. H., 526, 573, 602, 607-8, 618-19, 621, 625, 708; death, 673-4
Meakins, Col. J. C., 428
Medical and Chirurgical Faculty of Maryland, 241, 243*n*, 274-5; centennial, 153; dedication of Osler Hall, 289-90
Medical education, Mr. Eliot on, 497
Medical history, *see* HC Addresses: Historical; Harvard Medical Society; Johns Hopkins Historical Club
Medical illustration, 158
Medical Research Committee, 402; meeting in Paris (May 1918), 428-9
Medical Society of London, 546-7
Medicine, as career, 565-6; at the crossroads, 632; realignments in, 368-70; teaching of, 506
Medulloblastomas, 509, 521, 579
Mencken, H. L., 469, 694
Mendel, L. B., 37, 634; HC's appreciation of, 672
Meningiomas, 491; early case of, 260; cervical, 267; HC's first successful case, 308 *et seq.;* of olfactory groove, 538, 548-9; of tuberculum sellae, 561; origin of, 489
Meningioma monograph, 260, 261, 628, 640, 645, 674, 679, 685, 686-7, 693, 697, 700
Meningitis, hexamethylenamin for, 285; serum for, 285
Meningoceles, 268
Meralgia paraesthetica, 263
Merriam, J. C., 612
Metlin, Bessie, 126
Meyer, A. W., 252
Meyer, Adolf, letters to HC, 337, 448-9
Meyer, George, 459
Meyer, H. H., 294, 671
Michaud, Jeanne, 183
Mikulicz, J. von, 166, 238
Miles, Gen. N. A., 124, 312
Milford, Humphrey, 466
Miller, Mrs., 127, 129
Miller, J. A., 652
Miller, R. T. Jr., 218
Mills, C. W., 220, 226
Milmore, Martin, 73
Miner, L. M. S., 567
Minkowski, Oskar, 366
Minot, C. S., 54, 56
Minot, G. R., 353
Mitchell, J. F., 140, 155, 157, 159, 238
Mitchell, J. K., 226-7, 324; letter to HC, 305
Mitchell, S. Weir, 76, 228, 287-9, 330, 413, 459, 566, 692; HC memorabilia, 226; letters to HC, 286, 324
Mix, C. L., 58
Mixter, S. J., 59, 88, 109
Moffitt, H. C., 71, 75
Moltke, H. C. B., Count von, 60, 176
Molyneux, Sir Thomas, 485
Monks, G. H., 71-3, 356
Monrad-Krohn, G. H., 488
Montclair Yale Club of New Jersey, 599
Montreal Neurological Institute, 443; opening, 645-6
Moore, E. H., 35-6
Moore, G. F., 357, 359, 512
Morehouse, G., 330, 413
Morelle, Jean, 526, 558, 592, 608, 698
Morgan, J. P. Jr., 354
Morgenthau, Henry Jr., 650
Morley, John, 367
Morris, G. S., 110
Morris, Sir Henry, 368-9, 464
Morris, Sir Malcolm, 164, 294
Morse, J. T. Jr., 357, 361; letters to HC, 358-9
Morton, J. J., 433, 537*n*, 541, 605; reminiscences of early days at Brigham, 362-3
Morton, W. T. G., 278
Mosher, H. P., 506-7
Mosle, A. H., 59, 207
Moss, Bartholomew, 485
Mosso, Angelo, 184-6, 193, 199; letter to HC, 187
Motor area, 197, 256, 257
Mott, Valentine, 8
Moynihan, Berkeley, Baron, 314, 429, 591, 593-4
Müller, Friedrich von, 180, 190, 294, 328, 367, 369
Müller, Johannes, 181

Münsterberg, Hugo, 403
Mütter Lecture, 211
Muirhead, A. M., 707; letter to Lady Osler, 469-70
Mumford, J. G., 88, 207, 252, 254, 313, 318, 333, 375-6; letters to HC, 336, 337, 339
Murray, G. R., 478
Muscle perfusion experiments, 184
Musser, J. H., 295
Mussolini, Benito, 622, 696-7, 700-1
Mygatt, Comfort, 7

Naffziger, H. C., 245, 365*n*, 366*n*
Nager, F. A., 583
Napier, John, 324, 329
Nathan Smith Medical Club, 657
National Academy of Sciences, 327, 408, 451, 612, 629-30, 658-9, 660, 673, 681; organization, 407
National Association for the Study of Epilepsy, 312
National Hospital, London, 164, 235, 314, 376, 445
National Institute of Neurology, 443 *et seq.*, 645
National Institute of Social Sciences, 661
National Research Council, 407 *et seq.*, 658; Scientific Advisory Board, 659
National Security League, 404
Naunyn, Bernard, 192-4
Neale, L. E., 330
Nerve anastomosis, in facial paralysis, 266
Nerve-muscle, effect of salt on, 184*n*, 222-4
Neurological surgeons, 501-3; training of, 305
Neurological surgery, HC's early interest in, 96; study abroad, 162 *et seq.;* HC's beginning, 204; early development of, 256-7; technical advances, 268-9; special field, 239, 266, 305, 471; in war, 440*n*, 451; HC's final report on special field, 604-5
Neurosurgical assistants (1908), 278
New England Surgical Dressings Committee, 415, 501
New Haven Hospital, 332-3, 384, 517
New Haven Medical Society, 640
New York Academy of Medicine, 496, 625
New York Hospital, 7, 50, 74; call to, 331
New York Neurological Institute, 445
New York Neurological Society, 287, 615
New York University. Bellevue Hospital, call to, 331
Newcomb, Simon, 250, 255, 263, 265
Newell, F. S., 107
Newhall, C. S., 14
Newton, Mr. and Mrs. A. E., 544
Newton, F. C., 500, 544
Newton, H. F., 544, 556
Newton, Sir Isaac, 201, 554
Nichols, E. H., 214, 335
Nicolaus *of Cusa,* 484
Nicoll, Allardyce, 682
Nightingale, Florence, 483, 493
Noguchi, Hideyo, 236, 685
North, Elisha, 627
North Atlantic Medical Society, 234
North End Hospital, Boston, 83
Northwestern University, Evanston, Ill., 620
Norton, Charles Eliot, 227
Nothnagel, Hermann, 191-2
Novaro, G. F., 188
Nové-Josserand, Gabriel, 173
Noyes, Alfred, 366
Noyes, H. F., 42
Noyes, Raymond, 427
Noyes, W.S.G., 70-1
Nutting, M. A., 253
Nuyens, B. W. T., 582
Nyström, Gunnar, 474, 580, 589, 658

Ochsner, A. J., 169, 471, 486
O'Connell, Daniel, 429
Ogden, H. V., 312, 375
Ogden, J. B., 82
Ohio University, Athens, 27-8
Olausson, Carl, 581
'Old maids of both sexes', 128
Oldberg, Eric, 557*n*
Olfactory groove meningiomas, 538, 548-9
Olivecrona, Herbert, 580, 608
Oljenick, Ignaz, 582, 592, 608, 698
Ollier, Louis, 173
Opie, E. L., 147, 338
Oporinus, Johannes, 562, 625
Oppenheim, Moriz, 294
Optic atrophy, with chiasmal lesions, 582
Optic chiasm, syndrome of, 582
Optic nerve, diagram of decussation of fibres, 258
Orthopedics, 92, 121, 126
Ortschild, J. F., 220-1, 245, 251, 279-80
Osgood, R. B., 390-2, 428, 630
Osler, Sir Edmond B., 361
Osler, Edward Revere, 165, 206-7, 239, 246, 250, 283, 401, 434, 452, 457, 464, 468, 595; death, 424-5
Osler, Mrs. F. L., 250
Osler, Grace R., Lady, 143, 165, 206-7, 225, 228, 237, 242-3, 246, 250, 255, 290, 329, 370, 401, 452, 457, 462, 467-8, 488, 524, 545, 547, 574, 595, 707; letters to HC, 425, 459, 461; to KC, 328, 425; letters from HC, 458-61; from A. M. Muir-

head, 469-70; from C. R. L. Fletcher, 470; from P. S. Allen, 470-1
Osler, Sir William, vii, 68, 74, 86, 101, 111-12, 115, 120, 130, 132, 135, 139, 142, 145, 148, 153, 156-7, 159, 161, 163-7, 169, 193, 195-6, 200, 203-8, 210, 224, 228*n*, 229-32, 234-5, 237, 239, 241, 247, 249-52, 255, 275-6, 283, 287-90, 292, 307, 312, 314, 326, 329-30, 339, 343, 364, 367-71, 373, 375, 388, 401-2, 415, 439, 452, 457, 499, 530, 546, 549, 562, 566, 586, 646-7, 698-9, 707, 713
memorabilia, 206-8
Baltimore doorplate, 207
presentation of D.N.B., 228
'Fixed period' address, 242-3
farewell dinner and departure from Baltimore, 244
visit (Jan. 1906), 246; (Dec. 1906), 250
painting by Sargent, 246
Principles and practice of medicine, 266
remarks at P.B.B.H., 365
note to *The Times*, 369-70
death of, 453
HC's early appreciation, 458
memorial meeting, 472
Bibliotheca Osleriana, 574-5
letters to HC, 149, 205, 284, 324, 341, 361, 425; to HKC, 233; to KC, 425; letter from HC, 453
Osler biography, vii, 224, 360-1, 424, 457 *et seq.*, 474, 476-7, 481, 486-7, 491, 504, 508, 511, 514, 520-1, 523-4, 528, 544, 551, 564, 631
quotations from, 207, 234-6, 367-8, 456
dedication, 378
HC asked to undertake, 457
accepts, 458-9
plan of procedure, 460
aftermath, 462
Pulitzer prize, 462
anonymity of author, 463
Welch's criticism, 464-7
appreciations of, 467-71
corrigenda list, 671
Osler Club, London, 594, 698
Osler Hall, 289-90
Osler Library, dedication, 574
Osler testimonial fund, 288-9
Osten-Sacken, Baron, 359
Osteomas of orbit, 546
Otis, C. A., 26*n*
Oughterson, A. W., 669
Ould, R. F., 167
Owen, Edmund, 91
Owen, Thomas, 483
Oxford. University, 236; Medical School, 235; Press, 463

Paccioli, Luca, 663, 666
Packard, A. S., 37*n*
Packard, F. R., 211
Paddock, Alice, 126
Paddy, Sir William, 292
Paderewski, I. J., 63-4
Page, A. K., 73
Page, Mrs. C. G., 632
Paget, Sir James, 51, 164, 293
Paget, Stephen, 167, 256*n*, 370, 429, 566
Painter, C. F., 58, 62, 71-3, 92-3
Pan American Medical Congress, San Francisco, 405
Papen, Franz von, 403
Parasympathetic center, 591 *et seq.*, 603-4, 623
Paré, Ambroise, 137, 174, 234, 567, 695
Paris hospitals, 171
Park, E. A., 237
Parker, Peter, 518
Parkman, Francis, 359
Parkman, Dr. and Mrs. Samuel, 484*n*
Parks, Helen, 391
Parmelee, E. J., 422, 433
Parran, Thomas Jr., 651-2
Parsons, Herbert, 71
Parsons, Julia, letter from, 22
Parsons, Louisa, HC's tribute to, 493-4
Parsons, Richard, 19
Partridge, John, 241-2
Pasteur, Louis, 51, 370, 465, 522, 524, 558, 566; centenary celebration of, 494 *et seq.*
Pasteur Institute, 496
Pater, Walter, viii, 2
Pathological Society of Philadelphia, 255
Pathology, 121; caring for own specimens, 273
Patin, Gui, 284
Paton, Stewart, 228*n*
Patterson, Maj. Gen. R. U., 420, 666
Pattison, A. R., 698
Paulesco, N. C., 280, 298, 523
Pavlov, I. P., 606-7, 622-3, 645, 685, 711; at Physiological Congress, 577-9; HC's appreciation of, 671
Payne, O. H., 284
Payr, Erwin, 328
Peabody, F. G., 420; letter to HC, 642
Peabody, F. W., 531
Pearce, R. M., 474
Peary, R. E., 76
Pechkranz, S., 272*n*
Peerenboom, C. A., 563

Penfield, W. G., 443, 608, 645; note about HC, 646
Penn, William, 212
Pennell, Mr. and Mrs. Joseph, 172
Pennsylvania. University, 75; Medical dept., Philadelphia, 8; Osler at, 111
Pennsylvania Hospital, Philadelphia, 211
Pepper, William, 466-7
Peptic ulcers, neurogenic, 603
Pepys, Samuel, 71, 89
Percival, Thomas, 549
Perimetry, *see* Visual fields
Perineal zoster, 266
Peripheral nerves, regeneration, 266-7
Peritonitis, gonococcal, 151
Perkins, C. E., 359
Perkins, Frances, 655-6; letter from HC, 650; from Mr. Sydenstricker, 652-3
Perkins, Mrs. H. T., viii, 702*n*
Perkins, William, 359
Perry, Bliss, 357-9, 459, 461; reminiscence, 360
Perry, Gardner, 71
Perry, T. S., 357-9, 361, 399
Pershing, Gen. J. J., 308*n*, 427, 432, 452, 696
Perthes, Georg, 328
Peter Bent Brigham Hospital, Boston, 60, 202, 224, 281, 286, 319, 336-7, 341*n*, 344 *et seq.*, 390-1, 410, 415, 455-6, 471, 491, 498, 504, 507, 520, 552, 628, 630
  American Ambulance, vote, 389
  annual reports, 363, 472
  architect's drawings, 344
  autopsies, 363-4
  Board of Trustees, 344-5
  'Cosmos and Damian', 364
  examination of house officers, 526
  founder's will, 335
  funds for travel abroad, 354
  general surgical service, 543-4
  HC's budget, 557*n*
  Harvey Cushing Fellowship fund, 557
  metabolism laboratory, 543
  negotiations with HC, 338
  opening, 364-5; Founder's Day, 376
  organization, 342 *et seq.*
  organization of staffs, 347 *et seq.*
  paying beds, 345-6
  Philip Gray Fund, 557
  Physician-in-Chief, 343
  private ward privilege, 555-6
  retirement age, 351-2
  reunions, 10th (May 1923), 500; 15th (1928), 559-60; 20th (1933), 631-2
  Surgeon-in-Chief Emeritus, 626
  Surgeon-in-Chief Fund, 556
  Surgeon-in-Chief 'pro tempore', 472-3; list of incumbents, 473-4
  surgical team (1912), 362
  travelling fellowship in surgery, 556
  voluntary graduate assistants, 525-6, 584
  X-ray Dept., 543
Peters, A. J., 484
Peters, G. G., 557*n*
Peters, J. P., 622, 651
Peters, Rudolf, 622
Peterson, Rev. V. A., 23, 26*n*
Peterson, Mrs. V. A. (Cornelia Cushing), 23
Peterson, W., 224
Petit-Dutaillis, Daniel, 608
Pflüger, E. F. W., 195
Pflüger, Ernst, 190
Phelps, Marian, later wife of Count Franz von Rottenburg, 74-5, 176, 195
Phelps, W. L., 76, 533, 645, 683
Phelps, W. W., 176
Philadelphia. University of Pennsylvania. Medical dept., *see* Pennsylvania University
Philadelphia Neurological Society, 262
Phillips, A. W., 35-6
Phillips, John, 574
Phipps, Henry, 242, 279, 290; letter to HC, 243
Phipps Dispensary, opening, 242
Phipps Psychiatric Clinic, opening, 364
Phrenological Society, 319
Phrenology, history of, 544
'Physician and surgeon', address, 492
Pickering, E. C., 416
Piersol, G. M., 652
Pilcher, Cobb, 526
Pilcher, L. S., 252, 254, 386
Pinchot, Gifford, 305
Piotet, G., 709
Piozzi, Mrs., 227
Pitcher, Nazareth, *see* Cushing, Mrs. Mathew
Pithotomy Club, 239
Pittsfield. Berkshire Medical School, *see* Berkshire Medical School
Pittsfield Athenaeum Library, 8
Pituitary body, HC's prophecy about, 267; *see also* Hypophysis
Pituitrin, intraventricular injections, 591, 603-4, 623
Platt, Abial, 8
Platt, Charlotte, 8
Platt, Mary Ann, *see* Cushing, Mrs. Erastus
Platter, Felix, 293-4
Poincaré, Henri, 554
Pol, Nicolaus, 600
Polyuria, hypophysial, 365-6, 525-6

Poncet, Antonin, 173
Porter, C. A., 77-8, 88, 101, 108, 155, 336, 339, 506; letter to HC, 116
Porter, C. B., 70, 74-5, 78, 104, 107, 109, 125, 260, 354
Porter, Horace, 124
Porter, John, 72
Porter, W. T., 202, 213
Postcentral gyrus, 200, 314
Pott, Percival, 73, 293, 429
Power, Sir D'Arcy, 473, 547, 594, 697-8; letter to HC, 508
Pratt, J. H., 472, 478*n*
Pratt, J. W., 62, 99
Prescott, Miss, 34, 38
Price, Lucien, 544, 645, 657; review of *Consecratio medici*, 562-3; review of *Surgeon's Journal*, 672; letter to HC, 513; letters from HC, 512-13
Priestley, Joseph, 252
Princeton University, 44
Pritchett, H. S., 357-9, 379, 447
Provincial Surgical Society, 313
Psychic disturbances, in endocrine disorders, 364
Pumpelly, Raphael, 357-9
Pupin, Michael, 627, 700
Pure Food & Drug Act, 680
Puritan Club, 73, 75
Putnam, C. R.L., 71, 88; reminiscences, 45, 59
Putnam, Herbert, 688
Putnam, J. J., 261*n*
Putnam, T. J., 523, 525, 532, 543*n*, 553, 559, 565, 576, 608; reminiscence, 506-7; letter from HC, 618
Putti, Vittorio, 474, 582, 618-19, 624, 628, 673, 679, 701

Quain, Jones, 56, 117
Quaritch, Bernard, 236
Quervain, Fritz de, 584, 609
Quinby, W. C., 221, 362, 543-4, 585
Quincy, John, 5*n*

Raab, William, 615
Radcliffe, John, 167, 247
Radisics, Eugène de, 294
Ramón y Cajal, Santiago, 645, 698
Rand, C. W., 362*n*; recollections, 440
Rappelye, W. C., 661
Rathke's pouch cyst, 272
Ray, B. S., 611, 619
'Realignments in medicine,' 368-70
Recklinghausen, F. D. von, 193
Redfield, A. C., 577
Reed, Walter, 111, 150-1, 252, 387, 566; letters to HC, 154-5
Reford, L. L., 220-1, 245, 280, 523
Rehn, Ludwig, 328
Reid, Doris, 250
Reid, Edith G. (Mrs. H. F.), 119, 250; letters from HC, 229, 640
Reid, H. F., 124, 682
Reinach, Salomon, 399
Remsen, I. D., 110, 155, 207, 224, 327
Rensselaer Medical Society, Troy, 248
Repplier, Agnes, 566
Réunion Neurologique Internationale Annuelle, 3me (Paris 1922), 487
Reverdin, Auguste, 174
Revere, Grace Linzee, *see* Osler, Lady
Revere, Mrs. John, 207, 246
Reynolds, Maj. Gen. C. R., 666
Reynolds, J. P., 319, 345-6; letter to F. B. Harrington, 344
Reynolds, Sir Joshua, 167, 201, 226, 293
Reynolds, Lawrence, 478*n*, 543, 708
Rhazes, 292
Rhodes, J. F., 359-61, 505; HC's reminiscences, 356; HC's obituary, 545-6; letters to HC, 357, 358
Rhodes, W. C., 39, 45, 144
Richards, E. L., 42
Richards, T. W., 359, 416
Richardson, E. P., 531
Richardson, H. H., 359
Richardson, M. H., 54, 58, 67-9, 71-5, 77, 104, 107, 109, 166-7, 259, 286, 319, 336, 341-2, 353; letters to HC, 280, 340
Richardson, W. L., 82, 286
Riddoch, George, 597, 698
Riley, Gen., 505
Riley, H. A., 606
Ringer, Sidney, 212, 222
Ripley, A. L., 35-6, 76, 636; letter from HC, 418
Riva-Rocci, Scipione, 190, 212, 215; pneumatic cuff, 94, 213-14, 216
Rixey, P. M., 305
Rixford, Emmet, 473
Robb, Hunter, 115, 116*n*, 123, 153
Robbia, Luca della, 188
Roberts, S. C., 690
Roberts, S. R., 652
Robertson, O. H., 434
Robin, A., 252
Robson, Sir A. Mayo, 162-3, 172
Rochester. University, 605; Medical History Club, 587; School of Medicine, opening, 541
Rockefeller, J. D. Sr., 237, 290, 450
Rockefeller, Mrs. J. D. Sr., 27*n*
Rockefeller, J. D. Jr., 629

Rockefeller Foundation, 405, 443, 447, 450-1, 464
Rockefeller Institute, 111, 248, 306, 447, 449, 475
Röntgen, W. C., 104-5, 106*n*
Röntgen diagnosis, of meningiomas, 543
Roesler, Max, letter to HC, 568
Rogers, O. F. Jr., 391
Rolleston, Sir Humphry D., 167, 235, 284, 293, 458, 474, 547, 558, 676; recollection, 548
Rollins, C. P., 692
Roosevelt, F. D., 161, 517, 573, 590, 627, 644-5, 649, 658, 660, 669, 675, 685, 701; letters to HC, 654, 664, 666, 670, 676; letters from HC, 653-4, 664-5
Roosevelt, Mrs. F. D., 627, 676
Roosevelt, James, 517, 571, 573, 592, 594, 639, 659, 682
Roosevelt Mrs. James (Betsey Cushing), 282, 288, 317, 374, 514, 517, 544, 547, 594, 676, 680, 682; birth, 275; engagement, 573; wedding, 590
Roosevelt, Kate, 676
Roosevelt, Theodore, 208, 308*n*, 404, 653
Root, Mary, 63-4
Rosebery, A. P. P., 5th Earl, 167
Rosenau, M. J., 494
Rosenow, E. C., 150
Ross, J. P., 570, 698
Ross, Ronald, 237
Roth, Moritz, 293
Rottenburg, Franz von, 195
Roussy, Gustave, 474, 638
Roux, César, 174-5, 177
Roux, Émile, 154, 639
Rovsing, Thorkild, 294-5
Rowfant Club, 241
Rowland, Augustus, 110
Royal Academy of Medicine of Ireland, 550
Royal Army Medical Corps, 399-404, 415, 420, 423
Royal College of Physicians, 167, 226, 235, 371*n*
Royal College of Surgeons, 226, 253, 366, 371; centennial celebration, 166; dedication of Bowlby plaque, 592-3; Hunterian Museum, 164-5, 168, 292; laboratory at Down, 597
Royal College of Surgeons in Ireland, 429; welcome to members at American College of Surgeons, 485; National Cancer campaign, 550
Royal Library at Stockholm, 581
Royal Society, London, 632, 658
Royal Society of Medicine, 551
Royal Victoria Hospital, Montreal, 112*n*
Royal Zoological Society, 430
Ruhräh, John, 230, 660
'Rumpies,' 199
Russell, James, 500
Russell, W. W., 228*n*
Rutherford, E. R., Baron, 687, 705, 710
Ryff, W. H., 695

Sabin, Florence, 204, 218
Sabin, H. L., 8
Sachs, Bernard, 278, 606, 608
Sachs, Ernest, 270, 278, 455, 612; letters from HC, 257, 279
Sage, Henry, 56-7, 64, 66-7
Sahli, Hermann, 176, 180, 190
St. Bartholomew's Hospital, London, 488
St. George's Hospital, London, 165
St. Luke's Hospital, New York, 74
St. Margaret's Hospital, Boston, 78
St. Martin, Alexis, 205
St. Thomas's Hospital, London, 165
Salisbury, R. A. C., 3d Marquis of, 167
Salmon, T. W., 443, 445, 447-8
Salpêtrière, Paris, 445
Salt, effect of, on intracranial tension, 471; on nerve-muscle, 184*n*, 222-4
Sanarelli, Giuseppe, 154-5
Sanderson, Sir J. B., 48
Santayana, George, 670
Sarbó, A. de, 294-5
Sargent, C. S., 357, 359, 505
Sargent, J. S., 246, 505; painting of "Big Four," 246; unveiling of "Big Four," 251; letter to HC, 506
Sargent, Percy, 399, 401, 431
Sarton, George, 478n, 484, 703; letter from ACK, 704
The Saturday Club, 356-61, 372, 374, 416, 419, 461, 479, 493, 505
Saunders, Lawrence, 694
Scarff, J. E., 565
Schäfer, E. A., *see* Sharpey-Schafer, Sir E. A.
Schaltenbrand, Georges, 575, 582, 607-8, 698
Schaltenbrand, H. H., 702*n*
Schedel, Hartmann, 583
Schleich, C. L., 142
Schloffer, H., 301-2
Schmidt, A., 232
Schmiedeberg, Oswald, 194
Schneekloth, Gustave, 355, 371-2, 514, 585, 590, 611, 621
Schreiber, Frederic, 565, 608; reminiscence, 569
Schreiber, Julius, 192
Schwab, S. I., 435-6, 443, 445, 447; letter to HC, 441; letter from HC, 454

Schwann, Theodor, 181
Schweinitz, George de, 320, 459
Scott, Gen. Hugh, 312
Scott, J. A., 228*n*
Scroll and Key, 43-5, 51, 75-6, 274
Scudder, C. L., 58-9, 62-3, 65, 67-8, 71-2, 93, 98
Sears, H. F., 65, 71, 82, 86-7, 93, 531
Sedgwick, A. G., 359
Sedgwick, Ellery, 416, 512, 696
Selva, Julio, 73
Senn, Nicholas, 71, 260
Sensory area, 200, 262 *et seq.*
Sepsis, postoperative, 555
Servetus, Michael, 284, 289-90, 292
Service de Santé, 402
Seymour, Charles, letter to HC, 648
Seymour, G. D., 662
Seymour, T. D., 34-6
Shadwell, C. L., 236, 284
Shapley, Harlow, 520
Sharpe, William, 245, 303, 320
Sharpey-Schafer, Sir E. A., 200, 300, 371, 523-4, 660; Herter Lecture, 276; letter on pituitary, 298; letter to HC, 325
Shattuck, F. C., 54, 73-4, 104, 286, 382, 475, 482, 512, 531; letter to HC, 338
Shattuck Lecture, 365
Shaw, Caroline, *see* Cushing, Mrs. W. D.
Shearn, M. E., 134
Sheehan, Donal, letter to HC, 654
Shepley, J. H., viii, 423, 459-60, 462
Sheppard, J. T., 690
Sherman, John, 124
Sherrington, Sir Charles S., 162, 195-200, 217, 234, 267, 271, 292, 314, 444, 491, 522, 553-4, 595, 597, 606-9, 625, 645, 697-8; letters to HC, 196, 199
Sherrington, Lady, 553, 597
Shipley, Sir Arthur E., 475
Shippen, William, 228
Shock, avoidance of, 213
Sigerist, H. E., 611-13, 628, 636, 639, 703
Silliman, Benjamin, 37
Silliman Lectures, Osler's plans for, 361; by Hubble, 668
Silver clips, 314, 536
Simmons, G. H., 289, 509; HC's speech at dinner, 510
Singer, C. J., 589
Sizer, Theodore, 690*n*
Sjöqvist, Olof, 706-7
Skillen, James, 93, 482-4
Skull, hemangioma of, 492*n*
Skull and Bones, 43-5
Slater, James, reminiscence, 525
Sloggett, Sir Arthur, 420, 429*n*
Smart, E. F., 459-60
Smith, D. A., *see* Strathcona, 1st Baron
Smith, F. Hopkinson, 71
Smith, F. R., 228*n*
Smith, G. M., 237, 686; letter from HC, 238
Smith, H. E., 47, 333
Smith, M. C., 478*n*
Smith, Nathan, 565, 567
Smith, S. L., 144
Smith, Theobald, 150, 497; letter to HC, 154
Smith, W. H., letter from HC, 710
Smith-Petersen, M. N., 391
Society of British Neurological Surgeons, 549, 551
Society of Clinical Surgery, 354*n*; conception, 169; formation, 231; meetings, 239, 245, 255, 282, 298, 364, 375, 474, 533, 707; 1st trip abroad (1904), 313-14; 2nd trip abroad (1909), 328
Society of Neurological Surgeons, 454-5, 494, 554, 612, 616
Solley, J. B., 179, 194; reminiscence, 183
Sosman, M. C., 543, 708
Southard, E. E., 447
Southern Tri-State Medical Society, 148
Spanish-American war, 140, 146-7
Spielmann, M. H., 206, 529-30
Spiller, W. G., 196, 262, 263*n*
Spinal cord, 122; tumor, 267, 554
Spinal injuries, gunshot, 122-3, 135, 261
Spinal meningitis, operation for, 149
Splenectomy in anemia, 139
Sprat, Thomas, 324
Spurling, R. G., 617
Spurzheim, J. G., 319, 544
Stagg, A. A., 43
Stammers, F. A. R., 584
Stanton, M. E., viii, 506-7, 546, 572, 633, 660, 668, 675
Starling, E. H., 274-5, 325
Starr, C. L., 473
Starr, M. A., letter to HC, 324
Stedman, H. R., 478*n*
Steele, Sir Richard, 241
Steiner, W. R., 385, 627, 629, 679, 682
Sterling, John, 684
Sternberg, Surg. Gen. G. M., 71, 150, 154
Stettinius, E. R., 688
Stevenson, R. L., 128
Stewart, G. N., 284
Stewart, George, 714
Stewart, J. A., 166
Stiles, Sir Harold J., 473, 500, 583
Stiles, Margaret, 75-6
Stilling, Heinrich, 175-6
Stimson, L. A., 50
Stirling, William, 181
Stirling-Maxwell, Sir John M., 292

Stirling-Maxwell, Sir William, 292, 329
Stockard, C. R., 660
Stokes, A. P., 385, 480-1, 645
Stokes, Admiral C. F., 305
Stone, A. K., 70-2, 88
Stone, H. B., 221-2
Storer, Malcolm, 477-8, 494
Storey, Moorfield, 357, 359
Storrow, J. J., 419
Strasser, Hans, 180, 190-1
Strathcona, 1st Baron (Donald A. Smith), 367, 371
Strathcona, Lady, 368, 371
Street, Julian, 404
Streeter, E. C., 386*n*, 472, 475, 477-8, 482, 529, 545, 600, 686, 695, 701; letter to HC 483; letter from HC, 484
Strong, C. P., 72
Strong, R. P., 130, 132, 360, 390, 392, 395, 420, 432, 435
Strong Memorial Hospital, Rochester, 541
Styles, Capt., 699
Sudhoff, K. F.J., 324, 693
Surgeon's Journal, *see* HC Books
Swedish Royal Academy of Sciences, 645
Swieten, Gerhard, Freiherr van, 5*n*
Swift, Jonathan, 241-2, 485
Sydenstricker, Edgar, 650, 655; letter to Miss Perkins, 652; letter from HC, 651
Sylvester, J. J., 110, 263
Syme, James, 429, 500
Symonds, C. P., 525, 558
Syracuse University. College of Medicine, Centenary celebration, 644

Taeuber, H. W., 607, 624
Taft, H. D., 35-6
Taft, W. H., 285*n*, 304-5, 366, 403-4; letter to HC, 468
Taneyhill, G. L., Jr., 217
Tarbell, E. C., 276; portrait, copy of, 304-5; letter to HC, 277; to HKC, 277
Taste fibres, 266
Tavern Club, Boston, 359-61, 474
Taylor, Alexander, 26*n*
Taylor, Capt., pilot, 428
Taylor, E. W., 260, 478*n*; 60th birthday, 531-3
Taylor, Sir William, 485
Teacher, J. H., 201, 548
Teel, H. M., 615
Terry Lectures, 675, 703
Thacher, H. C., 220
Thackeray, W. M., 227
Thayer, W. R., 416
Thayer, W. S., 86, 101, 116, 148, 208, 228, 295-6, 435, 457, 466, 468, 473, 521, 575
Third circulation, 522-3
Thomas, C. C, 563, 604, 686, 700
Thomas, H. M., 204, 228*n*
Thomas, J. J., 26*n*, 27
Thompson, Francis, 231
Thompson, Henry, 34
Thompson, K. W., 557, 689
Thoms, Herbert, 317, 657, 682; letter from HC, 318
Thomson, E. H., viii
Thomson, Elihu, 104-5
Thorndike, Lynn, 698
Thorndike, Paul, 76, 88
Thorndike, Mrs. Paul, 62
Thyroid tumors, treatment of, 141*n*
Tic douloureux, 263*n*; *see also* Trigeminal neuralgia
Tilden, C. J., letter from HC, 691
Tilney, Frederick, letter to HC, 503
Tilton, E. L., 530
Tinker, C. B., 586, 691
Titian, 189, 201, 296
Toronto Academy of Medicine, 318
Toronto General Hospital, 365
Toulmin, H., 228*n*
Tourniquet, cranial, 268, 536
Towne, E. B., 362*n*
Townsend, J. B., 45
Towse, Sir Beachcroft, 431
Trask, W. R., 345
Trigeminal nerve, sensory distribution, 264-5
Trigeminal neuralgia, 262; ganglionectomy, 158, 262, 265*n*, 266*n*, 451
Trimble, I. R., 147
Trinity College, Dublin, 550
Tri-State Medical Society, 471
Trousseau, Armand, 137
Trout, H. H., 139*n*
Trudeau, E. L., 233, 566
Truesdale, P. E., 478*n*
Tudor and Stuart Club, 526
Tugo, O. C., 422-3; memorial to, 484
Turin Academy of Sciences, 187
Turnbull, H. M., 625
Turner, G. G., 479
Tweedy, H. H., 89
Tyler, W. L., 7-8
Typhoid fever, case resembling, 151; exploratory laparotomy, 150, 157; intestinal perforation, 146*n*, 148-150
Tyson, James, 235, 289

'Uglies,' 304
Union Boat Club, Boston, 73, 75, 92
Union College, Schenectady, N.Y., 11
U.S. Army. Base Hospital No. 5, 412 *et*

seq.; preliminary negotiations, 412-14; 'Battle of Boston Common,' 416-18; overseas, 419, *et seq.;* bombing of, 422-3; history of, 451-3; Tugo Circle dedicated, 484; parapet wall dedication, 564-5
U.S. Army. Medical Dept., history of war, 450
U.S. Library of Congress, 123, 665
U.S. Sanitary Commission, 13, 420, 501, 679
U.S. Surgeon General's Office. Library, 110, 560, 663-5, 676
University College, London; 1st lecture before Medical Research Society, 638
University College Hospital, London, 165

Vallery-Radot, R., 566
Valverde, Juan, 392
Vanderbilt, H. S., 685
Vanderbilt Clinic, 74
Van Dessel, Arthur, 526
Van Dyke, Henry, 253
Van Rensselaer, Mrs. Schuyler, 172
Van Slyke, D. D., 622
Van Wagenen, W. P. 541, 617, 643
Vaschide, N., 215*n*
Vasomotor center, mechanism of, 187
Vaughan, Mrs. W. W., 484*n*
Vennison, Capt. *of Saxonia,* 420
Ventriculography, 490
Vesalius, Andreas, viii, 168, 174, 189, 201, 206, 225, 230, 233, 237, 291-2, 294-5, 327, 328-9, 373, 392, 453, 458, 548, 560, 563, 594, 624, 639, 666, 668, 676, 687, 695, 709-10, 712; Bio-bibliography of, 702, 704-6; copy of Titian portrait, 296; 400th anniversary of birth, 385-6; Iconography, 230, 529-30; muscle and skeletal plates, 679
Victoria, Queen of England, 167
Vienna. Allgemeines Krankenhaus, 294, 343
Viets, H. R., 95*n*, 96, 101, 260*n*, 447, 478*n*, 484, 494, 531-2, 554, 567, 570, 621, 624-5, 701
Vincent, Beth, 390-1
Vincent, Clovis, 554, 558, 598, 698, 709
Vincent, George, 447, 554; letter from HC, 448
Vinson, R. E., 619
Virchow, Rudolf, 51, 181-2
Virginia. University, 275, 331
Visual fields, 319; alterations in, 290; in brain tumors, 320; in pituitary lesions, 365*n*
Volkmann, Richard von, 182
Voynich, W. M., 529

Wadsworth, Eliot, 419
Walcott, F. C., 52, 251, 521, 588-9, 627, 629, 644, 671, 696, 705-6
Walcott, H. P., 336, 341, 358-9, 382, 416-17, 482
Waldeyer, W., 239
Walker, C. B., 320, 365, 708
Walker, Emery, 463
Wallace, Sir Cuthbert, 399, 473, 486-8, 698; letter from C. E. Bird, 487
Wallace, F. W., 72
Wallace, Henry, 650, 656-7
Waller, Erik, 579-80, 667-8, 694
Walley, W. P., 359
Walpole, Horace, 227, 544
Walters, Henry, 694
Walton, G. L., 261*n*
War wounds, first experiences with, 393 *et seq.;* British experiences with, 399-401; treatment in infection, 408-9; cranio-cerebral, 423*n*, 440*n*; of nervous system, 440*n*, 451; follow-up, 423
Ware, John, 54*n*
Warfield, Edwin, 290
Warfield, R. B., 289
Warren, J. C., 54, 69, 72-5, 95, 104-5, 109, 164, 166-7, 336-7, 339, 341, 359, 360*n*, 364, 376, 554; letters to HC, 319, 340, 354; letter from HC, 475
Warren Triennial Prize, 232
Warrington Academy and Dispensary, collection, 252
Washburn, F. A., 278, 481-2; letter from HC, 95
Washington University, St. Louis, 405; Medical School, 346; call to, 331, 337
Waterhouse, Benjamin, 407
Watson, Frank, 82
Watson, John, 567
Watson, Rollo, 31
Watzka, Adolph, 706, 708
Webster, J. P., 216; reminiscence, 249
Wednesday Evening Club, Boston, 357
Weed, L. H., 221, 317*n*, 356, 362-3, 368, 374, 443-5, 447-9, 471, 494, 523; letters to HC, 512, 524; to KC, 528; letters from HC, 444, 527, 530
Weeks, Edward, 666
Wegefarth, Paul, 362
Wegman, Myron, 616
Weigert, K., 111
Weil, Ernst, 607, 624, 695-6
Weir, J. F., 74, 164, 166
Weir Mitchell Lecture, 375
Weisenberg, T. H., 503
Welch, Hopestill, 641
Welch, W. H., 111-12, 120, 143, 149-51, 153, 158, 161, 178, 203-4, 219, 229, 234, 238,

242-3, 246, 248, 251-3, 271-5, 284, 289-90, 327, 330, 335, 343, 355, 373, 376, 379, 419, 443, 445-7, 464 479, 496, 504, 517-18, 530, 558, 573, 584-9, 599-604, 606-11, 627, 639, 649, 653, 677, 705, 708; Ether Day address, 277-8; Birthdays (60th), 312; (75th), 521; (80th), 587-9; review of 'Osler,' 465-6; HC's reminiscence of, 519-20, 585, 628-30; death of, 640-1; HC's appreciation, 641-2; letters to HC, 133, 156-7, 241, 307, 340, 480, 613; letters from HC, 466, 612; from Pres. Wilson, 408
Welch, W. W., 642
Welch Institute of Pathology, 290
Welch Lecture, 591, 603-4
Welch Library, 246, 573; early plans for, 530-1; HC's address at, 583-4; dedication of H. B. Jacobs room, 208 *et seq.*, 616
Wells, E. H., letter from HC, 469
Wells, Spencer, 139
Wenckebach, K. F., 193, 710
West, Benjamin, 241
West, Olin, 651
West London Medico-Chirurgical Society, 488
Westcott, T. S., 149
Western Reserve Historical Society, 15
Western Reserve University, 6, 23, 452; Medical School, 6, 19, 23, 156; HC's first call, 156; dedication of H. K. Cushing Laboratory, 284; dedication of new medical building, 511; HC asked to return, 318, 503-4, 619-20
Wheatland, Richard, 612
Wheeler, D. W., 453
Wheeler, W. M., 567
Wheelock, John, 566
Whipple, G. H., 221, 541, 681
White, F. W., 58, 70-2, 88
White, J. C. (1833-1916), 54*n*
White, J. C. (1895-), 669
White, J. W., 167, 206, 566
White, Perygrine, 78
Whitehead, A. N., 597
Whitlock, Brand, 432
Whitman, Walt, 441
Whitman, Winslow, 71, 74, 77
Whitney, Mrs. H. P., 388
Whitney, W. F., 319, 475
Whittier, C. A., 359
Whytt, Robert, 523
Wickham, Ethel, 74
Wiegand, Willy, 624-5, 679-80
Wiggers, C. J., 284
Wilhelm II, ex-Emperor of Germany, 367, 387
Wilhelm, Crown Prince, 624
Wilkie, D. P. D., 473, 583
Williams, C. C., 75
Williams family, 644
Williams, Betsey Maria, *see* Cushing, Mrs. H. K.
Williams, C. T., 16-17, 33, 513
Williams, Day, 17
Williams, E. M., 28-31
Williams, E. P., 20, 88-91, 144, 265
Williams, Mrs. E. P. (Aunt Louise), 60, 89-91, 144
Williams, Ebenezer, 7, 16
Williams, Elizabeth, *see* Ladd, Mrs. G. T.
Williams, F. H., 105
Williams, G. F., 75
Williams, J. Whitridge, letter from HC, 326
Williams, Laura G., 72
Williams, Ray, 144
Williams, Reba, *see* Baldwin, Mrs. A. D.
Williams, W. C., 17, 34
Williams, William, 16
Williams, Mrs. William (Lucy Fitch), 16
Williams College, 8
Williams College. Medical dept., *see* Berkshire Medical School, Pittsfield
Williamson, Samuel, 13
Willis, Thomas, 593
Willyoung coil, 122
Wilms, Max, 328
Wilson, C. T. R., 705
Wilson, Marion, 391
Wilson, P. D., 391
Wilson, S. A.K., 293
Wilson, Woodrow, 208, 224, 387, 404, 407, 412, 414, 496-7; letter to Dr. Welch, 408
Wing, D. G., 692
Winslow, C.-E. A., 651, 682
Winslow, Josiah, 77
Winternitz, M. C., 385, 479-81, 517-18, 586, 626, 634, 642, 644, 648, 663, 713
Wintersnight Club, Boston, 357
Winthrop, John, 662
Wishard, W. M. Jr., excerpts from student notebook, 499-500
Wislocki, G. B., 221, 447
Witte, E. E., 650, 653-4; letter from HC *et al.*, 655-6
Wölfler, Anton, 142
Wolbach, S. B., 436, 495, 642-3
Wolsey, Thomas, Card., 324
Women's Peace Party, 403
Wood, E. S., 54, 56
Wood, H. C., 74, 228
Wood, Maj. Gen. Leonard, 260, 285, 289, 306, 387, 404, 412-14, 419, 429, 489,

491, 552, 633, 635*n*, 700; HC's operations on, 308-12; diagram of operation, 311; death of, 551
Wood, Mrs. Leonard, 308*n*, 551
Wood, Robert, 682
Woods, Sir Robert, 485
Woolsey, George, 143
Woolsey, Thomas, *see* Wolsey, T.
Worcester, Alfred, 129*n*
World War I, casualty figures, 438-9
Wotton, William, 324
Wright, A. W., reminiscence, 498-9
Wright, Sir Almroth E., 400, 409, 429, 468, 698
Wright, H. P., 42, 46, 55
Wright, William, 625
Wroth, L. C., 690

X-rays, 104-6, 121, 122, 126

Yale College, curriculum, 35-7; growth in '90's, 37; fence, 41; library, 37, 52; Tap day, 44-5
Yale Library Associates, 681
Yale Medical Alumni Association, address by HC, 248
Yale Medical Society, 639, 658
Yale University, vii-viii, 3, 11-12, 16, 21-2, 26, 33-53, 71, 224, 247, 274, 366, 452, 505; alumni luncheon (1921), 481; (1937), 682-4; bicentennial, 207; Commencement, 1934, 644-5
Yale University. Library, viii, 110, 586, 645, 648, 677; new librarian and perlustration, 688
Yale University. School of Medicine, 379, 480
call to, 248, 331 *et seq.*, 586, 634 *et seq.*
full-time, 384-5
centennial, 385
HC's advice to, 505
reorganization (1920), 517 *et seq.*
dedication of Sterling Hall of Medicine, 518-19
William Harvey Cushing Fellowship, 556
Alpha Omega Alpha Lecture, 616
Historical Library, ii, vii, 253, 318, 423, 686, 702*n;* Vesalius portrait, 530; first thoughts about, 646-7; plans for housing, 648, 663, 667; ACK's book shelf plans, 667; funds voted for, 711-12
Medical Library, 350*n*, 530, 648, 663, 702*n*, 711
See also Brain Tumor Registry
Yale University, Sheffield Scientific School, 37, 42
Yerkes, R. M., 288, 340, 586; letter to HC, 283; letter from HC, 283
Young, Archibald, 548
Young, H. H., 150, 160, 172, 237-8, 289
Young, John, 201, 548

Zimmerman, H. M., 658, 713
Zimmermann, Ágoston, 180, 190
Zinsser, Hans, 531, 630

This first edition of *Harvey Cushing—A Biography* was printed by The Collegiate Press of Menasha, Wisconsin in August 1946. The book was designed by Reinhold Frederic Gehner. The composition is Linotype Baskerville in eleven, nine and eight point sizes. The paper is 50-pound substance Eggshell for the text pages and 70-pound substance coated for the halftone illustrations. The binding cloth is Holliston's Rex, stamped in gold.